THE SIXTEENTH
MARCEL GROSSMANN MEETING
**On Recent Developments in Theoretical and Experimental
General Relativity, Astrophysics and Relativistic Field Theories**

PART C

THE SIXTEENTH
MARCEL GROSSMANN MEETING

On Recent Developments in Theoretical and Experimental
General Relativity, Astrophysics and Relativistic Field Theories

Proceedings of the MG16 Meeting
on General Relativity
Online, 5–10 July 2021

Editors

Remo Ruffini
University of Rome "La Sapienza", Rome, Italy
International Center for Relativistic Astrophysics Network (ICRANet), Pescara, Italy

Gregory Vereshchagin
International Center for Relativistic Astrophysics Network (ICRANet), Pescara, Italy

Series Editor

Remo Ruffini
University of Rome "La Sapienza", Rome, Italy
International Center for Relativistic Astrophysics Network (ICRANet), Pescara, Italy

World Scientific

NEW JERSEY · LONDON · SINGAPORE · BEIJING · SHANGHAI · HONG KONG · TAIPEI · CHENNAI

Published by

World Scientific Publishing Co. Pte. Ltd.

5 Toh Tuck Link, Singapore 596224

USA office: 27 Warren Street, Suite 401-402, Hackensack, NJ 07601

UK office: 57 Shelton Street, Covent Garden, London WC2H 9HE

Library of Congress Cataloging-in-Publication Data
Names: Marcel Grossmann Meeting on General Relativity (16th : 2021 : Online) | Ruffini, Remo, editor. | Vereshchagin, Gregory, editor.
Title: The sixteenth Marcel Grossmann meeting on recent developments in theoretical and experimental general relativity, astrophysics, and relativistic field theories : proceedings of the MG16 meeting on general relativity online, 5–10 July 2021 / editors: Remo Ruffini, University of Rome "La Sapienza", Rome, Italy, International Center for Relativistic Astrophysics Network (ICRANet), Pescara, Italy, Gregory Vereshchagin, International Center for Relativistic Astrophysics Network (ICRANet), Pescara, Italy.
Other titles: Proceedings of the MG16 meeting on general relativity online, 5–10 July 2021
Description: New Jersey : World Scientific, [2023] | Includes bibliographical references.
Identifiers: LCCN 2022047088 | ISBN 9789811269769 (set ; hardcover) | ISBN 9789811266584 (v. 1) | ISBN 9789811266591 (v. 2) | ISBN 9789811266607 (v. 3) | ISBN 9789811266614 (v. 4) | ISBN 9789811269776 (set ; ebook)
Subjects: LCSH: General relativity (Physics)--Congresses. | Gravitation--Congresses. | Quantum gravity--Congresses. | Cosmology--Congresses. | Astrophysics--Congresses.
Classification: LCC QC173.6 .M37 2021 | DDC 523.01--dc23/eng/20220929
LC record available at https://lccn.loc.gov/2022047088

British Library Cataloguing-in-Publication Data
A catalogue record for this book is available from the British Library.

Copyright © 2023 by Editors

All rights reserved.

This is an Open Access volume published by World Scientific Publishing Company. It is distributed under the terms of the Creative Commons Attribution-Non Commercial 4.0 (CC BY-NC) License. Further distribution of this work is permitted, provided the original work is properly cited.

For any available supplementary material, please visit
https://www.worldscientific.com/worldscibooks/10.1142/13149#t=suppl

Typeset by Stallion Press
Email: enquiries@stallionpress.com

Printed in Singapore

THE MARCEL GROSSMANN MEETINGS
Series Editor: REMO RUFFINI
Publications in the Series of Proceedings

Proceedings of the Sixteenth Marcel Grossmann Meeting on General Relativity
(Virtual Meeting, 2021)
Edited by G. Vereshchagin, R. Ruffini
World Scientific, 2022

Proceedings of the Fifteenth Marcel Grossmann Meeting on General Relativity
(Rome, Italy, 2018)
Edited by E.S. Battistelli, R.T. Jantzen, R. Ruffini
World Scientific, 2022

Proceedings of the Fourteenth Marcel Grossmann Meeting on General Relativity
(Rome, Italy, 2015)
Edited by M. Bianchi, R.T. Jantzen, R. Ruffini
World Scientific, 2017

Proceedings of the Thirteenth Marcel Grossmann Meeting on General Relativity
(Stockholm, Sweden, 2012)
Edited by K. Rosquist, R.T. Jantzen, R. Ruffini
World Scientific, 2015

Proceedings of the Twelfth Marcel Grossmann Meeting on General Relativity
(Paris, France, 2009)
Edited by T. Damour, R.T. Jantzen, R. Ruffini
World Scientific, 2012

Proceedings of the Eleventh Marcel Grossmann Meeting on General Relativity
(Berlin, Germany, 2006)
Edited by H. Kleinert, R.T. Jantzen, R. Ruffini
World Scientific, 2007

Proceedings of the Tenth Marcel Grossmann Meeting on General Relativity
(Rio de Janiero, Brazil, 2003)
Edited by M. Novello, S. Perez-Bergliaffa, R. Ruffini
World Scientific, 2005

Proceedings of the Ninth Marcel Grossmann Meeting on General Relativity
(Rome, Italy, 2000)
Edited by V.G. Gurzadyan, R.T. Jantzen, R. Ruffini
World Scientific, 2002

Proceedings of the Eighth Marcel Grossmann Meeting on General Relativity
(Jerusalem, Israel, 1997)
Edited by T. Piran
World Scientific, 1998

Proceedings of the Seventh Marcel Grossmann Meeting on General Relativity
(Stanford, USA, 1994)
Edited by R.T. Jantzen and G.M. Keiser
World Scientific, 1996

Proceedings of the Sixth Marcel Grossmann Meeting on General Relativity
(Kyoto, Japan, 1991)
Edited by H. Sato and T. Nakamura
World Scientific, 1992

Proceedings of the Fifth Marcel Grossmann Meeting on General Relativity
(Perth, Australia, 1988)
Edited by D.G. Blair and M.J. Buckingham
World Scientific, 1989

Proceedings of the Fourth Marcel Grossmann Meeting on General Relativity
(Rome, Italy, 1985)
Edited by R. Ruffini
World Scientific, 1986

Proceedings of the Third Marcel Grossmann Meeting on General Relativity
(Shanghai, People's Republic of China, 1982)
Edited by Hu Ning
Science Press – Beijing and North-Holland Publishing Company, 1983

Proceedings of the Second Marcel Grossmann Meeting on General Relativity
(Trieste, Italy, 1979)
Edited by R. Ruffini
North-Holland Publishing Company, 1982

Proceedings of the First Marcel Grossmann Meeting on General Relativity
(Trieste, Italy, 1975)
Edited by R. Ruffini
North-Holland Publishing Company, 1977

SPONSORS

International Center for Relativistic Astrophysics Network (ICRANet)
International Center for Relativistic Astrophysics (ICRA)

FREEDOM OF MOVEMENT FOR SCIENTISTS

The Marcel Grossmann Meetings were founded with the premise that scientists of all nations have a right to meet to exchange knowledge independent of national borders.

ACKNOWLEDGEMENTS

We acknowledge the outstanding job done before, during and after the meeting by the ICRANet/ICRA administrative and secretarial staff: Cristina Adamo, Silvia Latorre, Elisabetta Natale, and Cinzia di Niccolo. Finally this meeting and its proceedings could not have functioned without the dedicated IT support of the ICRANet system manager Gabriele Brandolini, with some temporary assistance from Domenico La Selva and Damiano Verzulli. We would like to thank Linda Kwan from World Scientific for valuable assistance during preparation of these proceedings.

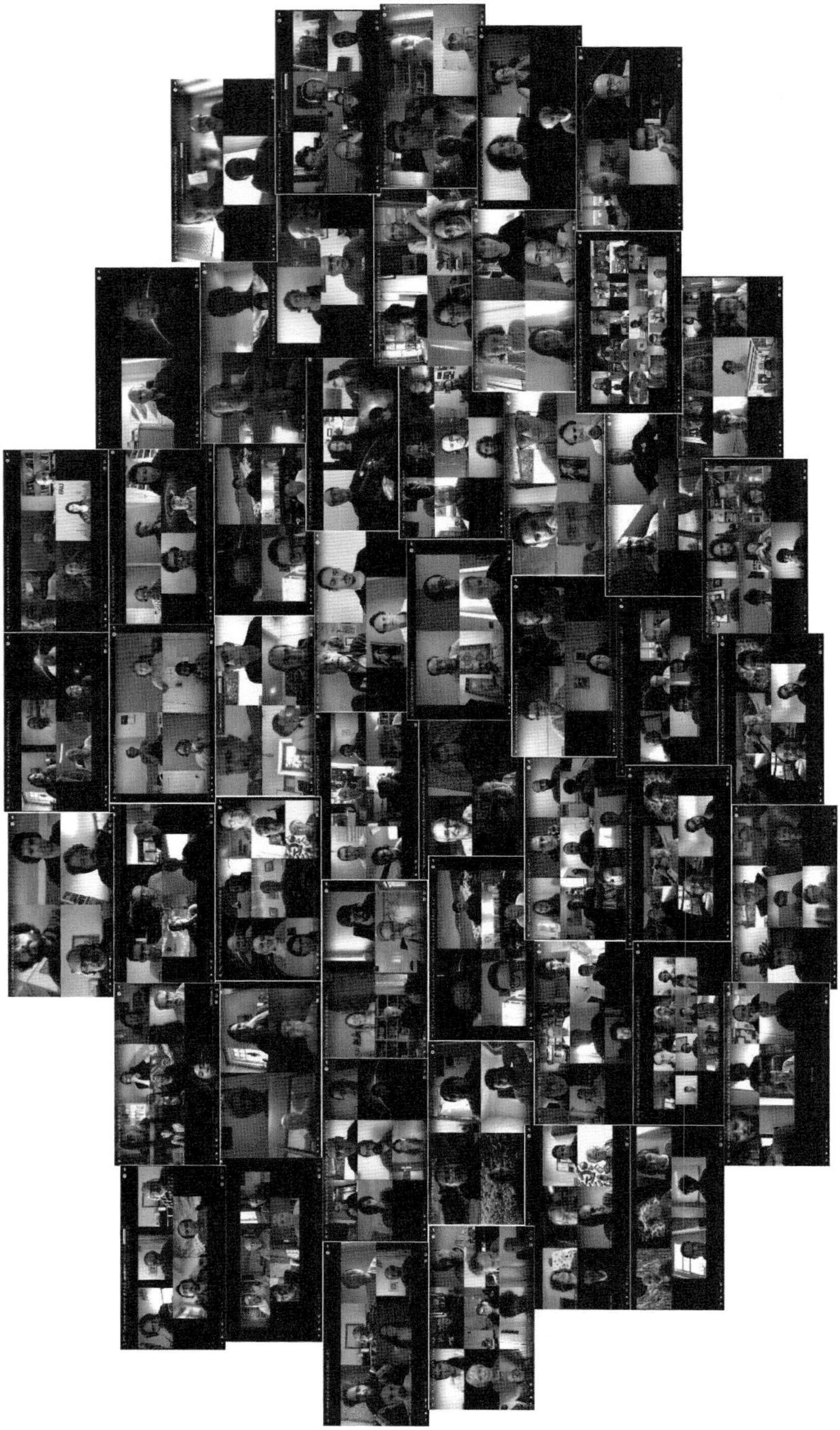

ORGANIZING BODIES
OF THE SIXTEENTH MARCEL GROSSMANN MEETING

INTERNATIONAL ORGANIZING COMMITTEE

Blair David, Choquet Bruhat Yvonne, Damour Thibault, De Bernardis Paolo, Everitt C. W. Francis, Fryer Chris, Haensch Theodor, Henneaux Marc, Jones Christine, Kerr Roy, Kleinert Hagen, Kunz Jutta, Laemmerzahl Claus, Longair Malcolm, Mirabel Felix, Mirzoyan Razmik, Piran Tsvi, Rueda Jorge, Ruffini Remo (chair), Sasaki Misao, Sato Humitaka, Sunyaev Rashid, 't Hooft Gerard, Weinberg Steven, Yau Shing-Tung, Zhang Bing

LOCAL ORGANIZING COMMITTEE

Adamo Cristina, Bianco Carlo Luciano, Brandolini Gabriele A., di Niccolo Cinzia, Latorre Silvia, La Selva Domenico, Li Liang, Loppini Alessandro, Natale Elisabetta, Verzulli Damiano, Vereshchagin Gregory (chair), Wang Yu

INTERNATIONAL COORDINATING COMMITTEE

ALBANIA: Hafizi M. - ARGENTINA: Arguelles C., Scoccola C., Reula O., Romero G.E. - ARMENIA: Sahakyan N. - AUSTRALIA: Blair D., Ju L., Lun A., Manchester D., Melatos A., Quinn P., Scott S.M., Steele J.D. - AUSTRIA: Aichelburg P.C., Schindler S. - BELARUS: Kilin S., Prakapenia M., Siutsou I. - BELGIUM: Henneaux M. - BOLIVIA: Aguirre C.B. - BOSNIA: Pasic V. - BRAZIL: Barres de Almeida U., Coelho Goulart J., Dalmolin F.T., de Lima Rafael C.R., Guzzo M., Maia C., Malheiro M., Romero Filho C.A., Shellard R.C., Zen Vasconcellos C. - BULGARIA: Yazadjiev S. - CANADA: Singh D., Smolin L., Turok N. - CHILE: Bauer F., Bunster W.C., Giacomini A. - CHINA (MAINLAND): Cai R., Cai Y., Cao Z., Chang J., Chen J., Chen X., Dai Z., Feng L.-L., Han W., Jing Y., Li T.-P., Lin W., Lou Y.-Q., Luo J., Mei J., Tam T., Wang A., Wang Y., Wu X.-P., Wu Y.-L., Yuan Y.-F., Zhang B.-B., Zhang S.-N., Zhao G. - CHINA (TAIWAN): Chen Chiang-Mei, Chen Pisin, Lee Da-Shin, Lee Wo-Lung, Ni Wei-Tou - COLOMBIA: Bargueño de Retes P., Gonzalez G., Higuera Garzon M.A., Núñez L., Romano A.E., Valenzuela Toledo C.A., Zuluaga J.I. - CROATIA: Dominis Prester D., Karlica M., Milekovic M., Smolcic V., Smolic I., Suric T. - CUBA: Perez Martinez A., Pérez Rojas H. - CZECH REPUBLIC: Bicak J., Stuchlik Z. - DENMARK: Naselsky P. - ECUADOR: Contreras E. - EGYPT: Tawfik A.N., Wanas M.I. - ESTONIA: Einasto J., Saar E. - FINLAND: Poutanen J., Volovik G. - FRANCE: Brillet A., Buchert T., Chardonnet P., Coullet P., de Freitas Pacheco J.A., Deruelle N., Iliopoulos J., Lamanna G., Mignard F. - GEORGIA: Lavrelashvili George, Machabeli Giorgi - GERMANY: Biermann P., Blumlein J., Di Piazza A., Fritzsch H., Genzel R., Gilmozzi R., Hasinger G., Hehl F., Keitel C., Kiefer C., Mirzoyan R.,

Neugebauer G., Nicolai H., Renn J., Ringwald A., Ruediger A. - GREECE: Batakis N.A., Cotsakis S., Vagenas E.C. - HUNGARY: Fodor G., Levai P. - ICELAND: Bjornsson G., Jakobsson P. - INDIA: Chakrabarti S.K., Iyer B., Padmanabhan T., Souradeep T. - IRAN: Baghram S., Bavarsad E., Eslam Panah B., Firouzjahi H., Haghighat M., Mansouri R., Mashhoon B., Shakeri S., Sobouti Y., Taghi Mirtorabi M. - IRELAND: O'Murchada N. - ISRAEL: Milgrom M., Nakar E., Pe'er A., Piran T. - ITALY: Belinski V., Bianchi M., Bianco C.L., Cherubini C., Della Valle M., Falciano S., Filippi S., Haardt F., Menotti P., Merafina M., Pani P., Ricci F., Treves A., Vereshchagin G.V., Vitale S., Xue S.- S. - JAPAN: Fujimoto M.-K., Makishima K., Nakamura T., Sato K., Shibata M. - KAZAKHSTAN: Abishev M., Aimuratov Y., Boshkayev K., Mychelkin E.G., Spitaleri C. - KOREA (PYEONGYANG): Kim J.S. - KOREA (SEOUL): Kim S.P., Kim S.-W., Lee H.K., Lee H.-W., van Putten M. - KYRGYZSTAN: Gurovich V.Ts. - LIBYA: Gadri M. - MEXICO: Breton N., Cervantes-Cota J.L., Fraija Cabrera N.I., García-Diaz A.A., Macías Alvarez A., Mielke Eckehard W., Quevedo H., Rodriguez L.F. - NETHERLANDS: Slagter R. - NEW ZEALAND: Visser M., Wiltshire D. - NORWAY: Elgaroy O., Fonseca Mota D., Knutsen H. - PAKISTAN: Qadir A., Qamar S. - PERU: Vargas T. - POLAND: Belczynski K., Demianski M., Lewandowski Jerzy, Nurowski P., Sokolowski L. - PORTUGAL: Costa M., Da Silva A., Lemos J.P.S., Lobo F., Moniz P., Silva L.O. - ROMANIA: Visinescu M. - RUSSIA: Aksenov A., Arkhangelskaja I., Bisnovatyi-Kogan G., Blinnikov S., Chechetikin V.M., Cherepaschuk A.M., Khriplovich I., Lipunov V.M., Lukash V.N., Novikov I., Rudenko V.N., Starobinsky A.A. - SERBIA: Djordjevic G., Jovanovic P., Knezevic Z., Pankov-Hzvojevic M., Popovic L., Prodanovic T., Sijacki D., Simic S. - SLOVAKIA: Balek V. - SLOVENIA: Cadez A., Gomboc A., Zavrtanik D. - SOUTH AFRICA: Larena J., Maharaj S. - SPAIN: Elizalde E., Ibanez J., Perez M.J., Verdaguer E. - SWEDEN: Abramowicz M.A., Marklund M., Ryde F. - SWITZERLAND: Durrer R., Jetzer P. - TURKEY: Aliev A., Gurses M. - UKRAINE: Novosyadlyj B., Zaslavskii O., Zhuk A. - UNITED ARAB EMIRATES: Fernini I. - UNITED KINGDOM: Cruise A.M., Frenk Carlos S., Green M., Mavromatos N., Perry M., Willingale R. - USA: Abel T., Ashtekar A., Bardeen J., Carlstrom J., Cornish N., Dermer C., Fan X., Flanagan E., Fraschetti F., Fryer C., Incera V., Jantzen R.T. (chairperson), Kolb R., Laguna P., Lousto C., Madau Piero, Mathews Grant, Matzner Richard, Melia Fulvio, Mester John, Michelson Peter, Nordtvedt Kenneth, Parker Leonard, Pretorius F., Pullin J., Shapiro I., Shapiro S., Shoemaker D., Smoot G., Stiavelli M., Teukolsky S., van Nieuwenhuizen P., Zhang B. - UZBEKISTAN: Ahmedov B., Zalaletdinov R.M. - VATICAN CITY: Gionti G. - VENEZUELA: Fuenmayor E. - VIETNAM: Long H.N.

MARCEL GROSSMANN AWARDS

Sixteenth Marcel Grossmann Meeting

Institutional Awards

"for the creation of the world's best X-ray map of the entire sky, for the discovery of millions of previously unknown accreting supermassive black holes at cosmological redshifts, for the detection of X-rays from tens of thousands of galaxy clusters, filled mainly with dark matter, and for permitting the detailed investigation of the growth of the large-scale structure of the universe during the era of dark energy dominance".

S.A. LAVOCHKIN ASSOCIATION
- presented to its Designer General **Alexander Shirshakov**

MAX PLANCK INSTITUTE FOR EXTRATERRESTRIAL PHYSICS (MPE)
- presented to Professor **Peter Predehl**, Principal Investigator of eROSITA

SPACE RESEARCH INSTITUTE (IKI) OF THE RUSSIAN ACADEMY OF SCIENCES
- presented to Professor **Rashid Sunyaev,** Principal Investigator of SRG Observatory in Russia

Individual Awards

DEMETRIOS CHRISTODOULOU
"For his many lasting contributions to the foundation of mathematical physics including the dynamics of relativistic gravitational fields. Notably for: contributing in 1971, at the age of 19, to derive with Remo Ruffini the mass-energy formula of black holes as a function of their angular momentum, charge and irreducible mass. Christodoulou turned then to the study of partial differential equations and mathematical physics, to which he remained dedicated for the rest of his career. Highlights in this area include the theoretical discovery of the nonlinear memory effect of gravitational waves (Phys. Rev. Letters 1991), the monograph (1993) in collaboration with Sergiu Klainerman on the global nonlinear stability of the Minkowski spacetime, the monograph (2009) on the formation of black holes in pure general relativity by imploding gravitational waves, and the monographs (2007 and 2019) on the formation and further development of shocks in fluids."

GERARD 't HOOFT
"for his persistent devotion to the study of the quantum field theory boundary conditions at the black hole horizon".

TSVI PIRAN
"for extending Relativistic astrophysics across international frontiers, a true companion in the search for the deeper meaning of Einstein's great theory".

STEVEN WEINBERG
"for unwavering support for the MG meetings since their inception, a true companion in the search for the deeper meaning of Einstein's great theory".

Each recipient is presented with a silver casting of the TEST sculpture by the artist A. Pierelli. The original casting was presented to His Holiness Pope John Paul II on the first occasion of the Marcel Grossmann Awards.

15th Marcel Grossmann Meeting
July 2018, Rome, Italy

Institutional Awards

PLANCK SCIENTIFIC COLLABORATION (ESA)
"for obtaining important constraints on the models of inflationary stage of the Universe and level of primordial non-Gaussianity; measuring with unprecedented sensitivity gravitational lensing of Cosmic Microwave Background fluctuations by large-scale structure of the Universe and corresponding B-polarization of CMB, the imprint on the CMB of hot gas in galaxy clusters; getting unique information about the time of reionization of our Universe and distribution and properties of the dust and magnetic fields in our Galaxy"

- presented to Jean-Loup Puget, the Principal Investigator of the High Frequency Instrument (HFI)

HANSEN EXPERIMENTAL PHYSICS LABORATORY AT STANFORD UNIVERSITY
"to HEPL for having developed interdepartmental activities at Stanford University at the frontier of fundamental physics, astrophysics and technology"

- presented to Research Professor Leo Hollberg, HEPL Assistant Director

Individual Awards

LYMAN PAGE
"for his collaboration with David Wilkinson in realizing the NASA Explorer WMAP mission and as founding director of the Atacama Cosmology Telescope"

RASHID ALIEVICH SUNYAEV
"for the development of theoretical tools in the scrutinising, through the CMB, of the first observable electromagnetic appearance of our Universe"

SHING-TUNG YAU
"for the proof of the positivity of total mass in the theory of general relativity and perfecting as well the concept of quasi-local mass, for his proof of the Calabi conjecture, for his continuous inspiring role in the study of black holes physics"

14th Marcel Grossmann Meeting
July 2015, Rome, Italy

Institutional Award

EUROPEAN SPACE AGENCY (ESA)
"for the tremendous success of its scientific space missions in astronomy, astrophysics, cosmology and fundamental physics which have revolutionized our knowledge of the Universe and hugely benefited science and mankind"

- presented to its Director General Johann-Dietrich Woerner

Individual Awards

KEN'ICHI NOMOTO
"for heralding the role of binary systems in the evolution of massive stars"

MARTIN REES
"for fostering Research in black holes, gravitational waves and cosmology"

YAKOV G. SINAI
"for applying the mathematics of chaotic systems to physics and cosmology"

SACHIKO TSURUTA
"for pioneering the physics of hot neutron stars and their cooling"

FRANK C.N. YANG
"for deepening Einstein's geometrical approach to physics in the best tradition of Paul Dirac and Hermann Weyl"

T.D. LEE (award received by Yu-Qing Lou on behalf of Prof. T.D. Lee)
"for his work on white dwarfs motivating Enrico Fermi's return to astrophysics and guiding the basic understanding of neutron star matter and fields"

13th Marcel Grossmann Meeting
July 2012, Stockholm, Sweden

Institutional Award

ALBANOVA
for its innovative status as a joint institute established by Stockholm University and the Royal Institute of Technology and for fostering contributions to cosmology and astrophysics in the profound scientific tradition established by Oskar Klein.

- presented to the Rector of Stockholm University, Prof. Kåre Bremer.

Individual Awards

DAVID ARNETT
for exploring the nuclear physics and yet unsolved problems of the endpoint of thermonuclear evolution of stars, leading to new avenues of research in physics and astrophysics.

VLADIMIR BELINSKI and I.M. KHALATNIKOV
for the discovery of a general solution of the Einstein equations with a cosmological singularity of an oscillatory chaotic character known as the BKL singularity.

FILIPPO FRONTERA
for guiding the Gamma-ray Burst Monitor Project on board the BeppoSAX satellite, which led to the discovery of GRB X-ray afterglows, and to their optical identification.

12th Marcel Grossmann Meeting
July 2009, Paris, France

Institutional Award

INSTITUT DES HAUTES ÉSTUDES SCIENTIFIQUE (IHÉS)
for its outstanding contributions to mathematics and theoretical physics, and notably for having renewed basic geometrical concepts, and having developed new mathematical and physical aspects of spacetime.

- presented to Prof. Jean-Pierre Bourguignon

Individual Awards

JAAN EINASTO
for pioneering contributions in the discovery of dark matter and cosmic web and fostering research in the historical Tartu Observatory.

CHRISTINE JONES
for her fundamental contributions to the X-ray studies of galaxies and clusters tracing their formation and evolution and for her role in collaborations using clusters to study dark matter and in analyzing the effects of outbursts from supermassive black holes on the intracluster gas.

MICHAEL KRAMER
for his fundamental contributions to pulsar astrophysics, and notably for having first confirmed the existence of spin-orbit precession in binary pulsars.

11th Marcel Grossmann Meeting
July 2006, Berlin, Germany

Institutional Award

FREIE UNIVERSITÄT BERLIN

for the successful endeavor of re-establishing — in the spirit of the Humboldt tradition — freedom of thinking and teaching within a democratic society in a rapidly evolving cosmos

- presented to Dr. Dieter Lenzen, President of FUB

Individual Awards

ROY KERR

for his fundamental contribution to Einstein's theory of general relativity: "The gravitational field of a spinning mass as an example of algebraically special metrics."

GEORGE COYNE

for his committed support for the international development of relativistic astrophysics and for his dedication to fostering an enlightened relationship between science and religion.

JOACHIM TRUMPER

for his outstanding scientific contributions to the physics of compact astrophysical objects and for leading the highly successful ROSAT mission which discovered more than 200,000 galactic and extragalactic X-ray sources: a major step in the observational capabilities of X-ray astronomy and in the knowledge of our universe.

10th Marcel Grossmann Meeting
July 2003, Rio de Janeiro, Brazil

Institutional Award

CBPF (Brazilian Center for Research in Physics)
for its role as a teaching and research institution and as a place originating fundamental physics ideas in the exploration of the universe.

- presented to its founders Cesar Lattes, Josè Leite Lopez and Jayme Tiomno

Individual Awards

YVONNE CHOQUET-BRUHAT AND JAMES W. YORK, JR.
for separate as well as joint work in establishing the mathematical framework for proving the existence and uniqueness of solutions to Einstein's gravitational field equations.

YUVAL NE'EMAN
for his contributions to science, epistemology, mathematics and physics from subnuclear to space sciences.

9th Marcel Grossmann Meeting
July 2000, Rome, Italy

Institutional Award

SOLVAY INSTITUTES

for identifying and recording in discussions by the protagonists the crucial developments of physics and astrophysics in the twentieth century.

- presented to Jacques Solvay

Individual Awards

CECILLE AND BRYCE DEWITT

for promoting General Relativity and Mathematics research and inventing the "summer school" concept.

RICCARDO GIACCONI

for opening, five successive times, new highways for exploring the Universe.

ROGER PENROSE

for extending the mathematical and geometrical foundations of General Relativity.

8th Marcel Grossmann Meeting
June 1997, Jerusalem

Institutional Award

HEBREW UNIVERSITY
for its role as a cradle of Science and Humanities and for hosting the manuscripts of Albert Einstein.

- presented to M. Magidor, President of the Hebrew University of Jerusalem

Individual Awards

TULLIO REGGE
for his contributions to the interface between mathematics and physics leading to new fields of research of paramount importance in relativistic astrophysics and particle physics.

FRANCIS EVERITT
for leading the development of extremely precise space experiments utilizing superconducting technology to test General Relativity and the Equivalence Principle.

7th Marcel Grossmann Meeting
June 1994, Stanford, USA

Institutional Award

SPACE TELESCOPE SCIENCE INSTITUTE
for its critical role in the direction and operation of the Hubble Space Telescope, a truly unique international laboratory for the investigation and testing of general relativity in the context of modern astrophysics and cosmology.

- presented to Peter Stockman

Individual Awards

SUBRAHMANYAN CHANDRASEKHAR
for his contributions to the analysis of gravitational phenomena from Newton to Einstein and especially for leading the way to relativistic astrophysics with the concept of critical mass for gravitational collapse.

JIM WILSON
for having built on his experience in nuclear physics, thermonuclear reactions, and extensive numerical simulation to create a new testing ground for the novel concepts of relativistic astrophysics.

6th Marcel Grossmann Meeting
June 1991, Kyoto, Japan

Institutional Award

RITP

for keeping alive first in Hiroshima and them in Kyoto research in relativity, cosmology, and relativistic field theory and the development of a school of international acclaim.

- presented to Professor K. Tomita

Individual Awards

MINORU ODA

for participating in the pioneering work of the early sixties in X-ray astronomy and for his subsequent molding of an agile and diversified Japanese scientific space program investigating the deepest aspects of relativistic astrophysics.

STEPHEN HAWKING

for his contributions to the understanding of spacetime singularities and of the large scale structure of the Universe and of its quantum origins.

5th Marcel Grossmann Meeting
August 1988, Perth, Australia

Institutional Award

THE UNIVERSITY OF WESTERN AUSTRALIA
for its contributions to relativistic astrophysics.

- presented to the Vice Chancellor, Professor Robert Smith

Individual Awards

SATIO HAYAKAWA
for his contributions to research in gamma, X-ray and infrared radiation as well as cosmic rays.

JOHN ARCHIBALD WHEELER
for his contributions to geometrodynamics and Einstein's visions.

4th Marcel Grossmann Meeting
July 1985, Rome, Italy

Institutional Award

THE VATICAN OBSERVATORY
for its contributions to the origin and development of astrophysics.

- presented to His Holiness Pope John Paul II

Individual Awards

WILLIAM FAIRBANK
for his work in gravitation and low temperature physics.

ABDUS SALAM
for his work in unifying fundamental interactions.

Institutional Awards for the Spektrum-Roentgen-Gamma (SRG) mission

"for the creation of the world's best X-ray map of the entire sky, for the discovery of millions of previously unknown accreting supermassive black holes at cosmological redshifts, for the detection of X-rays from tens of thousands of galaxy clusters, filled mainly with dark matter, and for permitting the detailed investigation of the growth of the large-scale structure of the universe during the era of dark energy dominance".

S.A. LAVOCHKIN ASSOCIATION
- presented to its Designer General **Alexander Shirshakov**

MAX PLANCK INSTITUTE FOR EXTRATERRESTRIAL PHYSICS (MPE)
- presented to Professor **Peter Predehl**, Principal Investigator of eROSITA

SPACE RESEARCH INSTITUTE (IKI) OF THE RUSSIAN ACADEMY OF SCIENCES
- presented to Professor **Rashid Sunyaev**, Principal Investigator of SRG Observatory in Russia

On Tuesday June 29, 2021, the following 31 astro-ph appeared:

1. https://arxiv.org/abs/2106.14517
2. https://arxiv.org/abs/2106.14518
3. https://arxiv.org/abs/2106.14519
4. https://arxiv.org/abs/2106.14520
5. https://arxiv.org/abs/2106.14521
6. https://arxiv.org/abs/2106.14522
7. https://arxiv.org/abs/2106.14523
8. https://arxiv.org/abs/2106.14524
9. https://arxiv.org/abs/2106.14525
10. https://arxiv.org/abs/2106.14526
11. https://arxiv.org/abs/2106.14527
12. https://arxiv.org/abs/2106.14528
13. https://arxiv.org/abs/2106.14529
14. https://arxiv.org/abs/2106.14530
15. https://arxiv.org/abs/2106.14531
16. https://arxiv.org/abs/2106.14532
17. https://arxiv.org/abs/2106.14533
18. https://arxiv.org/abs/2106.14534
19. https://arxiv.org/abs/2106.14535
20. https://arxiv.org/abs/2106.14536
21. https://arxiv.org/abs/2106.14537
22. https://arxiv.org/abs/2106.14541
23. https://arxiv.org/abs/2106.14542
24. https://arxiv.org/abs/2106.14543
25. https://arxiv.org/abs/2106.14544
26. https://arxiv.org/abs/2106.14545
27. https://arxiv.org/abs/2106.14546
28. https://arxiv.org/abs/2106.14547
29. https://arxiv.org/abs/2106.14548
30. https://arxiv.org/abs/2106.14549
31. https://arxiv.org/abs/2106.14550

S.A. LAVOCHKIN ASSOCIATION
presented to its Designer General **Alexander Shirshakov**

Dr Alexander Shirshakov

S.A. Lavochkin Association created the Navigator space platform carrying German eRosita and Russian ART-XC X-Ray Telescopes, organized the launch of SRG Orbital X-Ray Observatory to the second Lagrangian point of the Sun-Earth system at a distance of 1.5 million km from the Earth and managed the observatory flight and the daily reception of its scientific data on Earth for 23.5 months.

Dr Alexander Shirshakov, Designer General of the S.A. Lavochkin Association, is specialized in design, manufacture, testing, launch and control of S/C for scientific purposes. Among those S/C launched, there are the «Radiostron» Astrophysical Observatory (2011) and the «Spektr-RG» space observatory (2019), while the planned S/C launches are «Luna-25» and «Exomars».

Dr Shirshakov started his career in 1973, working as an engineer of the State Unitary Enterprise «NPO named by S.A. Lavochkin» in Khimki (Russian Federation). Starting from 1989 he has played multiple roles within the Lavochkin Association, been appointed head of the group, head of the sector, head of department, deputy head of the complex, head of the branch, director of the center, deputy head of the Design Bureau, deputy General Designer and deputy General Director.

Dr Shirshakov is an editorial board Member of the reviewed edition of «Vestnik of Lavochkin Association». Since 2017, he is also member of the General Designer council. He has been awarded Honored Mechanical engineer of the Russian Federation as well as Agency-level award of the Russian Federal Space Agency.

MAX PLANCK INSTITUTE FOR EXTRATERRESTRIAL PHYSICS (MPE)
presented to Professor **Peter Predehl**, Principal Investigator of eROSITA

Professor Peter Predehl

eROSITA is the soft X-ray telescope on-board the Russian-German Spektr-RG mission which was successfully launched from Baikonur on July 13, 2019 and placed in a halo orbit around the L2 point. 30 years after ROSAT, eROSITA performs an all-sky survey with an unprecedented sensitivity, spectral and angular resolution. Clusters of galaxies are the largest collapsed objects in the Universe. Their formation and evolution is dominated by gravity, i.e. Dark Matter, while their large scale distribution and number density depends on the geometry of the Universe, i.e. Dark Energy. X-ray observations of clusters of galaxies provide information on the rate of expansion of the Universe, the fraction of mass in visible matter, and the amplitude of primordial fluctuations which are the origin of clusters of galaxies and the whole structure of the universe. eROSITA has been designed to detect at least 100.000 clusters of galaxies and to detect systematically more than 3 million obscured accreting Black Holes. eROSITA will also allow to study the physics of galactic X-ray source populations, like pre-main sequence stars, supernova remnants and X-ray binaries. The eROSITA telescope consists of seven identical Wolter-1 mirror modules. A novel detector system has been developed by MPE on the basis of the successful XMM-Newton pn-CCD technology. MPE is the scientific lead institute of eROSITA, responsible for the development of the instrument, the operation, the analysis software and data archive. Peter Predehl led this development as Principal Investigator of eROSITA and German lead scientist of the SRG mission for more than 15 years until the completion of the first of eight surveys in 2020. At this time eROSITA has already discovered more than 1 million X-ray sources, more than all X-ray observatories of the last 50 years together. This demonstrates that the design goals of the mission will easily be fulfilled.

SPACE RESEARCH INSTITUTE (IKI) OF THE RUSSIAN ACADEMY OF SCIENCES
presented to Professor **Rashid Sunyaev**

Professor Rashid Sunyaev

Space Research Institute (IKI) of the Russian Academy of Sciences was responsible for developing the overall concept and scientific program of the SRG Orbital observatory and played a leading role in developing the ART-XC telescope and the entire SRG observatory as part of the Russian space science program carried out by Roskosmos Corporation in the interests of the Russian Academy of Sciences.

During the flight to the L2 point of the Sun-Earth system, SRG with German (eRosita) and Russian (ART-XC named after Mikhail Pavlinsky) X-ray Telescopes aboard performed calibrations and long duration Performance Verification observations of a dozen of targets and deep fields. Starting in the middle of December 2019, the SRG scanned the whole sky three times. During these scans, SRG discovered two million point X-ray sources: mainly quasars, stars with hot and bright coronae, and more than 30 thousand clusters of galaxies. There is a competition and synergy in the search for clusters of galaxies between SRG and the ground-based Atacama Cosmology and South Pole Telescopes, which are searching for clusters of galaxies in microwave spectral band using Sunyaev-Zeldovich effect.

SRG provided the X-Ray map of the whole sky in hard and soft bands, the last is now the best among existing. The huge samples of the X-ray selected quasars at the redshifts up to $z = 6.2$ and clusters of galaxies will be used for well-known cosmological tests and detailed study of the growth of the large scale structure of the Universe during and after reionization. SRG/eRosita is discovering every day several extragalactic objects which increased or decreased their brightness more than 10 times during half of the year after the previous scan of the same one-degree wide strip on the sky. A significant part of these objects has observational properties similar to the Events of Tidal Disruption of a star orbiting in the vicinity of the supermassive black hole. ART-XC discovered a lot of bright galactic and extragalactic transients.

Rashid Sunyaev is the Principal Investigator of SRG mission in Russia, director-emeritus of the Max-Planck Institute for Astrophysics and Maureen and John Hendricks distinguished visiting professor of the Institute for Advanced Study, Princeton.

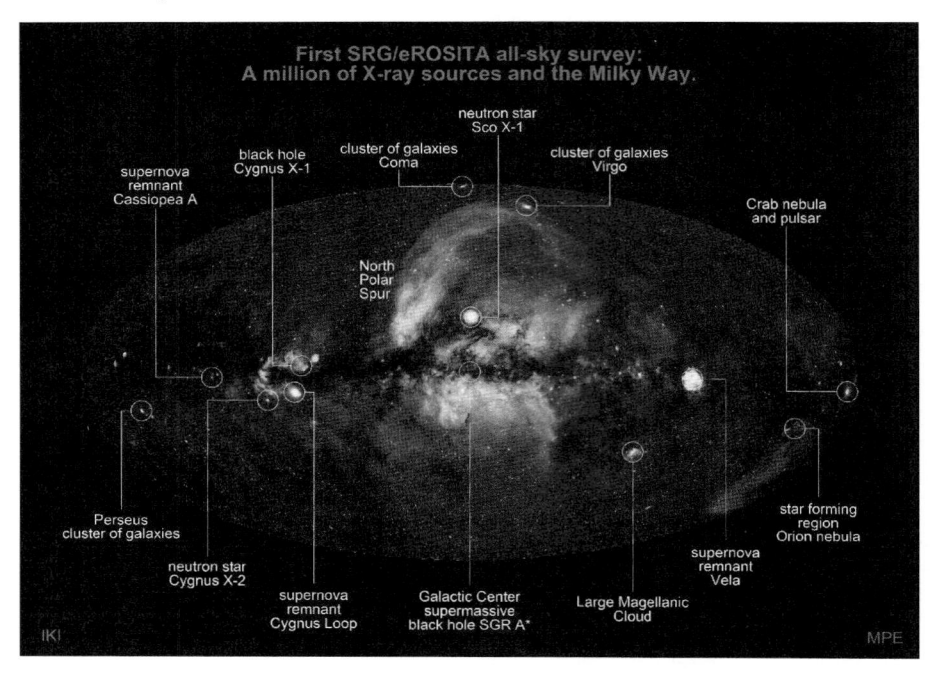

Individual Awards

Professor **DEMETRIOS CHRISTODOULOU**

"For his many lasting contributions to the foundation of mathematical physics including the dynamics of relativistic gravitational fields. Notably for: contributing in 1971, at the age of 19, to derive with Remo Ruffini the mass-energy formula of black holes as a function of their angular momentum, charge and irreducible mass. Christodoulou turned then to the study of partial differential equations and mathematical physics, to which he remained dedicated for the rest of his career. Highlights in this area include the theoretical discovery of the nonlinear memory effect of gravitational waves (Phys. Rev. Letters 1991), the monograph (1993) in collaboration with Sergiu Klainerman on the global nonlinear stability of the Minkowski spacetime, the monograph (2009) on the formation of black holes in pure general relativity by imploding gravitational waves, and the monographs (2007 and 2019) on the formation and further development of shocks in fluids."

Professor Demetrios Christodoulou

It was back in 1967 that Achille Papapetrou mentioned the case of the 16-year-old Demetrios Christodoulou to John Archibad Wheeler. Wheeler interviewed Demetrios in Paris and brought him immediately to Princeton where he was registered as an undergraduate at the university. After one year he entered the graduate school and started collaborating with me. At the time I was working with Wheeler on the effective potential approach to geodesics co-rotating and counter-rotating (see e.g. reference in The Classical Theory of Fields (Landau and Lifshitz, 1980) in the Kerr metric (later renamed as ISCO; see e.g. (Gravitation Misner, Thorne, Wheeler, 1973). In parallel, Frank Zerilli was working on the gravitational radiation emitted by the fall of a test particle in a Schwarzschild black hole (Zerilli 1970). From these limited conceptual arena Charles Misner and later Kip Thorne launched a program for the detection of gravitational waves on the Earth; see e.g. Misner 1974, Abbott et al. 2016, Abbott et al. 2017. See however Davis et al. 1972, Rodriguez et al. 2018 and J.A. Rueda et al. 2018.

A new approach started with the arrival of Demetrios: he was just creating mathematics following his needs. We identified the reversible and irreversible transformations of a Kerr black hole. Wheeler advanced a thermodynamic analogy. I addressed the need of identifying the concept of irreducible mass (from the Italian "irriducibile"), and was Demetrios's contribution to integrate, overnight, the differential equation for infinitesimal reversible transformations which led to the finite mass-energy formula of a Kerr black hole. That evening, while walking back home through IAS woods, I expressed to Wheeler the great relevance of the newly found formula by Demetrios and proposed to let Demetrios be the single author of this article, admiring his great mathematical talent. Wheeler agreed. The Editor of PRL objected since in that two pages article the Fig. 2 by Wheeler and myself was still unpublished. Actually that Fig. 2 followed a discussion I previously had with Penrose in Florence (Penrose 1961) which allowed us to present there, for the first time, a "Penrose Process". Some difficulties in achieving this process were obvious from the example in Fig. 2, which Roger later recognized himself (Penrose & Floyd 1971). The Editor finally agreed on our written request and the paper appeared on September 17, 1970 (Christodoulou, 1970). On January 1971 appeared my article with Johnny introducing the Black Hole (Ruffini & Wheeler, 1971), with the new physics we were developing in Princeton, including the concept of the "ergosphere". On march 1 1971 we submitted the mass formula of the Kerr Newmann metric, including the relation between the surface area of the horizon and the irreducible (Christodoulou & Ruffini, 1971). On March 11, 1971 the same results were independently confirmed by Steven Hawking, extending further the applicability of our equation (Hawking 1971).

The thesis was successfully discussed by a committee including Eugene Wigner (see Fig. 1), one of the closest collaborators of Albert Einstein and David Wilkinson (see Fig. 2), the head of the NASA WMAP mission, and Johnny and myself as supervisors. The new message was clear: Black Holes, far from being a sink of energy, were energy sources emitting "in principle" 50% of their mass energy, being extractable (Christodoulou & Ruffini, 1971).

Fig. 1 and Fig. 2: Demetrios during his thesis presentation with Eugene Wigner (Fig. 1) and David Wilkinson (Fig.2). Johnny and I were supervisors, ready to intervene in case of need, but no need of intervention was necessary! Wigner elaborated the aphorism of Niels Bohr "Interesting = wrong" in the most definite "very interesting if true = totally wrong".

Demetrios turned soon to the study of partial differential equations and mathematical physics, to which he dedicated for the rest of his career and results were published in four monographs: (Christodoulou and Klainerman 1994, Christodoulou 2007, Christodoulou 2009, Christodoulou 2019). In 1968, Johnny proposed to Demetrios the collapse of a "geon" composed of massless scalar field as a second topic for his thesis. It took almost forty years for him to solve this problem, extended by Demetrios to the focusing of gravitational waves leading to black hole formation (Christodoulou 2009).

A "long march" started on 12 December 1970 with the launch of the Uhuru satellite by Riccardo Giacconi. Early in 1971 an almost daily conversation with him and Herb Gursky at the Smithsonian Astrophysical Observatory, leading to the discovery of binary X-ray sources. This was soon followedby the announcement of Cygnus X1 identified as the first black hole in our galaxy (Ruffini 1973); see e.g. Gursky & Ruffini 1975, which contained as well the first publicannouncement of the Discovery of Gamma Ray burst, as well as Giacconi & Ruffini 1980, 2009; see Figs. 3 and 4).

Fig. 3: Prof. Remo Ruffini receiving the Cressy Morrison Award of the New York Academy of Sciences, 1972 for the discovery of the first Black Hole in our galaxy Cygnus X1.

Fig. 4: In the second row, from left to right, there are, among others: E. T. Newman, S. Chandrasekhar (Nobel 1983), R. Giacconi (Nobel 2002), R. Ruffini, A. Treves, A. Hewish (Nobel 1974), D. Arnett, J.H. Taylor (Nobel 1993), J. Wilson, R. Penrose (Nobel 2020), as well as J. Bahcall, T. Damour, T. Piran et al.

Today, after fifty years, this "long march" has reached a definite result: through the grandest observational multi-wavelength effort in the history of mankind, from space, ground and underground observatories, we are finally finding evidence that black holes are "alive" and their "extractable energy" in our mass formula (Christodoulou & Ruffini, 1971), is the energy source of the most energetic cosmological sources: gamma ray bursts (GRBs),the active galactic nuclei (AGNs) as well as the ultra-high energy cosmic rays (UHECRs) (Ruffini et al. 2021 and references therein). Their "inner engine", has three independent components: 1) a Kerr black hole which is neither in a stationary state nor in vacuum, 2) a background magnetic field aligned with the black hole rotation axis, and 3) an extremely diluted fully ionized plasma (Moradi et al. 2021).There is no role in this inner engine for ISCO. Indeed a new electro dynamical field equations describe the synchrotron radiation emitted close to the black hole horizon, they point to a discrete and repetitive emission of "blackholic quanta" in the MeV and in the GeV. The magnitudes and the emission time scales of these quanta, for M87 and GRB 130427A, are expressed as a function of the above three parameters (Rueda & Ruffini, 2021). A long lasting GeV emission with a luminosity decreasing as a temporal power law, allows for the first time in GRBs, the determination of the black hole mass and spin as well as their time evolution perfectly fulfilling our mass energy formula (Christodoulou & Ruffini, 1971): a long lasting emission process profoundly different from the traditional process of continued gravitational contraction.

Remo Ruffini

Professor GERARD 't HOOFT

"for his persistent devotion to the study of the quantum field theory boundary conditions at the black hole horizon".

Prof. Gerard 't Hooft has been a full Professor at the Utrecht University (the Netherlands), since 1977. Nowadays, he is an Emeritus Professor at that University. During his career, he has paid extended scientific visits to CERN (Geneva), Harvard, Stanford, Princeton and Duke University, NC. In 1999, together with M. Veltman, he received the Nobel Prize in Physics, awarded by The Royal Swedish Academy of Sciences, *"For elucidating the quantum structure of electroweak interactions in physics"*.

Prof. 't Hooft's main subjects of research includes:

– Gauge Theories for the sub-atomic particles and forces, various aspects and ingredients of what is now called "The Standard Model of the sub-atomic particles: renormalizability, topological features such as magnetic monopoles and instantons, 1/N expansions.

– Theories for the quantization of the gravitational force and black holes: producing models for the quantum properties of a black hole, as derived from Standard Model and General Relativity alone; its topological features such as antipodal identification.

Professor Gerard 't Hooft

– Fundamental theories underlying quantum mechanics, in particular returning determinism and reality to the dynamics of the tiniest material entities in his universe.

Prof. 't Hooft has been awarded the Wolf Prize of the State of Israel (1982), the Pius XI Medal (Vatican City, 1983), the Lorentz Medal (KNAW Amsterdam, 1986) as well as the Spinoza Premium (Netherlands Organization for Scientific Research NWO, 1995).

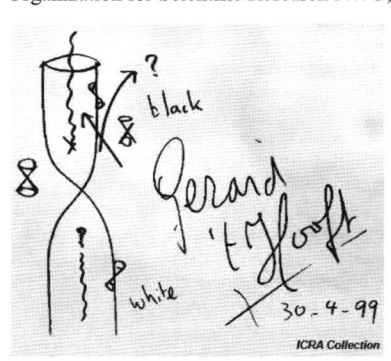

Fig. 2: The signature of Gerard 't Hooft on the wall of ICRA Room 301 (April 4, 1999).

A special event took place at ICRA on April 30, 1999. Prof. Ruffini invited Gerard 't Hooft to Rome to discuss a boundary condition for a quantum field on the black hole horizon, a topic Prof. Ruffini discussed in a previous article "Black-hole evaporation in the Klein-Sauter-Heisenberg-Euler formalism" with Thibault Damour (Phys. Rev. D 14, 332, 1976), but which needed to be examined in more detail. Prof. Ruffini planned to direct Gerard's attention to some specific aspects of this problem. Because we have traditionally been very attentive in spending ICRA travel funds, ICRA offered Gerard to come to Rome on a reduced fare weekend ticket arriving Friday and departing Monday. He had a great relaxing weekend together with Prof. Ruffini following his seminar, which among other things allowed Gerard to sign the wall in our ICRA Room (see Fig. 2), and during this splendid Rome spring weekend he also was able to find a missing factor of 2 in a formula in Prof. Ruffini's 1971 paper with Demetri Christodoulou on the black hole mass formula. The following October, Gerard received the Nobel prize, which meant that we could no longer get away with bringing him to Rome on a cheap ticket! Ever since Gerard has been in our MG IOC helping us with the preparation of the meetings. We are very happy to announce this MG16 Award to Gerard 't Hooft with the motivating phrase *"for his persistent devotion to the study of the quantum field theory boundary conditions at the black hole horizon"*.

Remo Ruffini

Professor **TSVI PIRAN**

"for extending relativistic astrophysics across international frontiers, a true companion in the search for the deeper meaning of Einstein's great theory".

Professor Tsvi Piran

Tsvi Piran is the emeritus Schwartzmann professor at the Hebrew University of Jerusalem. He obtained his PhD in Physics, in 1976 from the Hebrew University working on the collisional Penrose process. Piran returned to the Hebrew University at 1981after being a post doc at Oxford and Texas and a long-term member at the IAS at Princeton. In 1982 he initiated and directed the first ever summer school on Gravitational Waves that took place at Les Houches. Piran was a visiting professor at Harvard, Columbia and New York and a Moore scholar at Caltech.

Piran's research deals with numerous aspects of relativistic astrophysics, ranging from the foundation of numerical relativity to modeling of observer relativistic phenomena and analytic work on the fate of gravitational collapse. Piran's research work focuses mostly on black holes and in particular on gamma-ray bursts. He was among the first to point out their cosmological origin and their association with merging neutron stars and heavy r-process nucleo synthesis. Piran's achievements were recognized in the 2019 EMET prize for Physics.

Professor **STEVEN WEINBERG**

"for unwavering support for the MG meetings since their inception, a true companion in the search for the deeper meaning of Einstein's great theory".

Professor Steven Weinberg. Photo courtesy of Matt Valentine.

Steven Weinberg is a member of the Physics and Astronomy Departments at The University of Texas at Austin. His research has covered a broad range of topics in quantum field theory, elementary particle physics and cosmology. He has been honored with numerous awards, including the Nobel Prize in Physics, the National Medal of Science, the Heinemann Prize in Mathematical Physics and in 2020, the Breakthrough Prize. He is a member of the US National Academy of Sciences, Britain's Royal Society, and other academies in the USA and abroad. The American Philosophical Society awarded him the Benjamin Franklin Medal, with a citation that said he is "considered by many to be the preeminent theoretical physicist alive in the world today." His books for physicists include *Gravitation and Cosmology*, the three-volume work *The Quantum Theory of Fields*, *Cosmology* and published in April of 2021, *Foundations of Modern Physics*. Educated at Cornell, Copenhagen, and Princeton, he also holds honorary degrees from sixteen other universities. He taught at Columbia, Berkeley, M.I.T., and Harvard, where he was Higgins Professor of Physics, before coming to Texas in 1982.

Fig. 1: Chuo Pei Yuan and Cheng Ning Yang at MG2 in Trieste, Italy (1979).

The Sixteenth Marcel Grossmann Meeting (MG16) is a very special one in many respects: it will take place during a pandemic and in spite of the many difficulties, we have decided not to postpone it but to organize it as a virtual meeting. As described on the MG series webpage, these meetings started in 1975 with the first meeting at the International Centre for Theoretical Physics (ICTP) in Trieste (Italy) that I organized with Nobel Prize winner Abdus Salam. A second meeting followed in 1979, with a significantly larger participation including Nobel Laurate Cheng Ning Yang and a Chinese delegation led by Chuo Pei Yuan (see Fig. 1), including Fang Li-Zhi who had accompanied me during my entire first visit to China in 1979. The first truly international MG meeting followed in 1982 in Shanghai (China):this represented an especially important step forward both for the meeting and for China. A multi-millennia *"motto"* in China, which was then proclaimed on banners everywhere, read *"Friends from all over the world are welcomed"*.

We were soon at an impasse over the participation of scientists from Israel, since no diplomatic relations existed between China and Israel at that time and the Israeli scientists were not to be allowed to attend the meeting. A long negotiation began. The boundary conditions were clearly set by Steven Weinberg, a member of the present MG16 IOC: no MG meetings on Einstein's theory of general relativity could occur without the participation of Israeli scientists. The intervention of Yuval Ne'emann, also a member of the MG IOC then as well as the Minister of Science of Israel (see Fig.2), proposed a compromise that would admit at least one Israeli scientist. I went to Beijing alone, meeting every morning for a week with 12 Chinese representatives led by Chuo Pei Yuan going over all possible options. I stayed in an isolated villa not far from Tiananmen Square, accompanied by the 3 volumes of Matteo Ricci (RI MA TO) to keep me company. No solution was in sight the entire week. At the last moment, just before my departure, an agreement was finally reached allowing two Israeli scientists into China. The historic compromise would admit Gerard Tauber and Tsvi Piran into China using a special ICRA travel document I had proposed for them to be able to participate in the meeting, accepted by the Chinese Ambassador in Rome. This modified the thousand-year Chinese *"motto"* to read *"Scientists from all over the world are welcomed"*. The event was extremely beneficial for China and signaled the truly international nature of the MG meetings.

Fig. 2: From right to left: Chaim Weizmann, President of Israel; Yuval Ne'emann, Minister of Science of Israel; R. Ruffini.

I kept on meeting Tauber in the years which followed (see Fig. 3). Soon after, Yuval Ne'emann visited China. The development of bilateral relations, including military cooperation and economical tights, grow exponentially until the establishment of normal diplomatic relations between Israel and China in 1992.

Fig. 3: From right to left: Arrigo Finzi, Remo Ruffini, Gerard Tauber and Konrad Bleuler.

Fig. 4: Albert Einstein, Hideki Yukawa and John. A. Wheeler with a handwritten dedication to Remo Ruffini "To Remo Ruffini, companion in the search for the deeper meaning of Einstein great theory. With warm regards, John Wheeler 5 April 1968".

Given their key role played in the foundations of the MG meetings, I am very happy to propose on behalf of the MG16 IOC, two special Marcel Grossmann Individual Awards: one to Steven Weinberg for *"for unwavering support for the MG meetings since their inception, a true companion in the search for the deeper meaning of Einstein's great theory"* and another one to Tsvi Piran, *"for extending Relativistic astrophysics across international frontiers, a true companion in the search for the deeper meaning of Einstein's great theory"*, in the words of John A. Wheeler's photo dedication to me (see Fig. 4).

Remo Ruffini

PREFACE

Since 1975, the Marcel Grossmann Meetings on Recent Developments in Theoretical and Experimental General Relativity, Gravitation, and Relativistic Field Theories have been organized in order to provide opportunities for discussing recent advances in gravitation, general relativity and relativistic field theories, emphasizing mathematical foundations, physical predictions and experimental tests. The objective of these meetings is to elicit exchange among scientists that may deepen our understanding of spacetime structures as well as to review the status of ongoing experiments aimed at testing Einstein's theory of gravitation either from the ground or from space. Previous meetings have been held in Trieste (MG1: 1975) and (MG2: 1979), Shanghai (MG3: 1982), Rome (MG4: 1985, MG9: 2000), Perth (MG5: 1988), Kyoto (MG6: 1991), Stanford (MG7: 1994), Jerusalem (MG8: 1997), Rio (MG10: 2003), Berlin (MG11: 2006), Paris (MG12: 2009), Stockholm (MG13: 2012), MG14 in 2015 and MG15 in 2018 both in Rome.

Due to the COVID-19 pandemic spreading in the last two years the decision was taken to organize the Sixteenth Marcel Grossmann meeting for the first time in history entirely online. Despite numerous challenges, related to the organization of large worldwide event, MG16 showed the strongest ever interest from the scientific community with a record-breaking number of almost 1200 registered participants and of more than 1000 speakers.

The traditional six-day schedule has been modified to account for different time zones of the speakers and each day the program of the meeting was divided in three blocks with the reference to the Central European Summer Time. The first block was starting at 06:30 in the morning, allowing comfortable time for speakers from Asia and Oceania. The second block was held in the daytime in Europe and Africa. The third block was starting in the afternoon and ending at 19:30 allowing accommodation of the speakers from the Americas. Each day the blocks of plenary sessions were interchanging with the blocks of about 30 parallel sessions each, making this one of the most intense MG meetings ever. All this was possible thanks to recent developments in communication technologies. The Indico open-source software was selected as a web platform for this meeting, while Zoom platform was adopted for the video-conferencing. The meeting was streamed on ICRANet YouTube channel.

The meeting started on Monday July 5 with the Award ceremony. The individual awards went to Demetrios Christodoulou, Tsvi Piran, Gerard 't Hooft and Steven Weinberg, while the Institutional Awards went to the S.A. Lavochkin Association, to the Max Planck Institute for Extraterrestrial Physics – MPE and to the Space Research Institute IKI of the Russian Academy of Sciences. Overall there were 54 plenary talks, 4 public lectures and 5 roundtables and about 90 parallel sessions. The plenary session "Events in Relativistics Astrophysics" on Monday have seen the contributions from Rashid Sunyaev, Michael Kramer, James Miller-Jones, Felix Mirabel. The public lectures were delivered by Razmik Mirzoyan, Asghar Qadir and Mohammad Bagheri. Plenary talks on Tuesday session "Black holes and the Quantum" by Juan Maldacena, Ahmed Almheiri, Gerard 't Hooft, Mihalis Dafermos, Sergiu Klainerman, Abhay Ashtekar and Frank Wilczek were bracketed by two roundtables on "New results from SRG/eRosita" with the participation of Andrea Merloni, Prof. Rashid Sunyaev, Alexander Lutovinov, Chandreyee Maitra, Esra Bulbul and "Solar neutrinos and Borexino" with the participation of Gianpaolo Bellini and Wick Haxton. Plenary talks on Wednesday in the session "Lambda CDM tensions" by George Efstathiou, Scolnic Daniel, Marc Kamionkowski, Wendy Freedman, Priya Natarajan and Licia Verde were followed by the roundtable "Precision cosmology" with the participation of Licia Verde, Marc Kamionkowski, Piero Rosati, and the public lecture by Francis Halzen. Two blocks of Thursday plenary sessions "Black holes in GRBs" and "Precision tests" included the talks by Roy Kerr, Yuan Ha, Lorenzo Amati, Elena Pian, Carlos Raúl Argüelles, Di Li, Jianglai Liu, Claus Lämmerzahl, Gerhard Heinzel and Ignazio Ciufolini and were followed by the roundtable "GRB 170817A and GRB 190829A" with the participation of Eleonora Troja, Liang Li, Rahim Moradi, Jorge Armando Rueda Hernandez. Two plenary blocks on Friday "Massive stars" and "Physics behind stellar collapse" included the talks by Selma de Mink, Norbert Langer, Jiri Bicak and Tomáš Ledvinka, Ivan De Mitri, Rahim Moradi and Giancarlo Cella. Finally, two plenary blocks on Saturday "Current and future missions" have seen the talks by Shuang-Nan Zhang, Weimin Yuan, Makoto Tashiro, Ruoyu Liu, Jean-Luc Atteia, Jim Hinton and Nicholas White and were followed by the roundtable "What is in our Galactic center" with the participation of Reinhard Genzel, Carlos Raúl Argüelles, Andreas Krut, Jorge Armando Rueda Hernandez, Eduar Becerra Vergara. The program of the meeting can be found at the official website http://www.icra.it/mg/mg16 and at ICRANet Indico website https://indico.icranet.org/event/1/.

These proceedings include about 400 papers containing the results presented at the Sixteenth Marcel Grossmann meeting. The plenary papers from the meeting have been published in International Journal of Modern Physics D as they were submitted. The table of contents includes also the links to YouTube videos with talks given at the meeting and cover plenary talks, public lectures, roundtables and all parallel sessions. The general link to the videos from MG16 is: https://www.youtube.com/watch?v=QFe1lsSid-o&list=PLr5RLbSWSonsaOnZukBDs0qsNIWM8AvRF.

As the editors we would like to express our gratitude to all the chairpersons of the parallel sessions at MG16, who peer-reviewed the papers submitted for these proceedings, as well as to the ICRANet secretariat office and in particular to Cinzia di Niccolo, Elisabetta Natale and Yasmina Di Domizio, as well as to ICRANet system manager Gabriele Brandolini for their help in preparation of this publication.

Remo Ruffini and Gregory Vereshchagin
November 2021

Contents

Publications in this Series	v
Sponsors and Acknowledgements	vii
Organizing Committees	ix
Marcel Grossmann Awards	xi
Preface	xxxvi

PART A
PLENARY SESSIONS

New results from testing relativistic gravity with radio pulsars *Michael Kramer*	3
Dragging of inertial frames by matter and waves *Jiří Bičák and Tomáš Ledvinka*	22
Probes of the progenitors, engines and physics behind stellar collapse *Chris L. Fryer*	39
The observation of high-energy neutrinos from the cosmos: Lessons learned for multimessenger astronomy *Francis Halzen*	59
The first results of PandaX-4T *Jianglai Liu on behalf of the PandaX Collaboration*	85
XRISM: X-ray imaging and spectroscopy mission *Makoto S. Tashiro and the XRISM team*	95
The SVOM mission *J.-L. Atteia, B. Cordier and J. Wei on behalf of the SVOM Collaboration*	104
Quantum field theory with boundary conditions at the horizons *Gerard 't Hooft*	133

The development of general relativity and the cosmological constant
Asghar Qadir 143

The irreducible mass of Christodoulou-Ruffini-Hawking mass formula
Yuan K. Ha 154

Reshaping our understanding on structure formation with the quantum nature of the dark matter
C. R. Argüelles, E. A. Becerra-Vergara, A. Krut et al. 164

First results of LHAASO
Ruo-Yu Liu for the LHAASO Collaboration 180

On the MG16 awards 2021
Remo Ruffini 196

The white dwarf binary merger model of GRB 170817A
J. A. Rueda, R. Ruffini, Liang Li et al. 217

PARALLEL SESSIONS

Accretion

• MHD Processes Near Compact Objects
Chairperson: Sergey Moiseenko
YouTube link: https://youtu.be/2WMTg06ZmV8

A semi-implicit multidimensional unstructured gas dynamical solver for astrophysical applications
Ilya A. Kondratyev and Sergey G. Moiseenko 242

Magnetized neutron stars propagating through a non-uniform ISM
O. D. Toropina, M. M. Romanova and R. V. E. Lovelace 255

Calculation of the kinetic coefficients of arbitrary degenerate electrons in magnetized dense matter
M. V. Glushikhina and G. S. Bisnovatyi-Kogan 264

Modeling of magnetic fields of accretion discs, using no-z- and RZ-approximations
M. V. Pashentseva and E. A. Mikhailov 272

• Accretion Discs and Jets
Chairpersons: Audrey Trova and Shokoufe Faraji
YouTube link: https://youtu.be/29Wj9RCVEKw

Limiting effects in tori clusters
D. Pugliese and Z. Stulchik 280

Hydrodynamical transport of angular momentum in accretion disks
in the presence of nonlinear perturbations due to noise
Subham Ghosh and Banibrata Mukhopadhyay 295

Properties of accretion disc models in the background quadrupole
Shokoufe Faraji 307

Magnetized tori around a uniformly accelerating black hole
Shokoufe Faraji and Audrey Trova 317

Multifrequency behaviour of high mass X-ray binaries
(Time lag between optical and X-ray outbursts)
Franco Giovannelli 321

Active Galactic Nuclei

• The Black Hole in M87
Chairpersons: Brian Punsly and Jorge Rueda
YouTube link: https://youtu.be/l1lTgksyJag

Rotation of the crescent image of M87* and polarization of its ESE hotspot
Krzysztof Nalewajko 339

Magnetic reconnection in jet-accretion disk systems
*Chandra B. Singh, Elisabete M. de Gouveia Dal Pino,
Luis H. S. Kadowaki et al.* 344

• Machine Learning in Astronomy: AGN, Transient Events, Cosmology and Others
Chairpersons: Rahim Moradi and Yu Wang
YouTube link: https://youtu.be/ErqrmMZQsBk

Exact fractal model of the universe and possible machine learning
methods for the verification of the fractality
A. A. Kirillov, E. P. Savelova and P. O. Vladykina 352

Estimating the photometric redshifts of galaxies and QSOs using
regression techniques in machine learning
A. Momtaz, M. H. Salimi and S. Shakeri 368

Deep learning in quasar physics
*F. Rastegar Nia, M. T. Mirtorabi, R. Moradi, Y. Wang
and A. Vafaei Sadr* 382

Cosmological density field emulation and gravitational wave inference
based on dimensionality reduction and supervised machine learning
Miguel Conceição, António da Silva and Alberto Krone-Martins 391

Unsupervised photometric detection of galaxy cluster candidates in
large surveys
Ana Carvalho, Alberto Krone-Martins and Antonio da Silva 409

• **Multiwavelength and Multi-Messenger Observations of Active Galactic Nuclei**
Chairpersons: Paolo Giommi and Narek Sahakyan

YouTube link: https://youtu.be/-Hyu2NQsExg

Time-dependent lepto-hadronic modeling of the emission processes in
blazar jets
S. Gasparyan, D. Bégué and N. Sahakyan 429

Multiwavelength study of high-redshift blazars
G. Harutyunyan and D. Israyelyan 445

Alternative Theories

• Extended Theories of Gravity and Quantum Cosmology
Chairpersons: Yi-Fu Cai and Wentao Luo

YouTube links: https://youtu.be/ADRr9DfV5zM
https://youtu.be/eOzpiC1cFkU
https://youtu.be/kYzJds_JIp8

Quantum gravity phenomenology from thermodynamics of spacetime
A. Alonso-Serrano and M. Liška 462

Gauge theory of gravity based on the correspondence between
the 1st and the 2nd order formalisms
David Benisty 479

$U(1)$ local strings in hybrid metric-Palatini gravity
Tiberiu Harko, Francisco S. N. Lobo and Hilberto M. R. da Silva 485

Inflationary supersymmetric FRLW quantum cosmology
N. E. Martínez-Pérez, C. Ramirez and V. M. Vázquez-Báez 499

Effective $f(R)$ actions for modified loop quantum cosmologies
Ana Rita Ribeiro, Daniele Vernieri and Francisco S. N. Lobo 517

Probing multiverse using gravitational wave observations
Moe Kukihara and Kazuhiro Hayama 531

Operator ordering ambiguity in observables of quantum cosmology
Harkirat Singh Sahota and Kinjalk Lochan 538

Decoupled quark stars in self-interacting Brans-Dicke gravity
M. Sharif and Amal Majid 548

Big-bounce in projectively invariant Nieh-Yan models: The Bianchi I case
*Flavio Bombacigno, Simon Boudet, Gonzalo J. Olmo
and Giovanni Montani* 561

Late time cosmology with derivatives of matter Lagrangian
Shahab Shahidi 576

On the semiclassical and quantum picture of the Bianchi I polymer dynamics
E. Giovannetti, G. Montani and S. Schiattarella 588

Quantum corrections to the Bianchi II transition under local rotational invariance
Sara F. Uria, David Brizuela and Ana Alonso-Serrano 597

- **Mathematical Problems of Relativistic Physics: Classical and Quantum**
Chairpersons: A. Shadi Tahvildar-Zadeh and Michael Kiessling
YouTube links: https://youtu.be/9Dr3M9Kb2jo
https://youtu.be/gMOykpapJ5A

The hypercomplex medium as storage of physical equations
Alexander P. Yefremov 605

The Maxwell-Bopp-Landé-Thomas-Podolsky-Einstein system for a static point source
Érik Amorim 619

On recent developments in the theory of relativistic dissipative fluids
V. Hoang 627

Adiabatic solutions in general relativity as null geodesics on the space of boundary diffeomorphisms
Emine Şeyma Kutluk 635

The point spectrum of the Dirac Hamiltonian on the zero-gravity Kerr-Newman spacetime
M. Kiessling, E. Ling and A. S. Tahvildar-Zadeh 648

Causal fermion systems: Classical gravity and beyond
Felix Finster 661

Newman-Penrose-Debye formalism for fields of various spins in pp-wave backgrounds
Aleksandr Kulitskii and Elena Yu Melkumova 679

Gravitational geometric phase
*Banibrata Mukhopadhyay, Tanuman Ghosh and
Soumya Kanti Ganguly* 689

Retarded potentials and radiation in odd dimensions
D. V. Gal'tsov and M. Khlopunov 699

Wave propagation in the anti-deSitter optical metric
D. García-Peláez and C. S. López-Monsalvo 713

New approaches to constrained dynamics and Hamilton-Jacobi
procedures in general relativity
D. Salisbury, J. Renn and K. Sundermeyer 719

Orientability of space from electromagnetic quantum fluctuations
N. A. Lemos and M. J. Rebouças 725

Essential self-adjointness of Dirac operators under the influence of
general-relativistic gravity
Michael K.-H. Kiessling, A. Shadi Tahvildar-Zadeh and Ebru Toprak 736

- **Wormholes, Energy Conditions and Time Machines**
Chairpersons: Francisco Lobo and Diego Rubiera-Garcia

YouTube links: https://youtu.be/tu_3Wqcd9Ys
https://youtu.be/NqN1c-2fv8Y

Relic magnetic wormholes as possible source of toroidal magnetic
fields in galaxies
A. A. Kirillov and E. P. Savelova 743

Wormhole geometries induced by action-dependent Lagrangian theories
Ismael Ayuso, Francisco S. N. Lobo and José P. Mimoso 756

Gravitational lensing by wormholes in binary systems
S. Pietroni 774

Hyper-fast positive energy warp drives
E. W. Lentz 779

From black-bounce to traversable wormhole, and beyond
Alex Simpson 787

Tractor beams, pressor beams, and stressor beams within the context
of general relativity
Matt Visser, Jessica Santiago and Sebastian Schuster 808

A singularity theorem for evaporating black holes
E.-A. Kontou, B. Freivogel and D. Krommydas 822

Circularly symmetric thin-shell wormholes in F(R) gravity with
(2+1)-dimensions
Cecilia Bejarano, Ernesto F. Eiroa and Griselda Figueroa-Aguirre 831

Warp drive dynamic solutions considering different fluid sources
*Osvaldo L. Santos-Pereira, Everton M. C. Abreu and
Marcelo B. Ribeiro* 840

Symmetries and geometry of spacetime: Towards a new paradigm
Francisco Cabral, Francisco S. N. Lobo and Diego Rubiera-Garcia 856

- **Theories of gravity: Alternatives to the cosmological and particle standard models**
Chairpersons: Stefano Bellucci and Orlando Luongo

YouTube links: https://youtu.be/-aQcrYoQfBM
https://youtu.be/WsCwPb5OQhY
https://youtu.be/JMnrUfBgqVU
https://youtu.be/pPhZY-bbsew

Thermodynamics of scalar-tensor gravity: A new approach
Valerio Faraoni 876

Two body dynamics in a quadratic modification of general relativity
Soham Bhattacharyya 883

Alternatives to Λ: Torsion, generalized couplings, and scale invariance
C. J. A. P. Martins, C. M. J. Marques, C. B. D. Fernandes et al. 907

Model-independent test of scalar-tensor gravity theory by
reconstructing scalar mode of GW170817
Yuya Gushima and Kazuhiro Hayama 921

Cosmology in the novel scalar-tensor representation of $f(R,T)$ gravity
Tiago B. Gonçalves, João Luís Rosa and Francisco S. N. Lobo 932

On the interaction between electromagnetic, gravitational, and plasma
related perturbations on LRS class II spacetimes
P. Semrén 943

Condition for expansion-collapse duality between Einstein and
Jordan frames
Dipayan Mukherjee, H. K. Jassal and Kinjalk Lochan 958

The model of dark energy based on the quantum-mechanical
uncertainty relation
Yu. V. Dumin 967

- **Conformal Dilaton Gravity and Related Issues**
Chairperson: Reinoud Jan Slagter

YouTube link: https://youtu.be/A3Ygi3YBs5A

Conformal dilaton gravity, antipodal mapping and black hole physics
on a warped spacetime
R. J. Slagter 978

From neutrino masses to the full size of the universe — Some
intriguing aspects of the tetron model
B. Lampe 999

Summary parallel session AT5
Reinoud Jan Slagter 1014

- **Horava-Lifshitz Gravity**
Chairperson: Anzhong Wang

YouTube links: https://youtu.be/vPT1dH1zITE
https://youtu.be/5z7zhpiDOpw

Boundary conditions for the Klein-Gordon field on Lifshitz spacetimes
Lissa de Souza Campos 1017

Dynamical system analysis of Bianchi-I spacetimes in $f(R)$ gravity
Saikat Chakraborty, Kazuharu Bamba and Alberto Saa 1026

Cosmological implications in modified Hořava-Lifshitz gravity
Abdul Jawad, Kazuharu Bamba and Farwa Khurshid 1038

Finite action principle and wormholes
Jan Chojnacki and Jan Kwapisz 1046

Strange quark stars in Hořava gravity
Grigoris Panotopoulos 1054

Shadows of Kerr-like black holes in $4D$ Einstein–Gauss–Bonnet
gravity and constraints from EHT observations
Sushant G. Ghosh and Rahul Kumar Walia 1069

Wormhole interaction in 2d Hořava-Lifshitz quantum gravity
Jan Ambjørn, Yuki Hiraga, Yoshiyasu Ito and Yuki Sato 1084

Nature of singularities in vector-tensor theories of gravity
V. H. Satheeshkumar 1095

Hořava-Lifshitz and Einstein-Æther gravity in the light of Event Horizon Telescope observations of M87*
Emmanuel N. Saridakis 1104

Hořava-Lifshitz gravity in (3 + 1) dimensions coupled with anisotropic matter and possible constraints from GRB 170817A
Tao Zhang and Fu-Wen Shu 1112

Summary of the parallel session AT6
Anzhong Wang 1119

• **Ghost-Free Models of Modified Gravity: Massive Gravity, Horndeski and DHOST Theories, Other Related Models; Their Properties and Solutions**
Chairpersons: Dmitry Gal'tsov and Michael Volkov

YouTube links: https://youtu.be/l8KHUPnT2D8
https://youtu.be/48OHIKpgNqs

Non-local R^2-like inflation, gravitational waves and Non-Gaussianities
K. Sravan Kumar 1124

Palatini kinetic scalar-tensor theory: Analytical and numerical solutions
D. V. Gal'tsov and D. S. Bushuev 1136

PART B

Black Holes: Theory and Observations/Experiments

• **Theoretical and Observational Studies of Astrophysical Black Holes**
Chairperson: Alexander Zakharov

YouTube links: https://youtu.be/fiv_MH-N2kw
https://youtu.be/GYoOb17GvE8

Reconstruction of a star motion in the vicinity of black hole from the redshift of the electromagnetic spectrum
S. O. Komarov and A. K. Gorbatsievich 1151

Shadows of hairy Kerr black holes and constraints from M87*
Sushant G. Ghosh and Misba Afrin 1167

Displacement memory and BMS symmetries
Shailesh Kumar 1179

Physical black holes in semiclassical gravity
Sebastian Murk and Daniel R. Terno 1196

- **Black Hole Thermodynamics**

Chairperson: Hernando Quevedo

YouTube links: https://youtu.be/XmZDf5mrXQk
https://youtu.be/amseL2qykfk

Information recovery from evaporating rotating charged black holes
Zhi-Wei Wang, Samuel L. Braunstein and Saurya Das 1212

Black hole thermodynamics from entanglement mechanics
S. Mahesh Chandran and S. Shankaranarayanan 1223

Thermodynamics of charged black hole
M. Sharif and Amjad Khan 1238

Rindler trajectories and Rindler horizons in the Schwarzschild spacetime
Kajol Paithankar and Sanved Kolekar 1250

Linear growth of the two-point function for the Unruh state in
$1 + 1$ dimensional black holes
Paul R. Anderson, Zachary P. Scofield and Jennie Traschen 1255

Stress-energy tensor for a quantized scalar field in a four-dimensional
black hole that forms from the collapse of a null shell
*Shohreh Gholizadeh Siahmazg, Paul R. Anderson, Raymond D. Clark
and Alessandro Fabbri* 1265

Microscopic model building for black hole membranes from constraints
of symmetry
Swastik Bhattacharya and S. Shankaranarayanan 1275

Einstein-Maxwell-Dilaton-Axion mass formulas for black holes with
struts and strings
Dmitri Gal'tsov, Gérard Clément and Igor Bogush 1291

- **Black Holes in Alternative Theories of Gravity**

Chairpersons: Jutta Kunz and Kamal Hajian

YouTube links: https://youtu.be/FRNGJKhiw7c
https://youtu.be/Tjfmuut1Eo0

Holography for rotating black holes in $f(T)$ gravity
Masoud Ghezelbash 1308

Infinitely degenerate exact Ricci-flat solutions in $f(R)$ gravity
Semin Xavier, Jose Mathew and S. Shankaranarayanan 1319

Universe in a black hole with spin and torsion
Nikodem Popławski 1327

Asymptotically flat black hole solution in modified gravity
Surajit Kalita and Banibrata Mukhopadhyay 1337

Shadow of a charged black hole surrounded by an anisotropic matter field
Javier Badía and Ernesto F. Eiroa 1343

Constraining modified gravity theories with physical black holes
Sebastian Murk 1351

Penrose suggestion as to pre-Planck-era black holes showing up in present universe data sets discussed, with a possible candidate as to GW radiation which may provide initial CMBR data
A. W. Beckwith 1359

Summary of the parallel session BH3
Kamal Hajian and Jutta Kunz 1372

Binaries

• Explosive Events Associated with Compact-Object Binary Mergers
Chairpersons: Chris Belczynski and Jorge Rueda

YouTube links: https://youtu.be/Dwq1ZU3gKrg
https://youtu.be/nw02ylI6R2M

Uncertainties in kilonova modeling
C. L. Fryer, C. J. Fontes, O. Korobkin et al. 1391

• Post-Newtonian and Post-Minkowskian Corrections for Binary Gravitating Systems
Chairperson: Johannes Bluemlein

YouTube link: https://youtu.be/wfiLG5r08yE

Tutti-Frutti method: Recent developments in the PN/PM/SF treatment of the gravitational two-body problem
Donato Bini and Andrea Geralico 1405

• Multichannel Studies of Nonstationary Relativistic Stars
Chairperson: Vladimir Lipunov

YouTube link: https://youtu.be/usn2PlU_qFA

GRB observations on cubesate satellites in the Universat–SOCRAT project
Sergey I. Svertilov, Michail I. Panasyuk, Vitaly V. Bogomolov et al. 1412

Multiwavelength observations of GRB160625B by MASTER,
Lomonosov, Konus-Wind and three stage collapse
V. M. Lipunov, V. A. Sadovnichy, M. I. Panasyuk et al. 1429

The role of the magnetic fields in GRB outflows
N. Jordana-Mitjans, C. G. Mundell, S. Kobayashi et al. 1449

MASTER optical observations of the blazar TXS0506+056 during the
IC170922A
V. M. Lipunov, K. Zhirkov, V. G. Kornilov et al. 1467

Boson Stars

• Scalar Fields in Cosmology
Chairpersons: Carlos Herdeiro and Alfredo Macias

YouTube links: https://youtu.be/SyLoguueGKk
https://youtu.be/f9nuo8Jvw-w

A short review on nonlinear perturbation theory of structure
formation for modified gravity
Jorge L. Cervantes-Cota and Alejandro Aviles 1474

Testing modified gravity theories with marked statistics
Alejandro Aviles 1494

Dark matter as condensed phase of generic bosons
Elías Castellanos and Jorge Mastache 1513

Cosmic Microwave Background

• Cosmic Backgrounds from Radio to Far-IR
Chairperson: Carlo Burigana

YouTube link: https://youtu.be/4e3Cj5wahck

New Planck tSZ map and its cosmological analysis
H. Tanimura, M. Douspis and N. Aghanim 1527

The CMB dipole: Eppur si muove
R. M. Sullivan and D. Scott 1532

High angular resolution Sunyaev Zel'dovich observations: The case of
MISTRAL
E. S. Battistelli, E. Barbavara, P. de Bernardis et al. 1542

Cosmological and astrophysical results exploiting magnification bias
with high-z sub-millimetre galaxies
L. Bonavera, M. M. Cueli and J. Gonzalez-Nuevo 1557

The impact of the Lorentz symmetry violation on the CMB polarization
Seddigheh Tizchang, Rohoollah Mohammadi and She-Sheng Xue 1571

Cosmic backgrounds from the radio to the far-infrared: Recent results and perspectives from cosmological and astrophysical surveys
Carlo Burigana, Elia Sefano Battistelli, Laura Bonavera et al. 1579

- **New Horizons in Cosmology with CMB Spectral Distortions**

Chairpersons: Jens Chluba and Andrea Ravenni

YouTube links: https://youtu.be/uBYLO4Smw3o
https://youtu.be/5oAPfzAe35k

CMB μT cross-correlations as a probe of PBH scenarios
Ogan Özsoy and Gianmassimo Tasinato 1609

Theoretical and numerical aspects of CMB spectral distortions from non-thermal energy injections
Sandeep Kumar Acharya, Jens Chluba and Abir Sarkar 1628

BISOU: A balloon project to measure the CMB spectral distortions
B. Maffei, M. H. Abitbol, N. Aghanim et al. 1633

Cosmic microwave background spectral distortions constraints on decaying dark matter particles and axion-like particles using *COBE/FIRAS* and *EDGES*
Boris Bolliet 1645

The COSmic Monopole Observer (COSMO)
S. Masi, E. Battistelli, P. de Bernardis et al. 1654

- **Status of the H_0 and σ_8 Tensions: Theoretical Models and Model-Independent Constraints**

Chairpersons: Joan Solà Peracaula and Adrià Gómez-Valent

YouTube links: https://youtu.be/VNWZ1Bzjus4
https://youtu.be/zEBOCwvetKE
https://youtu.be/nzgC7qV9H_Y

Measuring the Hubble constant H_0 from gravitational lensing
Liliya L. R. Williams 1672

Extra components consistency in the Hubble tension and BBN
Osamu Seto and Yo Toda 1686

Gravitational anomalies, axions and a string-inspired running vacuum model in Cosmology
Nick E. Mavromatos 1693

Early and not so early dark energy. What do cosmological observations tell us about them?
Adrià Gómez-Valent, Ziyang Zheng, Luca Amendola, Valeria Pettorino and Christof Wetterich 1713

Renormalized ρ_{vac} without m^4 terms
Cristian Moreno-Pulido and Joan Solà Peracaula 1733

BD-ΛCDM and running vacuum models: Theoretical background and current observational status
Javier de Cruz Pérez, Joan Solà Peracaula, Adrià Gómez-Valent and Cristian Moreno-Pulido 1752

Cosmological tensions: Hints for a new concordance model?
E. Di Valentino 1770

Solving both H_0 and σ_8 tensions in $f(T)$ gravity
Emmanuel N. Saridakis 1783

Precision Cosmology and Hubble tension in the era of LSS surveys
G. Fanizza 1792

- **Effects of Primordial Perturbations Enhancement: From Black Holes Formation to CMB Anomalies**
Chairpersons: Antonio Enea Romano and Krzysztof Turzynski
YouTube link: https://youtu.be/frjjONXbd1M

Primordial black holes arise when the inflaton falls
Keisuke Inomata 1803

Effects of the modification of gravity on the production of primordial black holes
Sergio Andrés Vallejo Peña 1809

Cosmic Strings

- **Cosmic Strings**
Chairpersons: Reinoud Jan Slagter and Batool Imtiaz
YouTube link: https://youtu.be/ZpaU82ZUHzM

$U(1)$ local strings in generalized hybrid metric-Palatini gravity
Hilberto M. R. da Silva, Tiberiu Harko, Francisco S. N. Lobo and João Luís Rosa 1820

New evidence of the azimuthal alignment of quasars spin vector in Large Quasar Groups and cosmic strings
R. J. Slagter 1835

Summary parallel session cosmic strings I
Reinoud Jan Slagter and Batool Imtiaz 1848

- **From Cosmic Strings to Superstrings**
Chairpersons: Carlos Martins and Ivan Rybak
YouTube link: https://youtu.be/LJFtV_4aSAg

Scaling solutions of wiggly cosmic strings
A. R. R. Almeida and C. J. A. P. Martins 1851

High resolution calibration of string network evolution
J. R. C. C. C. Correia and C. J. A. P. Martins 1871

Radiation from Global Cosmic Strings using adaptive mesh refinement
Amelia Drew and E. P. S. Shellard 1891

Analysing the scaling density of axion strings
A. Lopez-Eiguren 1898

Electroweak axion string and superconductivity
Yu Hamada, Yoshihiko Abe and Koichi Yoshioka 1912

Dark Energy and Large Scale Structure

- **Dark Energy and the Accelerating Universe**
Chairpersons: Alexei Starobinky and David Polarski
YouTube links: https://youtu.be/JZEPRS_rqbE
https://youtu.be/3aG_AT4UzWE
https://youtu.be/ZlTWquG-pFk

Hints for the $H_0 - r_d$ tension in uncorrelated Baryon Acoustic Oscillations dataset
Denitsa Staicova 1923

Observational constraints on nonlinear matter extensions of general relativity
E.-A. Kolonia and C. J. A. P. Martins 1935

Constraining the dark energy-dark matter interaction model using low-redshift observations
Archana Sangwan, Joseph P. J. and S. Shankaranarayanan 1948

On the evolution of inhomogeneous perturbations in the ΛCDM model and $f(R)$ modified gravity theories
T. Schiavone and G. Montani 1961

Soft dark energy and soft dark matter
Emmanuel N. Saridakis 1970

A simple parametrisation for coupled dark energy
Vitor da Fonseca, Nelson J. Nunes and Tiago Barreiro 1979

- **Cosmography with Gravitational Lensing**
Chairpersons: Claudio Grillo and Mimoza Hafizi
YouTube link: https://youtu.be/FXplIAvUDBM

A tale of two double quasars: Hubble constant tension or biases?
L. J. Goicoechea and V. N. Shalyapin 1990

Dark Matter

- **Interacting Dark Matter**
Chairpersons: Nikolaos Mavromatos
YouTube links: https://youtu.be/zOshKJlwD-Y
https://youtu.be/JR44dh2GYik

Dark energy and dark matter unification from dynamical space time:
BBN constraints
D. Benisty 2005

Entropy and irreversible processes in gravity and cosmology
Llorenç Espinosa-Portalés and Juan García-Bellido 2013

LHC experiments for long-lived particles of the dark sector
Vasiliki A. Mitsou 2029

Constraining the interactions in the dark sector with cosmological data
Adrià Gómez-Valent, Valeria Pettorino and Luca Amendola 2050

Running vacuum interacting with dark matter or with running
gravitational coupling. Phenomenological implications
Joan Solà Peracaula 2069

Dark matter properties from the Fornax globular cluster timing:
Dynamical friction and cored profiles
D. Blas 2089

Growth of linear perturbations in a universe with superfluid dark matter
S. Banerjee, S. Bera and D. F. Mota 2101

Interacting dark sector in the late Universe: Mapping fields and fluids,
and observational signatures
Joseph P. J. and S. Shankaranarayanan 2119

The role of self interactions in the cosmological evolution of warm
dark matter
R. Yunis, C. R. Argüelles, D. López Nacir et al. 2127

Interaction energy between a charged medium and its electromagnetic field as a dark matter candidate
Mayeul Arminjon 2139

• **Dark Matter Searches with Liquid Xenon and Argon Detectors and Self Gravitating Systems and Dark Matter**
Chairpersons: Marco Merafina and Soroush Shakeri and She-Sheng Xue
YouTube link: https://youtu.be/H9oGYnGq9pI

The maximum mass of dilute axion stars
Pierre-Henri Chavanis 2149

A dark matter solution for the XENON1T electron excess and the galactic center 511 keV line
Yasaman Farzan 2174

Preliminary results of rich galaxy clusters' spatial distribution analysis on CfA2 Redshift Survey data: Compact objects or dark matter presence at redshift less 0.032
I. V. Arkhangelskaja, A. M. Galper, L. N. Khanh and D. N. Dorosheva 2189

• **Dark Matter: Beyond ΛCDM**
Chairpersons: Carlos Argüelles and Andreas Krut
YouTube links: https://youtu.be/hdKeo5L7pYE
https://youtu.be/i0IPHXzmV-s

Probing the nature of dark matter with Milky Way subhaloes
M. R. Lovell 2202

Addressing classical cosmological back-reaction with multiple scales
Yonadav Barry Ginat 2217

Imaging formation process for DM profiles
Omar de J. Cabrera-Rosas and Tonatiuh Matos 2222

The self-gravitating Fermi gas in Newtonian gravity and general relativity
Pierre-Henri Chavanis 2230

• **Dark Matter and Rare Processes**
Chairpersons: Carlos Rita Bernabei and Zurab Berezhiani
YouTube links: https://youtu.be/wheVrbETP_0
https://youtu.be/dVdZ4TIDxt0

The dark matter: DAMA/LIBRA and its perspectives
R. Bernabei, P. Belli, V. Caracciolo et al. 2252

Dark matter directionality approach
R. Bernabei, P. Belli, V. Caracciolo et al. 2272

Collapse models under test by high sensitivity γ-ray and X-ray measurements
C. Curceanu, Kristian Piscicchia, Massimiliano Bazzi et al. 2288

Leptophilic dark matter at linear colliders
P. S. Bhupal Dev 2296

DM6 session: Dark matter and rare processes
R. Bernabei and Z. Berezhiani 2316

- **The Nature of Galactic Halos**
Chairpersons: Francesco De Paolis and Asghar Qadir
YouTube link: https://youtu.be/qIwVnNxi0n0

Primordial black holes as dark matter candidates in the Galactic halo
Lindita Hamolli, Mimoza Hafizi, Francesco De Paolis and Achille A. Nucita 2319

Giant cosmic ray halos around M31 and the Milky Way
S. Recchia, S. Gabici, F. A. Aharonian and V. Niro 2335

A nearly complete census of intergalactic gas using the kinematic Sunyaev-Zel'dovich effect
Chaves-Montero, Jonás 2345

Searching for Intermediate Mass Black Holes in the Milky Way's galactic halo
A. Franco, A. A. Nucita, F. De Paolis, F. Strafella and M. Maiorano . . . 2352

Virial clouds evolution from the last scattering up to the formation of first stars
Noraiz Tahir, Asghar Qadir, Muhammad Sakhi and Francesco De Paolis 2360

Testing Weyl-modified gravity on M31 and Milky Way
Muhammad Bilal and Asghar Qadir 2365

PART C

Education

- **Teaching Einsteinian Physics to School Students**
Chairpersons: David Blair and Matteo Luca Ruggiero
YouTube links: https://youtu.be/W-WV6J8kprg
https://youtu.be/UHYpwKQ09SU

Teaching relativity: A paradigm change
F. Herrmann and M. Pohlig 2371

Teaching relativity: Computer-aided modeling
F. Herrmann and M. Pohlig 2381

Solstices and Equinoxes in 1703 at the meridian line of St. Maria degli Angeli in Rome, and the stellar aberration of Sirius
Costantino Sigismondi and Silvia Pietroni 2388

Positional astrometry at arcsecond accuracy using historical instruments, with light equipment
Costantino Sigismondi and Lorenzo Ricciardi 2398

Daily, seasonal, and equinoctial solar paths on a school soccer field
Costantino Sigismondi 2411

Teaching relativity at the AstroCamp
C. J. A. P. Martins 2415

Sungrazing comets as General Relativistic gravitational probes
Silvia Pietroni and Costantino Sigismondi 2424

The three Summer solstice's markers of 1721 unveiled in the Basilica of Santa Maria degli Angeli in Rome
Costantino Sigismondi 2428

Einstein-First: Bringing children our best understanding of reality
A. Popkova, K. Adams, S. Boublil et al. 2438

Exact Solutions

• Exact Solutions in Four and Higher Dimensions
Chairpersons: David Blair and Matteo Luca Ruggiero
YouTube link: https://youtu.be/GHZUS5-4gVQ

Kundt spacetimes in the Einstein–Gauss–Bonnet theory
R. Švarc, J. Podolský and O. Hruška 2453

Exact decoupled solutions in curvature-matter coupled gravity
M. Sharif and Fizza Furqan 2464

Tolman-Oppenheimer-Volkov conditions beyond spherical symmetry
José P. Mimoso, Alan Maciel and Morgan Le Delliou 2479

A spherically symmetric stiff fluid spacetime in light of cosmic structure formation
Daniele Gregoris 2497

- **Exact Solutions (Including Higher Dimensions)**
Chairperson: Susan Scott

YouTube link: https://youtu.be/-hJjJvmmOew

Three-parameter solution for the null-surface formulation in
2+1 dimensions
Tina A. Harriott and J. G. Williams 2510

New exact stationary cylindrical anisotropic fluid solution of GR
M.-N. Célérier 2522

Early Universe

- **Quantum Fields**
Chairperson: Andrei Lebed

YouTube links: https://youtu.be/BLaTp0r0TkQ
https://youtu.be/ZifgaSDy5Vc

Hydrodynamic representation and energy balance for the Dirac and
Weyl fermions in curved space-times
Tonatiuh Matos, Omar Gallegos and Pierre-Henri Chavanis 2533

Breakdown of the Equivalence Principle for a composite quantum body
A. G. Lebed 2551

Extended DeWitt-Schwinger subtraction scheme, heavy fields and
decoupling
Antonio Ferreiro and Jose Navarro-Salas 2557

Renormalization and decoupling for the Yukawa model in curved
spacetime
Sergi Nadal-Gisbert, Antonio Ferreiro and José Navarro-Salas 2562

Trace anomaly and evaporation of spherical black holes
P. Meda 2573

On decay of the false Unruh vacuum
A. Shkerin 2587

Behaviour of noise kernel in de Sitter and FRW space-times
Ankit Dhanuka and Kinjalk Lochan 2600

Breaking Buchdahl: Ultracompact stars in semiclassical gravity
*Julio Arrechea, Carlos Barceló, Raúl Carballo-Rubio and
Luis J. Garay* 2608

Einstein anomaly with tensors of odd order in six dimensional
curved space
Kohei Yamamoto and Satoshi Yajima 2619

Quantum memory and BMS symmetries
Sanved Kolekar and Jorma Louko 2623

- **Topological Methods, Global Existence Problems, and Spacetime Singularities**
Chairperson: Spiros Cotsakis
YouTube link: https://youtu.be/H8Itnc_C10c

Gravitational singularities, scattering maps for bouncing, and
structure-preserving algorithms
Philippe G. LeFloch 2630

Brane-world asymptotics in a nonlinear fluid bulk
I. Antoniadis, S. Cotsakis and Ifigeneia Klaoudatou 2645

Primordial synchronization of Mixmaster spatial points
Spiros Cotsakis 2657

- **The Early Universe**
Chairperson: Stefano Ansoldi
YouTube links: https://youtu.be/m80hHWgOlFs
https://youtu.be/6tyaZ8MMVtw

Quintessential inflation from Lorentzian slow roll
David Benisty 2663

Condensed light, quantum black holes and L-CDM cosmology:
Experimentally suggested and tested unified approach to dark matter,
dark energy, cosmogenesis and two-stage inflation
Victor Borsevici 2672

Helical magnetic fields lead to baryogenesis
Ashu Kushwaha and S. Shankaranarayanan 2692

Polymer Quantization of the Isotropic Universe: Comparison with the
Bounce of Loop Quantum Cosmology
G. Barca, E. Giovannetti, F. Mandini and G. Montani 2700

General relativistic evolution equations for density perturbations in
open, flat and closed FLRW universes and the problem of structure
formation
Pieter G. Miedema 2708

Constraining beyond ΛCDM models with 21cm intensity mapping
forecast observations combined with latest CMB data
M. Berti 2726

Entropy and irreversible processes in gravity and cosmology
Llorenç Espinosa-Portalés and Juan García-Bellido 2737

Fundamental Interactions and Stellar Evolution

• Why and How the Sun and the Stars Shine: The Borexino Experiment

Chairpersons: Giampaolo Bellini, Dmitry Naumov, Gioacchino Ranucci, Gemma Testera

YouTube links: https://youtu.be/hh5wDnM8miU
https://youtu.be/TG-HgBf7W4s
https://youtu.be/HLiis2LFeEs

Experimental detection of the CNO cycle
B. Caccianiga, N. Rossi, G. Testera et al. 2753

Borexino detector performances
A. Caminata, M. Agostini, K. Altenmüller et al. 2765

Study of antineutrinos from the Earth and the Cosmos with the
Borexino detector
Sandra Zavatarelli, M. Agostini, K. Altenmuller et al. 2774

Unveiling the engine of the Sun: Measurements of the pp-chain solar
neutrinos with Borexino
D. Guffanti, A. C. Re and O. Smirnov 2785

Electron neutrino survival probability in the energy range
200 keV–15 MeV
Marco Pallavicini on behalf of the Borexino Collaboration 2804

The relevance of pp-chain and CNO-cycle neutrino measurements for
solar physics
F. L. Villante and A. M. Serenelli 2815

Role of the CNO cycles in stars
A. Ianni 2835

Geoneutrino observation
Tadao Mitsui for the KamLAND Collaboration 2840

Synthesis of the session: Why and how the Sun and the stars shine
Gianpaolo Bellini 2845

- **Rotation in Stellar Evolution**
Chairperson: Georges Meynet

YouTube link: https://youtu.be/9LNoiwa0nv8

The internal rotation of low-mass stars from solar and stellar seismology
G. Buldgen and P. Eggenberger 2848

The rotation of supermassive stars
L. Haemmerlé 2865

Fast Transients

- **What Can We Learn from a Growing Sample of Fast Radio Bursts?**
Chairpersons: Duncan Lorimer, Victoria Kaspi and Bing Zhang

YouTube links: https://youtu.be/yo4n1SgfUrQ
https://youtu.be/NwGooPauhjU

Cosmology with high-redshift FRBs
A. Fialkov 2880

- **Non Standard Cosmological Probes**
Chairpersons: Duncan Lorimer, Victoria Kaspi and Bing Zhang

YouTube links: https://youtu.be/EEFUgiFeMck
https://youtu.be/Ryb15AINfMs

Closing the cosmological loop with the redshift drift
*C. J. A. P. Martins, C. S. Alves, J. Esteves, A. Lapel
and B. G. Pereira* 2890

Gamma-Ray Bursts as potential cosmological probes
L. Izzo 2906

Surface brightness fluctuations: The method and future applications
Michele Cantiello 2915

Preliminary results of analysis of Ia supernovae redshift distributions
on data of the Asiago Supernova and Open Supernova Catalogues
I. V. Arkhangelskaja 2930

- **Photospheric Emission in GRBs**
Chairpersons: Gregory Vereshchagin and Damien Bégué

YouTube links: https://youtu.be/ZifnzoUXIFc
https://youtu.be/n7vWAVhFXiU

Understanding prompt emission: Where do we stand?
Asaf Pe'er 2946

On explaining prompt emission from GRB central engines with
photospheric emission model
M. Bhattacharya and P. Kumar 2957

Monte Carlo simulations of photospheric emission in Gamma Ray Bursts
T. M. Parsotan and D. Lazzati 2972

The photosphere emission spectrum of hybrid relativistic outflow for
Gamma-Ray Bursts
Yan-Zhi Meng, Jin-Jun Geng and Xue-Feng Wu 2982

On diffusive photospheres in Gamma-Ray Bursts
G. V. Vereshchagin 2989

Summary of the parallel session GB3
G. V. Vereshchagin and D. Bégué 3002

• **High and Very High Energy Emission from Gamma-Ray Bursts**
Chairpersons: Francesco Longo and Fabian Schüssler

YouTube links: https://youtu.be/ZUkLyyYowaM
https://youtu.be/zwN1mNVeUzA

Synchrotron and synchrotron self-Compton emission components in
GRBs detected at very high energies
Jagdish C. Joshi, Vikas Chand and Soebur Razzaque 3009

The VERITAS gamma-ray burst follow-up program
D. Ribeiro for the VERITAS Collaboration 3017

MAGIC view of Gamma-Ray Bursts at very high energies
A. Berti on behalf of the MAGIC Collaboration 3030

Prospects for VHE monitoring of gamma-ray bursts with SWGO
G. La Mura, U. Barres de Almeida, R. Conceição et al. 3041

Theoretical implications on the very high energy emission from
GRB 190114C
*D. Miceli, A. Berti, Z. Bosnjak et al. on behalf of the
MAGIC Collaboration* 3052

AGILE and GRBs: 13 years of observations
A. Ursi on behalf of the AGILE Team 3062

Searching for Gamma-Ray Bursts with the High-Altitude Water
Cherenkov (HAWC) observatory
K. L. Engel for the HAWC Collaboration 3074

- **Electromagnetic Counterparts of Compact Binary Mergers**
  Chairpersons: Jonathan Granot and Paz Beniamini
  YouTube link: https://youtu.be/AS7bwaT48us

  CALET search for gamma-ray counterparts of gravitational wave events
  Masaki Mori for the CALET Collaboration 3084

- **Unusual and New Types of Gamma-Ray Bursts**
  Chairperson: Binbin Zhang
  YouTube link: https://youtu.be/VrF0iU8Q6us

  Off-axis jet scenario for early afterglow emission of low-luminosity Gamma-Ray Burst GRB 190829A
  Yuri Sato, Kaori Obayashi, Ryo Yamazaki, Kohta Murase and Yutaka Ohira 3095

- **Gamma-Ray Burst Correlations: Observational Challenges and Theoretical Interpretation**
  Chairpersons: Maria Giovanna Dainotti and Liang Li
  YouTube links: https://youtu.be/gcEy2h6y1jg
  https://youtu.be/m2pCT6RAmI0
  https://youtu.be/GTCvcVhBjN4

  GRB prompt phase spectra under backscattering dominated model
  Mukesh Kumar Vyas, Asaf Pe'er and David Eichler 3101

  Applying models of pulsar wind nebulae to explain X-ray plateaux following short Gamma-Ray Bursts
  L. C. Strang and A. Melatos 3107

  Searching for strange quark planets
  Xu Wang, Yong-Feng Huang and Bing Li 3118

  Probe the universe by using Gamma-Ray Bursts with X-ray plateaus
  Fan Xu and Yong-Feng Huang 3124

  A new perspective on cosmology through Supernovae Ia and Gamma Ray Bursts
  B. De Simone, V. Nielson, E. Rinaldi and M. G. Dainotti 3130

  Theory of plateau phase in Gamma-Ray Bursts
  Asaf Pe'er 3141

  Exploring the canonical behaviour of long Gamma-Ray Bursts using an intrinsic multi-wavelength afterglow correlation
  S. R. Oates, J. L. Racusin, M. De Pasquale et al. 3150

- **GRB 170817A and Binary Models**
  Chairpersons: Marica Branchesi and Giulia Stratta
  YouTube link: https://youtu.be/FRBvkaLX5WU

  Kilonova emission observed so far: A comparison with AT2017gfo
  A. Rossi 3162

- **Binary-Driven Hypernovae of Type 1, 2 and 3**
  Chairpersons: Carlo Luciano Bianco, Christian Cherubini and Simonetta Filippi
  YouTube link: https://youtu.be/8IFLfget3C0

  Neutrinos and gamma-ray production from proton-proton interactions in binary-driven hypernovae framework
  S. Campion, J. D. Melon Fuksman and J. A. Rueda Hernandez 3172

  General relativistic turbulence in spherically symmetric core-collapse supernovae simulations
  L. Boccioli, G. J. Mathews and E. P. O'Connor 3184

Gravitational Waves

- **Sources of Gravitational Waves**
  Chairperson: Andrew Melatos
  YouTube links: https://youtu.be/Lr8b9nKsFm4
  https://youtu.be/xuqJOXPDyVY
  https://youtu.be/qzOrgojHsMg
  https://youtu.be/KCJoWMd71pE

  Mountain formation by repeated, inhomogeneous crustal failure in a neutron star
  A. D. Kerin and A. Melatos 3194

  Gravitational waves from neutrino mass generating phase transitions
  Nobuchika Okada and Osamu Seto 3206

  Efficiency of registration of chirp bursts and signals of collapsing stars by the Euro-Asian network of GW interferometers
  V. N. Rudenko, S. L. Andrusenko, D. P. Krichevskiy and G. D. Manucharyan 3219

  Joint analysis method on gravitational waves and low-energy neutrinos to detect core-collapse supernovae
  O. Halim, C. Casentini, M. Drago et al. 3228

- **Mid-frequency Gravitational Waves (0.1–10 Hz): Sources and Detection Methods**
  Chairperson: Wei-Tou Ni
  YouTube link: https://youtu.be/sJ6A7a73Vxw

A cryogenic and superconducting inertial sensor for the Lunar
Gravitational–Wave Antenna, the Einstein Telescope and Selene-physics
F. Badaracco, J. V. van Heijningen, E. C. Ferreira and A. Perali 3245

Space gravitational wave antenna DECIGO and B-DECIGO
S. Kawamura and the DECIGO working group 3254

Summary of the parallel session GW2
Dongfeng Gao, Wei-Tou Ni, Jin Wang et al. 3261

- **Numerical Relativity and Gravitational Wave Observations**
  Chairperson: Nigel Bishop
  YouTube links: https://youtu.be/eZPytAU4Zmk
  https://youtu.be/th-3KqkxDnU

Salient features of the optimised PyCBC IMBH search
Koustav Chandra, Archana Pai, V. Villa-Ortega et al. 3277

Matter shells modifying gravitational wave signals
Monos Naidoo, Nigel T. Bishop and Petrus J. van der Walt 3286

Odd-dimensional gravitational waves from a binary system on
a three-brane
D. V. Gal'tsov and M. Khlopunov 3301

Developments in numerical relativity and gravitational wave observations
Nigel T. Bishop 3309

High Energy

- **Very High Energy Gamma Rays**
  Chairpersons: Razmik Mirzoyan and Alessandro De Angelis
  YouTube link: https://youtu.be/jHM1RH20ZyM

Insights into the Galactic Center environment from VHE gamma-ray
observations with ground-based facilities
C. Fruck 3316

The TAIGA experiment
M. Tluczykont, I. I. Astapov, A. K. Awad et al. 3324

Science perspectives of the Southern Wide-field Gamma-ray
Observatory (SWGO)
K. L. Engel for the SWGO Collaboration 3343

- **Future Missions for High-Energy Astrophysics**
  Chairpersons: Filippo Frontera and Shaolin Xiong
  YouTube link: https://youtu.be/JgDsZX6RUkU

Laue lenses: Focusing optics for hard X/soft Gamma-ray astronomy
L. Ferro, M. Moita, P. Rosati et al. 3355

ASTENA: A mission concept for a deep study of the transient gamma-ray sky and for nuclear astrophysics
E. Virgilli, F. Frontera, P. Rosati et al. on behalf of the ASTENA Collaboration 3368

Polarimetric prospects of a new hard X-soft gamma-ray space mission for next decades
M. Moita, L. Ferro, F. Frontera et al. 3385

- **The SRG Mission: First Results from eROSITA and ART-XC**
Chairperson: Andrea Merloni
YouTube link: https://youtu.be/l0t1B716UcM

Prospect for WHIM detection in the cosmic web by *SRG/eROSITA*
H. Tanimura and N. Aghanim 3400

- **eXTP – Enhanced X-Ray Timing and Polarimetry Mission**
Chairpersons: Marco Feroci and Fangjun Lu
YouTube link: https://youtu.be/3d08eKmsImI

The role of eXTP in the multi-messenger astronomy era
G. Stratta and Gor Oganesyan 3403

- **Observations of HE and UHE Cosmic Rays**
Chairpersons: Ivan De Mitri and Fabio Gargano
YouTube link: https://youtu.be/l9DZyBMWO5c

CALET on the ISS: The first 5 years
Pier Simone Marrocchesi for the CALET Collaboration 3427

The fluxes of charged cosmic rays as measured by the DAMPE satellite
Paolo Bernardini on behalf of the DAMPE Collaboration 3442

Recent results from the Pierre Auger Observatory
E. Roulet for the Pierre Auger Collaboration 3449

The HERD space mission
F.C.T. Barbato on behalf of the HERD Collaboration 3455

PART D

History of Relativity

- **The "Fall and Rise" of Betelgeuse**
Chairperson: Costantino Sigismondi
YouTube link: https://youtu.be/VmbrE2gYmOM

The observation of the stars in daytime and near the horizon
Costantino Sigismondi and Paolo Ochner 3471

Fall and Rise of Betelgeuse: The summary of HR1 session
Costantino Sigismondi and Paolo Ochner 3475

Photometry of Betelgeuse at daylight
Otmar Nickel 3479

Evidence for dynamical changes in Betelgeuse using multi-wavelength data
Sneha Kachhara, Sandip V. George, Ranjeev Misra and G. Ambika 3485

The curious case of Betelgeuse
Jacco Th. van Loon 3494

Variable stars observed from city sites: The 2500 AAVSO-SGQ database
Costantino Sigismondi and Paolo Ochner 3501

Betelgeuse: An introductory course to observational astronomy
Costantino Sigismondi and Tiziana Pompa 3507

The meridian line of the Vatican obelisk to study the stellar aberration
Costantino Sigismondi and Lorenzo Ricciardi 3513

Betelgeuse, Sirius and the stars in the roman *Settecento*
Costantino Sigismondi 3519

- **History of Relativity, Gravitation and Cosmology**
Chairperson: Luis Crispino

YouTube link: https://youtu.be/RNbPUSp95PQ

On Einstein's last bid to keep a stationary cosmology
Salvador Galindo-Uribarri and Jorge L. Cervantes-Cota 3536

Jayme Tiomno: Relativity, gravity, cosmology, and the
Marcel Grossmann Meetings
William D. Brewer 3547

A look inside Feynman's route to gravitation
M. Di Mauro, S. Esposito and A. Naddeo 3563

Towards detecting gravitational waves: A contribution by
Richard Feynman
M. Di Mauro, S. Esposito and A. Naddeo 3576

Stellar gravitational collapse, singularity formation and theory breakdown
Kiril Maltsev 3596

The Hamilton-Jacobi analysis by Peter Bergmann and Arthur Komar
of classical general relativity
D. Salisbury 3626

- **Time and Philosophy in Physics**
Chairperson: Shokoufe Faraji

YouTube link: https://youtu.be/986v-V5JJEk

The passage of time and top-down causation
Barbara Drossel 3631

Explaining time's passage
Jonathan J. Dickau 3646

A glimpse to Feynman's contributions to the debate on the
foundations of quantum mechanics
M. Di Mauro, S. Esposito and A. Naddeo 3657

Summary of the parallel session HR3
Shokoufe Faraji 3671

Neutron Stars

- **Dense Matter in Compact Stars**
Chairpersons: Alessandro Drago and Jorge Rueda

YouTube links: https://youtu.be/U5Yr0oDVhqY
https://youtu.be/MvMDFh-1_bc

Massive compact stars in the two-families scenario
P. Char, A. Drago and G. Pagliara 3677

Quasi-universality of the magnetic deformation of neutron stars in
general relativity and beyond
J. Soldateschi, N. Bucciantini and L. Del Zanna 3684

Screening and elastic properties of the NS crust in the OCP
approximation
D. Barba González, C. Albertus Torres and M. A. Pérez-García . . 3703

Tidal deformability as a probe of dark matter in neutron stars
D. Rafiei Karkevandi, S. Shakeri, V. Sagun and O. Ivanytskyi . . . 3713

Binary neutron star mergers with quark matter equations of state
Atul Kedia, Hee Il Kim, Grant Mathews and In-Saeng Suh 3732

Probing dense matter physics with transiently-accreting neutron stars: The case of source MXB 1659-29
Melissa Mendes, Andrew Cumming, Charles Gale and Farrukh J. Fattoyev 3736

- **Compact Stars as Laboratories for Testing Strong Gravity**

Chairpersons: Aurora Perez Martinez and César Augusto Zen Vasconcellos

YouTube link: https://youtu.be/C1KGecdNEfs

Vacuum properties and astrophysical implications
A. Pérez Martínez, M. Pérez-Garcia, E. Rodríguez Querts and A. Romero Jorge 3756

Testing extended theories of gravity with GRBs
L. Mastrototaro 3762

- **Pulsar Power in Physics and Astrophysics and Pulsars and Pulsar Systems at High Energies**

Chairpersons: Andrea Possenti and Pak-Hin Tam

YouTube links: https://youtu.be/gAG29DZwUbM
https://youtu.be/ytdUBFrViHI

News and views regarding PSR J1757–1854, a highly-relativistic binary pulsar
A. D. Cameron, M. Bailes, V. Balakrishnan et al. 3774

On the origin of the unique isolated X-Ray pulsar 1E 161348-5055 with 6.7 hr. spin period
V. Yu. Kim 3785

Advantages of including globular cluster millisecond pulsars in Pulsar Timing Arrays
M. Maiorano, F. De Paolis, A. A. Nucita and A. Franco 3791

Searching for pulsars in globular clusters with the MeerKAT Radio Telescope
F. Abbate on behalf of the MeerTIME/TRAPUM Collaboration 3799

Precision Tests

- **Gravitational Lensing and Shadows**

Chairpersons: Perlick Volker and Oleg Tsupko

YouTube links: https://youtu.be/6DXXWpMJ3IQ
https://youtu.be/F-K1gXn71_Y
https://youtu.be/B-V8r2HMztw

Gravitational lensing by rotating Simpson–Visser black holes
Sushant G. Ghosh and Shafqat Ul Islam 3812

Killing tensors in foliated spacetimes and photon surfaces
Igor Bogush, Kirill Kobialko and Dmitri Gal'tsov 3827

Decoding black hole metrics from the interferometric pattern of relativistic images
V. Bozza 3839

Symplectic evolution of an observed light bundle
N. Uzun 3844

Shadow of black holes with a plasma environment in 4D Einstein-Gauss-Bonnet gravity
Javier Badía and Ernesto F. Eiroa 3856

Aspects of neutrino mass hierarchy in gravitational lensing
Himanshu Swami 3865

Photon regions in stationary axisymmetric spacetimes and umbilic conditions
K. V. Kobialko and D. V. Gal'tsov 3874

Gravitational lensing by charged accelerating black holes
Torben C. Frost 3885

- **Experimental Gravitation**
Chairpersons: Angela di Virgilio and Claus Lammerzahl

YouTube link: https://youtu.be/mXcxztQ0nyk
https://youtu.be/tE3gIUBviTc

A manmade experiment aimed to clarify the gravity law in the Solar system
Alexander P. Yefremov and Alexandra A. Vorobyeva 3905

Gravitomagnetic field generation using high permittivity materials in superconducting magnetic energy storage devices
G. V. Stephenson 3910

Large ring laser gyroscopes: Geometry stabilization and laser control
U. Giacomelli, N. Beverini, G. Carelli et al. 3920

Dark gravitomagnetism with LISA and gravitational waves space detectors
A. Tartaglia, M. Bassan, G. Pucacco, V. Ferroni and D. Vetrugno 3929

Light rays in the Solar system experiments: Phases and displacements
Pravin Kumar Dahal and Daniel R. Terno 3942

The Ginger project – preliminary results
C. Altucci, F. Bajardi, A. Basti et al. 3956

• **Variation of the Fundamental Constants, Tests of the Fundamental Symmetries and Probes of the Dark Sector**
Chairpersons: Angela Victor Flambaum and Yevgeny Stadnik
YouTube links: https://youtu.be/NAZA-0tWHak
https://youtu.be/juhDGBJ12Lg
https://youtu.be/zxGgDP2sn60

Varying fundamental constants and dark energy in the ESPRESSO era
C. J. A. P. Martins 3963

• **Dragging is Never Draggy: MAss and CHarge Flows in GR**
Chairperson: Oldrich Semerak
YouTube link: https://youtu.be/ho31IgLNxu8

Testing the general relativistic nature of the Milky Way rotation curve with Gaia DR2
Mariateresa Crosta 3970

Spinning cylinders in general relativity: A canonical form for the Lewis metrics of the Weyl class
L. Filipe O. Costa, José Natário and N. O. Santos 3982

Magnetized black holes: The role of rotation, boost, and accretion in twisting the field lines and accelerating particles
Ondřej Kopáček and Vladimír Karas 3999

Spinning particle: Is Newton-Wigner the only way?
V. Witzany 4010

Gravitomagnetic resonance and gravitational waves
Matteo Luca Ruggiero and Antonello Ortolan 4019

Quantum Gravity

• **Loop Quantum Gravity**
Chairpersons: Marcin Kisielowski and Jerzy Lewandowski
YouTube links: https://youtu.be/VaLPseYWh9E
https://youtu.be/WFIgMqrQ07U

Studying the EPRL spinfoam self-energy
Pietropaolo Frisoni 4026

A spin foam framework for the black-to-white hole transition
Farshid Soltani 4045

Holographic properties of the bulk-to-boundary transmission of information in regions of quantum space
Eugenia Colafranceschi 4062

- **Quantum Gravity Phenomenology**
  Chairpersons: Giovanni Amelino-Camelia and Jerzy Kowalski-Glikman

YouTube links: https://youtu.be/vYnVb2zNl0o
https://youtu.be/icK8z80Hm-Y
https://youtu.be/svXLa0yhyYY

Minimal length discretization and properties of modified metric tensor and geodesics
Abdel Nasser Tawfik, Fady T. Farouk, F. Salah Tarabia and Muhammad Maher 4074

The structure of the multiverse from the entanglement entropy
Samuel Barroso Bellido 4082

Effective field theory from relativistic Generalized Uncertainty Principle
Vasil N. Todorinov, Saurya Das and Pasquale Bosso 4088

Stelle gravity as the limit of quantum gravity with maximal momentum
V. Nenmeli, S. Shankaranarayanan, V. Todorinov and S. Das 4107

Baryon asymmetry and minimum length
Saurya Das, Mitja Fridman, Gaetano Lambiase and Elias C. Vagenas . . . 4114

On quantum gravity and quantum gravity phenomenology
Douglas Edmonds, Djordje Minic and Tatsu Takeuchi 4126

WKB approach to the gravity-matter dynamics: A cosmological implementation
G. Maniccia and G. Montani 4146

Natural evidence for fuzzy sphere noncommutative geometry: Super-Chandrasekhar white dwarfs
Surajit Kalita, T. R. Govindarajan and Banibrata Mukhopadhyay 4159

A model of polymer gravitational waves: Theory and some possible observational consequences
Angel Garcia-Chung, James B. Mertens, Saeed Rastgoo, Yaser Tavakoli and Paulo Vargas Moniz 4166

• **Loop Quantum Gravity: Cosmology and Black Holes**
Chairpersons: Jorge Pullin and Parampreet Singh

YouTube links: https://youtu.be/CAuAK31Ukho
https://youtu.be/JlYnEzRiRR0

Primordial power spectrum from a matter-ekpyrotic scenario in loop quantum cosmology
Bao-Fei Li, Sahil Saini and Parampreet Singh 4178

The primordial power spectra in modified loop quantum cosmology
Bao-Fei Li, Javier Olmedo, Parampreet Singh and Anzhong Wang 4188

Primordial perturbations in kinetically dominated regimes of classical and quantum cosmology
B. Elizaga Navascués, R. Jiménez-Llamas and G. A. Mena Marugán 4193

Revisiting the Hamiltonian formalism of the Ashtekar–Olmedo–Singh black hole model
Alejandro García-Quismondo and Guillermo A. Mena Marugán 4211

A comparison of different choices of clocks in a reduced phase space quantization in loop quantum cosmology with an inflationary potential using effective techniques
Kristina Giesel, Bao-Fei Li and Parampreet Singh 4228

Initial conditions in LQC/mLQCs
Bao-Fei Li, Parampreet Singh and Anzhong Wang 4234

Holonomy corrections in effective midisuperspace models
A. Alonso-Bardaji and D. Brizuela 4239

Infrared signatures of quantum bounce in collapsing geometry
Harkirat Singh Sahota and Kinjalk Lochan 4247

Effective black hole interior and the Raychadhuri equation
Keagan Blanchette, Saurya Das, Samantha Hergott and Saeed Rastgoo . . . 4256

Effect of loop quantization prescriptions on the physics of non-singular gravitational collapse
Kristina Giesel, Bao-Fei Li and Parampreet Singh 4267

Summary of the parallel session QG3
Jorge Pullin and Parampreet Singh 4272

Strong Field

• **Strong Electromagnetic and Gravitational Field Physics: From Laboratories to Early Universe**
Chairpersons: Sang Pyo Kim and She-Sheng Xue

YouTube links: https://youtu.be/kexqTayqFiU
https://youtu.be/laymGp6x9Hg

Reliable equations of state of viscous strong and electroweak matter
A. Tawfik 4277

Neutral fermion pair production by Sauter-like magnetic step
T. C. Adorno, Zi-Wang He, S. P. Gavrilov and D. M. Gitman 4290

On the magnetic field screening in strong crossed electromagnetic field
S. Campion, J. A. Rueda Hernandez, S.-S. Xue and R. Ruffini 4306

Particle creation by strong fields and quantum anomalies
José Navarro-Salas 4317

Constraints on the non-minimal coupling of electromagnetic fields from astrophysical observations
Susmita Jana and S. Shankaranarayanan 4326

New partial resummation of the QED effective action
Silvia Pla and José Navarro-Salas 4337

Can a detector detect soft photons
Sanved Kolekar and Jorma Louko 4347

Breaking of the adiabatic invariance in the production of particles by strong fields
P. Beltrán-Palau, A. Ferreiro, J. Navarro-Salas and S. Pla 4352

Dynamics of relativistic electrons in non-uniform magnetic fields and its applications in quantum computing and astrophysics
Srishty Aggarwal and Banibrata Mukhopadhyay 4362

Validity of the semiclassical approximation in 1+1 electrodynamics: Numerical solutions to the linear response equation
Ian M. Newsome 4374

On Kerr black hole perfect MHD processes in Doran coordinates
C. Cherubini, S. Filippi, A. Loppini et al. 4387

Tadpole contribution to magnetic photon-graviton conversion
N. Ahmadiniaz, F. Bastianelli, F. Karbstein and C. Schubert 4393

- **The Effects of (Non)Linear Electrodynamics on the Properties of Astrophysical/Gravitational Compact Objects**

  Chairperson: Seyed Hossein Hendi

  YouTube link: https://youtu.be/SAIAXtQhavE

  Correspondence of gamma radiation coming from GRBs and magnetars based on the effects of nonlinear vacuum electrodynamics
  Tursynbek Yernazarov, Medeu Abishev and Yerlan Aimuratov 4401

  Absorption of massless scalar waves by electrically charged regular black holes
  Marco A. A. de Paula, Luiz C. S. Leite and Luís C. B. Crispino 4410

White Dwarfs

- **White Dwarf Explosions**

  Chairpersons: Robert Fisher and María Pilar Ruiz Lapuente

  YouTube links: https://youtu.be/ndaW6u2xuOo
  https://youtu.be/IwjYaQaqJeI

  Modeling Type Ia supernovae with explosions in white dwarfs near and below the Chandrasekhar mass
  Friedrich K. Röpke, Florian Lach, Sabrina Gronow et al. 4420

  Type Ia supernovae and their explosive nucleosynthesis: Constraints on progenitors
  Shing-Chi Leung and Ken'ichi Nomoto 4427

  Charged polarized white dwarfs with finite temperature as a possible source of type Ia supernovae
  Sílvia P. Nunes, José D. V. Arbañil and Manuel Malheiro 4447

- **White Dwarfs, Magnetic Compact Stars and Nuclear Astrophysics**

  Chairpersons: Manuel Malheiro and Jaziel Goulart Coelho

  YouTube link: https://youtu.be/onicFElJQnA

  CTCV J2056-3014 and other fast-spinning white dwarfs
  C. V. Rodrigues, R. Lopes de Oliveira, A. Bruch et al. 4453

  Gravitational waves from fast-spinning white dwarfs
  M. F. Sousa, J. C. N. de Araujo and J. G. Coelho 4461

  Highly magnetized white dwarfs: Implications and current status
  B. Mukhopadhyay, M. Bhattacharya, A. J. Hackett et al. 4475

  Electron captures and stability of white dwarfs
  N. Chamel, L. Perot, A. F. Fantina et al. 4488

Massive hot white dwarfs: Consequences of finite temperature in the
structure and on the onset of instabilities
Sílvia P. Nunes, José D. V. Arbañil and Manuel Malheiro 4508

A study of the infrared emission of SGR/AXPs in a disk scenario and
its implications for their origin
Sarah Villanova Borges 4514

Particle acceleration and high energy emission in the white dwarf
binaries AE Aquarii and AR Scorpii
P. J. Meintjes, S. T. Madzime, Q. Kaplan et al. 4522

Study the effects of anisotropy on the highly magnetized white dwarfs
Debabrata Deb, Banibrata Mukhopadhyay and Fridolin Weber 4532

List of Participants   4545

PART C

Teaching relativity: A paradigm change

F. Herrmann* and M. Pohlig

Institute for Theoretical Solid State Physics, Karlsruhe Institute of Technology (KIT), Karlsruhe, Baden-Württemberg, Germany
* E-mail: f.herrmann@kit.edu
www.kit.edu

The teaching of relativity usually starts with kinematics: The invariance of the speed of light, clock synchronization, time dilatation and length contraction, the relativity of simultaneity, Lorentz transformation and the Minkowski diagram. The change of the reference frame is a central topic. Only afterwards problems of relativistic dynamics are discussed. Such an approach closely follows the historical development of the Special Theory of Relativity.

We believe that this access to relativity is unnecessarily complicated, and unsuitable for beginners. We present the basics of a teaching approach in which the initial postulate of relativity is the identity of energy and relativistic mass. Reference frame changes are largely avoided.

Keywords: Special relativity, additional postulate, reference frame change, relativistic dynamics.

1. Introduction

Relativity, and we mean for the moment only special relativity, is more than 100 years old, but still has not found its place in school. Just compare: Faraday-Maxwell electromagnetism, which is certainly not simpler than special relativity, would still not be included in the curricula 120 years after its creation, i.e. in 1980. There are several reasons for this deficiency. Here we want to discuss only one of them: Relativity is still taught today as it has originated historically. One starts with a very special relativistic effect, and works through with great effort to the more important and useful general statements. It is as if one enters a splendid palace not by the beautiful main portal, but by some shabby servants' entrance.

We describe the basics of a course on special relativity. The concept has been tested and is used at numerous secondary schools: parts of it already in the lower secondary school, the complete program in the upper secondary school. The course is part of the *Karlsruhe Physics Course*.[1] It can be downloaded from the Internet in various languages. A bilingual English-Chinese version was published recently.[2]

We do not describe the details of this course. We are merely presenting some ideas that underlie its development. Some of the topics we address are also discussed in articles of the column *Historical burdens on physics*.[3]

We justify our paradigm change in Section 2. We choose a different "entrance" to relativity. We substantiate our choice in section 2.1. In sections 2.2 and 2.3 we begin with a critical discussion of two popular topics: the reference frame change, and the role of the observer. Section 2.4 is about naming. How is the word mass used and how do we want to use it. Section 2.5 deals with the way to write Einstein's famous equation $E = mc^2$. We are thus prepared for our main topic, which will be treated in section 3: relativistic dynamics.

2. Paradigm change

2.1. *Additional postulate of the special theory of relativity*

The laws of the special theory of relativity, or special relativity for short, are obtained from those of classical mechanics by adding one extra postulate. Traditionally and for historical reasons, the choice was made for the invariance of the speed of light upon a change of the reference frame.

Once one has become aware that this choice as a starting point is only one of several possibilities, one discovers that completely new perspectives arise for the development of a teaching concept. We have decided to introduce the mass-energy equivalence as an additional postulate instead of the invariance of the speed of light.

With this choice, we arrive more quickly at that part of special relativity that we consider being the most important one, namely relativistic dynamics.

The traditional choice of the invariance of the speed of light has a rather incidental cause: when special relativity came into being, light was the only known system that behaved relativistically. Einstein's work – both his famous publication of 1905 *Zur Elektrodynamik bewegter Körper*[4] and his textbook *Grundzüge der Relativitätstheorie*[5] – begins with a detailed, and one can say somewhat tiring part on relativistic kinematics.

One might imagine what the course of history would have been if the first relativistic observation had been that a cup of hot coffee is heavier than a cup of cold coffee (or that the corresponding observation had been made with particles in an accelerator). The presentation of the theory of relativity in our textbooks would certainly be very different from what it is actually.

Of course, the mass-energy equivalence is not supported by our everyday experience (neither is the invariance of the speed of light). But one can make it easily plausible and discuss its consequences even in beginners' classes. It leads to surprising and at first unbelievable statements; but it does not lead to the cognitive conflicts one has to deal with in the traditional approach to relativistic kinematics, which questions our basic convictions about space and time.

2.2. *Reference frames and reference frame changes*

In the traditional approach to special relativity, the following topics are dealt with before relativistic dynamics is addressed:

The invariance of the speed of light
Clock synchronization

The relativity of simultaneity
Time dilatation and length contraction
Velocity addition
Lorentz transformation
Minkowski diagram

The problem with such an approach is that one begins with the most confusing part of the theory: the relationship between space and time.

Certainly, students can learn a lot of physics by analyzing the same process in different reference frames. But we should not forget that we are dealing with beginners, and it is better to stick to the old rule: Choose a suitable reference frame right at the beginning, i.e. a reference frame in which the description of your problem becomes as simple as possible, and don't change it anymore.

And above all, don't change the reference frame in the middle of dealing with your problem (as is usually done when discussing the twin paradox). By the way, in classical mechanics and electromagnetism, too, one can create the greatest confusion if one chooses the reference frame improperly or if one changes it in the middle of the discussion.

This is why our decision was not to make reference frame changes the main topic of our lessons and to avoid them as far as possible. Above all, the impression should not be created that special relativity is essentially a theory of reference frame changes – an impression that some presentations certainly arouse. Even the name relativity gives that impression.

2.3. *The observer*

Closely related to the question of the choice of the reference frame is the problem of the so-called observer. The observer seems to be particularly important in two areas of physics: in quantum physics (where the observer always appears as the one making a "measurement") and in the theory of relativity.

An observation is always made from a certain perspective. It thereby emphasizes something that does not play a particular role in the phenomenon to be described.

We believe the observation should not be in the foreground as long as the understanding of a process is the objective. This is especially true when teaching at school, i.e. beginners.

It is true that we get all the information about the world by observing and measuring. But the idea we form of the world is quite different from what we observe. So, if we wanted to explain the shape of the earth to someone, we would certainly not start with the shadow of the obelisk in Alexandria, but simply say: The earth is a sphere.

In our opinion when teaching physics we should primarily give a picture of what nature is like – not how it is perceived by an observer.

2.4. The use of the term mass

Mass is a physical quantity that until not so long ago did not cause any problems. It was known for which properties it is a measure.

With Einstein's special theory of relativity, this only changed insofar as the mass of a body became dependent on its velocity, temperature and other variables. It was no longer a quantity that had a characteristic value for a body or a particle.

Thus, a body, a particle, a field, or any other structure, has a mass that depends, among other things, on its velocity. The value that the mass assumes when the centre of mass of the particle or body is at rest is called its rest mass (symbol m_0). Even more appropriate would actually be the less common term *proper mass*, because when the centre of mass is at rest, this does not mean that the parts or particles of the system are at rest.

It is that simple, or, unfortunately, one must say: it could be that simple.

For there is an area of physics in which another use of the term mass has established itself: Particle physics. A particle has a well-defined rest mass. The rest mass is characteristic of the particle species. Among the various other parameters, such as electric charge, spin, lepton number, etc., it is considered the main characteristic. It seems to constitute the identity of the particle. For this property, a compact, plausible name was needed, and particle physicists simply called it mass. Thus, in particle physics, the term mass refers to only part of the quantity that describes the inertia of a particle.

However, this custom also spread beyond particle physics, and this results in several misunderstandings and ambiguities. What is to be understood by the mass of a macroscopic body that is at rest? Is it the mass that would be measured with a (very accurate) scale, or is it the sum of the (rest) masses of the particles that constitute the body? This is a question that particle physicists probably don't ask, but we teachers do.

We have therefore decided to use the term mass (symbol m) exclusively for the quantity that measures gravity and inertia, no matter what kind of object is considered and in what state it is. Thus, a hot cup of coffee has a larger mass than the same coffee when it is cold. A photon has a mass and a magnetic field has a mass (a liter of magnetic field near a neutron star has a mass of some hundred grams).

By the way, if one follows this use of the term mass, it makes no sense to say that mass is a "form of energy" or that mass can be converted into energy.

2.5. The identity of mass and energy

First, let us look at the term *mass-energy equivalence*. It is a pity that a simple fact is expressed so unclearly. The word equivalence is certainly not wrong, but why not say directly: Mass and energy are the same physical quantity.

If one were to ask someone who has never seen the equation $E = mc^2$ to express this fact in a formula, he would probably write something like this:

$$E = k \cdot m \, . \tag{1}$$

The factor k tells us how the units joule and kilogram are converted into each other. As the definitions of the units kilogram and joule are independent of the choice of the reference frame, k is a universal constant.

Its value is obtained by a measurement. One finds

$$k = 9 \cdot 10^{16} \, \text{J/kg} \, . \tag{2}$$

But what is wrong with writing

$$E = mc^2 \, ? \tag{3}$$

Every student learns in mathematics that a linear relationship between the variables x and y is written as

$$y = a \cdot x \, . \tag{4}$$

On the right side first the factor of proportionality a, and second the independent variable. The unbiased student might interpret the famous equation (3) this way: The energy is proportional to the square of the speed of light – and not: energy and mass are the same physical quantity. One might object: This can easily be explained to the students. Of course it can. But doesn't the statement become clearer if one writes $E = k \cdot m$? Would the iconic character of equation (3) survive if it were formulated in this way?

3. The laws of dynamics

In the *Karlsruhe Physics Course*[1], the extensive quantities energy, momentum, electric charge and entropy are introduced as basic quantities. Especially momentum and entropy have a very direct and vivid interpretation. Momentum is a measure of the "amount of motion", that is, what one would colloquially call "impetus" or "drive". Entropy measures almost perfectly what would colloquially be called the amount of heat (not to be confused with the rather difficult concept of heat that has established itself in physics).

Therefore, in the context of relativity, it is natural to ask in the first place for the dependence of different quantities on momentum. Momentum is our independent variable. We give momentum to a body or particle and ask how it reacts to it: How does its mass (= energy) behave? What happens to its velocity? In other words: We ask for the functions $E(p)$ and $v(p)$.

3.1. *The energy momentum relationship*

To derive $E(p)$, we take over as much as possible from non-relativistic physics. In addition, we only require the identity of mass and energy, i.e. we assume the validity of equation (1). We start with the change dE of the energy, that results from a change of the momentum dp.

$$dE = vdp .\tag{5}$$

With $p = m \cdot v$ we obtain

$$dE = \frac{p}{m}dp .\tag{6}$$

Replacing m with E/k, and reordering returns

$$EdE = kpdp .\tag{7}$$

We thus obtain

$$dE^2 = kdp^2 \tag{8}$$

and

$$E^2 = kp^2 + C ,\tag{9}$$

where C is the constant of integration.

The value of C can easily be determined, because for $p = 0$ the energy E assumes the value of the rest energy E_0. Thus, C must be equal to $E_0{}^2$. We therefore get

$$E^2 = E_0{}^2 + kp^2 \tag{10}$$

and for the sought-after relationship between energy and momentum we get:

$$E(p) = \sqrt{E_0{}^2 + kp^2} .\tag{11}$$

The red line in Figure 1 shows the graphic representation of relation (11). Two limiting cases are of particular interest.

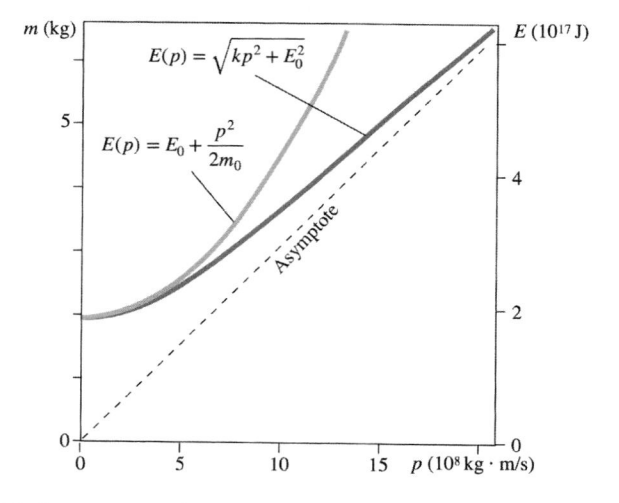

Fig. 1. Relationship between mass/energy and momentum (red line). For large values of the momentum the curve approaches the asymptote (dashed line), for small values the classical quadratic relation (grey line).

For small momentum values, equation (11) changes to

$$E(p) = E_0 + \frac{kp^2}{2E_0} = E_0 + \frac{p^2}{2m_0} . \tag{12}$$

We obtain the classical kinetic energy, increased by the rest energy (grey line in Figure 1).

If the momentum is very large, so that E_0^2 can be neglected in comparison with kp^2, equation (11) turns into

$$E(p) = \sqrt{k}p , \tag{13}$$

see the dashed line in Figure 1. For bodies whose rest mass is 0 kg, equation (13) applies for all values of the momentum, not only for large values (Figure 2). Thus, in the highly relativistic limiting case, energy and momentum are proportional to each other. This shows that there is a similarity between these quantities, which becomes even clearer when we solve equation (11) according to E_0^2

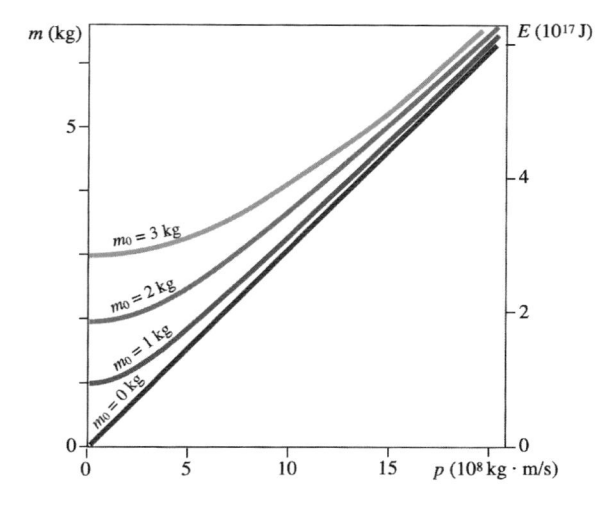

$$E_0^2 = E^2 - kp^2 . \tag{14}$$

Fig. 2. Energy momentum relationship for four different rest masses. For photons (rest mass zero) the relation is linear.

We thus have the rule: If the momentum of a body changes, its energy changes in such a way that the difference $E^2 - kp^2$ retains its value. This value is the square of the rest energy E_0.

3.2. The velocity momentum relationship

Now our second question: How does the velocity of a body depend on its momentum? We solve $p = mv$ for v, then apply equations (1) and (11) and obtain

$$v(p) = \frac{p}{m} = \frac{kp}{E} = \frac{kp}{\sqrt{E_0^2 + kp^2}} \ . \tag{15}$$

If we replace the rest energy with the rest mass we get

$$v(p) = \frac{kp}{\sqrt{k^2 m_0^2 + kp^2}} \ . \tag{16}$$

Figure 3 shows the dependence of the velocity on the momentum for different rest-masses. From equation (16) follows that the velocity of a body approaches a terminal value as the momentum increases. It is

$$\lim_{p \to \infty} v(p) = \lim_{p \to \infty} \frac{kp}{\sqrt{k^2 m_0^2 + kp^2}} = \sqrt{k} \ . \tag{17}$$

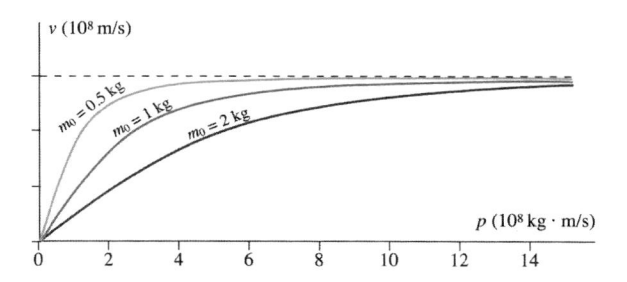

Fig. 3. Dependence of the velocity on the momentum for different rest masses.

Up to now, k only played the role of a conversion factor, but now it gets a physical meaning. Its value is the square of the terminal speed. Since k is a universal constant, its square root, i.e. the terminal speed, is also a universal constant. The terminal speed is the same for all bodies and particles and is independent of the reference frame.

This can be seen in Figure 3. The diagram also shows: the smaller the rest mass of a body is, the "faster" it approaches the terminal speed.

Let us come back to equation (16). We see: If one supplies momentum to a body, its velocity initially increases linearly with the momentum, while its mass almost does not change. This is the Newtonian limiting case. When its momentum has become very large, its velocity no longer changes, but its mass increases.

But what is the value of k and thus the value of the terminal speed? So far, nothing has been said about it. The answer to this question can only be obtained by a measurement. There are several ways to do that: Either one increases the momentum of a particle until its velocity no longer changes (in a particle accelerator) and then measures its velocity, or one measures the velocity of photons, i.e. particles of rest mass zero. Photons always move with the terminal speed.

Because of the great importance of the terminal speed, one gives it its own symbol

$$c := \sqrt{k} \ . \tag{18}$$

The measurement results in

$$c = 3 \cdot 10^8 \text{m/s} \tag{19}$$

and therefore

$$k = 9 \cdot 10^{16} \text{J/kg} \ . \tag{20}$$

The constant c is also called speed of light. But our derivation shows that light does not play a particular role in special relativity. That is why we prefer to call c terminal speed.

3.3. *Mass and inertia*

From classical physics we are used to consider mass as a measure of inertia. Let us first clarify what is meaningfully understood by inertia.

To determine the inertia of an object, we supply a certain amount of momentum to the object and we look at the resulting change in velocity. The more momentum $\mathrm{d}p$ is needed to achieve a desired change in velocity $\mathrm{d}v$, the greater the inertia.

Therefore we can define the inertia as

$$T := \frac{\mathrm{d}p}{\mathrm{d}v} \ . \tag{21}$$

We first consider a classical motion, i.e. a motion with $v \ll c$. We know the $p - v$ relationship to be

$$p = m \cdot v \ . \tag{22}$$

This results in

$$T = m \ , \tag{23}$$

which is no surprise.

If however the movement is relativistic, i.e. if no longer $v \ll c$, things become more complicated. From equation (15) we obtain

$$p(v) = \frac{m_0 v}{\sqrt{1 - \frac{v^2}{c^2}}} \tag{24}$$

and

$$T(v) = \frac{\mathrm{d}p}{\mathrm{d}v} = \frac{m_0}{\left(1 - \frac{v^2}{c^2}\right)^{\frac{3}{2}}} \ . \tag{25}$$

The inertia now depends on the velocity. It can no longer be described by a single number. By the way, it is also not identical with the so-called relativistic mass.

We know a similar behavior from other contexts. The current-voltage relationship of an ohmic resistor can be characterized by a single number, its resistance. In general, however, the resistive behavior of an electrical component cannot be characterized by a single number. What we need is the $U - I$ characteristic. The situation is like that of inertia. In general, one cannot say that the mass is a measure for the inertia of a body. Rather, the inertial behavior of a body is characterized by a characteristic curve, equation (25). Sometimes the quantity defined by equation (25) is called the longitudinal mass. We think this is rather clumsy. The simple facts are thereby somewhat obscured.

4. Conclusion

The development of a teaching concept for the school, in our case for the secondary school, is a balancing act.

On one hand, teaching at school differs fundamentally from popular science presentations. The latter can limit themselves to showcasing the spectacular, the impressive and the surprising of the scientific results – one can almost say: to exhibit them like objects in a museum.

School teaching has to meet other requirements. The statements must be logically coherent. They have to fit into the previous teaching and form a foundation for the future teaching, for example, at the university.

On the other hand, we must make sure that we do not treat high-school students like university students, that we do not overburden them. Let us not forget: One can calculate and prove without generating understanding.

It should also be borne in mind that most high school students a priori have no particular interest in physics.

We have tried to develop a course under these constraints. We would like to emphasize once again that the above remarks do not represent the content of our course. We have presented only what we believe is different in our approach from that of other textbooks.

References

1. F. Herrmann et al., *The Karlsruhe Physics Course* (2016), http://www.physikdidaktik.uni-karlsruhe.de/.
2. F. Herrmann et al., *The Karlsruhe Physics Course* (Guangzhou: Guangdong Education Publishing House , 2018), http://www.physikdidaktik.uni-karlsruhe.de/.
3. F. Herrmann, G. Job, *Historical burdens on physics* (2019), http://www.physikdidaktik.uni-karlsruhe.de/.
4. A. Einstein, *Zur Elektrodynamik bewegter Körper,* **Vol 10 (322)** , (Annalen der Physik, 1905), pp. 891–921.
5. A. Einstein, *Grundzüge der Relativitätstheorie*, 5th edn. (Berlin: Akademie-Verlag, 1970).

Teaching relativity: Computer-aided modeling

F. Herrmann and M. Pohlig*

*Institute for Theoretical Solid State Physics, Karlsruhe Institute of Technology (KIT),
Karlsruhe, Baden-Württemberg, Germany*
**E-mail: pohlig@kit.edu*
www.kit.edu

Mathematical derivations alone do not necessarily lead to physical understanding. Tools that can replace the mathematical treatment of a physical process and at the same time increase the physical understanding are computer-aided modeling programs, also called system dynamics software. Examples of such software are Stella, Berkeley Madonna, Wensim, Dynasys, Powersim or COACH 7. They solve differential equations and systems of differential equations with numerical methods. One works with a graphical user interface. We want to show how such a software can be used to get from a non-relativistic model to a relativistic model with only minimal modifications. Equating mass and energy alone, ensures that the model provides essential statements of relativistic dynamics: the existence of a terminal velocity for all physical motions, the relativistic dependence of the velocity of a body on its momentum, the relativistic relation between momentum and energy of a body.

Keywords: Teaching relativity, computer-aided modeling, system dynamic software, Coach 7.

1. Introduction

There are two reasons why learning relativity is difficult. First, there is a widespread belief that relativity is essentially a physics of reference frame changes. Second, mathematics, which seems to be indispensable for a first approach to relativity according to common usage, is a major, even often insurmountable, hurdle for many students. Therefore, the structure of our course follows two didactic recommendations: 1. avoid reference frame changes 2. reduce the use of mathematics to the most necessary. We fulfill the first recommendation by teaching dynamics before kinematics. Instead of postulating that the speed of light is invariant under reference frame changes, we declare from the very beginning that energy and mass are the same physical quantity. We call it energy when its value is measured in joules and mass when measured in kilograms. The second recommendation can be fulfilled if we use a suitable modeling software, a so-called system dynamics software (SDS). In a SDS, physical quantities and their relations are described by graphical symbols and are intuitively understandable. Since its usage is self-explanatory to a large extent, we do not need to go into details of the handling here.

As a representative of such a software we use COACH 7.[1]

2. Teaching relativity using a system dynamics software

2.1. *Momentum flow into a body*

We create a model for a body which is accelerated from rest. Its momentum, which is zero at the beginning, increases as a constant momentum current flows into it (as a force is exerted on it). In a first step we treat this model non-relativistically. In the second step, the model is transformed into a relativistic model by a small modification.

In a SDS model, momentum p and other substance-like (extensive) quantities such as electric charge Q, energy E, or entropy S are represented by boxes. All these quantities change their values by an inflow or an outflow. (Entropy can also change its value by being produced). In the model, these currents are represented by thick arrows, Figure 1. Since in our lessons momentum is not introduced as a derived quantity, it gets its own unit of measurement, the Huygens, abbreviated Hy. The unit of its current is Huygens per second (Hy/s). The unit Hy is SI-compatible. We thus have $1 \text{Hy/s} = 1 \text{ N}$.

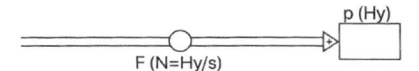

Fig. 1. A temporally constant momentum current F leads to a linear increase of the momentum p.

Since the body is accelerated from rest, its momentum at the beginning of its motion is 0 Hy. We assume the momentum current to be constant in time, we set e.g. $F = 1$ N. When the model is started, the simulation begins running and the actual momentum is calculated for previously defined time steps.

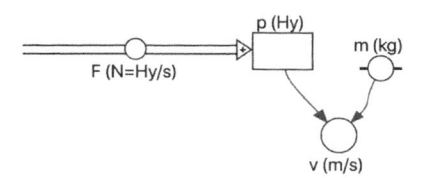

Fig. 2. The velocity is calculated from momentum and mass.

In order for our model to be able to tell us something about the velocity of the body, we must add the mass m of the body to the model, in Figure 2 represented by a circle. We choose $m = 1$ kg for a first simulation and $m = 2$ kg for the second one. The velocity is calculated using $v = p/m$. This relationship is stored in circular symbol for the velocity v. Thin, red arrows are pointing from the symbols for p and m to the symbol of v. This ensures that the actual values of p and m are available for the calculation of v at any instant of time during the simulation. In concrete terms, this means that while the simulation is running, the momentum is divided by the mass at fixed time steps, and thus the actual velocity v is calculated.

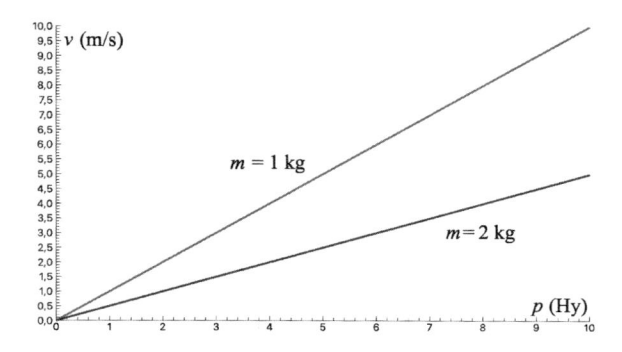

Fig. 3. $v - p$ diagrams or bodies of masses 1kg and 2 kg.

The dependencies of the various variables occurring in the model can be displayed graphically in output windows. Figure 3 shows the v-p diagrams for two bodies of masses 1 kg and 2 kg.

2.2. Together with momentum energy is flowing into the body

We now add the kinetic energy of the body to our model, Figure 4.

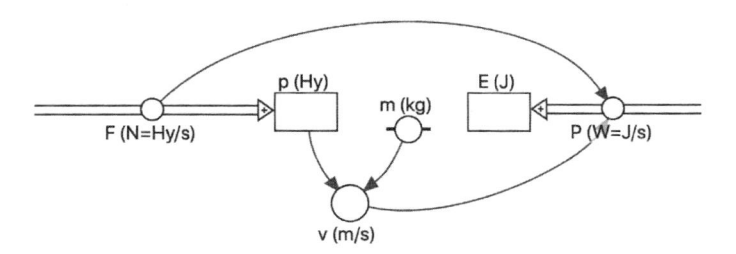

Fig. 4. The energy current P into the body is calculated from the velocity v of the body and the momentum current F (force).

Also the energy E is represented by a box. Since the body is accelerated from rest, not only the momentum but also the kinetic energy must have the initial value $E_{\text{int}} = 0$. Like the momentum current, the energy current (power) into the body is represented by a thick arrow. It can be calculated as $P = vF$. The software provides the energy-momentum diagrams for $m = 1$ kg and $m = 2$ kg, Figure 5.

These graphs could be described by the formula

$$E_{\text{kin}} = \frac{p^2}{2m}.\tag{1}$$

However, this equation has not been used by the SDS.

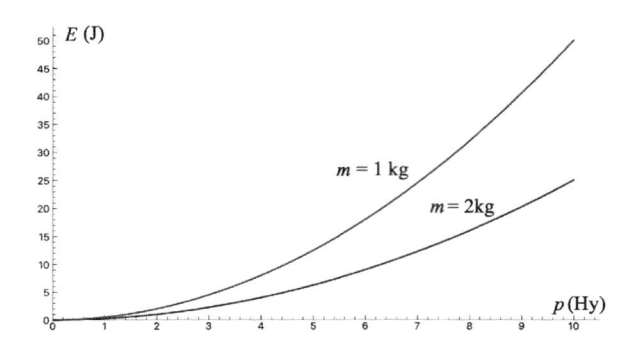

Fig. 5. $E - p$ diagrams generated with the SDS for $m = 1$ kg and $m = 2$ kg.

2.3. *From the classical to the relativistic model*

The two models described up to now serve as basic models for others, such as for "free fall in the gravitational field of the earth", for "falling with friction" and others.

If momentum is replaced by other substance-like quantities such as electric charge or entropy, analogous models are obtained from electricity and thermodynamics, respectively. In this way, students learn to use the modeling software as a tool in other subfields of physics. So when they create relativistic models, they are already familiar with the tool. We now want to create a relativistic model by modifying our non-relativistic model appropriately, Figure 4. For this purpose, only a small modification has to be made. The mass, which was originally a constant,

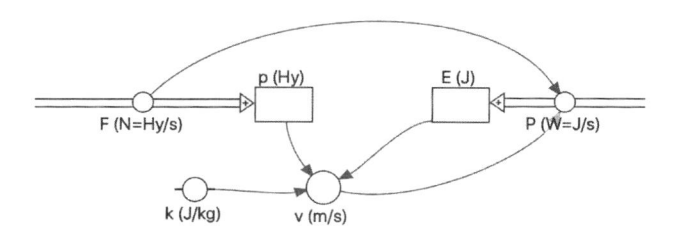

Fig. 6. Relativistic model: The constant mass is replaced by the total energy of the body.

is now identified with the energy[2] according to

$$E = k \cdot m \tag{2}$$

Here, the energy is no longer the kinetic energy but the total energy of the body. Figure 6 shows the modified model. The initial value of the energy is no longer 0 J, but it is equal to the value of the energy that the body has at rest. We choose $E_{\text{int}} = 10$ J and for another simulation $E_{\text{int}} = 5$ J. To transform the unit kilograms into joules, we have to multiply the mass by k. We first set its value arbitrarily to $k = 16$ J/kg. The actual true value of k will be discussed later. The velocity of the body is now calculated according to

$$v = \frac{p}{m} = \frac{kp}{E} . \tag{3}$$

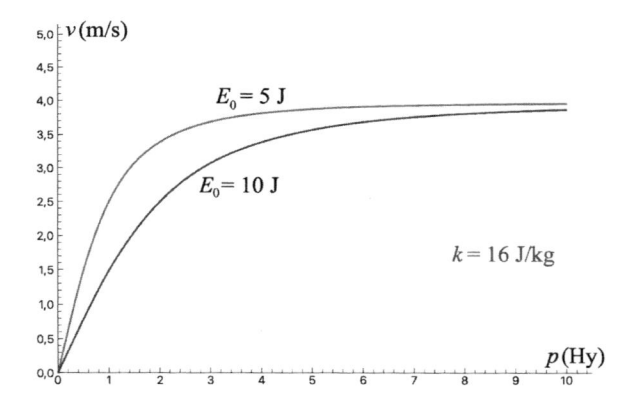

Fig. 7. $v - p$ diagrams obtained with the relativistic model.

As Figure 7 shows, the v-p diagrams are different from those in Figure 3. It can be seen that the velocities of both bodies approach a common terminal velocity of 4 m/s. One "plays" with further, freely chosen values for the rest energy and always finds the same terminal velocity. Furthermore, the v-p diagrams show that light bodies reach the terminal velocity quicker than heavy ones. Finally, one recognizes that for sufficiently small momentum values the velocity of a body increases linearly with momentum. This confirms what is already known from non-relativistic mechanics.

The diagrams are graphs of the relation

$$v(p) = \frac{p}{m} = \frac{kp}{E} = \frac{kp}{\sqrt{E_0^2 + kp^2}} . \tag{4}$$

However, we don't need to know this equation, or to derive it, in order to be able to read the important properties of this relationship from the diagrams.

The diagrams show that for relativistic motions the following rules hold:

- small momentum values: $v \sim p$
- large momentum values: $v = \sqrt{k}$

By choosing other initial values for the energy and other values for k, one easily gets convinced of the generality of these rules. For the diagrams in Figure 8, the values 9 J/kg, 16 J/kg and 25 J/kg were selected for k. The terminal velocity results to be 3 m/s, 4 m/s and 5 m/s, respectively.

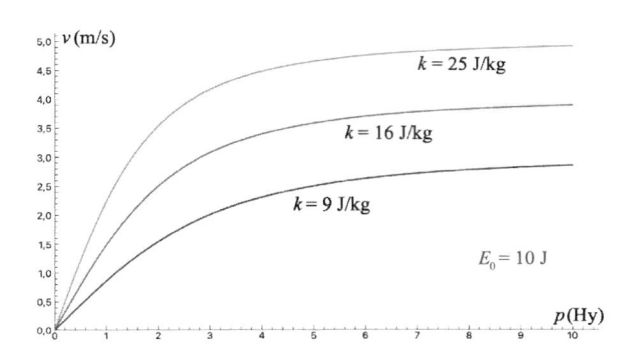

Fig. 8. $v - p$ diagrams for different k values.

We see that the value of the terminal velocity is just the square root of k. While k used to be merely a conversion factor between kilogram and joule, it now acquires a physical meaning. Moreover, from the fact that a conversion factor for units is universal, the terminal velocity also has a universal value. It must be a universal constant. For this reason, we give the square root of k, i.e. the terminal velocity, a symbol of its own, namely

$$c := \sqrt{k} \tag{5}$$

Up to now, we had chosen the value of k and thus also that of c arbitrarily. But which value has nature given to k resp. c? Experiments show that $k = 9 \cdot 10^{16}$ J/kg and therefore $\sqrt{k} = c = 3 \cdot 10^8$ m/s.

Another relationship that our model provides in the form of a diagram is that between energy and momentum, Figure 9. The diagrams shown are graphs of the equation:

$$E(p) = \sqrt{E_0{}^2 + kp^2} = \sqrt{E_0{}^2 + c^2 p^2} \tag{6}$$

For small momentum values we get the non-relativistic relation between kinetic energy and momentum, shifted by the rest energy of the body:

$$E(p) = \frac{p^2}{2m} + E_0 \tag{7}$$

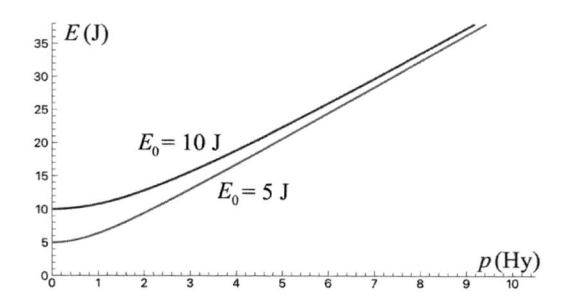

Fig. 9. $E - p$ relation in the relativistic model. The rest energy was set to 5 J and in the second run to 10 J.

Moreover, we see that the ratio of energy and momentum is the same for large values of the momentum.

$$E(p) = \sqrt{k} \cdot p = c \cdot p \tag{8}$$

3. Conclusion

A non-relativistic SDS model which describes the behavior of a body whose momentum increases linearly, i.e. into which a constant momentum current is flowing, becomes a relativistic model by a small modification. The change consists in equating the quantities mass and energy. The new model then provides diagrams that are well-known from relativistic physics. The software provides them without using the respective equations. From these diagrams, important results of relativity can be interpreted and understood. The use of computer-aided modeling in teaching has the advantage of getting rid of the mathematical ballast and that one can concentrate on the physical content. Our experience shows that even younger students can easily learn a software like COACH 7 and use it to work out challenging results in relativistic dynamics.

References

1. Coach 7 for Desktop and Tablet: CMA (Centre for Microcomputer Application https://cma-science.nl/downloads_en accessed July 26 2021.
2. Herrmann, F. et al., *The Karlsruhe Physics Course: Mechanics: for the upper secondary school*, (2019).
   http://www.physikdidaktik.uni-karlsruhe.de/index_en.html accessed August 2021.

Solstices and Equinoxes in 1703 at the meridian line of St. Maria degli Angeli in Rome, and the stellar aberration of Sirius

Costantino Sigismondi

ICRA, Sapienza University of Rome, Rome, Italy
E-mail: sigismondi@icra.it
http://www.icra.it/solar

Silvia Pietroni

Dipartimento di Fisica "E.R. Caianiello", Università di Salerno
Via Giovanni Paolo II 132, I-84084 Fisciano, Italy
Istituto Nazionale di Fisica Nucleare, Sezione di Napoli
Via Cintia, 80126, Napoli, Italy
E-mail: spietroni@unisa.it

The 1703 was the first year of full operation of the meridian line in the Basilica of St. Maria degli Angeli in Rome. The instants of solstices and equinoxes, the *Anni Cardines*, obtained by comparing transit timings of Sun and Sirius, also in daytime, are affected either by the East deviation of the meridian line of about 5' Eastward (geometrical effect), either by the stellar aberration of Sirius (relativistic effect). Similarly the seasonal shifts of Sirius' declination observed by Bianchini are here firstly recognized as depending on the stellar aberration in ecliptic latitude. The eccentricity of the Earth's orbit and the orientation of its axis in the space can be measured, since Ptolemy, by knowing the exact timing of the solstices and the equinoxes. The dates of 1703 equinoxes and solstices have been published by Francesco Bianchini in local roman mean time, referred to the local (roman) mean noon, i.e. after the solar meridian mean transit time. By using the observations of the three lunar eclipses of 1703 we found the equation of time for that year, and the UTC corresponding timings of the beginning of the seasons. This operation lead to find the contribution of the Sirius aberration to the instant calculated by Bianchini with respect to the current celestial mechanical models of IMCCE.

Keywords: St. Maria degli Angeli, Meridian Line, Stellar Aberration, Sirius, 1703, Solstices, Equinoxes, Ecliptic Longitude, UTC, UT1, TDT, TT, Roman mean time.

1. Stellar aberration measures in 1701 before Bradley's discovery

The stellar aberration was discovered by James Bradley in 1727, and the same astronomer discovered the nutation of the Earth's axis in 1737. At the meridian line of St. Maria degli Angeli, the giant Clementine Gnomon, built by astronomer Francesco Bianchini (1662-1729) and funded by the Cardinal Gianfrancesco Albani (1649-1721), elected pope on 23 November 1700 with the name of Clement XI.

The effects of stellar aberration have been detected on the Polaris (2006), and on Sirius (2021, present work).

The aberration of the Polaris influenced the measure of the latitude of the pinhole, the gnomon of the meridian line, made by Bianchini on January 1-8, 1701.

The aberration on Sirius affected the instant of the equinoxes and the solstices, calculated with the difference between solar and stellar meridian transit, the latter observed also in full daylight. To obtain such evidence of the first special relativistic effect observable, a complete calibration of the meridian line has been carried since 2018. With the IGEA observational campaign, Informatized Geometric Ephemerides for Astrometry: all the reference points present of the 45 meters long meridian line have been calibrated, by comparing solar observations and ephemerides.

At the Marcel Grossmann Meeting XI (Berlin, 2006) the evidences of Polaris' aberration were discovered in the latitude, from the measures by Bianchini at the Gnomon, and now at the Marcel Grossmann XVI edition we can afford the evidences on Sirius' stellar aberration with the increased precision on the calibration of this giant instrument, the second *Heliometer*, or solar telescope, of its times, after the one of Cassini in St. Petronio, Bologna.

2. Managing dates and timing of 1703, in local mean time

The equation of time shifts the instants of the meridian transit day by day with respect to an absolute time reference such as UTC. The eclipses' ephemerides are based upon the terrestrial dynamical time TDT, while the terrestrial rotational time UT1 includes the slowing down effect of the Earth's rotation in act since 1700. To translate 1703 local time to modern UTC to the nearest second we exploited the observations of the three lunar eclipses occurred in 1703, all made by Bianchini. The equation of time of that year come out from the comparison between the observed instants of eclipse's beginning and end -in local mean time- and the corresponding instants in TDT computed by the NASA ephemerides.

3. The dates and timing for 1703 lunar eclipses from NASA ephemerides

The three lunar eclipses of 1703 have been observed by Francesco Bianchini and published in the same book (Bianchini, 1703) where the great meridian line, the *Clementine Gnomon* was presented. The instants of beginning and end of lunar eclipses are independent of the position of the observers on the Earth, and they can be calculated with a suitable celestial mechanical model of the lunar orbit (provided by NASA). They occurred very close to the solstices, making the procedure of their absolute timing (expressed in TDT and then in UTC) particularly accurate.

The maximum phase of the eclipse is indicated in TD, terrestrial dynamical time to the nearest minute in the figures, and to second accuracy in the website. The maximum of the eclipse is recovered in local time after doing the average between starting time and ending time of the eclipse, to the nearest second. In the details of the *Canon of five millennia of lunar eclipses*, also the starting time and the ending time of the eclipses are provided. The eclipses have been observed by Bianchini at the telescope, improving the accuracy of the measurements.

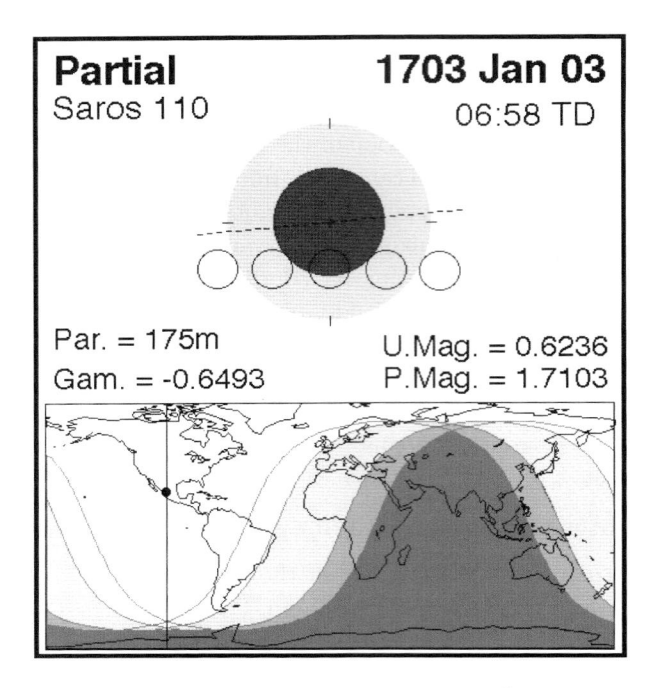

Fig. 1. The lunar eclipse of January 3rd 1703

4. Solstices and equinoxes and the equation of time in the ephemerides

The dynamical model for the Earth's orbit includes the perturbations of all planets, and they are implemented in the most advanced ephemerides. IMCCE provides an online service back to 4000 B. C. for the dates of the astronomical beginning of the seasons. The comparison with the corresponding instant of 1703 as calculated by Bianchini required a conversion into UTC of the local timings. It is available online a service, *Planetcalc*, with the equations of time, from 500 B. C.

We need a self-consistent derivation of the UTC timing of the equinoxes and the solstices in 1703, being the Equation of Time itself depending on the Earth's orbit eccentricity, which is derived from the the observed beginning of the seasons, namely the equinoxes and solstices.

The obliquity component goes to zero four times per year at the equinoxes and the solstices, while the eccentricity component vanishes twice per year at the apsides (aphelion and perihelion). This is well shown in *Planetcalc* website.

5. Synchronization of the equation of time with lunar eclipses in 1703

The dates of the apsides (as shown in Sigismondi and Pietroni, 2019) and the obliquity of the year are used to compute the equation of time for that year,

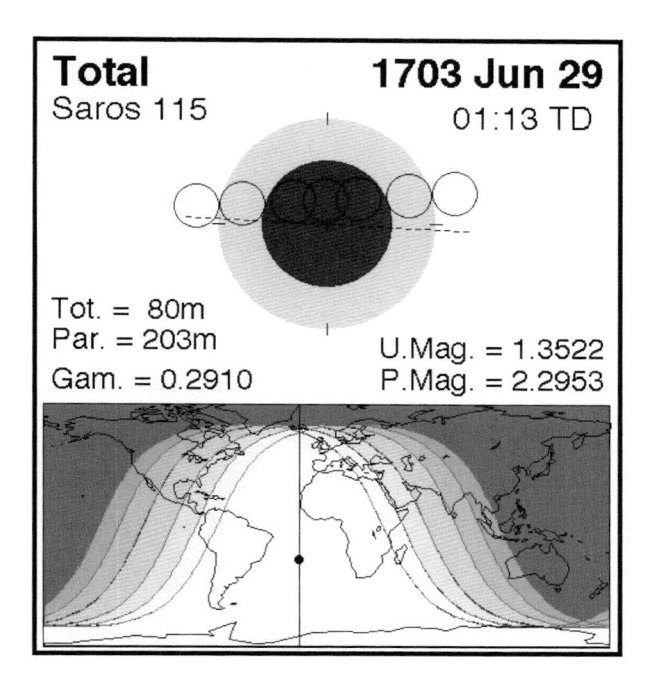

Fig. 2. The lunar eclipse of June 29th 1703

but an independent synchronization with UTC is needed, to verify the IMCCE ephemerides, and the lunar eclipses were used exactly to assure that synchronization. On June 22nd 1703 the equation of time of Planetcalc is -1.11 minutes, and in 28th June, last solar transit before the lunar eclipse, it is -2.38 minutes. It means that this local noon should occur 2 m 22 s before a mean solar noon fixed (e.g. CET Central European Time). For Rome the mean noon is at 12:10 CET, then 12:12:22 the transit time for 28th June, 1703. The eclipse was computed as maximum at 1:13 TD on 29th June, so 2:13 CET. Bianchini's beginning of totality is at 13:18:15 after solar meridian transit of 28th June, and the end (emersion) is 14:38:15. The middle of totality (maximum phase) is at 13:28:15, obtained by averaging. The solar transit in the same publication occurred at 12:07:36 so that the eclipse's maximum was at 02:05:51. The terrestrial dynamical time for the eclipse has been computed (Espenak and Meeus, 2009) on 02:12:47 (1:13 TD in figure 1). The TD, is ahead with respect to Bianchini's roman mean time of 6 min 56 s.

6. Including $\Delta UT1$ in the final timing

The procedure shown in detail for June 29th has been applied to the other eclipses of 1703, that Bianchini observed also with Filippo Maraldi (January 3rd) and alone (December 23rd), recovering the Roman average time adopted by Bianchini for his observations, with respect to the Terrestrial Dynamical Time. The adopted value

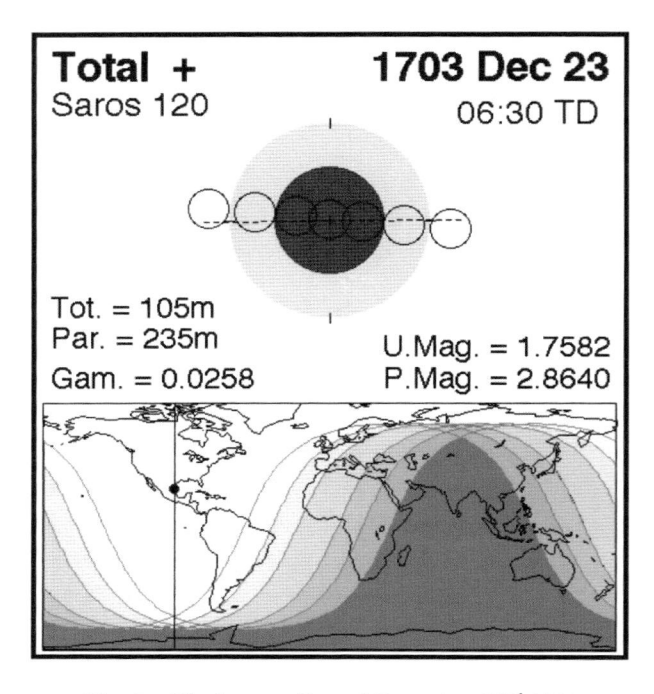

Fig. 3. The lunar eclipse of December 23rd 1703

1) Dates of the *Anni Cardines* A, B, C, D.
2) Length of the seasons a, b, c, d -->
3) --> eccentricity e and direction of the apsides

4) e+ε => Equation of Time

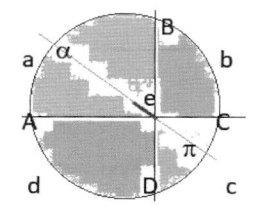

Fig. 4. The connection between the beginning of seasons' times and the eccentricity, and the equation of time. Aphelion α and perihelion π, the apsides, are also sketched.

1) Meridian transit (observed) = Mean Local Noon + Equation of Time (definition)

2) Eclipse's start (observed) = Mean Local Noon + Time delay (measured)

3) Eclipse's start (calculated) = Terrestrial Dynamical Time (calculated, NASA)

Fig. 5. The relations existing between Mean Noon, Equation of time, solar transit time and terrestrial dynamical time TD.

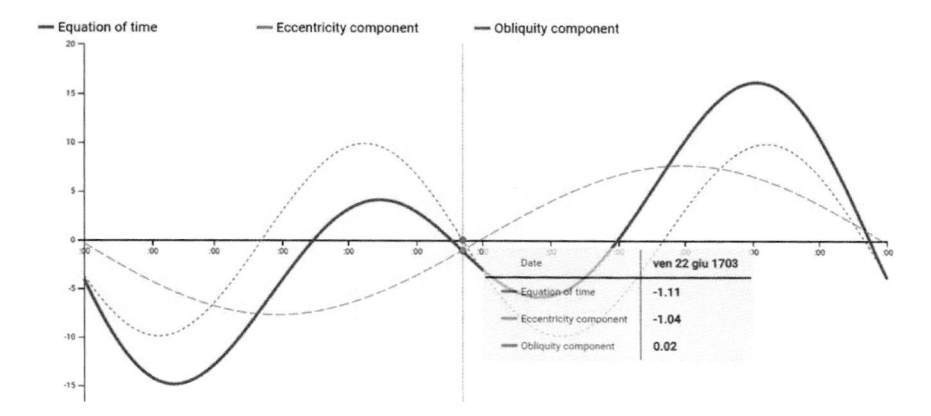

Fig. 6. The equation of time for 1703, as computed with Planetcalc.

for ΔUT1, of 7-8 seconds for the 1703, and due to the de-rotation effect of the Earth upon continental uplift after the ice age, is added to TD to obtain the coordinate universal time UTC for these observations, and for the dates and timing of solstices and equinoxes in 1703. These instants of seasons' beginning dates have been used for studying the aberration effect on the solstices and equinoxes in 1703 at the meridian line of St. Maria degli Angeli in Rome, demonstrating that Sirius' aberration and the deviation from Celestial North of the meridian line have caused the departure from IMCCE calculated times for 1703 seasons' starts (Sigismondi, 2021).

7. The dates and timing for 1703 *anni cardines*

Bianchini used the term *Anni Cardines* for the solstices and the equinoxes, because they are related to:

- Inclination of the Earth's axis on the ecliptic plane (the plane of the orbit), called *obliquity*;
- Position of the apsides in the Earth's orbit, which determines the *eccentricity*.

They were published in the book *De Nummo et Gnomone Clementino* of 1703, as well as on a marble epigraph in the presbytherium.

These instants are expressed in mean local time, after/before the mean meridian transit or midnight (anti-)transit. So to recover their instants as expressed in UTC it was necessary to recover three lunar eclipses observed in the same year and published by Bianchini in the same book (Bianchini, 1703): January 3, June 29 and December 23 (see below). After this operation of synchronization, we made the comparison with the IMCCE ephemerides for 1703.

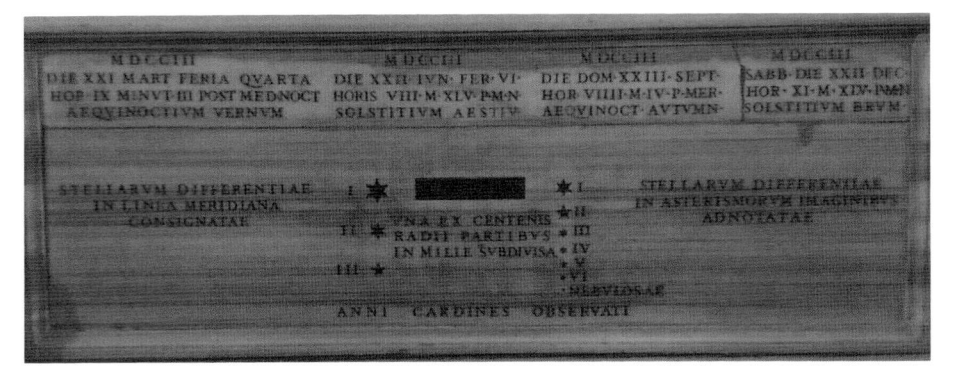

Fig. 7. The epigraph of 1703 *Anni Cardines* in the presbytherium of St. Maria degli Angeli in Rome.

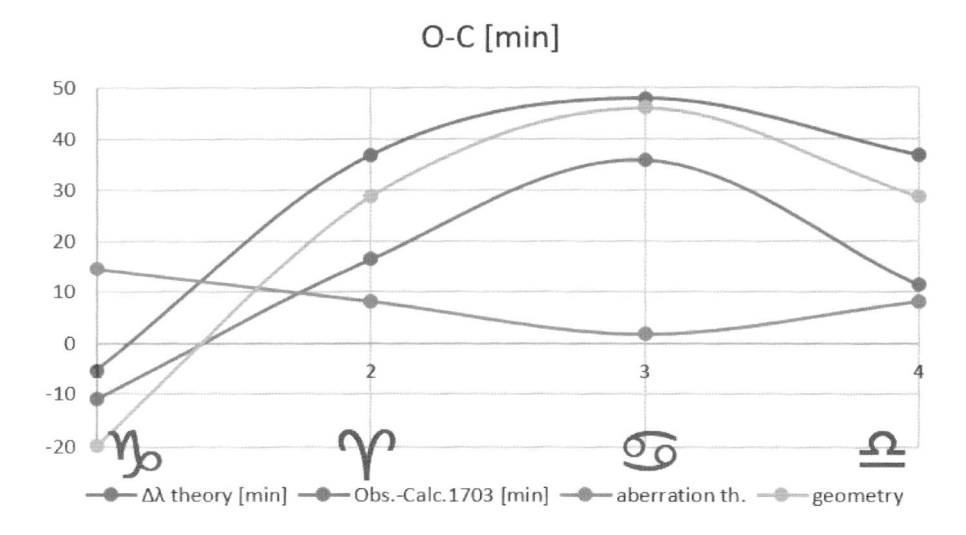

Fig. 8. The epigraph's timings translated into UTC and compared with IMCCE ephemerides.

8. Sirius' aberration and the East deviation of the line

Before the present analysis it was not clear that Bianchini used only Sirius for timing the solar meridian transits, also in daytime. The reason can be practical: Sirius is the brightest star in the sky and it can be seen in full daylight with a telescope through the open window 60 cm × 40 cm located over the pinhole. I made personally observations of meridian transits of Antares, Ras Alhague and Venus in daytime, outdoor at the meridian line of the Vatican obelisk, and the brightness of the star is crucial. Nevertheless on the meridian line of St. Maria degli Angeli there are reported 22 stars, with their ecliptic coordinates of 1701. This lead us to intend that all the 22 stars were used during the measurements (Bedinsky and Nastasi,

2007), while only Sirius was certainly used, after the examination of the documents of Bianchini.

The *Anni Cardines* are with ecliptic longitude 0°, 90°, 180°, 270°.

Sirius in 1701 had ecliptic longitude 97°57′53″ (fig. 3), and it was supposed to change only for the precession, until James Bradley discovered the aberration in 1727.

9. Seasonal aberration in ecliptic latitude

Francesco Bianchini (1703) considered also the meridian shift of Sirius, as of seasonal and of meteorological cause. Here I have demonstrated that it was due to the stellar aberration in ecliptic latitude (being Sirius not on the ecliptic plane but nearly at −40°).

Fig. 9. The coordinates of Sirius in 1701 from the Stellar Atlas of Philippe de la Hire, as reported on the meridian line of St. Maria degli Angeli.

10. Discussion

The measurements reported by Bianchini on the epigraph are plotted in orange, and they are in very good agreement with the blue line which includes the effects of the line's deviation (geometry in yellow) and of the stellar aberration in grey. The geometrical effect is much larger, nevertheless the aberration's contribution matches exactly as needed, especially in the cases of opposition (Sun in Capricorn) and conjunction (Sun in Cancer) with the star. The accuracy of the method applied

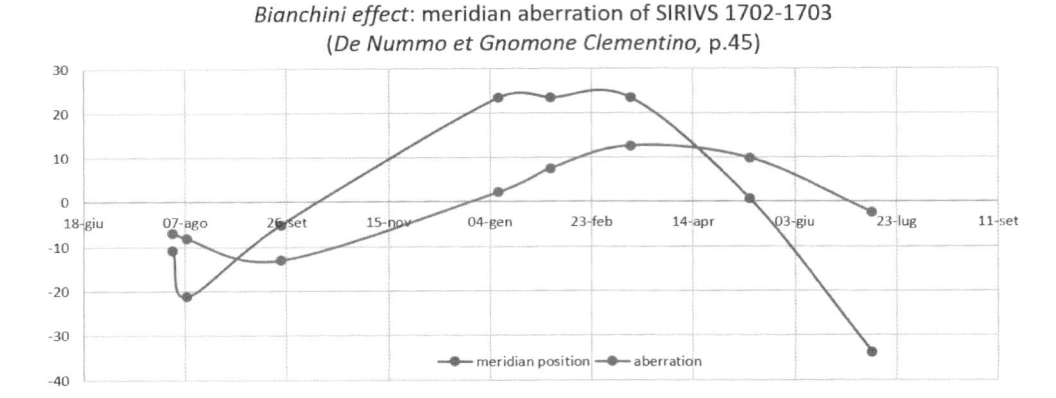

Fig. 10. The meridian position of Sirius along the year. Bianchini thought it was a meteorological effect, while it is due to aberration in ecliptic latitude.

at the Clementine meridian line is enough to recover the *Anni Cardines* within 10 minutes, as Bianchini declared in his book. The departure from this value, up to 30 minutes, is due to a systematic error (the deviation of the whole line toward East of 5.2', or 70 mm at its Northern extreme, 45 meters from the pinhole's vertical) combined with the special relativistic effect of the stellar aberration of Sirius, used in all measurements.

11. Conclusions

An important contribution of this paper is the verification that Sirius was the star always used in the meridian measurements, to compute the ecliptic coordinates of the Sun with respect to a fixed star. Finally the effect of meridian shift of Sirius along the year, was clearly recognized by Bianchini as seasonal, and it is, not because of seasonal humidity variations, but of special relativistic origin: due to the stellar aberration in ecliptic latitude, which is a rather big effect being Sirius of ecliptic latitude $b = -40°$.

The operation of synchronizing the mean solar time of Rome in 1703 with the Terrestrial Dynamical Time and then with the Universal Time Coordinated, has made possible recovering the Equation of Time of 1703 and the comparison between modern ephemerides and these data, to distinguish clearly the stellar aberration's contribution of Sirius, from the one due to the Eastward deviation of the line.

References

1. Bianchini, Francesco, Roma (1703), *De Nummo et Gnomone Clementino*, https://archive.org/details/bub_gb_IYtGjIE_X64C.
2. Bradley, James, (1727), *A New Discovered Motion of the Fix'd Stars*, https://www.if.ufrj.br/~marta/caronte-hipertexto/movimentosdaterra/bradley.pdf.

3. Sigismondi, Costantino, Proc. of MG X (2008), https://ui.adsabs.harvard.edu/abs/2008mgm..conf.2470S/abstract.
4. Bedinsky, Magdalena, Nastasi, Monica, (2007), *Le Stelle e la Meridiana*, http://www.santamariadegliangeliroma.it/paginamastersing.html?codice_url=posizione_delle_stelle&ramo_home=La_Meridiana.
5. Sigismondi, Costantino, *Earth's Obliquity and Stellar Aberration Detected at the Clementine Gnomon (Rome, 1703)* (2021), https://www.mdpi.com/2673-9984/2/1/49.
6. Bianchini, Francesco (1703), *Lunar eclipse of 29 June 1703 observed with Gabriele Manfredi*, https://archive.org/details/bub_gb_IYtGjIE_X64C/page/n325/mode/2up1
7. Espenak, Fred & Meeus, Jaan (2009), *Five Millennium Canon of Lunar Eclipses*, https://eclipse.gsfc.nasa.gov/SEpubs/5MCLE.html
8. IMCCE, Paris (2021), *DATES DES SAISONS POUR UNE ANNEE DONNEE*, https://promenade.imcce.fr/fr/pages4/439.html
9. Planetcalc LLC, Moscow (2021), *PLANETCALC Online calculators*, https://planetcalc.com/9198/.
10. Sigismondi, Costantino, *Earth's Obliquity and Stellar Aberration Detected at the Clementine Gnomon (Rome, 1703)* (2021), https://www.mdpi.com/2673-9984/2/1/49.
11. Sigismondi, Costantino and Silvia Pietroni, *L'eccentricità ed apogeo dell'orbita della Terra misurata a Santa Maria degli Angeli nel 1703*, Gerbertus **12**, 115 (2019). http://www.icra.it/gerbertus/2019/Gerb-12-2019-Sigismondi-Pietroni-eccen-115-120.pdf.

Positional astrometry at arcsecond accuracy using historical instruments, with light equipment

Costantino Sigismondi

ICRA, Sapienza University of Rome,
Rome, Italy
E-mail: sigismondi@icra.it
http://www.icra.it/solar

Lorenzo Ricciardi

University of Rome 3,
Rome, Italy

It is possible to make solar astrometry at arcsecond level using a meter, a watch and a smartphone at the Clementine Gnomon (1702, a giant pinhole-camera obscura). Similarly at the Vatican obelisk's meridian line (1817) the transit timing's accuracy is better than one second with the same instruments, and a small monocular. The differential positions with respect to the zodiacal marble disks allow to reach the arcsecond accuracy even outdoor.

Keywords: Video-timing, Equation of time, Spherical Astronomy, St. Maria degli Angeli, Vatican Obelisk, Meridian Line, Solstices, Equinoxes, Zodiacal signs, UTC, Ephemerides, Altazimuthal coordinates.

1. The giant pinhole camera obscura of the Clementine Gnomon (1702)

Measures of solar astrometry at arcsecond level have been done with a pencil, a meter, a watch and a smartphone at the Clementine Gnomon (1702). The Clementine meridian line is 45 meter long. The new calibration tables of the reference points on the meridian line in the Basilica of St. Maria degli Angeli, have been recently published (2021). Each measure of the solar image position is referred to its nearby marker with known position with respect to the pinhole, within ±0.5 mm. The solar images limbs can be located on the floor within ±1 mm. 2 arcseconds of angular position accuracy is obtained for winter observations with focal length of nearly 50 meters, while 5 arcsec is reached in summer with 21 m length involved. The pencil is used for signing the limbs' positions on the meridian line, the meter is sufficient to measure the distances of these limbs from the nearest reference point (there are 42 of them along the line), the watch synchronized with UTC is video recorded along with the solar transit to get the single frame accuracy on contact's times. A timing accuracy down to 0.3 s is reached with the average air turbulence conditions. This result is observed by N parallel transits averaged.

Examples on application of Cassini's and Laplace's corrections for air refraction on the observed data to obtain the real celestial coordinates of the date are presented (Sigismondi, 2019). This research was aimed to understand the Bianchini's effect, claimed in the book De Nummo et Gnomone Clementino (Bianchini, 1703). According to his observations Sirius changed its meridian position during the seasons because of some meteorological effect. We proved that the relativistic stellar aberration was the cause, thanks to this whole series of accurate observations of the Sun during all kind of weather conditions. This historical instrument gives the possibility to see the arcsecond, as half of a millimetre during winter, as no other instrument in the World, at the same time to many people. A set of more than 100 transits video is also presented for remote observations during all year's seasons.

Fig. 1. The ellipses of the Sun on 20 August 1702 on the meridian line of St. Maria degli Angeli. They are an example of measurement of the solar image on the floor with respect to the references on the meridian line [e.g. the number 55's marker].

2. The outdoor Vatican obelisk's meridian line (1817)

At the Vatican obelisk's meridian line solar positions as well as stellar and planetary transits have been measured. The obelisk of St. Peter's square has a meridian line since 1817. This line is two times longer than the Clementine line, and it allows potentially accurate measurements, despite the low contrast obtainable outdoor.

A scheme of the correspondence between the features on the top of the obelisk and the marble zodiacal disks on the square is published in figure 2.

The limit of the penumbra of the obelisk's shadow has been recovered with an accuracy of 2 mm during the Summer solstices of 2020 and 2021, repeatedly, by

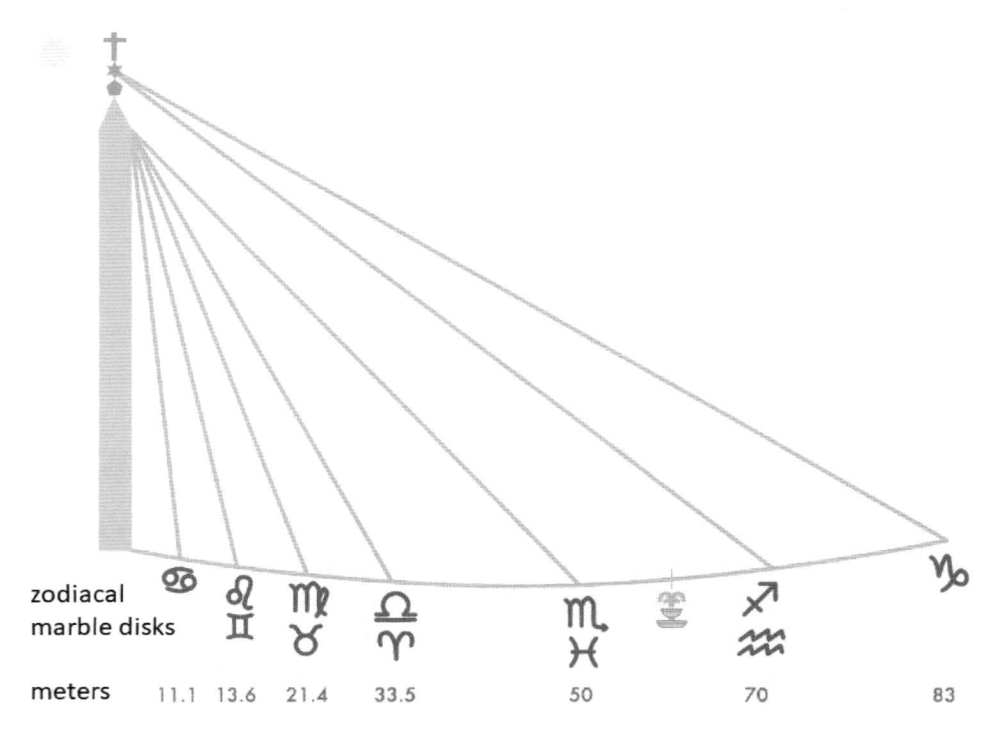

Fig. 2. The zodiacal signs on the meridian line of St. Peter's square as connected with the top of the obelisk. The distances from the axis of the obelisk are reported in meters from all the zodiacal marble disks.

moving the smartphone used for the video making, up and down near the limit and observing its cast shadow. The shadow's limits measured during 20 minutes of observations (fig. 3) on the Cancer and Leo's disks showed the rotation of the obelisk with respect to the East-West direction of 24 mm around its axis. This is the first indication on the astronomical accuracy of the re-collocation of the obelisk in September 1586 (Sigismondi, 2016). Observing the shadow's penumbra the massive presence of Sahara's sand in the upper roman atmosphere has been detectable. The contrast of the shadow almost vanished at noon time during the most sandy days. These observations were confirmed by the aerobiological measurements made in Tor Vergata University in the same period, and by the following presence of dry sand all over the city (Travaglini, 2021).

Moreover the projection of the image of the Sun when being occulted by the obelisk, obtained by a monocular 7×18, on the marble zodiacal disks (or on movable cardboard projection screen) has been video recorded during the meridian transits, attaining a timing accuracy of 1 second. The 18 mm-lens telescope projects on the marble a sharp image of the Sun, of about 30-45 mm of length, screened by the direct sunlight (fig. 4).

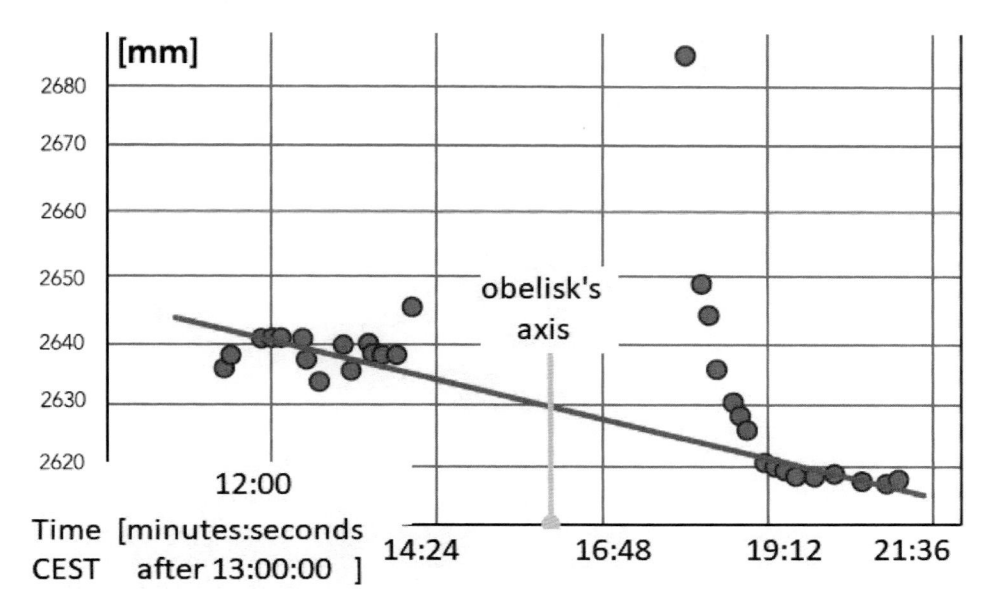

Fig. 3. The rotation of the obelisk with respect to East-West direction determines the variation of the shadow's length detected around the meridian time (24 July 2021) on the Leo disk, measured from the Cancer's black star.

2.1. Parallax error

The crucial problem of the all direct observations (with or without telescope) is the on-axis location of the lens or of the eye. It is a parallax error.

A mm shift from the meridian axis, with 4 mm/s velocity of the shadow corresponds to 0.25 s of timing shift. From the summer to the winter solstice the ground velocity of the shadow ranges from 2 to 6 mm/s, making the corresponding accuracy on the timing ranging from 0.5 to 0.2 s per mm.

To obtain a timing absolute accuracy ranging from 1 s to 3 s the parallax problem has to be solved. The solar shadow have not this problem, but their contrast makes the accuracy ± 3 s. Using a telescope to project the eclipses on the marble disks we improved the accuracy to ± 0.5s. The naked eye measurements of the stellar and planetary alignments while standing on the meridian line show an accuracy of ± 1, reduced to ± 0.5 s by using a ground mirror posed exactly in the middle of the meridian line and aiming at it. and the planetary/stellar transits observed with the mini-telescope standing on the meridian line. Stellar transits with the naked eye at the monocular are easier to be seen and audio-recorded because of the strong illumination of the square by night.

The achievable accuracy on many measurements from the same point, as for Antares' transits on the Capricorn disk, has been ± 10 arcsec on the central azimuth of the meridian transit behind the obelisk. The first video record of a full daytime transit (October 28, 2021 of Venus) confirms that result within a σ, as well as the transit of Fomalhaut observed on November 4, 2021 from the same disk.

Fig. 4. The approach of the Sun to Scorpio black star in 2021 on the marble disk in S. Peter's square: the three dimensional star on top of the obelisk is projected next to the black star. That black star is 4 cm wide.

3. Solstices, zodiacal signs and equinoxes

In the solstices the solar altitude above the horizon reach a maximum (June) or a minimum (December) well represented by a parabola. In St. Maria degli Angeli the influence of the aphelion (4-6 July) and of the perihelion (2-4 January) on the measured altitude of the Sun is well visible as the minimum/maximum's shift of the fitting parabola on dates symmetrical to the solstice and more and more widely spaced. For St. Peter's meridian line the approach to Scorpio zodiacal sign shows already well the change in solar meridian altitude day by day, projected on the marble disk (fig. 5).

Fig. 5. The approach of the Sun to Scorpio from 16 to 23 October 2021, looking at the obelisk of St. Peter's from the Scorpio's black star on the marble disk. The solar profile is reported with light yellow circles.

For a more precise measurement of the winter solstice a solid metal holder has been prepared for the mini-telescope. The principle is the same of the tripod with fixed angle, with a larger stability to guarantee high precision measurements, with the image shifting of $4-5\%$ of its length of 40-50 mm during the solstice's days.

4. Equinoxes and linear interpolation

The parabolae for the solstices and the linear interpolation for all zodiacal signs' ingresses are required to fit the observed data. This is a very good training for data analysis practice.

The observations of the equinoxes require the accurate knowledge of the Gnomon's height and geographical coordinates, and two observations: one before and another after the equinox, are necessary to have the possibility of interpolation.

Fig. 6. The fixed-angle monocular-holder built as Winter solstice meter.

These measurements confirmed the accuracy of ±10 minutes claimed by Bianchini, provided the systematic deviation of the line from the Celestial North. Similar result is obtained at St. Peter's square meridian line.

5. Level function of the mini-telescope at fixed angle

The mini-telescope with a fixed inclination can be used to test the horizontality of the seven disks. The Virgo's one shows a larger inclination because there the meridian line is reaching its minimum level in the square, before the equinox and toward the Scorpio's disk. The St. Peter's square is concave, allowing to convey the rainwater to the sewage system.

6. Special measurements

The meridian line of St. Maria degli Angeli allows to measure the position of the Sun with a great precision. The solstices can be measured also off-meridian as differential measures, always from the same reference point on the floor of the Basilica (e.g. the Summer solstice "royal" marker along the 173° azimut). The precision of 1 mm yields an angular accuracy in the range of a few arcseconds. The zodiacal marble disk of St. Peter's square meridian line have been used as fixed references, to make differential measurements of meridian transits. These differential measures

Fig. 7. The measurements of the Fall equinox on September 23, 2019 in the Basilica of St. Maria degli Angeli.

are used to recover their relative alignment with North and the obelisk's axis, and the alignment between the Sun entering the sign, the black star of the disk (see fig. 4) and the ending top features of the obelisk. The accuracy here is within 2 mm, as the one attained with the penumbral limit measured directly (fig. 3).

The measures of planetary and stellar transits have been:

- Antares from July 21 to August 21 (before sunset), Capricorn
- Ras Alhague, August 21-September 6, Virgo
- Fomalhaut, November 4 2021, Capricorn
- Saturn, Sagittarius, October 2021
- Venus in full daytime, 19-28 October 2021, Capricorn
- Jupiter, October 2021, Scorpio
- δ Capricorni, October 2021, in Scorpio
- μ and ϵ Aquarii, respectively of magnitude 4.91 and 3.96 under an unusual clear sky for Rome on October 11, 2021.

Fig. 8. The measurements of the Fall equinox on September 23, 2021 in St. Peter's square, on the meridian line. The solar image is the ellipse on the intersection of the two meters-tapes.

The lunar transits have been also recorded, and the lunar limb position precisely located. The planetary transits timing with a precision of a second allow to detect directly the nature of their motion (direct or retrograde) by comparing with the previous transit and the sidereal day length. The stellar and planetary transit paralleled the solar ones to measure the local western deviations of the meridian line on all the zodiacal disks. In particular Antares, Venus and Fomalhaut were used for the last point in the Capricorn solstice. The stellar transits allow to measure the sidereal day and the stellar aberration with a 0.01 s precision obtained over several days, either with naked eye video recorded measures (Sigismondi, 2021, these Proceedings).

6.1. *Distances on the meridian line in St. Peter's square*

The accuracy on the measures made on the floor of the square would require the use of metal meters at least 50 m long, or total stations, but due to security requirements in the square this is not possible. So we adopted a technique used in Athletics Track & Field to measure the long jump run-up length with the feet. The length of 10 adjacent feet with shoes is accurately measured to find its own unit with a mm accuracy. Distances up to 300 feet are accurate within 1%, as we could verify from the center of the colonnade of St. Peter's square, by measuring the distances of some columns from their centre.

Fig. 9. The mini-telescope and its tripode, used also as level-meter. The image of the Sun is evidenced inside the cloudlet.

7. The marble zodiacal disks and the Gregorian cycle of four centuries

There is a 4-years periodicity in the ingress' dates into the zodiacal signs, due to the Julian leap year. The 29th of February resets almost completely the 5 h 49 m 11 s of average excess of the tropical year versus the civil one of 365 days. But only over 4 centuries the Gregorian reformation of the calendar is complete. Then the sequence of the dates represented in figure 10 with the addition of 22 December, Solstice in Capricorn (fig. 6, logo), is the result of a rounding to the day of these instants. The complete sequence corresponding to the dates represented on the marble disks happened in 1815. Here the procedure applied to the IMCCE calculated dates:

- Spring in Aries 21 March 1815 11h31m UT become 21 March
- Summer in Cancer 22 June 1815 8h59m UT become 22 June
- Autumn in Libra 23 September 1815 à 22h43m UT become 23 September
- Winter in Capricorn 22 December 1815 à 15h44m UT become 22 December

This sequence will be the same for all 12 zodiacal signs ingresses in the year 2215.

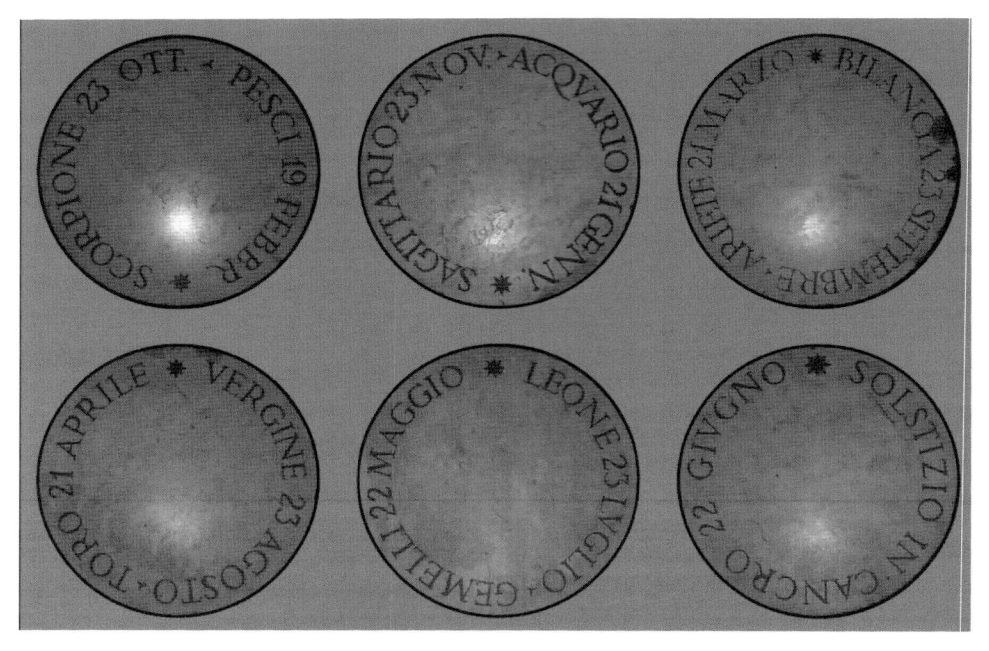

Fig. 10. Six of seven zodiacal disks: the Solstice in Capricorn 22 December is in the circular logo of figure 6. The dates of the zodiacal ingresses are the ones of 1815, and they will repeat in 2215.

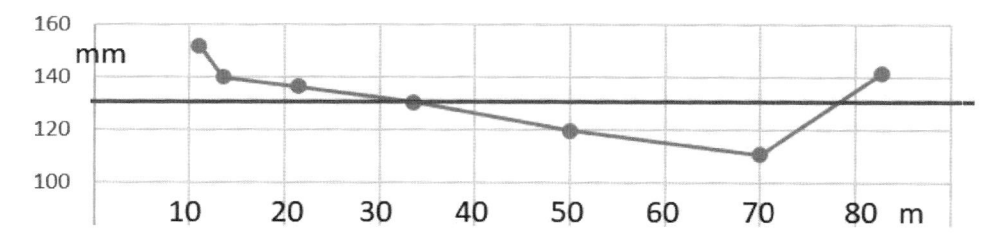

Fig. 11. On the seven zodiacal disks the meridian line is always West of the axis of the obelisk. The cross above the obelisk is also West of its axis, and it was reliably the sighting scope for the alignment of the austral zodiacal disks.

8. Deviation of the meridian line of St. Peter from Celestial North

The deviation of the meridian line has been measured from the obelisk's axis, and it is Westward.

The cross does not cast its shadow on the black stars of Leo and Cancer's disks; while it does from the Virgo-Taurus disk on.

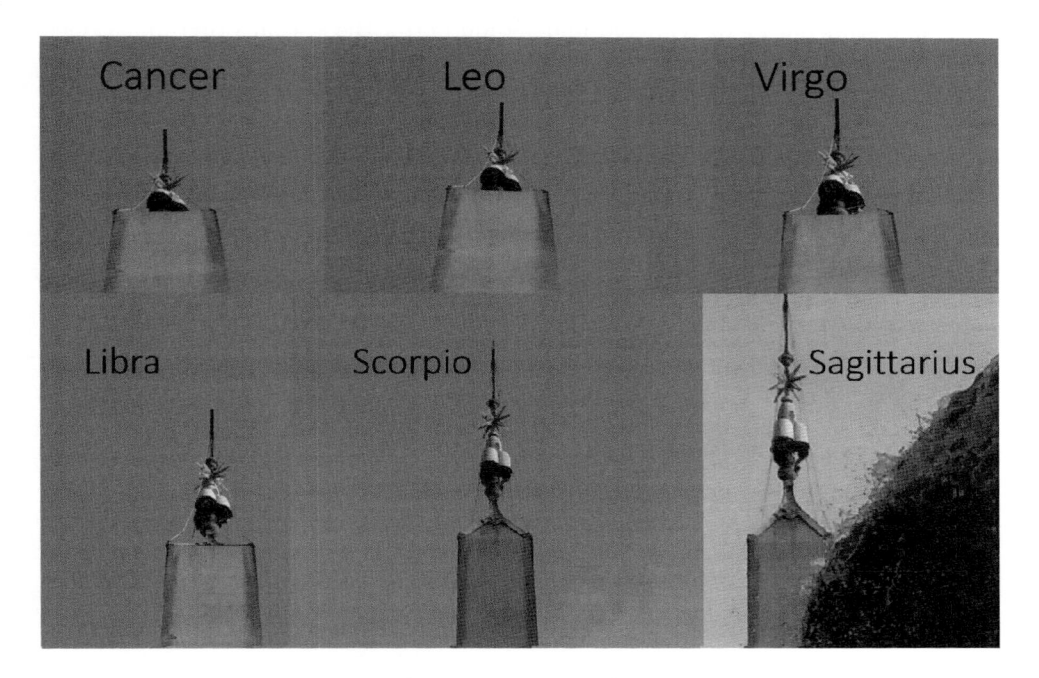

Fig. 12. The top of the obelisk as seen from all zodiacal disks.

9. Conclusions and perspectives

The positions of the celestial bodies is at the basis of Celestial Mechanics, and every gravitational theory: either Newtonian or Einstenian. To distinguish the latter are necessaries data with arcsecond level of accuracy. The measurements made at the historical meridian lines of St. Maria degli Angeli and St. Peter's square, with light equipment included:

- small meter tape
- radio synchronized watch
- a smartphone used for video and/or audio records
- "calibrated" feet
- a monocular 7×18 on small tripode

All these measurements on field allowed to know:

- the absolute calibration of the line's orientation
- the motion of the Sun, Moon and planets with respect to reference stars
- the stellar aberration with respect to the atomic time UTC
- Sun and planets' motion controlled with ephemerides (Stellarium 0.20.2)
- the variation of the Earth's rotation time $\Delta UT1$

Young students 14-15 years old understand better the season's rhythm as ruled by the solar rays' inclination at noon, as well as the astronomical observation considered as a real physics experiment, requiring calibration and errorbar evaluations, and long time basis (like the whole month needed for measuring the Sidereal Day up to 0.01 s). Also the data analysis experience with linear and parabolic fits has been mentioned. Finally, last but not least, the relevance of astronomy in the cultural heritage, owing the importance of the historical places were they can experience it: St. Maria degli Angeli, Diocletian's baths transformed into church by Michelangelo, and St. Peter's square realized along the centuries by the contributions of several popes, cardinals artists and scientists, namely Sixtus V, Domenico Fontana, Egnazio Danti, Pietro Maccarani and Filippo Luigi Gigli for the meridian line and Gianlorenzo Bernini for the colonnade's astronomical orientation from solstices' sunrises and sunsets.

References

1. Stellarium Astronomical Software (2021), http://stellarium.org/.
2. Solar transit on the Clementine Gnomon of September 23rd 2020, https://youtu.be/bhuH5FOi2tk.
3. Solar transit on St. Peter's meridian line of September 23rd 2021, https://youtu.be/eQU4B85DV7A.
4. Solar transit on St. Peter's meridian line of October 1st 2021, https://youtu.be/zfOwtO6pOl8.
5. Dates of seasons for any year, IMCCE, Paris, 2021, https://promenade.imcce.fr/en/pages4/439.html.
6. Venus transit of 27 October 2021 in St. Peter's square, https://drive.google.com/drive/u/2/folders/1ugl5TkhzQnE9qJcfJgx2BkiNnUIfKRAX.
7. Youtube Transits in St. Maria degli Angeli and Ostia's sunsets, https://docs.google.com/document/d/1TnbBfweA_-2_q-ZoC5Oi7HHOLKIyINUD8Dm5nnHqzMc/edit?usp=sharing.
8. Francesco Bianchini, De Nummo et Gnomone Clementino, Roma (1703) p. 45, https://archive.org/details/bub_gb_IYtGjIE_X64C/page/n289/mode/2up.
9. Costantino Sigismondi, Gerbertus **9**, 27 (2016).
10. Alessandro Travaglini, Pollens bulletin, Rome, Tor Vergata University (2020-2021), https://drive.google.com/drive/u/2/folders/17q3TgxmNp9L81P7_5Xy-VqKKJjokr7NI.
11. Costantino Sigismondi, *The meridian line of the Vatican obelisk to study the stellar aberration*, MG16 Proceedings (2021).

Daily, seasonal, and equinoctial solar paths on a school soccer field

Costantino Sigismondi

ICRA, Sapienza University of Rome,
Rome, Italy
E-mail: sigismondi@icra.it
http://www.icra.it/solar

The shadow of a wall cast by the Sun on a soccer field has been used to measure the change of the altitude and azimuth of the Sun along the day and through the seasons. The change of curvature parameter of the daily hyperbola shadow's path, has been recovered in the days around the spring equinox 2021. The study of the daily paths has been possible with chalk and meter during school days, on this field, and the data have been reported on a spreadsheet. The students were impressed by this whole-year experiment, while normally at school the experimental sessions are one-hour long.

Keywords: Solstices, Equinoxes, Shadows, Altitude, Azimuth.

1. Sun's paths on a soccer field

The shadow of a 10 meters wall (its vertex) cast on the soccer field of the Technical Institute Galileo Ferraris in Rome, 41.878 415° N, 12.454 662° E, coordinates WGS84 of the gnomon (fig. 2), has been used to perform daily measures with an accuracy up to a few millimeters. The gnomon's shadow, measured from the bottom and from the side of the field with a tape meter, in the best sets of measurements, presented rms below 1 mm. The hyperbolae drawn by the Sun through these shadows changed their aperture coefficient from Winter to Spring, passing to zero at the equinox. The students learned literally "on field" what means accuracy to the millimeter level, during several months. They learned how to do linear interpolations and extrapolations to predict the positions of the shadows in the next 10 minutes... or in the days without data (weekends and holidays).

The curvature radius of the hyperbolae is also measurable with three points along 20 minutes, repeated 3 times in a hour lesson.

All these achievements are possible during a single hour of lesson. The students remember well past situations, because they made practical actions.

The experience presented here with 14 and 15 years old students, started in February through May 2021.

The spring equinox was calculated by interpolation of aperture's parameters these months, with good agreement with the actual date.

The activity in open air and the use of the chalk on the field to mark the shadows' limits, the use of the meter and the care for the zero positions, have been appreciated alternatives to the normal indoor teaching.

2. Procedure

The positions of the shadow's cusp (e.g. fig. 3) are taken with respect the corner of the field as x and y. The curve connecting the daily positions (about ten each time) is plotted to see immediately its form. The meridian point (a, b) is measured and made center of a new coordinates system, with the appropriate translation. The meridian axis has an equation computed in the first days of observations, by marking the position of the shadow at the very instant of the meridian transit. Its angle α with respect to the axis x and y of the soccer field is used to apply the following rotation.

$$\begin{cases} x' = (x-a)\cos(\alpha) - (y-b)\sin(\alpha) + a \\ y' = (x-a)\sin(\alpha) + (y-b)\cos(\alpha) + b \end{cases}$$

Fig. 1. The equation of the roto-translation around the meridian point (a,b), to obtain a curve symmetric to the y' axis, with its vertex on the new origin (0,0).

A parabola fits with fair approximation the curve so obtained, by using a common spreadsheet (e.g Excel, LibreOffice, OpenOffice). The hyperbolic fit requires more passages, not automatically implemented in the spreadsheets.

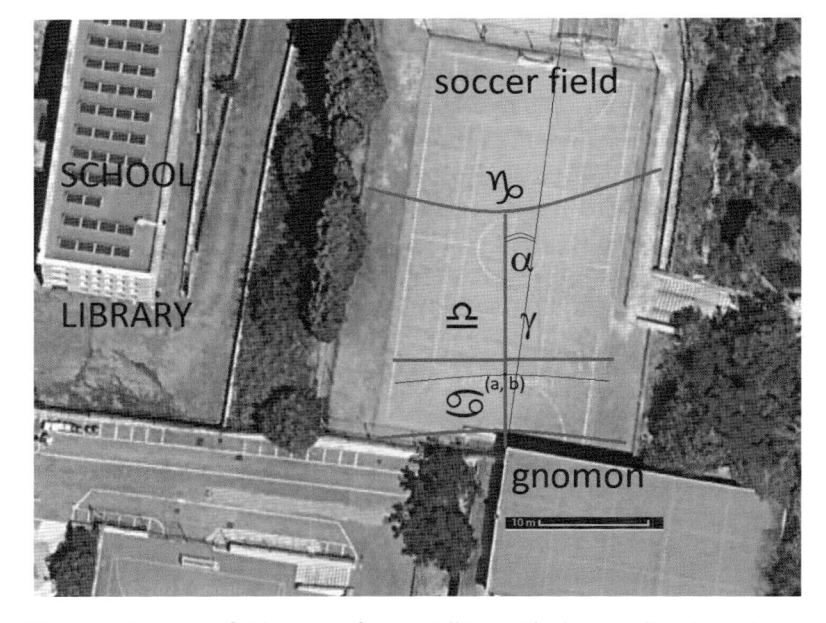

Fig. 2. The school's soccer field as seen from satellite, with the meridian line scheme superimposed.

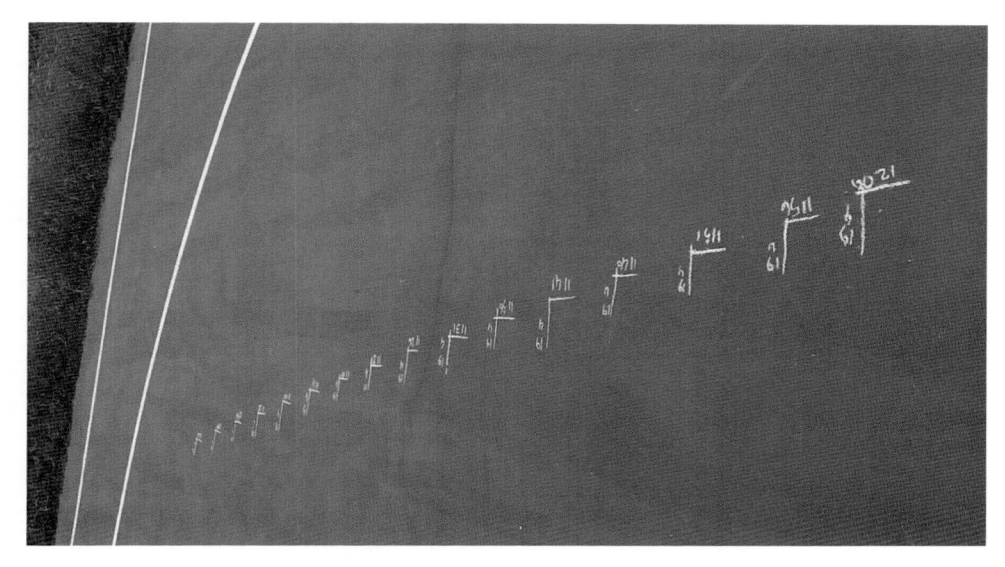

Fig. 3. The hourly path of the shadow's limit from 10:46 to 12:06 of 9 April 2021: the progress of the gnomon's shadow is visible.

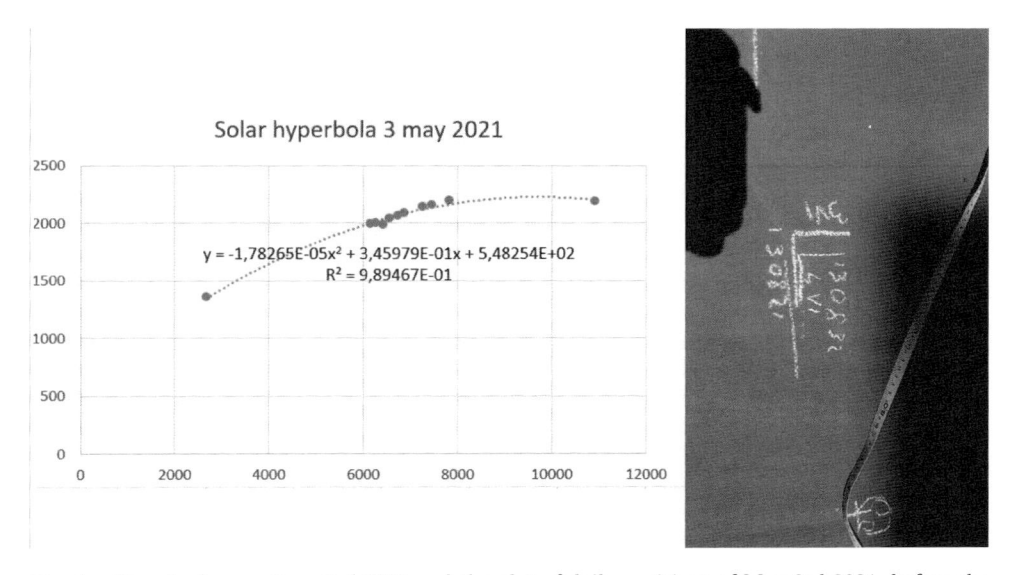

Fig. 4. The shadow on June 3rd 2021 and the plot of daily positions of May 3rd 2021, before the roto-translation.

3. Conclusions

The method presented is to fit the hyperbola of the shadow's positions of the wall's cusp on the soccer field, with the equation of a parabola. The accuracy achieved is within 20 arcseconds, or 2 mm for each position of the shadow on the field. The path of two consecutive days, even near the summer solstice (where the positions are very close one to another), are well distinguishable each day from the other one. This procedure has been adapted to Excel spreadsheet, and the hyperbolic fits have been realized with the parabolae. The results obtained in the soccer field allowed to check the curvature's change during the equinox, and they have been published in detail (2021).

This is a suitable introduction to the trigonometrical methods of Celestial Mechanics, affordable by many schools and all students. These practical activities, made with increasing accuracy, may pave the way to understand the problems in experimental general relativity.

Reference

1. Sigismondi, C., Gerbertus, vol. 14, pp. 33-38 (2021) *L'equinozio e le parabole osculatrici*, http://www.icra.it/gerbertus/2021/Gerb-14-2021-Sigismondi-Parabole_osculatrici-33-38.pdf.

Teaching relativity at the AstroCamp

C. J. A. P. Martins

*Centro de Astrofísica da Universidade do Porto, and
Instituto de Astrofísica e Ciências do Espaço, Universidade do Porto,
Rua das Estrelas, 4150-762 Porto, Portugal
E-mail: Carlos.Martins@astro.up.pt*

The AstroCamp is an academic excellence program in the field of astronomy and physics for students in the last 3 years of pre-university education, which often includes a course (or a significant part thereof) on Relativity. After an introduction to the principles, goals and structure of the camp, I describe the approach followed by camp lecturers (myself and others) for teaching Special and General Relativity, and some lessons learned and feedback from the students. I also provide some thoughts on the differences between the physics and mathematics secondary school curricula in Portugal and in other countries, and on how these curricula could be modernized.

Keywords: AstroCamp; Secondary education; Summer schools; Relativity.

1. The AstroCamp vision

The AstroCamp[a] is an academic excellence program in the field of astronomy and physics, organized by CAUP and the Paredes de Coura municipality (with the support of several national and international partners) for students in the last 3 years of pre-university education, i.e. roughly 15-18 year old students.

Our key goals are

(a) Promote scientific knowledge, with high-quality training in a secluded and tranquil setting
(b) Stimulate student curiosity and skills of critical thinking, team work and group responsibility
(c) Stimulate interactions between students with different backgrounds and life experiences but common interests

The camp was created in 2012, and now accepts applications from 42 eligible countries. Participation is strictly by invitation, after an application period (in April) and a selection phase (in May) which includes an interview in English. The camp itself takes place in August, in the Corno de Bico Protected Landscape area of the Paredes de Coura municipality (in the northwest of Portugal) and lasts 15 days. One of our points of principle is that for students in Portuguese schools the camp has no costs. Some students from other countries will also have support, others

---
[a]https://www.astro.up.pt/astrocamp/

may need to pay part of the costs or find their own support locally. In any case, significant efforts are made to keep costs low, and the maximum cost for foreign students is 400 Euro.

The main academic activity consists of two courses (each with 15h of lectures and a 2h written exam), given by currently active researchers with a PhD in a relevant area. Depending on the year, more than two courses are offered, but each student will only take two of them. In most of the 10 editions so far, one course or a significant part thereof was devoted to Relativity (both Special and General). This is to a large extent driven by the camp students themselves: one of the principles of the camp is that students are involved in the choice of the courses offered in the camp, and Relatively is clearly the prime example of a topic that the students feel is not satisfactorily covered in their school classes (if it is at all), and for which their school teachers are often unable to provide further information.

Other camp activities include observational and/or computational projects, stargazing sessions and documentaries, community service projects and evening talks which in early editions were open to the local public, but are now webcast live. There are also several other recreational activities such as hiking (including an overnight hike coinciding with the peak of the Perseids meteor shower). Interested students can also engage in several post-camp projects at CAUP and elsewhere. Our guiding vision is to provide the students with unique opportunities beyond the standard school systems, also after the camp. The extent to which students make use of all of these is of course up to them.

The camp is residential, with all students, teachers and camp monitors (university students, which most often are AstroCamp alumni) staying in the camp for the full 15 days. (Exceptionally, teachers may stay for reduced periods.) Due to COVID-19, the 2020 edition exceptionally had a hybrid format, with students living in Portugal in residence at the camp, and students living in other countries joining virtually in all activities where this was feasible. In the 2021 edition only one student had to participate remotely, and we naturally hope that the 2022 edition will be fully residential again.

2. Some statistics and outcomes

In the first four editions the camp only accepted applications from Portuguese students studying in Portuguese schools. Starting in 2016 the list of eligible countries has expanded, and currently the camp can accept applications from students matriculated in one of the last 3 years of pre-university education in any of 42 eligible countries[b], provided they are national citizens from one of these countries.

---

[b]These are: Andorra, Argentina, Austria, Belgium, Brazil, Bulgaria, Canada, Chile, Croatia, Cyprus, Czechia, Denmark, Estonia, Finland, France, Germany, Greece, Hungary, Iceland, Ireland, Italy, Latvia, Liechtenstein, Lithuania, Luxembourg, Malta, Monaco, Netherlands, Norway, Poland, Portugal, Romania, San Marino, Serbia, Slovakia, Slovenia, Spain, Sweden, Switzerland, United Kingdom, United States of America and Uruguay.

In the 10 editions so far the camp had a total of 133 accepted students with 15 different nationalities. Some basic statistical information on the participants can be found in Table 1. It is worthy of note that the camp does not have quotas of any kind; the outcomes are therefore the result of the merit and academic potential of the candidates.

Table 1. Basic statistical information on the 2012-2021 Astro-Camp students.

Accepted Students	2012-2015 Editions	2016-2021 Editions
Portuguese	100%	53%
Foreign	N/A	47%
Grade 10	24%	31%
Grade 11	52%	47%
Grade 12	24%	22%
Boys	47%	40%
Girls	53%	60%

Note: Grades 10, 11 and 12 are the names of the last three years of secondary education in the Portuguese school system. The student ages corresponding to these grades are country-specific, but broadly speaking Grade 10 students are 15 or 16 years old, while Grade 12 students are 17 or 18 years old.

One of the most rewarding deliverables of the AstroCamp is our Solar System Trail. This is the second scale model of the Solar System, in the Iberian Peninsula (and one of only sixteen in Europe, as far as we know), that is accurate both in terms of the sizes and of the distances of the objects. It was built during the first four AstroCamps, and a full hiking trail which follows the objects in the system—the Sun, the planets up to Neptune (including the Earth's Moon), and Ceres—was officially opened on 13 August 2016. The trail has recently been included among the teaching resources for Grade 7 students, so for a new generation of Portuguese students this may well be providing their first contact with astronomy. The trail also has an accompanying website[c] which at the time of writing only has a Portuguese version but is due to be expanded and replicated in at least 10 different languages in early 2022.

Most editions of the camp also included a computational project, lasting about 20 hours, aiming to provide the students with an introduction to scientific programming and statistics and data analysis in astrophysics. In several cases, the students continued working on these projects after the camp, and contributed to peer-reviewed publications in top academic journals.[1-3] At least one more such publication is expected soon.

---

[c]https://www.astro.up.pt/trilhosistemasolar/

3. Teaching special and general relativity

As previously mentioned, One AstroCamp principle is that students are involved in the choices of the courses taught in the camp, as well as in the ones they actually take. This is a multi-stage process, which we run in parallel with the student applications. A call for courses is issued at the beginning of each calendar year, and the submitted proposals undergo a scientific and pedagogical check, leading to a courses shortlist. The students shortlisted for the interviews are then asked to rank the shortlisted courses according to their preferences; this is done in a double-blind way—students don't know who would teach each course, and organizers don't know individual student preferences until after the student places are assigned. The courses to be offered are then decided and assignment to students, and a final tweaking of course contents can be done if there are overlaps between them. As an example, in the 2021 edition the shortlist included 6 courses, of which 3 were taught in the camp (with each student taking 2 of them).

So far, courses on Relativity/Cosmology (or containing at least ca. 5 hours of content on this) have always been selected by the students when offered. Various lecturers have been involved (in addition to the author), from Canada, Germany, Italy, The Netherlands, Portugal, Spain and the UK, some of them teaching twice.

Topics are covered both at the conceptual and (at least for some of them) also at the more detailed mathematical level. In our experience, most students also enjoy learning about the relevant historical context and background.

Galilean relativity topics covered include

(a) Galilean mechanics and acceleration
(b) Inertial frames and Galilean Transformations
(c) Historical developments from Galileo to Newton (Gassendi, Huygens, Descartes, etc)
(d) Newton's Laws and Equivalence Principle (inertial and gravitational masses)
(e) The XIX Century background to Relativity: Mechanics versus Electromagnetism

Special relativity topics covered include

(a) Derivation and interpretation of the Lorentz-Fitzgerald transformations
(b) Minkowski geometry and spacetime diagrams
(c) Special Relativity and the Principle of Relativity
(d) Invariance of the speed of light and its consequences
(e) Time dilation and Lorentz contraction: Cosmic rays and Twin paradox
(f) Physical meaning of inertial frames

Finally, topics pertaining to applications of relativity covered include

(a) Relativity and the GPS
(b) The Schwarzschild solution and black hole properties

(c) Derivation of the Friedmann and Raychaudhuri equations, and simple solutions thereof
(d) Cosmology, including Hubble's law and simple FLRW universes
(e) Gravitational waves, including their detection

Examples of conceptual questions on these topics that have been previously used in AstroCamp course exams are listed in the Appendix. Student feedback clearly shows that the Newtonian physics curriculum is unattractive, and often containing significant misconceptions. Camp students usually follow conceptual aspects very well (even when finding some of them counter-intuitive); any difficulties usually pertain to their mathematical background, which is partially correlated with their age.

4. Lessons learned, and the COVID-19 impact

The experience of ten camp editions (of which six included foreign students) reveals significant differences between the secondary school curricula in different countries, and sometimes in different regions of the same country. There are also country-specific differences between public and private (or international) schools. In Portugal, it is clear that private schools (and even a few public schools) routinely apply grade inflation. This further reinforces the prior expectation that grades alone do not provide a fair selection process. This is why, from the first edition, the application procedure includes a student motivation letter, a teacher recommendation letter and, importantly, an interview to shortlisted candidates.

Since the camp accepts students from the last three years of secondary education, one challenge for the camp teachers is that the mathematical background will be quite diverse. Specifically, derivatives introduced at different ages in different countries, and integrals are not a given even for Grade 12 students, who have finished secondary education and are about to start university. However, in our experience this is not a problem for bright students: through direct interaction with teachers or camp monitors, they can quickly gain a working knowledge, e.g. of differentiation rules, which allows then the follow the course contents that rely on them.

One rather surprising lesson is that schools can actually be a bottleneck in disseminating information on the AstroCamp to students. Specifically, from our experience less than 20% of Portuguese schools that receive direct camp information from us (including, in some editions, A4 or A3 sized posters and leaflets) actually transmit it to their students, and the fraction of students that find out about the camp through a school teacher is small—while the number is not trivial to estimate, it is clearly below 50%.

A recent challenge was provided by COVID-19. This led to a hybrid format edition in 2020, with foreign students interacting with camp teachers, monitors (including some online tutors) and students in residence at the camp through online collaboration tools such as Zoom, Discord and Colaboratory online collaboration.

This was was nevertheless very successful despite the fact that foreign students participating in this edition had a very limited experience of the camp, and clearly demonstrates that remote collaboration tools enable new teaching and mentoring opportunities, which we intend to pursue.

A more surprising realization emerged in the 2021 edition, in that the COVID-19 impact on students' cognitive and social skills and emotional maturity was clearly visible. Inter alia, although the level of the courses and exams has been kept constant in recent editions (roughly at the level of a course from first year undergraduate physics degree at a top Portuguese university), the average grades of the students were lower and, in particular, for the first time in ten editions two students failed their exams. It is likely that this impact will be noticeable for several years to came. This is all the more scary since these are bright students—the impact on average ones may be much more serious.

As the AstroCamp starts its second decade, this is a good time to revise and update its format, structure and rules, also taking into account the most recent challenges. There is clearly some room for growth—more in extension and scope than in numbers—making the camp an international reference for events of this kind.

5. Epilogue: Improving Portuguese secondary scientific education

The experience of 10 years of organizing the AstroCamp (together with teaching one course in each edition, and leading other scientific activities therein) also leads to the conclusion that the Portuguese secondary education system, in scientific areas, is clearly lagging behind those of other developed countries, and needs urgent revision and modernization.

In an effort to contribute to an urgent and much needed debate, I may suggest four very specific measures

(a) It is clear that Portuguese students are, on average, far less familiar with scientific programming that their foreign peers. (The Portuguese school system current offers a 'Computational Applications' subject, but this is a total waste of time[d].) One must urgently introduce a compulsory scientific programming subject in Grades 10 to 12 grades, using languages such as Python, Octave or Julia, and connected to other subjects, especially Physics, Chemistry, Biology and Mathematics.
(b) In the Portuguese school system, Physics and Chemistry are taught as a single subject in Grades 10 and 11, and are only separate subject in Grade 12.

---

[d]As well as an insult to the intelligence of most students, were it not for the fact that it allows an easy high grade to be obtained, which will count towards the students' university application.

Moreover, very few students take Grade 12 Physics, either because the school does not offer it or because the students consider it a hard subject (form the perspective of getting a good grade) and prefer softer subjects such as English, Psychology or the infamous Computational Applications. This is a crass mistake. Physics and Chemistry should be separate subjects from Grade 10 (and, arguably, even earlier).

(c) The Portuguese school system has national exams which, depending on the subject, are either at the end of Grade 11 or Grade 12. The former, which currently include the Physics exam, is a clear mistake. The Physics national exam (and indeed all national exams) should be cumulative and at the end of Grade 12. Moreover, Grade 12 Physics should be made compulsory for students intending to apply for university physics and engineering degrees

(d) Last but not least, these is a vast disconnect between the secondary school environment and that of university (not to mention that of research, business, etc). A way to bridge the gap would be to reward students with top results in national exams with summer internships at research labs or tech companies (with the student matching done by the hosts). As a way to foster equal opportunities, these internships should not be merely awarded to the students with the numerically highest grades but, for example, to the student with the highest grade in each district (or, more ambitiously, each municipality in Portugal—in the former case this kind of program would reach about 20 students, while in the latter it would reach about 300.

All of these are, at least in principle, easy to implement and would have dramatic and comparatively rapid (as well as quantifiable) impacts. The main bottlenecks, other than political will are our blatant 'teaching to the test approach' (manifest in the blind acceptance of school rankings, but partially stemming from the university numerus clausus system), and the pathological reluctance of teacher unions to any kind of change. The latter can be, at least in part, ascribed to the fact that most secondary school science teachers are in their 50s or 60s. This is especially relevant in the context of the first of the above points, since these teachers and have little computing literacy, and none in coding and scientific programming. Nevertheless, delaying the modernization of the system, with these and other measures, simply increases the personal and financial costs for future generations.

Acknowledgments

This work was financed by FEDER—Fundo Europeu de Desenvolvimento Regional funds through the COMPETE 2020—Operational Programme for Competitiveness and Internationalisation (POCI), and by Portuguese funds through FCT - Fundação para a Ciência e a Tecnologia in the framework of the project POCI-01-0145-FEDER-028987 and PTDC/FIS-AST/28987/2017.

Appendix A. Conceptual question examples

The following is a partial list of relevant conceptual questions that have been used in at least one AstroCamp exam. Except for the last one (with is a proposed essay topic) they are all multiple choice questions.

Two inertial observers measure the speed of the same beam of light and obtain the same finite value. This would surprise Newton because

(a) According to him the speed of anything should depend on the frame of reference.
(b) He expected the speed of light to be infinite in inertial frames.
(c) In inertial reference frames he believed light to be stationary.
(d) He believed light should have an infinite speed in all frames.

The Michelson-Morley experiments were an attempt to

(a) Measure the speed of light.
(b) Test the Lorentz-Fitzgerald transformations.
(c) Measure the Earth's speed relative to the Sun.
(d) Detect the Earth's movement relative to the aether.

Relative to an object at rest, a moving object is

(a) Shorter and younger.
(b) Longer and older.
(c) Shorter and older.
(d) Longer and younger.

Special relativity (SR) and general relativity (GR) corrections must be taken into account for the GPS system to work. If these satellites were moved to LEO,

(a) Both corrections would decrease.
(b) The SR correction would decrease and the GR one would increase.
(c) The SR correction would increase and the GR one would decrease.
(d) Both corrections would increase.

If an astronaut in a windowless rocket feels pressed against the back of her seat, she won't be able to tell

(a) Whether the rocket is accelerating or moving at constant speed.
(b) Whether she is accelerating or resting on the surface of some planet.
(c) Whether the rocket it moving at constant speed in space or at rest in space.
(d) Whether she is at rest in space or freely falling towards some planet.

A green animal lives on an extremely dense planet. When observed from space,

(a) It will look green.
(b) It will look white.

(c) It will look blue.
(d) It will look red.

Which of these is not a direct test of the Einstein Equivalence Principle?

(a) Measurements of gravitational redshift.
(b) Tests of the stability of fundamental couplings.
(c) Measurements of the precession of Mercury's perihelion.
(d) Tests of the universality of free fall.

Essay topic: Describe the relation between physical reality and the mathematical models with which we describe it. In particular, comment on how this relation may differ in the contexts of the pure and applied physical sciences (e.g., theoretical physics and engineering).

References

1. C. J. A. P. Martins, A. M. M. Pinho, R. F. C. Alves, M. Pino, C. I. S. A. Rocha and M. von Wietersheim, Dark energy and Equivalence Principle constraints from astrophysical tests of the stability of the fine-structure constant, *JCAP* **08**, p. 047 (2015).
2. C. S. Alves, A. C. O. Leite, C. J. A. P. Martins, T. A. Silva, S. A. Berge and B. S. A. Silva, Current and future constraints on extended Bekenstein-type models for a varying fine-structure constant, *Phys. Rev. D* **97**, p. 023522 (2018).
3. M. C. F. Faria, C. J. A. P. Martins, F. Chiti and B. S. A. Silva, Low redshift constraints on energy-momentum-powered gravity models, *Astron. Astrophys.* **625**, p. A127 (2019).

Sungrazing comets as General Relativistic gravitational probes

Silvia Pietroni

Dipartimento di Fisica "E.R. Caianiello", Università di Salerno
Via Giovanni Paolo II 132, I-84084 Fisciano, Italy
Istituto Nazionale di Fisica Nucleare, Sezione di Napoli
Via Cintia, 80126, Napoli, Italy
spietroni@unisa.it

Costantino Sigismondi

ICRA - International Center for Relativistic Astrophysics, Sapienza Università di Roma
Piazzale Aldo Moro 5, 00185 Roma, Italy
sigismondi@icra.it

Among the celestial bodies of the solar system, the ones passing closer to the solar mass are the sungrazing comets. The sungrazers can approach the Sun with a perihelion more than 60 times closer than Mercury, experiencing a local effect of perihelion relativistic precession 60 times larger. Mercury requires 15 years, or sixty orbits, to totalize the same effect. The sungrazers have generally no more than a single orbit, because they vanish at the perihelion passage. The observability of such phenomena with SOHO coronagraphs is discussed.

Keywords: Sungrazing comets, perihelion relativistic precession

1. Generalities on sungrazing comet

The sungrazing comets are a class of comets whose known number significantly increased in the last 26 years, since the SOHO coronagraphes entered in function, at the rhythm of about hundred per year. The gravitational studies on such comets, starting from Newton are presented in the references.[1-21]

Their orbital parameters suggest their grouping as related to a few parent bodies, and we recall the statistical work on comets made by Enrico Fermi in 1922 as thesis for the Normal School of Pisa.

The sungrazing comets are the celestial bodies which approach more closely the mass of the Sun: then their orbital parameters are influenced by both General Relativity and non-gravitational effects, like mass loss and outgassing. The General Relativity effects and the non-gravitational effects are compared to understand the observational accuracy required on Mercury's perihelion. The studies carried by Le Verrier and Newcomb in the second part of XIX century, were possible because the orbit of Mercury is rather eccentric e=0.2056. When some objects may graze the solar surface, a very high eccentricity e=0.99 is considered to produce some visible effect. The accuracy on the determination of the orbital parameters of sungrazing comets is also investigated, to enforce with observations all these theoretical concepts. The identification of new sungrazing comets is possible online, at the SOHO website, and it has been realized by the high school students of Galileo Ferraris Institute, Rome, as curricular activity, with great enthusiasm, especially with the real time discoveries of January 18, 2021 (fig. 3).

2. Measurability of the relativistic precession

$$\delta\theta = 6\pi \cdot GM_\odot a/c^2 b^2$$

Planet	a (mean) AU	e	Perturbation [arcsec/cy]	$e \cdot \delta\theta$ [arcsec/cy]
Mercury	0.38709893	0.20563069	43.03	8.847
Venus	0.72333199	0.00677323	8.63	0.059
Earth	1.00000011	0.01671022	3.84	0.064
Mars	1.52366231	0.09341233	1.35	0.126
Jupiter	5.20336301	0.04839266	0.06	0.003

Fig. 1. The relative observability from Mercury to Jupiter, as indicated by Dennis Sciama (1972).

The eccentricity larger than 0.99, that the sungrazer can present, and a perihelion's advancement of $60 \times 43''$ produces an effective visibility of 43', larger than the apparent diameter of the Sun.

The problem is that the comet is rarely visible after the perihelion, because it vanishes, and when it is visible the effect is small due to a less close encounter with the photosphere.

3. Conclusions and perspectives

The sungrazers are comets belonging to groups with similar geometrical parameters, originated by a close encounter of a big comet with the solar photosphere. They experienced the largest General Relativistic effect of perihelion precession possible in our solar system, even if for only one passage. The amplitude of such effect can be such as 0.75°, but its measurability with the SOHO coronagraph is very difficult due to the relative inclination angles with Earth's orbit; moreover the sungrazers vanish after the passage to the perihelion due to the closeness with the photosphere. The possibility to "discover" averagely a new sungrazer each week makes interesting the discussion of such effect in secondary school's physics class, where the students become protagonist of the discoveries through inspecting the SOHO movie theatre, in real time. The introduction to observational General Relativity can be effective through this approach, for the young students.

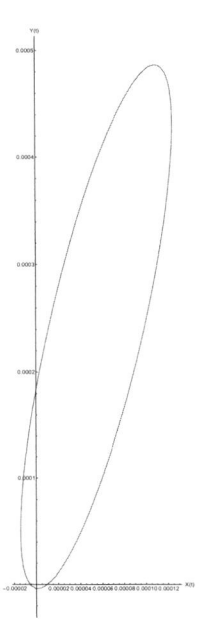

Fig. 2. One complete orbit of a sungrazer comet calculated with a computer code developed by Bozza and Pietroni (2021), distance given in parsecs; orbital parameters: semimajor axes $a \simeq 52 AU \simeq 7.64 \times 10^{12}$ meters, eccentricity $e = 0.98$, inclination $i = 160°$, period $P = 360$ ys. The relativistic Lagrangian has been used to evaluate the perihelion advancement, and compared with the non-relativistic one. The interaction with the solar atmosphere is not taken into account, to close the orbit.

Fig. 3. Two sungrazer comets at the same time on January 17, 2021, observed by SOHO C3 coronagraphs, and "discovered" at school in real time.

References

1. T. Scarmato, Sungrazer comet c/2012 s1 (ison): Curve of light, nucleus size, rotation and peculiar structures in the coma and tail (2014).
2. R. Ruffini and C. Sigismondi, *Nonlinear Gravitodynamics* (World Scientific, 2003).
3. M. M. Knight and K. J. Walsh, Will comet ison (c/2012 s1) survive perihelion?, *The Astrophysical Journal* **776**, p. L5 (Sep 2013).
4. S. Giordano, J. C. Raymond, P. Lamy, M. Uzzo and D. Dobrzycka, Probing the solar wind acceleration region with the sun-grazing comet c/2002 s2, *The Astrophysical Journal* **798**, p. 47 (Dec 2014).
5. Z. Sekanina and R. Kracht, Strong erosion-driven nongravitational effects in orbital motions of the kreutz sungrazing system's dwarf comets, *The Astrophysical Journal* **801**, p. 135 (Mar 2015).
6. A. Sekhar, D. J. Asher, S. C. Werner, J. Vaubaillon and G. Li, Change in general relativistic precession rates due to lidov–kozai oscillations in solar system, *Monthly Notices of the Royal Astronomical Society* **468**, p. 1405–1414 (Mar 2017).
7. O. Ivanova, V. Reshetnyk, Y. Skorov, J. Blum, Z. S. Krišandová, J. Svoreň, P. Korsun, V. Afanasiev, I. Luk'yanyk and M. Andreev, The optical characteristics of the dust of sungrazing comet c/2012 s1 (ison) observed at large heliocentric distances, *Icarus* **313**, p. 1–14 (Oct 2018).
8. J. C. Raymond and S. Giordano, Probing coronal magnetic fields with sungrazing comets: H i ly from pickup ions, *The Astrophysical Journal* **887**, p. 45 (Dec 2019).
9. M.-T. Hui and Q.-Z. Ye, Observations of disintegrating long-period comet c/2019 y4 (atlas): A sibling of c/1844 y1 (great comet), *The Astronomical Journal* **160**, p. 91 (Jul 2020).
10. D. Jewitt, Systematics and consequences of comet nucleus outgassing torques, *The Astronomical Journal* **161**, p. 261 (May 2021).
11. B. Gundlach, J. Blum, Y. V. Skorov and H. U. Keller, A note on the survival of the sungrazing comet c/2011 w3 (lovejoy) within the roche limit (2012).
12. I. Haranas, O. Ragos and I. Gkigkitzis, The lens-thirring effect in the anomalistic period of celestial bodies (2013).
13. Z. Sekanina, Comments on a recent review paper on near-sun comets (2019).
14. K. Battams and M. M. Knight, Soho comets: 20 years and 3000 objects later, *Philosophical Transactions of the Royal Society A: Mathematical, Physical and Engineering Sciences* **375**, p. 20160257 (May 2017).
15. C. Sigismondi, Astrometry and relativity, *Nuovo Cimento B Serie* **120**, p. 1169 (October 2005).
16. C. Sigismondi and F. Maiolino, Enrico Fermi and the statistics of comets, *Nuovo Cimento B Serie* **117**, p. 1207 (September 2002).
17. C. Sigismondi, The Eddington's Eclispe and a Possible Replica of the Experiment of Light Bending, *arXiv e-prints*, p. arXiv:1507.03879 (July 2015).
18. C. Sigismondi, The Eddington's eclispe replicated with the images of the SOHO coronographs, in *Fourteenth Marcel Grossmann Meeting — MG14*, eds. M. Bianchi, R. T. Jansen and R. RuffiniJanuary 2018.
19. C. Sigismondi, L'algoritmo di correzione per l'estinzione atmosfera a occhio nudo e studio su foto da webcam e da SOHO, *Gerbertvs, International Academic Publication on History of Medieval Science* **13**, 17 (July 2020).
20. D. W. Sciama, *La relatività generale. Fondamenti fisici della teoria.* 1972.
21. Soho movie theater website https://soho.nascom.nasa.gov/data/Theater/.

The three Summer solstice's markers of 1721 unveiled in the Basilica of Santa Maria degli Angeli in Rome

Costantino Sigismondi

ICRA, Sapienza University of Rome,
Rome, Italy
E-mail: sigismondi@icra.it
http://www.icra.it/solar

The solar image is projected through a pinhole inside a camera obscura in the great meridian line in the Basilica of Santa Maria degli Angeli in Rome: the daily path of 1721 summer solstice has been recovered as passing through three markers on the floor of the Basilica, near the summer part of the meridian line. The function of these three markers was considered ornamental until now, because no written documents have been found on them. Moreover two of the three markers today are no longer illuminated by the Sun, after 1750.

The same technique has been applied to the three solar markers in St. Maria degli Angeli, finding that they belong to the same 1721 solstice of three centuries ago, within a few millimeters of accuracy.

Keywords: St. Maria degli Angeli, Meridian Line, 1721, Solstices, Equinoxes, Maria Clementyna Sobieska, James III Stuart.

1. The 1721 Summer solstice perpetuated in St. Maria degli Angeli

The Meridian Line of Santa Maria degli Angeli in Rome has been realized in 1700-1702 upon the will of Pope Clement XI, since when he was Cardinal, after the project of Francesco Bianchini (1662-1729) to measure with unprecedented accuracy the tropical year and the variation of the obliquity of the ecliptic. At this Great Gnomon the seasonal effects on the atmospheric refraction and the effects of stellar aberrations were measured, but while the first were recognized the latter become systematic effects included in the errors of measurements.

At the Marcel Grossmann Meeting of Berlin (2006) this discovery was firstly presented; after other historical data were analyzed (2014), while in International Astronomical Union General Assembly of 2018 in Vienna the recognition of two brass markers as solstice markers was announced.

The two markers belong to the summer solstice because they are on the same daily hyperbola of the solar center entering Cancer in 1721. One of the two brass markers, named after this paper the King's marker, is no longer illuminated by the Sun since 1750 Vanvitelli's renovations of the Basilica, which modified the pinhole's visibility from all the floor.

A third marble marker, considered as ornamental until now, it is on the same hyperbola and it is on the floor of the Basilica, about 7 meters far from the other.

The different material of this third marker delayed our discovery of the strict correlation of the three markers. This marble was dedicated to the King James III Stuart in 1721; the well known inscription says: FELIX TEMPORVM REPARATIO meaning "Return to good times", very probably after his marriage in 1719 1st of September (Francesca Ceci, 2021), with Maria Klementyna Sobieska and the birth of their son on 31 December 1720.

These markers are offset with respect to the great meridian line, because on the Cancer's marble no more modifications were possible. This chronological sequence explains also why in his book of 1703, Bianchini did not mention these markers.

Fig. 1. Two markers: King James' (Jacobus in Latin) III in marble and Klementyna Sobieska's in brass, the one still illuminated by the Sun.

2. Observations and inspections

The three solstice's ellipses, two in brass (half ellipses, as the only one still illuminated by the Sun in the right-side of figure 1) and one in marble (whole ellipse, left-side figure 1) with the dedicational epigraph containing the date (adding together the capital letters as Latin numbers) are no longer hit by the Sun's image, excepted the last one, before the meridian line.

In 2018 the two brass decorations have been recognized as half ellipses of the Summer solstice's Sun. This year 2021, exactly three centuries after their realization, the all three markers have been recognized as belonging to the same "memorial addition" to the great meridian line.

With this addition, made very reliably by Francesco Bianchini, the royal couple Maria Clementyna Sobieska (1701-1735) and James III Stuart (1688-1766), king without land, married since 1719 and living in Rome under the protection of the pope, has been celebrated by realizing three summer solstice markers.

Fig. 2. The cenotaph of King James III in St. Peter's Basilica, were he is buried.

Fig. 3. Maria Klementyna Sobieska: the same image used in her cenotaph, in St. Peter's Basilica, in front of James III (painter Martin van Meytens, according to Wikipedia 2021.

3. Fitting the three positions with one hyperbola

The giant pinhole meridian line has been somewhat reproduced in a school environment, with the possibility to mark the soil with chalk and to bring many measurements with the meter, that are impossible in the Basilica. The hyperbolic paths of the Sun's shadow on the floor showed clearly the change of curvature from North to South at the spring equinox. The same method developed to fit the equation of the hyperbola to the shadow's positions of the cusp of a wall on the soccer field (Sigismondi, 2021, these Proceedings) has been applied on these three positions, marked by the historical ellipses.

These three ellipses have been considered as ancient observations, marked on the floor of the Basilica at their exact position.

The hyperbolic fits has been realized either with a parabola, either with an hyperbola: a millimeter accuracy in the positions of the Sun on the 1721 Summer solstice's path has been found in Santa Maria degli Angeli. The equation of the hyperbola of the 1721 summer solstice has been recovered with respect to the current solstice (2021) at 33.38 centesimal parts on the meridian line (on the body of Cancer in fig. 4). The meridian line is the y- axis, the origin is the 33.38 point on it, and the x-axis is perpendicular to the meridian line.

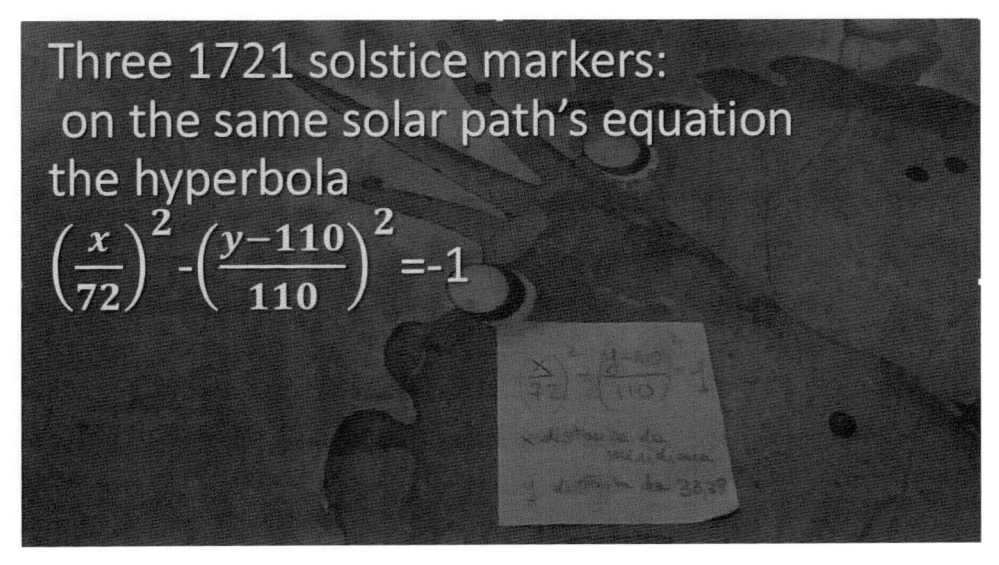

Three 1721 solstice markers:
on the same solar path's equation
the hyperbola
$$\left(\frac{x}{72}\right)^2 - \left(\frac{y-110}{110}\right)^2 = -1$$

Fig. 4. The equation of the 1721 summer solstice's path as derived from the three markers. The parameters in the equation are expressed in meters.

4. Obliquity variation in three centuries

In 2021 the difference of Earth orbit's obliquity has been evident after 3 centuries, as a shift of 15 mm (fig. 5). The brass' profile is the 1721 one, while the luminous disk is the 2021 solar position. The new pinhole installed for the 2018 IGEA[a] campaign[9] has the same position along the meridian axis of 1702.

Fig. 5. Obliquity meter: differential measure of June 20, 2020 compared with 1721 at the Summer solstice. The image of the Sun is formed over the Queen's marker, the second in the sequence.

---

[a]IGEA standing for Informatized Geometric Ephemerides for Astrometry, started on October 27, 2018 and was named in honor of Igea Contessa (1918 Oct 27-2009 Dec 11)

Fig. 6. The marble marker with the inscription. A pencil shows its dimension.

5. Conclusions: High science in *Roman Settecento*

It is natural that the policy of the popes during the life of James III Stuart was oriented toward the restauration of the catholic dinasty at the throne, and Francesco Bianchini as close friend of Clement XI collaborated to this policy. The title of the new work of J. L. Heilbron (to appear in 2022) dedicated to Bianchini seems not to depart significantly from his approach in *The Sun in the Church* of 1999, with *tranchant* sentences on the papal policy of 1700. This paper along with the other one concerning the aberration of Sirius and the Equation of time in 1703 complete a 20 years' cycle of measurements and studies on the meridian line of St. Maria degli Angeli, inspired by Heilbron's book (1999), but in the direction of showing the prestige and the accuracy of roman astronomy, on the cutting edge of celestial mechanics of the eigtheenth century, instead of an easy *bavardage* on the court's intrigues as the forthcoming new title suggests.

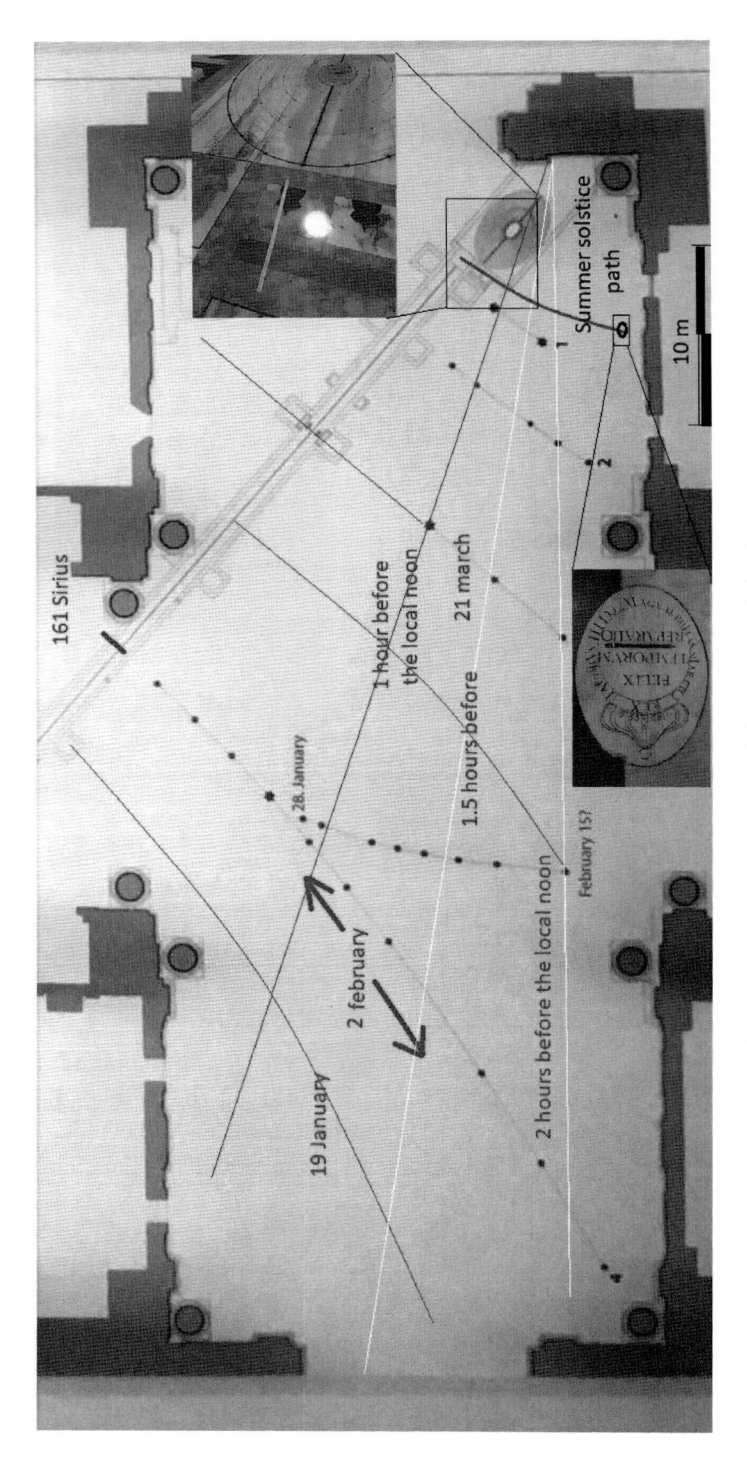

Fig. 7. Location on the map of the Basilica of the three markers.

Fig. 8. The Sun between the two brass markers, and the boreal line with the ellipses of the Jubilee years. The great meridian line starts on the left of this photo, taken on 4th July 2021 at 13:01. The Sun moves left in this photo, from the King's to the Queen's marker.

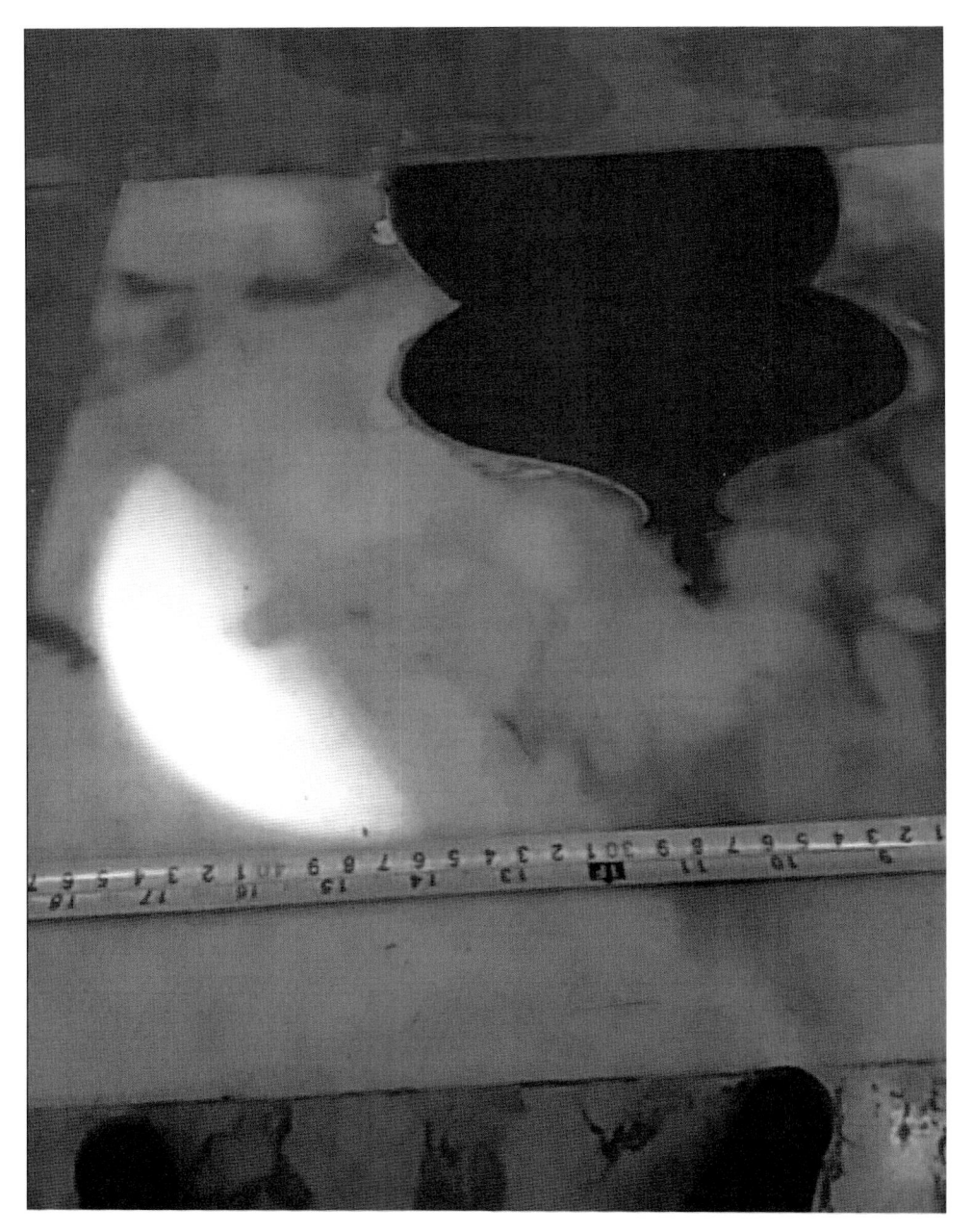

Fig. 9. The Sun's image appeared just after the King's marker on July 3rd 2021 at 12:58. It is the King's one because it was hit first by the Sun. Nowadays the Sun does not illuminates parts of the floor of the Basilica from the pinhole, after the intervents of Luigi Vanvitelli in 1750, which obscurated with a decorative arch the pinhole. Roger J. Boscovich cut the arch in correspondence of the meridian line, and the above image of the Sun is appearing from this cut.

References

1. Bianchini, F. (1703), *De Nummo et Gnomone Clementino* https://archive.org/details/dekalendarioetcy00bian
2. Sigismondi, C., et al., IAU General Assembly, Vienna (2018) *The rediscovery of the obliquity meter in the meridian line of St. Maria degli Angeli in Rome* http://homepages.vub.ac.be/~csterken/C3_Science_meeting.pdf
3. Sigismondi, C., (2008) *MG XI Proceedings* , https://ui.adsabs.harvard.edu/abs/2008mgm..conf.2470S/abstract.
4. Sigismondi, C., et al., *Measures of the Earth obliquity during the 1701 winter solstice at the Clementine meridian line in Rome*Proceedings of the Journées 2014 "Systèmes de référence spatio-temporels" https://ui.adsabs.harvard.edu/abs/2015jsrs.conf..116A/abstract.
5. Ceci, F. and G. Breccola *1 settembre 1719 a Trecento anni dalle nozze regali a Montefiascone* Edizioni, ArcheoAres, Terni (2021) https://www.facebook.com/accademia.polacca/photos/a.416643071829557/1709674122526439/?type=3&theater
6. Heilbron, J. L. *The Incomparable Monsignor: Francesco Bianchini's world of science, history, and court intrigue* (to appear in 2022) https://www.barnesandnoble.com/w/the-incomparable-monsignor-jl-heilbron/1140143257#
7. Heilbron, J. L. *The Sun in the Church* Harvard University Press, 1999.
8. Sigismondi, C., Gerbertus, vol. 14, pp. 33-38 (2021) *L'equinozio e le parabole osculatrici* http://www.icra.it/gerbertus/2021/Gerb-14-2021-Sigismondi-Parabole_osculatrici-33-38.pdf.
9. Sigismondi, C., *Earth's Obliquity and Stellar Aberration Detected at the Clementine Gnomon (Rome, 1703)* Phys. Sci. Forum 2021, **2(1)**, 49 https://www.mdpi.com/2673-9984/2/1/49/htm
10. Catamo, M. and C. Lucarini, *Il Cielo in Basilica*, Arpa-Agami Roma, 2011 2nd ed.

Einstein-First: Bringing children our best understanding of reality

A. Popkova*, K. Adams, S. Boublil, R. K. Choudhary, E. Horne, L. Ju, T. Kaur, D. McGoran,
D. Wood, M. Zadnik and D. G. Blair

*Department of Physics, The University of Western Australia, 35 Stirling Highway, Crawley
Perth, WA 6009, Australia*
23134632@student.uwa.edu.au

D. F. Treagust

*STEM Education Research Group, School of Education, Curtin University, Kent Street,
Bentley, Perth WA 6102, Australia School of Education, Curtin University*
d.treagust@curtin.edu.au

The Einstein-First project is designed to resolve a conflict between modern science and the science taught at school, which is a significant cause of students' negative attitudes to STEM. Our program resolves these contradictions by teaching our best understanding of the universe, dubbed Einsteinian Physics, from an early age. We use models and group activities in a carefully crafted 8-year learning progression, to give students a basic understanding of the language and concepts describing our physical universe, from quarks to the big bang. Einstein-First works with teachers to develop courses, lesson plans and training workshops. These components all contribute to curriculum trials where student learning and attitude outcomes can be assessed. Every trial of curriculum modules or short intervention programs has yielded exciting, positive outcomes including surprising gender equalising effects and benefits for less academic and disadvantaged students. There are multiple classroom trials in place in local partner schools. In this paper we present an overview of the Einstein-First program and give examples of the ability of students from age 8 to 12 to comprehend modern scientific concepts.

Keywords: Einsteinian Physics; Science Education

1. Introduction

The experimental educational project called Einstein-First is a collaboration of scientists and educators who are concerned about the current school science curriculum which: a) includes misconceptions b) is irrelevant c) does not meet needs of people in the modern world. The existing science curriculum completely ignores the modern, awesome discoveries of relativistic astrophysics and makes teaching of modern concepts impossible.[1] For example, the first direct observation of gravitational waves in 2015 and the rapid development of gravitational wave astronomy, have provided a new spectrum for understanding the Universe as well as providing evidence to support the theory of relativity predicted by Einstein a century ago.[2] The discovery of gravitational waves has inspired new developments in areas such as optomechanics, the quantum mechanics of gravitational wave detectors, as well as observational investigations of black holes, neutron stars and heavy element nucleosynthesis.[3] Also, in the last century, science has given us knowledge of the tiniest things in the universe and vast distances to the edge of the visible universe, and with it, the modern technologies on which our lives depend. Recently, in 2021, the Nobel prize in physics was awarded for modelling of complex systems related to climate change and the discovery of the interplay of disorder and fluctuations in physical systems from atomic to planetary scales.[4] These are all examples of modern discoveries that are not included in the current Australian science curriculum.

Primary and secondary school science curricula still rely on outdated scientific paradigms of traditional Newtonian physics based on classical concepts, research methods, postulates, and standards. Thus, the revelations of modern science and even the vocabulary of modern physics is denied to early and middle school students. The consequences of this situation may be that students are not able to digest the core concepts related to new discoveries during higher level of schooling with the subsequent loss of students' interest in the science presented as being irrelevant to real life events across the world.[5] Einsteinian physics, encompassing both general relativity and quantum mechanics provides a better understanding of modern reality and is relevant to students' everyday life. Unfortunately, general relativity and quantum mechanics have typically been reserved for specialist high school physics subjects and mainly taught at the tertiary level. For the overwhelming majority of students, modern physics may be inaccessible. Year 10 is the last year of compulsory science in Australian schools and can be the last opportunity for the education system to foster scientific literacy on our school population.

One reason for keeping children away from Einsteinian physics is because these concepts are considered to be difficult to comprehend at an early age. In 2004 Kathleen E. Metz stated "Science frameworks have frequently limited the content targeted for the early grades to such simple and concrete ideas that they offer little explanatory power. Even pre-schoolers seek explanation".[6] Einstein-First has demonstrated, through numerous studies and peer reviewed published results that Einsteinian physics can be successfully integrated into a curriculum at all levels of schooling from Year 3 to Year 10[7–11] when taught at the appropriate level. These results concur with the statement of the distinguished Harvard and Oxford educator Jerome Bruner that: "Any subject can be taught effectively in some intellectually honest form to any child at any stage of development".[12] In a spirit of Bruner, this project is designed to test the introduction of general relativity and quantum mechanics to children in a manner that will be powerful, fun and mind-expanding.

Another reason for the opposition to the teaching of Einsteinian physics in primary and lower secondary school is the false belief that advanced mathematics is a prerequisite for understanding modern physics. While advanced mathematics is not required, new mathematical skills are important. To allow children to understand the scales of the universe from atoms to galaxies, we need to also rethink mathematics education. Understanding the main concepts of Einsteinian Physics requires the development of students' mathematical concepts in three important ways: a) understanding the vast range of scales of the universe, which necessitates the development of logarithmic thinking[13] b) the development of probabilistic thinking,[14] and c) the development of vector understanding.[15] These skills also have importance for understanding the financial world, global issues such as environmental problems, gambling and risks, and skills such as drone navigation.

Overall, education needs to remain relevant in order to impart knowledge of the modern world to the new generation. Furthermore, physics practitioners, who are at the forefront of modern investigations and discoveries, should be part of the educational partnership to ensure that contemporary scientific trends find their way into the school curriculum at every level. For that reason, "Sharing our best understanding of reality with kids" is the driving motivation of the Einstein -First project.

Our vision is that every student, by Year 10, the last compulsory year of science in Australia, will have knowledge of our best understanding of the nature of space, time and gravity, the quantum world of atoms and photons, and the universe from quarks to the big bang. We want to give students the language of science so that no one need suffer from science illiteracy. We want students to know the epic stories of the struggle to understand the universe, which we teach through plays, songs and games. We want two common phrases to become obsolete: "I can't understand science" and "You must be a genius to understand that stuff".

In 2019 the Australian Research Council funded a five-year project to develop an integrated Einsteinian Physics-focused curriculum across primary and secondary schools. An early outcome has been the book *Teaching Einsteinian Physics in Schools*, published in August of 2021.[16] To produce this book, we had to find out if young children could understand Einsteinian concepts. To do this we developed activities that would make Einsteinian concepts intuitively understandable. Then we conducted trials and gathered evidence, which showed that young children comprehended and enjoyed learning Einsteinian concepts.[17] The successes of the Einstein-First program has been demonstrated also through studies on; long-term impact,[18] gender benefits,[19] advantages for underachieving students[7,9] and positive teacher response.[20] Particularly with further trials we made three specific exciting discoveries:

(1) the less-academic students developed knowledge and understanding on a par with the more-academic students[7,9],
(2) students' attitudes to science improved strongly[17] and
(3) girls entered programs with less knowledge than boys but on completion had performance on a par with boys when learning more difficult concepts.[19]

The goal of Einstein-First is to modernize school science so that all students by Year 10, should have a basic understanding of the science behind modern technology, and the universe, from its tiniest components like atoms to vast structures like our Milky Way galaxy.

2. Einstein–First Overview

2.1. *Einsteinian physics*

In the early 1900's, discoveries by Albert Einstein and others revolutionised our understanding of physical reality. Evidence of the existence of photons led to quantum theory, and evidence that space is curved confirmed Einstein's general theory of relativity. Today, the theories we term Einsteinian Physics have been tested to exquisite precision, with the crowning glory being the recent detections of gravitational waves from colliding black holes and neutron stars, the 2017 Nobel Prize announcement and the three million dollar Breakthrough Prize shared by the gravitational waves discovery team, including four members of this project. The Einsteinian conceptions of space, time, gravity, light, energy and matter represent our deepest understanding of the Universe. Einsteinian Physics unleashed the technological revolution that underpins modern civilisation, forming the basis for computers, mobile phones, GPS and more. Gravitational wave detectors themselves harness concepts of space as a rippling, stretchable fabric, as well as the quantum properties of light and quantum uncertainty, which underpins their exquisite measurement technology.

The Einstein-First project aims to introduce Einsteinian Physics starting with Year 3. For this age, we focus on Einsteinian concepts of understanding the atomic nature of matter (Brownian motion), Einstein's proof that light comes as photons, photons have momentum and that heat in solids fluctuates as phonons (1917).

2.2. *Educational contradictions*

Einstein and his collaborators revolutionized our understanding of space, time, light, matter and gravity. Einsteinian Physics, developed about 100 years ago, has extraordinary explanatory power, and has enabled the development of technologies that revolutionised our lives such as mobile phones, cameras, solar panels, and medical imaging. Despite the power and importance of Einsteinian physics, children from Primary to Year 10 are taught 19th century physics concepts in school, sometimes implicitly and sometimes explicitly. Hence the modern understanding of physical reality is withheld from the majority of students. The few students who do specialise in physics in Year 11 and Year 12 have to learn a new paradigm. This situation is grossly inefficient and leads to the general view that science is a domain for experts alone.

2.3. *Children's awareness*

Children pick up bits of modern science from media, the internet, and children's books but at school almost all of this relevant, modern and exciting science is withheld. From an early age most have heard of time warps, black holes and $E = mc^2$, but school learning contradicts all this. They currently teach that time is absolute, geometry is Euclidean, and mass does not change with energy. Children are aware that most of their school science is "old stuff" because there is more modern science on *The Simpsons* than there is in the classroom. Hence students see school science as being boring and irrelevant.

Many teachers and schools do wonderful things with robots, coding and more, to enhance STEM education but usually within the outdated curriculum. We realized that we needed to address the fundamentals and start at primary school when students are best able to assimilate the new language of Einsteinian physics.

2.4. *How the contradictions in science education arose*

New theories that change our way of thinking are always hard to get used to. When the new physics was discovered, people claimed that the new theories were much too complex for ordinary people to understand. Physicists did little to dispel these views and curriculum designers accepted them. This combined with early views of education theorists (now dispelled by recent research[21,22]) that children cannot learn abstract concepts. In the 1930s atoms, photons, electrons and curved space were all newly discovered concepts that were inferred but not directly observed.

However, in the modern era all the things that were conceptual have changed their status: they are now observed, imaged and part of observational reality, and a few clicks away on the internet. Because physical science underpins everything from biology to plate tectonics, the lack of conceptual foundations means that the key motivational content of science — the ongoing stream of scientific discoveries – is not taught and hence students adopt a negative attitudes towards existing science curricula. Also, the few students who specialise must suffer an abrupt shift in paradigm from Newtonian to Einsteinian physics that makes their learning more difficult.

2.5. *International partnerships*

There is widespread concern that school curricula do not meet the needs of modern children. The development of the Einsteinian Physics curriculum started with a collaboration of Australian and multinational teams. Currently, there is a lot evidence from different groups around the world, including our partner researchers, that middle school and even primary school children can understand concepts of mass and gravity,[23] theory of relativity,[24] theory of atoms[25,26] and the connection between wavelength and momentum.[27] However there is no evidence in the literature that any school jurisdictions in the world are embracing the need for modernising the curriculum. This modernization includes both the physics concepts and the associated mathematical concepts needed to understand the Universe.

2.6. *A contradiction-free curriculum*

We are working to overcome the deep-seated conflict between children's learning in schools and the current science that underpins all modern technology. During the years of rapid childhood learning when minds are most fluid, children are learning obsolete 19th century concepts that contradict modern science. Awesome discoveries are withheld because both the concepts and language are inaccessible to young learners. Here are some examples:

(1) In Year 3 students learn about heat without reference to atoms because atoms are considered too conceptual, and not to be taught until children are 12-14 years old.
(2) Children are taught that mass is always conserved in chemical reactions despite the fact that recent conceptually simple experiments are able to measure the mass loss of an atom when it emits a photon, a consequence of Einstein's $E = mc^2$.
(3) Students learn implicitly that time is absolute even though our GPS navigators must correct for the time warp between Earth and the satellites' orbits.

The modernization of the school curriculum requires the integration of new knowledge with innovative approaches. To identify a new learning methods and activities, the Einstein-First project encompasses two key ideas: a) "never underestimate the child's abilities to absorb new information and cope with new ideas",[28] and b) the central concept of the theory of constructivism in education that is "complex ideas can be taught at a simplified level first, then re-visited at more complex levels later on".[12]

Our learning framework is divided into the three stages.

1. Primary School: Opening minds to Einsteinian concepts and creating expectations. We use qualitative and experiential activity-based learning to emphasise the language of Einsteinian Physics.
2. Middle School: Basic understanding of Einsteinian concepts, using semi-quantitative activity-based learning, including the use of graphs and simple calculations.
3. High School: Developing a quantitative understanding of Einsteinian concepts, as well as a quantitative understanding, that includes calculations.

Einstein-First is creating a seamless learning progression that begins in early primary school and is designed to ensure that every student develops an intuitive understanding of physical reality. Currently, Einstein-First is developing curricula for every school level from Year 3 to Year 10 as well as introducing the language of modern science in Year 2. The modules of curriculum are presented below:

Year 3	Atom frenzy and Hot stuff
Year 4	May the forces be with you
Year 5	Fantastic photons and Our place in the universe
Year 6	Electric world
Year 7	Warp spacetime: Gravity from the Earth to black holes
Year 8	From mc^2 to renewable energy
Year 9	Quantum world: quarks to photons
Year 10	Climate change to cosmology

2.7. How have we made Einsteinian physics accessible? Models, toys, analogies and drama

Einsteinian physics is imagined by most primary and secondary school teachers to be impossibly difficult. This is because those who learnt the 19th century paradigm cannot envisage ideas like space having a shape, and matter having properties of both waves and particles. Children, however, accept Einstenian concepts with ease when taught with appropriate models and activities.

In order to make modern physics understandable we use multiple, interactive methods that are discussed in detail here.

2.7.1. Activities and toys

Most of the universe is beyond the reach of our normal senses it is either, too big, too small or invisible. We need to find creative analogies and models so that concepts and ideas can become tangible. We understand and remember things not just with abstract thought, but with our bodies, by doing things. Furthermore, for all children toys are critical means of learning.

Our diversity of toys and models are simple, robust, and inexpensive. They allow students to learn complex concepts intuitively, mainly through group activities. For example, students roll steel balls around a central mass on a stretched lycra sheet (often called a space-time simulator). The 2D lycra sheet is our toy space-time. The balls orbit the central mass due to the curvature of the membrane caused by the central mass. These orbits resemble the orbit of planets around stars. The greater the central mass, the greater the curvature of space-time and the stronger the force of gravitation exerted on the orbiting bodies.

2.7.2. Crossing boundaries, playing Einstein

The discovery of Einsteinian physics was the culmination of centuries of enquiry by scientists all over the world. There were intellectual battles between scientists, notably between holists and atomists in the 19th century. The holists who believed that matter was smooth and continuous forever, lost the battle when conclusive evidence was found for electrons (1897), photons (1905) and atoms (1911). Bringing these human stories to life helps students understand the progress and process of science and shows science as an epic human endeavour. In our reading plays, often performed in drama lessons, inquisitive students mix with scientists from across the ages, enacting the process of discoveries. Characters such as Einstein, sing songs and recite aphorisms that help cement the Einsteinian vocabulary with fun and humor.

2.7.3. Mathematics for the modern world

To allow children to understand the scales of the universe from atoms and galaxies, we need to rethink mathematics education. Modern science understanding depends on fundamental mathematical areas that go beyond primary school arithmetic. Einstein-First has introduced early activity-based learning in three crucial areas: huge and tiny (powers of ten), maths of arrows (graphical vectors), and maths of chance. In our use of mathematics we are creating seamless learning progressions that begins in early primary school, designed to ensure that everyone develops an intuitive understanding of concepts crucial for understanding, for example, the size of the whole observable universe, the electromagnetic spectrum and the quantum world. This mathematics also has social importance for understanding money, weather, risks and gambling. Starting at the youngest ages, we teach these topics with fun activities designed to open children's minds to ideas that mathematics is more than numbers, maths is easy, and maths is fun.

3. Methods of Einstein-First

In this section we present examples of four activities of Einstein-First methods to deliver concepts of modern science and associated mathematics concepts of probability, big and small numbers, and vectors.

3.1. *Early learning of powers of 2 and powers of ten by cutting up tape measure*

Exponential notation is essential to our ability to comprehend the scale of the Universe from the tiniest component to the Hubble volume. To introduce exponential notations we use a paper cutting activity. Students cut a one meter paper tape measure into repeated halves. Then they cut another one meter paper tape measure into tenth to learnt that ten powers of two are approximately three powers of ten. Then this exercise is mentally extrapolated to find how many times this process needs to be continued to reach the size of the atom.

3.2. *The entire Universe in a single book*

To introduce big and small numbers and the scale of the Universe we have developed a novel long-term activity consisting of the creation of a 130 page book called *Powers of the Universe*. All numbers describing the known Universe can be placed in this book. Each page is a power of ten. Line position on each page is designated for various quantities, all expressed in SI units. For example there are line bands for distances, masses, energy etc. Students use all possible methods (e.g., using Google) to discover numbers at all scales. For example, they start the book at the page labelled -37, while they indicate, that 10^{-37} is the rest mass of the neutrino. Page +90 shows the total number of photons in the Universe and page +2 is the mass of a human.

Through this activity, students investigate the scale of our universe and expand their knowledge and their ability to envisage big and small numbers.

3.3. *Children pushing a car to discover vector addition*

In order to introduce the concept of vectors at early age we use activity in which students push their teacher's car. Students in the class altogether push a car on a flat car park under the supervision of a class teacher. Teachers use creative questioning to encourage all students to contribute answers about what happened and why it happened. In this way, students represent the pushing forces by vectors and learn rules of head to tail adding vectors. Then we introduce the concept of the resultant. To reinforce the learning, students use magnetic arrows on magnetic boards to investigate the sum of the vectors from where they find out that the resultant is not dependent on an order of adding arrows.

3.4. *A boy and his atom. Feeling hidden atoms pattern*

The world's smallest movie *A boy and his atom* is used to introduce atoms and molecules, and how we are able to see and move them. Students watch a short video from IMB[29] and discuss how the Atomic Force Microscopy works. Students work in pairs. One student makes the image using playdough and toy atoms in a form of marbles and covers it with a piece of cloth. Then the other student determines the hidden pattern by feeling in the same way that an atomic force microscope "feel" when it scans a surface. Finally, the student draws a picture of the pattern.

All of these activities mentioned above along with others were included in recent short programs for students from Year 3 to 8.

4. Four Recent Programs

The Einstein-First project has held short programs in schools over the previous six months to teach students about atoms and molecules, heat, forces, light and gravity. Group activities, hands-on learning and team competitions were all parts of the programs. Students' attitudes and knowledge were assessed using pre- and post-questionnaires that students completed on the first and last day of the programs. Assessments of the attitudes and knowledge were administrated for 15 minutes before and after the programs. Every lesson was delivered using the following method:

a) The first 15 minutes were used to review what they had learnt in the previous lesson and to introduce the idea they would be learning that day;
b) The main part of the lesson was dedicated to the associated activity and concepts; and
c) The final 15 minutes were set out for discussion or completion of the worksheets.

4.1. *Discovering black holes*

This four-week, eight-hour program was designed for motivated Year 7 and Year 8 students from various schools. This program had a total of 20 students, including a

6-year-old gifted student). The program was presented by current PhD students involved in the Einstein-First project. Each two hour session consisted of Einsteinian physics concepts as well as the mathematics that accompanied them. By doing activities on a space-time simulator (see section 2.7.1), students visualized the concept of gravity, black holes, and deflection of light. Students summarised their learning with the following phrase *"Space-time tells matter how to move; matter tells space-time how to curve."*

All of the above activities, as well as others in the program, require the development of mathematical skills to comprehend both big and small numbers. Understanding big and small numbers aids in comprehending the nature of supermassive black holes and how little displacements in the interferometer arms are essential to detect gravitational waves. For example the activity described in Section 3.1 was used for understanding powers of ten for these numbers.

4.2. How big is an atom? How small is a light year?

Twenty six Year 5 and 6 students participated in a four-session program on big and small numbers. The lessons were delivered by a mathematics teacher in the presence of the PhD student who developed the program. Each session lasted 1 hour, teaching mainly mathematics associated with Einsteinian physics. The main goal of the program was to teach students about the scale of the universe and how to use powers of ten to understand big and small numbers as described in Sections 3.1 and 3.2. Students also took part in a reading play called "Ten times Alice" in which the main character eats magic cookies or a magic liquid to grow ten times smaller or bigger than her companions. This play was created for students to practice proportional reasoning and multiplication by 10.

4.3. Vectors and forces

This short program was aimed at Year 4 students. The main goal of the program was to give an understanding of how vectors are used in physics and addition of vectors. There were 2.5 sessions that were presented to 27 students. The program was presented by the leader of the Einstein-First project with assistance of a current PhD student. Each session lasted 90 minutes and encompassed concepts of forces and geometry associated with them. We used the activity presented in Section 3.3 to practice vector addition and the concept of a resultant. After, children applied the ideas of vectors pulling wooden blocks with rubber bands in different direction to find the final movement (Fig. 1). The program also included activities with balance, for example, balancing a big wooden ruler horizontally on one finger to understand conception of the resultant.

4.4. Atom frenzy

Twenty-four Year 3 students participated in the 12-session atoms and molecules program delivered by the project's senior member and Phd student. Each session was

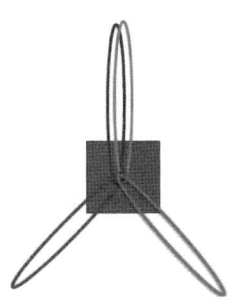

Fig. 1. Each coloured loop above represents a rubber band being pulled by an external force. Students are tasked with finding the resultant of four forces applied to wooden block with rubber bands as detailed in Section 4.3.

90 minutes and delivered through engaging, hands-on activities. We used various methods of understanding of atoms from children acting as atoms to boxes of balls that represent atoms, states of matter and heat. Students learnt three molecules H_2O, CO_2, O_2, N_2, using tennis and ping-pong balls with magnets inside representing toy atoms.

5. Results and Discussion

The section presents some outcomes of the programs described in Section 4.

5.1. Results from the programs "Discovering Black Holes" and "How big is an atom? How small is a light year?"

Students' understanding of the exponential function, writing numbers in scientific notations, and calculations significantly improved. Fig. 2 presents the results from the programs described in the sections 4.1 and 4.2. We evaluated students' choice to write big numbers such as *a) one hundred b) one million c) one trillion and d) one billion* before and after interventions. We discovered that just 26% of students chose powers of ten to write the numbers before the program. However, after the program, all students were able to write the numbers in powers of ten accurately. According to the research findings from program 4.2, 73% of participants chose to write numbers in powers of ten, compared to only 12 percent at the start.

Overall, we found that primary school students were capable of using powers of ten in reasoning about big numbers.

5.2. Results from the programs "Forces and vectors"

Results from the program 4.3 is shown in Fig. 3. A question was asked about force vectors and resultant to evaluate what they had learnt from the car-pushing activity (3.3). More than 80% of students accurately added vectors after the program.

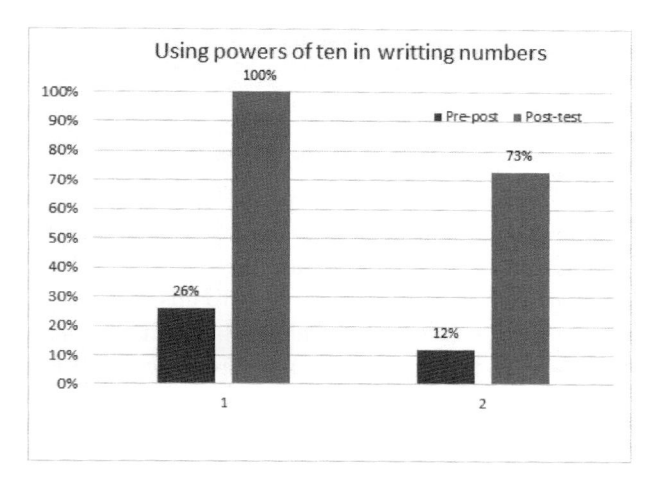

Fig. 2. The percentage of students using powers of ten in writing numbers before and after programs 1) 4.1 and 2) 4.2.
Q: Using powers of ten (or otherwise) write the numbers below: a)one hundred b) one million b) one billion c) one trillion.

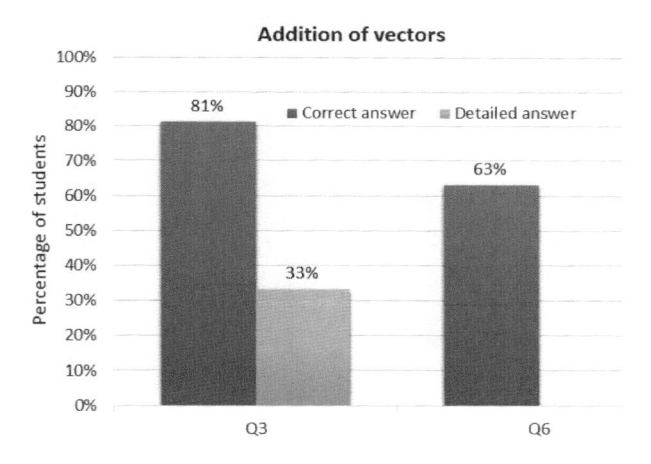

Fig. 3. The percentage of students, giving correct answers on the questions about arrows addition after program Vectors and Forces.
Q3: Eight children pushed the teacher's car, but seven children pushed in the opposite directions. Draw the resultant arrow? What was the total Force?
(Orange light indicates that one answer is correct. Yellow indicates that both answers are correct and detailed picture is provided.)
Q6: Four kids pull the wooden block in different direction using four rubber bands (the picture was provided) In what direction will the block move? Draw an arrow for the direction.

However, only 33% of students were able to determine the resultant of two opposing forces.

Q6 is an extension of Q3, indicating that 63% of students can add four arbitrary vectors to determine a resultant applied to wooden block with rubber bands (Fig. 1) and its final movement. The graph shows that the vast majority of student can grasp the notion of vectors and add them together.

5.3. *Results from the programs "Atom Frenzy"*

The results from the program 4.4 are shown in Fig. 4. Despite the fact that the Australian curriculum stipulated that atoms should not be introduced until the age of 14, 40% of students had a basic understanding of atoms prior to the program. Figure 3 indicates that 83% of students were able to answer *what is an atom?* after the program, compared to only 40% of students before the program. In addition, 75% of students expanded their answers by referencing atom structure, naming subatomic particles, or thinking them to be a part of molecules. Also 87.5% of students correctly identified atom number six as a carbon atom, drew its structure, and presented it as a component of carbon dioxide.

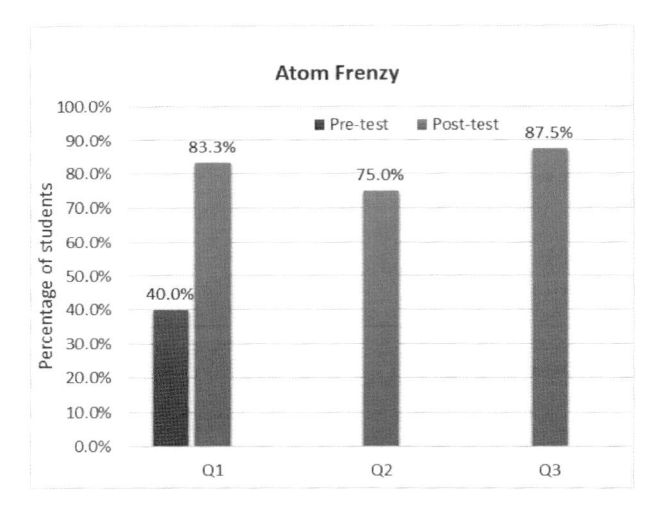

Fig. 4. The percentage of students, giving corrected answers on the questions about atoms before and after program Atom Frenzy?
Q1: Describe what you think an atom is.
Q2: Write down three things you know about atoms and the things they are made of.
Q3: Draw a picture of atom number 6.

Overall, outcomes of programs show that, the students demonstrated a considerable gain in their grasp of atoms, vectors, and the use of powers of ten as a technique of manipulating big and small numbers.

6. Conclusion

We have emphasized the vital necessity to rethink the science curriculum and mathematics associated with it. It has become obvious to introduce ideas that students find interesting and engaging especially because of the widespread decline of students' attitude to science. Einstein-First is an innovative experimental education project rethinking the physical science curriculum by developing an innovative approach for introducing Einsteinian Physics in school starting at an early age. We have given the general principle of our approach and examples of methods used to make the physics accessible to teachers and students alike. We have presented some results from recent short interventions, that have shown that students aged 11 to 14 years have shown competency with power of ten notation. Secondly, we have demonstrated that students aged 10 obtain high scores in understanding the concept of vectors, including vectors addition. Within the larger Einstein-First project, learning progressions of curricula have been created, starting with Year 3 and going up to Year 10. Einstein-First also considers Year 2 to be the pre-learning stage for modern physics vocabulary. Models and analogies, drama plays, and mathematical support modules are suggested to make concepts of modern physics digestible and fun to learn. It has been demonstrated that even short interventions can bring high outcomes in learning Einsteinian physics in both primary and early-secondary schools.

Acknowledgments

We very much thank the anonymous teachers, who facilitated and taught in the programs presented here. This research was supported by Australian Research Council Linkage Grant LP 180100859.

References

1. https://k10outline.scsa.wa.edu.au/home/teaching/curriculum-browser/science-v8.
2. R. Weiss, *Reviews of modern Physics* **90** (2018) 1.
3. B. Abbott et al., *Physical Review Letters* (2016) 131103.
4. https://www.nobelprize.org/prizes/physics/2021/press-release/.
5. P. Potvin, A. Hasni, *Journal of Science Education and Technology* **23** (2014) 784.
6. K. E. Metz, *Cognition and Instruction* **22** (2004) 219.
7. M. Pitts, G. Venville, D. Blair, M. Zadnik *Research in Science Education* **44** (2014) 363.
8. T. Kaur, D. Blair, J. Moschilla, W. Stannard, M. Zadnik, *Physics Education* **52** (2017) 065014.
9. T. Kaur, D. Blair, W. Stannard, D. Treagust, G. Venville, M. Zadnik, W. Mathews, D. Perks, *Research in Science Education* **50** (2019) 2505.
10. R. Choudhary, U. Kraus, M. Kersting, D. Blair, C. Zahn, Marjan Zadnik, *The Physics Educator* **1** (2019) 1950016.
11. R. Choudhary, D. Blair, *European Journal of Physics* **42** (2021) 035408.
12. Jerome Bruner, *The Process of education* (Harvard University Press, Cambridge, Manchester, London 1976).
13. S. Mahajan, *American Journal of Physics* **86** (2018) 859.
14. D. I. Sari, I. K. Budayasa, D. Juniati, Probabilistic Thinking of Elementary School Students in Solving Probability Tasks Based on Math Ability, *AIP Conference Proceedings 1867*, 2017, 1867, p. 020028.

15. W. Widada, D. Herawaty, Y. Beka, R. M. Sari, R. Riyani, K. Umam, Z. Nugroho, *Journal of Physics Conference* **1470** (2020) 012071.
16. M. Kersting, D. Blair, *Teaching Einsteinian Physics in Schools: An Essential Guide for Teachers in Training and Practice* (Taylor and Francis Group, 2021).
17. R. K Choudhary, A.Foppoli, T. Kaur, D. G. Blair, M. Zadnik, R. Meagher, *Physics Education* **53** (2018) 065020.
18. K. Adams, R. Dattatri, T. Kaur, D. Blair, *Physics Education* **56** (2021) 055031.
19. T. Kaur, D. Blair, R. K. Choudhary, Y. S. Dua, A. Foppoli, D. Treagust, M. Zadnik, *Physics Education* **55** (2020) 035029.
20. A. Foppoli, R. Choudhary, D. Blair, T. Kaur, J. Moschilla, M. Zadnik, *Physics Education* **54** (2019) 015001.
21. K. E. Metz, *Review of Educational Research* **65** (1995) 93.
22. National Research Council, *Taking science to school: Learning and teaching science in grades K-8*, (National Academies Press, 2007).
23. M. Luca Ruggiero, S. Mattiello, M. Leone, *Physics Education* **56** (2019) 065011.
24. M. Kersting, G. Schrocker, S. Papantoniou, *International Journal of Science Education* **43** (2021) 2044.
25. C. Haeusler, J. Donovan, *Research in Science Education* **50**, 2 (2020).
26. A. Mandrikas, E. Michailidi, D. Stavrou, *Research in Science Technological Education* **38** (2020) 337.
27. P. Bitzenbauer, J.-P. Meyn, *Physics Education* **55** (2020) 055031.
28. D. Whitebread, P. Coltman, *Teaching and Learning in the Early Years* (Taylor and Francis, United Kingdom, 2015).
29. https://research.ibm.com/articles/madewithatoms.shtml.
30. https://www.einsteinianphysics.com/.

Kundt spacetimes in the Einstein–Gauss–Bonnet theory

R. Švarc[*], J. Podolský[†] and O. Hruška

Institute of Theoretical Physics, Faculty of Mathematics and Physics, Charles University, Prague, V Holešovičkách 2, 180 00 Praha 8, Czech Republic
E-mail: [*]robert.svarc@mff.cuni.cz, [†]podolsky@mbox.troja.mff.cuni.cz
www.mff.cuni.cz

Based on our recent results we present the complete class of vacuum solutions in the Einstein–Gauss–Bonnet gravity which admit non-expanding, shear-free and twist-free null geodesic congruence and thus form the Kundt family of geometries. We explicitly derive the field equations and classify their solutions into three distinct subfamilies. Algebraic structure of the Weyl tensor is determined and using the corresponding scalars entering the invariant form of geodesic deviation equation we discuss the specific local physical properties of the gravitational field constrained by the EGB theory. Moreover, we analyze interesting subclasses of such vacuum solutions, namely all geometries with constant-curvature transverse space, and the class of pp-waves admitting a covariantly constant null vector field.

Keywords: Einstein–Gauss Bonnet theory; Kundt spacetimes; exact solutions; pp-waves.

1. Introduction

The Einstein–Gauss–Bonnet (EGB) theory represents the first and simultaneously the simplest non-trivial contribution of the Lovelock gravities[1] extending the classic Einstein–Hilbert action into higher dimensions $D \geq 5$ and keeping the second order field equations. This theory also arises in various scenarios, e.g., as the heterotic string theory limit for low energies.[2,3]

In particular, the EGB vacuum action in D-dimensions reads

$$S = \int \left[\kappa^{-1}(R - 2\Lambda_0) + \gamma\, L_{GB} \right] \sqrt{-g}\, \mathrm{d}^D \mathrm{x}, \qquad (1)$$

with the Gauss–Bonnet term defined as

$$L_{GB} \equiv R_{cdef}\, R^{cdef} - 4\, R_{cd}\, R^{cd} + R^2. \qquad (2)$$

Here R stands for the Ricci scalar, R_{cdef} and R_{cd} are Riemann and Ricci tensors, respectively, Λ_0, κ and γ are theory constants. Obviously, for $\gamma = 0$ the standard Einstein–Hilbert action of the general relativity is restored. The least action principle, i.e., variation $\delta S = 0$, leads to the field equations in the form

$$R_{ab} - \tfrac{1}{2} R\, g_{ab} + \Lambda_0\, g_{ab} + 2k\, H_{ab} = 0 \qquad \text{where} \qquad k \equiv \kappa\gamma, \qquad (3)$$

and

$$H_{ab} \equiv R\, R_{ab} - 2 R_{acbd}\, R^{cd} + R_{acde}\, R_b{}^{cde} - 2 R_{ac}\, R_b{}^c - \tfrac{1}{4}\, g_{ab}\, L_{GB}. \qquad (4)$$

The aim of this proceeding contribution is to briefly summarize main results of Ref. 4, where we explicitly derived and analyzed the second order field equations (3) in the case of so-called Kundt geometries,[5,6] see e.g. Ref. 7 for detail list of references, and compared properties of obtained EGB solutions with those extensively studied within general relativity.[8–11]

The Kundt geometries are defined via geometric assumption on existence of a specific affinely parametrized null geodesic congruence. In general, transverse deformations of such null congruence, generated by null vector field $\boldsymbol{k}$, are described by the optical scalars which characterize its twist, shear, and expansion, namely

$$A^2 = -k_{[a;b]}k^{a;b}, \qquad \sigma^2 = k_{(a;b)}k^{a;b} - \tfrac{1}{D-2}(k^a{}_{;a})^2, \qquad \Theta = \tfrac{1}{D-2}k^a{}_{;a}. \qquad (5)$$

Then, the Kundt spacetimes are those which admit the congruence with all above optical scalars vanishing, i.e., we deal with the non-twisting, shear-free, and non-expanding geometries. Simultaneously, presence of the non-twisting vector field $\boldsymbol{k}$ implies existence of the spacetime null foliation[8] with $\boldsymbol{k}$ being normal (tangent). In such a case, it is straightforward to introduce adapted set of coordinates $\{r, u, x^p\}$ in D dimensions, where $u = $ const labels null hypersurfaces generated by $\boldsymbol{k}$, r is an affine parameter along the non-twisting null congruence, i.e., $\boldsymbol{k} = \partial_r$, and the $(D-2)$-dimensional transverse subspace with $u = $ const and $r = $ const is covered by spatial coordinates x^p with $p = 2, \ldots, D-1$. Using these adapted coordinates the general non-twisting line element can be written as

$$\mathrm{d}s^2 = g_{pq}(r,u,x)\,\mathrm{d}x^p\mathrm{d}x^q + 2g_{up}(r,u,x)\,\mathrm{d}x^p\mathrm{d}u - 2\mathrm{d}u\mathrm{d}r + g_{uu}(r,u,x)\,\mathrm{d}u^2, \qquad (6)$$

where g_{pq} represents metric of the transverse space. Moreover, the shear-free condition implies

$$g_{pq} = \rho^2(r,u,x)\,g_{pq}(u,x) \qquad \text{with} \qquad \rho = \exp\left(\int \Theta(r,u,x)\,\mathrm{d}r\right). \qquad (7)$$

Finally, the non-expanding condition leads to the r-independent transverse space metric, i.e., $g_{pq} = g_{pq}(u,x)$. The most general Kundt line element can thus be expressed as

$$\mathrm{d}s^2 = g_{pq}(u,x)\,\mathrm{d}x^p\mathrm{d}x^q + 2g_{up}(r,u,x)\,\mathrm{d}x^p\mathrm{d}u - 2\mathrm{d}u\mathrm{d}r + g_{uu}(r,u,x)\,\mathrm{d}u^2. \qquad (8)$$

Moreover, in our contribution[4] we assume simplification corresponding to $g_{up} = 0$, i.e., our metric ansatz takes the form

$$\mathrm{d}s^2 = g_{pq}(u,x)\,\mathrm{d}x^p\mathrm{d}x^q - 2\mathrm{d}u\mathrm{d}r + g_{uu}(r,u,x)\,\mathrm{d}u^2, \qquad (9)$$

where the metric functions g_{pq} and g_{uu} have to be specified by the field equations (3).

Finally, let us briefly mention the most important members of the Kundt family of spacetimes studied within Einstein's general relativity. Definitely, the prominent role is played by spacetimes admitting a covariantly constant null vector field, which can be associated with $\boldsymbol{k}$, leading to all optical scalars vanishing. These *pp*-wave spacetimes were introduced by Brinkmann[12] in the context of conformal mapping. On the level of Kundt line element (8) this corresponds to all metric functions being r-independent. The spacetimes providing vanishing scalar curvature invariants of all orders (VSI spacetimes)[13] also belong to the Kundt class and their metric functions have to be of the form

$$g_{pq} = \delta_{pq}, \quad g_{up} = e_p(u,x) + r\, f_p(u,x), \quad g_{uu} = a(u,x)\, r^2 + b(u,x)\, r + c(u,x). \quad (10)$$

Moreover, the Kundt geometries include also various direct product spacetimes such as Bertotti–Robinson, Nariai, and Plebanski–Hacyan backgrounds, see e.g. Chap. 7 in Ref. 9, or toy models for null particles with internal spin called gyratons independently discovered by Bonnor[14] and Frolov.[15]

2. EGB field equations in the Kundt case

Let us analyze the specific constraints on the Kundt geometry (9) implied by the EGB field equations (3). These can be rewritten in alternative form

$$R_{ab} = \frac{2\Lambda_0}{D-2} g_{ab} - 2k \left(H_{ab} - \frac{g_{ab}}{D-2} H \right) \quad \text{with} \quad H = g^{ab} H_{ab}. \quad (11)$$

Calculating all the curvature tensors we find that the rr and rp components of (11) are identically satisfied and the only conditions we have to discuss are

$$R_{ru} = -\frac{2\Lambda_0}{D-2} - 2k \left(H_{ru} + \frac{1}{D-2} H \right), \quad R_{up} = -2k\, H_{up},$$

$$R_{pq} = \frac{2\Lambda_0}{D-2} g_{pq} - 2k \left(H_{pq} - \frac{g_{pq}}{D-2} H \right), \quad R_{uu} = \frac{2\Lambda_0}{D-2} g_{uu} - 2k \left(H_{uu} - \frac{g_{uu}}{D-2} H \right).$$

In particular, we obtain:

- ru-component connects the transverse space geometry described by the metric $g_{pq}(u,x)$ with the theory constants Λ_0 and k, namely

$$^S R - 2\Lambda_0 + k\left({}^S R^2_{klmn} - 4\, {}^S R^2_{mn} + {}^S R^2 \right) = 0, \quad (12)$$

where the superscript ^{S} denotes quantities calculated using the $(D-2)$-dimensional metric g_{pq}. Moreover, in the general relativity limit corresponding to $k=0$ the transverse space Ricci scalar $^S R$ has to be a constant, i.e., $^S R = 2\Lambda_0$.

- pq-component generically provides relation between the transverse space geometry and the r-dependence of the metric function g_{uu} via relation

$$Q_{pq}\, g_{uu,rr} + {}^S R_{pq}$$
$$+ 2k\big({}^S R_{pq}\, {}^S R - 2\, {}^S R_{pmqn}\, {}^S R^{mn}$$
$$+ {}^S R_{pklm}\, {}^S R_q{}^{klm} - 2\, {}^S R_{pm}\, {}^S R_q{}^m \big) = 0, \quad (13)$$

where Q_{pq} is a *fundamental quantity* important for the further discussion defined as

$$Q_{pq} \equiv -\tfrac{1}{2} g_{pq} + k\left(2\, {}^S R_{pq} - {}^S R\, g_{pq} \right). \quad (14)$$

To obtain a particular constraint we evaluate the *trace* of (13), namely

$$-Q\, g_{uu,rr} = 4\Lambda_0 - {}^S R \quad (15)$$

with
$$Q \equiv g^{pq} Q_{pq} = -\left[\tfrac{1}{2}(D-2) + k(D-4)\,{}^S R\right]. \qquad (16)$$

Obviously, the further discussion has to be split into three distinct cases, namely $Q \neq 0$, and $Q = 0$ with $Q_{pq} \neq 0$, or $Q_{pq} = 0$. In Einstein's theory we have $Q \neq 0$ and the condition (15) can be simply integrated to obtain the specific r-dependence of g_{uu}.

- up-component represents constraint on the spatial dependence of the metric function g_{uu} combined with the admitted u-dependence of the transverse space metric g_{pq},

$$Q_{pn}\, g^{nm} \left(g_{uu,rm} - 2g^{kl} g_{k[m,u||l]}\right)$$
$$+ 2k\big(-2\,{}^S R^{kl}\,\delta_p^m + {}^S R_p{}^{kml}\big) g_{k[m,u||l]} = 0, \qquad (17)$$

where the symbol $_{||}$ denotes covariant derivative on the transverse space.

- uu-component restricts the possible amplitudes of Kundt gravitational waves typically encoded in the second covariant derivative $g_{uu||pq}$. The condition becomes

$$Q^{pq}\left(g_{uu||pq} + g_{pq,uu} - \tfrac{1}{2} g_{uu,r}\, g_{pq,u} - \tfrac{1}{2} g^{kl} g_{kp,u}\, g_{lq,u}\right)$$
$$+ 2k\left(g^{ko} g^{ls} - 2\, g^{kl} g^{os}\right) g^{pq}\, g_{k[p,u||l]}\, g_{o[q,u||s]} = 0. \qquad (18)$$

The above equations represent a complete set of the constraints on the Kundt spacetime geometry implied by the EGB theory which have to be satisfied. In the following subsections we will discuss three particular cases defined with respect to the values of quantities Q, and Q_{pq}, respectively.

2.1. Case $Q \neq 0$ – generic case

In this non-degenerate case the pq-equation determines r-dependence of g_{uu} to be polynomial. Subsequently, the remaining equations are decoupled with respect to power in r. In particular,

- pq-equation trace (15) can be integrated to obtain

$$g_{uu}(r,u,x) = b(u,x)\, r^2 + c(u,x)\, r + d(u,x), \qquad (19)$$

where

$$b = \frac{4\Lambda_0 - {}^S R}{(D-2) + 2k\,(D-4)\,{}^S R}. \qquad (20)$$

With g_{uu} in hand the pq-equation restrict the transverse space geometry,

$$\left[(D-2) + 4k(D-4)\big(1 + k\,{}^S R\big)\,{}^S R + 16k\Lambda_0\right] {}^S R_{pq}$$
$$- \left(1 + 2k\,{}^S R\right)\left(4\Lambda_0 - {}^S R\right) g_{pq}$$
$$- 2k\left[(D-2) + 2k(D-4)\,{}^S R\right]\left(2\,{}^S R_{pmqn}\,{}^S R^{mn} - {}^S R_{pklm}\,{}^S R_q{}^{klm}\right.$$
$$\left. + 2\,{}^S R_{pm}\,{}^S R_q{}^m\right) = 0. \qquad (21)$$

In general relativity ($k = 0$) this condition implies that the transverse space has to be the Einstein space, i.e.,

$$^S R_{pq} = \frac{2\Lambda_0}{D-2} g_{pq}. \tag{22}$$

- up-component has a non-trivial part which determines the spatial dependence of $c(u, x)$ in (19) and couples it to the u-dependence of the spatial metric g_{km},

$$Q_{pn} g^{nm} \left(c_{,m} - 2 g^{kl} g_{k[m,u||l]} \right) \\ + 2k \left(-2\, ^S R^{kl} \delta_p^m + {}^S R_p{}^{kml} \right) g_{k[m,u||l]} = 0. \tag{23}$$

Basically, in general relativity this equation plays very similar role.

- uu-component gives two independent conditions implied by its parts linear in r, and r-independent, respectively,

$$Q^{pq} \left(c_{||pq} - b\, g_{pq,u} \right) = 0, \tag{24}$$
$$Q^{pq} \left(d_{||pq} - \tfrac{1}{2} c\, g_{pq,u} + g_{pq,uu} - \tfrac{1}{2} g^{kl} g_{kp,u}\, g_{lq,u} \right) \\ + 2k \left(g^{mo} g^{ns} - 2\, g^{mn} g^{os} \right) g^{pq} g_{m[p,u||n]}\, g_{o[q,u||s]} = 0. \tag{25}$$

These constraints can be understood as restrictions on the spatial dependence of g_{uu}. In particular, it gives a possible amplitudes $d_{||pq}$ of the Kundt gravitational waves.

2.2. Case $Q = 0$ with $Q_{pq} \neq 0$

In principal, there may occur a peculiar situation in which $Q_{pq} \neq 0$ and simultaneously $Q = 0$. In such a case the condition $Q = 0$ implies a strict constraint on the transverse-space scalar curvature, namely

$$^S R = -\frac{D-2}{2k(D-4)}, \tag{26}$$

which is a non-vanishing and constant. This case is clearly *not allowed* in the Einstein theory. Moreover, the trace of pq-equation gives

$$^S R = 4\Lambda_0. \tag{27}$$

These two conditions combined together represent an interesting coupling of all theory parameters in the form

$$8(D-4) k \Lambda_0 = -(D-2). \tag{28}$$

We can thus conclude that for any Gauss–Bonnet parameter $\gamma = k/\kappa$ there is a unique value of Λ_0. Simultaneously, parameters k and Λ_0 must have opposite signs and none of them can be vanishing. Finally, since $Q_{pq} \neq 0$, the pq-equation has to be satisfied for every pair p and q which again implies at most quadratic r-dependence of g_{uu} and thus all remaining equations are similar to those of the previous case.

2.3. Case $Q_{pq} = 0$ implying $Q = 0$

As in the previous case $Q = 0$ implies relation between the theory constants,

$$8(D-4)k\Lambda_0 = -(D-2) \quad \text{and} \quad {}^SR = 4\Lambda_0. \tag{29}$$

However, the condition $Q_{pq} = 0$ strongly constraints the transverse-space geometry,

$${}^SR_{pq} = \frac{1}{4k} g_{pq} + \frac{1}{2} {}^SR\, g_{pq}, \quad \text{i.e.} \quad {}^SR_{pq} = \frac{4\Lambda_0}{D-2} g_{pq} \equiv -\frac{1}{2k(D-4)} g_{pq}. \tag{30}$$

In this degenerate case the $(D-2)$-dimensional transverse space has to be the Einstein space. Interestingly, this subclass of EGB vacuum solutions does not allowed a straightforward limit to the Einstein theory. The constraints implied by the field equations become:

- pq-equation restricts the transverse-space Riemann tensor as

$${}^SR_{pklm}\,{}^SR_q{}^{klm} = 2\bigl[2k(D-4)\bigr]^{-2} g_{pq} \equiv -\frac{1}{k(D-4)} {}^SR_{pq}, \tag{31}$$

  and the ru-equation becomes identically satisfied.
- up-equation significantly simplifies to the form

$$\left(-\tfrac{8\Lambda_0}{D-2} \delta_p^m g^{kl} + {}^SR_p{}^{kml}\right) g_{k[m,u||l]} = 0. \tag{32}$$

- uu-component constraints only the transverse metric g_{pq} and its u-dependence as

$$\bigl(g^{ko}g^{ls} - 2 g^{kl}g^{os}\bigr) g^{pq}\, g_{k[p,u||l]}\, g_{o[q,u||s]} = 0. \tag{33}$$

Interestingly, the metric component $g_{uu}(r,u,x)$ remains *arbitrary function of all spacetime variables*. Moreover, for the spatial metric g_{pq} being u-independent the equations (32) and (33) are identically satisfied.

3. Analysis of the solution

In this section we summarize two methods employed in analysis of the general solution derived above. In particular, we discuss the structure of the Weyl tensor and describe relative motion of free test particles, respectively.

3.1. Algebraic structure

The higher-dimensional algebraic classification can be formulated in terms of the boost-weight irreducible components of any tensor with respect to a suitable null frame.[7,16] Such a frame in the case of Kundt geometries (9) takes the form

$$\boldsymbol{k} = \partial_r, \qquad \boldsymbol{l} = \tfrac{1}{2} g_{uu}\partial_r + \partial_u, \qquad \boldsymbol{m}_i = m_i^p\, \partial_p. \tag{34}$$

The Weyl tensor components sorted by their boost weights with respect to the generic null frame $\{\bm{k}, \bm{l}, \bm{m}_i\}$ are

$$\begin{aligned}
\Psi_{0ij} &= C_{abcd}\, k^a\, m_i^b\, k^c\, m_j^d\,, \\
\Psi_{1ijk} &= C_{abcd}\, k^a\, m_i^b\, m_j^c\, m_k^d\,, & \Psi_{1T^i} &= C_{abcd}\, k^a\, l^b\, k^c\, m_i^d\,, \\
\Psi_{2ijkl} &= C_{abcd}\, m_i^a\, m_j^b\, m_k^c\, m_l^d\,, & \Psi_{2S} &= C_{abcd}\, k^a\, l^b\, l^c\, k^d\,, \\
\Psi_{2ij} &= C_{abcd}\, k^a\, l^b\, m_i^c\, m_j^d\,, & \Psi_{2T^{ij}} &= C_{abcd}\, k^a\, m_i^b\, l^c\, m_j^d\,, \\
\Psi_{3ijk} &= C_{abcd}\, l^a\, m_i^b\, m_j^c\, m_k^d\,, & \Psi_{3T^i} &= C_{abcd}\, l^a\, k^b\, l^c\, m_i^d\,, \\
\Psi_{4ij} &= C_{abcd}\, l^a\, m_i^b\, l^c\, m_j^d\,.
\end{aligned} \qquad (35)$$

Moreover, their irreducible components identifying specific algebraic subtypes are defined[16] as

$$\begin{aligned}
\tilde{\Psi}_{1ijk} &= \Psi_{1ijk} - \tfrac{2}{D-3} \delta_{i[j} \Psi_{1T^{k]}}\,, \\
\tilde{\Psi}_{2T^{(ij)}} &= \Psi_{2T^{(ij)}} - \tfrac{1}{D-2} \delta_{ij} \Psi_{2S}\,, \\
\tilde{\Psi}_{2ijkl} &= \Psi_{2ijkl} - \tfrac{2}{D-4} \left(\delta_{ik} \tilde{\Psi}_{2T^{(jl)}} + \delta_{jl} \tilde{\Psi}_{2T^{(ik)}} - \delta_{il} \tilde{\Psi}_{2T^{(jk)}} - \delta_{jk} \tilde{\Psi}_{2T^{(il)}} \right) \\
& \quad - \tfrac{4\, \delta_{i[k} \delta_{l]j}}{(D-2)(D-3)} \Psi_{2S}\,, \\
\tilde{\Psi}_{3ijk} &= \Psi_{3ijk} - \tfrac{2}{D-3} \delta_{i[j} \Psi_{3T^{k]}}\,.
\end{aligned} \qquad (36)$$

The above quantities evaluated for the Kundt geometry (9) without employing any particular theory constraints imply:

- with respect to the natural null frame (34) the $+2$ and $+1$ boost-weight components Ψ_0 and Ψ_1 vanish identically and the analyzed spacetimes are *at least* of algebraic type II with $\bm{k} = \partial_r$ being a *double* degenerate Weyl aligned null direction (WAND),
- since $\Psi_{2ij} = 0$, the geometry (9) is of the algebraic *subtype* II(d).

Moreover, the specific EGB theory restrictions derived in the previous section enter the discussion and may affect the Weyl tensor structure. We observe:

- in the generic case $Q \neq 0$ the type II(d) remains in general unchanged,
- the case $Q = 0$ with $Q_{pq} \neq 0$ specializes to II(ad) $\Leftrightarrow \Psi_{2S} = 0$, i.e.,

$$b = -\frac{{}^S\!R}{(D-2)(D-3)} = -\frac{4\Lambda_0}{(D-2)(D-3)} = \frac{1}{2k(D-3)(D-4)}\,, \qquad (37)$$

- in the class $Q_{pq} = 0$ both the highest and the lowest non-trivial boost weights Ψ_2 and Ψ_4 contain *arbitrary* metric function g_{uu} and are thus in general non-vanishing. However, since the transverse space has to be the Einstein space we get $\tilde{\Psi}_{2T^{(ij)}} = 0$ which leads to the subtype II(bd).

Analogous discussion can be performed also for the Ricci tensor, see Ref. 4.

3.2. *Geodesic deviation*

To observe a physical nature of a given solution its useful to study relative motion of free test particles encoded in the geodesic deviation.[17] This is described the Jacobi equation

$$\frac{D^2 Z^a}{d\tau^2} = R^a{}_{bcd} u^b u^c Z^d, \qquad (38)$$

where Z^a are components of the separation vector of nearby geodesics, $R^a{}_{bcd}$ is the Riemann curvature tensor, and u^b are components of the fiducial observer 4-velocity, i.e., $\boldsymbol{u} = \dot{r}\,\partial_r + \dot{u}\,\partial_u + \dot{x}^p \partial_p$. To obtain coordinate-independent information it is natural to project (38) onto a suitable orthonormal frame $\{\boldsymbol{e}_{(0)}, \boldsymbol{e}_{(1)}, \boldsymbol{e}_{(i)}\}$ associated with some particular observer where we assume $\boldsymbol{e}_{(0)} \equiv \boldsymbol{u}$. This leads to $\ddot{Z}^{(a)} = R^{(a)}{}_{(0)(0)(b)} Z^{(b)}$ with $\ddot{Z}^{(a)} \equiv e_b^{(a)} \frac{D^2 Z^b}{d\tau^2}$ and $Z^{(b)} \equiv e_a^{(b)} Z^a$, where $a, b = 0, 1, \ldots, D-1$, which gives $\ddot{Z}^{(0)} = 0$. Moreover, using decomposition of the Riemann tensor we obtain the invariant form of the geodesic deviation equation,

$$\ddot{Z}^{(i)} = \left[C_{(i)(0)(0)(j)} + \frac{1}{D-2}\left(R_{(i)(j)} - \delta_{ij} R_{(0)(0)}\right) - \frac{R\,\delta_{ij}}{(D-1)(D-2)} \right] Z^{(j)}, \qquad (39)$$

where $i, j = 1, 2, \ldots, D-1$.

To explicitly analyze the specific effects of the EGB theory we restrict ourselves to the transversally static observers, i.e., we set $\sqrt{2}\,\dot{u} = 1$, $\dot{x}^p = 0$, which corresponds to the direct relation between observer's orthonormal frame $\{\boldsymbol{e}_{(0)}, \boldsymbol{e}_{(1)}, \boldsymbol{e}_{(i)}\}$ and the null frame (34), namely

$$\boldsymbol{k} = \tfrac{1}{\sqrt{2}}(\boldsymbol{u} + \boldsymbol{e}_{(1)}), \qquad \boldsymbol{l} = \tfrac{1}{\sqrt{2}}(\boldsymbol{u} - \boldsymbol{e}_{(1)}), \qquad \boldsymbol{m}_i = \boldsymbol{e}_{(i)}. \qquad (40)$$

The straightforward evaluation of all projections in (39) and expression of the Ricci tensor components using the EGB field equations give the decomposed form of the geodesic deviation equation,

$$\ddot{Z}^{(1)} = \frac{2(\Lambda_0 + 2kH/D)}{(D-1)(D-2)} Z^{(1)} + \Psi_{2S} Z^{(1)} - \frac{1}{\sqrt{2}} \Psi_{3T^j} Z^{(j)}$$
$$+ \frac{k}{D-2}\left(4\mathcal{H}_{ru} Z^{(1)} + \sqrt{2} m_j^p \mathcal{H}_{up} Z^{(j)}\right), \qquad (41)$$

$$\ddot{Z}^{(i)} = \frac{2(\Lambda_0 + 2kH/D)}{(D-1)(D-2)} Z^{(i)} - \Psi_{2T^{(ij)}} Z^{(j)} - \frac{1}{\sqrt{2}} \Psi_{3T^i} Z^{(1)} - \frac{1}{2} \Psi_{4^{ij}} Z^{(j)}$$
$$+ \frac{k}{D-2}\Big(-2 m_i^p m_j^q \mathcal{H}_{pq} Z^{(j)} + \sqrt{2} m_i^p \mathcal{H}_{up} Z^{(1)}$$
$$+ \left[(g_{uu} + 2)\mathcal{H}_{ru} + \mathcal{H}_{uu}\right] Z^{(i)} \Big), \qquad (42)$$

where the components of the traceless Gauss–Bonnet part $\mathcal{H}_{ab} \equiv H_{ab} - \tfrac{1}{D} H g_{ab}$ satisfy $2\mathcal{H}_{ru} = g^{pq} \mathcal{H}_{pq}$.

4. Example: Solutions with a constant-curvature transverse space

To explicitly demonstrate application of the above completely general constraints on the Kundt geometries within the EGB theory together with analysis of their properties we present a particular important case of (9) with an additional assumption that $(D-2)$-dimensional transverse space with the metric $g_{pq}(u,x)$ is of a *constant curvature*. In such a case the Riemann tensor can be written as

$$^S R_{pqmn} = \frac{^S R}{(D-3)(D-2)} \left(g_{pm} g_{qn} - g_{pn} g_{qm} \right), \tag{43}$$

and the transverse metric becomes conformally flat, namely

$$g_{pq} = \frac{\delta_{pq}}{P^2}, \quad \text{where} \quad P = 1 + \frac{^S R}{4(D-3)(D-2)} \left[(x^2)^2 + \cdots + (x^{D-1})^2 \right]. \tag{44}$$

The scalar curvature $^S R$ is then determined via the ru-equation (12) by generic theory parameters $k = \kappa\gamma$ and Λ_0,

$$^S R = \frac{(D-2)(D-3)}{2k(D-4)(D-5)} \left(\pm\sqrt{1 + 8k\Lambda_0 \frac{(D-4)(D-5)}{(D-2)(D-3)}} - 1 \right). \tag{45}$$

Immediately we can see that $D=5$ and $D=4$ are exceptional cases for which we have $^S R = 2\Lambda_0$ corresponding to the pure Einstein theory. Moreover, there are *two* branches of generic solutions in the EGB gravity where the "$+$" case has a GR limit while the "$-$" case is peculiar.

For generic values of the theory parameters we have $Q_{pq} \neq 0$ and the resulting line element becomes

$$ds^2 = \left[1 + \frac{^S R\, \delta_{mn} x^m x^n}{4(D-2)(D-3)} \right]^{-2} \delta_{pq}\, dx^p\, dx^q - 2\, du\, dr$$
$$+ \left[\frac{4\Lambda_0 - {}^S R}{(D-2) + 2k(D-4)\, ^S R}\, r^2 + c(u)\, r + d(u,x) \right] du^2, \tag{46}$$

where the scalar curvature $^S R$ is given by (45), $c(u)$ is arbitrary function, and $d(u,x)$ has to satisfy the Laplace equation,

$$g^{pq} d_{||pq} = 0. \tag{47}$$

The Weyl tensor algebraic type of such solution is II(bcd). However, for the flat transverse space, i.e., with $^S R = 0$, $g_{pq} = \delta_{pq}$, we have $\Lambda_0 = 0$ and all the Gauss–Bonnet corrections vanish which means that we effectively deal with the Einstein theory (subclass of VSI spacetimes of the Weyl-type N). These spacetimes can be interpreted as exact type II gravitational waves propagating on the type D(bcd) background corresponding to the direct-product (anti-)Nariai universe.

This interpretation is simply supported by analysis of relative accelerations in terms of the geodesic deviation. For the transversally static observer associated with the privileged null congruence we get a simple result,

$$\ddot{Z}^{(1)} = \frac{4\Lambda_0 - {}^S R}{(D-2) + 2k(D-4)\,{}^S R} Z^{(1)}, \qquad \ddot{Z}^{(i)} = -\frac{1}{2}\Psi_{4ij} Z^{(j)}, \qquad (48)$$

where the longitudinal spatial acceleration in the direction $e_{(1)}$ is determined by the direct-product background corresponding to the non-trivial coefficient of r^2 term in g_{uu}, The transverse accelerations in $D-2$ directions $e_{(i)}$ are given by $\Psi_{4ij} = -\frac{1}{2} m_i^p m_j^q d_{\|pq}$ and cause symmetric and traceless deformations representing the exact Kundt–EGB gravitational waves.

Finally, as a special case of the above solution we can set ${}^S R = 4\Lambda_0$ which makes the resulting metric r-independent and we are thus dealing with the pp-wave solution. Subsequently, the parameter Λ_0 can be vanishing, which leads to the classic solution analogous to the general relativity one, or it has to become

$$\Lambda_0 = -\frac{(D-2)(D-3)}{8k(D-4)(D-5)}. \qquad (49)$$

This *new* non-trivial class is only allowed in the EGB theory with $D > 5$ and its metric takes the form

$$ds^2 = \left(1 - \frac{\delta_{mn} x^m x^n}{8k(D-4)(D-5)}\right)^{-2} \delta_{pq}\,dx^p\,dx^q - 2\,du\,dr + d(u,x)\,du^2, \qquad (50)$$

where the Laplace equation (47) for the metric function $d(u,x)$ reflects the non-trivial transverse-space geometry corresponding to the Weyl-type II(bcd) solutions.

5. Conclusions

In this contribution we have summarized the main results of Ref. 4. In particular, we have described explicit class of the Kundt solutions to the Einstein–Gauss–Bonnet gravity. As the first step, the explicit form of the EGB field equations has been derived and geometrically distinct subclasses identified. We have also indicated differences in comparison with the classic solutions to the Einstein's general relativity. As a suitable tool characterizing the solutions we have briefly discussed the algebraic structure of the Weyl tensor and geodesic deviation. Finally, we have presented a particular example of the Kundt solutions with the constant-curvature transverse space including the EGB pp-waves.

Acknowledgments

This work was supported by the Czech Science Foundation Grant No. GAČR 20-05421S.

References

1. D. Lovelock, The Einstein tensor and its generalizations, *J. Math. Phys.* **12**, 498 (1971).
2. D. J. Gross and J. H. Sloan, The quartic effective action for the heterotic string, *Nucl. Phys. B* **291**, 41 (1987).
3. M. C. Bento and O. Bertolami, Maximally symmetric cosmological solutions of higher-curvature string effective theories with dilatons, *Phys. Lett. B* **368**, 198 (1996).
4. R. Švarc, J. Podolský, and O. Hruška, Kundt spacetimes in the Einstein-Gauss-Bonnet theory, *Phys. Rev. D* **102**, 084012 (2020).
5. W. Kundt, The plane-fronted gravitational waves, *Z. Physik* **163**, 77 (1961).
6. W. Kundt, Exact solutions of the field equations: Twist-free pure radiation fields, *Proc. Roy. Soc. A* **270**, 328 (1962).
7. J. Podolský and R. Švarc, Explicit algebraic classification of Kundt geometries in any dimension, *Class. Quantum Grav.* **30**, 125007 (2013).
8. H. Stephani, D. Kramer, M. MacCallum, C. Hoenselaers, and E. Herlt, *Exact Solutions of Einstein's Field Equations* (Cambridge University Press, Cambridge, 2003).
9. J. B. Griffiths and J. Podolský, *Exact Space-Times in Einstein's General Relativity* (Cambridge University Press, Cambridge, 2009).
10. J. Podolský and M. Žofka, General Kundt spacetimes in higher dimensions, *Class. Quantum Grav.* **26**, 105008 (2009).
11. A. Coley, S. Hervik, G. Papadopoulos, and N. Pelavas, Kundt spacetimes, *Class. Quantum Grav.* **26**, 105016 (2009).
12. H. W. Brinkmann, Einstein spaces which are mapped conformally on each other, *Math. Annal.* **94**, 119 (1925).
13. A. Coley, R. Milson, V. Pravda, and A. Pravdová, Vanishing scalar invariant spacetimes in higher dimensions, *Class. Quantum Grav.* **21**, 5519 (2004).
14. W. B. Bonnor, Spinning null fluid in general relativity, *Int. J. Theor. Phys.* **3**, 257 (1970).
15. V. P. Frolov and D. V. Fursaev, Gravitational field of a spinning radiation beam pulse in higher dimensions, *Phys. Rev. D* **71**, 104034 (2005).
16. M. Ortaggio, V. Pravda, and A. Pravdová, Algebraic classification of higher dimensional spacetimes based on null alignment, *Class. Quantum Grav.* **30**, 013001 (2013).
17. J. Podolský and R. Švarc, Interpreting spacetimes of any dimension using geodesic deviation, *Phys. Rev. D* **85**, 044057 (2012).

Exact decoupled solutions in curvature-matter coupled gravity

M. Sharif* and Fizza Furqan

Department of Mathematics, University of the Punjab,
Quaid-e-Azam Campus, Lahore-54590, Pakistan
*E-mail: msharif.math@pu.edu.pk
www.pu.edu.pk

This paper explores the extended gravitational decoupling procedure for a static sphere in the context of $f(\mathbb{R}, T)$ theory where $\mathbb{R}$ denotes the scalar curvature and T represents the trace of the energy-momentum tensor. This method extends the domain of a seed solution by including a new gravitational source. Deformations in radial and temporal metric potentials split the set of field equations into two subsystems associated with isotropic and additional matter sources. We utilize the Korkina-Orlyanskii spacetime as a solution for the system describing the seed source and use some physical constraints to extend it to anisotropic domain. A linear gravity model, $f(\mathbb{R}, T) = \mathbb{R} + 2\chi T$ (where χ couples geometry to matter) is employed to interpret the influence of the decoupling parameter on the developed solutions. It is found that physically acceptable solutions can be formulated in the background of $f(\mathbb{R}, T)$ gravity through the decoupling approach.

Keywords: $f(\mathbb{R}, T)$ gravity; Extended gravitational decoupling; Anisotropy.

1. Introduction

Numerous fascinating astronomical discoveries have opened the gateway to the mysteries of cosmic origin and evolution. In this regard, one of the significant developments is Hubble's discovery of an expanding universe.[1] Observations based upon redshifts of Type Ia supernovae provide evidence that the rate of this expansion is accelerating.[2] An unknown energy field (known as dark energy) possessing large negative pressure is assumed to be the source of this acceleration.[3] Einstein's general theory of relativity has successfully been employed to describe different astrophysical phenomena. However, this theory supports a universe experiencing a receding rate of expansion owing to gravitational attraction. Consequently, the cosmological constant was added in the field equations of general relativity (GR) to construct the ΛCDM model which has been used to justify the current cosmic behavior.[4] Nevertheless, this model is unable to solve the problems of fine-tuning[5] and cosmic coincidence.[6] The fine-tuning problem is concerned with the large discrepancy between the observed and predicted values of the cosmological constant whereas the cosmic coincidence problem questions the equal densities of dark matter (non-baryonic matter with strong gravitational field) and dark energy detected in the current era.

Modifications of GR are proposed to find a suitable explanation of these cosmic issues. The simplest modification replaced the Ricci scalar in the Einstein-Hilbert action by its generic function and was put forward by Buchdal[7] as the $f(\mathbb{R})$ theory. Harko et al.[8] introduced $f(\mathbb{R}, T)$ gravity by generalizing the $f(\mathbb{R})$ theory. The $f(\mathbb{R}, T)$ theory incorporates a non-zero covariant derivative of the trace of the energy-momentum tensor. This causes test particles to execute non-geodesic motion and produces acceleration. Various models of $f(\mathbb{R}, T)$ gravity have been developed to explore different cosmological events. The most widely used model is $f(\mathbb{R}, T) = f_1(\mathbb{R}) + f_2(T)$ where $f_2(T)$ is often set equal to $2\chi T$.[8] Houndjo[9] inspected the matter-dominated phase and late-time acceleration of the universe for this minimally coupled $f(\mathbb{R}, T)$ model. This theory also aids in understanding of gravitational effects at the quantum level.[10] Das et al.[11] used different equations of state to examine the properties of gravastar in the context of $f(\mathbb{R}, T)$ theory. Effects of the trace on the state variables of a white dwarf were discussed by Carvalho et al.[12] Moreover, the viability of relativistic interiors has been analyzed in this theory.[13]

Solutions of the Einstein field equations represent feasible stellar interiors. Therefore, they help in investigating the essential properties of compact objects. Models portraying physically acceptable astrophysical structures with extremely dense matter have been suggested to exhibit anisotropy. Ruderman[14] studied the existence of anisotropy in high density pure neutron matter. Canuto[15] reviewed the effects of deviations from local isotropy on various stellar characteristics. Impact of anisotropy generated during the phase transition from normal to pion-condensed matter was analyzed by Lovas et al.[16] Gleiser and Dev[17] revealed a stability range for anisotropic stars that was wider in contrast to their isotropic counterparts. Paul and Deb[18] constructed a class of viable relativistic models composed of anisotropic fluid in hydrostatic equilibrium.

However, extraction of analytic anisotropic solutions of the non-linear field equations is often difficult. Therefore, new methods to formulate viable solutions have been developed. In this respect, the decoupling approach allows us to extend known solutions of the field equations to more complex domains. This minimizes the requirement of additional constraints and simplifies the system of equations. Ovalle[19] introduced decoupling through the minimal geometric deformation (MGD) approach by addition of new matter sources. The MGD technique splits the original system of equations into two sets by deforming the radial metric coefficient. Both sets are solved individually and the complete solution is obtained by the principle of superposition.

The MGD technique has been employed extensively for the derivation of anisotropic extensions of well-known solutions. Ovalle et al.[20] utilized this technique to devise stellar models from the isotropic Tolman IV metric. Sharif and Sadiq[21] found well-behaved solutions for spherically symmetric matter configurations. Singh et al.[22] considered the MGD approach in relation to the embedding class-one condition. Furthermore, Sharif and collaborators[23] adopted this procedure to obtain realistic solutions in modified theories of gravity. The use of MGD decoupling has yielded several solutions of the $f(\mathbb{R}, T)$ field equations. Maurya and Tello-Ortiz[24] computed charged anisotropic extensions of the isotropic Durgapal-Fuloria model. Recently, Maurya et al.[25] utilized a linear $f(\mathbb{R}, T)$ model to develop a compact structure through the Korkina-Orlyanskii line element and ascertained its viability as well as stability through energy conditions and speed of sound criteria, respectively.

Despite the effectiveness of the MGD method, the scheme deforms only one metric function leading to a purely gravitational interaction between matter sources. Thus, Ovalle[26] proposed a technique incorporating transformations of both radial and temporal metric components known as the extended geometric deformation (EGD) approach. The continuity equation obtained through this procedure holds regardless of the absence or presence of matter sources. Contreras and Bargueño[27] developed a charged BTZ solution by implementing this technique in (1+2)-dimensional spacetime. Maurya et al.[28] extended an embedding class-one solution through the EGD approach. Sharif and Ama-Tul-Mughani[29] constructed viable solutions from the isotropic Krori-Barua metric under the influence of the electromagnetic field. Moreover, the EGD technique has also been employed with modified theories to produce feasible stellar interiors.[30]

In this work, we provide two anisotropic extensions of the Korkina-Orlyanskii spacetime using the EGD approach in connection to $f(\mathbb{R}, T)$ gravity. The salient features of the generated models are analyzed through energy conditions and stability criteria. This paper has been arranged as follows. In section **2**, we apply the EGD technique to decouple the field equations of $f(\mathbb{R}, T)$ theory. An anisotropic solution corresponding to certain constraints on the extra source is evaluated in section **3**. Physical relevance of the solution is also discussed in the same section. The last section summarizes the main results.

2. Basic Formalism in $f(\mathbb{R}, T)$ Theory

The action for $f(\mathbb{R}, T)$ theory incorporating the Lagrangian density (L_ϑ) of an additional source (ϑ) turns out to be[8]

$$S = \int \sqrt{-g} \left(\frac{f(\mathbb{R}, T)}{16\pi} + L_m + \alpha L_\vartheta \right) d^4 x, \tag{1}$$

where L_m, g and α indicate the matter Lagrangian, determinant of the metric tensor and dimensionless decoupling parameter, respectively. The energy-momentum tensors of the seed and additional sources are written as

$$T_{\omega\beta} = -\frac{2}{\sqrt{-g}} \frac{\delta(\sqrt{-g} L_m)}{\delta g^{\omega\beta}} = g_{\omega\beta} L_m - 2 \frac{\partial L_m}{\partial g^{\omega\beta}}, \tag{2}$$

$$\vartheta_{\omega\beta} = -\frac{2}{\sqrt{-g}} \frac{\delta(\sqrt{-g} L_\vartheta)}{\delta g^{\omega\beta}} = g_{\omega\beta} L_\vartheta - 2 \frac{\partial L_\vartheta}{\partial g^{\omega\beta}}. \tag{3}$$

while the field equations for $f(\mathbb{R},T)$ gravity are derived as

$$8\pi(T_{\omega\beta}+\alpha\vartheta_{\omega\beta})-f_T(\mathbb{R},T)(T_{\omega\beta}+\Theta_{\omega\beta})=(R_{\omega\beta}-\nabla_\omega\nabla_\beta+g_{\omega\beta}\Box)f_{\mathbb{R}}(\mathbb{R},T)$$
$$-\frac{1}{2}g_{\omega\beta}f(\mathbb{R},T). \quad (4)$$

Here ∇_ω symbolizes the covariant derivative operator while $f_{\mathbb{R}}(\mathbb{R},T)$ and $f_T(\mathbb{R},T)$ are derivatives of the generic function with respect to $\mathbb{R}$ and T, respectively. Moreover, $\Box=g^{\omega\beta}\nabla_\omega\nabla_\beta$ and $\Theta_{\omega\beta}=g_{\omega\beta}L_m-2T_{\omega\beta}-2g^{\delta\gamma}\frac{\partial^2 L_m}{\partial g^{\omega\beta}\partial g^{\delta\gamma}}$.

Covariant differentiation of Eq.(4) yields

$$\nabla^\omega T_{\omega\beta}=\frac{f_T(\mathbb{R},T)}{8\pi-f_T(\mathbb{R},T)}\left[(T_{\omega\beta}+\Theta_{\omega\beta})\nabla^\omega ln f_T(\mathbb{R},T)+\nabla^\omega\Theta_{\omega\beta}-\frac{1}{2}g_{\omega\beta}\nabla^\omega T\right.$$
$$\left.-\frac{8\pi\alpha}{f_T(\mathbb{R},T)}\nabla^\omega\vartheta_{\omega\beta}\right], \quad (5)$$

which shows the non-conserved energy-momentum tensor in $f(\mathbb{R},T)$ theory. The isotropic matter distribution is characterized by the following energy-momentum tensor

$$T_{\omega\beta}=(\rho+p)u_\omega u_\beta-pg_{\omega\beta}, \quad (6)$$

with isotropic pressure (p), matter density (ρ), four-velocity (u_ω) and $u_\omega u^\omega=1$. Since the matter Lagrangian appears explicitly in the field equations, in order to obtain the corresponding dynamics we set $L_m=-p$ corresponding to a perfect fluid.[31] This further leads to $\Theta_{\omega\beta}=-2T_{\omega\beta}-pg_{\omega\beta}$. We consider a minimally coupled $f(\mathbb{R},T)$ model of the form

$$f(\mathbb{R},T)=\mathbb{R}+2\chi T, \quad (7)$$

which provides

$$G_{\omega\beta}=8\pi(T_{\omega\beta}+\alpha\vartheta_{\omega\beta})+\chi Tg_{\omega\beta}+2\chi(T_{\omega\beta}+pg_{\omega\beta})$$
$$=8\pi\widetilde{T}_{\omega\beta}+8\pi\alpha\vartheta_{\omega\beta}=8\pi T_{\omega\beta}^{(eff)}, \quad (8)$$

where $\widetilde{T}_{\omega\beta}=T_{\omega\beta}(1+\frac{\chi}{4\pi})+\frac{\chi}{8\pi}(T+2p)g_{\omega\beta}$.

To describe the interior configuration of the stellar object, we choose a line element given by

$$ds^2=e^\nu dt^2-e^\eta dr^2-r^2(d\theta^2+\sin^2\theta d\phi^2), \quad (9)$$

where ν and η are functions of the radial coordinate. The field equations can now be rewritten as

$$\frac{1}{r^2}-e^{-\eta}\left(\frac{1}{r^2}-\frac{\eta'}{r}\right)=8\pi(\bar{\rho}+\alpha\vartheta_t^t), \quad (10)$$

$$-\frac{1}{r^2}+e^{-\eta}\left(\frac{1}{r^2}+\frac{\nu'}{r}\right)=8\pi(\bar{p}-\alpha\vartheta_r^r), \quad (11)$$

$$\frac{e^{-\eta}}{4}\left(2\nu''+\nu'^2-\eta'\nu'+2\frac{\nu'-\eta'}{r}\right)=8\pi(\bar{p}-\alpha\vartheta_\theta^\theta). \quad (12)$$

Here prime denotes derivative with respect to r while $\bar{\rho}$ and $\bar{p}$ are identified as follows

$$\bar{\rho} = \rho + \frac{\chi}{8\pi}(3\rho - p), \tag{13}$$

$$\bar{p} = p - \frac{\chi}{8\pi}(\rho - 3p). \tag{14}$$

The physical variables (total density and radial/tangential pressure) are defined as

$$\rho^{(tot)}(r) = \rho(r) + \alpha \vartheta_t^t, \tag{15}$$

$$p_r^{(tot)}(r) = p(r) - \alpha \vartheta_r^r, \tag{16}$$

$$p_t^{(tot)}(r) = p(r) - \alpha \vartheta_\theta^\theta, \tag{17}$$

whereas the anisotropy generated from involvement of an extra source is obtained as

$$\Delta = p_t^{(tot)}(r) - p_r^{(tot)}(r) = \alpha(\vartheta_r^r - \vartheta_\theta^\theta). \tag{18}$$

Seven unknowns appear in the system of equations (10)-(12). Therefore, to reduce the degrees of freedom and close the undetermined system, we adopt the EGD scheme.

2.1. *The EGD Approach*

The EGD approach disintegrates the field equations into two distinct sets through deformations in the temporal and radial metric potentials. To proceed with this technique, we consider a line element corresponding to perfect fluid

$$ds^2 = e^{\xi(r)}dt^2 - \frac{dr^2}{\mu(r)} - r^2(d\theta^2 + \sin^2\theta d\phi^2). \tag{19}$$

Taking non-zero values of the parameter α incorporates the effects of the source $\vartheta_{\omega\beta}$ in $T_{\omega\beta}$. The metric components linked to (ν, η)-frame are segregated as

$$\nu = \xi + \alpha h(r), \tag{20}$$

$$e^{-\eta(r)} = \mu + \alpha f(r), \tag{21}$$

where $h(r)$ and $f(r)$ represent temporal and radial deformation functions, respectively. Substitution of above transformations in the field equations decomposes the system into two sets. We acquire an array for the seed distribution given as

$$8\pi\bar{\rho} = -\frac{\mu'}{r} - \frac{\mu}{r^2} + \frac{1}{r^2} = 8\pi\rho + \chi(3\rho - p), \tag{22}$$

$$8\pi\bar{p} = \frac{\mu\xi'}{r} + \frac{\mu}{r^2} - \frac{1}{r^2} = 8\pi p - \chi(\rho - 3p), \tag{23}$$

$$8\pi\bar{p} = \frac{\mu}{4}(2\xi'' + (\xi')^2 + 2\frac{\xi'}{r}) + \frac{\mu'}{4}(\xi' + \frac{2}{r}) = 8\pi p - \chi(\rho - 3p). \tag{24}$$

The isotropic density and pressure are evaluated from the above equations as

$$\rho = \frac{\chi(\mu\xi'r + \mu - 1) + (8\pi + 3\chi)(-\mu'r - \mu + 1)}{r^2(8\pi + 2\chi)(8\pi + 4\chi)}, \quad (25)$$

$$p = \frac{\chi(-\mu'r - \mu + 1) + (8\pi + 3\chi)(\mu\xi'r + \mu - 1)}{r^2(8\pi + 2\chi)(8\pi + 4\chi)}. \quad (26)$$

The second system, related to the source $\vartheta_{\omega\beta}$, is obtained as

$$8\pi\vartheta_t^t = -\frac{f'}{r} - \frac{f}{r^2}, \quad (27)$$

$$8\pi\vartheta_r^r = -\frac{\mu h'}{r} - f\left(\frac{\xi'}{r} + \frac{\alpha h'}{r} + \frac{1}{r^2}\right), \quad (28)$$

$$8\pi\vartheta_\theta^\theta = -\frac{f}{4}\left(2\xi'' + 2\alpha h'' + (\xi')^2 + \alpha^2(h')^2 + 2\xi'\alpha h' + 2\frac{\xi'}{r} + 2\frac{\alpha h'}{r}\right)$$
$$- \frac{f'}{4}\left(\frac{2}{r} + \xi' + \alpha h'\right) - \mu\left(\frac{h''}{2} + \frac{\alpha(h')^2}{4} + \frac{\xi'h'}{2} + \frac{h'}{2r}\right) - \frac{\mu'h'}{4}. \quad (29)$$

The energy-momentum tensor corresponding to the line element (19) satisfies the Bianchi identity as

$$\nabla_\omega^{(\xi,\mu)}\widetilde{T}_\beta^\omega = -\frac{dp}{dr} - \frac{\xi'}{2}(\rho + p) + \frac{\chi}{2(4\pi + \chi)}\frac{d}{dr}(\rho - p) = 0, \quad (30)$$

while the divergence $\nabla_\omega \widetilde{T}_\beta^\omega$ associated with the system (22)-(24) yields

$$\nabla_\omega \widetilde{T}_\beta^\omega = \nabla_\omega^{(\xi,\mu)}\widetilde{T}_\beta^\omega + \alpha\frac{h'}{2}(\rho + p)\delta_\beta^1. \quad (31)$$

Furthermore, conservation of the additional source $\vartheta_{\omega\beta}$ is provided as

$$\nabla_\omega \vartheta_\beta^\omega = \frac{d\vartheta_r^r}{dr} - \frac{\xi'}{2}(\vartheta_t^t - \vartheta_r^r) - \frac{2}{r}(\vartheta_\theta^\theta - \vartheta_r^r) = -\frac{h'}{2}(\rho + p)\delta_\beta^1. \quad (32)$$

Consequently, the continuity equation for the effective energy-momentum tensor is constructed as follows

$$-\frac{dp}{dr} - \frac{\xi'}{2}(\rho + p) + \frac{\chi}{2(4\pi + \chi)}\frac{d}{dr}(\rho - p) + \alpha\left[\frac{d\vartheta_r^r}{dr} - \frac{\xi'}{2}(\vartheta_t^t - \vartheta_r^r) - \frac{2}{r}(\vartheta_\theta^\theta - \vartheta_r^r)\right] = 0. \quad (33)$$

An exchange of energy between the two sources ($\widetilde{T}_{\omega\beta}$ and $\vartheta_{\omega\beta}$) is evident from Eqs.(31) and (32) which allows successful implementation of the decoupling process. Meanwhile, decoupling in the case of MGD is possible only without a transfer of energy. Note that the system (22)-(24) consists of four unknowns (μ, ξ, ρ, p) whereas the system (27)-(29) comprises seven unknowns ($\mu, \xi, \rho, p, f, h, \vartheta_t^t, \vartheta_r^r, \vartheta_\theta^\theta$). The extraction of solutions can be simplified substantially by specifying a seed solution to the system of equations connected to the original energy-momentum tensor. As a result, the unknowns in the second array of equations decrease from seven to five. Hence, the EGD scheme facilitates the evaluation of anisotropic solutions by reducing the degrees of freedom.

3. Interior Anisotropic Solution

In this section, we use the Korkina-Orlyanskii solution for the system of equations (22)-(24). The metric coefficients of the Korkina-Orlyanskii spacetime have been previously utilized for the development of spherically symmetric static solutions to the Einstein-Maxwell system.[32] Moreover, this ansatz has helped examine the role of pressure anisotropy on charged stellar objects.[33] The metric components and corresponding physical variables in the framework of $f(\mathbb{R}, T)$ theory read

$$\mu(r) = \frac{1 + Ar^2}{1 + 2Ar^2}, \tag{34}$$

$$e^{\xi(r)} = C(1 + Ar^2)\left[D + \frac{\sqrt{1 + 2Ar^2}}{1 + Ar^2} - \sqrt{2}\ln\left(\sqrt{1 + 2Ar^2} + \sqrt{2 + 2Ar^2}\right)\right]^2, \tag{35}$$

$$\rho(r) = \frac{A}{8\chi^2 + 48\pi\chi + 64\pi^2}\left[\frac{\chi}{2Ar^2 + 1} + \frac{(3\chi + 8\pi)(2Ar^2 + 3)}{(2Ar^2 + 1)^2} - \frac{4\chi\left(A^2r^4 + Ar^2(\sqrt{Ar^2 + 1} + 2) + 1\right)}{(2A^2r^4 + 3Ar^2 + 1)^{3/2}(D + \psi(r))}\right], \tag{36}$$

$$p(r) = \frac{A}{8\chi^2 + 48\pi\chi + 64\pi^2}\left[\frac{\chi(2Ar^2 + 3)}{(2Ar^2 + 1)^2} + \frac{3\chi + 8\pi}{2Ar^2 + 1} - \frac{4(3\chi + 8\pi)\left(A^2r^4 + Ar^2(\sqrt{Ar^2 + 1} + 2) + 1\right)}{(2A^2r^4 + 3Ar^2 + 1)^{3/2}(D + \psi(r))}\right], \tag{37}$$

with $\psi(r) = \frac{\sqrt{1+2Ar^2}}{1+Ar^2} - \sqrt{2}\ln(\sqrt{1 + 2Ar^2} + \sqrt{2 + 2Ar^2})$. Here A, C and D are constants that are calculated by matching with the exterior Schwarzschild line element expressed as

$$ds^2 = \left(1 - \frac{2M}{r}\right)dt^2 - \frac{1}{\left(1 - \frac{2M}{r}\right)}dr^2 - r^2(d\theta^2 + \sin^2\theta d\phi^2), \tag{38}$$

where M is the total mass of the exterior geometry.

To ensure a smooth junction between the interior and exterior regions at $r = R$, the matching conditions were introduced by Darmois.[34] These conditions are given as

$$[ds^2]_{r=R} = 0, \tag{39}$$

$$[p_r^{(tot)}(r)]_{r=R} = 0. \tag{40}$$

which provide

$$A = \frac{2M}{R^2(R-4M)}, \tag{41}$$

$$C = \frac{1 - \frac{2M}{R}}{(AR^2+1)} \left[D - \sqrt{2}\ln\left(\sqrt{2AR^2+1} + \sqrt{2AR^2+2}\right) + \frac{\sqrt{2AR^2+1}}{AR^2+1} \right]^{-2}, \tag{42}$$

$$D = \frac{\sqrt{2AR^2+1}\,(D_2(R)\chi + 4\pi D_1(R)) + D_3(R)}{(AR^2+1)^{3/2}\,(4AR^2\chi + 8\pi AR^2 + 3\chi + 4\pi)}, \tag{43}$$

where

$$D_1(R) = 4 + 4A^2R^4 - \sqrt{1+AR^2} + 2AR^2(4 + \sqrt{1+AR^2}),$$
$$D_2(R) = 6 + 6A^2R^4 - 3\sqrt{1+AR^2} + 2AR^2(6 + \sqrt{1+AR^2}),$$
$$D_3(R) = (3\chi + 4\pi + 4\chi AR^2 + 8\pi AR^2)(1+AR^2)^{3/2}\sqrt{2}\ln\left[\sqrt{1+2AR^2} + \sqrt{2+2AR^2}\right].$$

We now produce a solution of Eqs.(27)-(29) corresponding to the extra source ϑ_ω. Because the number of unknowns (f, h, ϑ^t_t, ϑ^r_r, ϑ^θ_θ) is greater than the number of equations, two additional constraints need to be applied to close the system and extend the isotropic sector to anisotropic domain. The matching condition in Eq.(40) is fulfilled if

$$\vartheta^r_r(r) = p(r). \tag{44}$$

Thus, the above equation is selected as the first constraint. Accordingly, the physical entities of the anisotropic configuration are acquired through Eqs.(15)-(17) as

$$\rho^{(tot)}(r) = \rho(r) + \frac{\alpha}{8\pi}\left(-\frac{f'}{r} - \frac{f}{r^2}\right), \tag{45}$$

$$p_r^{(tot)}(r) = p(r)(1-\alpha), \tag{46}$$

$$p_t^{(tot)}(r) = p(r) - \frac{\alpha}{8\pi}\left[-\frac{f}{4}\left(2\xi'' + 2\alpha h'' + (\xi')^2 + \alpha^2(h')^2 + 2\xi'\alpha h' + 2\frac{\xi'}{r}\right.\right.$$
$$\left.\left. + 2\frac{\alpha h'}{r}\right) - \frac{f'}{4}\left(\frac{2}{r} + \xi' + \alpha h'\right) - \mu\left(\frac{h''}{2} + \frac{\alpha(h')^2}{4} + \frac{\xi'h'}{2} + \frac{h'}{2r}\right)\right.$$
$$\left. - \frac{\mu'h'}{4}\right]. \tag{47}$$

In the subsequent discussion, the respective anisotropic extension is generated by means of a second constraint.

3.1. Solution

Along with the mimic constraint stated in Eq.(44), we impose a condition on the anisotropy of the system developed through the conservation equation by Bowers and Liang.[35] The Bowers-Liang constraint takes the following precise form

$$\vartheta_\theta^\theta - \vartheta_r^r = jr\frac{\xi'}{2}(\vartheta_t^t + \vartheta_r^r). \tag{48}$$

Here j is an arbitrary constant for which we have defined a value of 2. This constraint has been used extensively with gravitational decoupling in search of feasible star models.[36,37] The geometric deformations $f(r)$ and $h(r)$ are obtained from Eqs.(44) and (48), respectively as

$$f(r) = \frac{1}{(\chi + 2\pi)(\chi + 4\pi)(\alpha rh(r) + r\xi'(r) + 1)}\left(-r\chi^2 h(r)\mu(r)\right.$$
$$+ \pi r\chi\mu'(r) - 6\pi r\chi h(r)\mu(r) - 8\pi^2 rh(r)\mu(r) - 3\pi r\chi\mu(r)\xi'(r)$$
$$\left. - 8\pi^2 r\mu(r)\xi'(r) - 2\pi\chi\mu(r) - 8\pi^2\mu(r) + 2\pi\chi + 8\pi^2\right), \tag{49}$$

$$\frac{1}{r}\left(r\left(h(r)\left(r\left(\alpha f'(r) + \mu'(r)\right) - 2\mu(r)\left((j-1)r\xi'(r) + 1\right)\right) + f'(r)\left((r\right.\right.\right.$$
$$- 2jr)\xi'(r) + 2) + 2r\mu(r)h'(r) + \alpha rh(r)^2\mu(r)\right) + f(r)\left(2\alpha r^2 h'(r)\right.$$
$$- 2\alpha rh(r)\left((j-1)r\xi'(r) + 1\right) + \alpha^2 r^2 h(r)^2 - 2jr^2\xi'(r)^2 - 4jr\xi'(r)$$
$$\left.\left. + 2r^2\xi''(r) + r^2\xi'(r)^2 - 2r\xi'(r) - 4\right)\right) = 0. \tag{50}$$

A numerical solution of the deformation function $h(r)$ is revealed by applying the initial condition $h(0) = 0$ to Eq.(50).

The deformed temporal and radial metric components are derived as

$$\nu(r) = \ln\left(C(1+Ar^2)\left[\frac{\sqrt{1+2Ar^2}}{1+Ar^2} - \sqrt{2}\ln\left(\sqrt{1+2Ar^2}\right.\right.\right.$$
$$\left.\left.\left. + \sqrt{2+2Ar^2}\right) + D\right]^2\right) + \alpha h(r), \tag{51}$$

$$e^{-\eta} = \frac{1+Ar^2}{1+2Ar^2} + \alpha\left[\frac{1}{(\chi + 2\pi)(\chi + 4\pi)(\alpha rh(r) + r\xi'(r) + 1)}(\pi r\chi\mu'(r)\right.$$
$$- r\chi^2 h(r)\mu(r) - 6\pi r\chi h(r)\mu(r) - 8\pi^2 rh(r)\mu(r) - 3\pi r\chi\mu(r)\xi'(r)$$
$$\left. - 8\pi^2 r\mu(r)\xi'(r) - 2\pi\chi\mu(r) - 8\pi^2\mu(r) + 2\pi\chi + 8\pi^2)\right], \tag{52}$$

while the matter variables are formulated through Eqs.(45)-(47). After the inclusion of anisotropy in the solution, matching of interior and exterior line elements yields the following expressions

$$\ln\left(1 - \frac{2M}{R}\right) = \ln\left(C(1 + AR^2)\left[\frac{\sqrt{1 + 2AR^2}}{1 + AR^2} - \sqrt{2}\ln\left(\sqrt{1 + 2AR^2}\right.\right.\right.$$
$$\left.\left.\left. + \sqrt{2 + 2AR^2}\right) + D\right]^2\right) + \alpha h(R), \qquad (53)$$

$$1 - \frac{2M}{R} = \frac{1 + AR^2}{1 + 2AR^2} + \alpha \left[\frac{1}{(\chi + 2\pi)(\chi + 4\pi)\left(\alpha Rh(R) + R\xi'(R) + 1\right)}\right.$$
$$\times \left(\pi R\chi\mu'(R) - R\chi^2 h(R)\mu(R) - 6\pi R\chi h(R)\mu(R) - 8\pi^2 \mu(R)\right.$$
$$- 8\pi^2 Rh(R)\mu(R) - 3\pi R\chi\mu(R)\xi'(R) - 8\pi^2 R\mu(R)\xi'(R)$$
$$\left. - 2\pi\chi\mu(R) + 2\pi\chi + 8\pi^2\right)\right]. \qquad (54)$$

which cannot determine the constants A and C. Hence, they are considered as free parameters and acquired from Eqs.(41) and (42). On the other hand, the condition $[p_r^{(tot)}(r)]_{r=R} = 0$ provides the constant D as computed in Eq.(43).

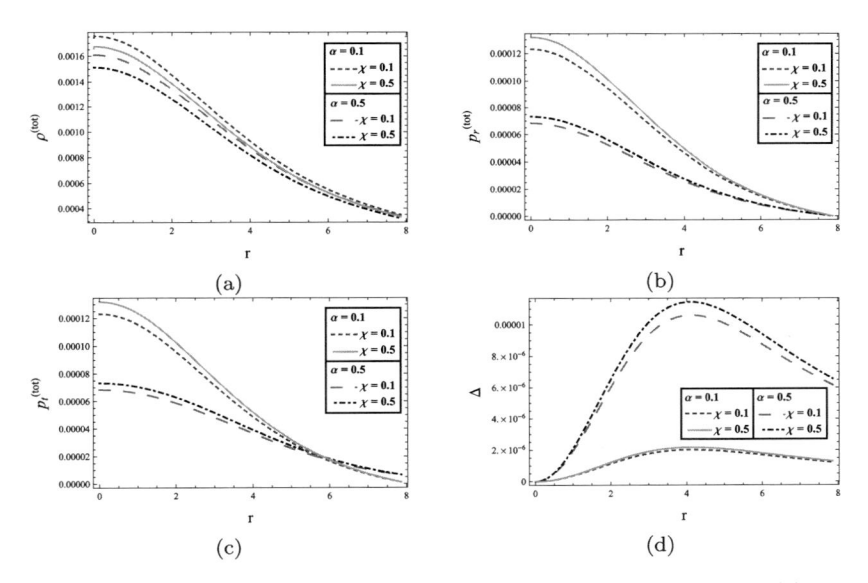

Fig. 1. Behavior of (a) density, (b) radial pressure, (c) tangential pressure and (d) anisotropy factor relative to radial coordinate.

The physical entities of the constructed setup are analyzed graphically for the star 4U 1538-52 with a mass of 1.28325km and a radius 7.866km.[38] The density and pressure components must be positive and decreasing from a maximum at the core. Figure 1 exhibits variations of these physical attributes relative to the radial coordinate. It is evident that the total energy density as well as both pressure components decrease continually from the center towards the surface. Moreover, the radial pressure vanishes at $r = R$ while the anisotropy displays a null value at

Table 1. State determinants of the stellar model corresponding to 4U 1538-52 ($M = 1.28325$ km and $R = 7.866$ km).

α	χ	$\rho_{\mathcal{C}}^{(tot)}$ (gm/cm^3)	$\rho_{\mathcal{S}}^{(tot)}$ (gm/cm^3)	$p_{\mathcal{C}}^{(tot)}$ $(dyne/cm^2)$	A	C	D
0.1	0.1	2.3466×10^{15}	4.6142×10^{14}	1.4790×10^{35}	0.0152	0.0179	5.3580
0.1	0.5	2.2355×10^{15}	4.3801×10^{14}	1.5824×10^{35}	0.0152	0.0189	5.2508
0.5	0.1	2.1526×10^{15}	4.5165×10^{14}	8.2173×10^{34}	0.0152	0.0179	5.3580
0.5	0.5	2.0268×10^{15}	4.2771×10^{14}	8.8221×10^{34}	0.0152	0.0189	5.2508

$r = 0$. The positive anisotropy factor suggests the presence of an outward-directed force. Higher values of χ cause the radial/tangential pressure and anisotropy to increase. Furthermore, the energy density declines as α and χ increase. Table 1 shows values of A, C and D along with the state determinants for different values of α and χ. The subscripts $\mathcal{C}$ and $\mathcal{S}$ denote that the quantity has been evaluated at the center and surface of the star, respectively.

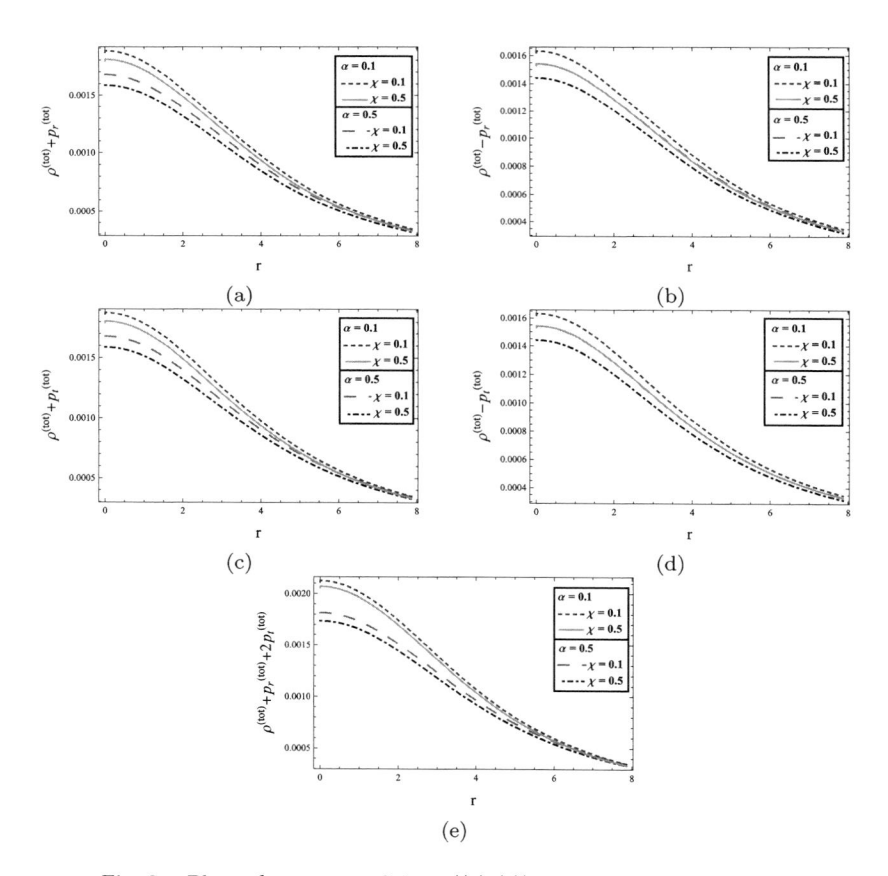

Fig. 2. Plots of energy conditions ((a)-(e)) against radial coordinate.

To verify the viability of the constructed solution, we place some bounds on the physical parameters called the energy conditions. These conditions, classified as null (NEC), weak (WEC), strong (SEC) and dominant (DEC), are presented as

NEC: $\rho^{(tot)} + p_r^{(tot)} \geq 0$, $\quad \rho^{(tot)} + p_t^{(tot)} \geq 0$,

WEC: $\rho^{(tot)} \geq 0$, $\quad \rho^{(tot)} + p_r^{(tot)} \geq 0$, $\quad \rho^{(tot)} + p_t^{(tot)} \geq 0$,

SEC: $\rho^{(tot)} + p_r^{(tot)} \geq 0$, $\quad \rho^{(tot)} + p_t^{(tot)} \geq 0$, $\quad \rho^{(tot)} + p_r^{(tot)} + 2p_t^{(tot)} \geq 0$,

DEC: $\rho^{(tot)} - p_r^{(tot)} \geq 0$, $\quad \rho^{(tot)} - p_t^{(tot)} \geq 0$.

Figure 2 demonstrates positive behavior of above inequalities. Therefore, the solution is viable for the considered values of α and χ.

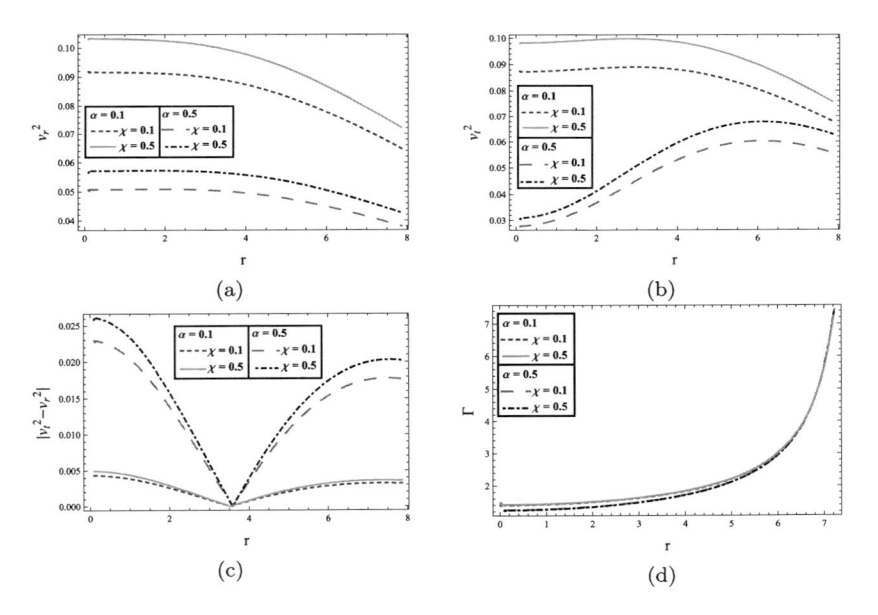

Fig. 3. Graphical representation of (a) v_r^2, (b) v_t^2, (c) $|v_t^2 - v_r^2|$ and (d) Γ.

Another important feature of anisotropic stellar models is stability to fluctuations in the physical variables. The causality constraint is one of the stability criteria which limits the radial ($v_r^2 = \frac{dp_r^{(tot)}}{d\rho^{(tot)}}$) and tangential ($v_t^2 = \frac{dp_t^{(tot)}}{d\rho^{(tot)}}$) sound speeds inside the static configuration as follows

$$0 \leq v_r^2 \leq c, \quad 0 \leq v_t^2 \leq c,$$

where $c = 1$ is the speed of light. Herrera[39] devised another approach to examine stability known as cracking. Cracking is caused by a sudden change in the direction of the radial force within a stellar configuration as a result of perturbations in density and anisotropy. Later, Abreu et al.[40] defined the potentially stable and unstable regions within a compact object through differences of sound speeds given as

$$-1 \leq v_t^2 - v_r^2 \leq 0 \Rightarrow \text{Potentially stable},$$
$$0 < v_t^2 - v_r^2 \leq 1 \Rightarrow \text{Potentially unstable}.$$

The above inequalities can be combined in to a single relation of the form $0 \leq |v_t^2 - v_r^2| \leq 1$.

In addition to the above constraints, an alternative tool to establish the stability of compact spheres is the adiabatic index which measures the resistance offered by a stellar configuration to perturbations in density. It is obtained as

$$\Gamma = \frac{p_r^{(tot)} + \rho^{(tot)}}{p_r^{(tot)}} v_r^2.$$

An adiabatic index greater than $4/3$ is proposed to indicate stable relativistic structures.[41] Figure 3 displays graphs of radial and temporal sound speeds as well as the adiabatic index for the developed solution. The sound speeds lie between 0 and 1 whereas the adiabatic index remains greater than $4/3$. Hence, we deduce that the resulting stellar model is stable.

4. Conclusions

In this paper, we have derived an anisotropic solution depicting the interior of a self-gravitating system in connection to $f(\mathbb{R}, T)$ gravity. The set of field equations (10)-(12) has been decoupled into two sets through the EGD scheme. These arrays separately describe the seed and anisotropic distributions. The Bianchi identity has been employed to examine energy transfer between the matter sources. We have considered the Korkina-Orlyanskii metric as a solution to the array corresponding to the isotropic configuration. Matching conditions on the hypersurface have been used to calculate the constants appearing in the solution. In order to extend the seed solution to anisotropic domain, we require two additional constraints. Thus, we have implemented the mimic constraint on ϑ_r^r along with the Bowers-Liang constraint. Physical relevance of the acquired solution has been investigated by employing the mass and radius of the star 4U 1538-53. For this purpose, we have performed graphical examination of the state determinants corresponding to $\alpha = 0.1, 0.5$ with $\chi = 0.1, 0.5$.

Plots for effective energy density, radial and tangential pressures have been found to monotonically decrease from the core. The anisotropy increases steadily from the center where $\Delta = 0$. The solution is viable and stable since all required quantities are in agreement with the energy bounds and speed of sound criteria. Furthermore, smaller values of the parameters α and χ give rise to denser, more compact and stable stellar models. Maurya et al.[25] evaluated an anisotropic, stable interior solution corresponding to a mimic constraint on pressure through the MGD technique. When compared to the solution obtained via the MGD approach, the EGD scheme has yielded a denser star model with higher anisotropy. Hence, we conclude that the construction of anisotropic and ultra-dense stellar interiors is attainable using the EGD approach in the framework of $f(\mathbb{R}, T)$ theory.

References

1. E. Hubble, A relation between distance and radial velocity among extra-galactic nebulae, *Proc. Nat. Acad. Sci.* **15**, 168 (1929).
2. A. G. Riess et al., Observational evidence from supernovae for an accelerating universe and a cosmological constant, *Astrophys. J.* **116**, 1009 (1998).
3. E. J. Copeland, M. Sami and S. Tsujikawa, Dynamics of dark energy, *Int. J. Mod. Phys. D* **15**, 1753 (2006).
4. D. Parkinson et al., The WiggleZ dark energy survey: Final data release and cosmological results, *Phys. Rev. D* **86**, 103518 (2012).
5. J. Martin, Everything you always wanted to know about the cosmological constant problem, *Comptes Rendus Physique* **13**, 566 (2012).
6. N. Sivanandam, Is the cosmological coincidence a problem?, *Phys. Rev. D* **87**, 083514 (2013).
7. H. A. Buchdahl, Non-linear Lagrangians and cosmological theory, *Mon. Not. R. Astron. Soc.* **150**, 1 (1970).
8. T. Harko et al., $f(\mathbb{R}, T)$ gravity, *Phys. Rev. D* **84**, 024020 (2011).
9. M. J. S. Houndjo, Reconstruction of $f(\mathbb{R}, T)$ gravity describing matter dominated and accelerated phases, *Int. J. Mod. Phys. D* **21**, 1250003 (2012).
10. M. X. Xu, T. Harko and S. D. Liang, Quantum Cosmology of $f(\mathbb{R}, T)$ gravity, *Eur. Phys. J. C* **76**, 449 (2016).
11. A. Das et al., Gravastars in $f(\mathbb{R}, T)$ gravity, *Phys. Rev. D* **95**, 124011 (2017).
12. G. A. Carvalho et al., Stellar equilibrium configurations of white dwarfs in the $f(\mathbb{R}, T)$ gravity, *Eur. Phys. J. C* **77**, 871 (2017).
13. D. Deb et al., Anisotropic strange stars under simplest minimal matter-geometry coupling in the $f(\mathbb{R}, T)$ gravity, *Phys. Rev. D* **97**, 084026 (2018); S. Hansraj and A. Banerjee, Dynamical behavior of the Tolman metrics in $f(\mathbb{R}, T)$ gravity, *Phys. Rev. D* **97**, 104020 (2018).
14. A. Ruderman, Pulsars: Structure and dynamics, *Annu. Rev. Astron. Astrophys.* **10**, 427 (1972).
15. V. Canuto, Equation of state at ultrahigh densities, *Annu. Rev. Astron. Astrophys.* **12**, 167 (1974).
16. I. Lovas, J. Németh and K. Sailor, Equilibrium between anisotropic normal and pion-condensed nuclear matter, *Nucl. Phy. A* **430**, 731 (1984).
17. M. Gleiser and K. Dev, Anistropic stars: Exact solutions and stability, *Int. J. Mod. Phys. D* **13**, 1389 (2004).
18. B. C. Paul and R. Deb, Relativistic solutions of anisotropic compact objects, *Astrophys. Space Sci.* **354**, 421 (2014).
19. J. Ovalle, Decoupling gravitational sources in general relativity: From perfect to anisotropic fluids, *Phys. Rev. D* **95**, 104019 (2017).
20. J. Ovalle et al., Anisotropic solutions by gravitational decoupling, *Eur. Phys. J. C* **78**, 122 (2018).
21. M. Sharif and S. Sadiq, Gravitational decoupled charged anisotropic spherical solutions, *Eur. Phys. J. C* **78**, 410 (2018).
22. K. N. Singh et al., Minimally deformed anisotropic model of class one space-time by gravitational decoupling, *Eur. Phys. J. C* **79**, 851 (2019).

23. M. Sharif and A. Waseem, Anisotropic spherical solutions by gravitational decoupling in $f(\mathbb{R})$ gravity, *Ann. Phys.* **405**, 14 (2019); M. Sharif and A. Majid, Decoupled anisotropic spheres in self-interacting Brans-Dicke gravity, *Chin. J. Phys.* **68**, 406 (2020).
24. S. K. Maurya and F. Tello-Ortiz, Charged anisotropic compact star in $f(\mathbb{R}, T)$ gravity: A minimal geometric deformation gravitational decoupling approach, *Phys. Dark Universe* **27**, 100442 (2020).
25. S. K. Maurya et al., Gravitational decoupling minimal geometric deformation model in modified gravity theory, *Phys. Dark Universe* **30**, 100640 (2020).
26. J. Ovalle, Decoupling gravitational sources in general relativity: The extended case, *Phys. Lett. B* **788**, 213 (2019).
27. E. Contreras and P. Bargueño, Extended gravitational decoupling in 2+1 dimensional space-times, *Class. Quantum Grav.* **36**, 215009 (2019).
28. S. K. Maurya, F. Tello-Ortiz and M. K. Jasim, An EGD model in the background of embedding class I space-time, *Eur. Phys. J. C* **80**, 918 (2020).
29. M. Sharif and Q. Ama-Tul-Mughani, Extended gravitational decoupled charged anisotropic solutions, *Chin. J. Phys.* **65**, 207 (2020).
30. M. Sharif and A. Majid, Extended gravitational decoupled solutions in self-interacting Brans-Dicke theory, *Phys. Dark Universe* **30**, 100610 (2020); M. Sharif and S. Saba, Extended gravitational decoupling approach in $f(G)$ gravity, *Int. J. Mod. Phys. D* **29**, 2050041 (2020).
31. J. D. Brown, Action functionals for relativistic perfect fluids, *Class. Quantum Grav.* **10**, 1579 (1993).
32. S. K. Maurya and Y. K. Gupta, Exact well behaved solutions of Einstein-Maxwell equations for relativistic charged superdense star models, *Astrophys. Space Sci.* **340**, 323 (2012).
33. S. K. Maurya, A. Banerjee and S. Hansraj, Role of pressure anisotropy on relativistic compact stars, *Phys. Rev. D* **97**, 044022 (2018).
34. G. Darmois, *Memorial Des Sciences Mathematiques* (Gauthier-Villars, Paris, 1927).
35. R. Bowers and E. Liang, Anisotropic spheres in general relativity, *Astrophys. J.* **188**, 657 (1974).
36. M. Sharif and A. Majid, Effects of charge on decoupled solutions in self-interacting Brans-Dicke theory, *Phys. Dark Universe* **32**, 100803 (2021).
37. G. Abellán et al., Regularity condition on the anisotropy induced by gravitational decoupling in the framework of MGD, *Eur. Phys. J. C* **80**, 177 (2020); E. Contreras, F. Tello-Ortiz and S. K. Maurya, Regular decoupling sector and exterior solutions in the context of MGD, *Class. Quantum Grav.* **37**, 155002 (2020).
38. M. L. Rawls et al., Refined neutron star mass determinations for six eclipsing x-ray pulsar binaries, *Astrophys. J.* **730**, 25 (2011).
39. L. Herrera, Cracking of self-gravitating compact objects, *Phys. Lett. A* **165**, 206 (1992).
40. H. Abreu, H. Hernandez and L. A. Nunez, Sound Speeds, cracking and stability of self-gravitating anisotropic compact objects, *Class. Quantum Gravit.* **24**, 4631 (2007).
41. H. Heintzmann and W. Hillebrandt, Neutron stars with an anisotropic equation of state-Mass, redshift and stability, *Astron. Astrophys.* **38**, 51 (1975).
42. S. K. Maurya, F. Tello-Ortiz and S. Ray, Decoupling gravitational sources in $f(\mathbb{R}, T)$ gravity under class I spacetime, *Phys. Dark Universe* **31**, 100753 (2021).

Tolman-Oppenheimer-Volkov conditions beyond spherical symmetry

José P. Mimoso

Departamento de Física and Instituto de Astrofísica e Ciências do Espaço,
Faculdade de Ciências da Universidade de Lisboa,
Campo Grande, Ed. C8 1749-016 Lisboa, Portugal
E-mail: jpmimoso@fc.ul.pt

Alan Maciel

Centro de Matemática, Computação e Cognição, Universidade Federal do ABC,
Avenida dos Estados 5001, CEP 09210-580, Santo André, São Paulo, Brazil
E-mail: alan.silva@ufabc.edu.br

Morgan Le Delliou

Institute of Theoretical Physics, School of Physical Science and Technology, Lanzhou University,
No. 222, South Tianshui Road, Lanzhou, Gansu 730000, P R China
E-mail: delliou@lzu.edu.cn, delliou@ift.unesp.br

The TOV equation is usually interpreted as the relativistic counterpart of the classical condition for hydrostatic equilibrium, and characterises the static equilibrium of bound, spherical distributions of matter such as stars. In the present work we aim at showing that a generalised TOV equation also determines the equilibrium of models endowed with other symmetries besides spherical. We resort to the dual null formalism applied to spacetimes with two dimensional spherical, planar and hyperbolic symmetries, and consider a perfect fluid as the source. Static configurations assume the existence of a time-like Killing vector field orthogonal to the surfaces of symmetry, and homogeneous dynamical solutions arise when the Killing field is space-like. In order to treat equally all the aforementioned cases, we discuss the definition of a quasi-local energy for the spacetimes with planar and hyperbolic foliations, since the Hawking-Hayward definition only applies to compact foliations. This procedure enables us to translate our geometrical formalism to the fluid dynamics language in a unified way, to find the generalised TOV equation, for the three cases when the solution is static, and to obtain the evolution equation, for the homogeneous spacetime cases. Remarkably, we show that the static solutions which are not spherically symmetric violate the weak energy condition (WEC). We also show that the counterpart of the TOV equation $\rho+P=0$, defines a cosmological constant-type behaviour, both in the hyperbolic and spherical cases. This implies a violation of the strong energy condition in both cases, added to the above mentioned violation of the weak energy condition in the hyperbolic case. We illustrate our unified treatment obtaining analogs of Schwarzschild interior solution, for an incompressible fluid $\rho = \rho_0$ constant.

Keywords: Gravitational collapse; hydrostatic equilibrium.

1. Introduction

The Tolman-Oppenheimer-Volkoff (TOV) equation[1,2] characterises spherical objects in equilibrium in the framework of General Relativity. It appears as the relativistic counterpart of the classical condition for hydrostatic equilibrium. Given the relevance of the spherical configurations in astrophysics, many solutions were investigated,[3–15] and more specifically, different formalisms[16–20] and solutions generating techniques have been developed.[21,22] Extensions of the TOV equation have also been investigated in the framework of modified gravity theories.[23–29]

Yet a unified characterization of the underlying features of the TOV equation has attracted little attention, and this is what concerns us in the present work. There is a widespread perception of the TOV equation as being restricted to the spherically symmetric case, but this is a misled assumption. So, in the present work we derive a generalised TOV equation that also characterises the equilibrium of models endowed with other symmetries besides the spherical.[a]

We adopt the dual null formalism[b] that offers a description of the spacetime based on the properties of the optical flow, and has the significant advantage of being a coordinate free formalism. In the literature it has been considered in connection with the behaviour of dynamical black holes,[35,36] the definition of energy in more general geometries,[37] the gravitational collapse of fluids,[38] and even with the definition of generalized horizons in modified gravity.[39] The dual null formalism has also been useful to explicit the "linear" behavior of gravity for sources that satisfy the hypotheses of the Birkhoff theorem.[31]

Here, we apply the dual null formalism to analyse, in a unified way, the spacetimes which admit a codimension-two foliation with constant curvature leaves.[40] This comprises the spherical, planar and hyperbolic symmetries, sourced by a perfect fluid. Aside from the Killing vector fields that are tangent to those surfaces of symmetry, we assume the existence of an additional symmetry generated by a Killing vector field orthogonal to those surfaces at each event. A particular case of this setup, where the symmetry is spherical and the Killing vector is timelike, corresponds to the spherically symmetric perfect fluid in hydrostatic equilibrium, which leads us to the well-known TOV equation. As we will show this celebrated equation arises most naturally in the dual-null framework which, moreover, allows us to generalize it for the planar and hyperbolic cases. This generalisation of the geometry underlying the TOV equation, stepping beyond spherical symmetry, is novel and leads to consequences which are far from trivial.[40]

Since in planar and hyperbolic geometries the spatial hypersurfaces are open, this extension requires the novel introduction of a mass-energy "parameter". In fact one needs to promote a generalization of the Misner-Sharp/Hawking-Hayward definitions of the mass-energy distribution, which overcomes the problem of the divergence of the latter quantities due to the natural threading with infinite surfaces.

---

[a]A similar prejudice applying to the Birkhoff theorem, has been addressed with its generalization to more general geometries by C. Bona,[30] and more recently by us in.[31]
[b]We follow here the nomenclature coined by Sean A. Hayward[32–34] although in some references this formalism is referred to as double-null.

Finally, our investigation of the planar and hyperbolic geometries reveals the violation of the weak energy condition in order to maintain hydrostatic equilibrium. This takes the form of negative effective mass, physically translating repulsive curvature effects, which suggest a link to repulsive source models, as those proposed to mimic dark energy, generate bouncing universes, or support classical wormholes.[41,42]

For completness, when the metric is characterised by a spacelike, rather than a timelike Killing vector, we have spatially homogeneous spacetimes that correspond to some of the Bianchi spacetimes, or Kantowski-Sachs, as expected. The hydrostatic equilibrium on those spacetimes is only possible when their source is a cosmological constant in the non flat cases, also implying the violation of energy conditions.

2. The dual null formalism

We consider metrics that have a codimension-two maximally symmetric foliation, and can be written as

$$\mathrm{d}s^2 = N_{ab}\mathrm{d}x^a\mathrm{d}x^b + Y^2(x^c)\left(\mathrm{d}\theta^2 + S_\epsilon^2\mathrm{d}\phi^2\right), \tag{1}$$

where

$$S_\epsilon = \begin{cases} \sin\theta, & \text{for } \epsilon = 1 \\ 1, & \text{for } \epsilon = 0 \\ \sinh\theta, & \text{for } \epsilon = -1 \end{cases},$$

and where we divide the tangent space $\mathcal{T}$ at each event in two orthogonal subspaces $\mathcal{T} = \mathcal{N} \oplus \mathcal{S}$. Here $\mathcal{S}$ is the subspace generated by the orbits of (θ, ϕ) and $\mathcal{N}$, the subspace of $\mathcal{T}$ orthogonal to $\mathcal{S}$. The x^a coordinates are chosen orthogonal to $\mathcal{S}$, which gives the metric in the warped sum form of Eq. (1).

We denote $s_{ab} = Y^2\gamma_{ab}$ the induced metric in each leaf of the foliation where $Y(x^c)$ is the warp factor. Evidently, $\gamma_{ab} := \delta_a^\theta\delta_b^\theta + S_\epsilon^2\delta_a^\phi\delta_b^\phi$ has constant curvature and does not depend on the coordinates x^a which identify each leaf Σ_{x^c}, defined as the locus spanned by the orbits of θ and ϕ for fixed x^c. We define an orthonormal two dimensional basis (n^a, e^a) for $\mathcal{N}$, whose induced metric is N_{ab}, according to Eq. (1). This basis satisfies

$$-n^a n_a = e^a e_a = 1, \quad n^a e_a = n^a s_{ab} = e^a s_{ab} = 0. \tag{2}$$

We may also define a dual null basis for the same subspace from n^a and e^a by

$$k^a = \frac{1}{2}(n^a + e^a), \quad l^a = \frac{1}{2}(n^a - e^a),$$
$$n^a = k^a + l^a, \quad e^a = k^a - l^a, \tag{3}$$

which satisfies

$$k^a k_a = l^a l_a = 0, \quad k^a l_a = -\frac{1}{2}. \tag{4}$$

The metric g_{ab} can be written as

$$g_{ab} = \frac{2}{k^c l_c} k_{(a} l_{b)} + s_{ab} \,. \tag{5}$$

We associate the null expansion for each null vector as follows

$$\Theta_k = \frac{1}{2} s^{ab} \mathcal{L}_k s_{ab} = \frac{1}{2} Y^{-2} \gamma^{ab} \mathcal{L}_k Y^2 \gamma_{ab} = \frac{2}{Y} k^a \partial_a Y \,. \tag{6}$$

We may extend the definition of null expansion to timelike and spacelike vectors in $\mathcal{N}$, calling it the two-expansion, since it measures the rate of variation of area, as in the null case. We may define the mean curvature form $\mathcal{K}_a = \partial_a \ln Y^2$, such that, we obtain for the two-expansion $\Theta_{(u)}$ of any vector u^a in $\mathcal{N}$

$$\Theta_{(u)} = u^a \mathcal{K}_a \,. \tag{7}$$

We describe our spacetimes by means of the behaviour of the null expansion, casting the Einstein equations, $G_{ab} = 8\pi T_{ab}$ in terms of expansions, i.e., by writing the Raychaudhuri equations and constraint equations[35, 43–45]

$$\mathcal{L}_k \Theta_{(k)} = \nu_k \Theta_{(k)} - \frac{\Theta_{(k)}^2}{2} - 8\pi T_{ab} k^a k^b \,, \tag{8a}$$

$$\mathcal{L}_l \Theta_{(l)} = \nu_l \Theta_{(l)} - \frac{\Theta_{(l)}^2}{2} - 8\pi T_{ab} l^a l^b \,, \tag{8b}$$

$$\mathcal{L}_k \Theta_{(l)} + \mathcal{L}_l \Theta_{(k)} = -\Theta_{(l)} \nu_k - \Theta_{(k)} \nu_l - 2\Theta_{(k)} \Theta_{(l)} + \epsilon \frac{2 k^a l_a}{Y^2} + 16\pi T_{ab} k^a l^b \,, \tag{8c}$$

where we included the inaffinities ν_k and ν_l, defined as

$$\nu_k = \frac{1}{k^c l_c} l^b k^a \nabla_a k_b \qquad \nu_l = \frac{1}{k^c l_c} k^b l^a \nabla_a l_b \,. \tag{9}$$

In the latter equations, for T_{ab}, if we take the source to be a perfect fluid[c], then the energy momentum tensor reduces to

$$T_{ab} = \rho n_a n_b + P(e_a e_b + s_{ab}) \,. \tag{10}$$

where we adapt our vector basis to the fluid source, such that n^a gives its flow. In the latter decomposition ρ is the energy density, and P is the isotropic pressure, both measured by an observer moving with 4-velocity n^a. By construction, the flow n^a is always orthogonal to the surfaces of symmetry and will be characterized by two quantities

$$\mathcal{A} = e^a \dot{n}_a = e^a n^b \nabla_b n_a \,, \qquad \mathcal{B} = e^a n'_a = e^a e^b \nabla_b n_a \,. \tag{11}$$

The scalar $\mathcal{A}$ gives us the acceleration of the flow, a positive sign meaning that the acceleration is outwards in the spherical, compact case. The scalar $\mathcal{B}$ gives the

---

[c]The equations in the case of a general fluid are given by us in Ref.[46].

change of direction of n^a as we travel along e^a. It is the $e-e$ component of the extrinsic curvature K_{ab} of the 3-space orthogonal to this flow, since

$$K_{ab} = \frac{1}{2}\mathcal{L}_n h_{ab}, \tag{12}$$

where $h_{ab} = g_{ab} + n_a n_b$. We may also write

$$h_{ab} = e_a e_b + Y^2 \gamma_{ab}, \tag{13}$$

which gives

$$K_{ab} = \mathcal{B} e_a e_b + \frac{\Theta_{(n)}}{2} Y^2 \gamma_{ab}. \tag{14}$$

The trace of Eq. (14) gives us the flow volumetric expansion $\Theta_3 = \nabla_a n^a = K^a_a$ as

$$\Theta_3 = \mathcal{B} + \Theta_{(n)}. \tag{15}$$

In order to relate our quantities with the flow scalars, we compute the shear scalar σ, by taking the symmetric traceless part of K_{ab}. We obtain

$$\sigma = \frac{\Theta_{(n)}}{6} - \frac{\mathcal{B}}{3}, \tag{16}$$

which implies

$$\frac{\Theta_3}{3} + \sigma = \frac{\Theta_{(n)}}{2}, \tag{17}$$

in agreement with the result obtained in Ref.[38].

Using the inaffinities of the null basis vectors, $\mathcal{A}$ and $\mathcal{B}$ can be expressed as

$$\mathcal{A} = \nu_k - \nu_l, \qquad \mathcal{B} = \nu_k + \nu_l. \tag{18}$$

Contracting the conservation of the energy-momentum tensor with e_b (Euler equation in[47]) we get

$$e_b \nabla_a T^{ab} = (\rho + P)\dot{n}^b e_b + e^a \nabla_a P = 0 \Rightarrow$$

$$\mathcal{A} = -\frac{e^a \partial_a P}{\rho + P}. \tag{19}$$

3. Orthogonal Killing vector

We now assume that our metric has a Killing vector orthogonal to maximally symmetric surfaces, as we are interested in static configurations. Our symmetry requirements imply that it commutes with the symmetry generators on the foliation. We denote this hypersurface orthogonal Killing vector field χ^a. It satisfies the Killing equation,

$$\mathcal{L}_\chi g_{ab} = 0. \tag{20}$$

Proposition 1. If a spacetime is described by a metric of the form (1) and admits an orthogonal Killing vector $\chi^a \in \mathcal{N}$, then $\Theta_\chi = 0$.

Proof. We may write, from Eq. (6), $\Theta_\chi = \frac{1}{2} s^{ab} \mathcal{L}_\chi s_{ab} = \frac{1}{2} Y^{-2} \gamma^{ab} \mathcal{L}_\chi Y^2 \gamma_{ab}$, and

$$g_{ab} = N_{ab} + Y^2 \gamma_{ab}. \tag{21}$$

Then

$$\begin{aligned} 0 = Y^{-2} \gamma^{ab} \mathcal{L}_\chi g_{ab} &= Y^{-2} \gamma^{ab} \mathcal{L}_\chi N_{ab} + 2\Theta_\chi \\ &= -Y^{-2} N^{ab} \mathcal{L}_\chi \gamma_{ab} + 2\Theta_\chi. \end{aligned} \tag{22}$$

However

$$\mathcal{L}_\chi \gamma_{ab} = 0, \tag{23}$$

since χ^a does not admit components in $\mathcal{S}$ and γ_{ab} doesn't depend on coordinates along $\mathcal{N}$. Therefore, Eq. (22) implies that $\Theta_\chi = 0$. □

Consequently, if there is an extra symmetry with orbits orthogonal to those of the maximally symmetric leaves of the foliation, the two-expansion of its generator vanishes. This also implies that if dY is spacelike, then χ_a is timelike and vice-versa. If dY is null, the Killing vector will also be null.

4. Extension of the mass-energy parameter to open geometries

There is a widely known mass-energy definition suitable to the spherically symmetric case, namely the Misner-Sharp mass-energy,[48,49] that is defined regardless of asymptotic assumptions. However, as we also intend to analyze nonspherical spacetimes in this work, we are led to consider a more general mass-energy definition, namely the Hawking-Hayward's (hereafter HH).[37,50] The HH mass-energy gives the mass-energy content inside a closed compact surface in terms of an integral over that surface, in a manner similar to the Gauss law in Newtonian gravity. This quasilocal mass-energy has been explored in different contexts, such as seen in Refs.[51–53].

Under our symmetry assumptions the Hawking-Hayward mass-energy enclosed by Σ is reduced to

$$M_\Sigma = \frac{1}{8\pi} \sqrt{\frac{A}{16\pi}} \int_\Sigma \left[\mathcal{R} - \frac{1}{k^a l_a} \Theta_{(k)} \Theta_{(l)} \right] d\Sigma \tag{24}$$

where $\mathcal{R}$ is the two-dimensional Ricci scalar and A is the area of Σ. We have included a factor of $-\dfrac{1}{k^a l_a}$ in the optical scalars part of the mass-energy, compared with the formula present in Ref.[37], in order to take account of our different normalization of the null normals. Our symmetry assumptions imply that the only non-vanishing optical scalar on Σ is the null expansion.

Since we assume that Σ is maximally symmetric, we have $\mathcal{R} = \dfrac{2\epsilon}{Y^2}$. We also have

$$\Theta_{(k)}\Theta_{(l)} = k^{(a}l^{b)}\partial_a \ln Y^2 \partial_b \ln Y^2 = \frac{k^c l_c}{2} g^{ab}\partial_a \ln Y^2 \partial_b \ln Y^2 =$$

$$\frac{1}{2}k^c l_c \|d\ln Y^2\|^2 = k^c l_c \frac{2}{Y^2}\|dY\|^2 \Rightarrow \frac{\Theta_{(k)}\Theta_{(l)}}{k^c l_c} = \frac{2}{Y^2}\|dY\|^2, \quad (25)$$

where we used Eq. (5) in the second step.

For the spherical case $\epsilon = 1$ and $A = 4\pi Y^2$, we obtain the known interpretation of $\|dY\|$ in terms of the Misner-Sharp mass-energy, which coincides with the Hawking-Hayward one

$$M_\Sigma = \frac{Y}{2}\left(1 - \|dY\|^2\right) \Leftrightarrow \|dY\|^2 = 1 - \frac{2M_\Sigma}{Y}. \quad (26)$$

In this work, we aim at treating all three symmetry types in the same manner. In the planar and hyperbolic cases ($\epsilon = 0$ and $\epsilon = -1$, respectively), the Hawking-Hayward mass is not conveniently defined for the integration domain set by our preferred foliation, as it requires a closed compact surface which is absent in the latter cases. Therefore, we need a mass-energy definition which might be equivalent to the HH mass-energy, but suitable to deal with (instead of adapted for) non compact domains in order to take advantage of the planar or hyperbolic symmetry.

We can make such an extension of the HH mass-energy, as long as their boundary correspond to a pair of symmetric two-surfaces of symmetry Σ corresponding to the same warp factor Y. Of course, those domains are infinite and have an infinite mass-energy content in general. However, as they are homogeneous along the surfaces of symmetry, we can successfully adapt the HH mass-energy definition in order to obtain a finite *mass-energy parameter* with those cases. They then describe an infinite mass-energy distribution, homogeneous along the surfaces of symmetry, with a finite density.

We proceed by first making the replacement

$$\frac{1}{8\pi}\sqrt{\frac{A}{16\pi}} \to \frac{Y}{4\pi\kappa}, \quad (27)$$

in order to keep its dimensionality, and eliminating the explicit dependence on the area of Σ. Evidently, by setting $\kappa = 4$ we recover the Hawking-Hayward mass-energy in the spherical case. This step is justified by the fact that originally this factor was introduced to correct the dimensionality of the mass-energy, and to make it match the Arnowitt-Deser-Misner (ADM) mass,[54] where both are well defined. Since our symmetric spacetimes allow an "areal scalar" as the warp factor Y, we can replace $\sqrt{A}$ by Y as the quantity with dimension of length associated to each surface of symmetry.

We then define the quasi-local mass-energy parameter $\mu(Y)$ by

$$M_\Sigma = \frac{\mu(Y)}{4\pi} \int S_\epsilon(\theta)\,\mathrm{d}\theta\mathrm{d}\phi, \tag{28}$$

and we write

$$\frac{Y}{4\pi\kappa}\left[\mathcal{R} - \frac{\Theta_{(k)}\Theta_{(l)}}{k^c l_c}\right]\int_\Sigma \mathrm{d}\Sigma = \frac{Y}{4\pi\kappa}\left[2\epsilon - 2\|\mathrm{d}Y\|^2\right]\int S_\epsilon(\Theta)\mathrm{d}\theta\mathrm{d}\phi. \tag{29}$$

Equating Eqs. (28) and (29) and eliminating the improper area integral on both sides we derive

$$\|\mathrm{d}Y\|^2 = \epsilon - \frac{\kappa\mu(Y)}{2Y}. \tag{30}$$

Equation (30) coincides with the known mass function [see Eq. (15.7a) in[55]] which appears as we integrate the Einstein equations of specific spacetimes with metrics of the form (1) for planar and hyperbolic symmetries. From now on, we will consider Eq. (30) with the choice $\kappa = 4$ as the mass-energy definition.

An alternative route to Eq. (30) can be obtained by computing the HH mass-energy in a finite domain, symmetric with respect to the central plane or wire, $Y = 0$, and taking the limit where the domain tends to be the whole surface. The finite integration domain consist of the union of

(1) a subset of the Σ_Y, that we denote Γ_r, bounded by a circle γ_r of radius r on the (θ, ϕ) coordinate plane and
(2) a compact surface given by the surfaces Δ_r defined by γ_r transported along Y orbits.

It forms a closed surface, corresponding to a part of a cylinder bounded by $Y = $ constant surfaces in the space of coordinates (Y, θ, ϕ). Therefore, the HH mass-energy enclosed by those surfaces will by finite, and given by

$$M_r = \frac{1}{8\pi}\sqrt{\frac{A_r}{16\pi}}\left(\int_{\Gamma_r}(\ldots)S_\epsilon\mathrm{d}\theta\mathrm{d}\phi + \int_{\Delta_r}(\ldots)\mathrm{d}\Delta\right) \tag{31}$$

where $(\ldots)$ replaces the integrand of Eq. (24). In the limit $r \to \infty$, the first integral in Eq. (31) scales as r^2 while the second one scales as r. This means that, in the limit $r \to \infty$, and repeating the replacement in Eq. (27) we obtain

$$\frac{M_r}{A_r} \to \frac{\mu(Y)}{4\pi Y^2}. \tag{32}$$

This relation is particularly adequate to obtain the extension of the TOV equation for the open geometries, as it will become apparent in the following section.

5. Evolution equations

5.1. *Timelike Killing vector*

We assume $\chi^a \chi_a < 0$. In this case, the spacetime is static, and $n^a \sim \chi^a$. Therefore, from Proposition 1, $\Theta_{(n)} = 0$ everywhere, and dY is spacelike, since it is orthogonal to n^a. If $\Theta_{(n)}$ vanishes everywhere, this means that the fluid has no radial velocity, therefore we are dealing with a static fluid with a flow parallel to the Killing vector field.

In order to characterize its static equilibrium, we realise the derivative of the flow 2-expansion along the flow itself is vanishing

$$\mathcal{L}_n \Theta_{(n)} = 0, \tag{33}$$

since $\Theta_{(n)} = 0$ everywhere.

We may write $\mathcal{L}_n \Theta_{(n)}$ in terms of the null expansions as

$$\mathcal{L}_n \Theta_{(n)} = \mathcal{L}_k \Theta_{(k)} + \mathcal{L}_l \Theta_{(l)} + \mathcal{L}_l \Theta_{(k)} + \mathcal{L}_k \Theta_{(l)}. \tag{34}$$

Substituting the Eqs. (8a), (8b), and (8c), we obtain

$$\mathcal{L}_n \Theta_{(n)} = -\frac{(\Theta_{(k)} + \Theta_{(l)})^2}{2} - \Theta_{(k)} \Theta_{(l)} - \frac{\epsilon}{Y^2} - 8\pi T_{ab} e^a e^b + \mathcal{A}(\Theta_{(k)} - \Theta_{(l)}). \tag{35}$$

Recall that we are assuming $\Theta_{(n)} = \Theta_{(k)} + \Theta_{(l)} = 0$, and that $\Theta_{(k)} - \Theta_{(l)} = \Theta_{(e)}$, using Eqs. (7) and (3). We identify here $\Theta_{(k)} \Theta_{(l)}$ as the mass term, since it equals $\frac{2}{Y^2} \|dY\|^2 = \frac{2}{Y^2} \left(\epsilon - \frac{2\mu(Y)}{Y} \right)$.

Taking the source to be a perfect fluid, (10), and contracting the divergence of the energy-momentum tensor with e_b (Euler equation in[47]) we get

$$e_b \nabla_a T^{ab} = (\rho + P) \dot{n}^b e_b + e^a \nabla_a P = 0 \Rightarrow$$

$$\mathcal{A} = -\frac{e^a \partial_a P}{\rho + P}. \tag{36}$$

Since $\Theta_{(n)} = 0$, e^a is proportional to ∂_Y, and as e^a is normalized, we have

$$e_a = \frac{1}{\|dY\|} \partial_a Y, \quad e^a = \|dY\| (\partial_Y)^a, \tag{37}$$

which gives us

$$\mathcal{A} \Theta_e = -\|dY\|^2 \frac{2}{Y} \frac{\partial_Y P}{\rho + P}. \tag{38}$$

Therefore, replacing $\|dY\|^2$ by its meaning in terms of mass, $\mathcal{L}_n \Theta_{(n)} = 0$ corresponds to[40]

$$\left(\frac{\epsilon}{Y^2} - \frac{2\mu(Y)}{Y^2} \right) \frac{\partial_Y P}{\rho + P} = -\frac{1}{Y} \frac{\mu(Y)}{Y^2} - 4\pi P, \tag{39}$$

that reveals that the generalization of the concept of mass-energy given by (32) is particularly suited to avoid the caveats of the divergence of that quantity if it were defined in accordance to the canon of the spherically symmetric models.

Of course the latter equation (39) can alternatively be cast under a more familiar form as

$$\frac{\partial_Y P}{\rho + P} = -\left(\frac{\mu(Y)}{Y^2} + 4\pi PY\right)\left(\epsilon - \frac{2\mu(Y)}{Y}\right)^{-1}, \qquad (40)$$

which is what we denote as *the unified TOV equation*. It reduces to the well-know TOV equation for spherically symmetric spacetimes when $\epsilon = 1$, and it corresponds to the equation of hydrostatic equilibrium for planar and hyperbolic geometries, in the cases where $\epsilon = 0$ and $\epsilon = -1$, respectively. This underlines the fact that the TOV equation is a hydrostatic equilibrium equation, and not an equation of state, as it is sometimes erroneously stated.

In order to determine $\mu(Y)$ we consider the $\mathcal{L}_e \Theta_{(e)}$ Raychaudhuri equation

$$\mathcal{L}_e \Theta_{(e)} = \mathcal{B}\Theta_{(n)} - \frac{\Theta_{(e)}^2}{2} + \frac{1}{4}\left(\Theta_{(n)}^2 - \Theta_{(e)}^2\right) \\ + \frac{\epsilon}{Y^2} - 8\pi T_{ab} n^a n^b, \qquad (41)$$

which, by using $\Theta_{(n)} = 0$, and Eq. (37) lead us to

$$\|\mathrm{d}Y\|\partial_Y\left(\frac{2}{Y}\|\mathrm{d}Y\|\right) = -\frac{3}{Y^2}\|\mathrm{d}Y\|^2 + \frac{\epsilon}{Y^2} - 8\pi\rho. \qquad (42)$$

Substituting Eq. (30) into Eq. (42), we obtain

$$\partial_Y \mu = 4\pi\rho Y^2, \qquad (43)$$

which looks like the mass-energy equation of spherical symmetry. Here, it should be interpreted as the mass-energy equation in the spherical case, and as a mass-energy parameter equation in the planar and hyperbolic cases. Furthermore, Eqs. (43) and (30) imply that, if the *weak energy condition (WEC)*[56] *holds*, only the spherically symmetric case admits static regular solutions. Indeed, as those solutions require $\|\mathrm{d}Y\|^2 > 0$, that implies $\mu < 0$ for $\epsilon \leq 0$ and, as in regular spacetimes,

$$\mu(Y) = 4\pi \int_0^Y \rho(y) y^2 \mathrm{d}y, \qquad (44)$$

this imposes $\rho < 0$.

With Eq. (43), the last requirement to solve Eq. (40) is the equation of state of the fluid, $f(\rho, P) = 0$ which should come from specific physical considerations.

5.2. *Spacelike Killing vector: The cosmological cases*

In the case of a spacelike Killing vector, $\mathrm{d}Y$ is timelike, the flow n_a is orthogonal to the Killing vector, and the unitary base vector e^a is parallel to it. This imposes no constraint on the sign of μ according to Eq. (30), and thus there is no need to violate energy conditions in order to consider these solutions, thoroughly studied in cosmology.[57]

Combining the dynamical equation given by $\mathcal{L}_e \Theta_{(e)} = 0$, and Proposition 1, we have $\Theta_{(e)} = 0$. Replacing Eq. (16) in Eq. (41), we derive

$$\frac{3}{4}\Theta_{(n)}^2 - 3\sigma \Theta_{(n)} + \frac{\epsilon}{Y^2} = 8\pi \rho, \qquad (45)$$

and, using Eq. (17), we can express this Eq. (45) in terms of the volume expansion Θ_3 obtaining

$$\frac{\Theta_3^2}{3} - 3\sigma^2 = 8\pi \rho - \frac{\epsilon}{Y^2}, \qquad (46)$$

which corresponds to the generalised Friedmann constraint equation for the evolution of a homogeneous and anisotropic universe. In the case $\sigma = 0$, we may identify $\Theta_3 = 3H$, and we recover the usual Friedmann equation for the flat ($\epsilon = 0$) and open ($\epsilon = -1$) spatially isotropic universes. Notice though that $\sigma = 0$ also yields anisotropic, cosmological solutions when the matter content is not a perfect fluid.[58]

The $\mathcal{L}_n \Theta_{(n)}$ Raychaudhuri equation gives the evolution of $\Theta_{(n)}$. Using Eq. (35) we obtain

$$\mathcal{L}_n \Theta_{(n)} = -\frac{3}{4}\Theta_{(n)}^2 - \frac{\epsilon}{Y^2} - 8\pi T_{ab} e^a e^b, \qquad (47)$$

so that subtracting Eq. (45) from Eq. (47), we further derive

$$\mathcal{L}_n \Theta_{(n)} = -3\sigma \Theta_{(n)} - 8\pi (\rho + P), \qquad (48)$$

which, together with an equation of state relating ρ and P closes our system. By adding half of the Eq. (48) with one third of Eq. (46), we obtain:

$$\mathcal{L}_n \left(\frac{\Theta_3}{3}\right) + \left(\frac{\Theta_3}{3}\right)^2 =$$
$$- 2\sigma \left(\frac{\Theta_3}{3} + \sigma\right) - \frac{\epsilon}{3Y^2} - \frac{4\pi}{3}(\rho + 3P). \qquad (49)$$

Those homogeneous and anisotropic spacetimes belong to a subclass of Bianchi models,[59,60] with the case $\epsilon = 0$ corresponding to Bianchi type I universes, $\epsilon = -1$ corresponding to the Bianchi type III models, and $\epsilon = 1$ to the Kantowski-Sachs spacetimes.[61]

In this work we are mainly focused on the hydrostatic equilibrium situations. Thus, our interest will be directed to understanding whether it is possible to find a correspondence between the TOV equation of static equilibrium, and some condition applying to the spatially homogeneous models.

Imposing staticity amounts in the present case to have $\Theta_3 = 0$, $\mathcal{L}_n \Theta_3 = 0$, and $\sigma = 0$ in Eqs. (46) and (49). Reconciling the reduced equations simply requires

$$\rho + P = 0, \qquad (50)$$

in the $\epsilon = \pm 1$ cases, and has no realisation when $\epsilon = 0$, as $\rho = 0$ from Eq.(46). Hence we conclude that the TOV condition interpreted as a cornerstone of stability yields the well-known equation of state characterising a cosmological constant in the non flat cases. In hindsight, one could have anticipated this result which emerges here in a self-consistent way. Moreover we see that strong energy condition (SEC) is violated for both cases $\epsilon = \pm 1$, whilst the WEC is additionally violated for the $\epsilon = -1$ case, as follows from Eq. (46).

6. An illustration: Incompressible fluid solutions

Using our unified TOV equation, Eq. (40), we may look for static perfect fluid solutions for all three symmetries considered here. By choosing a timelike coordinate T along the flow, making $n_a = -\alpha(Y)\mathrm{d}T$, and the warp factor Y, we obtain the following line element in the (T, Y) coordinates:

$$\mathrm{d}s^2 = -\alpha^2(Y)\mathrm{d}T^2 + \frac{\mathrm{d}Y^2}{\epsilon - \frac{2\mu(Y)}{Y}} + Y^2 \mathrm{d}\Omega_\epsilon, \tag{51}$$

where $\mathrm{d}\Omega_\epsilon = \left(\mathrm{d}\theta^2 + S_\epsilon^2 \mathrm{d}\phi^2\right)$ and the functions α and μ will be given by solving Einstein equations, i.e., Eqs. (40) and (30).

Here, we will apply our unified treatment to find the analogs of Schwarzschild interior solution, that is, we will use the equation of state of an incompressible fluid $\rho = \rho_0$ constant. It is important to note that, as we have discussed in Sec. 5.1, the static solutions with $\epsilon \neq 1$ violate the WEC, therefore we should take $\rho_0 < 0$ in those cases.

Equation (36) implies

$$\frac{\alpha'}{\alpha} = -\frac{P'}{\rho + P} \Rightarrow \alpha = \frac{c_0}{\rho_0 + P}, \tag{52}$$

where c_0 is an integration constant that can be set by rescaling the time coordinate and the prime denotes Y differentiation.

Equation (43) gives us

$$\mu(Y) = \frac{4\pi\rho_0 Y^3}{3}, \tag{53}$$

which we replace in Eq. (40) to obtain

$$P(Y) = \rho_0 \left(\frac{2\sqrt{|\epsilon - \frac{Y_s}{Y_g}|}}{3\sqrt{|\epsilon - \frac{Y_s}{Y_g}|} - \sqrt{|\epsilon - \frac{Y_s Y^2}{Y_s^3}|}} - 1 \right). \tag{54}$$

where Y_g is the analog of the radius of the object and is the least positive number that satisfy $P(Y_g) = 0$, $Y_s = \dfrac{8\pi\rho_0 Y_g^3}{3}$ is the analog of the Schwarzschild radius, although it can not be interpreted as a location since it will be a negative number. This gives

$$\alpha = \frac{1}{2}\left(3\sqrt{\left|\epsilon - \frac{Y_s}{Y_g}\right|} - \sqrt{\left|\epsilon - \frac{Y_s Y^2}{Y_g^3}\right|}\right) \tag{55}$$

which has a similar form to the interior Schwarzschild solution, where we only change the sign of the mass-energy parameter and change the value of ϵ in the formula. Of course the physical properties are very distinct, since the solutions violate the WEC.

In Fig. 1 we compare the pressure for the three cases. From the slope of the curves, we notice that only the hyperbolic case presents $P' > 0$, compensating the repulsive gravity force in this setup. This is the opposite of the more familiar situations presented in the spherical and planar cases, where gravity is attractive, with $P' < 0$ sustaining the weight of the configuration. We can also see that the planar case admits a positive pressure for $0 < Y < Y_g$. That means that, as long as mass-energy is negative, we may have static plane configurations over a finite Y interval. On the other hand, the hyperbolic solution only admits positive pressure for $Y > Y_g$, so there is no analog of the Schwarzschild interior solution for this foliation, although it can be interpreted as an exterior fluid solution to an internal void. It can thus be matched to a hyperbolic vacuum solution for $Y < Y_g$, found as a particular case in Ref.[31]:

$$ds^2 = -\left(\frac{2m}{Y} - 1\right)dt^2 + \frac{dY^2}{\frac{2m}{Y} - 1} + Y^2(d\theta^2 + \sinh^2\theta d\phi^2), \tag{56}$$

where the parameter $m = |\mu|$. The peculiarities of the hyperbolic solutions with regard to the energy conditions are also found in the work.[42]

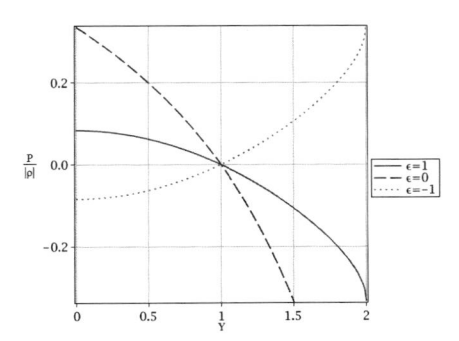

Fig. 1. Pressure as function of Y for $Y_g = 1$ and $|Y_s| = 0.25$ for $\epsilon = 1$, $\epsilon = 0$ and $\epsilon = -1$.

The equation of state consisting of a negative energy density with a positive pressure might be achieved by some kind of phantom field, but a Lagrangian description of the fluid is beyond the scope of this work. However, our simple incompressible model, with constant energy density, but varying pressure, is reminiscent of a constant time surface of a McVittie or Shah-Vaidya spacetime, which admits a Lagrangian scalar field as source.[62,63] This suggests the possibility that there exist field models in the literature which can source the solutions presented in this paper.

We notice that the planar solutions may also represent a subclass of cylindrical solutions (see Refs.[64,65]) if we select one coordinate along the plane to be periodic. Thus, our planar solution may be interpreted as a static cylinder of fluid with boundary given by $Y = Y_g$. At this surface, the solution must be matched with a vacuum solution.

Actually, all fluid configurations found can be matched with the corresponding static solutions presented in Ref.[31] which arise from applying Birkhoff theorem for external fluid sources that satisfy the hypotheses of the theorem. In those cases there is a matter content present outside, the most common examples being an electromagnetic field, and a cosmological constant. Therefore the matching surface will correspond to a surface where $P(Y)$ matches the pressure of the exterior solution, in a manner similar to the way in which an uncompressible charged sphere is matched to a Reissner-Nordström solution in Ref.[66].

7. Conclusion

In this paper we analysed spacetimes with a two-dimensional maximally symmetric foliation sourced by a perfect fluid. We proved that in those cases, if there is a Killing vector orthogonal to the leaves, its two-expansion vanishes, which allows us to simplify our dynamical equations in terms of the two-expansion of a unit vector orthogonal to the Killing field.

When the Killing vector χ^a is timelike, we find that the flow lines must be tangent to χ^a, and as this is true at all times, the equations describe a hydrostatic equilibrium, governed by a (generalised) TOV equation. When the Killing vector is spacelike, we have instead a spatially homogeneous dynamical spacetime. The result is a subclass of Bianchi universes, with only one shear degree of freedom. The corresponding equation gives the evolution of expansion and shear scalars.

Our approach relates the mass parameter to the geometrically defined quasi-local mass-energies of Misner-Sharp and Hawking-Hayward by slightly changing its definition in order to apply it to our infinite mass-energy distributions. This innovation is in itself a step towards addressing the open issue of defining mass/energy in gravitation and cosmology, c.f the recent works of,[67] and others[68,69] on this subject.

Using these concepts we could recover the physical interpretation of the geometrical quantities appearing in the equilibrium/evolution equations, translate the dual null formalism to the more usual relativistic fluid dynamics framework, and show that the TOV equation arises as a particular case of those equations. Henceforth the generalizations of the TOV equation appear automatically by just setting $\epsilon = 0$ or -1 accordingly.

From this treatment it emerges the fact that the only static fluid solutions that satisfy the WEC are the spherical ones, as the other two cases require a negative energy density.

In what regards the spatially homogeneous spacetimes, the hydrostatic equilibrium condition also implies a violation of the SEC[70, 71] for the non planar solutions, constraining the equation of state for the perfect fluid to be that of a cosmological constant[d].

In order to illustrate the analogy between the planar, hyperbolic and spherical cases we studied the static solutions for an incompressible fluid. We found that, besides the known case of spherically symmetric spacetimes, we can obtain a static interior fluid configuration only in the case of planar symmetric spacetimes. In the hyperbolic case, the static configuration is an exterior solution that can surround an inner vacuum region.

Our unified way to describe three classes of spacetimes foliated with codimension-two leaves of constant curvature leads the way to further generalizations that we will address elsewhere.

Acknowledgements

The work of M.Le D. has been supported by Lanzhou University starting fund and by the Fundamental Research Funds for the Central Universities (Grant No.lzujbky-2019-25). The work of JPM was supported by FCT/MCTES through national funds (PIDDAC) by the grants UID/FIS/04434/2019, UIDB/04434/2020 and UIDP/04434/2020. as well as by CERN/FIS-PAR/0037/2019 and PTDC/FIS-OUT/29048/2017. The authors wish to thank Xu Yumeng for helpful discussions.

References

1. R. C. Tolman, Effect of inhomogeneity on cosmological models, *Proc. Natl. Acad. Sci. U.S.A.* **20**, 169 (March 1934).
2. J. R. Oppenheimer and G. M. Volkoff, On massive neutron cores, *Phys. Rev.* **55**, 374 (February 1939).
3. W. H. Zurek and D. N. Page, Black-hole thermodynamics and singular solutions of the Tolman-Oppenheimer-Volkoff equation, *Phys. Rev.* **D29**, 628 (1984).
4. M. S. R. Delgaty and K. Lake, Physical acceptability of isolated, static, spherically symmetric, perfect fluid solutions of Einstein's equations, *Comput. Phys. Commun.* **115**, 395 (1998).
5. S. Berger, R. Hojman and J. Santamarina, General Exact Solutions of Einstein Equations for Static Perfect Fluids With Spherical Symmetry, *J. Math. Phys.* **28**, p. 2949 (1987).
6. G. Fodor, Generating spherically symmetric static perfect fluid solutions (2000).
7. K. Dev and M. Gleiser, Anisotropic stars: Exact solutions, *Gen. Rel. Grav.* **34**, 1793 (2002).

---

[d]There are several arguments in the literature suggesting the canonical energy conditions should be abandoned as a criterion of viability.[72]

8. S. Rahman and M. Visser, Space-time geometry of static fluid spheres, *Class. Quant. Grav.* **19**, 935 (2002).
9. V. Gorini, U. Moschella, A. Yu. Kamenshchik, V. Pasquier and A. A. Starobinsky, Tolman-Oppenheimer-Volkoff equations in presence of the Chaplygin gas: stars and wormhole-like solutions, *Phys. Rev.* **D78**, p. 064064 (2008).
10. L. Zou, F.-Y. Li and H. Wen, Exact solutions of the Einstein-Maxwell equations in charged perfect fluid spheres for the generalized Tolman-Oppenheimer-Volkoff equations, *Int. J. Mod. Phys.* **D22**, p. 1350009 (2013).
11. L. Herrera and W. Barreto, General relativistic polytropes for anisotropic matter: The general formalism and applications, *Phys. Rev.* **D88**, p. 084022 (2013).
12. F. Özel and P. Freire, Masses, Radii, and the Equation of State of Neutron Stars, *Ann. Rev. Astron. Astrophys.* **54**, 401 (2016).
13. L. Herrera and A. Di Prisco, Self-similarity in static axially symmetric relativistic fluids, *Int. J. Mod. Phys.* **D27**, p. 1750176 (2017).
14. V. Faraoni, Embedding black holes and other inhomogeneities in the universe in various theories of gravity: a short review, *Universe* **4**, p. 109 (2018).
15. Y. X. Martins, L. F. A. Campos, D. d. S. P. Teixeira and R. J. Biezuner, Existence and Classification of Pseudo-Asymptotic Solutions for Tolman-Oppenheimer-Volkoff Systems, *Annals Phys.* **409**, p. 167929 (2019).
16. J. D. V. Arbañil, J. P. S. Lemos and V. T. Zanchin, Polytropic spheres with electric charge: compact stars, the Oppenheimer-Volkoff and Buchdahl limits, and quasiblack holes, *Phys. Rev.* **D88**, p. 084023 (2013).
17. S. Carloni and D. Vernieri, Covariant Tolman-Oppenheimer-Volkoff equations. I. The isotropic case, *Phys. Rev.* **D97**, p. 124056 (2018).
18. S. Carloni and D. Vernieri, Covariant Tolman-Oppenheimer-Volkoff equations. II. The anisotropic case, *Phys. Rev.* **D97**, p. 124057 (2018).
19. A. A. Isayev, Comment on "Covariant Tolman-Oppenheimer-Volkoff equations. II. The anisotropic case", *Phys. Rev.* **D98**, p. 088503 (2018).
20. P. Papadopoulos and J. A. Font, Relativistic hydrodynamics on space - like and null surfaces: Formalism and computations of spherically symmetric space-times, *Phys. Rev.* **D61**, p. 024015 (2000).
21. K. Lake, All static spherically symmetric perfect-fluid solutions of Einstein's equations, *Phys. Rev. D* **67**, p. 104015 (May 2003).
22. P. Boonserm, M. Visser and S. Weinfurtner, Solution generating theorems for the TOV equation, *Phys. Rev.* **D76**, p. 044024 (2007).
23. G. J. Olmo, H. Sanchis-Alepuz and S. Tripathi, Stellar Structure Equations in Extended Palatini Gravity, *Phys. Rev.* **D86**, p. 104039 (2012).
24. K. Glampedakis, G. Pappas, H. O. Silva and E. Berti, Post-Tolman-Oppenheimer-Volkoff formalism for relativistic stars, *Phys. Rev.* **D92**, p. 024056 (2015).
25. R. Jain, B. G. Sidharth and C. Corda, On the Jeans Theorem and the 'Tolman-Oppenheimer-Volkoff Equation' in R^2 Gravity, *Adv. High Energy Phys.* **2016**, p. 2601741 (2016).
26. H. Velten, A. M. Oliveira and A. Wojnar, A free parametrized TOV: Modified Gravity from Newtonian to Relativistic Stars, *PoS* **MPCS2015**, p. 025 (2016).
27. A. Wojnar and H. Velten, Equilibrium and stability of relativistic stars in extended theories of gravity, *Eur. Phys. J.* **C76**, p. 697 (2016).
28. K. A. Bronnikov, J. C. Fabris, O. F. Piattella and E. C. Santos, Static, spherically symmetric solutions with a scalar field in Rastall gravity, *Gen. Rel. Grav.* **48**, p. 162 (2016).

29. A. V. Astashenok, S. D. Odintsov and A. de la Cruz-Dombriz, The realistic models of relativistic stars in $f(R) = R + \alpha R^2$ gravity, *Class. Quant. Grav.* **34**, p. 205008 (2017).
30. C. Bona, A new proof of the generalized birkhoff theorem, *Journal of Mathematical Physics* **29**, 1440 (1988).
31. A. Maciel, M. Le Delliou and J. P. Mimoso, Revisiting the Birkhoff theorem from a dual null point of view, *Phys. Rev.* **D98**, p. 024016 (2018).
32. S. A. Hayward, Dual - null dynamics, *Ann. Inst. H. Poincare Phys. Theor.* **59**, 399 (1993).
33. S. A. Hayward, Dual-null dynamics of the einstein field, *Classical and Quantum Gravity* **10**, 779 (apr 1993).
34. S. A. Hayward, The general solution to the einstein equations on a null surface, *Classical and Quantum Gravity* **10**, 773 (apr 1993).
35. S. A. Hayward, General laws of black-hole dynamics, *Phys. Rev. D* **49**, 6467 (June 1994).
36. J. M. Senovilla, Trapped surfaces, *Int. J. Mod. Phys. D* **20**, p. 2139 (2011).
37. S. A. Hayward, Quasilocal gravitational energy, *Phys. Rev. D* **49**, 831 (January 1994).
38. A. Maciel, M. Le Delliou and J. P. Mimoso, Dual null formalism for the collapse of fluids in a cosmological background, *Phys. Rev.* **D92**, p. 083525 (2015).
39. A. Maciel, Quasilocal approach to general universal horizons, *Phys. Rev. D* **93**, p. 104013 (2016).
40. A. Maciel, M. Le Delliou and J. P. Mimoso, New perspectives on the TOV equilibrium from a dual null approach, *Classical and Quantum Gravity* **37**, p. 125005 (June 2020).
41. C. Cattoen and M. Visser, Necessary and sufficient conditions for big bangs, bounces, crunches, rips, sudden singularities, and extremality events, *Class.Quant.Grav.* **22**, 4913 (2005).
42. F. S. N. Lobo and J. P. Mimoso, Possibility of hyperbolic tunneling, *Phys. Rev.* **D82**, p. 044034 (2010).
43. R. M. Wald, *General Relativity* (The University of Chicago Press, Chicago, 1984).
44. S. W. Hawking and G. F. R. Ellis, *The Large Scale Structure of Space-Time* (Cambridge University Press, Cambridge, 1973).
45. S. Carroll, *Spacetime and Geometry* (Addison-Wesley Publishing Company, San Francisco, 2004).
46. A. Maciel, M. Le Delliou and J. P. Mimoso, New perspectives on the TOV equilibrium from a dual null approach, *Class. Quant. Grav.* **37**, p. 125005 (2020).
47. J. P. Mimoso, M. Le Delliou and F. C. Mena, Separating expansion from contraction in spherically symmetric models with a perfect fluid: Generalization of the tolman-oppenheimer-volkoff condition and application to models with a cosmological constant, *Phys. Rev. D* **81**, p. 123514 (June 2010).
48. C. W. Misner and D. H. Sharp, Relativistic equations for adiabatic, spherically symmetric gravitational collapse, *Phys. Rev.* **136**, B571 (October 1964).
49. S. A. Hayward, Gravitational energy in spherical symmetry, *Phys. Rev. D* **53**, 1938 (1996).
50. V. Faraoni, Is the Hawking quasilocal energy "Newtonian"?, *Symmetry* **7**, 2038 (2015).
51. S. A. Hayward, Unified first law of black-hole dynamics and relativistic thermodynamics, *Classical Quantum Gravity* **15**, 3147 (1998).
52. A. Prain, V. Vitagliano, V. Faraoni and M. Lapierre-Léonard, Hawking–Hayward quasi-local energy under conformal transformations, *Class. Quant. Grav.* **33**, p. 145008 (2016).

53. V. Faraoni and J. Coté, Quasilocal mass and multipole expansion in scalar-tensor gravity (2019).
54. R. L. Arnowitt, S. Deser and C. W. Misner, Dynamical structure and definition of energy in general relativity, *Phys. Rev.* **116**, 1322 (1959).
55. H. Stephani, D. Kramer, M. MacCallum, C. Hoenselaers and E. Herlt, *Exact Solutions of Einstein's Field Equations*, Cambridge Monographs on Mathematical Physics, 2nd edn. (Cambridge University Press, Cambridge, England, 2009).
56. P. Martin-Moruno and M. Visser, Classical and semi-classical energy conditions, *Fundam. Theor. Phys.* **189**, 193 (2017).
57. G. F. R. Ellis and H. van Elst, Cosmological models: Cargese lectures 1998, *NATO Sci. Ser. C* **541**, 1 (1999).
58. J. P. Mimoso and P. Crawford, Shear - free anisotropic cosmological models, *Class. Quant. Grav.* **10**, 315 (1993).
59. L. Bianchi, On the three-dimensional spaces which admit a continuous group of motions, *General Relativity and Gravitation* **33**, 2171 (2001).
60. G. F. R. Ellis and M. A. H. MacCallum, A Class of homogeneous cosmological models, *Commun. Math. Phys.* **12**, 108 (1969).
61. R. Kantowski and R. K. Sachs, Some spatially homogeneous anisotropic relativistic cosmological models, *J. Math. Phys.* **7**, p. 443 (1966).
62. E. Abdalla, N. Afshordi, M. Fontanini, D. C. Guariento and E. Papantonopoulos, Cosmological black holes from self-gravitating fields, *Phys. Rev. D* **89**, p. 104018 (May 2014).
63. D. C. Guariento, A. Maciel, M. M. C. Mello and V. T. Zanchin, Charged cosmological black holes: a thorough study of a family of solutions, *Phys. Rev.* **D100**, p. 104050 (2019).
64. F. C. Mena, Cylindrically symmetric models of gravitational collapse to black holes: A short review, *Int. J. Mod. Phys.* **D24**, p. 1542021 (2015).
65. K. Bronnikov, N. O. Santos and A. Wang, Cylindrical Systems in General Relativity (2019).
66. J. D. V. Arbañil, J. P. S. Lemos and V. T. Zanchin, Incompressible relativistic spheres: Electrically charged stars, compactness bounds, and quasiblack hole configurations, *Phys. Rev.* **D89**, p. 104054 (2014).
67. V. Faraoni, Quasilocal energy in modified gravity, *Classical Quantum Gravity* **33**, p. 015007 (2016).
68. H. Barzegar, P. T. Chrusciel and M. Hörzinger, Energy in higher-dimensional spacetimes, *Phys. Rev.* **D96**, p. 124002 (2017).
69. M.-T. Wang and S.-T. Yau, Quasilocal mass in general relativity, *Phys. Rev. Lett.* **102**, p. 021101 (2009).
70. S. Capozziello, F. S. N. Lobo and J. P. Mimoso, Energy conditions in modified gravity, *Phys. Lett.* **B730**, 280 (2014).
71. S. Capozziello, F. S. N. Lobo and J. P. Mimoso, Generalized energy conditions in Extended Theories of Gravity, *Phys. Rev.* **D91**, p. 124019 (2015).
72. C. Barcelo and M. Visser, Twilight for the energy conditions?, *Int. J. Mod. Phys.* **D11**, 1553 (2002).

A spherically symmetric stiff fluid spacetime in light of cosmic structure formation

Daniele Gregoris

School of Science, Jiangsu University of Science and Technology, Zhenjiang 212003, China
E-mail: danielegregoris@libero.it

We will report here a critical inspection of the Penrose conjecture according to which the gravitational entropy should be quantified via the Weyl curvature, with the Clifton-Ellis-Tavakol entropy being one specific realization of this proposal. In fact, we will show that in some exact inhomogeneous and anisotropic cosmological models which arise as exact solutions in general relativity with either closed and open topologies, the Clifton-Ellis-Tavakol gravitational entropy is increasing in time despite the decrease of the magnitude of the Weyl curvature: this is possible thanks to the growth of the spatial shearing effects. The matter content driving the dynamics of this class of models comes in the form of a stiffened fluid which can be relevant in the early universe. We choose the values of the free parameters entering the metric tensor consistently with the holographic principle and the second law of thermodynamics. Our study can be of interest in light of the modeling of the formation of some primordial structures, like the Large Quasar Groups, as suggested by the growth of gravitational entropy, and whose existence cannot be accounted for by standard perturbation methods over a homogeneous background.

Keywords: Exact solution; stiff matter; gravitational entropy.

1. Introduction

Our Universe contains a plethora of different astrophysical structures with different sizes such as galaxies, clusters of galaxies, filaments, voids,... The formation process for cosmic structures of sizes smaller than 150 Mpc, which is the length scale above which the universe is considered to be homogeneous,[1] can be described with perturbation schemes applied to a homogeneous background as the Friedman-Lemaître-Robertson-Walker one.[2,3] However, there is observational evidence of the existence of astrophysical structures like the one known as the "axis of evil"[4] which challenge the Copernican principle because they come with an alignment of matter along a preferred direction and their sizes are larger than 150 Mpc. Other examples are the Large Quasar Groups with sizes in the range of 70-350 Mpc.[5–8] Accounting for their existence by means of perturbation methods is problematic because the cosmic material would not cluster quickly enough for forming a bound system of this size: this is one among few other open questions affecting the standard model of cosmology.[12] Inhomogeneous cosmology may offer an alternative route for developing theoretical frameworks which can describe the evolution of matter perturbations undergoing a local collapse which can lead to the formation of an astrophysical structure. For example, in a dust Szekeres spacetime the density contrast grows eight times quicker than in the linear perturbation regime making the process of formation of astrophysical structures more efficient.[13] There is also observational evidence of exotic astrophysical structures with non-standard size which should have formed in the early universe, as a supermassive black hole at redshift $z \sim 10$,[9,10] and the Huge Quasar Group at redshift $z \sim 1.27$,[11] whose existence cannot be explained by invoking effects played by an inhomogeneous spacetime supported by dust (which can be interpreted as pressureless dark matter). Therefore, the issue becomes to provide an appropriate theoretical framework in which spatial shear effects and tidal effects can trigger a local collapse in an overall expanding background supported by a matter content consistent with the early stages of evolution of the universe.

In the primordial universe shearing effects may play an important role, as compared to the one of the matter content, even though they are almost negligible at the present day.[14] Moreover, it has been argued that in early cosmic epochs the matter content may come in the form of a stiff fluid[a],[15–19] which is the effective hydrodynamical realization of a massless scalar field according to the canonical formalism.[20,21] More in detail, in[18,19] it has been argued that the early universe should be filled with cold baryons which fulfill the equation of state $p = \rho$, and that if cosmic matter is described as a relativistic self-gravitating Bose-Einstein condensate, then the cosmic evolution would experience a stiff-matter dominated era. Indeed the development of specific algorithms for integrating the Einstein field equations when the matter content is a stiff fluid has received attention in the literature;[22–28] then a number of exact and analytical solutions expressible in terms of elementary functions has been found obeying to a variety of symmetry groups,[29–32] just to mention a few examples.

One specific solution to the Einstein equations that we have adopted in our own research,[33] and which was found and investigated from the mathematical perspective by a number of different authors,[34–38] reads as (see also page 261 in[39]):

$$ds^2 = -\left(\frac{r}{2}\right)^2 dt^2 + \frac{dr^2}{\epsilon + Cr^2} + r^2 \left[\frac{\epsilon}{2} + h(t)\right](d\theta^2 + \sin^2\theta d\phi^2), \tag{1}$$

where the "generalized scale factor" can either be

$$h(t) = A\sin(t) + B\cos(t) \quad \text{if} \quad \epsilon = -1, \tag{2}$$

$$h(t) = -\left(\frac{t}{2}\right)^2 + 2At + B \quad \text{if} \quad \epsilon = 0, \tag{3}$$

$$h(t) = Ae^t + Be^{-t} \quad \text{if} \quad \epsilon = 1, \tag{4}$$

according to the topology of the spacetime. We can note that the model (1) depends on three free parameters A, B, and C, and that only its angular part, and not the

---

[a]A stiff fluid is a perfect fluid, e.g. it is fully described by its adiabatic pressure p and energy density ρ, whose equation of state in natural units is $p = \rho$, and with matter-energy tensor $T^\mu{}_\nu = \text{diag}[-\rho, p, p, p]$.

radial one, is expanding. The spacetime is supported by a fluid obeying to a stiffened equation of state

$$p = \rho + \frac{3C}{4\pi}. \tag{5}$$

which reduces to the case of a stiff fluid, i.e. of a massless scalar field, in the limit of $C \to 0$. Thus, this latter parameter, which does not affect directly the time evolution of the generalized scale factor $h(t)$ as we can appreciate from (2)-(3)-(4), would instead make the cosmic fluid pressure to be non-zero but equal to a constant in an empty space for which $\rho = 0$; more in general th equation of state (5) can be written in the form $p = \omega(\rho)\rho$ in which the density-dependent equation of state parameter can be interpreted as a chameleon field.[40, 41] The Hubble function, invariant shear, cosmic energy density and Weyl curvature of the spacetime (1) are given by

$$H = \frac{4\dot{h}(t)}{3(\epsilon + 2h(t))r}, \tag{6}$$

$$\sigma^2 = \frac{4\dot{h}(t)^2}{3(\epsilon + 2h(t))^2 r^2} = \frac{3H^2}{4}, \tag{7}$$

$$\rho = -\frac{c^2(\mathcal{R} + 18C)}{16\pi G}, \quad R = -2\frac{\epsilon + \mathcal{R} + 6Cr^2(\epsilon + 2h(t))^2}{r^2(\epsilon + 2h(t))^2}, \tag{8}$$

$$\Psi_2 = -\frac{\mathcal{R} + \epsilon}{3r^2(2h(t) + \epsilon)^2}, \tag{9}$$

where an overdot denotes a derivative with respect to the cosmic time. In the computation of the latter quantity we have applied the Newman-Penrose formalism,[42] and the following notation has been introduced:

$$\begin{aligned}\mathcal{R} &= 4(A^2 + B^2) \quad \text{for} \quad \epsilon = -1, \\ \mathcal{R} &= 4(4A^2 + B) \quad \text{for} \quad \epsilon = 0, \\ \mathcal{R} &= -16AB \quad \text{for} \quad \epsilon = 1.\end{aligned} \tag{10}$$

Since we have a nonzero Weyl scalar Ψ_2, some tidal forces are present in the cosmological model (1),[43] and they can trigger a local gravitational collapse whose evolution then experiences the non-standard spatial shearing effects described by σ^2, potentially taming the previously mentioned problems of accounting for the existence of some astrophysical structures observed in the early universe. For exploring this topic, in our research[33] we have computed the gravitational entropy for the cosmology (1) by following the Clifton-Ellis-Tavakol proposal,[44] in which we have implemented some numerical values for the free parameters A, B, and C which are consistent with the thermodynamical requirements formulated through the cosmological holographic principle and the second law of thermodynamics. We have obtained that the gravitational entropy can be increasing even in the time intervals in which the strength of the Weyl curvature is decreasing, and therefore we have claimed that *Thermodynamics of shearing massless scalar field spacetimes is inconsistent with the Weyl curvature hypothesis* according to which the conformal curvature can be adopted as a measure for the gravitational entropy.[45] Our result is due to the effects played by the spatial shear which accounts for the spatial anisotropies.

This *MG16 conference proceeding* is organized as follows: in Sect. 2 we impose the holographic principle and the second law of thermodynamics to the spacetime (1) showing how they can set some constraints on the behavior of various relevant physical quantities. In Sect. 3 we introduce the Clifton-Ellis-Tavakol entropy, discuss its importance in the modeling of the formation of astrophysical structures, and report on our specific results for the spacetime under investigation. In Sect. 4 we formulate the two messages that according to us the reader should take at home regardless the technicalities involved in this project. Finally in Sect. 5 we put our research into the larger perspective of the studies of gravitational entropy in inhomogeneous cosmology.

2. Imposing the thermodynamical requirements

According to the cosmological holographic principle, as formulated by Bousso, the matter entropy S_m inside a region bounded by a "horizon" should be smaller than the area A_H of the horizon itself, or more precisely $S_m \leq A_H/4$.[46] We can see that the celebrated Bekenstein-Hawking entropy for static black holes[47,48] constitutes the limiting case of this more general principle. For a dynamical spacetime we consider appropriate to work with the dynamical apparent horizon as the boundary of the region we are interested in; by introducing the areal radius

$$\tilde{r} = r\sqrt{\frac{\epsilon}{2} + h(t)}, \tag{11}$$

the location $\tilde{r}_H$ of the dynamical apparent horizon is such that[49]

$$||\nabla \tilde{r}||^2_{\tilde{r}=\tilde{r}_H} = 0. \tag{12}$$

In a time-evolving configuration, the dynamical apparent horizon is not the unique choice for the boundary of the region to which the cosmological holographic principle can be imposed; however in the homogeneous and isotropic Friedman universe assuming the space to be filled with some form of dark energy the first and second law of thermodynamics have been shown to hold for the dynamical apparent horizon, but not if one works with the cosmic horizon,[50] providing a motivation for choosing our route.[51,52]

Since the fluid energy density should be non-negative all along the time evolution of the system, we found that C should be non-positive; under this restriction, equation (12) admits a solution only for the topology $\epsilon = 1$. Setting the parameters A and B to be positive guarantees both a well-defined cosmic energy density and the existence of a solution for the equation determining the location of the dynamical apparent horizon. Taking into account that $A_H = 4\pi \tilde{r}_H^2$ and that $S_m = \alpha \tilde{r}_H^3$, with

α an overall proportionality constant, it can be seen after some computations that the holographic principle is further constraining the value of C, i.e. of the deviations of the equation of state of the cosmic matter from a stiff fluid. The cosmological consequences of these restrictions on the values of the arbitrary model parameters are:

- If we compute the deceleration parameter as in,[53] it would be negative;
- Since $\epsilon + 2h(t) \neq 0$, there would be no initial singularity in this cosmology because there would not exist a time t_B at which the energy density (8) would diverge.

On the other hand, imposing the second law of thermodynamics to the matter content would require $\dot{S}_m > 0$, which can be translated into the equivalent condition $\frac{d\tilde{r}_H}{dt} > 0$. After some algebraic manipulations, we could recast this condition as $Ae^t - Be^{-t} > 0$; thus, the cosmological consequences within the model (1) of imposing the second law are:

- The lower limit on the size of the universe $h(t) > 2Be^{-t}$ is established;
- The lower limit on the age of universe $t > \frac{1}{2} \ln \frac{B}{A}$ is established;
- The Weyl curvature Ψ_2 is a time-decreasing quantity.

3. Computing the gravitational entropy

"Entropy" can be naively regarded as a measure of the disorder within a system (as related to the existence of an arrow of time), or as a quantification of the number of different microscopic realizations compatible with the same macroscopic system (statistical entropy). Therefore, in cosmology, as astrophysical structures form in one specific spatial regions rather than in others with the whole universe remaining homogeneous on large enough length scales, the gravitational entropy should increase. Since when an observer looks at the universe from its location it may or may not detect an astrophysical structure, the growth of gravitational entropy should be accompanied by an increase of the spatial anisotropy. One specific way of computing the density s_{grav} of gravitational entropy in Petrov type D spacetime, as for example (1), is due to Clifton-Ellis-Tavakol[44]:

$$T_{\text{grav}} \dot{s}_{\text{grav}} = -dV \sigma_{\mu\nu} \left(\pi^{\mu\nu}_{\text{grav}} + \frac{(\rho + p)}{3\rho_{\text{grav}}} E^{\mu\nu} \right). \tag{13}$$

The ingredients of this formula are the following:

- The temperature of the free gravitational field defined as

$$T_{\text{grav}} = \frac{|u_{a;b} l^a n^b|}{\pi} = \frac{r}{8\pi \sqrt{Cr^2 + \epsilon}}, \tag{14}$$

where u^a is the matter-comoving observer four-velocity, and l^a and n^a are part of the null coframe containing the dt and dr contributions.

- The volume element
$$dV = \frac{r^2 \sin\theta(\epsilon + 2h(t))}{2\sqrt{Cr^2 + \epsilon}} \, dr d\theta d\phi \,. \tag{15}$$
- The shear tensor $\sigma_{\mu\nu}$ which describes the rate of distortion of a given region with fixed volume during the cosmic evolution.
- The gravitational energy defined in terms of the Weyl curvature as:
$$\rho_{\text{grav}} := 16\pi |\Psi_2| \,. \tag{16}$$
- The gravitational anisotropic pressure also defined in terms of the Weyl curvature as:
$$\pi_{\mu\nu}^{\text{grav}} := \frac{|\Psi_2|}{16\pi}(-x_a x_b + y_a y_b + z_a z_b + u^a u^b) \,, \tag{17}$$
in which x_a, y_a, z_a constitute the spacelike vectors in the orthonormal base for the metric (1).
- The gravito-electric tensor $E_{\mu\nu}$ which accounts for tidal effects, which are indeed necessary for having a gravitational collapse.

We have considered the approach (13) to be a sound proposal for computing the gravitational entropy because, as pointed out in,[44] it delivers a non-negative entropy, it is consistent with the Hawking-Bekenstein entropy of black holes, it provides a vanishing entropy in and only in conformally flat spacetimes (as for example in the homogeneous and isotropic Friedman-Lemaître-Robertson-Walker universe in which astrophysical structures cannot form due to the lack of any matter density contrast), and it is related to the growth of anisotropies in the spacetime (as they indeed increase during the structure formation phase).

Thus, it does not come as a surprise that the conjecture of a connection between gravitational entropy and Weyl curvature has been regarded as a useful tool for the description of the formation of astrophysical structures in various inhomogeneous models. For example, in[54] a relationship between the growth of gravitational entropy and the amplitude of initial fluctuations of spatial curvature at the last scattering time has been found, while the possible saturation of its value at a certain time has been investigated in[55] for the Lemaître-Tolman-Bondi universe, in[56] more in general for the class of silent universes for which the gravitomagnetic part of the Weyl curvature vanishes, and in[57] for a perturbed Friedman spacetime. Furthermore, a gravitational entropy quantified via the Weyl curvature is consistent with the generalized second law in the void Lemaître-Tolman-Bondi universe,[58] and the specific Clifton-Ellis-Tavakol entropy has been shown to be a time increasing function in a number of cosmological models.[59]

Our explicit computations for the Clifton-Ellis-Tavakol gravitational entropy delivered the result
$$T_{\text{grav}} \dot{s}_{\text{grav}} = dV \frac{64\pi \dot{h}(t)(1 - 16AB)}{3(2h(t) + \epsilon)^3 r^3} \,. \tag{18}$$

Here we have restricted ourselves to the spacetime (4) because, as mentioned in Sect. 2, it is the only case within (1) for which a thermodynamical investigation based on the cosmological holographic principle was possible. Then, implementing the constraints on the free parameters obtained from such analysis and those arising from the second law of thermodynamics, we have found that a challenge to the Weyl curvature conjecture proposed by Penrose[45] is posed. In fact, the gravitational entropy is increasing even when the gravito-electric curvature as measured by Ψ_2 in (9) is not, and thus the latter cannot be considered too naively as a measure of the former.

4. Discussion

Quantifying the effects that the interactions between small-scale inhomogeneities (e.g. galaxies, galaxy clusters, voids, filaments, etc...) have on the large-scale evolution of the Universe is not a trivial task, and the debate in the literature about their importance is still open.[61] There exists in fact a range of completely different claims from that they have no effects at all to the one that they can bring an energy budget which can be responsible for the observed accelerated expansion of the universe without the need of a cosmological constant; see[62] for a review of different approaches and their predictions. Once endowed with a cosmological model formulated in terms of a metric tensor solution of the field equations of the underlying gravitational theory, it is necessary to investigate its physical applicability. Some widely applied cosmological tests which can assess the suitability of a mathematical solution of the Einstein equations as a cosmological model rely on supernovae data,[63-65] cosmic microwave background data,[66,67] or baryon acoustic oscillations data,[68,69] and clearly require data-analysis skills. For example, the inhomogeneous dust Lemaître-Tolman-Bondi model has been shown to be in tension with the kinematic Sunyaev-Zel'dovich effect[70] although it is not with observations related to the luminosity distance of supernovae, without the need of dark energy but assuming that the observer is located inside a giant void;[71] more in general the development of "model independent" tests for inhomogeneous cosmology constitutes a line of current research.[72-74] However, in Sect. 2 we have explained how "theoretical" requirements can also be exploited for constraining the values of the free model parameters and for extracting cosmological information about the model under investigation. We had previously applied the same way of thinking to the Stephani cosmological model by estimating the strength of spatial inhomogeneities, the matter abundance and the size of the universe by imposing the cosmological holographic principle and the second law of thermodynamics[75] (however this latter spacetime is conformally flat and therefore it does not offer any viable possibility for an investigation of the gravitational entropy). Thus, the first take at home message from our research is:

- By working with solely pen and paper, we can constrain a given cosmological model known in terms of its metric tensor by imposing the thermodynamical requirements which follow from the cosmological holographic principle and the second law of thermodynamics.

In Sect. 3 we have mentioned that the Clifton-Ellis-Tavakol gravitational entropy is increasing in time for the spacetime (1) although the Weyl curvature is not thanks to the presence of a term given by shear tensor which is inserted by hands in its formulation. The fact that spatial shearing effects are developing in the same time interval in which the gravitational entropy is increasing is a fundamental consistency check for the mathematical formula adopted for the latter. In fact, both these quantities are expected to increase during the structure formation phase because the universe is becoming anisotropic and inhomogeneous, with the former being measured by the shear tensor while the latter can be regarded as an increase of the level of "disorder" of the system which should be quantified via an appropriate entropy quantity. Thus, our second take at home message, whose consequences will be further explored in the next Sect. 5 is:

- Implementing the Weyl curvature conjecture according to which the Weyl curvature should serve as a measure for the gravitational entropy is not as simple as it may look like at a first sight and other ingredients may be necessary in the construction of a mathematical formula for the gravitational entropy.

5. Outlook

The search for an appropriate inhomogeneous cosmological model which can provide a viable framework for addressing the issue of the formation of astrophysical structures with sizes larger than 150 Mpc (and which is also in agreement with other datasets), and the formulation of an appropriate measure for the "gravitational entropy" in the spirit of the Weyl curvature conjecture are two related problems. Therefore, we consider appropriate to investigate various notions of gravitational entropy as the following:

-
$$S = \frac{C_{\mu\nu\rho\sigma}C^{\mu\nu\rho\sigma}}{R_{\mu\nu}R^{\mu\nu}} \tag{19}$$

where $C_{\mu\nu\rho\sigma}$ and $R_{\mu\nu}$ are respectively the Weyl and Ricci tensor, and its spatially integrated version

$$\tilde{S} = \int dV S. \tag{20}$$

This formula has arisen in the context of cosmologies exhibiting an anisotropic singularity.[76] However this proposal cannot be applied to vacuum spacetimes because of the vanishing of the Ricci tensor.

- Eq. (19) but multiplied by the square root of the determinant of the spatial metric h as suggested in[77]:
$$S = \sqrt{h}\frac{C_{\mu\nu\rho\sigma}C^{\mu\nu\rho\sigma}}{R_{\mu\nu}R^{\mu\nu}}, \qquad (21)$$
which would be something in between the two proposals of the previous step.
- Applying a spatially averaging scheme and writing the entropy as[78,79]
$$S = V_\mathcal{D}\left\langle \rho \ln \frac{\rho}{\langle\rho\rangle_\mathcal{D}}\right\rangle_\mathcal{D}, \qquad (22)$$
where angular brackets denote an average over the spatial domain of interest $\mathcal{D}$.
- The Clifton-Ellis-Tavakol entropy that we have already talked about in Sect. 3.

These inequivalent ways of computing the gravitational entropy should be applied to the general line element describing a spherically symmetric dynamical spacetime (see page 251 in[39])
$$ds^2 = -e^{2\nu(t,r)}dt^2 + e^{2\lambda(t,r)}dr^2 + Y^2(t,r)(d\theta^2 + \sin^2\theta d\phi^2) \qquad (23)$$
in a set of future projects. Intuitively, we expect that demanding the simultaneous growth of shear, Weyl curvature and gravitational entropy would provide some information on the increasing/decreasing and concavity properties of the functions $\nu(t,r)$, $\lambda(t,r)$ and $Y(t,r)$, which then will be implemented into the Einstein equations for understanding which types of matter content permit to achieve this goal.

All the previously mentioned proposals for computing the gravitational entropy are directly sensitive to the matter content of the spacetime. In fact in some of them the energy density (Hosoya-Buchert-Morita) and possibly also the pressure (Clifton-Ellis-Tavakol) appear explicitly; in other cases as in (19)-(20)-(21) they are inserted via the Ricci tensor, which is connected to the matter content of the universe as we can see from the Einstein equations written in the form
$$R_{\mu\nu} = 8\pi\left(T_{\mu\nu} - \frac{1}{2}g_{\mu\nu}T\right). \qquad (24)$$
A more conservative proposal which has been formulated recently in the context of black hole physics argues that it is possible to write the density s of gravitational entropy just in terms of the frame component of the Weyl tensor W and of its Newman-Penrose derivative DW as[80]
$$s = \left|\frac{DW}{W}\right|. \qquad (25)$$
The applicability of such formalism in inhomogeneous cosmology and in particular the investigation of its relationship to the spatial anisotropies quantified by the shear tensor would constitute a subject of future studies.

Acknowledgments

The author thanks the organizers of the online 16 Marcel Grossmann conference.

References

1. V. Springel, et al., Simulating the joint evolution of quasars, galaxies and their large-scale distribution, *Nature* **435**, 629 (2005).
2. E. Lifshitz, Republication of: On the gravitational stability of the expanding universe, *J. Phys. (USSR)* **10** (1946) 116; *Gen. Rel. Grav.* **49**, 18 (2017).
3. P. J. E. Peebles, and J. T. Yu, Primeval adiabatic perturbation in an expanding universe, *Astrophys. J.* **162**, 815 (1970).
4. K. Land, and J. Magueijo, Examination of evidence for a preferred axis in the cosmic radiation anisotropy, *Phys. Rev. Lett.* **95**, 071301 (2005).
5. M. Scrimgeour, et al., The WiggleZ Dark Energy Survey: the transition to large-scale cosmic homogeneity, *Mon. Not. Roy. Astron. Soc.* **425**, 116 (2012).
6. J. K. Yadav, J. S. Bagla, and N. Khandai, Fractal dimension as a measure of the scale of homogeneity, *Mon. Not. Roy. Astron. Soc.* **405**, 2009 (2010).
7. F. Sylos Labini, Super-homogeneity and inhomogeneities in the large scale matter distribution, *PoS Cosmology* **002**, 2009 (2009).
8. F. Sylos Labini, N. L. Vasilyev, Y. V. Baryshev, and M. Lopez-Corredoira, Absence of anti-correlations and of baryon acoustic oscillations in the galaxy correlation function from the Sloan Digital Sky Survey DR7, *Astron. Astrophys.* **505**, 981 (2009).
9. D. J. Mortlock, et al., A luminous quasar at a redshift of $z = 7.085$, *Nature* **474**, 616 (2011).
10. Y. Matsuoka et al., Subaru high-z exploration of lowluminosity quasars (SHELLQs). I. Discovery of 15 quasars and bright galaxies at $5.7 < z < 6.9$, *Astrophys. J.* **828**, 26 (2016).
11. R. G. Clowes, et al., A structure in the early universe at $z \sim 1.3$ that exceeds the homogeneity scale of the R-W concordance cosmology, *Mon. Not. Roy. Astron. Soc.* **429**, 2910 (2013).
12. A. D. Dolgov, Beasts in Lambda-CDM Zoo, *Physics of Atomic Nuclei* **80**, 987 (2017).
13. K. Bolejko, Structure formation in the quasispherical Szekeres model, *Phys. Rev. D* **73**, 123508 (2006).
14. A. Coley, and W. C. Lim, Spikes and matter inhomogeneities in massless scalar field models, *Class. Quantum Grav.* **33**, 015009 (2016).
15. E. M. Lifshitz, and I. M. Khalatnikov, Investigations in relativistic cosmology, *Adv. Phys.* **12**, 185 (1963).
16. V. A. Belinski, I. M. Khalatnikov, and E. M. Lifshitz, Oscillatory approach to the singular point in relativistic cosmology, *Adv. Phys.* **19**, 525 (1970).
17. V. A. Belinski, I. M. Khalatnikov, and E. M. Lifshitz, A general solution of the Einstein equations with a time singularity, *Adv. Phys.* **31**, 639 (1982).
18. J. B. Zel'dovic, A hypothesis, unifying the structure and the entropy of the Universe, *Mont. Not. Roy. Astron. Soc.* **160**, 1 (1972).
19. P. -H. Chavanis, Cosmology with a stiff matter era, *Phys. Rev. D* **92**, 103004 (2015).
20. D. H. Lyth, and A. Riotto, Particle physics models of inflation and the cosmological density perturbation, *Phys. Rep.* **314**, 1 (1999).
21. C. Armendariz-Picon, T. Damour, and V. F. Mukhanov, k-Inflation, *Phys. Lett. B* **458**, 209 (1999).
22. R. Geroch, A method for generating solutions of Einstein's equations, *J. Math. Phys.* **12**, 918 (1971).

23. R. Geroch, A method for generating new solutions of Einstein's equation. II., *J. Math. Phys.* **13**, 394 (1972).
24. D. Garfinkle, E. N. Glass, and J. P. Krisch, Solution generating with perfect fluids, *Gen. Rel. Grav.* **29**, 467 (1997).
25. H. Stephani, Symmetries of Einstein's field equations with a perfect fluid source as examples of Lie-Bäcklund symmetries, *J. Math. Phys.* **29**, 1650 (1988).
26. R. Hirota, Direct method of finding exact solutions of nonlinear evolution equations, in "Bäcklund transformations, the inverse scattering method, solitons, and their applications", *Lect. Not. Math. R.M. Miura eds.* **515** (1976).
27. V. A. Belinski, and V. E. Zakharov, Steady-state gravitational solitons with axial symmetry, *Sov. Phys. JETP* **50**, 1 (1979); *Zh. Eksp. Teor. Fiz.* **77**, 3 (1979).
28. J. Wainwright, W. C. W. Ince, and B. J. Marshman, Spatially homogeneous and inhomogeneous cosmologies with equation of state $p = \mu$, *Gen. Rel. Grav.* **10**, 259 (1979).
29. D. Gregoris, W. C. Lim, and A. Coley, Stiff fluid spike solutions from Bianchi type V seed solutions, *Class. Quantum Grav.* **34**, 235013 (2017).
30. M. Marklund, and M. Bradley, Invariant construction of solutions to Einstein's field equations - LRS perfect fluids II, *Class. Quantum Grav.* **16**, 1577 (1999).
31. A. Coley, D. Gregoris, and W. C. Lim, On the first G_1 stiff fluid spike solution in general relativity, *Class. Quantum Grav.* **33**, 215010 (2016).
32. D. Gregoris, On the connection between cosmological parameters and peculiar motion in a G_2 massless scalar field spacetime, *Int. J. Mod. Phys. D* 2150099 (2021).
33. D. Gregoris, Y. C. Ong, and B. Wang, Thermodynamics of shearing massless scalar field spacetimes is inconsistent with the Weyl curvature hypothesis, *Phys. Rev. D* **102** 023539 (2020).
34. C. Leibovitz, Time-dependent solutions of Einstein's equations, *Phys. Rev. D* **4**, 2949 (1971).
35. K. Lake, Remark concerning spherically symmetric nonstatic solutions to the Einstein equations in the comoving frame, *Gen. Rel. Grav.* **15**, 357 (1983).
36. N. van den Bergh and P. Wils, Exact solutions for nonstatic perfect fluid spheres with shear and an equation of state, *Gen. Rel. Grav.* **17**, 223 (1985).
37. B. Collins and J. M. Lang, A class of self-similar perfect fluid spacetimes, and a generalisation, *Class. Quantum Grav.* **4**, 61 (1987).
38. S. D. Maharaj, R. Maartens, and M. Maharaj, A note on a class of spherically symmetric solutions, *Nuovo Cimento B* **108**, 1 (1993).
39. H. Stephani, D. Kramer, M. MacCallum, C. Hoenselaers, and E. Herlt, *Exact solutions of Einstein's field equations* (Cambridge University Press, Cambridge, England, 2002).
40. J. Khoury, and A. Weltman, Chameleon fields: Awaiting surprises for tests of gravity in space, *Phys. Rev. Lett.* **93**, 171104 (2004).
41. J. Khoury, and A. Weltman, Chameleon cosmology, *Phys. Rev. D* **69**, 044026 (2004).
42. E. Newman, and R. Penrose, An approach to gravitational radiation by a method of spin coefficients, *J. Math. Phys* **3**, 566 (1962).
43. J. C. Baez, and E. F. Bunn, The meaning of Einstein's equation, *Amer. Jour. Phys.* **73**, 644 (2005).
44. T. Clifton, G. F. R. Ellis, and R. Tavakol, A gravitational entropy proposal, *Class. Quantum Grav.* **30**, 125009 (2013).
45. R. Penrose, Singularities and time-asymmetry, in *General Relativity: An Einstein Centenary Survey*, edited by S. W. Hawking and W. Israel (Cambridge University Press, Cambridge, England, 1979).
46. R. Bousso, The holographic principle, *Rev. Mod. Phys.* **74**, 825 (2002).

47. S. W. Hawking, Particle creation by black holes, *Comm. Math. Phys.* **43**, 199 (1975).
48. J. D. Bekenstein, Black holes and entropy, *Phys. Rev. D* **7**, 2333, (1973).
49. A. Ashtekar, and B. Krishnan, Isolated and dynamical horizons and their applications, *Living Rev. Relativity* **7**, 10 (2004).
50. B. Wang, Y. Gong, and E. Abdalla, Thermodynamics of an accelerated expanding universe, *Phys. Rev. D* **74**, 083520 (2006).
51. V. Faraoni, Cosmological apparent and trapping horizons, *Phys. Rev. D* **84**, 024003 (2011).
52. D. Bak, and S.-J. Rey, Cosmic holography, *Class. Quantum Grav.* **17**, L83 (2000).
53. G. F. R. Ellis, and H. van Elst, Cosmological models, *Cargése lectures 1998*, [arXiv:gr-qc/9812046].
54. R. A. Sussman, and J. Larena, Gravitational entropy of local cosmic voids, *Class. Quantum Grav.* **32**, 165012 (2015).
55. R. A. Sussman, and J. Larena, Gravitational entropies in LTB dust models, *Class. Quantum Grav.* **31**, 075021 (2014).
56. K. Bolejko, Gravitational entropy and the cosmological no-hair conjecture, *Phys. Rev. D* **97**, 083515 (2018).
57. G. Marozzi, J.-P. Uzan, O. Umeh, and C. Clarkson, Cosmological evolution of the gravitational entropy of the large-scale structure, *Gen. Rel. Grav.* **47**, 114 (2015).
58. P. Mishra, and T. P. Singh, Thermodynamics and Lemaitre-Tolman-Bondi void models, *Phys. Rev. D* **89**, 123007 (2014).
59. S. Chakraborty, S. Guha, and R. Goswami, An investigation on gravitational entropy of cosmological models, *Int. J. Mod. Phys. D* **30**, 2150051 (2021).
60. T. Buchert, et al., Is there proof that backreaction of inhomogeneities is irrelevant in cosmology?, *Class. Quantum Grav.* **32**, 215021 (2015).
61. T. Buchert, et al., Is there proof that backreaction of inhomogeneities is irrelevant in cosmology?, *Class. Quantum Grav.* **32**, 215021 (2015).
62. C. Clarkson, G. Ellis, J. Larena, and O. Umeh, Does the growth of structure affect our dynamical models of the universe? The averaging, backreaction, and fitting problems in cosmology, *Rep. Prog. Phys.* **74**, 112901 (2011).
63. A. G. Riess, et al., Observational evidence from supernovae for an accelerating universe and a cosmological constant, *Astron. J.* **116**, 1009 (1998).
64. S. Perlmutter, et al. (The Supernova Cosmology Project), Measurements of Omega and Lambda from 42 high-redshift supernovae, *Astrophys. J.* **517**, 565 (1999).
65. D. M. Scolnic, The complete light-curve sample of spectroscopically confirmed type Ia supernovae from Pan-STARRS1 and cosmological constraints from the combined pantheon sample, *Astrophys. J.* **859**, 101 (2018).
66. E. Komatsu, et al., Seven-year Wilkinson microwave anisotropy probe (WMAP) observations: cosmological interpretation, *Astrophys. J. Suppl.* **192**, 18 (2011).
67. R. Keisler, et al., A measurement of the damping tail of the cosmic microwave background power spectrum with the South Pole Telescope, *Astrophys. J.* **743**, 28 (2011).
68. D. J. Eisenstein, et al., Detection of the baryon acoustic peak in the large-scale correlation function of SDSS luminous red galaxies, *Astrophys. J.* **633**, 560 (2005).
69. S. Cole, et al. (The 2dFGRS Team), The 2dF Galaxy Redshift Survey: Power-spectrum analysis of the final dataset and cosmological implications, *Mon. Not. R. Astron. Soc.* **362**, 505 (2005).
70. P. Bull, T. Clifton, and P. G. Ferreira, The kSZ effect as a test of general radial inhomogeneity in LTB cosmology, *Phys. Rev. D* **85**, 024002 (2012).
71. T. Clifton, P. G. Ferreira, and K. Land, Living in a void: Testing the Copernican principle with distant supernovae, *Phys. Rev. Lett.* **101**, 131302 (2008).

72. L. H. Dam, A. Heinesen, and D. L. Wiltshire, Apparent cosmic acceleration from type Ia supernovae, *Mon. Not. R. Astron. Soc.* **472**, 835 (2017).
73. A. Heinesen, C. Blake, Y.-Z. Li, and D. L. Wiltshire, Baryon acoustic oscillation methods for generic curvature: Application to the SDSS-III baryon oscillation spectroscopic survey, *J. Cosmol. Astropart. Phys.* **03**, 003 (2019).
74. J. Trost Nielsen, A. Guffanti, and S. Sarkar, Marginal evidence for cosmic acceleration from Type Ia supernovae, *Sci. Rep.* **6**, 35596 (2016).
75. D. Gregoris, Y. C. Ong, B. Wang, Holographic principle and the second law in Stephani cosmology revisited, *Eur. Phys. J. Plus* **135**, 246 (2020).
76. J. Wainwright, and P. J. Anderson, Isotropic singularities and isotropization in a class of Bianchi Type-VI_h cosmologies, *Gen. Rel. Grav.* **16**, 609 (1984).
77. Ø. Grøn, and S. Hervik, Gravitational entropy and quantum cosmology, *Class. Quantum Grav.* **18**, 601 (2001).
78. A. Hosoya, T. Buchert, M. Morita, Information entropy in cosmology, *Phys. Rev. Lett.* **92**, 141302 (2004).
79. R. Sussman, Weighed scalar averaging in LTB dust models: Part I. Statistical fluctuations and gravitational entropy, *Class. Quantum Grav.* **30**, 065015 (2013).
80. D. Gregoris, and Y. C. Ong, Understanding Gravitational Entropy of Black Holes: A New Proposal via Curvature Invariants, arXiv:gr-qc/3945089.

Three-parameter solution for the null-surface formulation in 2+1 dimensions

Tina A. Harriott

Department of Mathematics and Statistics, Mount Saint Vincent University,
Halifax, Nova Scotia, B3M 2J6, Canada
E-mail: tina.harriott@msvu.ca
www.msvu.ca

J. G. Williams

Department of Mathematics and Computer Science,
and the Winnipeg Institute for Theoretical Physics, Brandon University,
Brandon, Manitoba, R7A 6A9, Canada
E-mail: williams@brandonu.ca

The null-surface formuation (NSF) of general relativity is equivalent to standard general relativity but uses families of null surfaces rather than the metric or connection. The NSF can be constructed in dimension 3+1, in any dimension higher, and also in dimension 2+1, which is a special case: In 2+1 dimensions, the main NSF field equation is equivalent to Cartan's metricity condition. The latter arose in differential equation theory to address the problem of classifying solutions of 4 third-order ordinary differential equations. Solving the NSF/Cartan equation has proved challenging, and only three solutions are known to date. This talk presents a fourth solution, which depends upon three independent parameters. Two of the previously known solutions are included as special cases. Energy conditions and possible source terms are examined. The physical interpretation is discussed in detail.

Keywords: Null-surface formulation; NSF; metricity condition; low dimensional gravity; imperfect fluid.

1. Introduction

The NSF[1–3] uses families of null surfaces, rather than a metric, and can be presented in terms of a function Z that specifies the families. More commonly, the NSF is described in terms of a function Λ that is related to Z by differentiation. If required, a metric can be constructed up to a conformal factor from a knowledge of either Z or Λ and an auxiliary function Ω. Forni, Iriondo, Kozameh and Parisi,[4,5] Tanimoto,[6] and Silva-Ortigoza[7] have constructed a (2+1)-dimensional version of the NSF. A brief summary of the 2+1 NSF is given in the remainder of this section. The sections that follow will present a new solution and list its properties.

The equation $u = Z(x^a; \varphi)$ defines a surface, with x^a ($a = 0, 1, 2$) being spacetime coordinates and $\varphi \in S^1$ being an angular variable. The role of φ is to label the surfaces. For the surfaces to be *null* with respect to a spacetime metric $g_{bc}(x^a)$, the gradient of Z must satisfy

$$g^{bc}(x^a) Z_{,b}(x^a;\varphi) Z_{,c}(x^a;\varphi) = 0, \quad (1)$$

where $Z_{,a} \equiv \partial_a Z \equiv \partial Z/\partial x^a$. Equation (1) and its derivatives with respect to φ lead to the *metricity conditions*, which ensure that the nullness requirement is satisfied. The metricity conditions are most easily expressed in terms of coordinates that are naturally adapted to the surfaces.[4–6] Such coordinates are called *intrinsic coordinates*,[2] and are denoted

$$u := Z(x^a;\varphi),$$
$$\omega := \partial u \equiv \partial Z(x^a;\varphi),$$
$$\rho := \partial \omega = \partial^2 u \equiv \partial^2 Z(x^a;\varphi),$$

where $\partial := \partial/\partial\varphi$ is the derivative with respect to φ when the x^a are held fixed. In principle, the above equations can be inverted to give

$$x^a = x^a(u,\omega,\rho,\varphi).$$

The third derivative of Z (i.e. of u) is denoted by Λ:

$$\Lambda(u,\omega,\rho,\varphi) := \partial^3 Z(x^a(u,\omega,\rho,\varphi);\varphi).$$

If Λ is known, then Z can be determined by integration. The intrinsic coordinates u, ω and ρ are φ-dependent and it can be shown that the action of the differential operator ∂ on a function $f(u,\omega,\rho,\varphi)$ is given by[4,6]

$$\partial = \partial' + \omega\,\partial_u + \rho\,\partial_\omega + \Lambda\,\partial_\rho,$$

where ∂' denotes the derivative with respect to φ when u, ω and ρ are held fixed.

Equation (1) leads to the following form for the inverse metric g^{ij},[4,6] expressed in terms of the u,ω,φ coordinates, with the signature of g^{ab}, and hence of g^{ij}, being chosen to be $(-++)$:

$$[g^{ij}] = \Omega^2\,[\gamma^{ij}] = \Omega^2 \begin{pmatrix} 0 & 0 & -1 \\ 0 & 1 & \frac{1}{3}\partial_\rho\Lambda \\ -1 & \frac{1}{3}\partial_\rho\Lambda & \frac{1}{3}\partial(\partial_\rho\Lambda) - \frac{1}{9}(\partial_\rho\Lambda)^2 - \partial_\omega\Lambda \end{pmatrix}.$$

It follows that the components of the metric g_{ij} are

$$[g_{ij}] = \Omega^{-2}\,[\gamma_{ij}] = \Omega^{-2} \begin{pmatrix} -\frac{1}{3}\partial(\partial_\rho\Lambda) + \frac{2}{9}(\partial_\rho\Lambda)^2 + \partial_\omega\Lambda & \frac{1}{3}\partial_\rho\Lambda & -1 \\ \frac{1}{3}\partial_\rho\Lambda & 1 & 0 \\ -1 & 0 & 0 \end{pmatrix}, \quad (2)$$

where γ_{ij} is called the *unphysical* metric. Equations (1) and (2) can be used to derive the following metricity conditions.[4,6]

$$2[\partial(\partial_\rho\Lambda) - \partial_\omega\Lambda - \tfrac{2}{9}(\partial_\rho\Lambda)^2]\partial_\rho\Lambda - \partial^2(\partial_\rho\Lambda) + 3\,\partial(\partial_\omega\Lambda) - 6\,\partial_u\Lambda = 0, \quad (3)$$

$$3\,\partial\Omega = \Omega\,\partial_\rho\Lambda. \quad (4)$$

Equations (3) and (4) ensure that Λ will determine a null surface with respect to *some* spacetime metric $g_{bc}(x^a)$. Equation (3) is the main metricity condition. Equation (4) is the secondary metricity condition. If the two metricity conditions are satisfied, then the Einstein equations, $G_{ij} = \kappa T_{ij}$, will be satisfied if the following equation holds:[4]

$$\partial_\rho^2 \Omega = \kappa T_{\rho\rho} \Omega. \tag{5}$$

Finding a solution in the NSF approach requires solving the coupled set of NSF field equations, Eqs (3), (4) and (5), for Λ and Ω. In 2+1 dimensions, only three nontrivial solutions of the NSF equations have been found to date.[8–10] The present paper introduces a new family of solutions.

2. Solution

The form of the differential operator ∂ suggests looking for solutions that are additively separable. Consider solutions that take the form

$$\Lambda(u, \omega, \rho) = -a\omega + h(\rho + au) = -a\omega + h(x), \tag{6}$$

where a is a constant. Writing $x := \rho + au$, will convert the main metricity condition, Eq. (3), into an ordinary differential equation with x as the independent variable:

$$h^2 \frac{d^3 h}{dx^3} - h \frac{dh}{dx} \frac{d^2 h}{dx^2} + \frac{4}{9}\left(\frac{dh}{dx}\right)^3 + 4a \frac{dh}{dx} = 0. \tag{7}$$

The solution of Eq. (7), together with Eq. (6), represents a solution of the main metricity condition. After introducing a new dependent variable $y := h^{2/3}$, and replacing h by $y^{3/2}$, Eq. (6) becomes

$$\Lambda(u, \omega, \rho) = -a\omega + [y(\rho + au)]^{3/2} \equiv -a\omega + [y(x)]^{3/2}, \tag{8}$$

and Eq. (7) becomes

$$\frac{d^3 y}{dx^3} + 4a\, y^{-3} \frac{dy}{dx} = 0,$$

which can be rewritten

$$\frac{d}{dx}\left(\frac{d^2 y}{dx^2} - 2a y^{-2}\right) = 0,$$

and leads to

$$\frac{d^2 y}{dx^2} - 2a y^{-2} = k,$$

where k is a constant. A further integration can be achieved by multiplying by dy/dx to give

$$\frac{dy}{dx} \frac{d^2 y}{dx^2} - 2a y^{-2} \frac{dy}{dx} - k \frac{dy}{dx} = 0,$$

which leads to
$$\left(\frac{dy}{dx}\right)^2 + 4ay^{-1} - 2ky = -A,$$

where A is a constant. The minus sign in front of A has been inserted for later convenience. It follows that
$$\frac{dy}{dx} = \pm\left(2ky - A - 4ay^{-1}\right)^{1/2},$$

and so
$$x = \pm\int \frac{dy}{\sqrt{2ky - A - 4ay^{-1}}},$$

$$\pm \int \frac{y\,dy}{\sqrt{y\left(2ky^2 - Ay - 4a\right)}}. \quad (9)$$

Equation (9) expresses y as an implicit function of x and, together with Eq. (8), represents an exact solution of the main metricity condition, Eq. (3). Although the right side of Eq. (9) can be evaluated in terms of elliptic integrals of the first and second kinds, the result is too complicated for the equation to be inverted to give y as an explicit function of x. Simplifications arise when some of the constants, A, a, and k, are zero. For example, if $A \neq 0, k \neq 0$, and $a = 0$, the solution becomes the perfect fluid, Petrov-type D, solution that the present authors reported in an earlier paper.[8] The special case where $k \neq 0, a \neq 0$, and $A = 0$ was also reported in an earlier paper, where the spacetime was determined to be of Petrov-type I and the source was represented by a minimally coupled scalar field.[9]

Now consider the secondary metricity condition, Eq. (4),
$$3\,\partial\Omega = \Omega\,\partial_\rho\Lambda.$$

As with Λ, assume that Ω depends upon u and ρ through the combination $\rho + au$, but assume that Ω is independent of ω. Thus $\Omega = \Omega(\rho + au)$. Using $\Lambda = -a\omega + h = -a\omega + y^{3/2}$, it follows that
$$\Omega = h^{1/3} = y^{1/2}.$$

The third NSF equation, Eq. (5),
$$\partial_\rho^2 \Omega = \kappa T_{\rho\rho}\,\Omega,$$

then implies
$$T_{\rho\rho} = \frac{1}{2\kappa\,y^2}\left\{y\frac{d^2y}{dx^2} - \frac{1}{2}\left(\frac{dy}{dx}\right)^2\right\}.$$

It follows that
$$T_{\rho\rho} = \frac{1}{4\kappa\,y^2}\left(A + 8ay^{-1}\right) = \frac{1}{4\kappa\,y^2}\,W,$$

where W is defined by
$$W := A + 8ay^{-1}. \tag{10}$$

For any null vector V, the null energy condition requires $R_{ij} V^i V^j \geq 0$, which is equivalent to $G_{ij} V^i V^j \geq 0$. The vector $V^\rho = \partial_\rho \equiv (0,0,1)$ is null and so $T_{\rho\rho} \geq 0$, or equivalently $W \geq 0$, is a *necessary* condition for the null energy condition to hold. Henceforth, it will be assumed that $W \geq 0$.

3. Metric and Curvature

The form of the solution given in Section 2 implies
$$\partial_\rho^2 y = 2a\, y^{-2} + k, \tag{11}$$
and
$$(\partial_\rho y)^2 = 2k\, y - A - 4a\, y^{-1}. \tag{12}$$

Equations (11) and (12), together with the fact that $\Omega = y^{1/2}$, lead to the following expression for the metric g_{ij}:

$$[g_{ij}] = \Omega^{-2}[\gamma_{ij}] = \begin{pmatrix} -\left(\frac{1}{4}A + 3ay^{-1}\right) & \frac{1}{2}y^{-1/2}\partial_\rho y & -y^{-1} \\ \frac{1}{2}y^{-1/2}\partial_\rho y & y^{-1} & 0 \\ -y^{-1} & 0 & 0 \end{pmatrix}. \tag{13}$$

Hence $g := \det g_{ij} = -y^{-3}$. The inverse metric is

$$[g^{ij}] = \Omega^2[\gamma^{ij}] = \begin{pmatrix} 0 & 0 & -y \\ 0 & y & \frac{1}{2}y^{3/2}\partial_\rho y \\ -y & \frac{1}{2}y^{3/2}\partial_\rho y & \frac{1}{2}ky^3 + 2ay \end{pmatrix}.$$

Equations (11), (12), and (13) can be used to find the Christoffel symbols and the Ricci tensor R_{ij}, which are listed in the appendix. The scalar curvature is constant:
$$R = \frac{1}{32} A^2 + ka. \tag{14}$$

If the constants A, a, and k, are all assumed to be positive (which is consistent with $W > 0$), then it is straightforward to show that the matrix $[R_{ij}]$ is positive definite. This implies that the null, weak, and strong energy conditions are all satisfied.

Being a theory of null surfaces, the NSF does not distinguish between conformally related spacetimes. Thus NSF solutions that correspond to conformally flat spacetimes are considered to be trivial. In 2+1 dimensions, the Cotton-York tensor is defined by[11]

$$C^i_j := \varepsilon^{ikp}\left(R_{pj} - \frac{1}{4}R\, g_{pj}\right)_{;k}$$

and provides a test for conformal flatness: A (2+1)-dimensional spacetime is conformally flat if and only if $C^i_j = 0$. For the solution considered in the present paper, $C^i_j \neq 0$ (except for the trivial case where the constants A, k, and a are all zero). Thus the spacetime is not conformally flat. The components C^i_j are listed in the appendix.

4. Fluid Source: Kinematics

Begin by assuming that the source is a fluid. Equation (10) and the discussion around the null-energy condition gave $W := A + 8ay^{-1} \geq 0$. Make the further assumption that $W + 4ay^{-1} > 0$ so that

$$\frac{1}{4}A + 3ay^{-1} > 0.$$

It follows from Eq. (13) that $g_{uu} < 0$. The form of the Ricci tensor, R_{ij}, given in the appendix then suggests the following convenient choice for the fluid velocity vector U,

$$(U^u, U^\omega, U^\rho) := a^{-1/2} y^{1/2} \left(1,\, 0,\, -\tfrac{1}{8}Wy\right),$$

$$(U_u, U_\omega, U_\rho) = a^{-1/2} y^{-1/2} \left(-\tfrac{1}{8}Wy - a,\, \tfrac{1}{2}y^{1/2}\partial_\rho y,\, -1\right),$$

which, using the R_{ij} given in the appendix, leads to

$$R_{ij} U^i U^j = \frac{1}{8} A R a^{-1} y. \tag{15}$$

Note that $U^i U_i = -1$, as required. The covariant derivative $U_{i;j}$ can be written as a sum[12] (p. 85)

$$U_{i;j} = \omega_{ij} + \sigma_{ij} + \frac{1}{2}\theta h_{ij} - \dot{U}_i U_j,$$

where the projection tensor h_{ij}, the acceleration vector $\dot{U}_i$, the vorticity tensor ω_{ij}, the expansion θ, and the shear tensor σ_{ij} are defined by

$$h_{ij} := g_{ij} + U_i U_j,$$

$$\dot{U}_i := U_{i;j} U^j,$$

$$\omega_{ij} := \frac{1}{2}\left(U_{i;k} h^k_j - U_{j;k} h^k_i\right),$$

$$\theta := U^i_{;i},$$

$$\sigma_{ij} := \frac{1}{2}\left(U_{i;k} h^k_j + U_{j;k} h^k_i\right) - \frac{1}{2}\theta h_{ij}.$$

The coefficient of θ, both in the expression for $U_{i;j}$ and in the expression for σ_{ij}, is $\frac{1}{2}$ (instead of $\frac{1}{3}$, as would be the case in 3+1 dimensions). This follows because the trace $h^i{}_i$ of the projection tensor is 2 (instead of 3). The components of $U_{i;j}$ and other kinematic quantities, including the acceleration vector $\dot{U}^i$, are listed in the appendix. The divergence of the acceleration vector, $\dot{U}^i{}_{;i}$, is

$$\dot{U}^i{}_{;i} = \frac{1}{8}(A - 4ky)Ra^{-1}y. \tag{16}$$

The expansion scalar, θ, measures the isotropic volume expansion of the fluid and is found to be zero:

$$\theta = 0. \tag{17}$$

The scalar vorticity ω and the scalar shear σ are given by

$$\omega^2 := \frac{1}{2}\omega^{ij}\omega_{ij} = \frac{1}{4}R^2 a^{-2} y^2, \tag{18}$$

$$\sigma^2 := \frac{1}{2}\sigma^{ij}\sigma_{ij} = \frac{1}{128}A^2 Ra^{-2} y^2. \tag{19}$$

Raychaudhuri's equation can be written[13] (p. 5295)

$$\dot{\theta} = -\frac{1}{2}\theta^2 - R_{ij}U^i U^j - 2\left(\sigma^2 - \omega^2\right) + \dot{U}^i{}_{;i}.$$

Using Eqs (15) to (19), it is straightforward to verify that Raychaudhuri's equation holds.

5. Fluid Source: Dynamics

In analysing the Einstein field equations, $G_{ij} = R_{ij} - \frac{1}{2}R g_{ij}$, the velocity U^i and the projection tensor h_{ij} can be used to write the stress energy tensor as a sum of separate terms[12] (p. 91)

$$T_{ij} = \mu U_i U_j + p h_{ij} + q_i U_j + U_i q_j + \pi_{ij},$$

where $q_i U^i = 0$, $\pi_{ij} U^j = 0$, and $\pi^i{}_i = 0$. The function μ denotes the total mass-energy density, p the isotropic pressure (which may include a contribution from the bulk viscosity), q^i the heat-flux vector, and π_{ij} the trace-free anisotropic pressure due to processes such as dynamic viscosity. It follows that

$$T^i{}_i = 2p - \mu,$$

and

$$\kappa(2p - \mu) = -\frac{1}{2}R.$$

Hence the Einstein field equations can be rewritten

$$R_{ij} = \kappa\left[T_{ij} - (2p - \mu)g_{ij}\right]$$

and then decomposed using U^i and $h^j{}_k$ to produce the following equivalent set of equations:

$$R_{ij}\, U^i U^j = 2\kappa\, p,$$

$$R_{ij}\, U^i h^j{}_m = -\kappa\, q_m,$$

$$R_{ij}\, h^i{}_m h^j{}_n = \kappa\,(\mu - p)\, h_{mn} + \kappa\, \pi_{mn}.$$

It follows that the pressure p is given by

$$p = \frac{1}{16\kappa} a^{-1} y AR,$$

and that the mass-energy density μ is given by

$$\mu = \frac{1}{8\kappa} a^{-1} y AR + \frac{1}{2\kappa} R.$$

The components q_i of the heat-flux vector are given by

$$q_u = \frac{1}{64\kappa} a^{-3/2} y^{3/2} AWR,$$

$$q_\omega = -\frac{1}{16\kappa} a^{-3/2} y AR\, \partial_\rho y,$$

$$q_\rho = \frac{1}{8\kappa} a^{-3/2} y^{1/2} AR.$$

Heat flow is related to temperature and acceleration by the temperature gradient law[12] (p. 96),

$$q^i = -\lambda h^{ij}\left(T_{,j} + T\dot{U}_j\right),$$

where λ denotes the coefficient of thermal conductivity. It can be checked that this law is satisfied identically. However, the usual phenomenological equation of state relating anisotropic pressure to the shear is *not* satisfied: $\pi_{ij} \neq -2\eta\sigma_{ij}$ (η being the coefficient of shear viscosity). Situations where this equation of state may not hold have been considered by MacCallum, Stewart, and Schmidt.[14]

6. Summary and Conclusions

A family of (2+1)-dimensional null-surface formulation solutions has been introduced and involves three parameters, A, a, and k. Since the solutions that make up the family all satisfy the NSF main metricity condition, they automatically satisfy Cartan's metricity condition.[15–17] The family of solutions led to a metric and to the Einstein equations being satisfied. An imperfect fluid was presented as a possible source. The mass-energy density and the pressure were shown to be positive. The scalar expansion was found to be zero. The scalar vorticity and scalar shear were found to be nonzero, and simple formulas were derived. The temperature gradient law was satisfied. It was pointed out that the special choices $\{A \neq 0, k \neq 0, a = 0\}$ and $\{k \neq 0, a \neq 0, A = 0\}$ correspond to two solutions that were reported earlier by the present authors.[8,9]

Acknowledgements

The authors would like to thank Dr. Alan Coley for a number of helpful comments. We would also like to acknowledge the generous hospitality of Dr. Ted Newman during our visits to the University of Pittsburgh.

Appendix

The Christoffel symbols are

$$\Gamma^u_{uu} = -a\Gamma^u_{\omega\omega} = -a\Gamma^\omega_{\omega\rho} = 2^{-1}ay^{-1}\,\partial_\rho y,$$

$$\Gamma^u_{u\omega} = 8^{-1}Ay^{-1/2} + ay^{-3/2},$$

$$\Gamma^u_{u\rho} = \Gamma^u_{\omega\rho} = \Gamma^u_{\rho\rho} = \Gamma^\omega_{\rho\rho} = 0,$$

$$\Gamma^\omega_{uu} = 2^{-1}Aay^{-1/2} + 3a^2 y^{-3/2} - 2^{-1}kay^{1/2},$$

$$\Gamma^\omega_{u\omega} = -(16^{-1}A + ay^{-1})\,\partial_\rho y,$$

$$\Gamma^\omega_{u\rho} = 8^{-1}Ay^{-1/2} + ay^{-3/2},$$

$$\Gamma^\omega_{\omega\omega} = -4^{-1}Ay^{-1/2} - ay^{-3/2} + 2^{-1}ky^{1/2},$$

$$\Gamma^\rho_{uu} = -2^{-1}a\left(-4^{-1}A + 3ay^{-1} + 2^{-1}ky\right)\partial_\rho y,$$

$$\Gamma^\rho_{u\omega} = -(16^{-1}Aky^{3/2} + a^2 y^{-3/2} + kay^{1/2}),$$

$$\Gamma^\rho_{u\rho} = (16^{-1}A - ay^{-1})\,\partial_\rho y,$$

$$\Gamma^\rho_{\omega\omega} = (2^{-1}ay^{-1} + 4^{-1}ky)\,\partial_\rho y,$$

$$\Gamma^\rho_{\omega\rho} = 8^{-1}Ay^{-1/2} - 2^{-1}ky^{1/2},$$

$$\Gamma^\rho_{\rho\rho} = -y^{-1}\,\partial_\rho y.$$

Using the abbreviation $W := A + 8ay^{-1}$, the Ricci tensor can be written as a matrix, $[R_{ij}]$:

$$[R_{ij}] = \begin{pmatrix} \frac{1}{256}(A^3 + W^3) + \frac{1}{8}Aka & -\frac{1}{64}AW\,y^{-1/2}\partial_\rho y & \frac{1}{32}W^2\,y^{-1} \\ -\frac{1}{64}AW\,y^{-1/2}\partial_\rho y & -\frac{1}{32}A^2\,y^{-1} + \frac{1}{8}Ak & -\frac{1}{8}A\,y^{-3/2}\partial_\rho y \\ \frac{1}{32}W^2\,y^{-1} & -\frac{1}{8}A\,y^{-3/2}\partial_\rho y & \frac{1}{4}W\,y^{-2} \end{pmatrix}.$$

The scalar curvature, R, is given in Eq. (14).

The covariant derivatives of the velocity can be written as a matrix, $[U_{i;j}]$:

$$\begin{pmatrix} -\frac{1}{8}a^{1/2}y^{-1/2}W\partial_\rho y & -\frac{1}{64}a^{-1/2}W^2 & -\frac{1}{16}a^{-1/2}y^{-1/2}W\partial_\rho y \\ a^{-1/2}\left(\frac{1}{2}ka - \frac{1}{64}W^2 + a^2 y^{-2}\right) & \frac{1}{16}a^{-1/2}y^{-1/2}A\partial_\rho y & \frac{1}{2}a^{-1/2}y^{-1}\left(ky - \frac{1}{4}A\right) \\ -a^{1/2}y^{-3/2}\partial_\rho y & -\frac{1}{8}a^{-1/2}y^{-1}W & -\frac{1}{2}a^{-1/2}y^{-3/2}\partial_\rho y \end{pmatrix}$$

The acceleration vector, $\dot{U}_i$, is defined by $\dot{U}_i := U_{i;j}U^j$, and its components are

$$\dot{U}^u = \left(1 - \frac{1}{16}Wa^{-1}y\right)\partial_\rho y,$$

$$\dot{U}^\omega = \frac{1}{4}Wy^{1/2}\left(1 - \frac{1}{16}Wa^{-1}y\right) - \frac{1}{2}Ra^{-1}y^{3/2},$$

$$= a^{-1}y^{3/2}\left(-R + \frac{1}{2}ka + a^2 y^{-2}\right),$$

$$\dot{U}^\rho = -a\left(1 - \frac{1}{16}Wa^{-1}y\right)\partial_\rho y - \frac{1}{4}Ra^{-1}y^2\partial_\rho y.$$

The only nonzero components of the vorticity tensor, ω_{ij}, are

$$\omega_{u\omega} = -\omega_{\omega u} = -\frac{1}{16}WRa^{-3/2}y,$$

$$\omega_{\omega\rho} = -\omega_{\rho\omega} = \frac{1}{2}Ra^{-3/2}.$$

The components of the shear tensor, σ_{ij}, are

$$\sigma_{uu} = -\frac{1}{1024}AW^2 a^{-3/2}y^{3/2}\partial_\rho y,$$

$$\sigma_{u\omega} = \sigma_{\omega u} = \frac{1}{128}W^2 ka^{-3/2}y^2 - \frac{1}{16}WRa^{-3/2}y,$$

$$\sigma_{u\rho} = \sigma_{u\rho} = -\frac{1}{128}AWa^{-3/2}y^{1/2}\,\partial_\rho y,$$

$$\sigma_{\omega\omega} = -\frac{1}{32}Aka^{-3/2}y^{3/2}\,\partial_\rho y,$$

$$\sigma_{\omega\rho} = \sigma_{\rho\omega} = \frac{1}{16}Wka^{-3/2}y - \frac{1}{2}Ra^{-3/2},$$

$$\sigma_{\rho\rho} = -\frac{1}{16}Aa^{-3/2}y^{-1/2}\,\partial_\rho y.$$

The components of the Cotton-York tensor, C^i_j, are

$$C^u{}_u = -\frac{1}{4}W\left(R + \frac{1}{32}AW\right),$$

$$= -\frac{1}{4}A\left(R + \frac{1}{32}W^2\right) - 2Ray^{-1},$$

$$C^u{}_\omega = y^{-1/2}\left(\frac{1}{2}R + \frac{1}{32}A^2\right)\partial_\rho y,$$

$$C^u{}_\rho = -Ry^{-1} - \frac{1}{16}AWy^{-1},$$

$$C^\omega{}_u = ay^{-1/2}\left(\frac{1}{2}R + \frac{1}{32}AW\right)\partial_\rho y,$$

$$C^\omega{}_\omega = \frac{1}{128}A^2W + Ray^{-1},$$

$$C^\omega{}_\rho = \frac{1}{4}Aay^{-3/2}\,\partial_\rho y,$$

$$C^\rho{}_u = \frac{1}{128}AW^2a - 2Ra^2y^{-1} + \frac{1}{2}RWa,$$

$$C^\rho{}_\omega = -ay^{-1/2}\left(\frac{1}{2}R + \frac{1}{32}A^2\right)\partial_\rho y,$$

$$C^\rho{}_\rho = \frac{1}{2}Aa^2y^{-2} - 2ka^2y^{-1} + \frac{1}{4}AR + 3Ray^{-1},$$

$$= \frac{1}{16}AWay^{-1} + \frac{1}{4}AR + Ray^{-1}.$$

References

1. S. Frittelli, C. N. Kozameh and E. T. Newman, Lorentzian metrics from characteristic surfaces, *J. Math. Phys.* **36**, 4975 (1995).
2. S. Frittelli, C. N. Kozameh and E. T. Newman, GR via characteristic surfaces, *J. Math. Phys.* **36**, 4984 (1995).
3. S. Frittelli, C. N. Kozameh and E. T. Newman, Linearized Einstein theory via null surfaces, *J. Math. Phys.* **36**, 5005 (1995).
4. D. M. Forni, N. Iriondo and C. N. Kozameh, Null surfaces formulation in three dimensions, *J. Math. Phys.* **41**, 5517 (2000).
5. D. M. Forni, N. Iriondo, C. N. Kozameh and M. F. Parisi, Understanding singularities in Cartan's and null surface formulation geometric structures, *J. Math. Phys.* **43**, 1584 (2002).
6. M. Tanimoto, On the Null Surface Formalism, gr-qc/9703003, (1997).
7. G. Silva-Ortigoza, Null surfaces and their singularities in three-dimensional Minkowski space-time, *Gen. Rel. Grav.* **32**, 2243 (2000).
8. T. A. Harriott and J. G. Williams, Solution for the null-surface formulation of general relativity in 2+1 dimensions, *Gen. Rel. Grav.* **46**, 1666 (2018).
9. T. A. Harriott and J. G. Williams, Three-variable solution in the (2 + 1)-dimensional null-surface formulation, *Gen. Rel. Grav.* **50**, 39 (2018).
10. T. A. Harriott and J. G. Williams, Petrov type-N solution for the null-surface formulation in 2 + 1 dimensions, *Gen. Rel. Grav.* **51**, 98 (2019).
11. A. A. Garcia-Diaz, *Exact Solutions in Three-Dimensional Gravity* (Cambridge University Press, 2017).
12. G. F. R. Ellis, R. Maartens and M. A. H. MacCallum, *Relativistic Cosmology* (Cambridge University Press, 2021).
13. J. D. Barrow, D. J. Shaw and C. G. Tsagas, Cosmology in three dimensions: Steps towards the general solution, *Class. Q. Grav.* **23**, 5291 (2006).
14. M. A. H. MacCallum, J. M. Stewart and B. Schmidt, Anisotropic stresses in homogeneous cosmologies, *Commun. Math. Phys.* **17**, 343 (1970).
15. E. Cartan, Les espaces generalises et l'integration de certaines classes d'equations differentielles, *C. R. Acad. Sci* **206**, 1425 (1938).
16. E. Cartan, La geometria de las ecuaciones diferenciales de tercer orden, *Rev. Mat. Hispano-Amer.* **4**, 1 (1941).
17. E. Cartan, Sur une classe d'espaces de Weyl, *Ann. Sc. Ec. Norm. Sup. (3)* **60**, 1 (1943).

New exact stationary cylindrical anisotropic fluid solution of GR

M.-N. Célérier

Laboratoire Univers et THéories, Observatoire de Paris,
Université PSL, CNRS, Université de Paris,
5, Place Jules Janssen, Meudon, 92190, France
E-mail: marie-noelle.celerier@obspm.fr

In a previous paper, the properties of interior spacetimes sourced by stationary cylindrical anisotropic fluids have been analytically studied for both nonrigid and rigid rotation. The gravito-electromagnetic features of different classes of such GR solutions have been described. Their regularity conditions and those for their junction to a vacuum exterior have also been provided. A new class of rigidly rotating exact solutions to Einstein's field equations satisfying a physically consistent equation of state for anisotropic fluids is displayed here. Its physical properties are discussed.

Keywords: General Relativity; exact solution; cylindrical symmetry; anisotropic fluids

1. Introduction

Cylindrically symmetric spacetimes have attracted much attention and have been extensively investigated in General Relativity (GR) for a number of purposes.[1,2] A recent review has been displayed in.[3]

The results presented here have been obtained as a continuation of a couple of previous works. The rigid rotation of stationary spacetimes sourced by a cylindrically symmetric anisotropic fluid has been considered in.[4] This study has been subsequently extended to nonrigidly rotating fluids,[5] while the analysis of the rigid case proposed in[4] has been supplemented, with a focuss on its Weyl tensor gravito-electromagnetic properties. Both were matched to a stationary vacuum exterior of the Lewis type.[6]

The new results displayed here consist of a class of exact interior solutions to the Einstein field equations for a rigidly rotating cylindrically symmetric anisotropic fluid bounded by a cylindrical hypersurface through which it is matched to an exterior Lewis vacuum of the Weyl class.[7] The particular case of an axially directed principal stress is considered here as a first step towards the analysis of anisotropy in this framework.[8] The main physical properties of these spacetimes are also discussed.

This contribution is organized as follows: in Section 2, the stress-energy tensor and the stationary cylindrically symmetric line element to be used in the following are set up. In Section 3, the new exact solution is constructed, from the field equations first displayed, through its regularity and junction conditions, up to its final form. A number of mathematical and physical properties pertaining to this solution are analyzed in Section 4. The conclusions are displayed in Section 5.

2. Cylindrical spacetime inside the source

A rigidly rotating stationary cylindrically symmetric anisotropic nondissipative fluid bounded by a cylindrical surface Σ whose principal stresses P_r, P_z and P_ϕ obey the equation of state $P_r = P_\phi = 0$ is considered. Its stress-energy tensor can be written as

$$T_{\alpha\beta} = \rho V_\alpha V_\beta + P_z S_\alpha S_\beta, \tag{1}$$

where ρ is the energy density of the fluid, V_α is its timelike 4-velocity, and S_α is a spacelike 4-vector, satisfying

$$V^\alpha V_\alpha = -1, \quad S^\alpha S_\alpha = 1, \quad V^\alpha S_\alpha = 0. \tag{2}$$

It is assumed, for the inside Σ spacetime, that the spacelike ∂_z Killing vector is hypersurface orthogonal, such as to ease its subsequent matching to the exterior Lewis metric. Hence, its stationary cylindrically symmetric line element reads

$$ds^2 = -f dt^2 + 2k dt d\phi + e^\mu (dr^2 + dz^2) + l d\phi^2, \tag{3}$$

where f, k, μ and l are real functions of the radial coordinate r only. Owing to cylindrical symmetry, the coordinates satisfy the following ranges

$$-\infty \leq t \leq +\infty, \quad 0 \leq r, \quad -\infty \leq z \leq +\infty, \quad 0 \leq \phi \leq 2\pi. \tag{4}$$

Now, still due to cylindrical symmetry, the two limits of the ϕ coordinate are topologically identified. These coordinates are numbered $x^0 = t$, $x^1 = r$, $x^2 = z$ and $x^3 = \phi$.

3. Rigidly rotating new solution

3.1. *Equation of state and 4-velocity of the fluid*

Choosing a corotating frame for the stationary fluid source,[4,5,8] the fluid 4-velocity can be written as

$$V^\alpha = v\delta_0^\alpha, \tag{5}$$

where v is a function of r only. The timelike condition for V^α, provided in (2), thus becomes

$$fv^2 = 1. \tag{6}$$

The spacelike 4-vector verifying conditions (2) can be chosen as

$$S^\alpha = e^{-\mu/2}\delta_2^\alpha, \tag{7}$$

and a function $D(r)$, which will proved useful for the calculations, is defined as

$$D^2 = fl + k^2. \tag{8}$$

3.2. Field equations

With the above choices, and using (5)-(8) into (1), one obtains the stress-energy tensor components corresponding to the five non-vanishing Einstein tensor components and the five field equations for the inside Σ spacetime follow.

A new function $h(r)$ defined as $h(r) \equiv P_z(r)/\rho(r)$, allows to write them as

$$G_{00} = \frac{e^{-\mu}}{2}\left[-f\mu'' - 2f\frac{D''}{D} + f'' - f'\frac{D'}{D} + \frac{3f(f'l' + k'^2)}{2D^2}\right] = \kappa\rho f, \tag{9}$$

$$G_{03} = \frac{e^{-\mu}}{2}\left[k\mu'' + 2k\frac{D''}{D} - k'' + k'\frac{D'}{D} - \frac{3k(f'l' + k'^2)}{2D^2}\right] = -\kappa\rho k, \tag{10}$$

$$G_{11} = \frac{\mu' D'}{2D} + \frac{f'l' + k'^2}{4D^2} = 0, \tag{11}$$

$$G_{22} = \frac{D''}{D} - \frac{\mu' D'}{2D} - \frac{f'l' + k'^2}{4D^2} = \kappa\rho h e^{\mu}, \tag{12}$$

$$G_{33} = \frac{e^{-\mu}}{2}\left[l\mu'' + 2l\frac{D''}{D} - l'' + l'\frac{D'}{D} - \frac{3l(f'l' + k'^2)}{2D^2}\right] = \kappa\rho\frac{k^2}{f}, \tag{13}$$

where the primes stand for differentiation with respect to r.

3.3. Bianchi identity

The stress-energy tensor conservation is analogous to the Bianchi identity that reads

$$T^{\beta}_{1;\beta} = 0. \tag{14}$$

From (1), we have

$$T^{\alpha\beta} = \rho V^{\alpha} V^{\beta} + P_z S^{\alpha} S^{\beta}, \tag{15}$$

with V^{α} given by (5), and the space-like vector S^{α} given by (7), inserted into (15). Using (3) and (6), the Bianchi identity (14) reduces to

$$T^{\beta}_{1;\beta} = \frac{1}{2}\rho\frac{f'}{f} - \frac{1}{2}P_z\mu' = 0, \tag{16}$$

which, when the $h(r)$ function defined above is inserted, becomes

$$\frac{f'}{f} - h\mu' = 0. \tag{17}$$

3.4. *Solving the field equations*

Since only five independent differential equations are available for six unknowns, i.e., the four metric functions f, k, e^μ and l, the energy density ρ, and the pressure defined by h, the set of equations needs to be closed by an additional one. The particular assumption displayed in[5] as Eq. (111), and amounting to make a particular choice of coordinates issued from an arbitrary constraint on the Weyl tensor components, is chosen for this purpose as

$$\mu' = \frac{2h'}{1-h} + \frac{2h'}{h}, \qquad (18)$$

which can be integrated as

$$e^\mu = c_\mu \frac{h^2}{(1-h)^2}, \qquad (19)$$

where c_μ is an integration constant. Inserting (18) into the Bianchi identity (17), one obtains

$$\frac{f'}{f} = \frac{2h'}{1-h}, \qquad (20)$$

which can be integrated as

$$f = \frac{c_f}{(1-h)^2}, \qquad (21)$$

c_f being another integration constant.

Now, (9) combined with (10), gives

$$\left(\frac{kf' - fk'}{D}\right)' = 0, \qquad (22)$$

which can be integrated as[4]

$$kf' - fk' = 2cD, \qquad (23)$$

where $2c$ is an integration constant, the factor 2 being chosen here for further convenience. Considered as a first order ordinary differential equation for $k(r)$, (23) possesses as a general solution

$$k = f\left(c_0 - 2c \int_{r_0}^{r} \frac{D(v)}{f(v)^2} dv\right), \qquad (24)$$

where c_0 and r_0 are new integration constants. With (21) inserted, it can be written as

$$k = \frac{c_f}{(1-h)^2}\left[c_0 - \frac{2c}{c_f^2} \int_{r_0}^{r} (1-h(v))^4 D(v) dv\right]. \qquad (25)$$

The last metric function l follows from (8) as

$$l = \frac{(1-h)^2}{c_f}\left\{D^2 - \frac{c_f^2}{(1-h)^4}\left[c_0 - \frac{2c}{c_f^2} \int_{r_0}^{r} (1-h(v))^4 D(v) dv\right]^2\right\}. \qquad (26)$$

3.5. *Interim results*

The field equations (9), (11) and (12), or, equivalently, (10), (11) and (12), give an expression for D'/D as a function of h and of its first and second derivatives. Then, inserting (19), (21), (25), (26) and the expression found for D'/D into (11) gives an expression for ρ depending on the same function h and its derivatives. Then inserting the same expressions into (9), or equivalently into (13), one obtains another expression for ρ still using h and derivatives

Equalizing both expressions for ρ yields a second order ordinary differential equation for h whose general solution allows one to calculate both the first and second derivatives of this h function. They are thus inserted into the previously obtained expressions for ρ and D'/D which can be integrated as

$$D^2 = c_f^2 c_k^2 \frac{(-2\ln h + 4h - h^2 + c_\beta)}{(1-h)(1+h)}. \tag{27}$$

Now (27) inserted into (25) gives, after integration,

$$k = \frac{c_f}{(1-h)^2} \left[c_0 + c_k(-2\ln h + 4h - h^2 + c_\beta) \right]. \tag{28}$$

Finally, the last metric function l emerges from inserting f, k and D into (8), which gives

$$l = c_f c_k^2 \frac{(1-h)}{(1+h)}(-2\ln h + 4h - h^2 + c_\beta) - \frac{c_f}{(1-h)^2} \left[c_0 + c_k(-2\ln h + 4h - h^2 + c_\beta) \right]^2. \tag{29}$$

3.6. *Regularity conditions*

The regularity conditions on the symmetry axis for metric (3) have already been displayed in.[4,5] However, since they will be needed in the following, their main outcomes are recalled briefly here.

To impose elementary flatness in the rotation axis vicinity, the norm X of the Killing vector ∂_ϕ must satisfy[2]

$$\lim_{r \to 0} \frac{g^{\alpha\beta} X_{,\alpha} X_{,\beta}}{4X} = 1, \tag{30}$$

where $X = g_{\phi\phi}$. Eqs. (3) and (30) yield

$$\lim_{r \to 0} \frac{e^{-\mu} l'^2}{4l} = 1. \tag{31}$$

The requirement that $g_{\phi\phi}$ vanishes on the axis implies

$$l \stackrel{0}{=} 0, \tag{32}$$

where $\stackrel{0}{=}$ means that the values are taken at $r = 0$.

Since there cannot be singularities along the axis, spacetime is forced to tend there to flatness. The coordinates are thus scaled such that, for $r \to 0$, the metric should be written as
$$\mathrm{d}s^2 = -\mathrm{d}t^2 + 2\omega r^2 \mathrm{d}t\mathrm{d}\phi + \mathrm{d}r^2 + \mathrm{d}z^2 + r^2 \mathrm{d}\phi^2, \tag{33}$$
implying
$$f \stackrel{0}{=} e^\mu \stackrel{0}{=} 1, \qquad k \stackrel{0}{=} 0, \tag{34}$$
giving
$$D \stackrel{0}{=} 0, \tag{35}$$
and, from (31) and (33),
$$l' \stackrel{0}{=} 0. \tag{36}$$
Then, the addition of the requirement that the Einstein tensor components in (9)-(13) do not diverge, implies
$$f' \stackrel{0}{=} k' \stackrel{0}{=} k'' - k'\frac{D'}{D} \stackrel{0}{=} 0, \tag{37}$$
Inserting (19), (21) and (28) into (34) one obtains
$$c_f \stackrel{0}{=} (1-h)^2, \tag{38}$$
$$c_\mu \stackrel{0}{=} \frac{c_f}{h^2}, \tag{39}$$
$$c_0 = 0, \tag{40}$$
$$c_\beta \stackrel{0}{=} 2\ln h - 4h + h^2. \tag{41}$$
All the other regularity conditions are verified provided (40) and (41) are satisfied.

3.7. Junction conditions

These conditions have also been displayed in[4,5] for metric (3). For completeness, and also since they will be partially needed further on, they are recalled here briefly.

Since the system is stationary, the Lewis vacuum metric[6] is used to represent the exterior spacetime, and the Weyl class[7] is here chosen for real junction condition purpose. Its metric is
$$\mathrm{d}s^2 = -F\mathrm{d}t^2 + 2K\mathrm{d}t\mathrm{d}\phi + e^M(\mathrm{d}R^2 + \mathrm{d}z^2) + L\mathrm{d}\phi^2, \tag{42}$$
where
$$F = aR^{1-n} - a\delta^2 R^{1+n}, \tag{43}$$
$$K = -(1-ab\delta)\delta R^{1+n} - abR^{1-n}, \tag{44}$$

$$e^M = R^{(n^2-1)/2}, \tag{45}$$

$$L = \frac{(1-ab\delta)^2}{a} R^{1+n} - ab^2 R^{1-n}, \tag{46}$$

with

$$\delta = \frac{c}{an}, \tag{47}$$

where a, b, c and n are the real constants determining the Weyl class of the metrics.

In accordance with Darmois' junction conditions,[9] metric (3) and metric (42)'s coefficients and their derivatives must be continuous across the Σ surface. It has been shown in[4] that, for the most general anisotropic fluid, these conditions imply $P_r \stackrel{\Sigma}{=} 0$, which is in agreement with the equation of state of the here studied fluid which imposes $P_r = 0$ everywhere.

Hence the conditions for a smooth junction to a Lewis vacuum of the Weyl class are fulfilled by this solution.

3.8. Final form of the solution

The constraints (38)–(41) on the integration constants, imposed by the regularity conditions, and inserted into the metric functions as given in (21), (19), (28) and (29) lead to their final form which can be displayed as

$$f = \left(\frac{1-h_0}{1-h}\right)^2, \tag{48}$$

$$e^\mu = \left(\frac{1-h_0}{h_0}\right)^2 \left(\frac{h}{1-h}\right)^2, \tag{49}$$

$$k = (1-h_0)^2 c_k \frac{[2\ln\frac{h_0}{h} + 4(h-h_0) - (h^2-h_0^2)]}{(1-h)^2}, \tag{50}$$

$$l = (1-h_0)^2 c_k^2 \left[2\ln\frac{h_0}{h} + 4(h-h_0) - (h^2-h_0^2)\right]$$

$$\times \left\{\frac{1-h}{1+h} - \frac{[2\ln\frac{h_0}{h} + 4(h-h_0) - (h^2-h_0^2)]}{(1-h)^2}\right\}. \tag{51}$$

An implicit integral equation for $h(r)$ reads

$$r = \frac{(1-h_0)^2}{c} \int_{h_0}^{h} \left\{\frac{1+u}{u^2(1-u)^3 \left[2\ln\frac{h_0}{u} + 4(u-h_0) - (u^2-h_0^2)\right]}\right\}^{\frac{1}{2}} du, \tag{52}$$

where h_0 denotes the h value on the symmetry axis, i.e., $h_0 \equiv h(r=0)$. And the expression for ρ follows as

$$\rho = \frac{2c^2 h_0^2}{\kappa(1-h_0)^4} \frac{(1-h)^4}{h^2(1+h)^2} \left\{ \frac{h\left[2\ln\frac{h_0}{h} + 4(h-h_0) - (h^2 - h_0^2)\right]}{(1+h)} + 2(1-h)^2 \right\}. \tag{53}$$

Notice that the constant c_k appearing in (50) and (51) can be absorbed by a rescaling of the ϕ coordinate.

4. Physical properties of the solution

4.1. *Hydrodynamical scalars, vectors and tensors*

The timelike 4-vector V_α can be invariantly decomposed through the genuine tensor $V_{\alpha;\beta}$ into three independent parts such as

$$V_{\alpha;\beta} = -\dot{V}_\alpha V_\beta + \omega_{\alpha\beta} + \sigma_{\alpha\beta}, \tag{54}$$

where

$$\dot{V}_\alpha = V_{\alpha;\beta} V^\beta, \tag{55}$$

$$\omega_{\alpha\beta} = V_{[\alpha;\beta]} + \dot{V}_{[\alpha} V_{\beta]}, \tag{56}$$

$$\sigma_{\alpha\beta} = V_{(\alpha;\beta)} + \dot{V}_{(\alpha} V_{\beta)}. \tag{57}$$

These three quantities are, respectively, the acceleration vector, the rotation tensor, and the shear tensor. For the timelike 4-vector given by (5), their nonzero components[5] are

$$\dot{V}_1 = \frac{1}{2}\frac{f'}{f}, \tag{58}$$

which becomes, with (48) inserted,

$$\dot{V}_1 = \frac{c}{(1-h_0)^2} h \left\{ \frac{(1-h)}{(1+h)} \left[2\ln\frac{h_0}{h} + 4(h-h_0) - (h^2 - h_0^2)\right] \right\}^{\frac{1}{2}} \tag{59}$$

and

$$2\omega_{13} = -(2kv' + k'v). \tag{60}$$

From (58), the acceleration vector modulus is therefore

$$\dot{V}^\alpha \dot{V}_\alpha = \frac{1}{4}\frac{f'^2}{f^2} e^{-\mu}, \tag{61}$$

which becomes, with (48) and (49) inserted, and with (52) differentiated with respect to r

$$\dot{V}^\alpha \dot{V}_\alpha = \frac{c^2 h_0^2}{(1-h_0)^6} \frac{(1-h)^3}{(1+h)} \left[2\ln\frac{h_0}{h} + 4(h-h_0) - (h^2 - h_0^2)\right]. \tag{62}$$

The rotation scalar, ω, defined by

$$\omega^2 = \frac{1}{2}\omega^{\alpha\beta}\omega_{\alpha\beta}, \tag{63}$$

follows as

$$\omega^2 = \frac{1}{4\mathrm{e}^{\mu}D^2}\left(k\frac{f'}{f} - k'\right)^2. \tag{64}$$

Inserting (23) into (64), one obtains

$$\omega^2 = \frac{c^2}{f^2 \mathrm{e}^{\mu}}, \tag{65}$$

As already stressed in,[4,5] the shear tensor vanishes for any rigidly rotating fluid.

4.2. Singularities

The solution exhibits three possible singularities.

One would occur for $h = +1$ where the whole metric function set diverges, which is not the case for the density ρ. Indeed, from its expression (53), the energy density is merely seen to vanish. Since a more complete analysis should be needed to conclude definitively, the question whether this locus is or not a mere coordinate singularity remains open.

For $h = -1$, l is the only metric function which diverges. However, at this location, ρ also happens to diverge and would change sign if h was allowed to reach values below -1, which is not the case as it is shown elsewhere.[8] However, this behaviour would imply a curvature singularity if such a value of h should be reachable.

A third singularity might occur for $h = 0$. Here, the density diverges and is no more defined if the h sign happens to become different from the h_0 sign, owing to the presence of $\ln h_0/h$ in its expression. We would be therefore confronted to another curvature singularity. However, as it is shown elsewhere,[8] such a singularity lies outside the domain of definition of these spacetimes

4.3. Integration constants and metric signature

Among the three integration constants, c, c_k and h_0, one, c_k, can be suppressed by a rescaling of the azimuthal coordinate ϕ.

Now, h_0 possesses an obvious physical interpretation from the consideration of the expression for $h(r)$ given by (52). Since the integral in the right hand side vanishes for $h = h_0$, such does r on the left hand side, and therefore, h_0 must be interpreted as the value of h on the axis. Notice that $h_0 = 1$, implying the vanishing of the whole set of metric functions, lies thus outside the domain of definition of the solution.

The parameter c is shown elsewhere[8] to represent the amplitude of the rotation scalar of the fluid on the axis.

Finally, the signature of the metric $(-+++)$ implies sign constraints on the components of the metric tensor, which, in turn, impose restrictions on the validity ranges of $h(r)$.[8]

5. Conclusions

Following the investigations of stationary cylindrical anisotropic gravitational fluids initiated in,[4,5] the case of rigidly rotating fluids with particular equation of state $P_r = P_\phi = 0$ has been considered here. A new exact solution of the field equations has thus been exhibited under the form of $h(r)$ functions for the metric and the density, with h defined as $h(r) = P_z(r)/\rho(r)$, and of an integral expression for h as a r function. As usual, this solution is valid in a given coordinate system which has been chosen such as to ease a direct physical interpretation. To allow any future use for astrophysical purposes, this solution has been forced to satisfy the regularity conditions on the symmetry axis and it has been matched to the Weyl class of the Lewis vacuum solution through a cylindrical Σ hypersurface.

A number of important physical properties have been analysed. The hydrodynamical scalars, vectors and tensors of the fluid have been computed such as to be used for further interpretation purpose. Three singularities have been identified and discussed. However, they will prove to be located outside the definition domain of the solution, which will thus appear as singularity-free.

The solution depends on two independent parameters, h_0, the value of the function $h(r)$ on the axis of symmetry, and c which represents the amplitude of the rotation scalar of the fluid on the axis.[8] It has been stressed that the signature of the metric implies constraints on the signs of the components of the metric tensor and this has been shown, in turn, to restrict the validity domain of the solution.

In,[8] the properties of the constant parameters h_0 and c have been analysed and the different classes of solutions which might be associated to these properties have been identified.

Now, the present display of this first particular class of solutions for a fluid with axially directed stress will be followed, in the future, by the study of other complementary cases which would hopefully provide us with a deeper understanding of stationary rotating cylinders of matter in GR.

References

1. J. B. Griffiths and J. Podolský, *Exact spacetimes in Einstein's General Relativity*, Cambridge Monographs on Mathematical Physics (Cambridge University Press, Cambridge, England, 2009).
2. H. Stephani, D. Kramer, M. MacCallum, C. Honselaers, and E. Herlt, *Exact Solutions to Einstein's Field Equations*, Cambridge Monographs on Mathematical Physics (Cambridge University Press, Cambridge, England, 2009).
3. K. A. Bronnikov, N. O. Santos, and A. Wang, Cylindrical systems in general relativity, Classical Quantum Gravity **37**, 113002 (2020).

4. F. Debbasch, L. Herrera, P. R. C. T. Pereira, and N. O. Santos, Stationary cylindrical anisotropic fluid, Gen. Relativ. Gravit. **38**, 1825 (2006).
5. M.-N. Célérier and N. O. Santos, Stationary cylindrical anisotropic fluid and new purely magnetic GR solutions, Phys. Rev. D **102**, 044026 (2020).
6. T. Lewis, Some special solutions of the equations of axially symmetric gravitational fields, Proc. R. Soc. A **136**, 176 (1932).
7. M. F. A. da Silva, L. Herrera, F. M. Paiva, and N.O. Santos, The parameters of the Lewis metric for the Weyl class, Gen. Relativ. Gravit. **27**, 859 (1995).
8. M.-N. Célérier, New classes of exact interior nonvacuum solutions to the GR field equations for spacetimes sourced by a rigidly rotating stationary cylindrical anisotropic fluid, Phys. Rev. D **104**, 064040 (2021).
9. G. Darmois, Les équations de la gravitation einsteinienne, *Mémorial des Sciences Mathématiques* fasc. XXV (Gauthier-Villars, Paris, 1927).

Hydrodynamic representation and energy balance for the Dirac and Weyl fermions in curved space-times

Tonatiuh Matos* and Omar Gallegos

*Departamento de Física, Centro de Investigación y de Estudios Avanzados del IPN,
A.P. 14-740, 07000 CDMX, México*
*E-mail: tonatiuh.matos@cinvestav.mx

Pierre-Henri Chavanis

Laboratoire de Physique Théorique, Université de Toulouse, CNRS, UPS, France

Using a generalized Madelung transformation, we derive the hydrodynamic representation of the Dirac equation in arbitrary curved space-times coupled to an electromagnetic field. We obtain Dirac-Euler equations for fermions involving a continuity equation and a first integral of the Bernoulli equation. Using the comparison of the Dirac and Klein-Gordon equations we obtain the balance equation for fermion particles. We also use the correspondence between fermions and bosons to derive the hydrodynamic representation of the Weyl equation which is a chiral form of the Dirac equation.

Keywords: Dirac equation; Weyl equation; Fermions; Hydrodynamics

1. Introduction

The Standard Model of elementary particles establishes that there exist two kinds of particles, fermions and bosons. In previous works,[1,2] the energy balance for bosons was derived starting from the general relativistic Klein-Gordon (KG) equation. In the present work, we study a system of fermions described by the Dirac equation in arbitrary curved space-times taking into account electromagnetic effects. We also use the Weyl equation which is a chiral form of the Dirac equation due to the relationship between the Lie algebras of the symmetry groups for both systems of particles. We give the hydrodynamic representation of the Dirac and Weyl equations for fermions using previous results obtained for boson particles.

Many examples of fermion particles in strong gravitational fields can be found in nature. Indeed, the curvature of space-time plays an important role in a neutron star, in the early Universe, or in a fermion cloud (e.g. a dark matter halo) in the vicinity of a black hole. We need to develop a general framework to identify what are the different energy contributions in such systems. In this work we use the geometrical decomposition of the metric in 3+1 slices and the tetrad formalism to study the particle spin in an arbitrary space-time. We define the gamma matrices in curved space-times and derive the generalized Dirac and Weyl equations. Then, using the Madelung transformation, we introduce a hydrodynamic representation of the Dirac and Weyl spinors. This hydrodynamic representation can help us to describe the fermionic system in a general framework.

2. Field Equations

We use the tetrad formalism for the space-time geometry, and the canonical expansion of the space-time in a 3+1 ADM decomposition,[3-8] such that the coordinate t is the parameter of evolution. The 3+1 metric reads

$$ds^2 = N^2 c^2 dt^2 - h_{ij} \left(dx^i + N^i c\, dt\right) \left(dx^j + N^j c\, dt\right), \qquad (1)$$

where N represents the lapse function which measures the proper time of the observers traveling along the world line, N^i is the shift vector that measures the displacement of the observers between the spatial slices and h_{ij} is the 3-dimensional slice-metric. In what follows $i, j, k, l = 1, 2, 3$; $a, b, c = 0, 1, 2, 3$ are the internal indices and $\mu, \nu, \alpha = 0, 1, 2, 3$ the space-time indices. We write eq. (1) in the tetrad formalism as $ds^2 = \eta_{ab} e^a{}_\mu e^b{}_\nu dx^\mu dx^\nu$, where $\eta_{ab} = \mathrm{diag}(1, -1, -1, -1)$. Here $e^a = e^a{}_\mu dx^\mu$ is the set of one-forms base of the cotangent space at the space-time manifold given by

$$\begin{aligned} e^0 &= N dt, \\ e^k &= \hat{e}^k{}_i \left(dx^i + N^i c\, dt\right), \end{aligned} \qquad (2)$$

with inverse

$$\begin{aligned} e_0 &= \frac{1}{N}\left(\frac{\partial}{c\,\partial t} - N^j \frac{\partial}{\partial x^j}\right), \\ e_k &= \hat{e}_k{}^j \frac{\partial}{\partial x^j}, \end{aligned} \qquad (3)$$

where $\hat{e}^k = \hat{e}^k{}_i dx^i$ are the one-form base to the three-dimensional slice of the cotangent manifold, such that $h_{ij} = \delta_{kl} \hat{e}^k{}_i \hat{e}^l{}_j$. We can also define the set of vectors base of the tangent-space to the space-time as $e_a = e_a{}^\mu \partial_\mu$, such that $e^a e_b = \delta^a_b$. We will use the tetrad formalism[3,6-10] to describe the space-time geometry where the fermion particles are located.

The action of a fermion system in curved space-time coupled to an electromagnetic field A_μ is given by $S[\psi, \partial_\mu \psi] = \int \mathcal{L}(\psi, \partial_\mu \psi(x^\mu))\, d^4 x$, where $\mathcal{L} = \mathcal{L}(\psi, \partial_\mu \psi(x^\mu))$ is the Lagrangian density[11-13]

$$\mathcal{L} = \sqrt{-g}\, \frac{i\hbar c}{2} \left[\psi^\dagger B \gamma^\mu (D_\mu \psi) - (D_\mu \psi)^\dagger B \gamma^\mu \psi + \frac{2imc}{\hbar} \psi^\dagger B \psi\right]. \qquad (4)$$

Here $D_\mu = \nabla_\mu + \frac{iq}{\hbar c} A_\mu$ is the total covariant derivative accounting for electromagnetic effects. The covariant derivative of a spinor $\psi = (\psi_{\dot\nu})$ is given by $\nabla_\mu(\psi_{\dot\nu}) = \partial_\mu(\psi_{\dot\nu}) + \Gamma^{\dot\alpha}_{\mu\dot\nu}(\psi_{\dot\alpha})$, where $\Gamma^{\dot\alpha}_{\mu\dot\nu}$ is the spin connection.[3,14] Using the least action principle it is possible to obtain from eq. (4) the corresponding Dirac equation. This equation is given by

$$[i\hbar \gamma^\mu (\nabla_\mu + iq A_\mu) - mc]\psi = 0, \qquad (5)$$

where $\hbar$, c are the Planck constant and the speed of light respectively, while q, m are the charge and mass of the fermion particle and ψ is its spinor. Besides, the gamma matrices γ^μ are related to the spin and space-time geometry. They can be written as $\gamma^\mu = e^\mu_a \tilde{\gamma}^a$, where $\tilde{\gamma}^a$ are the gamma matrices in flat space-time, which are well-know from Quantum Field Theory (QFT).[15-17] Therefore,

$$\gamma^0 = N\tilde{\gamma}^0,$$
$$\gamma^k = \hat{e}^k{}_j(\tilde{\gamma}^j + N^j \tilde{\gamma}^0). \tag{6}$$

In general, these matrices fulfill the following anti-commutation relation[3,18]

$$\{\gamma^\mu, \gamma^\nu\} = \gamma^\mu \gamma^\nu + \gamma^\nu \gamma^\mu = 2g^{\mu\nu}, \tag{7}$$

where $g_{\mu\nu}$ represents the metric that describes the space-time geometry. Furthermore, as we know, the gamma matrices in flat space-time are related to the Pauli matrices, which describe the spin of the fermion particles. In general, the gamma matrices obey the following relation[11-13,19]

$$(\gamma^\mu)^\dagger = B\gamma^\mu B^{-1}, \tag{8}$$

where B is a hermitian matrix, i.e. $B^\dagger = B$, that is uniquely determined by the gamma matrices γ^μ. As usual, we denote by $B^\dagger$ the conjugate (or Hermitian) transpose of B. We note that in QFT the relation (8) is fulfilled when $B = \tilde{\gamma}^0$ and the gamma matrices are in flat space-time. From the action (4) of the fermion system we can find the equation for the transpose conjugated spinor by making an infinitesimal variation of this action with respect to ψ. Another way of getting this equation of motion is to take the transpose conjugate of the Dirac equation (5) and using (8). In this manner we find that the transpose conjugated Dirac equation in curved space-time is given by

$$i\left(\nabla_\mu \bar{\psi}\right)\gamma^\mu - i\psi^\dagger \nabla_\mu (B\gamma^\mu) + i\bar{\psi}\nabla_\mu \gamma^\mu + \bar{\psi}A_\mu \gamma^\mu + m\bar{\psi} = 0. \tag{9}$$

To simplify the notations, here and in the following we use $mc/\hbar \to m$ in natural units ($c = \hbar = 1$). We consider that $(\nabla_\mu \psi)^\dagger = \nabla_\mu \psi^\dagger$, and we denote the adjoint spinor as $\bar{\psi} = \psi^\dagger B$. Using the gamma matrices in flat space-time and the fact that $B = \tilde{\gamma}^0$ we recover the definition of $\bar{\psi}$ in QFT and the transpose conjugated Dirac equation. However, in an arbitrary space-time $\nabla_\mu \gamma^\mu$ is distinct from zero, since $\gamma^\mu = e^\mu_a \tilde{\gamma}^a$, so in general $\nabla_\mu e^\mu_a$ is non-zero.

We can get the conserved charge from the Noether theorem.[20] The Dirac current is

$$J^\mu = \bar{\psi}\gamma^\mu \psi = \psi^\dagger B\gamma^\mu \psi. \tag{10}$$

To obtain the continuity equation

$$\nabla_\mu J^\mu = 0 \tag{11}$$

for the Dirac current, we take the covariant derivative of eq. (10). This gives

$$\nabla_\mu J^\mu = (\nabla_\mu \bar{\psi})\gamma^\mu \psi + \bar{\psi}(\nabla_\mu \gamma^\mu)\psi + \bar{\psi}\gamma^\mu \nabla_\mu \psi. \tag{12}$$

If we multiply the Dirac equation (5) by $\bar{\psi}$ and its transpose conjugate (9) by ψ and sum both equations, it follows that

$$\nabla_\mu J^\mu = \psi^\dagger \nabla_\mu (B\gamma^\mu) \psi. \tag{13}$$

If we require that the continuity equation (11) is fulfilled, i.e., that the number of particles is conserved, then we need $\nabla_\mu (B\gamma^\mu) = 0$, or equivalently

$$(\nabla_\mu B)\gamma^\mu = -B\nabla_\mu \gamma^\mu. \tag{14}$$

At this point, we want to emphasize the consistency conditions for the continuity equation (11). Some authors[21] impose $\nabla_\mu \gamma^\nu = 0$ while others[22] impose $\nabla_\mu B = 0$. These conditions are independent of each other, i.e., in general the condition of Ref.[21] is not fulfilled in Ref.[22] and *vice versa*. In Refs.[12,13] the authors conclude that the condition $\nabla_\mu(B\gamma^\nu) = 0$ is the most convenient because it is implied by $\nabla_\mu \gamma^\nu = 0$ and $\nabla_\mu B = 0$.

In addition, we can note that the matrix B can be obtained for a general metric (1) by solving the differential equation

$$\left(\nabla_0(BN) + \nabla_j(B\hat{e}_i^j N^i)\right)\tilde{\gamma}^0 - \nabla_j(B\hat{e}_i^j)\tilde{\gamma}^i = 0, \tag{15}$$

which follows from eq. (14). Using the condition (14), it is possible to rewrite the transpose conjugated Dirac equation (9) as

$$i\left(\nabla_\mu \bar{\psi}\right)\gamma^\mu + i\bar{\psi}\nabla_\mu \gamma^\mu + \bar{\psi}A_\mu \gamma^\mu + m\bar{\psi} = 0. \tag{16}$$

In order to find the conserved quantity resulting from the continuity equation, we take an arbitrary surface $\mathcal{S}$ enclosing the volume $\mathcal{V}$ which contains the whole system. Let k^j be an orthonormal vector to $\mathcal{S}$ such that

$$\int_\mathcal{V} \nabla_\mu J^\mu dV = \int_\mathcal{V} \nabla_0 J^0 dV + \int_\mathcal{S} k_j J^j dS = 0. \tag{17}$$

We assume that far away from the source, J^μ is negligible. Then, the surface integral in eq. (17) vanishes, and we obtain

$$\frac{dQ}{dt} = \int_\mathcal{V} \nabla_0 J^0 dV = 0, \tag{18}$$

where $Q = \int_\mathcal{V} J^0 dV$ is the conserved charge and dV is the curved volume element $dV = \sqrt{-g}d^4x$. In QFT this charge is identified with the number of fermions or with the electric charge of the system. In flat space-time we have $B = \tilde{\gamma}^0$, so that $J^0 = \psi^\dagger \psi = n$ represents the number density of fermion particles. In curved space-time J^0 (which is determined by γ^0 and by the generalized gamma matrices) has a different interpretation. The form of B given by eqs. (8) and (14) for each metric is related to the gamma matrices and to the tetrad formalism.

With the Maxwell four-potential we can define the Faraday tensor

$$F_{\mu\nu} = \nabla_\mu A_\nu - \nabla_\nu A_\mu. \tag{19}$$

In the electromagnetic theory, the Faraday tensor $F_{\mu\nu}$ satisfies the Maxwell field equations

$$\nabla_\nu F^{\nu\mu} = J^{E\mu}, \qquad (20)$$

where $J^{E\mu}$ is the four-electromagnetic current.

The problem of the Energy Balance for boson particles in a curved space-time is studied in Ref.[1], where the conserved 4-current associated with the KG equation describing the evolution of a complex scalar field $\Phi(x^\mu)$ is defined. We can generalize this idea by defining a new 4-current J_μ^{KG}, changing the scalar field by a spinor and the complex conjugate scalar field by the conjugate transpose of the spinor. Namely, the KG current is redefined as

$$J_\mu^{KG} = i\frac{q}{2m^2}\left[\psi\left(\nabla_\mu - iqA_\mu\right)\psi^\dagger - \psi^\dagger\left(\nabla_\mu + iqA_\mu\right)\psi\right]. \qquad (21)$$

3. Dirac Hydrodynamic Representation

Analogously to the hydrodynamic representation of the Schrödinger equation, which was introduced by Madelung,[23] we derive the hydrodynamic representation of the Dirac equation. We carry out the following generalized Madelung transformation for each component of the spinor $\psi = \psi(x^\mu)$ as follows

$$\psi = \exp(i\theta)R, \qquad (22)$$

where R is a spinor and θ is a function. For the case where we consider a Dirac electron-like fermion, $\theta = \theta(x^\mu)$, the spinor ψ reads

$$\psi = \begin{pmatrix} R_{\dot{1}} \\ R_{\dot{2}} \\ R_{\dot{3}} \\ R_{\dot{4}} \end{pmatrix} \exp(i\theta) = R\exp(i\theta), \qquad (23)$$

where we use the notation $\dot{\mu}, \dot{\nu}, ... = \dot{1}, \cdots, \dot{4}$ for the spinor indices such that

$$R = \begin{pmatrix} R_{\dot{1}} \\ R_{\dot{2}} \\ R_{\dot{3}} \\ R_{\dot{4}} \end{pmatrix} = \begin{pmatrix} \sqrt{n_{\dot{1}}} \\ \sqrt{n_{\dot{2}}} \\ \sqrt{n_{\dot{3}}} \\ \sqrt{n_{\dot{4}}} \end{pmatrix}. \qquad (24)$$

In the appendix we show some exact solutions of the Dirac equation with this ansatz in flat space-time. Here the dot indices represent elements of each component and we do not use the sum convention when the indices are up and down. On the other hand, we assume this notation $R_{\dot{\mu}} = \sqrt{n_{\dot{\mu}}}$ to (24), where $n_{\dot{\mu}}$ is the number density, represents the modulus of $\psi_{\dot{\mu}}$ and θ is its phase (both are real variables). In general, $n_{\dot{\mu}}$ is different for each component of the spinor. Note that the covariant derivative of the spinor ψ in terms of its decomposition (23) is $\nabla_\mu(\psi_{\dot{\nu}}) = \partial_\mu(R_{\dot{\nu}}e^{i\theta}) + \Gamma_{\mu\dot{\nu}}^{\dot{\alpha}}(R_{\dot{\alpha}}e^{i\theta}) = (\partial_\mu R_{\dot{\nu}})e^{i\theta} + i(\partial_\mu\theta)R_{\dot{\nu}}e^{i\theta} + \Gamma_{\mu\dot{\nu}}^{\dot{\alpha}}(R_{\dot{\alpha}}e^{i\theta})$, implying that $\nabla_\mu\theta = \partial_\mu\theta$.

Using the transformation (23) in eq. (5), the Dirac equation in terms of the variables R and θ reads

$$\exp(i\theta)\gamma^\mu \left(i\nabla_\mu R - (\nabla_\mu \theta)R - qA_\mu R - \frac{m}{4}\gamma_\mu R\right) = 0. \tag{25}$$

To get the last term, we used the property of the gamma matrices that $\gamma_\mu \gamma^\mu = 4\mathbb{I}$, where $\mathbb{I}$ is the 4×4 identity matrix. This property results from the anti-commutation relation of the gamma matrices. Similarly, the continuity equation (11) with (10) can be written with these new variables as

$$\left(\nabla_\mu R^T\right) K^\mu R + R^T K^\mu \left(\nabla_\mu R\right) = 0, \tag{26}$$

where R^T denotes the transpose of R and $K^\mu = B\gamma^\mu$. Observe that K^μ is hermitian ($K^{\mu\dagger} = K^\mu$).

In conclusion, we have introduced the hydrodynamic representation of the Dirac equation (25) and its conjugate transpose equation by making the change of variables from eq. (22).

4. Dirac-Euler Equation

As for the Klein-Gordon equation,[1,2] we define the 4-velocity v_μ by

$$mv_{\mu\dot{\nu}} = \nabla_\mu S_{\dot{\nu}} + qA_\mu. \tag{27}$$

Here, $S(x^\mu)$ is a phase with components $S_{\dot{\alpha}} = \theta_{\dot{\nu}}\delta^{\dot{\nu}}{}_{\dot{\alpha}} - \omega_{\dot{\nu}}\delta^{\dot{\nu}}{}_{\dot{\alpha}}t$ where $\omega_{\dot{\nu}}$ are constants that can be related to the mass of the fermion particle by $\omega_{\dot{\nu}} = mc^2/\hbar$ and $\theta_{\dot{\nu}} = \theta$. In this manner we can write

$$\nabla_\mu \theta_{\dot{\alpha}} \delta^{\dot{\alpha}}{}_{\dot{\nu}} = (mv_{\mu\dot{\alpha}} - \omega_{\dot{\alpha}}\delta^0{}_\mu)\delta^{\dot{\alpha}}{}_{\dot{\nu}} - qA_\mu. \tag{28}$$

We interpret $n_{\dot{\nu}}$ as the density number of fermions and $v_{\mu\dot{\nu}}$ as its velocity. Actually, eq. (25) can be interpreted as the first integral of the Bernoulli equation for fermions in an arbitrary space-time. To see this, we apply the operator $i\gamma^\mu D_\mu = i\gamma^\mu \nabla_\mu - q\gamma^\mu A_\mu$ to the Dirac equation (5) written under the form $i\gamma^\mu \nabla_\mu \psi = q\gamma^\mu A_\mu \psi - m\psi$. This yields

$$-\gamma^\mu\gamma^\nu \left(\nabla_\mu \nabla_\nu \psi + iq(\nabla_\mu A_\nu)\psi + iqA_\mu(\nabla_\nu \psi) + iqA_\nu(\nabla_\mu \psi) - q^2 A_\mu A_\nu \psi\right) - $$
$$m^2\psi - \gamma^\mu(\nabla_\mu \gamma^\nu)(\nabla_\nu \psi + iqA_\nu \psi) = 0. \tag{29}$$

Using the relation (7) in eq. (29) we obtain

$$\Box_E \psi + m^2\psi + \frac{i}{2}q\gamma^\mu \gamma^\nu F_{\mu\nu}\psi + \gamma^\mu(\nabla_\mu \gamma^\nu)(D_\nu \psi) = 0, \tag{30}$$

where we have defined the D'Alambertian operator in the presence of an electromagnetic field by $\Box_E = (\nabla_\mu + iqA_\mu)(\nabla^\mu + iqA^\mu)$ and the anti-symmetric Faraday tensor by $F_{\mu\nu} = \nabla_\mu A_\nu - \nabla_\nu A_\mu$. Eq. (30) is similar to the Klein-Gordon equation with an electromagnetic source except that here ψ is a spinor instead of a complex SF. The last term of eq. (30) contains the covariant derivative of γ^μ which vanishes in a flat space-time. According to Refs.[1,2] if we apply the transformation (22) to eq. (30), we could expect to obtain the continuity equation for the imaginary part and the Bernoulli equation for the real part. However, in the case of the Dirac equation the four components are mixed by the presence of the four dimensional spinor ψ. Hence, we obtain the following expression

$$i\left[2(mv^\mu - \omega\delta_0^\mu)\nabla_\mu R - qA_\mu + q\nabla_\mu(A^\mu R) + \nabla_\mu(mv^\mu - \omega\delta_0^\mu - qA^\mu)R\right] + \left(m^2 v_\mu v^\mu + 2m\omega v^0 + \frac{\omega^2}{N^2} + m^2\right)R - \Box R + \frac{i}{2}q\gamma^\mu\gamma^\nu F_{\mu\nu}R + \gamma^\mu(\nabla_\mu\gamma^\nu)(i(mv_\nu + \omega\nabla_\nu t)R + D_\nu R) = 0. \quad (31)$$

Here, we have defined $\Box = \nabla^\nu\nabla_\nu$ and we have introduced the diagonal matrices $v_\mu = v_{\mu\hat{\nu}}\delta^{\hat{\nu}}_{\hat{\alpha}}$ and $\omega = \omega_{\hat{\nu}}\delta^{\hat{\nu}}_{\hat{\alpha}}$. For bosons, the real and imaginary parts separate into two independent equations, namely, the continuity equation and the Bernoulli equation.[1,2] But in the spinor case, the last line of equation (31) mixes both the imaginary and real parts and there is no natural separation into real and imaginary parts. The system remains coupled.

5. Weyl Representation

The Dirac equation for 1/2-spin particles is associated with the $SO(1,3)$ symmetry group. Nevertheless, we can introduce a new representation as in standard QFT, since there exists a surjective homomorphism between the $SO(1,3)$ and $SU(2) \otimes SU(2)$ Lie groups.

In terms of the Pauli matrices the 4×4 gamma matrices γ^μ can be written as two 2×2 block matrices

$$\gamma^0 = N\tilde{\gamma}^0 = N\begin{pmatrix} 0 & \mathbb{I} \\ \mathbb{I} & 0 \end{pmatrix}, \quad (32)$$

$$\gamma^j = \hat{e}^j{}_i(\tilde{\gamma}^i + N^i\tilde{\gamma}^0) = \begin{pmatrix} 0 & -\hat{e}^j{}_i(\tilde{\sigma}^i - N^i\mathbb{I}) \\ \hat{e}^j{}_i(\tilde{\sigma}^i + N^i\mathbb{I}) & 0 \end{pmatrix}, \quad (33)$$

where $\tilde{\sigma}^i$ are the 2×2 Pauli matrices in flat space-time and $\mathbb{I}$ is the 2×2 identity matrix. The γ^μ matrices satisfy $(\gamma^0)^\dagger = \gamma^0$ and $(\gamma^j)^\dagger = -\gamma^j + 2N^j\gamma^0/N$.

As we know, the special unitary group $SU(2)$ is formed by the set of 2×2 complex matrices A, which satisfy $\det(A) = 1$. Explicitly, we have

$$A = \begin{pmatrix} a & -\bar{b} \\ b & \bar{a} \end{pmatrix}, \quad (34)$$

with $\det(A) = |a|^2 + |b|^2 = 1$, where a and b are complex parameters. Equivalently, we have the identity $A^\dagger = A^{-1}$.

The Lie algebra $\mathfrak{su}(2)$ associated to the $SU(2)$ Lie group is given by the exponential map

$$\exp(\mathfrak{su}(2)) \rightarrow SU(2). \quad (35)$$

For any element X of the Lie algebra, we have $\exp(X)\exp(X)^\dagger = \mathbb{I}$, implying that $X + X^\dagger = 0$. In what follows, we will indistinctly use $\exp(X)$ and e^X as the exponential map.

In the Weyl representation we can write a Dirac fermion as a four-spinor ψ made of two spinors each of which having two components, for instance

$$\psi = \begin{pmatrix} \psi_R \\ \psi_L \end{pmatrix}, \tag{36}$$

where ψ_R and ψ_L are the right- and the left- handed Weyl spinors, respectively. If we write the adjoint spinor $\bar\psi$ and use the Weyl representation, it follows that

$$\bar\psi = \psi^\dagger B = \left(\psi_R^\dagger, \psi_L^\dagger\right) B, \tag{37}$$

where B is the matrix from eqs. (8) and (14). If we use the relation (8) it is straightforward to see that the matrix B must have the following form

$$B = \begin{pmatrix} 0 & B_\zeta \\ B_\zeta & 0 \end{pmatrix}, \tag{38}$$

where the 2×2 matrix B_ζ is a diagonal matrix, $B_\zeta = b\mathbb{I}$, with $b = b(x^\mu)$. Therefore, we get $B = b\tilde\gamma^0$ and eq. (15) transforms into

$$\nabla_0(Nb) + \nabla_j(\hat{e}_i^j N^i b) = 0, \tag{39}$$
$$\nabla_j(\hat{e}_i^j b)\tilde\sigma^i = 0. \tag{40}$$

Using the definition of the spinor and its adjoint we can write the Dirac quadricurrent J^μ from eq. (10) as

$$J^\mu = \left(\psi_R^\dagger, \psi_L^\dagger\right) B\gamma^\mu \begin{pmatrix} \psi_R \\ \psi_L \end{pmatrix}, \tag{41}$$

where the gamma matrices are defined by eqs. (32) and (33) and, in general, B is given by the previously mentioned conditions. This yields

$$J^0 = Nb(\psi_R^\dagger \psi_R + \psi_L^\dagger \psi_L) = Nbn, \tag{42}$$
$$J^j = b\hat{e}^j_{\ i}(\psi_R^\dagger(\tilde\sigma^i + N^i\mathbb{I})\psi_R - \psi_L^\dagger(\tilde\sigma^i - N^i\mathbb{I})\psi_L). \tag{43}$$

In order to simplify the notation, we now define the vectors of 2×2 matrices $\mathbb{S}^a = (\mathbb{I}, \tilde\sigma^j + N^j\mathbb{I})$ and $\bar{\mathbb{S}}^a = (-\mathbb{I}, \tilde\sigma^j - N^j\mathbb{I})$ in terms of the Pauli matrices. $\mathbb{S}^a$ and $\bar{\mathbb{S}}^a$ are the (generalized) Pauli matrices in flat space-time. In terms of these new definitions, the density currents read

$$J^j = b\hat{e}^j_{\ i}(\psi_R^\dagger \mathbb{S}^i \psi_R - \psi_L^\dagger \bar{\mathbb{S}}^i \psi_L)$$
$$= b(\psi_R^\dagger \sigma^i \psi_R - \psi_L^\dagger \bar\sigma^i \psi_L), \tag{44}$$

where we have defined the 2×2 Pauli matrices in a curved space-time by $\sigma^\mu = e^\mu_a \mathbb{S}^a$ and $\bar\sigma^\mu = e^\mu_a \bar{\mathbb{S}}^a$. With this definition, the matrices γ^j read

$$\gamma^j = \begin{pmatrix} 0 & -\bar\sigma^j \\ \sigma^j & 0 \end{pmatrix}. \tag{45}$$

Furthermore, observe that the σ^j matrices follow the same commutation relations as the flat space-time Pauli matrices. This means that $[\sigma^i, \bar{\sigma}^j] = -\hat{e}^i_k \hat{e}^j_l [\tilde{\sigma}^k, \tilde{\sigma}^l]$. For the Weyl representation we have to obtain two equations for each Dirac fermion. Thus, we need to redefine the covariant derivative ∇_μ and the spinor affine connection Γ_μ,[14,24] which can be written as $\nabla_\mu = \partial_\mu + \Gamma_\mu$ and $\Gamma_\mu = \frac{1}{4}\bar{\sigma}_\nu \sigma^\nu_{;\mu}$ where $\sigma^\mu_{;\nu} = \partial_\nu \sigma^\mu + \Gamma^\mu_{\alpha\nu} \sigma^\alpha$. Nevertheless, in this representation we need to introduce two other notations due to the presence of $\bar{\sigma}^\mu$. Let $\bar{\nabla}_\mu$ and $\tilde{\Gamma}_\mu$ be the bar covariant derivative and the bar spinor affine connection, respectively, defined by $\bar{\nabla}_\mu = \partial_\mu + \tilde{\Gamma}_\mu$ where $\tilde{\Gamma}_\mu = \frac{1}{4}\sigma_\nu \bar{\sigma}^\nu_{;\mu}$ (we stress that we use the greek indices for denoting the objects in curved space-time as the gamma and Pauli matrices).

We can now apply the Weyl representation to rewrite the Dirac equation (5) for a spinor with four components as

$$\begin{pmatrix} i\sigma^\mu \left(\bar{\nabla}_\mu + iqA_\mu\right)\psi_R - m\psi_L \\ i\bar{\sigma}^\mu \left(\nabla_\mu + iqA_\mu\right)\psi_L - m\psi_R \end{pmatrix} = \begin{pmatrix} 0 \\ 0 \end{pmatrix}. \tag{46}$$

These are the Weyl equations for a spinor in a curved space-time coupled to an electromagnetic field. If we apply the Weyl representation to the transpose conjugated Dirac equation (16), it is straightforward to obtain the Weyl equation for the adjoint spinor (37). However, we shall not write the adjoint spinor equation explicitly because the results are analogous to the spinor equation as we have seen in the previous sections.

If we set $B = b\tilde{\gamma}^0$, the current density now reads

$$J^\mu = b\left(\psi_R^\dagger \sigma^\mu \psi_R - \psi_L^\dagger \bar{\sigma}^\mu \psi_L\right). \tag{47}$$

Explicitly, we have

$$J^0 = Nbn, \tag{48}$$

$$J^j = b\hat{e}^j_i \left(\psi_R^\dagger \tilde{\sigma}^i \psi_R - \psi_L^\dagger \tilde{\sigma}^i \psi_L + \frac{N^i}{Nb^2} J^0\right). \tag{49}$$

On the other hand, the last line of eq. (31) can be obtained from the identities

$$\gamma^\mu \gamma^\nu F_{\mu\nu} \psi = \begin{cases} (2NN^k F_{0k} + i\hat{F}_{ij}\epsilon^{ij}{}_k \tilde{\sigma}^k)\psi_R \\ -(2NN^k F_{0k} - i\hat{F}_{ij}\epsilon^{ij}{}_k \tilde{\sigma}^k)\psi_L \end{cases}, \tag{50}$$

and using definition (45), we find that

$$\begin{aligned} \gamma^\mu(\nabla_\mu \gamma^\nu)(D_\nu \psi) &= \begin{cases} -\bar{\mathbb{S}}^a \mathbb{S}^b (\hat{\nabla}_a \hat{e}^\nu_b)(D_\nu \psi_R) \\ -\mathbb{S}^a \bar{\mathbb{S}}^b (\hat{\nabla}_a \hat{e}^\nu_b)(D_\nu \psi_L) \end{cases} \\ &= \begin{cases} (N(\nabla_0 N) - \bar{\sigma}^j(\nabla_j N))(D_0 \psi_R) + (N(\nabla_0 \sigma^i) - \bar{\sigma}^j(\nabla_j \sigma^i))(D_i \psi_R) \\ (N(\nabla_0 N) + \sigma^j(\nabla_j N))(D_0 \psi_L) - (N(\nabla_0 \bar{\sigma}^i) - \sigma^j(\nabla_j \bar{\sigma}^i))(D_i \psi_L) \end{cases} \\ &= \begin{cases} (\hat{\nabla}_0 N - \bar{\mathbb{S}}^k(\hat{\nabla}_k N))(D_0 \psi_R) + (\mathbb{S}^k \hat{\nabla}_0 \hat{e}^i_k - \bar{\mathbb{S}}^k \mathbb{S}^l \hat{\nabla}_k \hat{e}^i_l))(D_i \psi_R) \\ (\hat{\nabla}_0 N + \mathbb{S}^k(\hat{\nabla}_k N))(D_0 \psi_L) - (\mathbb{S}^k \hat{\nabla}_0 \hat{e}^i_k - \mathbb{S}^k \bar{\mathbb{S}}^l(\hat{\nabla}_k \hat{e}^i_l))(D_i \psi_L), \end{cases} \end{aligned} \tag{51}$$

where $\epsilon^{ij}{}_k$ is the usual Levi-Civita tensor, $\hat{F}_{ij} = \hat{e}_i^l \hat{e}_j^m F_{lm}$ is the directional Maxwell tensor $\hat{F}_{ij} = (\hat{e}_i^l \hat{\nabla}_j - \hat{e}_j^l \hat{\nabla}_i) A_l$, and $\hat{\nabla}_a = \hat{e}_a^\alpha \nabla_\alpha$ is the directional covariant derivative which defines the Cartan connection $\hat{\nabla}_c \hat{e}_b^\nu = \Gamma^a_{bc} \hat{e}_a^\nu$. The Cartan connection $\Gamma^a_{bc} = \hat{e}^a_\nu \hat{\nabla}_c \hat{e}_b^\nu$ determines the Cartan first fundamental form $d\hat{e}^a + \Gamma^a_b \wedge \hat{e}^b$ for the connections $\Gamma^a_b = \Gamma^a_{bd} \hat{e}^d$ with the property that $\Gamma_{ab} + \Gamma_{ba} = 0$, where $\Gamma_{ab} = \eta_{ad} \Gamma^d_b$.

6. Weyl Hydrodynamic Representation

We now have all the ingredients to propose a hydrodynamic representation for the Weyl fermions, following the same procedure as the one developed for the Schrödinger and KG equations in Refs.[1,2].

We start to propose our Madelung transformation in the Weyl spinor, using the exponential map, that is

$$\Psi = \begin{pmatrix} \psi_R \\ \psi_L \end{pmatrix} = \begin{pmatrix} R_R \\ R_L \end{pmatrix} e^{i\theta}. \tag{52}$$

Since ψ_R and ψ_L are two spinors, we observe that R_R and R_L are two two-dimensional vectors. The Weyl representation of the adjoint spinor $\bar{\Psi}$ when $B = b\tilde{\gamma}^0$ is

$$\bar{\Psi} = b \left(\psi_R^\dagger, \psi_L^\dagger \right) \tilde{\gamma}^0 = \left(R_R^\dagger, R_L^\dagger \right) e^{-i\theta}. \tag{53}$$

Since R is a real vector, the transposed conjugate is equal to the transposed, that is $R^\dagger = R^T$.

Using the Madelung transformation (52) in the Weyl equations (46) and applying the Lie algebra and the Lie group, we can get the following expression

$$\begin{pmatrix} -\sigma^\mu \left(\bar{\nabla}_\mu \theta_R \right) R_R + i\sigma^\mu \left(\bar{\nabla}_\mu R_R \right) - q\sigma^\mu A_\mu R_R \\ -\bar{\sigma}^\mu \left(\bar{\nabla}_\mu \theta_L \right) R_L + i\bar{\sigma}^\mu \left(\bar{\nabla}_\mu R_L \right) - q\bar{\sigma}^\mu A_\mu R_L \end{pmatrix} = \begin{pmatrix} mR_L \\ mR_R \end{pmatrix}. \tag{54}$$

These are the Weyl equations in curved space-time with the Madelung transformation. We can also apply the Madelung transformation (52) and (53) to the current density (47), thereby obtaining

$$J^\mu = b \left(R_R^T \bar{\sigma}^\mu R_R - R_L^T \sigma^\mu R_L \right). \tag{55}$$

Its components are

$$J^0 = Nb(R_R^T R_R + R_L^T R_L) = Nbn, \tag{56}$$

$$J^j = b \left(\hat{e}_3^j (n_{\dot{1}} - n_{\dot{2}} - n_{\dot{3}} + n_{\dot{4}}) + 2\hat{e}_1^j (\sqrt{n_{\dot{1}} n_{\dot{2}}} - \sqrt{n_{\dot{3}} n_{\dot{4}}}) + \hat{e}_i^j N^i n \right). \tag{57}$$

We note that the zero component, where $n = \sum_{\dot{\nu}=\dot{1}}^{\dot{4}} n_{\dot{\nu}}$ is the density number of fermions in the system, gives the number of both right- and left-handed particles. We can write the following expressions $|\psi_R|^2 = \psi_R^\dagger \psi_R = R_R^T R_R = n_R$ and $|\psi_L|^2 = \psi_L^\dagger \psi_L = R_L^T R_L = n_L$ for the right- and left-handed spinors, as in the Dirac case. Thus, n_R, n_L are the right- and left- handed particle number and $n = n_R + n_L$ is the total density number.

Furthermore, eq. (31) becomes

$$i\left[2(mv_R^\mu - \omega_R\delta_0^\mu)\nabla_\mu R_R - qA_\mu + q\nabla_\mu(A^\mu R_R) + \nabla_\mu(mv_R^\mu - \omega_R\delta_0^\mu - qA^\mu)R_R\right] +$$
$$\left(m^2 v_{R\mu}v_R^\mu + 2m\omega_R v_R^0 + \frac{\omega^2}{N^2} + m^2\right)R_R - \Box R_R +$$
$$(2NN^k F_{0k} + i\epsilon^{ij}{}_k \hat{F}_{ij}\tilde{\sigma}^k)R_R +$$
$$(N(\nabla_0 N) - \bar{\sigma}^j(\nabla_j N))((mv_{R0} - \omega_R)R_R + D_0 R_R) +$$
$$(N(\nabla_0 \sigma^i) - \bar{\sigma}^j(\nabla_j \sigma^i))(imv_{Ri}R_R + D_i R_R) = 0. \tag{58}$$

A similar equation is obtained for the left-handed spinor R_L with the substitution $R \longrightarrow L$ and $\mathbb{S} \longleftrightarrow \bar{\mathbb{S}}$ in eq. (58). Simplifying the first line in this equation for $\dot{\nu} = 1, 2$ corresponding to right-handed components, we get

$$i\frac{m}{\sqrt{n_{\dot\nu}}}\left[-\frac{\omega_{\dot\nu}}{m}\nabla_0 n_{\dot\nu} + \nabla_\mu(n_{\dot\nu} v_{\dot\nu}^\mu) + \frac{\omega_{\dot\nu}}{m}\Box t\right] +$$
$$\sqrt{n_{\dot\nu}}\left[m^2 v_{\mu R}v_{\dot\nu}^\mu + 2m\omega_{\dot\nu}v_{\dot\nu}^0 + \frac{\omega_R^2}{N^2} + m^2 - \frac{\Box\sqrt{n_{\dot\nu}}}{\sqrt{n_{\dot\nu}}}\right] +$$
$$(2NN^k F_{0k} + i\epsilon^{lj}{}_k \hat{F}_{lj}\tilde{\sigma}^k)R_R -$$
$$(\hat{\nabla}_a \hat{e}_b^\alpha)\bar{\mathbb{S}}^a \mathbb{S}^b((mv_{R\alpha} - \omega_{\dot\nu}\delta_\alpha^0)R_R + D_\alpha R_R) = 0. \tag{59}$$

The equation for the left-handed components $\dot\nu = 3, 4$ is obtained by changing $R_R \longrightarrow R_L$ and $\mathbb{S} \longleftrightarrow \bar{\mathbb{S}}$. Here, we have introduced the two-dimensional vectors $v_\mu = (v_{R\mu}, v_{L\mu})$ and $\omega = (\omega_R, \omega_L)$. Explicitly, they are given by

$$R = \begin{pmatrix} R_R \\ R_L \end{pmatrix} = \begin{pmatrix} R_{\dot 1} \\ R_{\dot 2} \\ R_{\dot 3} \\ R_{\dot 4} \end{pmatrix} = \begin{pmatrix} \sqrt{n_{\dot 1}} \\ \sqrt{n_{\dot 2}} \\ \sqrt{n_{\dot 3}} \\ \sqrt{n_{\dot 4}} \end{pmatrix}, \tag{60}$$

$$v_\mu = \begin{pmatrix} v_{R\mu} & 0 \\ 0 & v_{L\mu} \end{pmatrix} = \begin{pmatrix} v_{\mu\dot 1} & 0 & 0 & 0 \\ 0 & v_{\mu\dot 2} & 0 & 0 \\ 0 & 0 & v_{\mu\dot 3} & 0 \\ 0 & 0 & 0 & v_{\mu\dot 4} \end{pmatrix}, \tag{61}$$

$$\omega = \begin{pmatrix} \omega_R & 0 \\ 0 & \omega_L \end{pmatrix} = \begin{pmatrix} \omega_{\dot 1} & 0 & 0 & 0 \\ 0 & \omega_{\dot 2} & 0 & 0 \\ 0 & 0 & \omega_{\dot 3} & 0 \\ 0 & 0 & 0 & \omega_{\dot 4} \end{pmatrix}. \tag{62}$$

We now write the last two lines of eq. (59) explicitly and separate them into imaginary and real parts, respectively. Using the Pauli representation of the $\tilde{\sigma}^j$ matrices

$$\tilde{\sigma}^1 = \begin{pmatrix} 0 & 1 \\ 1 & 0 \end{pmatrix}, \quad \tilde{\sigma}^2 = \begin{pmatrix} 0 & -i \\ i & 0 \end{pmatrix}, \quad \tilde{\sigma}^3 = \begin{pmatrix} 1 & 0 \\ 0 & -1 \end{pmatrix}, \tag{63}$$

we obtain for $\dot{\nu} = \dot{1}$:

$$\frac{m}{\sqrt{n_{\dot{1}}}}\left[-\frac{\omega_{\dot{1}}}{m}\nabla_0 n_{\dot{1}} + \nabla_\mu(n_{\dot{1}}v_{\dot{1}}^\mu) + \frac{\omega_{\dot{1}}}{m}\Box t\right] =$$

$$F_{12}\sqrt{n_{\dot{1}}} + F_{23}\sqrt{n_{\dot{2}}} - 2\Gamma_{21}^a((m\hat{v}_{a\dot{1}} - \omega_{\dot{1}}\hat{\delta}_a^0)\sqrt{n_{\dot{1}}} + \hat{D}_a\sqrt{n_{\dot{1}}}) -$$
$$2(\Gamma_{21}^a N^1 - \Gamma_{32}^a N^3 + \Gamma_{20}^a + \Gamma_{32}^a)((m\hat{v}_{a\dot{2}} - \omega_{\dot{2}}\hat{\delta}_a^0)\sqrt{n_{\dot{2}}} + \hat{D}_a\sqrt{n_{\dot{2}}}),$$

$$\sqrt{n_{\dot{1}}}\left[m^2 v_{\mu\dot{1}}v_{\dot{1}}^\mu + 2m\omega_{\dot{1}}v_{\dot{1}}^0 + \frac{\omega_{\dot{1}}^2}{N^2} + m^2 - \frac{\Box\sqrt{n_{\dot{1}}}}{\sqrt{n_{\dot{1}}}}\right] =$$

$$2N(F_{01}N^1 + F_{02}N^2 + F_{03}N^3)\sqrt{n_{\dot{1}}} - F_{13}\sqrt{n_{\dot{2}}} +$$
$$\left[\Gamma_{11}^a(1-(N^1)^2) + \Gamma_{22}^a(1-(N^2)^2) + \Gamma_{33}^a(1-(N^3)^2) +\right.$$
$$2\Gamma_{31}^a N^1 + 2\Gamma_{32}^a N^2 - \Gamma_{00}^a + 2\Gamma_{30}^a\bigr]((m\hat{v}_{a\dot{1}} - \omega_{\dot{1}}\hat{\delta}_a^0)\sqrt{n_{\dot{1}}} + \hat{D}_a\sqrt{n_{\dot{1}}}) +$$
$$(-2\Gamma_{21}^a N^2 - 2\Gamma_{31}^a N^3 + 2\Gamma_{10}^a + 2\Gamma_{31}^a)((m\hat{v}_{a\dot{2}} - \omega_{\dot{2}}\hat{\delta}_a^0)\sqrt{n_{\dot{2}}} + \hat{D}_a\sqrt{n_{\dot{2}}}), \quad (64)$$

for $\dot{\nu} = \dot{2}$:

$$\frac{m}{\sqrt{n_{\dot{2}}}}\left[-\frac{\omega_{\dot{2}}}{m}\nabla_0 n_{\dot{2}} + \nabla_\mu(n_{\dot{2}}v_{\dot{2}}^\mu) + \frac{\omega_{\dot{2}}}{m}\Box t\right] =$$

$$-F_{12}\sqrt{n_{\dot{2}}} + F_{23}\sqrt{n_{\dot{1}}} + 2\Gamma_{21}^a((m\hat{v}_{a\dot{2}} - \omega_{\dot{2}}\hat{\delta}_a^0)\sqrt{n_{\dot{2}}} + \hat{D}_a\sqrt{n_{\dot{2}}}) +$$
$$2(\Gamma_{21}^a N^1 - \Gamma_{32}^a N^3 + \Gamma_{20}^a - \Gamma_{32}^a)(m\hat{v}_{a\dot{1}} - \omega_{\dot{1}}\hat{\delta}_a^0)\sqrt{n_{\dot{1}}} + \hat{D}_a\sqrt{n_{\dot{1}}}),$$

$$\sqrt{n_{\dot{2}}}\left[m^2 v_{\mu\dot{2}}v_{\dot{2}}^\mu + 2m\omega_{\dot{2}}v_{\dot{2}}^0 + \frac{\omega_{\dot{2}}^2}{N^2} + m^2 - \frac{\Box\sqrt{n_{\dot{2}}}}{\sqrt{n_{\dot{2}}}}\right] =$$

$$2N(F_{01}N^1 + F_{02}N^2 + F_{03}N^3)\sqrt{n_{\dot{2}}} + F_{13}\sqrt{n_{\dot{1}}} +$$
$$\left[\Gamma_{11}^a(1-(N^1)^2) + \Gamma_{22}^a(1-(N^2)^2) + \Gamma_{33}^a(1-(N^3)^2) +\right.$$
$$-2\Gamma_{31}^a N^1 - 2\Gamma_{32}^a N^2 - \Gamma_{00}^a - 2\Gamma_{30}^a\bigr]((m\hat{v}_{a\dot{2}} - \omega_{\dot{2}}\hat{\delta}_a^0)\sqrt{n_{\dot{2}}} + \hat{D}_a\sqrt{n_{\dot{2}}}) +$$
$$(-2\Gamma_{21}^a N^2 - 2\Gamma_{31}^a N^3 + 2\Gamma_{10}^a - 2\Gamma_{31}^a)((m\hat{v}_{a\dot{1}} - \omega_{\dot{1}}\hat{\delta}_a^0)\sqrt{n_{\dot{1}}} + \hat{D}_a\sqrt{n_{\dot{1}}}), \quad (65)$$

for $\dot{\nu} = \dot{3}$:

$$\frac{m}{\sqrt{n_{\dot{3}}}}\left[-\frac{\omega_{\dot{3}}}{m}\nabla_0 n_{\dot{3}} + \nabla_\mu(n_{\dot{3}}v_{\dot{3}}^\mu) + \frac{\omega_{\dot{3}}}{m}\Box t\right] =$$

$$F_{12}\sqrt{n_{\dot{3}}} + F_{23}\sqrt{n_{\dot{4}}} - 2\Gamma_{21}^a((m\hat{v}_{a\dot{3}} - \omega_{\dot{3}}\hat{\delta}_a^0)\sqrt{n_{\dot{3}}} + \hat{D}_a\sqrt{n_{\dot{3}}}) +$$
$$2(\Gamma_{21}^a N^1 - \Gamma_{32}^a N^3 + \Gamma_{20}^a - \Gamma_{32}^a)((m\hat{v}_{a\dot{4}} - \omega_{\dot{4}}\hat{\delta}_a^0)\sqrt{n_{\dot{4}}} + \hat{D}_a\sqrt{n_{\dot{4}}}),$$

$$\sqrt{n_{\dot{3}}}\left[m^2 v_{\mu\dot{3}}v_{\dot{3}}^\mu + 2m\omega_{\dot{3}}v_{\dot{3}}^0 + \frac{\omega_{\dot{3}}^2}{N^2} + m^2 - \frac{\Box\sqrt{n_{\dot{3}}}}{\sqrt{n_{\dot{3}}}}\right] =$$

$$2N(F_{01}N^1 + F_{02}N^2 + F_{03}N^3)\sqrt{n_{\dot{3}}} - F_{13}\sqrt{n_{\dot{4}}} +$$
$$\left[\Gamma_{11}^a(1-(N^1)^2) + \Gamma_{22}^a(1-(N^2)^2) + \Gamma_{33}^a(1-(N^3)^2) +\right.$$
$$-2\Gamma_{31}^a N^1 - 2\Gamma_{32}^a N^2 - \Gamma_{00}^a - 2\Gamma_{30}^a\bigr]((m\hat{v}_{a\dot{3}} - \omega_{\dot{3}}\hat{\delta}_a^0)\sqrt{n_{\dot{3}}} + \hat{D}_a\sqrt{n_{\dot{3}}}) +$$
$$(2\Gamma_{21}^a N^2 + 2\Gamma_{31}^a N^3 - 2\Gamma_{10}^a + 2\Gamma_{31}^a)((m\hat{v}_{a\dot{4}} - \omega_{\dot{4}}\hat{\delta}_a^0)\sqrt{n_{\dot{4}}} + \hat{D}_a\sqrt{n_{\dot{4}}}), \quad (66)$$

and for $\dot{\nu} = \dot{4}$:

$$\frac{m}{\sqrt{n_{\dot{4}}}}\left[-\frac{\omega_{\dot{4}}}{m}\nabla_0 n_{\dot{4}} + \nabla_\mu(n_{\dot{4}} v_{\dot{4}}^\mu) + \frac{\omega_{\dot{4}}}{m}\Box t\right] =$$

$$-F_{12}\sqrt{n_{\dot{4}}} + F_{23}\sqrt{n_{\dot{3}}} + 2\Gamma_{21}^a((m\hat{v}_{a\dot{4}} - \omega_{\dot{4}}\hat{\delta}_a^0)\sqrt{n_{\dot{4}}} + \hat{D}_a\sqrt{n_{\dot{4}}}) -$$

$$2(\Gamma_{21}^a N^1 - \Gamma_{32}^a N^3 + \Gamma_{20}^a + \Gamma_{32}^a)((m\hat{v}_{a\dot{3}} - \omega_{\dot{3}}\hat{\delta}_a^0)\sqrt{n_{\dot{3}}} + \hat{D}_a\sqrt{n_{\dot{3}}}),$$

$$\sqrt{n_{\dot{4}}}\left[m^2 v_{\mu\dot{4}} v_{\dot{4}}^\mu + 2m\omega_{\dot{4}} v_{\dot{4}}^0 + \frac{\omega_{\dot{4}}^2}{N^2} + m^2 - \frac{\Box\sqrt{n_{\dot{4}}}}{\sqrt{n_{\dot{4}}}}\right] =$$

$$2N(F_{01}N^1 + F_{02}N^2 + F_{03}N^3)\sqrt{n_{\dot{4}}} + F_{13}\sqrt{n_{\dot{3}}} +$$

$$\left[\Gamma_{11}^a(1 - (N^1)^2) + \Gamma_{22}^a(1 - (N^2)^2) + \Gamma_{33}^a(1 - (N^3)^2) + \right.$$

$$\left. 2\Gamma_{31}^a N^1 + 2\Gamma_{32}^a N^2 - \Gamma_{00}^a + 2\Gamma_{30}^a\right]((m\hat{v}_{a\dot{4}} - \omega_{\dot{4}}\hat{\delta}_a^0)\sqrt{n_{\dot{4}}} + \hat{D}_a\sqrt{n_{\dot{4}}}) +$$

$$(2\Gamma_{21}^a N^2 + 2\Gamma_{31}^a N^3 - 2\Gamma_{10}^a - 2\Gamma_{31}^a)((m\hat{v}_{a\dot{3}} - \omega_{\dot{3}}\hat{\delta}_a^0)\sqrt{n_{\dot{3}}} + \hat{D}_a\sqrt{n_{\dot{3}}}), \quad (67)$$

where we have used that $\Gamma_{ab} + \Gamma_{ba} = 0$ and defined the directional quantities $v_{a\dot{\nu}} = v_{R\alpha\dot{\nu}}\hat{e}_a^\alpha$, $\hat{\delta}_a^0 = \delta_\alpha^0 \hat{e}_a^\alpha = N\delta_a^0$ and $\hat{D}_a = \hat{e}_a^\alpha D_\alpha$.

The first line of eq. (59) represents the continuity equation of the fermionic fluid. The second line is the Bernoulli equation. In this respect, we note that eq. (25) is the first integral of this equation. Finally, the last three lines of eq. (59) are the source of the fermionic fluid, something that is not present in the case of bosons. This is because the Dirac equation was introduced in Ref.[25] in order to eliminate the negative probability problem of the KG equation. As a result, the Dirac equation involves only first derivatives while the KG equation is a second order equation.

Observe that the structure of equations (64)-(67) is

$$\frac{m}{\sqrt{n_{\dot{\nu}}}}\left[-\frac{\omega_{\dot{\nu}}}{m}\nabla_0 n_{\dot{\nu}} + \nabla_\mu(n_{\dot{\nu}} v_{\dot{\nu}}^\mu) + \frac{\omega_{\dot{\nu}}}{m}\Box t\right] =$$

$$e_{1\dot{\nu}}F_{12}\sqrt{n_{\dot{\nu}}} + F_{23}\sqrt{n_{\ddot{\nu}}} - 2e_{1\dot{\nu}}\Gamma_{21}^a((m\hat{v}_{a\dot{\nu}} - \omega_{\dot{\nu}}\hat{\delta}_a^0)\sqrt{n_{\dot{\nu}}} + \hat{D}_a\sqrt{n_{\dot{\nu}}}) -$$

$$2(\Gamma_{21}^a N^1 - \Gamma_{32}^a N^3 + \Gamma_{20}^a + e_{2\dot{\nu}}\Gamma_{32}^a)((m\hat{v}_{a\ddot{\nu}} - \omega_{\ddot{\nu}}\hat{\delta}_a^0)\sqrt{n_{\ddot{\nu}}} + \hat{D}_a\sqrt{n_{\ddot{\nu}}}),$$

$$\sqrt{n_{\dot{\nu}}}\left[m^2 v_{\mu\dot{\nu}} v_{\dot{\nu}}^\mu + 2m\omega_{\dot{\nu}} v_{\dot{\nu}}^0 + \frac{\omega_{\dot{\nu}}^2}{N^2} + m^2 - \frac{\Box\sqrt{n_{\dot{\nu}}}}{\sqrt{n_{\dot{\nu}}}}\right] =$$

$$2N(F_{01}N^1 + F_{02}N^2 + F_{03}N^3)\sqrt{n_{\dot{\nu}}} - e_{1\dot{\nu}}F_{13}\sqrt{n_{\ddot{\nu}}} +$$

$$\left[\Gamma_{11}^a(1 - (N^1)^2) + \Gamma_{22}^a(1 - (N^2)^2) + \Gamma_{33}^a(1 - (N^3)^2) + \right.$$

$$\left. 2e_{2\dot{\nu}}(\Gamma_{31}^a N^1 + \Gamma_{32}^a N^2 + \Gamma_{30}^a) - \Gamma_{00}^a\right]((m\hat{v}_{a\dot{\nu}} - \omega_{\dot{\nu}}\hat{\delta}_a^0)\sqrt{n_{\dot{\nu}}} + \hat{D}_a\sqrt{n_{\dot{\nu}}}) +$$

$$(-2e_{3\dot{\nu}}(\Gamma_{21}^a N^2 + \Gamma_{31}^a N^3 - \Gamma_{10}^a) + 2e_{1\dot{\nu}}\Gamma_{31}^a)((m\hat{v}_{a\ddot{\nu}} - \omega_{\ddot{\nu}}\hat{\delta}_a^0)\sqrt{n_{\ddot{\nu}}} + \hat{D}_a\sqrt{n_{\ddot{\nu}}}), \quad (68)$$

where the coefficients $e_{i\dot{\nu}}$ are ± 1 with $e_{1\dot{\nu}} = (+,-,+,-)$, $e_{2\dot{\nu}} = (+,-,+,-)$ and $e_{3\dot{\nu}} = (+,+,-,-)$, and the sub-index $\ddot{\nu}$ is the conjugate of the sub-index $\dot{\nu}$ such that $\ddot{1} = \dot{2}$, $\ddot{2} = \dot{1}$, $\ddot{3} = \dot{4}$ and $\ddot{4} = \dot{3}$.

7. Energy Balance

We can also write equation (30) as a Schrödinger-like equation. If we perform the transformation $\psi = \Psi e^{i\omega_0 t}$, where Ψ is a four spinor that depends on all the variables x^μ, equation (30) becomes

$$i\nabla^0\Psi - \frac{1}{2\omega_0}\Box_E\Psi + \frac{m^2}{2\omega_0}\Psi + \left(-\frac{\omega_0}{N^2} - 2qA^0 + i\Box t\right)\Psi +$$
$$\frac{1}{2\omega_0}\begin{pmatrix} 2NN^k F_{0k} + i\hat{F}_{ij}\epsilon^{ij}{}_k\tilde{\sigma}^k & 0 \\ 0 & -2NN^k F_{0k} + i\hat{F}_{ij}\epsilon^{ij}{}_k\tilde{\sigma}^k \end{pmatrix}\Psi -$$
$$\frac{1}{2\omega_0}\begin{pmatrix} \bar{\mathbb{S}}^a\mathbb{S}^b & 0 \\ 0 & \mathbb{S}^a\bar{\mathbb{S}}^b \end{pmatrix}\Gamma^d_{ba}(\hat{D}_d\Psi + i\omega_0 N\delta^0_d\Psi) = 0. \quad (69)$$

Equation (69) is the generalization of the Schrödinger equation for fermions with electromagnetic field interaction in an arbitrary space-time.

Finally, from equation (59) we can identify the different energy contributions to the Fermi gas, and obtain an energy balance equation for fermions analogous to the one obtained for bosons in Refs.[1,2]. In order to simplify the notations, we can re-write equation (59) in terms of the $\dot{\nu}$ coefficients with the understanding that the subindex R refers to each component $R = \dot{1}, \dot{2}$ individually. We get

$$i\left[-\omega_{\dot\nu}\nabla_0 \ln(n_{\dot\nu}) + \frac{m\nabla_\mu(n_{\dot\nu}v^\mu_{\dot\nu})}{n_{\dot\nu}} + \frac{\omega_{\dot\nu}}{n_{\dot\nu}}\Box t\right] +$$
$$2m^2\left(K_{\dot\nu} + \frac{1}{m}\omega_{\dot\nu}v^0_{\dot\nu} + \frac{1}{2}U^N_{\dot\nu} + U^Q_{\dot\nu}\right) + E_{\dot\nu} + U^S_{\dot\nu} = 0. \quad (70)$$

This equation is valid for right handed fermions. The result is the same for left handed fermions changing $R_R \longrightarrow R_L$ in the first line, and $\mathbb{S} \longleftrightarrow \bar{\mathbb{S}}$ in the second line.

The first line in eq. (70) describes the free density evolution of the fermions, while the contribution of the different energy terms appears in the second line. The first one is the kinetic energy $K_{\dot\nu}$ defined as

$$K_{\dot\nu} = \frac{1}{2}v_{\dot\nu\mu}v^\mu_{\dot\nu}. \quad (71)$$

The lapse potential $U^N_{\dot\nu}$ is given by

$$U^N_{\dot\nu} = \frac{\omega^2_{\dot\nu}}{m^2}\frac{1}{N^2} + 1. \quad (72)$$

It represents the energy contribution due to the chosen lapse function N. The quantum potential $U^Q_{\dot\nu}$ is defined as

$$U^Q_{\dot\nu} = -\frac{1}{2m^2}\frac{\Box\sqrt{n_{\dot\nu}}}{\sqrt{n_{\dot\nu}}}. \quad (73)$$

The contribution of the electromagnetic interaction $E_{\dot\nu}$ is given by

$$E_{\dot\nu} = (2NN^k F_{0k} + i\epsilon^{lj}{}_k \hat{F}_{lj}\tilde{\sigma}^k)|_{\dot\nu},$$
$$= 2N(F_{01}N^1 + F_{02}N^2 + F_{03}N^3) - e_{1\dot\nu}F_{13}\sqrt{\frac{n_{\ddot\nu}}{n_{\dot\nu}}} + i\left(e_{1\dot\nu}F_{12} + F_{23}\sqrt{\frac{n_{\ddot\nu}}{n_{\dot\nu}}}\right). \tag{74}$$

It depends on the Faraday tensor, shift vector and lapse function that are related to the Pauli matrices. This relationship is due to the interaction between the electromagnetic field and the fermionic spin. Finally, the potential $U_{\dot\nu}^S$ describes the interaction between the spin and the geometry of space-time. It is given by

$$\begin{aligned}
U_{\dot\nu}^S &= -\left((m\hat{v}_{Rd} - \omega_{\dot\nu}\hat{\delta}_d^0) + \frac{\hat{D}_\alpha \sqrt{n_{\dot\nu}}}{\sqrt{n_{\dot\nu}}}\right)\Gamma_{ba}^d \bar{\mathbb{S}}^a \mathbb{S}^b|_{\dot\nu}, \\
&= \left[\Gamma_{11}^a(1-(N^1)^2) + \Gamma_{22}^a(1-(N^2)^2) + \Gamma_{33}^a(1-(N^3)^2) \right.\\
&\quad + 2e_{2\dot\nu}(\Gamma_{31}^a N^1 + \Gamma_{32}^a N^2 + \Gamma_{30}^a) - \Gamma_{00}^a\bigg]\left((m\hat{v}_{a\dot\nu} - \omega_{\dot\nu}\hat{\delta}_a^0) + \frac{\hat{D}_\alpha\sqrt{n_{\dot\nu}}}{\sqrt{n_{\dot\nu}}}\right) \\
&\quad + (-2e_{3\dot\nu}(\Gamma_{21}^a N^2 + \Gamma_{31}^a N^3 - \Gamma_{10}^a) + 2e_{1\dot\nu}\Gamma_{31}^a)\left((m\hat{v}_{a\dot\nu} - \omega_{\dot\nu}\hat{\delta}_a^0)\sqrt{\frac{n_{\ddot\nu}}{n_{\dot\nu}}} + \frac{\hat{D}_\alpha\sqrt{n_{\ddot\nu}}}{\sqrt{n_{\dot\nu}}}\right) \\
&\quad + i\left[-2e_{1\dot\nu}\Gamma_{21}^a\left((m\hat{v}_{a\dot\nu} - \omega_{\dot\nu}\hat{\delta}_a^0) + \frac{\hat{D}_\alpha\sqrt{n_{\dot\nu}}}{\sqrt{n_{\dot\nu}}}\right)\right. \\
&\quad \left.\left. - 2(\Gamma_{21}^a N^1 - \Gamma_{32}^a N^3 + \Gamma_{20}^a + e_{2\dot\nu}\Gamma_{32}^a)\left((m\hat{v}_{a\dot\nu} - \omega_{\dot\nu}\hat{\delta}_a^0)\sqrt{\frac{n_{\ddot\nu}}{n_{\dot\nu}}} + \frac{\hat{D}_\alpha\sqrt{n_{\ddot\nu}}}{\sqrt{n_{\dot\nu}}}\right)\right]\right.
\end{aligned} \tag{75}$$

for $\dot\nu = \dot{1}, \dot{2}$, and by making the substitution $\mathbb{S} \longleftrightarrow \bar{\mathbb{S}}$ for $\dot\nu = \dot{3}, \dot{4}$. In the foregoing equations, the notation $|_{\dot\nu}$ means that we have to evaluate the quantity at the corresponding $\dot\nu$. Note that $U_{\dot\nu}^S$ disappears if we assume a flat space-time or if we consider particles without spin. Furthermore, $U_{\dot\nu}^S$ is constructed with the generalized gamma matrices (45), which are related to the spin (the Pauli matrices) and to the space-time geometry (tetrads).

8. Conclusions

The main difference between the hydrodynamic representation of bosons[1,2] and fermions concerns the form of the Bernoulli equation. For bosons, after making the Madelung transformation, we can separate the KG equation into real and imaginary parts. By contrast, for fermion particles we have to work with the complete equations of motion because the real and imaginary parts cannot be separated easily. This is related to the fact that the gamma matrices are a representation of the $SO(1,3)$ group.

The spin is a fundamental outcome of the Dirac equation[25] which combines both elements of special relativity and quantum mechanics and was introduced to solve the problem of negative probability present in the KG equation – first proposed as a relativistic generalization of the Schrödinger equation. Here, we observe that the general relativistic Dirac equation involves an additional contribution due to geometry and spin through the generalized gamma and Pauli matrices. These terms arise from endowing a quantum field with a curvature (geometry) given by a metric in General Relativity. Such a contribution is absent in a flat space-time and in a system without spin as for a scalar field.

With this work we open the possibility of studying in detail the behavior of fermions in different situations (such as massive stars or dark matter halos harboring a central black hole) where general relativity effects may be important. We solved the problem of energy balance for both bosons and fermions. In this manner, we can compare the result of the hydrodynamic representation for classical and quantum fluids in the various geometries mentioned above.

Acknowledgments

This work was partially supported by CONACyT México under grants: A1-S-8742, 304001, 376127; Project No. 269652 and Fronteras Project 281;Xiuhcoatl and Abacus clusters at Cinvestav, IPN; I0101/131/07 C-234/07 of the Instituto Avanzado de Cosmología (IAC) collaboration (http:// www.iac.edu.mx). O.G. acknowledges financial support from CONACyT doctoral fellowship and appreaciates Angelica C. Aguirre Castañón for her valuable review and support. Works of T.M. are partially supported by Conacyt through the Fondo Sectorial de Investigación para la Educación, grant CB-2014-1, No. 240512.

Appendix A. Solutions to the Dirac equation in flat space-time

Equation (5) in flat space-time, using the Pauli matrices (63), reads

$$\begin{bmatrix} \frac{\partial}{\partial t}\psi_y - \frac{\partial}{\partial x}\psi_z + i\frac{\partial}{\partial y}\psi_z - \frac{\partial}{\partial z}\psi_y - m\psi_t \\ \frac{\partial}{\partial t}\psi_z - \frac{\partial}{\partial x}\psi_y - i\frac{\partial}{\partial y}\psi_y + \frac{\partial}{\partial z}\psi_z - m\psi_x \\ \frac{\partial}{\partial t}\psi_t + \frac{\partial}{\partial x}\psi_x - i\frac{\partial}{\partial y}\psi_x + \frac{\partial}{\partial z}\psi_t - m\psi_y \\ \frac{\partial}{\partial t}\psi_x + \frac{\partial}{\partial x}\psi_t + i\frac{\partial}{\partial y}\psi_t - \frac{\partial}{\partial z}\psi_x - m\psi_z \end{bmatrix} = 0, \qquad (A.1)$$

where we have defined the spinor as $\psi = (\psi_{\hat{\mu}}) = (\psi_x, \psi_y, \psi_z, \psi_t)^T$. In order to find an exact solution of the previous equation, we use the ansatz $\psi_{\hat{\mu}} = R_{0\hat{\mu}} \exp(i(x_0 x + y_0 y + z_0 z + t_0 t))$, where $x_0 \cdots t_0$ and $R_{0\hat{\mu}}$ are constants. Here we have the simplest solutions of the Dirac equation where the exponential is the same for all components.

We obtain four linear equations

$$iR_{0z}\zeta_0^* + iR_{0y}\eta_0 + mR_{0t} = 0,$$
$$iR_{0y}\zeta_0 - iR_{0z}\xi_0 + mR_{0x} = 0,$$
$$R_{0x}\zeta_0^* + R_{0t}\xi_0 + imR_{0y} = 0,$$
$$R_{0t}\zeta_0 - R_{0x}\eta_0 + imR_{0z} = 0, \qquad (A.2)$$

where $\zeta_0 = x_0 + iy_0$, $\eta_0 = z_0 - t_0$, and $\xi_0 = z_0 + t_0$. The solution of these equations is

$$R_{0t} = -\frac{1}{m}(iR_{0y}\eta_0 + iR_{0z}\zeta_0),$$
$$R_{0x} = \frac{1}{m}(iR_{0z}\xi_0 - iR_{0y}\zeta_0^*), \qquad (A.3)$$

where $x_0^2 + y_0^2 + z_0^2 - t_0^2 = m^2$.

Now we use the ansatz $\psi_\mu = R_{0\mu}\exp(i\theta)$, where θ is an arbitrary function of the coordinates. Substituting this ansatz into (A.1) we obtain

$$iR_{0z}Z_0^* + iR_{0y}E_0 + mR_{0t} = 0,$$
$$iR_{0y}Z_0 - iR_{0z}F_0 + mR_{0x} = 0,$$
$$R_{0x}Z_0^* + R_{0t}F_0 + imR_{0y} = 0,$$
$$R_{0t}Z_0 - R_{0x}E_0 + imR_{0z} = 0, \qquad (A.4)$$

where $Z_0 = \theta_{,x} + i\theta_{,y}$, $E_0 = \theta_{,z} - \theta_{,t}$, and $F_0 = \theta_{,z} + \theta_{,t}$. The solution of the previous system of differential equations is

$$\theta = F(X) - it$$
$$+ \frac{m}{2R_{0t}R_{0z} + 2R_{0x}R_{0y}}\left(i\zeta_0^*(R_{0x}^2 - R_{0z}^2) - i\zeta_0(R_{0y}^2 - R_{0t}^2)\right), \qquad (A.5)$$

where $F(X)$ is an arbitrary function of

$$X = \frac{R_{0t}(-\zeta R_{0y} - \zeta^* R_{0x} + \xi R_{0y} - \eta R_{0z})}{2R_{0t}R_{0z} + 2R_{0x}R_{0y}}. \qquad (A.6)$$

References

1. T. Matos, A. Avilez, T. Bernal, P.H. Chavanis, Gen. Rel. Grav. **51**, 159 (2019).
2. P.H. Chavanis, T. Matos, Eur. Phys. J. Plus **132**, 30 (2017).
3. P. Collas, D. Klein, *The Dirac Equation in Curved Spacetime: A Guide for Calculations* (Springer Briefs in Physics, Springer, 2019).
4. R.L. Arnowitt, S. Deser, C.W. Misner, Gen. Rel. Grav. **40**, 1997 (2008).
5. M. Alcubierre, *Introduction to 3+1 Numerical Relativity* (International Series of Monographs on Physics, Oxford, 2008).
6. S.W. Hawking, G.F.R. Ellis, *The Large Scale Structure of Space-Time* (Cambridge Monographs on Mathematical Physics, Cambridge University Press, 2011).
7. M. Nakahara, *Geometry, topology and physics* (IOP Publishing, 2003).
8. O. Gallegos, T. Matos, Gen. Rel. Grav. **53**, 50 (2021).

9. R. Penrose, W. Rindler, *Spinors and Space-time. Vol. 2: Spinor and Twistor Methods in Space-time Geometry* (Cambridge Monographs on Mathematical Physics, Cambridge University Press, 1988).
10. R. M. Wald, *General Relativity* (The University of Chicago Press, 1984).
11. M. Arminjon, F. Reifler, Braz. J. Phys. **40**, 242 (2010).
12. M. Arminjon, F. Reifler, Braz. J. Phys. **43**, 64 (2013).
13. M. Arminjon, F. Reifler, Int. J. Geom. Meth. Mod. Phys. **09**, 1250026 (2012).
14. N.J. Poplawski, arXiv:0710.3982.
15. S. Weinberg, *The Quantum Theory of Fields* (Press Syndicate of the University of Cambridge, 1995).
16. I.J.R. Aitchison, A.J.G. Hey, *Gauge Theories in Particles Physics Volume 1: From Relativistic Quantum Mechanics to QED* (CRC Press, 2003).
17. T. Lancaster, S.J. Blundell, *Quantum Field Theory for the Gifted Amateur* (Oxford University Press, 2014).
18. N.D. Birrell, P.C.W. Davies, *Quantum Fields in Curved Space* (Cambridge Monographs on Mathematical Physics, Cambridge Univ. Press 1984).
19. M.D. Pollock, Acta Physica Polonica B **41**, 8 (2010).
20. E. Noether, Nachr. d. Kgl. Ges d. Wiss (Math. phys. Klasse), Göttingen, 235 (1918).
21. D.R. Brill, J.A. Wheeler, Rev. Mod. Phys. **29**, 465 (1957).
22. L. Parker, Phys. Rev. D **22**, 1922 (1980).
23. E. Madelung, Zeitschrift fr̈ Physik **40**, 322 (1927).
24. Y-Q Gu, gr-qc/0610001.
25. P.A.M. Dirac, Proc. Roy. Soc. Lond. A **117**, 610 (1928).

Breakdown of the Equivalence Principle for a composite quantum body

A. G. Lebed

Department of Physics, University of Arizona,
Tucson, Arizona 85721, USA and
L.D. Landau Institute for Theoretical Physics,
Kosygina Street 2, Moscow 117334, Russia
E-mail: lebed@arizona.edu
www.university of arizona.edu

We derive the semiclassical Hamiltonian for electron in a hydrogen atom in a weak gravitational field, which takes into account the quantum effects of electron motion in the atom. We show that this Hamiltonian predicts a breakdown of the equivalence between electron passive gravitational mass and its energy in the absence of the gravitational field. More strictly, we demonstrate that quantum measurement of electron mass, which initially is in a ground state and has energy E_1, can give the following quantized values: $m_n = m_e + \frac{E_n}{c^2}$, where E_n is energy of electron orbit nS in a hydrogen atom. We correct some drawbacks of our early pioneering papers and discuss some difficulties in the possible observations of the above mentioned mass quantization phenomenon.

Keywords: Equivalence Principle; Quantum gavity; Equivalence betweem mass and energy

1. Introduction

Einstein's Equivalence Principle (EEP) between gravitational and inertial masses is known to be a keystone of the classical General Relativity. In the current scientific literature, there exists a wide discussion if it can survive in the possible quantum theory of gravity. Since the quantum gravitation theory has not been elaborated yet, the EEP is often studied in framework of the so-called semiclassical approach to quantum gravity, where gravitational field is not quantized, but the matter is quantized.[1–5] Note that gravitational mass of a composite body is not a trivial notion even in classical General Relativity.[6–8] The reason for this is that gravitational field is not directly coupled to the total energy, E, but is coupled to combination, $E + V(\mathbf{r})$, where $V(\mathbf{r})$ is the so-called virial term.[6–8] In quantum case, as shown by us,[1,2,4,5] the existence of the virial term results in breakdown of the equivalence between active and passive gravitational masses and energy of a body with internal degrees of freedom. The goal of our current paper is to suggest new method which demonstrates that the virial term is responsible for inequivalence of passive gravitational mass and energy. Below, we demonstrate the above mentioned inequivalence for a hydrogen atom, which is the simplest quantum object with internal degrees of freedom. Of course our conclusions, obtained in the paper, are applied to any composite quantum body.

2. Quantization of Passive Electron Gravitational Mass

2.1. *Electron wave function with a definite energy in the absence of gravitational field*

Let us consider the case, where at $t < 0$ gravitational field is zero and electron occupies ground state in a hydrogen atom, characterizing by the wave function:

$$\Psi_1(r,t) = \exp\left(\frac{-im_e c^2 t}{\hbar}\right)\exp\left(\frac{-iE_1 t}{\hbar}\right)\Psi_1(r). \tag{1}$$

Note that the wave function (1) corresponds to the $1S$ electron orbit and is known to be a ground state solution of the following Schrödinger equation:

$$i\hbar\frac{\partial \Psi_1(r,t)}{\partial t} = \left[m_e c^2 - \frac{\hbar^2}{2m_e}\left(\frac{\partial^2}{\partial x^2} + \frac{\partial^2}{\partial y^2} + \frac{\partial^2}{\partial z^2}\right) - \frac{e^2}{r}\right]\Psi_1(r,t). \tag{2}$$

[Here E_1 is electron ground state energy, r is a distance between the electron with coordinates (x,y,z) and proton; m_e is the bare electron mass, $\hbar$ is the Planck constant, and c is the velocity of light.]

2.2. *Electron wave function in the presence of gravitational field*

Let us consider the following Gedanken experiment: we turn on a weak (e.g., the Earth's) gravitational field at $t = 0$. As known,[9] the interval, characterizing a curved spacetime in the so-called weak field approximation, can be written as

$$ds^2 = -\left(1 + 2\frac{\phi}{c^2}\right)(cdt)^2 + \left(1 - 2\frac{\phi}{c^2}\right)(dx^2 + dy^2 + dz^2), \quad \phi = -\frac{GM}{R}, \tag{3}$$

where M is mass of a source of gravity, G is the gravitational constant. Below we use the local Lorentz invariance property of a spacetime in general relativity.[9] To this end, it is convenient to introduce the proper local coordinates,

$$\tilde{t} = \left(1 + \frac{\phi}{c^2}\right)t, \quad \tilde{x} = \left(1 - \frac{\phi}{c^2}\right)x, \quad \tilde{y} = \left(1 - \frac{\phi}{c^2}\right)y, \quad \tilde{z} = \left(1 - \frac{\phi}{c^2}\right)z, \tag{4}$$

where the interval (3) has the Minkowski's form,

$$d\tilde{s}^2 = -(cd\tilde{t})^2 + (d\tilde{x}^2 + d\tilde{y}^2 + d\tilde{z}^2). \tag{5}$$

Due to the local Lorentz invariance, if we disregard the tidal terms (i.e., if we don't differentiate the gravitational potential ϕ), the wave functions, written in the local proper coordinates (4), obeys the same Schrödinger equation at $t, \tilde{t} > 0$:

$$i\hbar\frac{\partial \Psi(\tilde{\mathbf{r}},\tilde{t})}{\partial \tilde{t}} = \left[m_e c^2 - \frac{\hbar^2}{2m_e}\left(\frac{\partial^2}{\partial \tilde{x}^2} + \frac{\partial^2}{\partial \tilde{y}^2} + \frac{\partial^2}{\partial \tilde{z}^2}\right) - \frac{e^2}{\tilde{r}}\right]\Psi(\tilde{\mathbf{r}},\tilde{t}). \tag{6}$$

Nevertheless, it is important that the wave function (1) is not a solution of the Schrödinger equation (6) and, thus, is not anymore characterized by definite energy and weight in the gravitational field (3). To clarify this point, we rewrite Eq. (6) in initial, (t, x, y, z), spacetime coordinates:

$$i\hbar\frac{\partial \Psi(\mathbf{r},t)}{\partial t} = \left\{\left[m_e c^2 - \frac{\hbar^2}{2m_e}\left(\frac{\partial^2}{\partial x^2} + \frac{\partial^2}{\partial y^2} + \frac{\partial^2}{\partial z^2}\right) - \frac{e^2}{r}\right] \right.$$
$$\left. + \left(\frac{\phi}{c^2}\right)\left[m_e c^2 - \frac{\hbar^2}{2m_e}\left(\frac{\partial^2}{\partial x^2} + \frac{\partial^2}{\partial y^2} + \frac{\partial^2}{\partial z^2}\right) - \frac{e^2}{r} + \hat{V}(\mathbf{r})\right]\right\}\Psi(\mathbf{r},t), \quad (7)$$

where the virial operator[10] is equal to

$$\hat{V}(\mathbf{r}) = -2\frac{\hbar^2}{2m_e}\left(\frac{\partial^2}{\partial x^2} + \frac{\partial^2}{\partial y^2} + \frac{\partial^2}{\partial z^2}\right) - \frac{e^2}{r}. \quad (8)$$

From Eq. (8), it directly follows that the external gravitational field (3) is coupled not only to Hamiltonian (2) but also to the virial operator (8). Note that the Hamiltonian (7),(8) can be also obtained from the results,[11] where some different physical problem is considered, if we disregard all tidal terms.

It is important that the gravitational field (3) can be considered as a sudden perturbation, $\hat{H}_1(\mathbf{r},t)$, to Hamiltonian (2) in the absence of gravitational field:

$$\hat{H}_1(\mathbf{r},t) = \left(\frac{\phi}{c^2}\right)\left[m_e c^2 - \frac{\hbar^2}{2m_e}\left(\frac{\partial^2}{\partial x^2} + \frac{\partial^2}{\partial y^2} + \frac{\partial^2}{\partial z^2}\right) - \frac{e^2}{r} + \hat{V}(\mathbf{r})\right]\Theta(t), \quad (9)$$

where $\Theta(t)$ is the step-like function. Then, a general solution of Eq. (7) can be written in the following way:

$$\Psi(r,t) = \exp\left(\frac{-i\tilde{m}_e c^2 t}{\hbar}\right)\Psi_1^1(r)\exp\left(\frac{-i\tilde{E}_1 t}{\hbar}\right)$$
$$+ \exp\left(\frac{-im_e c^2 t}{\hbar}\right)\sum_{n>1}^{\infty} a_n \Psi_n(r)\exp\left(\frac{-iE_n t}{\hbar}\right), \quad (10)$$

where the wave functions $\Psi_n(r)$ are solutions for the nS orbits in a hydrogen atom and are normalized,

$$\int [\Psi_1^1(r)]^2 \, d^3r \simeq 1; \quad \int \Psi_n^2(r) \, d^3r = 1, \quad n > 1. \quad (11)$$

[It is easy to show that perturbation (9) can results only in non-zero quantum transitions between $1S$ and nS electron orbits, therefore, we keep in Eq. (10) only $\Psi_n(r)$ wave functions, which are real.]

2.3. *Matrix elements and probabilities*

According with the standard time-dependent perturbation theory,[10] the corrected wave-function of ground state, $\Psi_1^1(r)$, as well as the corrections to mass and energy of ground state in Eq. (10) can be written as:

$$\Psi_1^1(r) = \Psi_1(r) + \left(\frac{\phi}{c^2}\right)\sum_{n>1}^{\infty} \frac{V_{n,1}}{E_1 - E_n}\Psi_n(r),$$
$$\tilde{m}_e = \left(1 + \frac{\phi}{c^2}\right)m_e, \quad \tilde{E}_1 = \left(1 + \frac{\phi}{c^2}\right)E_1, \quad (12)$$

where $V_{n,1}$ is matrix element of the virial operator (8):

$$V_{n,1} = \int \Psi_n(r) \left[-2\frac{\hbar^2}{2m}\left(\frac{\partial^2}{\partial x^2} + \frac{\partial^2}{\partial y^2} + \frac{\partial^2}{\partial z^2}\right) - \frac{e^2}{r} \right] \Psi_1(r) d^3\mathbf{r}. \tag{13}$$

Note that the very last term in Eq. (12) corresponds to the so-called red shift in gravitational field. It is due to the expected contribution to passive gravitational mass from electron binding energy in the atom. As to the coefficients a_n with $n \neq 1$ in Eq. (10), they can be also written in terms of the virial operator matrix elements,

$$a_n = -\left(\frac{\phi}{c^2}\right)\left(\frac{V_{n,1}}{E_1 - E_n}\right). \tag{14}$$

It is important that the wave function (10)-(14), which corresponds to electron energy levels in the presence of the gravitational field (3) at $t > 0$, is a series of eigenfunctions of electron energy operator, taken in the absence of the field. Therefore, if we measure energy, in electron quantum state (10)-(14), we obtain the following quantized values for electron gravitational mass:

$$m_n = m_e + \frac{E_n}{c^2}, \tag{15}$$

where we omit the red shift effect. From Eqs.(10)-(15), we can state that the expected Einstein's equation, $m_1 = m_e + \frac{E_1}{c^2}$, survives in our case with probability close to 1, whereas with the following small probabilities,

$$P_n = |a_n|^2 = \left(\frac{\phi}{c^2}\right)^2 \frac{V_{n,1}^2}{(E_n - E_1)^2}, \quad n \neq 1, \tag{16}$$

it is broken. The reason for this breakdown is that, the virial term (8) does not commute with the Hamiltonian in the absence of gravitational field (2). As a result, electron wave functions with definite passive gravitational masses are not characterized by definite energies in the absence of gravitational field. Let us calculate probability P_2 near the Earth's surface, where $\frac{\phi^2}{c^4} \approx 0.49 \times 10^{-18}$. From Eq. (16), we obtain the following probability for $n = 2$ in a hydrogen atom:

$$P_2 = |a_2|^2 = 1.5 \times 10^{-19}, \tag{17}$$

where

$$\frac{V_{2,1}}{E_2 - E_1} = 0.56. \tag{18}$$

3. Experimental Aspects

Here, let us describe another Gedanken experiment, where gravitational field is adiabatically switched on. To this end, we consider wave function (1) to be valid at $t \to -\infty$ and apply the following perturbation due to gravitation for the Hamiltonian (2):

$$\hat{H}_2(\mathbf{r}, t) = \left(\frac{\phi}{c^2}\right)\left[m_e c^2 - \frac{\hbar^2}{2m_e}\left(\frac{\partial^2}{\partial x^2} + \frac{\partial^2}{\partial y^2} + \frac{\partial^2}{\partial z^2}\right) - \frac{e^2}{r} + \hat{V}(\mathbf{r})\right] \exp(\lambda t), \quad \lambda \to 0. \tag{19}$$

Then, at $t \simeq 0$ (i.e., in the presence of the field), the electron wave function can be written as

$$\Psi(r,t) = \exp\left(\frac{-i\tilde{m}_e c^2 t}{\hbar}\right)\Psi_1^1(r)\exp\left(\frac{-i\tilde{E}_1 t}{\hbar}\right)$$
$$+ \exp\left(\frac{-im_e c^2 t}{\hbar}\right)\sum_{n>1}^{\infty}\tilde{a}_n\Psi_n(r)\exp\left(\frac{-iE_n t}{\hbar}\right). \quad (20)$$

Application of the standard time-dependent perturbation theory[10] in the case of adiabatic switching on gravitational field gives:

$$\Psi_1^1(r) = \Psi_1(r) + \left(\frac{\phi}{c^2}\right)\sum_{n>1}^{\infty}\frac{V_{n,1}}{E_1 - E_n}\Psi_n(r),$$
$$\tilde{m}_e = \left(1 + \frac{\phi}{c^2}\right)m_e, \quad \tilde{E}_1 = \left(1 + \frac{\phi}{c^2}\right)E_1, \quad (21)$$

and

$$\tilde{a}_n = 0, \quad \tilde{P}_n = 0. \quad (22)$$

Thus, in adiabatic limit, the phenomenon of quantization of passive gravitational mass (15),(16) disappears. This means that the possible experimental observations of the above mentioned phenomenon has to be done in quickly changing gravitational field. It is important that step-like function, $\Theta(t)$, which was used to derive Eqs.(15),(16) does not mean motion of an atom or a source of gravity with velocity higher than the speed of light. We can use step-like function if significant change of gravitational field happens quicker that the period of quasiclassical rotation of electron in a hydrogen atom. In the case under consideration, we need the time about $\delta t \leq t_0 = \frac{2\pi\hbar}{E_2 - E_1} \sim 10^{-15} s$. We hope that there exist much more convenient quantum systems with higher values of the parameter t_0, where discussed above phenomenon could be observed. We recall that all excited energy levels are quasistationary and, thus, decay with time by emitting photons. Therefore, it is much more efficient to detect emitted photons than to directly measure a weight. Here, we also stress that we did not calculate the gravitational mass and weight of the atom with an accuracy ϕ^2/c^4 since we did not take in account terms of the order of ϕ^2/c^4 in the metric (3). As to the relatively small probability of the quantization (16), it is not too small and can be compensated by large value of Avogadro number, $N_A \approx 6 \times 10^{23}$. In other words, for macroscopic number of the atoms, we may have large number of emitted photons. For instance, the number of excited electrons (i.e., emitted photons) for 1000 moles of the atoms is estimated as

$$N_n = 2.95 \times 10^8 \times \left(\frac{V_{n,1}}{E_n - E_1}\right)^2, \quad N_2 = 0.9 \times 10^8. \quad (23)$$

4. Conclusion

In the paper, we have shown that energy is not equivalent to passive gravitational mass of the such simplest composite body as a hydrogen atom. This happens due to the existence in the electron Hamiltonian in gravitational field of the so-called virial term, which does not commute with the Hamiltonian, taken in the absence of the field. It is easy to show that this is a general property of any quantum system with internal degrees of freedom in General Relativity. Therefore, we can conclude that application of the basic quantum laws to General Relativity results in the breakdown of the equivalence between passive gravitational mass and energy. It is important that the non-zero matrix elements (16),(18) of the virial operator (8) are also responsible, as shown by us,[1,2,4] for breakdown of the equivalence between active gravitational mass and energy for a quantum body with internal degrees of freedom. Therefore, formulation of the EEP has to be significantly reinvestigated and changed in semiclassical gravity.

Acknowledgments

We are thankful to N.N. Bagmet (Lebed), V.A. Belinski, Steven Carlip, Fulvio Melia, Douglas Singleton, and V.E. Zakharov for fruitful and useful discussions.

References

1. A. G. Lebed, Breakdown of the equivalence between active gravitational mass and energy for a quantum body, *J. Phys.: Conf. Ser.* **738**, 012036 (2016).
2. A. G. Lebed, Inequivalence between gravitational mass and energy due to quantum effects at microscopic and macroscopic levels, *Int. J. of Mod. Phys. D* **26**, 1730022 (2017).
3. M. Zych and C. Brukner, Quantum formulation of the Einstein equivalence principle, *Nature Phys.* **14**, 1027 (2018).
4. A. G. Lebed, Breakdown of the equivalence between gravitational mass and energy due to quantum effects, *Int. J. of Mod. Phys. D* **28**, 1930020 (2019).
5. A. G. Lebed, Breakdown of the Einstein's Equivalence Principle for a quantum body, *Mod. Phys. Lett. A* **35**, 2030010 (2020).
6. C. W. Misner and P. Putnam, Active gravitational mass, *Phys. Rev.* **116**, 1045 (1959).
7. K. Nordtvedt, Post-Newtonian gravity: Its theory-experimental interface, *Class. Quantum Grav.* **11**, A119 (1994).
8. S. Carlip, Kinetic energy and the equivalence principle, *Am. J. Phys.* **66**, 409 (1998).
9. C. W. Misner, K. S. Thorne, and J. A. Wheeler, *Gravitation* (W.H. Freeman and Co, New York, USA, 1973).
10. D. Park, *Introduction to the Quantum Theory*, 3rd edn. (Dover Publications, New York, USA, 2005).
11. E. Fischbach, B. S. Freeman, and W.-K. Cheng, General-relativistic effects in hydrogen systems, *Phys. Rev. D* **23**, 2157 (1981).

Extended DeWitt-Schwinger subtraction scheme, heavy fields and decoupling*

Antonio Ferreiro

Centre for Astrophysics and Relativity, School of Mathematical Sciences, Dublin City University, Glasnevin, Dublin 9, Rep. of Ireland
E-mail: antonio.ferreiro@dcu.ie

Jose Navarro-Salas

Departamento de Física Teórica and IFIC, Centro Mixto Universidad de Valencia-CSIC Facultad de Física, Universidad de Valencia, Burjassot-46100, Valencia, Spain
E-mail: jnavarro@ific.uv.es

Keywords: Renormalization techniques; quantum field theories.

1. Introduction

A standard result of quantum field theory is the existence of divergences when computing observables. This requires the construction of techniques, called regularization and renormalization schemes, to overcome these infinities and produce well defined physical observables. A standard example is the computation of vacuum polarization effects in perturbative Quantum Electrodynamics (QED) which results in the well-known Lamb Shift an the anomalous magnetic momentum of the electron. As a byproduct of these methods, an arbitrary mass scale parameter μ present in the calculations implies a dependence under this scale of the different coupling constants of the theory.[1] Instead of becoming an obstacle it offers a very useful tool, the renormalization group equation,[1,2] to understand the behaviour of the theories at some particular ranges, without knowing the exact details of the theory. The relevant magnitudes that encode the information of this equation are the beta functions, $\beta_O = \mu \frac{dO_R}{d\mu}$, where O_R is any possible renormalized coupling constant of the theory.

At the level of quantum field theory in curved spacetime, similar divergences arise. These appear even when computing observables in the vacuum state since the standard method of regularizing the vacuum divergences in Minkowski, known as *normal ordering*, is not available anymore since it strictly depends on the definition of the vacuum state, which is not unique in this context. Nevertheless, many regularization methods, including Dimensional Regularization and Pauli-Villars have been inherit from the Minkowski spacetime case, and have obtained finite renormalized

---

*Talk given by A. Ferreiro at the Sixteenth Marcel Grossmann Meeting (2021).

quantities, e.g. the Feynman propagator $G(x,x')$ and the expectation value of the stress energy tensor T_{ab} for scalar, Dirac or gauge fields in curved spacetime.[3–5]

Most methods rely on the convenient expression of the propagator in terms of an integral in the DeWitt-Schwinger proper time

$$G(x,x') = \frac{\Delta^{1/2}(x,x')}{(4\pi)^2} \int_0^\infty \frac{ds}{(is)^2} e^{-im^2 s + \frac{\sigma(x,x')}{2is}} F(x,x',is) \,. \tag{1}$$

The advantage of expression (1) is that it admits an expansion

$$F(x,x',is) = \sum_{j=0}^\infty a_j(x,x')(is)^j. \tag{2}$$

Note that the effective action and consequently the stress-energy tensor can be derived from $G(x,x')$ in the limit $x' \to x$ where this expression becomes divergent. In the case of four dimensions $d=4$, the divergences are encoded and isolated in the first two terms of the expansion (the first three terms in case of the effective action). There are several ways to regulate expression (1). For instance, it can be analytically extended to higher dimension $d>4$, via dimensional regularization or it can be expanded in terms of point splitting parameter σ. The infinities are recovered in the case of $d \to 4$ and $\sigma \to 0$ respectively. It can be shown[3] that all the divergent pieces of the one loop corrections of a free field can be consistently reabsorbed in the original action

$$S_G = \int d^4x \sqrt{-g} \left(-\Lambda + \frac{1}{2\kappa} R + \alpha_1 C^2 + \alpha_2 R^2 + \alpha_3 E + \alpha_4 \Box R \right), \tag{3}$$

where $\kappa = 8\pi G$. It is in principle possible to use the DeWitt-Schwinger decomposition (1) to compute the exact one-loop contribution.[3,5] In this case, as a byproduct of the DeWitt-Schwinger decomposition we can construct a natural subtraction scheme without invoking any artificial regulator

$$G_{\text{ren}}(x,x) = \lim_{x' \to x} G(x,x') - \frac{1}{(4\pi)^2} \sum_{j=0}^1 a_j(x) \int_0^\infty \frac{ds}{(is)^{(2-j)}} e^{-im^2 s} \,. \tag{4}$$

We can also construct subtraction schemes from dimensional regularization or point splitting. In any case the different regularization and subtraction schemes differ in terms that can always be reabsorbed in the action (3).[4]

Note that the subtracted contribution of (4) needs to include an small imaginary $m^2 - i\epsilon$ to avoid an infrared singularity. In the mass-less case this is an obstacle since the infrared divergence is present in the limit $s \to 0$.[4] In order to overcome this problem we can insert an artificial parameter μ^2 as a mass-scale instead of m^2 in (4) and then take the limit $\mu^2 \to 0$. This has been done for instance to obtain the conformal anomaly.[3] However, another interesting approach is to maintain in all the potential calculations μ^2 different to zero and to modify consistently the coefficients $a_j(x)$ of (4) in order to ensure that no extra divergences appear in the case of $\mu^2 \neq 0$. In the most general case, without assuming $m^2 = 0$, the extended DeWitt-Schwinger subtraction scheme would be[6]

$$\bar{G}_{\text{ren}}(x,x) = \lim_{x' \to x} G(x,x') - \frac{1}{(4\pi)^2} \sum_{j=0}^{1} \bar{a}_j(x) \int_0^\infty \frac{ds}{(is)^{(2-j)}} e^{-i(m^2+\mu^2)s} . \qquad (5)$$

Here the the new coefficients are $\bar{a}_0 = 1$, $\bar{a}_1 = a_1 + \mu^2$ and $\bar{a}_2 = a_1\mu^2 + \frac{1}{2}\mu^4$ [a]. The introduction of this extra parameter is required for the massless limit. However, it also offers a possible running coupling interpretation analogue to the Minimal subtraction scheme in dimensional regularization. We will analyze this in the next section.

An important property of the regularization and renormalization program is that it should not spoil the decoupling of heavy massive fields in the low energy limit. For instance, we should not have to compute the vacuum polarization of the quark top mass when performing a low energy (below the top mass) scattering process in QED. The decoupling of heavy field in renormalizable theories has been well stated by the Appelquist-Carazzone theorem.[8] In the case of QED, Minimal Subtraction is not compatible with decoupling[9] and a different subtraction scheme has to be taken in order to have a physical interpretation of the μ parameter at low energy regime. A possible scheme is known as *Momentum subtraction scheme*,[9] which not only decouples the heavy fields, i.e., $\beta_O \to 0$ when $m^2 \to \infty$ but also recovers the Minimal Subtraction beta functions in the limit of $\mu^2 \to \infty$ or $m^2 \to 0$.

In the case of quantum fields in curved spacetime an analog to the Momentum subtraction scheme has been elusive. A notable result of the subtraction scheme of (5) is that it is consistent with the decoupling of heavy massive fields,[6] as we will show in the next section.

2. Running of the couplings and decoupling of massive fields

In order to compute the running of the couplings with the parameter μ it is useful to use the extended DeWitt-Schwinger subtraction scheme for the effective action, which can be constructed in a similar manner to (5).[7] It is also useful for pedagogical purposes to consider a complex scalar field interacting with an electromagnetic field obeying the Klein-Gordon equation

$$\left(g^{\mu\nu} D_\mu^x D_\nu^x + m^2 + \xi R\right) G(x,x') = -|g(x)|^{-1/2} \delta(x'-x), \qquad (6)$$

where $D_\mu = \nabla_\mu + iqA_\mu$. In this case, the extended DeWitt-Schwinger subtraction scheme takes the form[7]

$$W_{\text{ren}}^{(1)} = W^{(1)} - \frac{2i}{2(4\pi)^2} \int d^4x \sqrt{-g} \sum_{j=0}^{2} \bar{a}_j(x) \int_0^\infty \frac{ds}{(is)^{(3-j)}} e^{-i(m^2+\mu^2)s} \qquad (7)$$

---

[a] Note here that in terms of adiabatic order, the μ^2 in the exponential of (5) is of adiabatic order zero while the μ^2 of the coefficients are of adiabatic order two. This is equivalent to the methodology taken in[7] for Parker-Fulling adiabatic regularization.

where $W^{(1)}$ is the divergent one-loop effective action constructed from (1) and the coefficients are

$$\bar{a}_0(x) = 1, \qquad \bar{a}_1(x) = \left(\frac{1}{6} - \xi\right) R + \mu^2$$

$$\bar{a}_2(x) = \frac{1}{180} R_{\alpha\beta\gamma\delta} R^{\alpha\beta\gamma\delta} - \frac{1}{180} R^{\alpha\beta} R_{\alpha\beta} - \frac{1}{6}\left(\frac{1}{5} - \xi\right) \Box R$$

$$+ \frac{1}{12}\left(\xi - \frac{1}{6}\right)^2 R^2 - \frac{q^2}{12} F_{\mu\nu} F^{\mu\nu} + \left(\frac{1}{6} - \xi\right) R\mu^2 + \frac{1}{2}\mu^4 . \tag{8}$$

The subtraction terms of (7) can be absorbed into the original action

$$S^c = S_G + \int d^4x \sqrt{-g}\left(-\frac{1}{4} Z_A \tilde{F}_{\mu\nu} \tilde{F}^{\mu\nu} + (\tilde{D}_\mu \phi)^\dagger \tilde{D}^\mu \phi + m^2 |\phi|^2 + \xi R|\phi|^2\right) \tag{9}$$

with $\tilde{D}_\mu = \nabla_\mu + iq Z_A^{1/2} \tilde{A}_\mu$, where we have re-scaled the potential to introduce an extra coupling constant Z_A. The complete effective action would be

$$S^{(1)}_{\text{ren}} = W^{(1)}(m, \xi, q Z_A^{1/2}) + S^c(m, \xi, q, Z_A, \Lambda, \kappa, \alpha_i), \tag{10}$$

where we have made visible the explicit dependence of the bare couplings and fields. The complete action in terms of the physical renormalized couplings O_R is

$$S^{(1)}_{\text{ren}} = W^{(1)}_{\text{ren}}(m_R, \xi_R, q_R Z_R^{1/2}) + S^c_{\text{ren}}(Z_R, \Lambda_R, \kappa_R, \alpha_{iR}) \tag{11}$$

where S^c_{ren} is the original S^c upgrading the bare divergent coupling constants to the corresponding renormalized finite ones. In the particular case of a free complex scalar field, it is not difficult to see that expression (7) does not involve any divergent piece that need to be reabsorbed neither in m^2, nor ξ and the combination $qZ^{1/2}$ and therefore we can already write

$$\xi = \xi_R \qquad m = m_R \qquad q Z_A^{1/2} = q_R Z_{AR}^{1/2}. \tag{12}$$

This is of course not a general result and indeed this couplings constants could be divergent in theories including other interactions.[10] We will from now on drop the subscript $_R$ from these terms.

In order to compute the beta functions $\beta_O = \mu \frac{dO_R}{d\mu}$ we will impose the invariance of the renormalized action with respect to the arbitrary parameter μ

$$\mu \frac{d}{d\mu} S^{(1)}_{\text{ren}} = 0. \tag{13}$$

From (7), it is easy to check

$$\mu \frac{d}{d\mu} W^{(1)}_{\text{ren}} = \int d^4x \sqrt{-g} \frac{1}{16\pi^2(m^2 + \mu^2)} \left(2\mu^2 a_2(x) - 2\mu^4 a_1(x) - \mu^6\right). \tag{14}$$

Using (12), (13) and (14), we finally obtain the following beta functions

$$\beta_{\alpha 1} = -\frac{1}{960\pi^2}\frac{\mu^2}{m^2+\mu^2} \quad \beta_{\alpha 2} = -\frac{\left(\xi-\frac{1}{6}\right)^2}{16\pi^2}\frac{\mu^2}{m^2+\mu^2}$$

$$\beta_\Lambda = \frac{1}{16\pi^2}\frac{\mu^6}{m^2+\mu^2} \quad \beta_{\kappa^{-1}} = \frac{\xi-\frac{1}{6}}{4\pi^2}\frac{\mu^4}{m^2+\mu^2} \quad \beta_q = \frac{q_R^3}{48\pi^2}\frac{\mu^2}{m^2+\mu^2} \quad . \tag{15}$$

It can be easily checked that the running of dimensionless coupling constants coincides with the Minimal Subtraction beta functions,[11] but with the advantage that the structure $\frac{\mu^2}{m^2+\mu^2}$, similar to the cutoff Wilsonian scheme[12] makes a vanishing contribution when $m^2 \to \infty$ thus making this renormalization scheme compatible with decoupling of heavy massive fields. The remarkable result is that also the running of both the Newton constant and the cosmological constant also decouple in this limit, thus enforcing the fact that higher massive fields do not contribute to the low energy regime, even when the gravitational field is present.

References

1. M. E. Peskin and D. V. Schroeder, *An Introduction to Quantum Field Theory* (Addison-Wesley, Reading MA, 1995).
2. J.C. Collins, *Renormalization* (Cambridge University Press, Cambridge, England 1984).
3. N. D. Birrell and P. C. W. Davies, *Quantum Fields in Curved Space* (Cambridge University Press, Cambridge, England 1982).
4. R. M. Wald, *Quantum Field Theory in Curved Spacetime and Black Hole Thermodynamics* (University of Chicago Press, Chicago, 1994).
5. L. Parker and D. J. Toms, *Quantum Field Theory in Curved Spacetime: Quantized Fields and Gravity* (Cambridge University Press, Cambridge, England 2009).
6. A. Ferreiro and J. Navarro-Salas, *Phys. Rev. D* **102**, 045021 (2020).
7. A. Ferreiro and J. Navarro-Salas, *Phys. Lett. B* **792**, 81 (2019).
8. T. Appelquist and J. Carazzone, *Phys. Rev. D* **11**, 2856 (1975).
9. L. Alvarez-Gaume and M. A. Vazquez-Mozo, *An Invitation to Quantum Field Theory* (Springer-Verlag, Berlin, 2012).
10. A. Ferreiro, S. Nadal-Gisbert and J. Navarro-Salas, *Phys. Rev. D* **104**, 025003 (2021)
11. J. Solà, *J. Phys. Conf. Ser.* **453**, 012015 (2013).
12. T. J. Hollowood, *Renormalization Group and Fixed Points in Quantum Field Theory* (Springer, Heidelberg, 2013).

Renormalization and decoupling for the Yukawa model in curved spacetime

Sergi Nadal-Gisbert*, Antonio Ferreiro† and José Navarro-Salas‡

Departamento de Física Teórica and IFIC, Centro Mixto Universidad de Valencia-CSIC
Facultad de Física, Universidad de Valencia, Burjassot-46100, Valencia, Spain
E-mail: †*antonio.ferreiro@ific.uv.es,* **sergi.nadal@uv.es,* ‡*jnavarro@ific.uv.es*

We consider the renormalization of the one-loop effective action for the Yukawa interaction. We compute the beta functions in the generalized DeWitt-Schwinger subtraction scheme. For the quantized scalar field we obtain that all the beta functions exhibit decoupling for heavy fields as stated by the Appelquist-Carazzone theorem including also the gravitational couplings. For the quantized Dirac field, decoupling appears for almost all of them. We obtain the atypical result that the mass parameter of the background scalar field, does not decouple.[a]

Keywords: Decoupling, renormalization, running couplings, beta functions, one-loop effective Lagrangian, DeWitt-Schwinger expansion

1. Introduction

Regularization and renormalization of infinities of quantum fields in curved spacetime is a subtle subject. Infinite quantities emerge at the vacuum level and can not be erased due to the non-trivial structure of the classical gravitational background field. There are well established covariant and pragmatic methods to evaluate the vacuum expectation value of the stress-energy tensor in physically reasonable states.[2–7] For a general spacetime, the DeWitt-Schwinger technique[8–10] allows us to evaluate and renormalize the stress-energy tensor as well as the one-loop effective action which constitute a practical tool that encodes all the relevant information about the quantum effects of fields.

The regularization machinery usually incorporates an arbitrary, non physical, mass-scale parameter. Studying how the coupling constants depend on this scale, i.e., the running of the couplings, is very useful in physical situations where more formal computations are very involved. This is done by requiring that physical quantities should not depend on spurious parameters.[11–13] As a representative case, in dimensional regularization an arbitrary mass scale μ is introduced to compensate the fictitious dimensions. In the case of the DeWitt-Schwinger proper-time expansion a mass scale μ is usually introduced in the short distance logarithmic term $\log \mu^2 \sigma/2$ to overcome an infrared divergence for massless fields. Changing the

---

[a]Expanded version of the talk given by S. Nadal-Gisbert in the Sixteenth Marcel Grossmann Meeting (2021).

mass scale μ to μ' allows to obtain an effective running for the parameters of the Lagrangian.

Another important feature of effective field theories is that massive fields should decouple at low energies[14,15] as stated by the Appelquist-Carazzone theorem[16b]. This idea which lies at the heart of the effective field theories states that a field of mass m can not influence the physics at scales larger than m^{-1}. In a physical renormalization scheme this idea should be manifested in the beta functions of the theory if they want to describe both infrared and ultraviolet regimes. Moreover, in gravitational physics decoupling is crucial to get a proper physical interpretation in the cosmic infrared regime. This can be particularly relevant for the cosmological constant problem and for the running of the Newton's gravitational constant.[19-22] A partial list of works dealing with this issue in a curved space are.[23-28]

Recently, an arbitrary scale parameter μ has been introduced in the DeWitt-Schwinger subtraction scheme in order to consistently construct the subtraction terms avoiding the infrared divergences[29] (see also[30-32]). This was done for the free complex scalar field in the Einstein-Maxwell theory. This approach has the benefit of producing the decoupling of heavy fields. In this work we further extend this approach by including Yukawa interactions with spinor fields and scalars also coupled to gravity. This model has been broadly studied in dimensional regularization[24,33-35] also by including gauge fields.[36,37] We will concentrate in the simplest case of a scalar background coupled to a quantized dirac field and also to a scalar field. The aim of this work is to compute the beta functions in the generalized DeWitt-Schwinger renormalization approach and observe whether decoupling explicitly appears.

2. Interaction with a quantized scalar field and renormalization

Consider a quantized real scalar field φ coupled to a real scalar background ϕ via the Yukawa interaction $\frac{h^2}{2}\phi^2\varphi^2$

$$S = \int d^4x\sqrt{-g}\left\{-\Lambda + \frac{R}{16\pi G} + \frac{1}{2}\nabla^\mu\varphi\nabla_\mu\varphi - \frac{1}{2}\left(m^2 + \xi R\right)\varphi^2 \right. \\ \left. -\frac{h^2}{2}\phi^2\varphi^2 + \frac{1}{2}\nabla^\mu\phi\nabla_\mu\phi - V(\phi)\right\}, \tag{1}$$

where m^2 is the mass parameter for the quantized scalar, ξ is the coupling of φ^2 to the Ricci scalar, and $V(\phi)$ is a general potential that can contain interactions between the background field and the curvature but is independent of the quantized scalar field φ. The Feynman propagator G_F for φ satisfies

$$\left(\Box_x + m^2 + \xi R + h^2\phi^2\right)G_F(x,x') = -|g(x)|^{-1/2}\delta(x-x'). \tag{2}$$

---

[b]There are some situations were decoupling is violated. This typically happens on theories with spontaneously broken gauge symmetries.[17,18]

The effective action can be generated from this propagator by $S_{\text{eff}} = -i\frac{1}{2}\text{Tr}\log(-G_{\text{F}})$. The ultraviolet divergences of the one-loop effective Lagrangian can be explicitly manifested if one expresses the Feynman propagator as an integral in the proper time s,

$$G_{\text{F}}(x,x') = -i\int_0^\infty ds\, e^{-im^2 s}\langle x,s|x',0\rangle\ , \qquad (3)$$

where m^2 is understood to have an infinitesimal negative imaginary part ($m^2 \equiv m^2 - i\epsilon$). The heat kernel $\langle x,s|x',0\rangle$ can be expanded in powers of the proper time as follows

$$\langle x,s|x',0\rangle = i\frac{\Delta^{1/2}(x,x')}{(4\pi)^2(is)^2}\exp\frac{\sigma(x,x')}{2is}\sum_{j=0}^\infty a_j(x,x')(is)^j\ , \qquad (4)$$

where $\Delta(x,x')$ is the Van Vleck-Morette determinant and $\sigma(x,x')$ is the proper distance along the geodesic from x' to x. Therefore, the effective Lagrangian, defined as $S_{\text{eff}} = \int d^4x\sqrt{-g}L_{\text{eff}}$, has the following asymptotic expansion

$$L_{\text{eff}} = \frac{i}{2(4\pi)^2}\sum_{j=0}^\infty a_j(x)\int_0^\infty e^{-ism^2}(is)^{j-3}ds\ . \qquad (5)$$

The first coefficients $a_n(x,x')$ are given, in the coincidence limit $x\to x'$, by[5]

$$a_0(x) = 1\ , \qquad a_1(x) = \frac{1}{6}R - Q$$
$$a_2(x) = \frac{1}{180}R_{\alpha\beta\gamma\delta}R^{\alpha\beta\gamma\delta} - \frac{1}{180}R^{\alpha\beta}R_{\alpha\beta} - \frac{1}{30}\Box R + \frac{1}{72}R^2$$
$$+ \frac{1}{2}Q^2 - \frac{1}{6}RQ + \frac{1}{6}\Box Q + \frac{1}{12}W_{\mu\nu}W^{\mu\nu}\ , \qquad (6)$$

where for the case of a scalar field we have $W_{\mu\nu} \equiv [\nabla_\mu,\nabla_\nu] = 0$ and $Q = \xi R + h^2\phi^2$. Expansion (5) shows that the ultraviolet divergent terms of the effective Lagrangian are localized in the first three terms of the DeWitt-Schwinger expansion in the limit $s\to 0$ of the integral. The renormalization procedure can be performed by directly subtracting these divergent terms to the total one-loop contribution.

$$L_{\text{ren}} = \int_0^\infty ds\left[\frac{e^{-im^2 s}}{is}\langle x,s|x,0\rangle - \frac{i}{2(4\pi)^2}\sum_{j=0}^2 a_j(x)\frac{e^{-ism^2}}{(is)^{-j+3}}\right]\ , \qquad (7)$$

where the notation of L_{ren} has to be understood as the finite one-loop correction to the background Lagrangian. One can notice that the massless case inherits an infrared divergence ($s\to\infty$ limit). We avoid it by introducing a mass scale μ^2 in the exponential term of the DeWitt-Schwinger expansion by writing $\sum_j a_j(x)e^{-ism^2} \to \sum_j \bar a_j(x)e^{-is(m^2+\mu^2)}$ in (5). As mentioned in,[29] this is the unique way of introducing the μ parameter if we want the exponential form to remain. The main point of the introduction of the arbitrary parameter μ at the same level of the mass, is to obtain decoupling in the infrared behaviour of the beta functions, as we will see.

The DeWitt coefficients a_j are redefined by consistency with the adiabatic orders, $\bar{a}_0(x) = 1, \bar{a}_1(x) = a_1(x) + \mu^2, \bar{a}_2(x) = a_2(x) + a_1(x)\mu^2 + \frac{1}{2}\mu^4$, and renormalization is now performed by taking the difference $L_{\text{ren}}(\mu) = L_{\text{eff}} - L_{\text{div}}(\mu)$, as for the standard situation with $\mu = 0$, (7)

$$L_{\text{ren}}(\mu) = \int_0^\infty ds \left[\frac{e^{-im^2 s}}{is} \langle x, s | x, 0 \rangle - \frac{i}{2(4\pi)^2} \sum_{j=0}^{2} \bar{a}_j(x) \frac{e^{-is(m^2+\mu^2)}}{(is)^{-j+3}} \right]. \quad (8)$$

We note that the renormalized one-loop Lagrangian depends now on μ. This dependece in the arbitrary parameter μ has to be compensated by a running of the couplings of the background Lagrangian, thus the physical one-loop renormalized Lagrangian $L_{\text{phys}} = L_{\text{B}}(\mu) + L_{\text{ren}}(\mu)$ is μ-independent, where $L_{\text{B}}(\mu)$ refers to the background Lagrangian.

2.1. *Running of the coupling constants and decoupling*

The background Lagrangian required for renormalization is given by

$$L_{\text{B}} = L_{\text{grav}} + \frac{1}{2} Z \nabla^\mu \phi \nabla_\mu \phi - \frac{M^2}{2} Z \phi^2 - \frac{\xi_\phi}{2} R Z \phi^2 - \frac{\lambda}{4!} Z^2 \phi^4 + \gamma_1 \Box Z \phi^2 , \quad (9)$$

where

$$L_{\text{grav}} = -\Lambda + \frac{1}{2}\kappa R + \alpha_1 R^2 + \alpha_2 R_{\mu\nu} R^{\mu\nu} + \alpha_3 R_{\mu\nu\alpha\beta} R^{\mu\nu\alpha\beta} + \alpha_4 \Box R . \quad (10)$$

We have defined $\kappa = 1/8\pi G$. The new terms are required to absorb the divergences of the one-loop correction. The coupling Z will not receive any contribution from the scalar quantum fluctuations, therefore we can canonically normalize it to 1. The remaining couplings $\lambda(\mu), \kappa(\mu), \alpha_i(\mu), M(\mu)$, etc will inherit a dependence on the mass scale μ.

The beta functions and the running couplings are built from the renormalization process, therefore they get only contributions from the divergent terms. For this reason, it is enough to approximate (8) with the first three terms of the asymptotic expansion for the heat kernel.

$$L_{\text{ren}}(\mu) \approx \frac{i}{2(4\pi)^2} \int_0^\infty \frac{ds}{s^3} \left\{ e^{-im^2 s} \left[1 + (is)a_1(x) + (is)^2 a_2(x)\right] \right.$$
$$\left. - e^{-is(m^2+\mu^2)} \left[1 + (is)\bar{a}_1(x) + (is)^2 \bar{a}_2(x)\right] \right\} . \quad (11)$$

This is a finite integral that can now be computed. Its result depends on the DeWitt coefficients $a_0(x), a_1(x)$ and $a_2(x)$ and also with the arbitrary μ parameter. Requiring that the physical one-loop renormalized Lagrangian $L_{\text{phys}} = L_{\text{B}}(\mu) + L_{\text{ren}}(\mu)$ has to be μ-independent, leads to the running of the couplings and the beta functions.

$$\frac{dL_{\text{phys}}}{d\mu} = 0 \quad \rightarrow \quad \beta_i \frac{\partial L_B}{\partial q_i} = -\mu \frac{\partial L_{\text{ren}}}{\partial \mu} , \quad (12)$$

where q_i refers to all the parameters of the Lagrangian and $\beta_i = \mu \frac{\partial q_i}{\partial \mu}$. A representative of the beta functions that we obtain are

$$\beta_\lambda = \frac{3h^4}{4\pi^2} \frac{\mu^2}{m^2 + \mu^2} \qquad \beta_\Lambda = \frac{1}{32\pi^2} \frac{\mu^6}{m^2 + \mu^2}$$

$$\beta_\kappa = \frac{\bar{\xi}}{8\pi^2} \frac{\mu^4}{m^2 + \mu^2} \qquad \beta_{M^2} = -\frac{h^2}{8\pi^2} \frac{\mu^4}{m^2 + \mu^2}, \qquad (13)$$

where we have defined $\bar{\xi} = \left(\xi - \frac{1}{6}\right)$. The rest of beta functions can be found in Appendix A. Several remarks are worth of mention in these results. For the dimensionless parameters, like $\lambda(\mu)$, we obtain a factor of the form $\mu^2/(m^2 + \mu^2)$, this factor also arises in the hierarchy of beta functions in the Wilsonian renormalization approach for a scalar field theory.[38] Analyzing this factor it is easy to see that for $m^2 \gg \mu^2$ the dimensionless beta functions decouple as expected in the infrared regime. Moreover for $\mu^2 \gg m^2$ the ultraviolet regime is recovered as expected from dimensional regularization with MS (minimal subtraction).[33] Another important feature concerns the dimensional couplings. For the Newton and cosmological constants we recover the same result as in the free field theory. Furthermore, all the dimensional couplings also decouple when $m^2 \gg \mu^2$.

3. Renormalization for Dirac fields

In this section we consider a quantized Dirac field ψ coupled via Yukawa interaction $g_Y \phi \bar{\psi} \psi$ with a classical scalar background ϕ. The action is given by

$$S = \int d^4 x \sqrt{-g} \left(-\Lambda + \frac{R}{16\pi G} + \bar{\psi} \left(i\gamma^\mu \nabla_\mu - m \right) \psi - g_Y \phi \bar{\psi} \psi + \frac{1}{2} \nabla^\mu \phi \nabla_\mu \phi - V(\phi) \right), \qquad (14)$$

where the covariant derivative ∇_μ acting on the Dirac field is defined as the ordinary derivative plus the spin connection term. $\gamma^\mu(x)$ are the curved space Dirac matrices $\gamma^\mu(x) = e_a{}^\mu \gamma^a$, defined in terms of the usual Dirac matrices in Minkowski space γ^a and the vierbein $e_a{}^\mu$.

In order to build the DeWitt-Schwinger expansion one needs the Klein-Gordon equation for the Dirac field

$$(\Box_x + m^2 + Q) G_F(x, x') = -|g(x)|^{-1/2} \delta(x - x') . \qquad (15)$$

Consequently, the one-loop effective action takes the form $S_{\text{eff}}^{(1)} = \frac{1}{2} i \operatorname{Tr} \log(-G_F)$. One can expand the heat kernel in the proper time asymptotic series as for the scalar field (4) and make use of the same coefficients (6). In this case Q is given by

$$Q(x) = \frac{1}{4} R(x) + i g_Y \gamma^\mu \nabla_\mu \phi(x) + g_Y^2 \phi^2(x) + 2 g_Y m \phi(x) . \qquad (16)$$

It is important to stress the appearance of the last term in the above expression which is proportional to m. This contrast with the obtained expression for Q in the scalar case ($Q = \xi R + h^2 \phi^2$). Generically, all DeWitt coefficients a_n (or $\bar{a}_n$) are local geometrical quantities independent of the mass of the field. The Yukawa interaction for Dirac fermions introduces a mass-dependent term in the expression for $Q(x)$. This term will be the responsible of the violation of the decoupling characteristic for the background scalar mass parameter.

As in the previous section one gets the expression for the subtraction terms with the asymptotic expansion

$$L_{\text{div}}(\mu) = \frac{-i}{2(4\pi)^2} \sum_{j=0}^{2} \operatorname{tr} \bar{a}_j(x) \int_0^\infty e^{-is(m^2+\mu^2)} (is)^{j-3} ds . \tag{17}$$

The main difference with the scalar case is that one needs to take into account the trace of the spinor indices acting on the coefficients $\operatorname{tr} \bar{a}_j(x)$. We still have the modified DeWitt coefficients $\bar{a}_0(x) = 1$, $\bar{a}_1(x) = a_1(x) + \mu^2$, and $\bar{a}_2(x) = a_2(x) + \left(\frac{1}{6}R - Q\right)\mu^2 + \frac{1}{2}\mu^4$ related to the DeWitt coefficients (6) but now with Q given by (16) and $W_{\mu\nu} = [\nabla_\mu, \nabla_\nu] = -\frac{1}{8} R_{\mu\nu ab} [\gamma^a, \gamma^b]$.

3.1. *Running of the coupling constant and decoupling*

The background Lagrangian terms are required by renormalization in order to absorb the divergent terms coming from the one-loop correction (17)

$$L_B = L_{\text{grav}} + \frac{1}{2} Z \nabla^\mu \phi \nabla_\mu \phi - \frac{M^2}{2} Z \phi^2 - \frac{\xi}{2} R Z \phi^2 - \tau Z^{1/2} \phi - \frac{\eta}{3!} Z^{3/2} \phi^3$$
$$- \frac{\lambda}{4!} Z^2 \phi^4 - \xi_1 R Z^{1/2} \phi + \gamma_1 \Box Z \phi^2 + \gamma_2 \Box Z^{1/2} \phi , \tag{18}$$

where L_{grav} was given in (10). In the Dirac case, Z gets a contribution from the quantum fluctuations of the Dirac field. Therefore, it has a running that can be related to a running of the field ϕ by a reparametrization. We write $Z = 1 + \delta Z$ as usual, to take into account canonical normalization and the one-loop correction. For simplicity, we introduce new primed couplings to absorb Z, except for the kinetic term, where we leave Z explicitly

$$\frac{1}{2} Z \nabla^\mu \phi \nabla_\mu \phi - \frac{M'^2}{2} \phi^2 - \frac{\xi'}{2} R \phi^2 - \tau' \phi - \frac{\eta'}{3!} \phi^3 - \frac{\lambda'}{4!} \phi^4 - \xi'_1 R \phi + \gamma'_1 \Box \phi^2 + \gamma'_2 \Box \phi . \tag{19}$$

As for the scalars, we just need to consider the divergent part of the one-loop effective action (11) to compute the running of the parameters. Again, we impose that the physical one-loop renormalized Lagrangian $L_{\text{phys}} = L_B(\mu) + L_{\text{ren}}(\mu)$ must be independent of the value of μ. Therefore considering (12) for this background Lagrangian we can obtain the beta functions for the primed parameters. By direct differentiation and keeping one-loop order $\mathcal{O}(\hbar)$, it is straightforward to obtain the beta functions of the unprimed original couplings

$$\beta_{M^2} = \beta_{M'^2} - M^2\beta_Z \qquad \beta_\xi = \beta_{\xi'} - \xi\beta_Z$$
$$\beta_{\xi_1} = \beta_{\xi_1'} - \frac{1}{2}\xi_1\beta_Z \qquad \beta_\tau = \beta_{\tau'} - \frac{\tau}{2}\beta_Z$$
$$\beta_\eta = \beta_{\eta'} - \frac{3}{2}\eta\beta_Z \qquad \beta_\lambda = \beta_{\lambda'} - 2\lambda\beta_Z$$
$$\beta_{\gamma_1} = \beta_{\gamma_1'} - \gamma_1\beta_Z \qquad \beta_{\gamma_2} = \beta_{\gamma_2'} - \frac{1}{2}\gamma_2\beta_Z .$$

The result for all the beta functions can be seen in Appendix A. Let us analyze the different regimes of the scalar wave function Z as a representative of the dimensionless parameters.

$$\beta_Z = -\frac{g_Y^2}{4\pi^2}\frac{\mu^2}{m^2+\mu^2} . \qquad (20)$$

In the ultraviolet regime, $\mu \gg m$ we recover the result from dimensional regularization with MS.[33,34]

$$\beta_Z = -\frac{g_Y^2}{4\pi^2}\frac{\mu^2}{m^2+\mu^2} \to_{\mu\gg m} -\frac{g_Y^2}{4\pi^2} , \qquad (21)$$

while for the infrared regime, $\mu \ll m$, we find decoupling

$$\beta_Z = -\frac{g_Y^2}{4\pi^2}\frac{\mu^2}{m^2+\mu^2} \to_{\mu\ll m} -\frac{g_Y^2}{4\pi^2}\frac{\mu^2}{m^2} . \qquad (22)$$

The other beta functions for the dimensionless parameters exhibit the same behaviour. Decoupling of massive fields is manifested in the infrared regime and the ultraviolet regime agrees with the results of dimensional regularization with MS.[33,34]

Things are more involved for the dimensional constants. We observe different behaviours with the parameter μ. For example for the couplings $\Lambda(\mu)$, $\kappa(\mu)$ and $M'^2(\mu)$ we get

$$\beta_\Lambda = -\frac{1}{8\pi^2}\frac{\mu^6}{m^2+\mu^2} \qquad \beta_\kappa = -\frac{1}{24\pi^2}\frac{\mu^4}{m^2+\mu^2}$$
$$\beta_{M^2} = \frac{g_Y^2}{8\pi^2}\frac{\mu^2}{m^2+\mu^2}\left(+4\mu^2 - 8m^2 + 2M^2\right) . \qquad (23)$$

A common feature is that decoupling appears when $m^2 \gg \mu^2$ for all the dimensional couplings except for the background mass parameter M^2. In this case the beta function essentially reproduces the value obtained via dimensional regularization with MS times a factor of order μ^2/m^2. The origin of the term proportional to $-8m^2$ can be retrieved from the term $2g_Y m\phi$ in Q. This can be linked to the fact that when building the DeWitt-Schwinger expansion all the mass dependence is assumed to be encoded in the exponential term[39] in the form m^2 and this expansion does not work properly if Q inherits a mass dependence. The latter result shows that finding decoupling for all the coupling constants, of a given theory, although it is crucial to define a cosmic infrared regime, it is indeed a nontrivial task, as already emphasized in.[25]

Finally it is worth showing the finite expression for the running of the Newton gravitational constant G, the cosmological constant Λ and the scalar mass term M'^2 coming from the Dirac field at two different scales μ and μ_0.

$$\Lambda(\mu) = \Lambda_0 - \frac{1}{32\pi^2}\left((\mu^4 - \mu_0^4) - 2m^2(\mu^2 - \mu_0^2) + 2m^4 \log\left(\frac{m^2 + \mu^2}{m^2 + \mu_0^2}\right)\right), \qquad (24)$$

$$G(\mu) = \frac{G_0}{1 - \frac{G_0}{6\pi}\left(\mu^2 - \mu_0^2 - m^2 \log\left(\frac{m^2+\mu^2}{m^2+\mu_0^2}\right)\right)}, \qquad (25)$$

$$M'^2(\mu) = M_0'^2 + \frac{g_Y^2}{4\pi^2}\left((\mu^2 - \mu_0^2) - 3m^2 \log\left(\frac{m^2 + \mu^2}{m^2 + \mu_0^2}\right)\right), \qquad (26)$$

where G_0, Λ_0 and $M_0'^2$ are the parameters at the scale μ_0. Note the appearance of μ^4 and μ^2 terms. In more conventional approaches only the logarithmic terms are present. However these non-logarithmic terms can be traced to the non trivial quartic and quadratic divergences and are indeed responsible of the appearance of decoupling. Expanding $\Lambda(\mu)$ and $G(\mu)$ for $\mu^2 \gg m^2$ one can check that the runnings are suppressed by a factor μ^6/m^2 and μ^4/m^2. However for $M'^2(\mu)$ we still get a non suppressed term proportional to μ^2.

4. Conclusions and final comments

We have considered the one-loop effective action for a quantized scalar field and Dirac field coupled to a background scalar field and gravity. Using the upgraded DeWitt-Schwinger subtraction scheme we have renormalized the theory and computed the beta functions for all the parameters. As a remarkable result, for the dimensionless couplings we obtain the beta functions that satisfy both ultraviolet and infrared regimes. In the ultraviolet regime we recover the beta function from MS scheme. In the infrared regime the beta functions explicitly exhibit the decoupling property. For the dimensional parameters new μ^4 and μ^2 terms appear in the runnings. These terms signal the presence of quadratic and quartic divergences and are indeed the responsible for the decoupling in the running couplings. Therefore, the obtained beta functions of the dimensional parameters exhibit the property of decoupling in the low energy regime, including the Newton's and cosmological constant. The exception is for the contribution of the Dirac field to the scalar mass parameter. As stress before the reason is localized in the linear term $2g_y m\phi$ in Q.

Acknowledgments

This work has been partially supported by Spanish Ministerio de Economia, Industria y Competitividad Grants No. FIS2017-84440-C2-1-P (MINECO/FEDER,

EU) and No. FIS2017-91161-EXP, and also by the project PROMETEO/2020/079 (Generalitat Valenciana). A. F. is supported by the Severo Ochoa Ph.D. fellowship, Grant No. SEV-2014-0398-16-1, and the European Social Fund. S. N. is supported by the Universidad de Valencia, within the Atracció de Talent Ph.D fellowship No. UV-INV- 506 PREDOC19F1-1005367.

Appendix A

The obtained beta functions for the scalar one-loop correction are

$$\beta_{\xi_\phi} = \frac{h^2 \bar{\xi}}{8\pi^2} \frac{\mu^2}{m^2 + \mu^2} \qquad \beta_{\alpha_1} = -\frac{\bar{\xi}^2}{32\pi^2} \frac{\mu^2}{m^2 + \mu^2}$$

$$\beta_{\alpha_4} = -\frac{\xi - \frac{1}{5}}{96\pi^2} \frac{\mu^2}{m^2 + \mu^2} \qquad \beta_{\alpha_2} = \frac{1}{2880\pi^2} \frac{\mu^2}{m^2 + \mu^2}$$

$$\beta_{\alpha_3} = -\frac{1}{2880\pi^2} \frac{\mu^2}{m^2 + \mu^2} \qquad \beta_{\gamma_1} = -\frac{h^2}{96\pi^2} \frac{\mu^2}{m^2 + \mu^2}$$

$$\beta_\lambda = \frac{3h^4}{4\pi^2} \frac{\mu^2}{m^2 + \mu^2} \qquad \beta_\Lambda = \frac{1}{32\pi^2} \frac{\mu^6}{m^2 + \mu^2}$$

$$\beta_\kappa = \frac{\bar{\xi}}{8\pi^2} \frac{\mu^4}{m^2 + \mu^2} \qquad \beta_{M^2} = -\frac{h^2}{8\pi^2} \frac{\mu^4}{m^2 + \mu^2} \ . \tag{A.1}$$

Dimensionless beta functions for the Dirac field are:

$$\beta_Z = -\frac{g_Y^2}{4\pi^2} \frac{\mu^2}{m^2 + \mu^2}$$

$$\beta_\xi = -\frac{g_Y^2}{24\pi^2} \frac{\mu^2}{m^2 + \mu^2} (1 - 6\xi) \qquad \beta_\lambda = -\frac{g_Y^2}{8\pi^2} \frac{\mu^2}{m^2 + \mu^2} (24 g_Y^2 - 4\lambda)$$

$$\beta_{\alpha_1} = \frac{1}{1152\pi^2} \frac{\mu^2}{m^2 + \mu^2} \qquad \beta_{\alpha_2} = -\frac{1}{720\pi^2} \frac{\mu^2}{m^2 + \mu^2}$$

$$\beta_{\alpha_3} = -\frac{7}{5760\pi^2} \frac{\mu^2}{m^2 + \mu^2} \qquad \beta_{\alpha_4} = \frac{1}{480\pi^2} \frac{\mu^2}{m^2 + \mu^2}$$

$$\beta_{\gamma_1} = \frac{g_Y^2}{4\pi^2} \frac{\mu^2}{m^2 + \mu^2} \left(\frac{1}{6} + \gamma_1\right) \qquad \beta_{\gamma_2} = \frac{g_Y}{8\pi^2} \frac{\mu^2}{m^2 + \mu^2} \left(\frac{2}{3} m + \gamma_2\right) \ . \tag{A.2}$$

Dimensional beta functions for the Dirac field:

$$\beta_\Lambda = -\frac{1}{8\pi^2} \frac{\mu^6}{m^2 + \mu^2} \qquad \beta_{\xi_1} = \frac{g_Y}{8\pi^2} \frac{\mu^2}{m^2 + \mu^2} \left(-\frac{m}{3} + g_Y \xi_1\right)$$

$$\beta_\kappa = -\frac{1}{24\pi^2} \frac{\mu^4}{m^2 + \mu^2} \qquad \beta_\tau = -\frac{g_Y}{8\pi^2} \frac{\mu^2}{m^2 + \mu^2} \left(4m\mu^2 - \tau g_Y\right)$$

$$\beta_{M^2} = \frac{g_Y^2}{8\pi^2} \frac{\mu^2}{m^2 + \mu^2} \left(+4\mu^2 - 8m^2 + 2M^2\right) \qquad \beta_\eta = -\frac{g_Y^3}{8\pi^2} \frac{\mu^2}{m^2 + \mu^2} \left(24 g_Y m - 3\eta\right) \ . \tag{A.3}$$

References

1. A. Ferreiro, S. Nadal-Gisbert and J. Navarro-Salas, *Phys. Rev. D* **104**, 025003 (2021).
2. N. D. Birrell and P. C. W. Davies, *Quantum Fields in Curved Space* (Cambridge University Press, Cambridge, England 1982).
3. S. Fulling, *Aspects of Quantum Field Theory in Curved Space-Time* (Cambridge University Press, Cambridge, England 1989).
4. R. M. Wald, *Quantum Field Theory in Curved Spacetime and Black Hole Thermodynamics* (University of Chicago Press, Chicago, 1994).
5. L. Parker and D. J. Toms, *Quantum Field Theory in Curved Spacetime: Quantized Fields and Gravity* (Cambridge University Press, Cambridge, England 2009).
6. B.-L. B. Hu and E. Verdaguer, *Semiclassical and Stochastic Gravity* (Cambridge University Press, Cambridge, England 2020).
7. I. L. Buchbinder and I. L. Shapiro, *Introduction to Quantum Field Theory with Applications to Quantum Gravity* (Oxford University Press, Oxford, England, 2021).
8. J. Schwinger, *Phys. Rev.* **82**, 664 (1951).
9. B. S. DeWitt, *Dynamical Theory of Groups and Fields* (Gordon and Breach, New York 1965).
10. B. S. DeWitt, *Phys. Rep.* **19**, 295 (1975).
11. S. Weinberg, *The Quantum Theory of Fields* (Cambridge University Press, Cambridge, England 1995), Vol. 1, 2.
12. M. E. Peskin and D. V. Schroeder, *An Introduction to Quantum Field Theory* (Addison-Wesley, Reading MA, 1995).
13. L. Alvarez-Gaume and M. A. Vazquez-Mozo, *An Invitation to Quantum Field Theory* (Springer-Verlag, Berlin, 2012).
14. I. L. Shapiro and J. Solà, *J. High Energy Phys.* 02, (2002) 006.
15. A. Babić, B. Guberina, R. Horvat and H. Štefančić, *Phys. Rev. D* **65**, 085002 (2002).
16. T. Appelquist and J. Carazzone, *Phys. Rev. D* **11**, 2856 (1975).
17. J.C. Collins, *Renormalization* (Cambridge University Press, Cambridge, England 1984).
18. F. Feruglio, *Acta Phys. Polon. B* **25**, 1279 (1994).
19. S.M. Carroll, *Living Rev. Relativ.* **4**, 1 (2001).
20. J. Martin, *C.R. Phys* **13**, 566 (2012).
21. J. Solà, *J. Phys. Conf. Ser.* **453**, 012015 (2013).
22. M. Niedermaier and M. Reuter, *Living Rev. Rel.* **9**, 5 (2006). M. Reuter, arXiv: hep-th/0012069.
23. E.V. Gorbar and I. L. Shapiro, *J. High Energy Phys.* 02, (2003) 021; *J. High Energy Phys.* 06, (2003) 004.
24. E.V. Gorbar and I. L. Shapiro *J. High Energy Phys.* 02, (2004) 060.
25. S.A. Franchino-Viñas, T. de Paula Netto and O. Zanusso, *Universe*, **5**, 67 (2019).
26. S.A. Franchino-Viñas, T. D. Netto, I.L. Shapiro and O. Zanusso, *Phys. Lett. B* **790**, 229 (2019).
27. O. Antipin and B. Melic, *Eur. Phys. J. C* **77**, 583 (2017).
28. T. Markkanen, *Phys. Rev. D* **91**, 124011 (2015).
29. A. Ferreiro and J. Navarro-Salas, *Phys. Rev. D* **102**, 045021 (2020).
30. A. Ferreiro and J. Navarro-Salas, *Phys. Lett. B* **792**, 81 (2019).
31. C. Moreno-Pulido and J. Solà, *Eur. Phys. J. C* **80**, 692 (2020).
32. P. Beltran-Palau, A. del Río, S. Nadal-Gisbert and J. Navarro-Salas, *Phys. Rev. D* **103**, 105002 (2021).
33. D.J. Toms, *J. High Energy Phys.* 05 (2018) 139.

34. V.F. Barra, I.L. Buchbinder, J.G. Joaquim, A.R. Rodrigues, and I. Shapiro, *Eur. Phys. J.C* **79**, 458 (2019).
35. I.L. Buchbinder, A.R. Rodrigues, E.A. dos Reis and I. Shapiro, *Eur. Phys. J. C* **79**, 1002 (2019).
36. D.J. Toms, *Phys. Rev. D* **98**, 025015 (2018).
37. D.J. Toms, arXiv:1906.02515.
38. T. J. Hollowood, *Renormalization Group and Fixed Points in Quantum Field Theory* (Springer, Heidelberg, 2013).
39. S. M. Christensen, *Phys. Rev. D* **14**, 2490 (1976).

Trace anomaly and evaporation of spherical black holes

P. Meda

Dipartimento di Fisica, Università degli Studi di Genova,
Istituto Nazionale di Fisica Nucleare - Sezione di Genova,
Genova, 16146, Italia
E-mail: paolo.meda@ge.infn.it

The evaporation of four-dimensional spherically symmetric black holes is presented in the framework of quantum field theory in curved spacetimes and semiclassical gravity. It is discussed how the evaporation process can be sourced by the presence of the trace anomaly of a massless, conformally coupled scalar field outside the apparent horizon of the black hole.

Keywords: Evaporation; black hole; trace anomaly; semiclassical gravity; Vaidya spacetime

1. Quantum fields in curved spacetimes

From the time of the discovery made by Hawking that black holes can emit radiation,[1,2] black hole evaporation has become of great interest in analyzing the interplay between matter and gravity. A theoretical framework where modelling black hole evaporation is represented by quantum field theory in curved spacetimes,[3] which consists of describing the propagation of a quantum field over a classical curved background. On one side, the background is assumed to be a four-dimensional globally hyperbolic spacetime $(\mathcal{M}, g)$, where $\mathcal{M}$ is a smooth manifold and g a Lorentzian metric with signature $(-, +, +, +)$. On the other side, the quantum field is the fundamental observable, which is viewed as an operator-valued distribution living in a $*$-algebra $\mathcal{A}(\mathcal{M})$. For a real, free Klein-Gordon field ϕ the $*$-algebra is generated by the set of linear smeared fields $\{\phi(f), f \in \mathcal{D}(\mathcal{M})\}$ satisfying the following relations:

$$\phi(Pf) = 0, \qquad \phi(f)^* = \phi(\bar{f}), \qquad [\phi(f), \phi(h)] = \mathrm{i}\Delta(f, h).$$

Here, $P = -\Box_g + m^2 + \xi R$ is the Klein-Gordon operator constructed from the d'Alambertian operator $\Box_g = g^{\mu\nu} \nabla_\mu \nabla_\nu$ on $(\mathcal{M}, g)$, and $\Delta = \Delta_R - \Delta_A$ is the causal propagator of the spacetime, which is defined as the difference between the unique retarded and advanced fundamental solutions of P. A generic quantum state ω is a linear, positive, normalized functional over $\mathcal{A}(\mathcal{M})$, and it is determined by the n-point functions

$$\omega_n(f_1, \ldots, f_n) = \langle \phi(f_1) \ldots \phi(f_n) \rangle_\omega \in \mathcal{D}'(\mathcal{M}^n).$$

Actually, for Gaussian pure states it is sufficient to known the kernel of the two-point function $\omega_2(x', x) = \langle \phi(x')\phi(x) \rangle_\omega$.

Different from the flat case, where the Poincaré invariance selects a vacuum state uniquely as preferred reference state, in a curved spacetime there is not in principle a preferred notion of "vacuum" dictated by the symmetries of the spacetime. However, a guiding principle to select physically reasonable states in curved spacetimes is that Wick normal-ordered fields like $:\phi^2:$ and $:T_{\mu\nu}:$ should acquire finite expectation values when evaluated on ω. In globally hyperbolic spacetimes, the set of Hadamard states represents the right class where computing normal-ordered fields, because they share the same ultraviolet singular structure of the Minkowski vacuum two-point function $\langle 0|\phi(x')\phi(x)|0\rangle$. Given $\sigma(x',x)$ the one half of the signed geodesic distance between x' and x, the two-point function of a Hadamard state is always locally of the form

$$\omega_2(x',x) = \frac{1}{8\pi^2}\left(\mathscr{H}_{0^+}(x',x) + w(x',x)\right).$$

Here,

$$\mathscr{H}_{0^+}(x',x) = \lim_{\varepsilon\to 0^+} \frac{u(x',x)}{\sigma_\varepsilon} + \sum_{n\geq 0} v_n(x',x)\sigma(x',x)^n \log\left(\frac{\sigma_\varepsilon}{\mu^2}\right) \quad (1)$$

is the universal singularity called Hadamard parametrix viewed in the distributional sense, where $\sigma_\varepsilon(x',x) = \sigma(x',x) + i\epsilon(t(x') - t(x))$, t is any time function and $\mu > 0$ is a length scale. The coefficients $u(x',x)$, $v_n(x',x)$ are real-valued bi-scalars fixed by the geometry and the equation of motion, while $w(x',x)$ characterizes the state and must be chosen in such a way that ω_2 is a bi-solution of the Klein-Gordon equation. The Hadamard point-splitting regularization consists of subtracting the divergences contained in $\mathscr{H}_{0^+}(x',x)$ before computing the coinciding point limits: it generalizes the normal-ordering prescription in the flat spacetime, and it is also local and covariant, because only local geometry enters in the subtraction. This procedure, and more generally any prescription to obtain Wick observables, is always unique up to a fixed combination of local terms depending on the mass and on the curvature, whose coefficients represent the renormalization freedom of the quantum theory.[4,5]

1.1. *Semiclassical gravity, the quantum stress-energy tensor, and the trace anomaly*

Strictly related to a formulation of quantum fields propagating in curved backgrounds is the semiclassical theory of gravity, which aims to analyze the back-reaction of quantum fields on the spacetime geometry using the semiclassical Einstein equations

$$G_{\mu\nu} = 8\pi \langle :T_{\mu\nu}:\rangle_\omega \quad (2)$$

in units convention $G = c = \hbar = 1$. In this equations, the classical Einstein tensor is equated to the renormalized quantum stress-energy tensor evaluated in a certain quantum state ω. Any pair formed by a spacetime and a quantum state satisfying these equations constitutes a solution in semiclassical gravity: such a solution models a curved spacetime which incorporates quantum effects due to the propagation of the matter field, and it is expected to describe physical phenomena where the interplay between quantum matter and curvature becomes significant, like in the early Universe or in the vicinity of black holes. On the other hand, any semiclassical model represents an approximation of a more fundamental theory of quantum gravity, and thus it should be only valid in a regime where quantum gravity effects are negligible, and when fluctuations of the stress-energy tensor $:T_{\mu\nu}:$ are small.

A conserved quantum stress-energy tensor which can enter Eqs. (2) can be constructed in perturbative interacting quantum field theory in curved spacetimes according to the Hadamard point-splitting procedure.[5-7] For the stress-energy tensor of a free Klein-Gordon field

$$T_{\mu\nu} = \nabla_\mu \phi \nabla_\mu \phi - \frac{1}{2} g_{\mu\nu} \left(\nabla_\rho \phi \nabla^\rho \phi + m^2 \phi^2 \right) + \xi \left(G_{\mu\nu} \phi^2 - \nabla_\mu \nabla_\nu \phi^2 + g_{\mu\nu} \nabla_\rho \nabla^\rho \phi^2 \right),$$

the Hadamard renormalization procedure yields the following expectation value:

$$\langle :T_{\mu\nu}: \rangle_\omega (x) = \lim_{x' \to x} D_{\mu\nu} w(x', x),$$

where

$$D_{\mu\nu} = (1 - 2\xi) g_\mu^{\mu'} \nabla_{\mu'} \nabla_\nu - 2\xi \nabla_\mu \nabla_\nu + \xi G_{\mu\nu} +$$

$$g_{\mu\nu} \left\{ 2\xi \Box_g + \left(2\xi - \frac{1}{2} \right) g_\rho^{\rho'} \nabla_{\rho'} \nabla^\rho - \frac{1}{2} m^2 \right\} + \frac{1}{3} g_{\mu\nu} P$$

is the bi-differential operator which realizes the point-splitting of $T_{\mu\nu}$, and $w(x', x)$ is the smooth part of the Hadamard state ω. In this expression, unprimed and primed indices denote covariant derivatives in the points x and x', respectively, while $g_\nu^{\nu'}$ is the bitensor of parallel transport. The last term proportional to $g_{\mu\nu}$, which vanishes in the classical case, must be added to obtain $\nabla^\mu \langle :T_{\mu\nu}: \rangle_\omega (x) = 0$. However, any construction of a covariantly conserved expectation value of $:T_{\mu\nu}:$ leads to the violation of the classical conformal invariance of $T_{\mu\nu}$, and it gives rise to the so-called trace anomaly; namely, the trace of the quantum stress-energy tensor does not vanish for a massless, conformally coupled field, i.e., when $m = 0$ and $\xi = 1/6$, different from its classical counterpart. This anomalous trace does not depend on the choice of the quantum state, but it is a local contribution depending on the geometry and on the linear equation of motion of the matter field. In the Hadamard point-splitting regularization scheme and for a free scalar field ϕ, it is proportional to the Hadamard coefficient v_1 evaluated in the coinciding limit, and it reads in four dimensions as

$$\langle :T_\rho{}^\rho: \rangle_\omega = \lambda \left(C_{\alpha\beta\gamma\delta} C^{\alpha\beta\gamma\delta} + R_{\mu\nu} R^{\mu\nu} - \frac{1}{3} R^2 \right), \quad \lambda = \frac{1}{2880\pi^2}, \quad (3)$$

where $C_{\alpha\beta\gamma\delta}$ is the Weyl tensor, $R_{\mu\nu}$ is the Ricci tensor and R is the Ricci scalar. The $\Box_g R$ usually appearing in $\langle :T_\rho{}^\rho: \rangle_\omega$ was removed by a judicious choice of the renormalization constants, according to the previous discussion about local and covariant Wick observables in curved spacetimes. In the case of $\langle :T_\rho{}^\rho:\rangle_\omega$, the renormalization scalar freedom is[5]

$$Q = \tilde{\beta}_1 m^4 + \tilde{\beta}_2 m^2 R + \tilde{\beta}_3 R^2 + \tilde{\beta}_4 \Box_g R,$$

where $\tilde{\beta}_i \in \mathbb{R}$ are renormalization constants. Hence, in some special cases like the massless, conformally coupled field, the higher-order derivative term proportional to $\Box_g R$ can be always cancelled by choosing properly $\tilde{\beta}_4$, thus meeting the requirement that curvature terms do not contain non-classical higher order derivatives of the metric.[8]

2. Evaporation of spherically symmetric black holes

A model of evaporation of black holes which incorporates the back-reaction of the matter fields on the geometry can be fully developed in the framework of four-dimensional spherically symmetric spacetimes. In this class of geometries, invariants like the mass of the black hole and the area of the horizon can be provided thanks to the spherical symmetry[9]: the area of each two-sphere is $\mathcal{A} = 4\pi r^2$, where r is the radius, while the mass

$$m = \frac{r}{2}\left(1 - \nabla^\rho r \nabla_\rho r\right)$$

represents the Misner-Sharp energy enclosed inside the sphere. The metric of every spherically symmetric spacetime can be always represented in double-null coordinates with respect to the null normal directions ∂_V and ∂_U as

$$ds^2 = -2A(V,U)dVdU + r^2(V,U)d\Omega, \tag{4}$$

where $d\Omega = d\theta^2 + \sin^2\theta d\varphi^2$ denotes the line-element of the two-sphere of unit radius $\mathbb{S}^2$. The orientation of the spacetime can be fixed in such a way that $A(V,U) > 0$ and at spatial infinity $\partial_V r > 0$, $\partial_U r < 0$. To study evaporation, another convenient choice of parametrization is the Bardeen-Vaidya metric[10]

$$ds^2 = -e^{2\Psi(v,r)}\left(1 - \frac{2m(v,r)}{r}\right)dv^2 + 2e^{\Psi(v,r)}dvdr + r^2 d\Omega, \tag{5}$$

where v denotes the advanced time coordinate and parametrizes any ingoing radial null geodesic.

The notion of horizon in spherically symmetric black holes is encoded in the idea that no light rays can escape from this hypersurface, whereas they can fall inside. Namely, it is a future outer local trapping horizon.[11] To formulate this idea on mathematical grounds, one introduces a pair of null radial geodesic congruences with respect to the outgoing and ingoing directions ∂_V and ∂_U, respectively, and the relative expansion parameters

$$\theta_+ = \frac{2}{Ar}\partial_V r, \qquad \theta_- = \frac{2}{Ar}\partial_U r.$$

Each expansion parameter measures the rate of variation of the cross-sectional area of the geodesic congruence: $\theta_\pm = A^{-1}\partial_{V,U}\log(\mathcal{A})$, and it determines if the congruence is expanding or focusing along that null direction. Thus, the apparent horizon of a spherically symmetric black hole is defined as a three-manifold $\mathcal{H}$ foliated by closed surfaces such that

$$\theta_+ \stackrel{\mathcal{H}}{=} 0, \qquad \theta_- \stackrel{\mathcal{H}}{<} 0, \qquad \partial_U \theta_+ \stackrel{\mathcal{H}}{<} 0, \tag{6}$$

and it is located in $\mathcal{H}: r - 2m = 0$ (the subscript $\mathcal{H}$ labels the evaluation on the apparent horizon). The third condition captures the property that this trapping horizon is outer and it is referred to a black hole. In coordinates (v,r), the hypersurface $\mathcal{H}$ is a one-dimensional line $r_\mathcal{H}(v)$ in the plane (v,r), and hence the mass of an evaporating black hole is defined by the relation

$$M(v) = m(v, r_\mathcal{H}(v)) = \frac{r_\mathcal{H}(v)}{2}. \tag{7}$$

On spherically symmetric black holes, the mechanism of evaporation can be described in terms of the variation of the mass

$$\Delta M = \int_{\delta \mathcal{H}} \mathrm{d}m, \tag{8}$$

along a small portion $\delta \mathcal{H}$ of the apparent horizon. In coordinates (v,r), $\delta \mathcal{H}$ corresponds to the line enclosed between two points $P = (v_P, r_\mathcal{H}(v_P))$ and $Q = (v_Q, r_\mathcal{H}(v_Q))$ in the (v,r) plane, and the dynamics of $M(v)$ is fully determined by the rate of evaporation $\dot{M}(v) = \partial_v M(v)$. If one considers a generic stress-energy tensor $T_{\mu\nu}$, then the evolution of $M(v)$ is governed by the vv-component of the (semiclassical) Einstein equations evaluated on $\mathcal{H}$, which reads

$$\dot{M}(v) = \mathcal{A}_\mathcal{H}(v) T_{vv}(v, r_\mathcal{H}(v)), \tag{9}$$

where $\dot{M}(v)$ and $\mathcal{A}_\mathcal{H} = 4\pi r_\mathcal{H}^2$ denote the rate of evaporation and the area of the horizon, respectively. Thus,

$$\Delta M = 4\pi \int_{v_P}^{v_Q} \frac{M}{\kappa} T_{vv}(r_\mathcal{H}) \mathrm{d}v. \tag{10}$$

As $T_{vv} \stackrel{\mathcal{H}}{=} T_{VV}$, both $\dot{M}(v)$ and ΔM depend on the ingoing flux of matter which is falling inside the black hole from the horizon. Whenever quantum matter is involved in the back-reaction process, it may happen that the quantum stress-energy tensor $\langle :T_{\mu\nu}: \rangle_\omega$ violates the classical null energy condition on the horizon, and hence the ingoing quantum component $\langle :T_{VV}: \rangle_\omega$ may be negative on $\delta \mathcal{H}$. In the end, the presence of a negative ingoing flux on the horizon makes the black hole mass to evaporate with a negative rate $\dot{M}(v) < 0$.

2.1. The static black hole

The vacuum spherically symmetric spacetime is the Schwarzschild solution of the Einstein equations according to Birkhoff's theorem, and it describes a static spherical black hole of constant mass M.[12] A double-null parametrization for arbitrary $U, V > 0$ is the maximally extension of the Schwarzschild eternal black hole in the so-called Kruskal-Szekeres coordinates

$$ds^2 = -\frac{32M^3}{r}e^{-r/2M}dVdU + r^2(V,U)d\Omega,$$

where $r(V, U)$ is implicitly defined by

$$UV = \left(1 - \frac{r}{2M}\right)e^{r/2M}.$$

On the other hand, the Bardeen-Vaidya metric corresponds to the advanced Eddington-Finkelstein coordinates, with $\Psi(v, r) = 0$ and $m(v, r) = M$.

The static symmetry of the Schwarzschild spacetime reflects the existence of a Killing vector field $\xi = \frac{1}{4M}(V\partial_V - U\partial_U)$, which is unit timelike at infinity and it is hypersurface orthogonal. Due to the static symmetry, the apparent horizon coincides with the null event horizon of the black hole, which is located in the Schwarzschild radius $r = 2M$ (see Figure 1[a]). The surface gravity of the black hole is defined by the equation $\nabla^\mu \xi^2 = -2\kappa \xi^\mu$ and it constant along each null generator of ξ. Physically, the surface gravity represents the gravitational acceleration detected along the black hole horizon, and it is strictly positive on the event horizon.

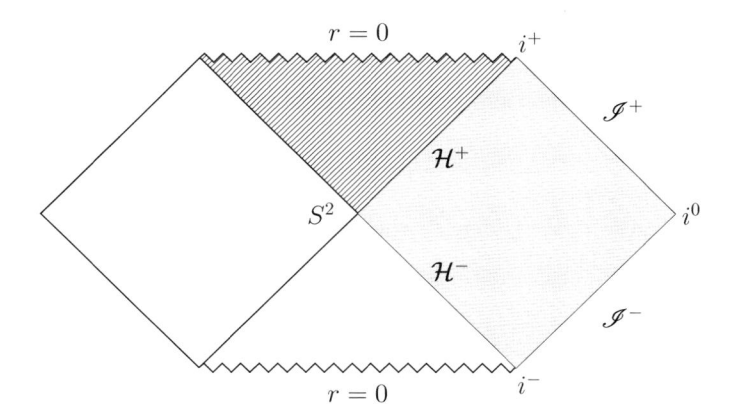

Fig. 1. Penrose diagram of the maximally extended Schwarzschild spacetime. The bifurcated Killing horizon $\mathcal{H} = \mathcal{H}^+ \cup \mathcal{H}^-$ associated to ξ is composed by two null surfaces $\mathcal{H}^\pm$ located in $U = 0$ and $V = 0$, respectively. The event horizon $\mathcal{H}^+$ corresponds to the future branch of $\mathcal{H}$, and it separates the outer region (grey region) from the black hole region (dashed region); the null surfaces intersects each other in the sphere of bifurcation S^2 located in $U = 0$, $V = 0$.

---

[a]Penrose diagrams were made in TikZ and are based on the Latex code posted in StackExchange.[13]

According to Hawking's works, a static black hole can emits thermal radiation at infinity in form of a flux of quantum particles, if the back-reaction is not taken into account and after assuming a vacuum state in the asymptotic past. The temperature of the radiation is the so-called Hawking temperature and it is proportional to the surface gravity of the black hole: in the units convention adopted in this paper it reads

$$T_H = \frac{\kappa}{2\pi} = \frac{1}{8\pi k_B M},$$

with k_B being the Boltzmann constant. The correspondence between the temperature of the radiation and the surface gravity lets to interpret the first law of black hole mechanics

$$dM = \frac{\kappa}{8\pi} d\mathcal{A} + \Omega dJ$$

from a thermodynamic point of view, with M and $\mathcal{A}/4$ playing the role of energy and entropy of the black hole, respectively. More recently,[14] it was shown that in case of a static black hole formed in a gravitational collapse, the Hawking radiation with temperature T_H always appears at future infinity whenever the state ω is a Hadamard state approaching the ground state near spatial infinity; for instance, in the case of the Unruh state,[15,16] which is regular on the horizon and respects the spherical symmetries of the spacetime.

Thus, the power of the radiation emitted from the black hole at future infinity is regarded as describing the evaporation of the black hole, because it can be instantaneously equated to the rate of loss of mass in the adiabatic approximation, namely neglecting how the spacetime is dynamically changing during the evaporation. Starting from this assumption, the negative ingoing flux on the horizon, that is, $\langle :T_{vv}: \rangle_\omega \stackrel{\mathcal{H}}{=} \langle :T_{VV}: \rangle_\omega$, can be related to the positive outgoing flux $\langle :T_{uu}: \rangle_\omega$ detected at infinity, where u denotes the retarded Eddington-Finkelstein coordinate parametrizing outgoing null geodesics. In the Unruh state, it holds that

$$\frac{\dot{M}(v)}{4\pi} = \lim_{r \to r_\mathcal{H}} \left(\langle :T_{VV}: \rangle_\omega r^2 \right) = -\lim_{r \to \infty} \left(\langle :T_{uu}: \rangle_\omega r^2 \right) = -\frac{L_\mathcal{H}}{4\pi}, \quad (11)$$

where $L_\mathcal{H} > 0$ denotes the luminosity of the black hole, namely the radial flux of particles measured by a static observer at large distance from the black hole.[17] Indeed, Eq. (11) loses meaning outside the adiabatic approximation, since the rate $\dot{M}(v)$ always vanishes in case of constant mass. It turns out, in fact, that the Schwarzschild spacetime is never a solution of the semiclassical Einstein equations, and hence an eternal black hole cannot be in equilibrium with the back-reaction of any quantum matter field in the semiclassical approach.

2.2. Dynamical black holes

The direct correspondence given in Eq. (11) between the ingoing negative flux and the positive outgoing flux holds in Schwarzschild spacetime thanks to the existence

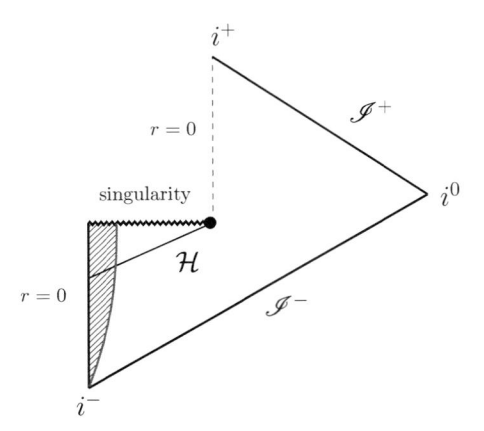

Fig. 2. Penrose diagram of a Schwarzschild gravitational collapse followed by evaporation and leaving an empty space at the end of the evolution. The black dot represents the end of the evaporation, and the dashed line denotes the new regular centre of the spacetime after the evaporation.[2]

of a global Killing field which is timelike outside the event horizon, but it is missing in arbitrary dynamical backgrounds. In this case, the mechanism of evaporation and the following emission of power radiated should be dealt separately as causally related processes: from one hand, evaporation is a local effect induced by the negative ingoing flux and affecting the horizon; on the other hand, the expected Hawking radiation is associated to the positive outgoing flux emitted to infinity, and it depends globally on the entire history of spacetime.

Moreover, the adiabatic approximation is unable to describe evaporations when the spacetime is treated with its full dynamics, since it does not give informations about the evolution of the apparent horizon. In this respect, the Penrose diagram shown in Figure 2 should be modified in case of dynamical backgrounds outside that approximation, because the dynamics of $\mathcal{H}$ depends sharply on the negative flux $\langle :T_{VV}: \rangle_\omega$, and the causal structure of the spacetime may be significantly modified in the back-reaction process. Conversely, a semiclassical model of evaporation should necessarily rely on the semiclassical Einstein equations (2) to study the variation of the mass $M(v)$ induced by the back-reaction of the quantum matter content, without further assumptions.

Contrary to Schwarzschild spacetimes modelling static black holes and event horizons, a general spherically symmetric spacetime describes a dynamical black hole, whose evolution is dictated by the dynamics of the apparent horizon (6). To define properties of spherically symmetric black holes like the surface gravity, there is a preferred choice of a vector field, which replaces the standard Killing vector field in stationary spacetimes. It is the Kodama vector[18] $K = g^{-1}(*_n dr)$, where $*_n$ denotes the Hodge operator in the two-dimensional spacetime normal to the two-sphere. This vector is timelike in the region outside the horizon, it becomes lightlike on $\mathcal{H}$, and eventually it is spacelike in the interior of the black hole. It also reduces to the Killing vector ξ in stationary spacetimes. Furthermore, it is divergenceless: $\nabla_\mu K^\mu = 0$, and it can be used to define conserved currents $T_{\mu\nu} K^\nu$ given any symmetric tensor $T_{\mu\nu}$ which respects the spherical symmetry. Finally, from the definition of K it holds that

$$\mathscr{L}_K K_\mu = K^\nu \left(\nabla_\nu K_\mu - \nabla_\mu K_\nu \right) \stackrel{\mathcal{H}}{=} \pm \kappa K_\mu, \qquad (12)$$

where $\mathscr{L}_K$ denotes the Lie derivative along K, and

$$\kappa \doteq \frac{1}{2} \Box_n r, \qquad (13)$$

where the d'Alambertian operator is evaluated in the two-dimensional normal spacetime. Namely, this quantity corresponds to the definition of the surface gravity for a dynamical black hole and it reduces to the standard one in the case of a Killing vector field. In particular, $\partial_U \theta_+ < 0$ implies that $\kappa > 0$ on $\mathcal{H}$.

In analogy with the static case, Hayward showed[9] that the four laws of black hole mechanics can be generalized in presence of spherical symmetry to apparent horizons using the properties of the Kodama vector and the definition of the surface gravity given in Eq. (13). In this class of spacetimes, the first law reads

$$m' = \frac{\kappa}{8\pi} \mathcal{A}' + w V', \qquad (14)$$

where the prime denotes the derivative along the horizon, i.e., $f' = \ell \cdot \nabla f$, and ℓ is any tangent vector to $\mathcal{H}$. Here, the second contribution in the right-hand side represents the variation of the work done by the matter on the horizon, where $V = \frac{4}{3} \pi r^3$ and $w = A^{-1} T_{UV}$. Furthermore, the same thermodynamic interpretation already seen in the static case can be given in terms of the Kodama surface gravity, with $\kappa/2\pi$ playing the role of dynamical local temperature of the apparent horizon with respect to the time parameter defined of the Kodama vector. This correspondence was shown in the dynamical case by studying the tunnelling probability of quantum matter across apparent horizons using the Hamilton-Jacobi method,[19,20] and by analyzing the scaling limit of the Hadamard two-point function on such horizons.[21]

According the previous section, cf. Eqs. (9) and (10), evaporation of spherically symmetric black holes is fully determined by the ingoing flux located on the horizon. However, in the absence of further symmetries it is very challenging to evaluate the component $\langle :T_{VV}: \rangle_\omega$, and, more generally, the renormalized quantum stress-energy tensor $\langle :T_{\mu\nu}: \rangle_\omega$, in a state ω which was a vacuum state in the past. On the other hand, the variation of the mass of the black hole can be constrained by the matter-geometry content in the causal past and outside the black hole horizon.[22] This is accomplished by applying the divergence theorem (Stokes' theorem) to the currents J_r and J_k obtained by contracting the stress-energy tensor with the gradient ∇r and with the Kodama vector K, respectively. The domain over which the divergence theorem is spherically symmetric and it has the form $D \times \mathbb{S}^2$, where D is a suitable region in the two-dimensional normal spacetime intersecting a portion of

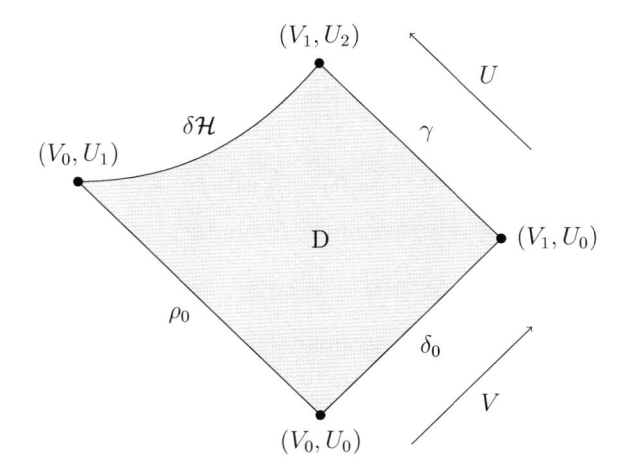

Fig. 3. Picture of the domain D. For spacelike $\delta\mathcal{H}$, $D \times \mathbb{S}^2 = J^+((V_0, U_0) \times \mathbb{S}^2) \cap J^-(\delta\mathcal{H} \times \mathbb{S}^2)$, with $U_2 < U_1$. The points $P = (V_0, U_1)$ and $Q = (V_1, U_2)$ denote the extreme values of $\delta\mathcal{H}$ in the (V, U) plane. In describing evaporation, the initial conditions are posed on $S_0 = \{(V, U, \theta, \varphi) \in \mathcal{M} \mid V = V_0, \ U = U_0\}$ and on the curves ρ_0 and δ_0 of the boundary ∂D.[22]

the apparent horizon. A representation of D for a spacelike portion of the horizon is pictured in Figure 3.

If one considers a stress-energy tensor $T_{\mu\nu}$ which respects the spherical symmetry and which satisfies vacuum-like initial condition at the boundary of $J^+(S_0)$, namely

$$T_{\mu\nu}(p) = 0, \qquad p \in \partial J^+(S_0), \tag{15}$$

then applying the divergence theorem to J_r yields

$$\Delta M = -(\mathcal{S} + \mathcal{W}), \tag{16}$$

where

$$\mathcal{S} = 2\pi \int_D \nabla \cdot J_r \mathrm{d}V_D, \tag{17}$$

$$\mathcal{W} = 4\pi \int_\gamma \frac{T_{UV} r^2}{A} (-\partial_U r) \mathrm{d}U. \tag{18}$$

Here, $\mathrm{d}V_D \doteq Ar^2 \mathrm{d}V \wedge \mathrm{d}U$ is the volume form on D in the (V, U) plane. Eq. (17) denotes the matter source inside the domain D which influences the variation of the mass, while Eq. (18) is related to the work done by the matter when evaluated on $\mathcal{H}$, in view of Hayward's first law (14). Moreover, applying the divergence theorem to J_K in spacetimes where $\mathcal{W} = 0$ yields

$$\left.\frac{\Delta M}{4\pi}\right|_{\mathcal{W}=0} = -\int_\gamma \frac{T_{UU} r^2}{A} \partial_V r \mathrm{d}U. \tag{19}$$

Namely, in the quantum case the variation of the mass is related to the outgoing flux $\langle :T_{UU}: \rangle_\omega$ across γ, which can interpreted as Hawking radiation sourced by $\mathcal{S}$ and emitted from the evaporating black hole to infinity. In this view, the relation (19) generalizes Eq. (11) to more general non-static, spherically symmetric black holes outside the adiabatic approximation.

2.3. *The trace anomaly as source of evaporation*

It is well known that the evaporation of a black hole, viewed as emission of Hawking radiation at infinity, can be ascribed to the presence of an anomalous trace in the stress-energy tensor of a quantum matter field in the vicinity of the horizon.[23–26] However, such analysis are often provided after making some approximations on the spacetime, like the adiabatic one. On the contrary, a full semiclassical approach to study the evaporation sourced by the trace anomaly should only rely on the semiclassical Einstein equations in four dimensions, without making further assumptions or referring to asymptotic effects which need global informations about the spacetime.

Based on the results presented in the previous section, the variation of the black hole mass can be related to the source term $\mathcal{S}$ given in Eq. (17), and to the boundary term $\mathcal{W}$ given in Eq. (18). Thus, it was proved[22] that the evaporation of a four-dimensional dynamical black hole can be induced by the trace anomaly (3) of a massless, conformally coupled scalar field affecting the horizon from the outside of the black hole, provided a weighted version of Eq. (16). This result is obtained using only the semiclassical Einstein equations (2), once the initial condition (15) is assumed on the state ω and a quantum averaged energy condition on $\langle :T_{UV}: \rangle_\omega$ is posed. Such a condition is of the form

$$\int_\gamma \frac{\langle :T_{UV}: \rangle_\omega r^2}{A} f(V,U) A dU \geq 0, \tag{20}$$

where γ is one of the boundary hypersurface of the domain $D \times \mathbb{S}^2$ (see Figure 3), and $f(V,U)$ is a certain strictly positive exponential function constructed from the geometry of the spacetime, whose role is to tame the contributions inside $\langle :T_\rho{}^\rho: \rangle_\omega$ which do not contribute to a negative variation of the mass. The form of the function f is similar to the ones entering usual quantum averaged weak energy conditions, which were shown to be valid both in flat and curved spacetimes for several values of the coupling-to-curvature parameter.[27]

In principle, it is difficult to verify if such an energy condition can be fulfilled by the quantum collapsing matter during the evaporation process, because the lack of a quantum state in spherically symmetric spacetimes which was a vacuum in the past prevents to evaluate $\langle :T_{\mu\nu}: \rangle_\omega$ on and outside the horizon. However, one can expect that this condition is satisfied in an approximate way by a background geometry which is not too different from the one obtained in a classical model of gravitational collapse. Indeed, classical solutions are approximately valid in semiclassical gravity, because quantum corrections are usually small outside the horizon, and thus one can assume that solutions of the full semiclassical equations maintain their classical form outside the horizon. To provide a simple application, consider the Vaidya spacetime

$$ds^2 = -\left(1 - \frac{2M(v)}{r}\right)dv^2 + 2dvdr + r^2 d\Omega,$$

which describes a null radiating spherically symmetric star with time-dependent mass $M(v)$. If one supposes that the quantum state fulfils $\langle :T_{UV}: \rangle_\omega = 0$, namely it makes the above metric a solution of Eqs. (2), then the negative ingoing flux on the horizon induced by the anomalous trace (3) can be evaluated explicitly, and it reads

$$\langle :T_{VV}: \rangle_\omega r^2 \stackrel{\mathcal{H}}{=} -\frac{3\lambda}{40 M(v)^2}.$$

Hence,

$$\dot{M}(v) = -\frac{3\pi\lambda}{10 M(v)^2}, \qquad \frac{dS_\mathcal{H}(v)}{dv} = -\frac{12\pi^2\lambda}{5M(v)},$$

where $S_\mathcal{H} = \mathcal{A}_\mathcal{H}/4$ denotes the Wald-Kodama entropy.

3. Conclusions

The evaporation of four-dimensional spherically symmetric black holes in semiclassical gravity can be fully ascribed to the presence of a negative ingoing flux on the horizon, which determines the global behaviour of the decreasing mass of the black hole. Whereas the evaporation of any static black hole can be described directly in terms of Hawking radiation and black hole luminosity, for dynamical black holes the variation of the mass can be constrained by the quantum matter content outside and in the causal past of the black hole, without directly referring to any expected radiation detected at infinity. When conformally coupled quantum scalar fields are involved, the evaporation can be sourced by the trace anomaly of the quantum stress-energy tensor, assuming vacuum-like initial conditions in the past, and an auxiliary quantum energy condition outside the horizon. It is, however, very challenging to extend these results to more generic quantum matter contents, due to the difficulties in evaluating the renormalized stress-energy tensor in a quantum state. In order to overcome this issue, a semiclassical analysis which takes advantage of some quantum energy conditions similar to the one presented in Eq. (20) might be viable in the future.

Acknowledgments

The author would like to thank Simone Roncallo for his careful reading of an earlier version of this proceeding.

References

1. S. W. Hawking, Black hole explosions?, *Nature* **248**, 30 (1974).
2. S. W. Hawking, Particle creation by black holes, *Communications in Mathematical Physics* **43**, p. 199 (1975).
3. S. Hollands and R. M. Wald, Quantum fields in curved spacetime, *Physics Reports* **574**, 1 (2015).
4. S. Hollands and R. M. Wald, Local wick polynomials and time ordered products of quantum fields in curved space-time, *Communications in Mathematical Physics* **223**, 289 (2001).
5. S. Hollands and R. M. Wald, Conservation of the stress tensor in perturbative interacting quantum field theory in curved spacetimes, *Reviews in Mathematical Physics* **17**, 227 (2005).
6. V. Moretti, Comments on the stress-energy tensor operator in curved spacetime, *Communications in Mathematical Physics* **232**, 189 (2003).
7. T. P. Hack, *Cosmological Applications of Algebraic Quantum Field Theory in Curved Spacetimes* (Springer International Publishing, 2016).
8. R. M. Wald, The back reaction effect in particle creation in curved spacetime, *Communications in Mathematical Physics* **54**, 1 (1977).
9. S. A. Hayward, Unified first law of black hole dynamics and relativistic thermodynamics, *Classical and Quantum Gravity* **15**, 3147 (1998).
10. J. M. Bardeen, Black holes do evaporate thermally, *Physical Review Letter* **46**, p. 382 (1981).
11. S. A. Hayward, General laws of black-hole dynamics, *Physical Review D* **49**, 6467 (1994).
12. R. M. Wald, *General Relativity* (Chicago University Press, Chicago, USA, 1984).
13. Nice scientific pictures show off https://tex.stackexchange.com/questions/158668/nice-scientific-pictures-show-off/209201, [Online; 05-February-2014].
14. K. Fredenhagen and R. Haag, On the derivation of hawking radiation associated with the formation of a black hole, *Communications in Mathematical Physics* **127**, p. 273 (1990).
15. W. G. Unruh, Notes on black-hole evaporation, *Physical Review D* **14**, 870 (1976).
16. C. Dappiaggi, V. Moretti and N. Pinamonti, Rigorous construction and Hadamard property of the Unruh state in Schwarzschild spacetime, *Advances in Theoretical and Mathematical Physics* **15**, 355 (2011).
17. P. Candelas, Vacuum polarization in schwarzschild space-time, *Physical Review D* **21**, p. 2185 (1980).
18. H. Kodama, Conserved energy flux for the spherically symmetric system and the backreaction problem in the black hole evaporation, *Progress of Theoretical Physics* **63**, p. 1217 (1980).
19. R. Di Criscienzo, M. Nadalini, L. Vanzo, S. Zerbini and G. Zoccatelli, On the hawking radiation as tunneling for a class of dynamical black holes, *Physics Letters B* **657**, 107 (2007).
20. L. Vanzo, G. Acquaviva and R. Di Criscienzo, Tunnelling methods and hawking's radiation: achievements and prospects, *Classical and Quantum Gravity* **28**, p. 183001 (2011).
21. F. Kurpicz, N. Pinamonti and R. Verch, Temperature and entropy-area relation of quantum matter near spherically symmetric outer trapping horizons, *Letters in Mathematical Physics* **111** (2021).

22. P. Meda, N. Pinamonti, S. Roncallo and N. Zanghì, Evaporation of four-dimensional dynamical black holes sourced by the quantum trace anomaly, *Classical and Quantum Gravity* **38**, p. 195022 (2021).
23. P. C. W. Davies, S. A. Fulling and W. G. Unruh, Energy momentum tensor near an evaporating black hole, *Physical Review D* **13**, 2720 (1976).
24. S. M. Christensen and S. A. Fulling, Trace anomalies and the hawking effect, *Physical Review D* **15**, 2088 (1977).
25. R. Balbinot and A. Barletta, The back reaction and the evolution of quantum black holes, *Classical and Quantum Gravity* **6**, 195 (1989).
26. F. Canfora and G. Vilasi, Trace anomaly and black holes evaporation (2003), arXiv:gr-qc/0302036.
27. E. A. Kontou and K. Sanders, Energy conditions in general relativity and quantum field theory, *Classical and Quantum Gravity* **37**, p. 193001 (2020).

On decay of the false Unruh vacuum

A. Shkerin

William I. Fine Theoretical Physics Institute, School of Physics and Astronomy,
University of Minnesota, Minneapolis, MN 55455, USA
E-mail: ashkerin@umn.edu

We provide a method to calculate the rate of false vacuum decay induced by a black hole. The method uses complex tunneling solutions and consistently takes into account the structure of quantum vacuum in the black hole metric via boundary conditions. We illustrate the technique by computing the rate of decay of the Unruh vacuum in a toy two-dimensional model of a scalar field with inverted Liouville potential in a background of a dilaton black hole.

Keywords: Black holes; false vacuum decay; Unruh vacuum; quantum fields and gravity

1. Introduction and motivation

There has been significant interest recently in the problem of black hole catalysis of vacuum decay.[1–15] A part of the motivation driving these studies comes from the fact that the Standard Model electroweak vacuum may not be absolutely stable.[16–22] Requiring the lifetime of the vacuum exceed the age of the Universe puts constraints on the parameters of the Standard Model, of its possible extensions, and of systems and environments which catalyze vacuum decay, including black holes.[23]

The catalyzing effect of a black hole (BH) is two-fold. First, it is a local spacetime inhomogeneity. Hence, as for any impurity, one expects for the BH to facilitate nucleation of bubbles of true vacuum in its vicinity. Second, associated with BHs is the quantum vacuum effect manifesting itself as Hawking radiation. As any field excitation, this radiation is expected to increase the decay rate. For small enough BHs, the catalyzing effects due to curved geometry and quantum vacuum may be equally important.

In the semiclassical regime, the vacuum decay is described by a (complex) classical solution of field equations. The solution — bounce — saturates the amplitude of transition from the false to the true vacuum regions. It is important to note that the vacuum is defined not only by classical field expectation values but also by the state of quantum fluctuations around these values. Different false vacuum states reveal themselves through different boundary conditions imposed on the bounce.

It is well-known how to look for the bounce solution in equilibrium systems.[24–27] Realistic BHs, however, are not in thermal equilibrium with their environment. In particular, this is true for hypothetical small primordial BHs that could exist in the early Universe but are completely evaporated by now.[28] It is desirable to have an approach to vacuum decay that can handle such non-equilibrium systems as a hot isolated BH in a comparatively low energy background. This system is described by the Unruh state.[29] In the Unruh vacuum, the BH emits Hawking radiation but does not receive anything from asymptotic infinity.

In this report, based on Ref. 30, we outline the recent progress made in the study of BH catalysis of false vacuum decay. In Sec. 2 we provide a general method to calculate the decay probability of a false vacuum state characterized by an arbitrary (Gaussian) density matrix. The method employs complex tunneling solutions and, when applied to a BH, allows one to discriminate between different vacuum states associated with the BH. In particular, it allows one to compute the rate of decay of the Unruh vacuum for which equilibrium methods are not applicable. In Sec. 3 we discuss the application of the method to a toy two-dimensional model of vacuum decay in the presence of a BH. Sec. 4 is dedicated to conclusions and outlook.

2. The method

To illustrate the method, we consider a real scalar field in the background of a dilaton BH in two dimensions.[31] The only region that is relevant for vacuum decay is the external (physical) patch of the BH spacetime.[30] It is convenient to introduce tortoise coordinates (t, x) covering this patch. Then the metric is read off from the line element

$$ds^2 = \Omega(x)(-dt^2 + dx^2) , \tag{1}$$

where the conformal factor takes the form

$$\Omega(x) = \frac{1}{1 + e^{-2\lambda x}} . \tag{2}$$

The parameter λ is related to the BH temperature T_{BH} as $\lambda = 2\pi T_{\text{BH}}$. For the sake of brevity, we will refer to λ itself as temperature. The horizon is located at $x \to -\infty$. Near the horizon, the conformal factor behaves as $\Omega(x) \approx e^{2\lambda x}$ and the metric (1) is approximately the Rindler one.[32] The physical size of the near-horizon region is

$$l_h \sim \int_{-\infty}^{0} dx\sqrt{\Omega} \sim \frac{1}{\lambda} . \tag{3}$$

In the opposite limit, $x \to \infty$, the metric is asymptotically flat. The vacuum boundary conditions are imposed in the remote past, $t \to -\infty$, on both sides of the physical patch, $x \to \pm\infty$.

Next, we take the following scalar field action

$$S = \frac{1}{\text{g}^2} \int d^2x \sqrt{-g} \left(-\frac{1}{2} g^{\mu\nu} \partial_\mu \varphi \partial_\nu \varphi - \frac{m^2 \varphi^2}{2} - V_{\text{int}}(\varphi) \right) . \tag{4}$$

Here $V_{\text{int}}(\varphi)$ is the interaction part of the tunneling potential chosen such that the false vacuum is located at $\varphi = 0$, and $V_{\text{int}}(0) = 0$. For convenience, we factored out the small coupling constant g that controls the semiclassical expansion. In the

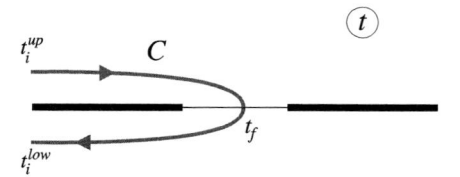

Fig. 1. Contour C in the complex time plane for the calculation of the vacuum decay probability. Black lines denote the branch-point singularities of the bounce in a theory with scalar potential unbounded from below.

background specified by eqs. (1) and (2), the action (4) becomes

$$S = \frac{1}{g^2} \int dt dx \left(-\frac{1}{2}\eta^{\mu\nu}\partial_\mu\varphi\partial_\nu\varphi - \frac{1}{2}\Omega m^2\varphi^2 - \Omega V_{\text{int}}(\varphi) \right) , \qquad (5)$$

where $\eta^{\mu\nu} = \text{diag}(-1, 1)$ is the Minkowski metric. We see that the dependence on the background is contained entirely in the (position-dependent) potential of the field φ.

Let us study linear perturbations around the false vacuum $\varphi = 0$. To this end, we neglect the self-interaction part of the potential V_{int}, and decompose φ using a complete set of positive- and negative-frequency modes:

$$\varphi_\omega^+(t,x) = f_\omega(x) e^{-i\omega t} , \quad \varphi_\omega^-(t,x) = f_\omega^*(x) e^{i\omega t} , \quad \omega > 0 . \qquad (6)$$

The equation for f_ω follows from the linearized field equation for φ and reads

$$-f_\omega'' + U_{\text{eff}}(x) f_\omega = \omega^2 f_\omega , \qquad (7)$$

where prime denotes derivative with respect to x. This is the Schrödinger equation with the potential

$$U_{\text{eff}}(x) = m^2 \Omega . \qquad (8)$$

Next, we turn to the construction of the bounce solution. Bounce φ_b is a regular solution of fields equations that saturates the transition amplitude from the false vacuum initial state to the basin of attraction of true vacuum. In our case, the field equation of motion is

$$\Box\varphi - U_{\text{eff}}(x)\varphi - \Omega V_{\text{int}}'(\varphi) = 0 . \qquad (9)$$

The bounce lives on a contour C in the complex time plane. The contour runs from the initial moment of time in the asymptotic past, $t = t_i^{up}$, as shown in Fig. 1, to the final moment $t = t_f$ and back to the asymptotic past, $t = t_i^{low}$. The contour must bypass singularities of the bounce. Assuming that the bounce is unique, its values on the upper and lower sides of the contour are complex conjugated, hence at $t = t_f$ it is real and can be analytically continued along the real time axis where it describes the evolution of the field after tunneling.

In the limits $t \to t_i^{up}$ and $t \to t_i^{low}$ the bounce must satisfy boundary conditions imposed by the false vacuum state. These boundary conditions turn out to be the same as for the time-ordered Green's function in the corresponding vacuum X.[30] The latter is defined as a time-ordered average of the field operators $\hat{\varphi}$ in the state X,

$$\mathcal{G}_X(t,x;t',x') = {}_X\langle T(\hat{\varphi}(t,x)\hat{\varphi}(t',x'))\rangle_X \ . \tag{10}$$

In turn, the field operator is composed out of the complete set of modes (6) in the standard way.[33]

A Green's function $\mathcal{G}$ satisfies the equation

$$(\Box - U_{\text{eff}}(x))\,\mathcal{G}(t,x;t',x') = i\delta(t-t')\delta(x-x') \ . \tag{11}$$

Using eq. (11), the field equation (9) can be recast into the integral form. To select a particular solution—bounce—of the integral equation, one should, first, adopt the time-integration contour C in the complex time plane and, second, choose a particular Green's function $\mathcal{G}_X$. Thus, we arrive at

$$\varphi_b(t,x) = -i \int_C dt' \int_{-\infty}^{\infty} dx' \mathcal{G}_X(t,x;t',x')\Omega(x')V'_{\text{int}}(\varphi_b(t',x')) \ . \tag{12}$$

This form of the bounce equation will be useful in what follows.

Finally, let us discuss the tunneling rate Γ. The latter is defined as the probability of tunneling per unit time. We are interested in the main exponential dependence and write

$$\Gamma \sim e^{-B} \ . \tag{13}$$

Up to boundary terms, the coefficient B equals the imaginary part of the bounce action computed along the contour C. One can show that[30]

$$B = -\frac{i}{g^2} \int_C dt \int_{-\infty}^{\infty} dx \left(\frac{1}{2}\varphi_b V'_{\text{int}}(\varphi_b) - V_{\text{int}}(\varphi_b)\right) \ . \tag{14}$$

3. The toy model

3.1. *Tunneling in flat spacetime*

In general, solving eq. (12) (or eq. (9) on the contour C with the vacuum boundary conditions) requires a numerical procedure. A big simplification of the problem happens in theories where the nonlinear core of the bounce, where it probes the true vacuum region, is much smaller in size than the Compton wavelength of the free field $\propto m^{-1}$. Then the source in the integral (12) is essentially point-like, and the solution outside the core is simply proportional to the Green's function $\mathcal{G}_X$. On the other hand, the core itself can be found in neglecting the mass term in the field equation (9). The full solution is constructed by matching the long-distance asymptotics of the core with the short-distance asymptotics of the Green's function.

To meet the above requirements, we consider the following interaction potential[30]

$$V_{\text{int}}(\varphi) = -2\kappa \left(e^{\varphi} - 1\right) \tag{15}$$

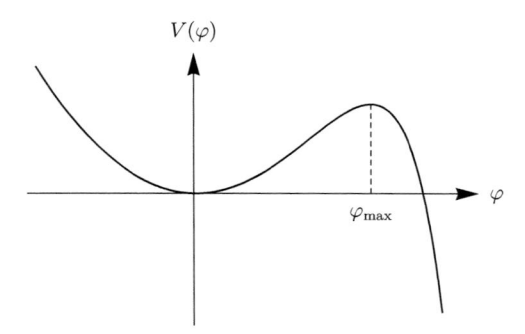

Fig. 2. The scalar field potential.

with $\kappa > 0$. In flat spacetime, the full scalar field potential $V(\varphi) = \frac{1}{2}m^2\varphi^2 + V_{\text{int}}(\varphi)$ is shown in Fig. 2. To ensure the applicability of the split-and-match procedure, the following relation between the parameters is adopted

$$\ln \frac{m}{\sqrt{\kappa}} \gg 1 \,. \tag{16}$$

Thanks to this hierarchy, the theory possesses two intrinsic energy scales: the mass scale m and the scale associated with the potential barrier $m \ln \frac{m}{\sqrt{\kappa}}$. Generally speaking, the first controls the width of the linear tail of the bounce, while the second determines the size of its core. The barrier separating the regions of false and true vacua has its maximum at

$$\varphi_{\max} \approx 2 \ln \frac{m}{\sqrt{\kappa}} \,, \tag{17}$$

where only the leading logarithmic term is taken into account.

To illustrate the matching procedure outlined above, let us discuss bounce in the flat-space Minkowski vacuum. Assume that the only singularities of the bounce are located on the real-time axis. Then, the contour C can be deformed into the contour C' that runs along the Euclidean time axis, see Fig. 3(a) for illustration. The vacuum boundary condition at C, which is provided by the Feynman Green's function, becomes the vanishing boundary condition at C'. Hence, the standard Euclidean approach is reproduced.[24, 25]

To find the core of the bounce, we neglect the mass term in eq. (9) and, using eq. (15), obtain

$$\Box \, \varphi_b |_{\text{core}} + 2\kappa e^{\varphi_b |_{\text{core}}} = 0 \,. \tag{18}$$

This is the Liouville equation, and its general solution is known. Next, the linear tail of the bounce is proportional to the (massive scalar) Feynman Green's function

$$\mathcal{G}_F(-i\tau, x; 0, 0) = \frac{1}{2\pi} K_0 \left(m\sqrt{\tau^2 + x^2 + i\epsilon} \right) \,, \tag{19}$$

where $\tau = it$ is the Euclidean time coordinate and K_0 is the modified Bessel function of the second kind. The core and the tail are matched in the region where, on the

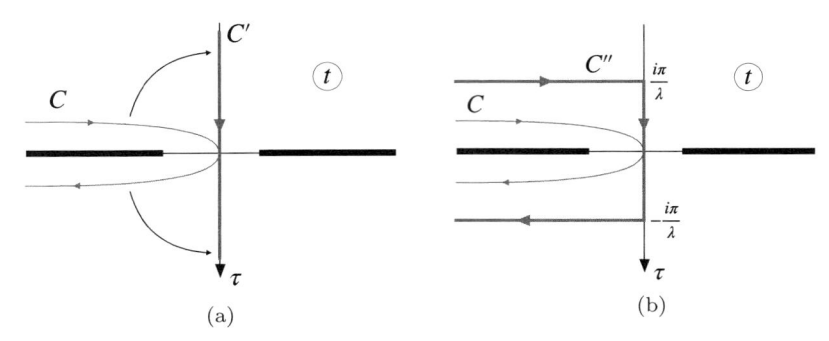

Fig. 3. (a) Deformation of the contour C into the Euclidean time contour C' used for the calculation of the flat-space Minkowski bounce. Black lines denote singularities of the bounce. (b) Deformation of C into C'' containing the Euclidean time segment which is used for the calculation of the Unruh bounce.

one hand, the solution to the Liouville equation is linearized and, on the other hand, the Green's function is approximated by its short-distance asymptotics. We obtain

$$\varphi_\text{b}|_\text{core} = \ln\left[\frac{4C_M^2}{(1+\kappa C_M^2(\tau^2+x^2))^2}\right] \tag{20}$$

$$\varphi_\text{b}|_\text{tail} = 8\pi\mathcal{G}_\text{F}(-i\tau,x;0,0) , \tag{21}$$

where $C_M = m^2 e^{2\gamma_E}/(2\kappa)$ and γ_E is the Euler constant. The matching region is defined by $(C_M\sqrt{\kappa})^{-1} \ll \sqrt{\tau^2+x^2} \ll m^{-1}$. Its existence is ensured by eq. (16). We see that the bounce is real for real τ, vanishes at infinity and has zero time derivative at $\tau = 0$. Hence, it is a valid tunneling solution. Moreover, it has no singularities apart from the ones on the real-time axis, which justifies the deformation of the contour C into C'.

The tunneling suppression is given by eq. (14) where one should substitute the core of the bounce (20). To the leading-log approximation, this gives

$$B_M = \frac{16\pi}{g^2}\ln\frac{m}{\sqrt{\kappa}} . \tag{22}$$

We observe that the suppression is enhanced by the large logarithm.

In the BH background (2), the linearized field equation (7) is still exactly solvable, and this allows us to compute explicitly the Green's functions of interest. The solvability of the equation for the core of the bounce is lost, but can be recovered in the two regions: near the horizon where the metric is approximately the Rindler one, and far away from the BH where the spacetime is asymptotically flat. From eq. (2) we see that the two regions are defined by $x < 0$, $|x| \gg \lambda^{-1}$ and $x > 0$, $|x| \gg \lambda^{-1}$, respectively. Although we do not have the explicit bounce solution in the transition region $|x| \lesssim \lambda^{-1}$, we will still be able to draw a qualitative picture of the evolution of the bounce across this region.

3.2. Decay of the Unruh vacuum near horizon

As discussed in introduction, the Unruh vacuum corresponds to a flux of thermal radiation propagating from the BH, whose spectrum is regularized by the m^2-asymptotics of the mode potential (8). In the absence of area growth in one spatial dimension, the flux enhances the vacuum decay rate at any distance from the BH. In the near-horizon region, the decay rate is additionally enhanced due to the accumulation of field excitations and curved geometry. Let us discuss the near-horizon case first.

To find the Unruh bounce in the BH vicinity, we have to integrate eq. (9) with $\Omega = e^{2\lambda x}$ along the contour C shown in Fig. 1 and satisfy the boundary condition imposed by the Unruh vacuum. The contour, in fact, can be deformed partially to the Euclidean time domain, as shown in Fig. 3(b). In the core region of the bounce the field equation reduces to

$$\Box \, \varphi_b|_{\text{core}} + 2\kappa e^{2\lambda x + \varphi_b|_{\text{core}}} = 0 \, . \tag{23}$$

This again admits a general solution. The tail of the bounce is determined by the time-ordered Unruh Green's function $\mathcal{G}_U$ computed in the BH vicinity. Overall, we write

$$\varphi_b|_{\text{core}} = \ln \left[\frac{4\lambda^2 b_{U1}}{\kappa \left(-2\lambda(v - v_1) \sinh\left(\frac{\lambda}{2}(u - u_1)\right) + b_{U1} e^{\frac{\lambda}{2}(u - u_1)} \right)^2} \right] - 2\lambda x \tag{24}$$

$$\varphi_b|_{\text{tail}} = 8\pi \mathcal{G}_U(t, x; 0, x_1) \, . \tag{25}$$

Here we defined $u = t - x$, $v = t + x$, and $u_1 = t - x_1$, $v_1 = t + x_1$. The parameter x_1 determines the position of the center of the bounce[a] and b_{U1} is found from matching the core and the tail. The expression for the Unruh Green's function at $m|x - x_1| \ll 1$ is given by eq. (A.2) from the appendix. Using it, we get

$$b_{U1} = \bar{b}_{U1} e^{-2\lambda x_1} \, , \qquad \bar{b}_{U1} = \frac{\kappa}{m^2} e^{\frac{32\lambda}{3\pi m} - 2\gamma_E - \frac{3}{2}} \, , \tag{26}$$

where we additionally assumed $\lambda \gg m$. We obtain a one-parameter family of solutions parametrized by x_1. This is an artefact of our approximation of the near-horizon geometry by the Rindler spacetime. Upon taking into account BH corrections to the Rindler metric, a unique tunneling solution is selected.

The bounce (24), (25) is real on the real-time axis and describes the tun-away toward the true vacuum $\varphi \to +\infty$ at positive time. Hence, it is a valid tunneling solution.

Investigating the applicability of the matching procedure, one arrives at the following condition[30]

$$\bar{b}_{U1} \lesssim 1 \, . \tag{27}$$

---

[a]We used the time translational invariance of the theory to put the center of the bounce at $t = 0$.

This inequality translates into the upper bound on the BH temperature, $\lambda \lesssim \lambda_{U1}$, where to the leading-log accuracy

$$\lambda_{U1} = \frac{3\pi m}{16} \ln \frac{m}{\sqrt{\kappa}} \,. \tag{28}$$

At $\lambda > \lambda_{U1}$, the bound (27) is violated and the matching procedure breaks down. This can be given a physical interpretation: at $\lambda \simeq \lambda_{U1}$ the nonlinear core of the bounce stops fitting the near-horizon region, as its physical size exceeds l_h, see eq. (3). The subsequent evolution of the bounce happens outside the BH vicinity, and we will discuss it below.

To compute the exponential suppression of the decay rate, we use the general expression (14) with the contour C'' depicted in Fig. 3(b). The result is[30]

$$B_{U1} = \frac{16\pi}{g^2} \left(\ln \sqrt{\frac{\lambda m}{\kappa}} - \frac{8\lambda}{3\pi m} \right) \,, \quad \lambda \lesssim \lambda_{U1} \,, \tag{29}$$

where for the sake of simplicity we omitted the order-one terms in the parentheses. We see that the suppression decreases with the BH temperature and becomes approximately half of the vacuum suppression at $\lambda \approx \lambda_{U1}$.

3.3. Decay of the Unruh vacuum away from the black hole

Far from the BH, the vacuum decay proceeds in the flat spacetime, and the only difference between the Unruh and Minkowski vacua is the presence of out-of-equilibrium field excitations. The question of how such excitations catalyze vacuum decay is interesting by itself.

Solving eq. (18) on the contour C'' and matching with the Unruh Green's function in the corresponding region, we arrive at the following solution

$$\varphi_b|_{\text{core}} = \ln \left[\frac{4\lambda^2 b_{U2}}{\kappa \left(-2\lambda(v-v_2) \sinh\left(\frac{\lambda}{2}(u-u_2)\right) + b_{U1} e^{\frac{\lambda}{2}(u-u_2)} \right)^2} \right] \tag{30}$$

$$\varphi_b|_{\text{tail}} = 8\pi \mathcal{G}_U(t, x; 0, x_2) \,, \tag{31}$$

where we denoted $u_2 = t - x_2$, $v_2 = t + x_2$, and the expression for $\mathcal{G}_U$ in the limit $|x - x_2| \ll m^{-1}$ and $\lambda \gg m$ is given in eq. (A.3) from the appendix. The parameter b_{U2} is found upon matching the core and the tail of the bounce and equals

$$b_{U2} = \frac{\kappa}{m^2} e^{\frac{8\lambda}{3\pi m} - 2\gamma_E + \frac{1}{2}} \,. \tag{32}$$

Similarly to the case studied above, one can take

$$b_{U2} \lesssim 1 \tag{33}$$

as a conservative condition for the validity of the bounce solution (30), (31). The bound (33) translates into the condition $\lambda \lesssim \lambda_{U2}$, where, to the leading-log accuracy,

$$\lambda_{U2} = \frac{3\pi m}{4} \ln \frac{m}{\sqrt{\kappa}} \,. \tag{34}$$

Finally, for the exponential suppression of the decay rate we get

$$B_{U2} = \frac{16\pi}{g^2}\left(\ln\sqrt{\frac{\lambda m}{\kappa}} - \frac{2\lambda}{3\pi m}\right), \qquad \lambda \lesssim \lambda_{U2}. \tag{35}$$

We see that the coefficient in the linear in λ term is smaller than in eq. (29). Thus, the tunneling far from the horizon is more suppressed, as expected. Again, the suppression becomes half of the flat space one when the critical temperature is reached.

What happens with the decay rate at $\lambda > \lambda_{U2}$? We could not find the relevant tunneling solution in this regime. Therefore, let us proceed with a different method. At $\lambda \gg m$, the dominant contribution to the Unruh Green's function comes from the modes with $\omega \sim m$. The occupation number of modes of the dominant frequency is large, being enhanced by λ/m. Hence, the flux of particles in the Unruh state is essentially classical. It is these modes that are relevant for vacuum decay. Therefore, the vacuum decay probability can be estimated as the probability of the classical field fluctuation to reach beyond the maximum of the potential barrier at $\varphi = \varphi_{\max}$, see eq. (17) and Fig. 2. To find the variance of classical fluctuations $(\delta\varphi)_U^2$, we take the Unruh Green's function at coincident points, upon renormalizing it by subtraction of the Green's function in empty space,

$$(\delta\varphi)_U^2 = g^2 \lim_{t,x\to 0}\left[\mathcal{G}_U(t,x;0,0) - \mathcal{G}_F(t,x;0,0)\right]. \tag{36}$$

Since the interaction quickly dies out at $\varphi < \varphi_{\max}$, one can take the field fluctuations to be Gaussian. Then we obtain the following estimation of the decay rate due to classical field fluctuations

$$\Gamma_{U2,\text{high}-\lambda} \sim \exp\left(-\frac{\varphi_{\max}^2}{2(\delta\varphi)_U^2}\right) \sim \exp\left(-\frac{6\pi^2 m}{g^2\lambda}\left(\ln\frac{m}{\sqrt{\kappa}}\right)^2\right). \tag{37}$$

As a consistency check, at $\lambda \approx \lambda_{U2}$ the stochastic estimate coincides with the bounce suppression (35) in the leading-log approximation.

Finally, let us go back to the near-horizon tunneling channel and see what happens with the decay rate after the critical temperature (28) is reached. At this point we can use again the stochastic estimate. We use the expression for the Unruh Green's function (A.3) to the right side from the barrier but not far from it and obtain

$$\Gamma_{U1,\text{high}-\lambda} \sim \exp\left(-\frac{3\pi^2 m}{2g^2\lambda}\left(\ln\frac{m}{\sqrt{\kappa}}\right)^2\right). \tag{38}$$

We observe that in the leading-log approximation the suppression is continuous across the transition from the low- to high-temperature regime.

4. Conclusions and outlook

In this report we discussed the method to compute the rate of decay of the false Unruh vacuum. We applied the method to a toy model of a real scalar field in

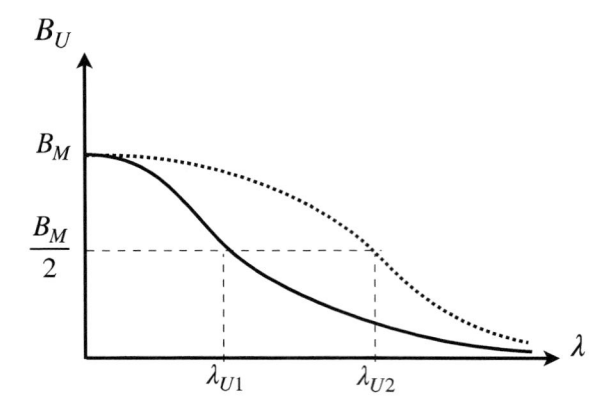

Fig. 4. Suppression of the Unruh vacuum decay as a function of BH temperature. The solid line represents the decay channel in the BH vicinity, and the dotted line shows the decay channel far from the BH. B_M, λ_{U1} and λ_{U2} are given in eqs. (22), (28) and (34), respectively.

the background of a dilaton BH in two dimensions. The results are summarized in Fig. 4. We see, in particular, that the decay channel far from the BH is suppressed as compared to the one close to the BH. This is in agreement with expectations. We also see that at high BH temperature the decay becomes unsuppressed.

Let us discuss to what extent our results are generalized to a realistic case such as a Schwarzschild BH in four dimensions. One should understand which features of the four-dimensional geometry are captured by the toy model in two dimensions, and which are not. For this, we can limit our discussion to the linear part of the theory. This is reasonable, since, as discussed above, properties of linear modes (or, more precisely, of Green's functions) are crucial for finding vacuum boundary conditions and, eventually, the decay rate. Then, one can readily compare the linear sector of the toy model with that of the spherical reduction of the free four-dimensional theory. More precisely, we can compare the greybody factors for linear perturbations. The four-dimensional greybody factor includes the barrier whose height depends on the size of the BH (and on its temperature). There is no such barrier in two dimensions. Its presence in four dimensions can change the results concerning the Unruh vacuum decay at high temperatures. Indeed, the barrier reduces the flux of Hawking radiation far from the BH and promotes the accumulation of Hawking quanta in the near-horizon region. In principle, our method allows us to take this effect into account, and we leave this study for future work.

Next, we found that the Unruh bounce does not exist above the certain temperature, both in the BH vicinity and in the asymptotically-flat region. Here, the situation is similar to the decay from a state in thermal equilibrium. It is known that a finite-temperature periodic instanton, which describes tunneling from such a state, yields to a static configuration—sphaleron—once the temperature exceeds a critical value.[34] The sphaleron corresponds to classical thermal jumps of the field over the barrier separating the false and true vacua. One can expect that in the case of Unruh vacuum a similar transition happens. We could not find the analog of sphaleron in the Unruh state analytically. However, thanks to the properties of our model, we were able to use the simple stochastic estimate and compute the decay rate above the critical temperature. Let us reiterate that the validity of the estimate relies on the two facts. First, (almost) any relevant for decay field fluctuation is Gaussian, as it follows from the scalar field potential. Second, the field excitations of relevant frequency, $\omega \sim m$, have large occupation numbers and, hence, can be treated as classical. In more general situations, the stochastic approach to vacuum decay can still be applicable, but would require a full-fledged numerical simulation. We also leave this for future work.

Acknowledgments

The author thanks S. Sibiryakov for useful discussions. The work was partially supported by the Department of Energy Grant DE-SC0011842.

Appendix A. Unruh Green's function

Here we quote the expressions for the (massive scalar) Unruh Green's function in two dimensions. We focus on the two regions: the near-horizon one ("left"), defined by the condition $x, x' < 0$, $|x|, |x'| \gg \lambda^{-1}$, and the asymptotically-flat one ("right"), determined by $x, x' > 0$, $|x|, |x'| \gg \lambda^{-1}$. Given that the metric (1) is static, we can set $t' = 0$ in the Green's function. Next, we consider the limit

$$|x - x'| \ll m^{-1}, \qquad |t| \ll m^{-1}. \tag{A.1}$$

Under these assumptions, the Unruh Green's function reads as follows[30]

$$\mathcal{G}_U(t, x; 0, x')|_{\text{left}} = -\frac{1}{4\pi} \ln\left[2\sinh\left(\frac{\lambda}{2}(x - x' - t)\right) m(x - x' + t) + i\epsilon\right]$$
$$- \frac{\lambda(x + x')}{4\pi} + \frac{4\lambda}{3\pi^2 m} + \frac{\ln 2 - \gamma_E}{4\pi} - \frac{3}{16\pi} \tag{A.2}$$

and

$$\mathcal{G}_U(t, x; 0, x')|_{\text{right}} = -\frac{1}{4\pi} \ln\left[2\sinh\left(\frac{\lambda}{2}(x - x' - t)\right) m(x - x' + t) + i\epsilon\right]$$
$$+ \begin{cases} -\frac{\lambda}{4\pi}(x + x') + \frac{4\lambda}{3\pi^2 m} + \frac{\ln 2 - \gamma_E}{4\pi} - \frac{3}{16\pi}, & x + x' \ll m^{-1} \\ \frac{\lambda}{3\pi^2 m} + \frac{\ln 2 - \gamma_E}{4\pi} + \frac{1}{16\pi}, & x + x' \gg m^{-1} \end{cases} \tag{A.3}$$

References

1. W. A. Hiscock, Can black holes nucleate vacuum phase transitions?, *Phys. Rev.* **D35**, 1161 (1987).

2. V. A. Berezin, V. A. Kuzmin and I. I. Tkachev, O(3) Invariant Tunneling in General Relativity, *Phys. Lett.* **B207**, 397 (1988).
3. P. B. Arnold, Gravity and false vacuum decay rates: O(3) solutions, *Nucl. Phys.* **B346**, 160 (1990).
4. V. A. Berezin, V. A. Kuzmin and I. I. Tkachev, Black holes initiate false vacuum decay, *Phys. Rev.* **D43**, 3112 (1991).
5. R. Gregory, I. G. Moss and B. Withers, Black holes as bubble nucleation sites, *JHEP* **03**, p. 081 (2014).
6. P. Burda, R. Gregory and I. Moss, Gravity and the stability of the Higgs vacuum, *Phys. Rev. Lett.* **115**, p. 071303 (2015).
7. P. Burda, R. Gregory and I. Moss, Vacuum metastability with black holes, *JHEP* **08**, p. 114 (2015).
8. P. Burda, R. Gregory and I. Moss, The fate of the Higgs vacuum, *JHEP* **06**, p. 025 (2016).
9. N. Tetradis, Black holes and Higgs stability, *JCAP* **1609**, p. 036 (2016).
10. D. Canko, I. Gialamas, G. Jelic-Cizmek, A. Riotto and N. Tetradis, On the Catalysis of the Electroweak Vacuum Decay by Black Holes at High Temperature, *Eur. Phys. J.* **C78**, p. 328 (2018).
11. D. Gorbunov, D. Levkov and A. Panin, Fatal youth of the Universe: Black hole threat for the electroweak vacuum during preheating, *JCAP* **1710**, p. 016 (2017).
12. K. Mukaida and M. Yamada, False Vacuum Decay Catalyzed by Black Holes, *Phys. Rev.* **D96**, p. 103514 (2017).
13. K. Kohri and H. Matsui, Electroweak Vacuum Collapse induced by Vacuum Fluctuations of the Higgs Field around Evaporating Black Holes, *Phys. Rev.* **D98**, p. 123509 (2018).
14. T. Hayashi, K. Kamada, N. Oshita and J. Yokoyama, On catalyzed vacuum decay around a radiating black hole and the crisis of the electroweak vacuum, *JHEP* **08**, p. 088 (2020).
15. T. Miyachi and J. Soda, False vacuum decay in a two-dimensional black hole spacetime, *Phys. Rev. D* **103**, p. 085009 (2021).
16. R. A. Flores and M. Sher, Upper Limits to Fermion Masses in the Glashow-Weinberg-Salam Model, *Phys. Rev. D* **27**, p. 1679 (1983).
17. M. Sher, Electroweak Higgs Potentials and Vacuum Stability, *Phys. Rept.* **179**, 273 (1989).
18. G. Isidori, G. Ridolfi and A. Strumia, On the metastability of the standard model vacuum, *Nucl. Phys. B* **609**, 387 (2001).
19. F. Bezrukov, M. Yu. Kalmykov, B. A. Kniehl and M. Shaposhnikov, Higgs Boson Mass and New Physics, *JHEP* **10**, p. 140 (2012).
20. G. Degrassi, S. Di Vita, J. Elias-Miro, J. R. Espinosa, G. F. Giudice, G. Isidori and A. Strumia, Higgs mass and vacuum stability in the Standard Model at NNLO, *JHEP* **08**, p. 098 (2012).
21. D. Buttazzo, G. Degrassi, P. P. Giardino, G. F. Giudice, F. Sala, A. Salvio and A. Strumia, Investigating the near-criticality of the Higgs boson, *JHEP* **12**, p. 089 (2013).
22. A. V. Bednyakov, B. A. Kniehl, A. F. Pikelner and O. L. Veretin, Stability of the Electroweak Vacuum: Gauge Independence and Advanced Precision, *Phys. Rev. Lett.* **115**, p. 201802 (2015).
23. T. Markkanen, A. Rajantie and S. Stopyra, Cosmological Aspects of Higgs Vacuum Metastability, *Front. Astron. Space Sci.* **5**, p. 40 (2018).
24. S. R. Coleman, The Fate of the False Vacuum. 1. Semiclassical Theory, *Phys. Rev.* **D15**, 2929 (1977), [Erratum: Phys. Rev. D16, 1248 (1977)].

25. C. G. Callan, Jr. and S. R. Coleman, The Fate of the False Vacuum. 2. First Quantum Corrections, *Phys. Rev.* **D16**, 1762 (1977).
26. S. R. Coleman, The Uses of Instantons, *Subnucl. Ser.* **15**, p. 805 (1979).
27. S. R. Coleman and F. De Luccia, Gravitational Effects on and of Vacuum Decay, *Phys. Rev.* **D21**, p. 3305 (1980).
28. B. Carr, K. Kohri, Y. Sendouda and J. Yokoyama, Constraints on Primordial Black Holes (2020).
29. W. G. Unruh, Notes on black hole evaporation, *Phys. Rev.* **D14**, p. 870 (1976).
30. A. Shkerin and S. Sibiryakov, Black hole induced false vacuum decay from first principles (5 2021).
31. C. G. Callan, Jr., S. B. Giddings, J. A. Harvey and A. Strominger, Evanescent black holes, *Phys. Rev.* **D45**, p. R1005 (1992).
32. W.-Y. Ai, Correspondence between Thermal and Quantum Vacuum Transitions around Horizons, *JHEP* **03**, p. 164 (2019).
33. N. D. Birrell and P. C. W. Davies, *Quantum Fields in Curved Space*, Cambridge Monographs on Mathematical Physics (Cambridge Univ. Press, Cambridge, UK, 1984).
34. A. D. Linde, Decay of the False Vacuum at Finite Temperature, *Nucl. Phys. B* **216**, p. 421 (1983), [Erratum: Nucl. Phys. B 223, 544 (1983)].

Behaviour of noise kernel in de Sitter and FRW space-times

Ankit Dhanuka* and Kinjalk Lochan[†]

Department of Physical Sciences,
Indian Institute of Science Education & Research (IISER)
Mohali, Sector 81 SAS Nagar, Manauli PO 140306 Punjab India
*E-mail: ph17006@iisermohali.ac.in
[†]E-mail: kinjalk@iisermohali.ac.in

Validity of the results of semiclassical analysis relies upon the assumption that the 2nd order or higher order corrections are negligible compared to 1st order semiclassical results which are based only on expectation values of operators. However, if the quantum fluctuations are large, then one may need to supplement semiclassical analysis with corrections coming from second order calculations. In the stochastic gravity paradigm, these fluctuations are quantified by noise kernel which are then supposed to act as a source of geometric fluctuations. In this work, we study the behaviour of noise kernel for a scalar field in de Sitter spacetime. We also carry out a similar analysis for some other FRW spacetimes invoking an equivalence that exists between scalar fields in de Sitter and FRW spacetimes.

Keywords: Stochastic gravity, Noise kernel etc.

1. Introduction

In semiclassical approach, we take matter fields to be quantum fields evolving over the classical geometry of a spacetime.[1] However, in this approach, we consider only the 1st order effects, for example, we replace classical stress energy tensor in Einstein's equations by the expectation value of the corresponding operator w.r.t. some quantum state in which the matter field is supposed to be. Now, conclusions drawn on the basis of such an analysis always rely on the implicit assumption that the 2nd or higher order quantum effects are relatively small and will not significantly affect the 1st order results. Though, in situations where higher order effects are appreciable, one may need to revisit the conclusions made on the basis of these 1st order calculations and may have to supplement them with 2nd or higher order calculations. For these considerations, one may resort to stochastic gravity[2,3] paradigm where one tries to incorporate the effects of quantum fluctuations, inherent in quantum matter fields, on the dynamics of classical background. These quantum fluctuations are quantified by what is called noise kernel which is given as follows:

$$N_{abcd} = \frac{1}{8}\{\hat{t}_{ab}, \hat{t}_{cd}\}, = \frac{1}{8}(\langle \hat{t}_{abcd}(x,x')\rangle + \langle \hat{t}_{cdab}(x,x')\rangle) \tag{1}$$

where $\hat{t}_{ab} = \hat{T}_{ab} - \langle \hat{T}_{ab} \rangle$, and

$$\langle \hat{t}_{abcd}(x,x') \rangle \equiv \langle \hat{t}_{ab}(x) \hat{t}_{cd}(x') \rangle$$
$$= \langle 0|\hat{T}_{ab}(x)\hat{T}_{cd}(x')|0\rangle - \langle 0|\hat{T}_{ab}(x)|0\rangle \langle 0|\hat{T}_{cd}(x')|0\rangle . \quad (2)$$

Stress energy quantum operator, $\hat{T}_{ab}$, is obtained by replacing classical fields by their quantum counterparts and the classical expression for stress energy tensor is obtained by taking the metric variation of the matter action, more precisely, $T_{ab}(x) = -\frac{2}{\sqrt{-g}} \frac{\delta S_M}{\delta g^{ab}(x)}$.

In this work, we are interested in studying the behaviour of noise kernel for scalar fields in a wide class of FRW spacetimes.[4,5] The line element for a general FRW spacetime is given by

$$ds^2 = a^2(\eta)(-d\eta^2 + d\vec{x}^2), \quad (3)$$

where the scale factor, $a(\eta)$, characterizes that spacetime. In particular, we are interested in de Sitter spacetime, with $a(\eta) = \frac{-1}{H\eta}$. de Sitter spacetime is a maximally symmetric spacetime and present day observations[6] suggest that the early universe went through a period of nearly de Sitter phase. Similarly, universe is also believed to have undergone through other FRW type periods/epochs. Therefore, studying these second order quantum effects in FRW settings is an important cosmological task and may be helpful in better understand the cosmological data. We make use of an equivalence that exists between scalar fields in de Sitter and FRW spacetimes, to study the noise kernel in FRW spacetimes in terms of the noise kernel in de Sitter spacetime. Equally important is the study of backreaction of the noise kernel on the classical geometry of spacetime, though in the present work, we largely ignore this aspect of the analysis.

2. Point-Splitting technique and Bunch Davies vacuum

Let's consider a minimally coupled massive scalar field in general space-time metric i.e.,

$$S[g_{\alpha\beta}, \phi] = -\frac{1}{2} \int d\eta d^3\vec{x} \sqrt{-g} \left(g^{\alpha\beta} \nabla_\alpha \phi \nabla_\beta \phi + m^2 \phi^2 \right). \quad (4)$$

We find that its stress energy operator is given by:

$$T_{\alpha\beta}(x) = \nabla_\alpha \phi \nabla_\beta \phi - \frac{1}{2} g_{\alpha\beta}(g^{\gamma\delta} \nabla_\gamma \phi \nabla_\delta \phi + m^2 \phi^2). \quad (5)$$

One can write the above stress energy expression in the following point-split form[7]

$$T_{ab}(x) = \lim_{y \to x} P_{ab}(x,y)\phi(x)\phi(y), \qquad (6)$$

where

$$P_{ab}(x,y) = \left(\delta^c_{(a}\delta^d_{b)} - \frac{1}{2}\left(\frac{g_{ab}(x)+g_{ab}(y)}{2}\right)\left(\frac{g^{cd}(x)+g^{cd}(y)}{2}\right)\right)\nabla^x_c\nabla^y_d$$

$$- \frac{1}{2}\left(\frac{g_{ab}(x)+g_{ab}(y)}{2}\right)m^2. \qquad (7)$$

Now substituting the above point split form in the formula for stress-energy two point correlator w.r.t the vacuum of the field, we find that

$$\langle t_{abcd}(x,x')\rangle = \lim_{\substack{y \to x \\ y' \to x'}} P_{ab}(x,y)P_{cd}(x',y')\langle 0|\phi(x)\phi(y)\phi(x')\phi(y')|0\rangle$$

$$- \lim_{\substack{y \to x \\ y' \to x'}} P_{ab}(x,y)P_{cd}(x',y')\langle 0|\phi(x)\phi(y)|0\rangle\langle 0|\phi(x')\phi(y')|0\rangle. \qquad (8)$$

After some manipulations, this becomes

$$\langle t_{abcd}(x,x')\rangle = 2 \lim_{\substack{y \to x \\ y' \to x'}} P_{ab}(x,y)P_{cd}(x',y')G(x,x')G(y,y'), \qquad (9)$$

where $G(x,x')$ is the Wightman function for the scalar field in the considered vacuum,

$$G(x,x') = \langle 0|\phi(x)\phi(x')|0\rangle. \qquad (10)$$

For de Sitter spacetime, we determine the behaviour of noise kernel for Bunch Davies vacuum[8,9] which is given by

$$G(Z) = (H^2/16\pi^2)\Gamma(a)\Gamma(b)\,_2F_1\left(a,b,2,\frac{1+Z}{2}\right), \qquad (11)$$

where $Z(x,x') = 1 + \frac{(\eta-\eta')^2 - (\vec{x}-\vec{x}')^2}{2\eta\eta'}$ and $a,b = \frac{3}{2} \pm \sqrt{\frac{9}{4} - \frac{m^2}{H^2}}$. We see that the Bunch Davies vacuum depends on the coordinates only through the invariant distance $Z(x,x')$ between them.

3. Noise Kernel in de Sitter universe

Since for de Sitter spacetime, $g_{ab} = \frac{1}{(H\eta)^2}\eta_{ab}$, we find that

$$\langle t_{abcd}(x,x')\rangle_{dS} = \Bigg(\nabla_b\nabla'_c G(x,x')\nabla_a\nabla'_d G(x,x') + \nabla_b\nabla'_d G(x,x')\nabla_a\nabla'_c G(x,x')$$
$$- \eta_{cd}\eta^{\rho\sigma}\nabla_a\nabla'_\rho G(x,x')\nabla_b\nabla'_\sigma G(x,x')$$
$$- \frac{1}{H^2\eta'^2}m^2\eta_{cd}\nabla_a G(x,x')\nabla_b G(x,x')$$
$$- \eta_{ab}\eta^{\gamma\delta}\nabla_\gamma\nabla'_c G(x,x')\nabla_\delta\nabla'_d G(x,x')$$
$$+ \frac{1}{2}\eta_{ab}\eta^{\gamma\delta}\eta_{cd}\eta^{\rho\sigma}\nabla_\gamma\nabla'_\rho G(x,x')\nabla_\delta\nabla'_\sigma G(x,x')$$
$$+ \frac{1}{2H^2\eta'^2}m^2\eta_{ab}\eta^{\gamma\delta}\eta_{cd}\nabla_\gamma G(x,x')\nabla_\delta G(x,x')$$
$$- \frac{1}{H^2\eta^2}m^2\eta_{ab}\nabla'_c G(x,x')\nabla'_d G(x,x')$$
$$+ \frac{1}{2H^2\eta^2}m^2\eta_{ab}\eta_{cd}\eta^{\rho\sigma}\nabla'_\rho G(x,x')\nabla'_\sigma G(x,x')$$
$$+ \frac{1}{2H^4\eta^2\eta'^2}m^4\eta_{ab}\eta_{cd}G(x,x')G(x,x')\Bigg). \quad (12)$$

In order to see whether the primordial fluctuations are significant or not in an expanding universe, we consider constant time sheets i.e., we take $\eta = \eta'$ and look at the behaviour of noise kernel in the limit in which $a(\eta) \to \infty$ i.e., $\eta \to 0$ limit. Therefore, for Bunch Davies vacuum, the $(a = b = c = d = 0)$ component of the stress energy correlator behaves in the following manner[10]:

$$\langle t_{00}(\eta,\vec{x})t_{00}(\eta,\vec{x}')\rangle_{dS}\Big|_{\text{late time}} = \frac{H^4\Gamma^2(\nu)\Gamma^2(\frac{5}{2}-\nu)}{\pi^5}\left[\frac{9\eta^{2-4\nu}}{32(\Delta\vec{x})^{6-4\nu}} + O(\eta^{4-4\nu})\right], \quad (13)$$

where $\nu = \sqrt{\frac{9}{4} - \frac{m^2}{H^2}}$.

From the above expression, we see that the above considered component of stress energy correlator vanishes in the $\eta \to 0$ limit when ν lies between $[0,\frac{1}{2})$ while it diverges in the same limit for ν lying between $(\frac{1}{2},\frac{3}{2}]$. At $\nu = \frac{1}{2}$, it becomes independent of ν and is given by $\frac{9H^4}{32\pi^4(\Delta\vec{x})^4}$. The range for ν is decided by the requirement that the mass of the field, m, cannot take imaginary values. Since energy density at any spacetime point, x, is given by $T_{ab}(x)t^a t^b$, where t^a is tangent vector to a comoving observer at that point, we find that the energy-energy density is given by:

$$\frac{<\hat{T}_{00}(\eta,\vec{x})\hat{T}_{00}(\eta',\vec{x}')>_{dS}}{(a(\eta)a(\eta'))^2}. \quad (14)$$

Using the above formula and the fact that $a(\eta) = -\frac{1}{H\eta}$, we find that the energy-energy correlator vanishes for all values of ν lying between $[0,\frac{3}{2}]$ except at $\frac{3}{2}$ for which it attains a constant value equal to $\frac{9H^4}{128\pi^4}$. One can also extend the above results to include all other components of the stress energy correlator as well as the non-minimal coupling.[10]

4. Noise Kernel for Friedmann spaces

As has already been stated, in order to study the behaviour of noise kernel in FRW spacetimes we make use of an equivalence between scalar fields in de Sitter and FRW spacetimes. So the idea is as follows[11]:

We consider a massless scalar field in a generic FRW universe i.e., $g_{\alpha\beta} = a^2(\eta)\eta_{\alpha\beta}$ with $a(\eta) = (H\eta)^{-q}$, with the action given by

$$S = -\frac{1}{2}\int d^4x\, a^4 \left(a^{-2}\eta^{\alpha\beta}\partial_\alpha\phi\,\partial_\beta\phi\right). \tag{15}$$

Under the transformation, $\phi(x) = (H\eta)^{-1+q}\psi(x)$, the action becomes

$$S = -\frac{1}{2}\int d^4x\, b^4 \left(b^{-2}\eta^{\alpha\beta}\partial_\alpha\psi\,\partial_\beta\psi - m_{eff}^2\psi^2\right), \tag{16}$$

where $b(\eta) = (H\eta)^{-1}$ and $m_{eff}^2 = H^2(1-q)(2+q)$. Therefore, with the above transformation, one can map a massless scalar field in a Friedmann universe with scaling factor, $a(\eta) = (H\eta)^{-q}$, to a massive scalar field in a de Sitter universe. From the relation, $m_{eff}^2 = H^2(1-q)(2+q)$, we conclude that the range $[0, \frac{3}{2}]$ of $\frac{m^2}{H^2}$ gets mapped to q between the range $[-2, 1]$. And since we are interested in the limit of η for which $a(\eta) \to \infty$, we find that, for $q \to [-2, 0]$, the late time limit corresponds to $\eta \to \infty$ while for $q \to [0, 1]$, the late time limit corresponds to $\eta \to 0$. From the above transformation between fields, we see that the Wightman functions in FRW spacetime and de Sitter spacetime are related by $G^{F.R.W.}(x, x') = (H\eta)^{q-1}(H\eta')^{q-1}G^{d.S.}(x, x')$. Using this relation between Wightman functions, we find that the stress energy correlator is given by:

$$\langle t_{00}(\eta, \vec{x}) t_{00}(\eta, \vec{x}')\rangle_{F.R.W.}$$

$$= (H\eta)^{4(q-1)}\Bigg[\frac{G^2}{2\eta^4}(q-1)^4 + GG'\bigg[\frac{(2q^3 - 7q^2 + 8q - 3)(\Delta\vec{x})^2}{2\eta^6} - \frac{(q-1)^2}{\eta^4}\bigg]$$

$$+ GG''\frac{(q-1)^2(\Delta\vec{x})^4}{4\eta^8} + G'G''\bigg[\frac{(q-\frac{3}{2})(\Delta\vec{x})^6}{4\eta^{10}} + \frac{(q-\frac{9}{4})(\Delta\vec{x})^4}{\eta^8} - \frac{(\Delta\vec{x})^2}{\eta^6}\bigg]$$

$$+ (G')^2\bigg[\frac{2}{\eta^4} + \frac{(q^2 - 5q + \frac{11}{2})(\Delta\vec{x})^2}{\eta^6} + \frac{(2q^2 - 6q + \frac{9}{2})(\Delta\vec{x})^4}{4\eta^8}\bigg]$$

$$+ (G'')^2\bigg[\frac{(\Delta\vec{x})^6}{4\eta^{10}} + \frac{(\Delta\vec{x})^8}{32\eta^{12}} + \frac{(\Delta\vec{x})^4}{2\eta^8}\bigg]\Bigg], \tag{17}$$

where $G(\eta, \vec{x}, \vec{x}')$ is the Wightman function in de Sitter universe[a]. Again taking the Wightman function to be the one corresponding to Bunch Davies vacuum, the

---

[a]We have suppressed the superscript d.S. in this expression.

behaviour of noise kernel for different cases can be summarized as follows[10]:

- $q = 1$: This is just massless scalar field case in de Sitter spacetime for which results are already given in the last section.
- $q \in (0,1)$: In this case, the late time universe correspond to $\eta \to 0$ limit. And we find that, in this limit, $\langle t_{00}(\eta, \vec{x}) t_{00}(\eta, \vec{x}') \rangle_{P.L.}\big|_{\eta \to 0} = \frac{H^{4q}(\Delta \vec{x})^{4q-8}}{8\pi^5}\Big((11 - 12q + 4q^2)(\Gamma(2-q))^2(\Gamma(0.5+q))^2\Big)$ i.e., it is time independent and it decreases with spatial distance.
- $q \in (-2, 0)$: In this case, the late time universe corresponds to $\eta \to \infty$. For this case, we have $\langle t_{00}(\eta, \vec{x}) t_{00}(\eta, \vec{x}') \rangle_{F.R.W.}\big|_{\text{late time}} = \lim_{\eta \to \infty} (H\eta)^{4q-4} \left[\frac{3H^4 \eta^4}{2\pi^4 (\Delta \vec{x})^8} + lower\ powers\ of\ \eta \right]$. This implies that there are no late time correlations in this case.
- $q = -2$: This is a slightly interesting case as in this case massless field in FRW spacetime goes to a massless scalar field in de Sitter spacetime. And because of this the stress energy correlator shows the infrared divergence as is present in Wightman function for a massless scalar in de Sitter spacetime.

Using the relation between the exponent, q, of the scale factor for a given FRW universe and the equation of state parameter, w, for the corresponding ideal fluid, i.e, $q = -2/(1+3w)$, we see that, for Friedmann universes with $q \in (0, 1]$, the equation of state parameter $w \in (-\infty, -1]$ whereas $w \in [0, \infty)$ for $q \in [-2, 0)$. Therefore, the results of the previous section with corresponding fluids can be summarized by the following diagram:

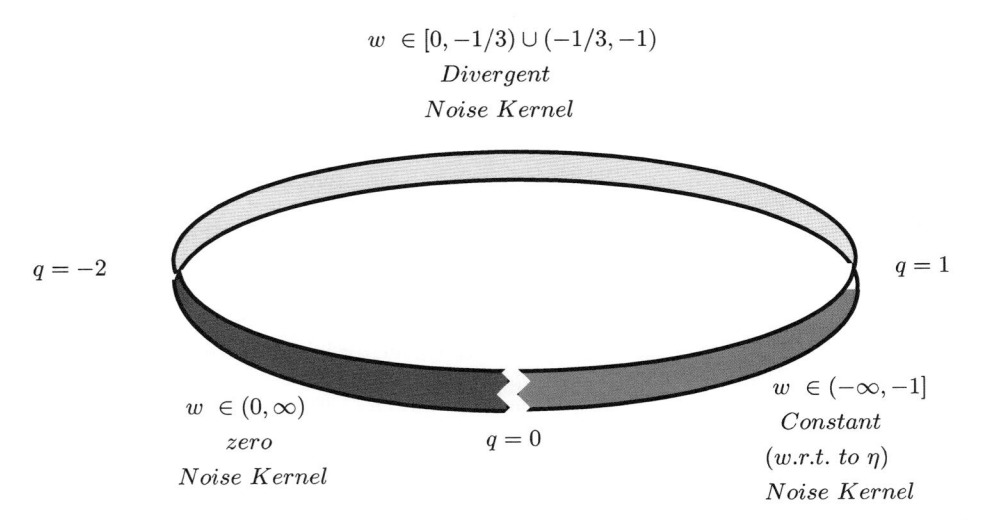

Fig. 1. Relation between different types of fluid (and the corresponding Friedmann space-times) and the behaviour of stress energy correlator in these regions.

Results for different epochs of the universe can be summarized in the following table[10]:

Table 1. Behaviour of the $(a=0, b=0, c=0, d=0)$ component of the stress-energy correlator and energy-energy correlator in the late time universe.[10]

	Radiation dominated $q=-1$	Dust dominated $q=-2$	de Sitter $q=1$ & $\nu \in [0, \frac{1}{2})$	de Sitter $q=1$ & $\nu \in (\frac{1}{2}, \frac{3}{2})$
$<t_{00}(\eta,\vec{x})t_{00}(\eta,\vec{x'})>$	0	∞	0	∞
$\frac{<t_{00}(\eta,\vec{x})t_{00}(\eta,\vec{x'})>}{(a(\eta))^4}$	0	∞	0	0

In the light of above results, we conclude that the semiclassical analyses alone may not be sufficient to draw any robust predictions about physical observables and questions related to the stability of the spacetimes. For example, for universe with positive equation of state parameter, the semiclassical analysis can still be trusted, at least in this stochastic approach, however, one may need to seriously relook at first order results for fluids with negative equation of state parameter and need to supplement them with, at least, 2nd order calculations. Similarly, for very light scalar fields, stochastic calculations may render the semiclasical conclusions invalid.[1,12]

References

1. L. E. Parker and D. Toms, *Quantum Field Theory in Curved Spacetime: Quantized Field and Gravity*, Cambridge Monographs on Mathematical Physics (Cambridge University Press, 8 2009).
2. N. G. Phillips and B. L. Hu, Noise kernel in stochastic gravity and stress energy bitensor of quantum fields in curved spacetimes, *Phys. Rev. D* **63**, p. 104001 (Apr 2001).
3. B. L. Hu and E. Verdaguer, Stochastic Gravity: Theory and Applications, *Living Rev. Rel.* **11**, p. 3 (2008).
4. G. Perez-Nadal, A. Roura and E. Verdaguer, Stress tensor fluctuations in de Sitter spacetime, *JCAP* **1005**, p. 036 (2010).
5. L. H. Ford and T. A. Roman, Minkowski vacuum stress tensor fluctuations, *Phys. Rev. D* **72**, p. 105010 (2005).
6. Y. Akrami et al., Planck 2018 results. X. Constraints on inflation, *Astron. Astrophys.* **641**, p. A10 (2020).
7. M. B. Fröb, Fully renormalized stress tensor correlator in flat space, *Phys. Rev. D* **88**, p. 045011 (2013).
8. B. Allen, Vacuum states in de sitter space, *Phys. Rev. D* **32**, 3136 (Dec 1985).
9. M. Spradlin, A. Strominger and A. Volovich, Les Houches lectures on de Sitter space, in *Les Houches Summer School: Session 76: Euro Summer School on Unity of Fundamental Physics: Gravity, Gauge Theory and Strings*, 10 2001.

10. A. Dhanuka and K. Lochan, Stress energy correlator in de Sitter spacetime: Its conformal masking or growth in connected Friedmann universes, *Phys. Rev. D* **102**, p. 085009 (2020).
11. K. Lochan, K. Rajeev, A. Vikram and T. Padmanabhan, Quantum correlators in Friedmann spacetimes: The omnipresent de Sitter spacetime and the invariant vacuum noise, *Phys. Rev. D* **98**, p. 105015 (2018).
12. L. H. Ford, Quantum instability of de sitter spacetime, *Phys. Rev. D* **31**, 710 (Feb 1985).

Breaking Buchdahl: Ultracompact stars in semiclassical gravity

Julio Arrechea*, Carlos Barceló[†]

*Institute of Astrophysics of Andalusia (IAA-CSIC),
Glorieta de la Astronomía, 18005 Granada, Spain*
*E-mail: arrechea@iaa.es, [†]E-mail: carlos@iaa.es

Raúl Carballo-Rubio

*Florida Space Institute, University of Central Florida,
12354 Research Parkway, Partnership 1, 32826 Orlando, FL, USA*
E-mail: Raul.CarballoRubio@ucf.edu

Luis J. Garay

*Universidad Complutense de Madrid, 28040 Madrid, Spain
and
Instituto de Estructura de la Materia (IEM-CSIC),
Serrano 121, 28006 Madrid, Spain*
E-mail: luisj.garay@ucm.es

The semiclassical approximation takes into account the gravitational contribution of zero-point energies. We model this contribution via the renormalized stress-energy tensor (RSET) of a massless scalar field, which we compute in a cutoff-regularized version of the Polyakov approximation. When the field is in the Boulware vacuum state (the natural vacuum for stellar geometries), the RSET works in favor of violating the Buchdahl compactness limit. We review the family of classical constant-density stellar solutions, paying particular attention to the notion of criticality—the presence of offsets in the mass function—and use it as a warm up for the analysis of the semiclassical set of solutions. For stars that surpass Buchdahl limit by far, the critical solution has an irregular pressure. This divergence in pressure moves inward by introducing a negative offset in the mass. In the semiclassical theory we find something rather different, namely that the critical configuration already displays a pressure that diverges exactly at the center of the structure. This drastic difference between the classical and semiclassical space of solutions suggests that semiclassical gravity could potentially allow for the existence of ultracompact stellar objects.

Keywords: Quantum fields in curved spacetimes, relativistic stars, semiclassical gravity

1. Introduction

In recent times, new windows have opened towards probing the nature of astrophysical black holes through both gravitational wave[1] and electromagnetic[2] observations. As observations aspire to unveiling the nature of these dark and compact objects, the issue of guessing what lurks behind their event horizons, assuming these long-lived surfaces exist in the first place, becomes more pressing than ever[a]. Among all

---

[a]Expanded version of the contributed talk by J.A. for the Sixteenth Marcel Grossmann Meeting (2021).

the different theories that, in principle, manage to change our notion of theoretical (Schwarzschild) black holes, semiclassical gravity stands out, mainly because it exhibits a conceptually well-stablished framework that has led to the discovery of effects such as cosmological particle creation[3] and Hawking evaporation.[4]

The main idea behind semiclassical gravity is that an effective geometrical description of the spacetime is retained, while the sources of this classical spacetime are of quantum origin. Therefore, this approximate scheme could be regarded as a conservative approach towards a theory of quantum gravity, in the sense that it captures the first corrections to classical general relativity originated by the zero-point energies of quantum matter fields. The presence of spacetime curvature modifies these zero-point energies in a way that cannot be renormalized away, the subsequent contribution from these zero-point energies to spacetime curvature being captured by the semiclassical field equations

$$G_{\mu\nu} = 8\pi \left(T_{\mu\nu} + \hbar \langle \hat{T}_{\mu\nu} \rangle \right), \qquad (1)$$

where $\langle \hat{T}_{\mu\nu} \rangle$ is the vacuum expectation value of the renormalized stress-energy tensor (RSET) of quantized fields. Obtaining analytical expressions for the RSET is an arduous task,[5] so it is typical to resort to highly symmetrical or dimensionally reduced models where the RSET can be computed explicitly.[6,7]

2. The Polyakov RSET: Boulware vs Buchdahl

For simplicity, we restrict our analysis to static and spherically symmetric spacetimes with line element

$$ds^2 = -e^{2\phi(r)}dt^2 + [1 - C(r)]^{-1} dr^2 + r^2 d\Omega^2, \qquad (2)$$

where $d\Omega^2$ is the line element of 2-spheres and ϕ, C are the redshift and compactness functions, respectively. The former measures the amount of redshift suffered by outgoing null rays and the latter is a measure of the amount of mass contained within concentrical spheres, namely $C(r) = 2m(r)/r$, with $m(r)$ the Misner-Sharp mass.[8]

An appealing method for obtaining a particularly simple RSET is via the s-wave Polyakov approximation.[9] This approximation models the RSET as that of a massless scalar field propagating in a $1+1$ dimensional spacetime [the t,r sector of (2)]. The resulting RSET is a function of the components of the metric[10] and has the form

$$\langle \hat{T}_{rr} \rangle^{(2)} = -\frac{l_{\rm P}^2 \psi^2}{2} + \langle {\rm SDT} \rangle, \quad \langle \hat{T}_{rt} \rangle^{(2)} = \langle \hat{T}_{tr} \rangle^{(2)} = 0,$$

$$\langle \hat{T}_{tt} \rangle^{(2)} = \frac{l_{\rm P}^2 e^{2\phi}}{2} \left[2\psi'(1-C) + \psi^2(1-C) - \psi C'\right] + \langle {\rm SDT} \rangle, \qquad (3)$$

where $\langle {\rm SDT} \rangle$ stands for state dependent terms, $l_{\rm P} = 1/\sqrt{12\pi}$, $\psi = \phi'$ and the $'$ denotes derivatives with respect to the r coordinate. These components are then identified with those of a 3 + 1 dimensional tensor

$$\langle \hat{T}_{\mu\nu} \rangle^{(\text{P})} = F(r) \delta^a_\mu \delta^b_\nu \langle \hat{T}_{ab} \rangle^{(2)}, \tag{4}$$

where Latin indices take $0, 1$ values and Greek indices take $0, 3$ values.

The Polyakov RSET provides an appropriate balance between simplicity and accuracy (see[11] for an extended discussion). There is an ambiguity in the 3 + 1-dimensional Polyakov RSET given by the radial function $F(r)$. Typically, this function is fixed to be $F(r) = 1/r^2$ to yield a covariantly conserved RSET with vanishing angular pressures. In turn, the resulting RSET is singular at $r = 0$, even computed over entirely regular stellar spacetimes. This poses a problem when backreaction is taken into account and it is the main motivation behind exploring other choices of regulator function. Following a conservative logic, we supplied the regulator with a cut-off of the form $F_{\text{CP}}(r) = 1/(r^2 + \alpha l_{\text{P}}^2)$, with $\alpha > 1$. This distortion of the regulator function induces a non-conservation of the RSET, which can be compensated by the introduction of angular pressures.[12]

In previous works[12, 13] we explored the sets of semiclassical vacuum and electrovacuum solutions using the cut-off regulator Polyakov RSET. In what follows we will consider the Boulware vacuum state, obtained by taking $\langle \text{SDT} \rangle = 0$, as it is the sole state compatible with staticity (absence of stationary fluxes) and asymptotic flatness. The Boulware state is singular at the Schwarzschild event horizon, hence backreaction will affect it in a non-perturbative manner. The semiclassical counterpart of the Schwarzschild black hole has its horizon replaced by the throat of an asymmetric wormhole. At finite affine distance inside this throat lives an undressed singularity. This result motivates the introduction of a classical matter fluid as the only semiclassically-consistent possibility of obtaining geometries devoid from singularities. We will explore whether these geometries are potentially able to mimic astrophysical black holes.

This potentiality comes from realizing that semiclassical physics provides several ways of surpassing the Buchdahl compactness bound[14] that applies to relativistic stars in hydrostatic equilibrium. The conditions for deriving this limit involve that (i) the star has a Schwarzschild exterior, (ii) pressures in the angular directions that do not surpass the pressure in the radial direction, and (iii) a density profile that is non-increasing outwards. Semiclassical corrections modify the exterior (vacuum) geometry so that it is no longer Schwarzschild but an asymmetric wormhole. The RSETs are anisotropic by construction, although this anisotropy is underestimated in regularized Polyakov-like approximations. Lastly, the violations of energy conditions provided by the RSET generate regions inside the star where the energy density decreases inwards.

In this contribution, we report on several results concerning the self-consistent solutions to (1). We will point out the remarkable differences that exist between constant-density stellar solutions in the classical and semiclassical theories. We will elaborate on the notion of criticality—a criteria for identifying stellar geometries that exhibit deficit or excess of mass that come from singular sources—and use it to obtain a family of *quasi-regular* semiclassical geometries. These quasi-regular geometries are characterized by a central (singular) core such that at its boundary the mass function is not trans-Planckian and pressures are finite.

3. Criticality in classical stars

First we give a brief summary of classical stellar equilibrium applied to the constant-density perfect fluid. In this simplified setting, the concept of criticality can be introduced in a clear fashion, paving the path toward the more involved analysis involving semiclassical corrections. The stress-energy tensor (SET) of the isotropic perfect fluid is

$$T_{\mu\nu} = (\rho + p)\, u_\mu u_\nu + p g_{\mu\nu}, \tag{5}$$

with p and ρ denoting the pressure and energy density measured by an observer comoving with the fluid with 4-velocity u^μ. In the following we will consider that the fluid obeys an equation of state of the form

$$\rho = \text{const.} \tag{6}$$

There are several reasons behind considering a constant-density fluid. First, this equation of state leaves the pressure of the fluid free to arrange itself in whichever form necessary to attain equilibrium. Second, the classical field equations admit (in some cases) analytical solutions. This characteristic is lost once we introduce semiclassical corrections. Finally, the constant-density assumption saturates one of the conditions necessary for the Buchdahl limit to hold.[15]

Covariant conservation of the classical SET yields

$$p' = -(\rho + p)\,\psi. \tag{7}$$

The rr and tt components of the classical field equations (1) take the form

$$C = \frac{-8\pi r^2 p + 2r\psi}{1 + 2r\psi}, \quad C' = 8\pi r \rho - \frac{C}{r}. \tag{8}$$

Expressions (6, 7, 8) form a closed system. The differential equation for C can be directly integrated, yielding

$$C = \frac{8}{3}\pi r^2 \rho + \frac{2m_0}{r}. \tag{9}$$

Here, m_0 is an arbitrary integration constant that accounts for a constant shift in the Misner-Sharp mass $m(r)$. The following relation

$$M_{\text{ADM}} = \int_0^R 4\pi r^2 \rho \, dr + m_0, \tag{10}$$

calls for interpreting m_0 as a term that compensates the disagreement between the mass generated by the whole fluid sphere and the ADM mass M_{ADM}. Therefore, regularity in the compactness of a classical star enforces $\rho = \rho_{\text{crit}} = 3C(R)/8\pi R^2$, where ρ_{crit} stands for the critical density. We use this value to distinguish three families of solutions

- Sub-critical regime ($\rho < \rho_{\rm crit}$): These solutions are characterized by a positive m_0 and can be interpreted as a fluid sphere with a mass excess whose gravitational pull cannot be withstood by finite pressures. Sub-critical solutions have infinite pressure singularities at some $r > 0$. For a fixed $C(R)$, the radius where this singularity appears nears the surface as ρ decreases.
- Critical regime ($\rho = \rho_{\rm crit}$): These solutions have a vanishing mass at $r = 0$ ($m_0 = 0$) and can be regular or irregular depending on whether the Buchdahl compactness bound is being surpassed. Critical solutions that surpass Buchdahl limit ($C(R) = 8/9$) display a pressure divergence at

$$R_{\rm div} = 3R\sqrt{1 - \frac{8}{9C(R)}}. \tag{11}$$

- Super-critical regime ($\rho > \rho_{\rm crit}$): Stellar geometries characterized by a negative m_0. The gravitational repulsion exherted by this negative mass tames the growing of the pressure of the fluid but at the cost of producing a curvature singularity at $r = 0$. As m_0 becomes more negative, the pressure at the core decreases, eventually becoming finite at $r = 0$ for some separatrix density.

Despite its apparent simplicity, this space of solutions reveals an important characteristic: for stars that surpass the Buchdahl limit, $C(R) = 8/9$, the respective separatrices for the pressure and mass functions do not overlap in any region. Fig. 1 shows integrations surrounding the critical solution, the only one with a regular compactness function[b]. The associated pressure profiles all develop singularities significantly far from $r = 0$. On the other hand, Fig. 2 shows integrations surrounding the solution separatrix in pressure, that is, the solution which is super-critical enough as to have a pressure that diverges exactly at $r = 0$. However, the price to pay for generating finite-pressure configurations is that the mass goes highly super-critical. At this point, enforcing the mass function to vanish at $r = 0$ would require introducing an additional positive mass contribution inside a small core. This sort of regularization cannot come without additional pathologies as the density of such sphere would necessarily be trans-Planckian. In what follows we will show that semiclassical corrections naturally provide this regularization mechanism for the mass, although they fail in achieving a strictly regular behavior at $r = 0$.

4. Semiclassical corrections in stellar spacetimes

The classical equations (8) guarantee the behavior of the compactness is independent from that of the pressure, although the converse is not true. The addition

---

[b]Recall that $C = 2m/r$, so only a Misner-Sharp mass that vanishes at the origin returns a non-singular compactness.

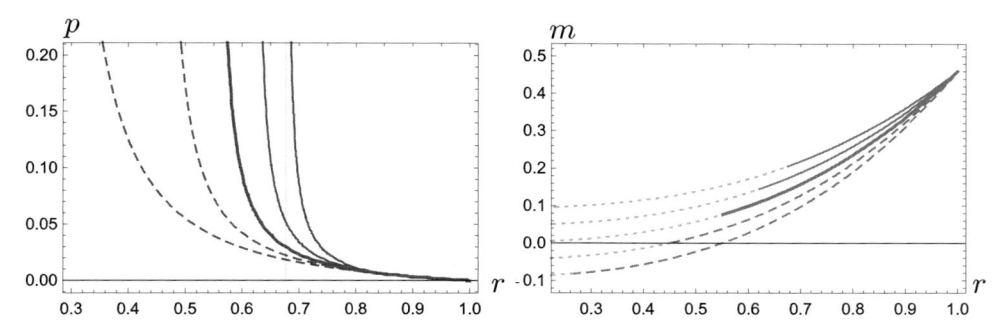

Fig. 1. Pressure (left panel) and Misner-Sharp mass (right panel) profiles surrounding the critical solution of a star with $C(R) = 0.92$ and $R = 1$. The thick, continuous line denotes the critical solution, while thin lines are sub-critical and dashed lines are super-critical stars. The only solution regular in the mass (critical) has a highly irregular pressure. The mass curves have been analytically extended for pictorical purposes, but the associated pressure profiles are singular. From right to left (top to bottom) $\rho/\rho_{\text{crit}} = \{0.8, 0.9, 1.0, 1.1, 1.2\}$.

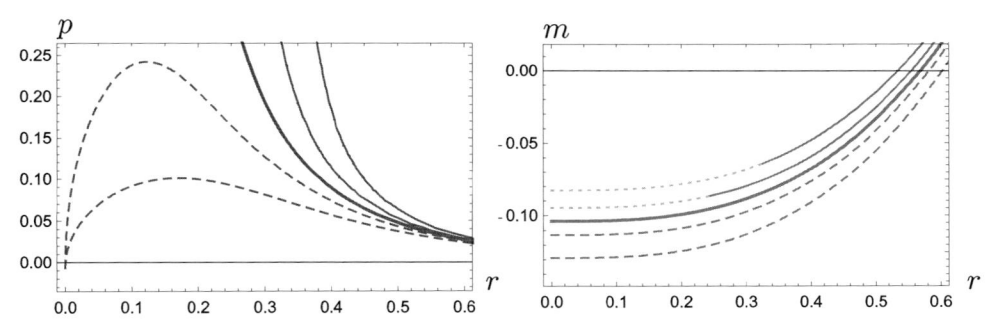

Fig. 2. Pressure (left panel) and Misner-Sharp mass (right panel) profiles surrounding the pressure-separatrix solution of a star with $C(R) = 0.92$ and $R = 1$. The thick, continuous line denotes the separatrix solution, while thin lines are infinite-pressure solutions and dashed lines are finite-pressure ones. Note that making the pressure everywhere finite enforces a negative central mass. All integrations are super-critical because $m_0 < 0$. From right to left (top to bottom) $\rho/\rho_{\text{crit}} \simeq \{1.18, 1.21, 1.23, 1.25, 1.28\}$.

of semiclassical corrections intertwines the behavior of both functions. As a consequence, when we analyze the semiclassical equations, the notion of criticality becomes more involved. This is because the differential equation for the compactness cannot be integrated analytically, so we lack an explicit expression that informs about the value of ρ_{crit}. The most relevant departure of semiclassical stars with respect to their classical counterparts is that, in the semiclassical theory, the separatrix solutions in mass and pressure overlap in a narrow region of the parameter space. In the following we will catalogue the space of semiclassical constant-density solutions and elaborate on this aspect.

Introducing the cut-off regularized Polyakov RSET (4) as a curvature source in the field equations (1), they result in

$$C = \frac{-8\pi r^2 p + 2r\psi + l_{\rm P}^2 r^2 \psi^2/\left(r^2 + \alpha l_{\rm P}^2\right)}{1 + 2r\psi + l_{\rm P}^2 r^2 \psi^2/(r^2 + \alpha l_{\rm P}^2)}, \tag{12}$$

$$C' = \frac{8\pi r^2 \rho - C + l_{\rm P}^2 r^2 \left(\psi^2 + 2\psi'\right)(1-C)/\left(r^2 + \alpha l_{\rm P}^2\right)}{r + l_{\rm P}^2 r^2 \psi/\left(r^2 + \alpha l_{\rm P}^2\right)}. \tag{13}$$

Semiclassical corrections to stellar spacetimes are typically negligible (they are proportional to $\hbar$) unless the geometries under consideration are able to explore and stimulate the energetic contributions of the Boulware state as to compensate their suppression of order $\hbar$. The scale that can potentially compensate this screening of semiclassical effects is the compactness of the star. In the following, we will be considering spheres of fluid whose surface is located very close and above the throat of the vacuum wormhole geometry $[C(R) \to 1]$. Such a configuration is defined by the following boundary conditions

$$p(R) = 0, \quad \phi(R) = \phi_{\rm S}, \quad \psi(R) = \frac{R^2 + \alpha l_{\rm P}^2}{R l_{\rm P}^2}\left[\sqrt{1 + \frac{R^2}{R^2 + \alpha l_{\rm P}^2}\frac{C(R)}{1 - C(R)}} - 1\right], \tag{14}$$

and a given value of ρ and $C(R)$. Here, the parameter $\phi_{\rm S}$ is obtained through a numerical integration of the vacuum equations from the asymptotic region inwards.

Plugging the boundary conditions (14) in the field equations (12, 13) we obtain expressions for $\psi'(R)$ and $C'(R)$. Then, the semiclassical energy density and radial pressure at $r = R$ are

$$\rho_{\rm sc} = -\langle \hat{T}^t_t \rangle^{({\rm P})} = -\frac{1}{8\pi R^2} + \rho + \mathcal{O}\left(\sqrt{1-C}\right),$$

$$p^r_{\rm sc} = \langle \hat{T}^r_r \rangle^{({\rm P})} = -\frac{1}{8\pi R^2} + \mathcal{O}\left(\sqrt{1-C}\right),$$

$$p^\theta_{\rm sc} = \langle \hat{T}^\theta_\theta \rangle^{({\rm P})} = -\frac{\alpha l_{\rm P}^2}{8\pi R^2\left(R^2 + \alpha l_{\rm P}^2\right)} + \mathcal{O}\left(\sqrt{1-C}\right). \tag{15}$$

The RSET components are comparable in magnitude to the classical SET at the surface. In fact, as long as $\rho \lesssim 1/8\pi R^2$ the total RSET violates energy conditions at the surface. Additionally, for more realistic equations of state with a classical energy density that vanishes at the surface, the total RSET will violate all pointwise energy conditions there.

Vacuum polarization provides an extra contribution to the Misner-Sharp mass of the spacetime. This contribution is negative in the vacuum region and permeates it entirely. In the interior of the star it can be overall positive or negative depending on the value of ρ. The equivalent to formula (10) in the semiclassical theory is

$$M_{\rm ADM} = \int_0^\infty 4\pi r^2 \left[\Theta\left(R - r\right)\rho + \rho_{\rm sc}\right]dr + m_0, \tag{16}$$

where Θ is the Heaviside step function. Since the total energy density is now intertwined to the pressure and redshift of the geometry through Eq. (13), the critical value of the classical density (recall, the value that corresponds to a vanishing m_0) cannot be determined analytically. In turn, a numerical exploration of the space of solutions is needed. We dedicate the rest of this note to highlight the chief results from our exploration[c].

Concerning the Buchdahl limit, we have found that the classical Buchdahl bound of $C(R) = 8/9$ gets perturbatively modified by semiclassical corrections. These correction makes the most compact configuration which is regular in p and C have $C(R) < 8/9$. This result follows from $\rho_{\rm sc}$ in (16) amounting to an overall positive contribution throughout the interior of the structure. In fact, the greatest positive contribution comes from the region $r \sim \sqrt{\alpha} l_{\rm P}$, precisely where the physics of the Polyakov RSET is driven by the regulator function. Using a local, more refined approximation to the RSET[16] the energetic contribution near the center of constant-density stars that are approaching Buchdahl limit turns out to be negative. The cutoff-Polyakov RSET could be incorrectly estimating the magnitude and sign of the energetic contribution from the vacuum near the center of compact fluid spheres.

In our exploration of the semiclassical space of solutions (see Fig. 3 for a pictorical representation) we found the following regimes

- Sub-critical regime ($\rho \ll \rho_{\rm crit}$, regions I and III of the diagram in Fig. 3): These solutions are asymmetric wormholes with characteristics akin to the vacuum solution, but filled with a classical fluid of diverging pressures. As ρ is increased, the throat of the wormhole progressively shrinks. When the throat is very small compared to the overall size of the star, we identify a new regime not present in the classical theory.
- Quasi-regular regime ($\rho \sim \rho_{\rm crit}$, narrow orange band in Fig. 3): This sub-family is comprised by super-critical solutions that lie below Buchdahl limit and sub-critical solutions of any compactness with an extremely tiny wormhole throat. In this regime, we can always identify a central core of radius $r_{\rm core} \ll R$. At the boundary of this core the pressure remains finite and the Misner-Sharp mass can be made as small as desired.
- Critical regime ($\rho = \rho_{\rm crit}$, black line in Fig. 3): Sub-Buchdahl stars amount to a perturbative correction over the classical geometries and are regular. Super-Buchdahl stars are irregular but extend all the way to $r = 0$, contrary to their classical counterparts. These solutions have infinite positive pressure and infinite negative mass at $r = 0$.
- Super-critical regime ($\rho > \rho_{\rm crit}$, regions II and IV of the diagram in Fig. 3): They correspond to perturbative corrections over the classical solutions, with the caveat that the Misner-Sharp mass is now infinite and negative at $r = 0$, which strengthens the central singularity. Pressure is finite everywhere.

---

[c]We refer the reader to[11] for details.

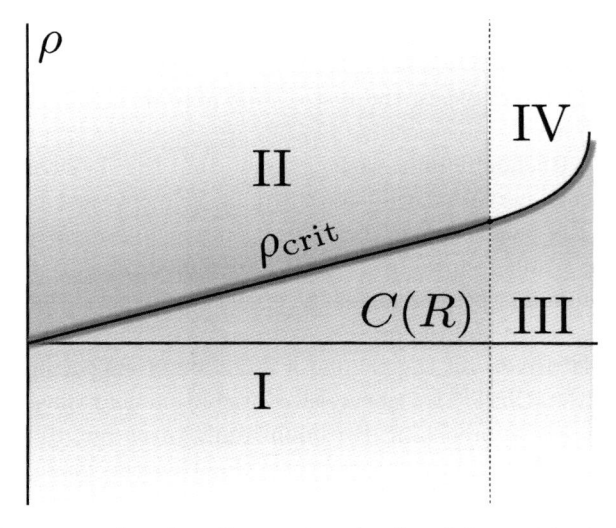

Fig. 3. Pictorial representation of an $R = \text{const.} \gg l_{\text{P}}$ slice of the semiclassical constant-density stellar space of solutions. The vertical and horizontal axes represent the energy density and surface compactness of stars. The black curve denotes critical configurations. Its intersection with the vertical, dotted line represents the Buchdahl limit, or the most compact structure regular in both p and C. We distinguish four regions: regions I and II for sub- and super-critical stars below Buchdahl limit and regions III and IV for sub- and super-critical stars above Buchdahl limit. The narrow orange band that surrounds the ρ_{crit} line denotes the quasi-regular regime which spans through regions I, II and III.

Figure 4 shows the pressure and mass profiles for various configurations surrounding the critical solution of a star that surpasses the Buchdahl limit (rightmost portion of diagram 3). There are several crucial differences between these diagrams and those from Figures 1 and 2. Firstly, the critical solution (thick line), albeit singular, coincides with the separatrix solution for the pressure. In the classical case, the critical solution and the separatrix in the pressure were distant in the space of parameters. Here, because of the way quantum corrections operate, we find a coincidence between these two solutions. Secondly, quasi-regular configurations (thin lines) for which the Misner-Sharp mass vanishes near the center of spherical symmetry are very different from their classical counterparts. Enforcing the mass function to vanish at $r = 0$ no longer requires the introduction of arbitrarily high masses inside small cores: Semiclassical corrections already provides a significant part of this contribution.

5. Conclusions

In this work we have reviewed the classical stellar solutions of constant density under our particular scope, with the aim of understanding properly the solutions that incorporate vacuum polarization contributions. We have not been able to find strictly regular configurations that surpass a Buchdahl limit (which receives perturbative

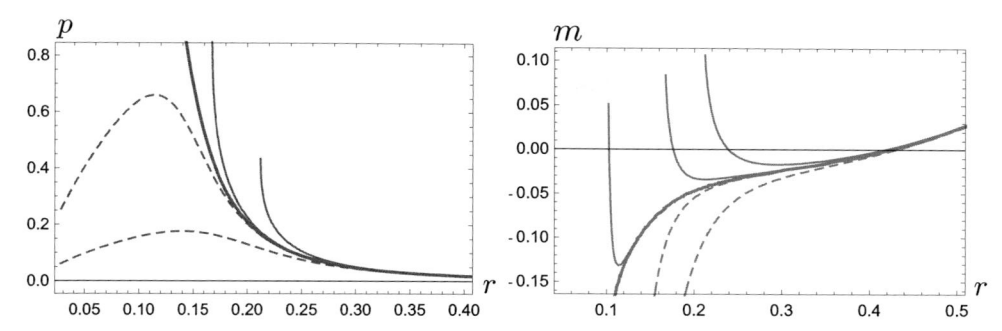

Fig. 4. Pressure (left panel) and Misner-Sharp mass (right panel) profiles surrounding the critical solution of a semiclassical star with $C(R) = 0.92, R = 1$ and $\alpha = 1.01$. The thick line denotes the critical solution (the separatrix between distinct compactness behaviors), while the thin lines are sub-critical and the dashed lines are super-critical. In the right panel the quasi-regular regime can be observed. Quasi-regular solutions are characterized by a mass function that vanishes in the innermost regions of the star. By a suitable choice of ρ, this vanishing can be achieved as close to $r = 0$ as desired. From right to left (top to bottom) the densities utilized are $\rho/\rho_{\text{crit}} = \{0.9990, 0.9998, 0.9999, 1, 1.0001, 1.0010\}$, where the critical density $\rho_{\text{crit}} \simeq 0.1214$ is determined numerically within a precision of 10^{-6}.

corrections). However, the study of singular solutions hints towards semiclassical gravity being able to regularize at the same time the pressure and mass of ultra-compact configurations. This notion is what we have attempted to capture in the notiont of quasi-regular configurations.

We believe that the crudity of the approximations used here for the semiclassical source could be preventing the quasi-regular solutions from appearing as regular in the first place. Ideally, these analyses should be revisited when more accurate approximations to the RSET are available. As an intermediate step in this direction, it is possible to ask whether a deformation of the regulator function from its cutoff-regulator form F_{CP} just inside the central core of the structure is sufficient to generate entirely regular and ultracompact configurations. The results of this ongoing investigation will appear in a forthcoming publication.

References

1. B. P. Abbott, R. Abbott, T. D. Abbott, M. R. Abernathy, F. Acernese, K. Ackley, C. Adams, T. Adams, P. Addesso, R. X. Adhikari, V. B. Adya, Affeldt and et. al., Observation of gravitational waves from a binary black hole merger, *Phys. Rev. Lett.* **116**, p. 061102 (Feb 2016).
2. K. Akiyama *et al.*, First M87 Event Horizon Telescope Results. I. The Shadow of the Supermassive Black Hole, *Astrophys. J. Lett.* **875**, p. L1 (2019).
3. L. Parker, Particle creation in expanding universes, *Phys. Rev. Lett.* **21**, 562 (Aug 1968).
4. S. W. Hawking, Breakdown of predictability in gravitational collapse, *Phys. Rev. D* **14**, 2460 (Nov 1976).
5. R. M. Wald, Axiomatic Renormalization of the Stress Tensor of a Conformally Invariant Field in Conformally Flat Space-Times, *Annals Phys.* **110**, 472 (1978).

6. M. R. Brown and A. C. Ottewill, Effective actions and conformal transformations, *Phys. Rev. D* **31**, 2514 (May 1985).
7. V. P. Frolov and A. I. Zel'nikov, Killing approximation for vacuum and thermal stress-energy tensor in static space-times, *Phys. Rev. D* **35**, 3031 (May 1987).
8. C. W. Misner and D. H. Sharp, Relativistic equations for adiabatic, spherically symmetric gravitational collapse, *Phys. Rev.* **136**, B571 (1964).
9. A. M. Polyakov, Quantum Geometry of Bosonic Strings, *Phys. Lett.* **B103**, 207 (1981).
10. P. C. W. Davies and S. A. Fulling, Quantum vacuum energy in two dimensional space-times, *Proceedings of the Royal Society of London. Series A, Mathematical and Physical Sciences* **354**, 59 (1977).
11. J. Arrechea, C. Barceló, R. Carballo-Rubio and L. J. Garay, Semiclassical constant-density spheres in a regularized Polyakov approximation, *Phys. Rev. D* **104**, p. 084071 (2021).
12. J. Arrechea, C. Barceló, R. Carballo-Rubio and L. J. Garay, Schwarzschild geometry counterpart in semiclassical gravity, *Phys. Rev. D* **101**, p. 064059 (Mar 2020).
13. J. Arrechea, C. Barceló, R. Carballo-Rubio and L. J. Garay, Reissner-Nordström geometry counterpart in semiclassical gravity (2 2021).
14. H. A. Buchdahl, General relativistic fluid spheres, *Phys. Rev.* **116**, 1027 (Nov 1959).
15. A. Urbano and H. Veermäe, On gravitational echoes from ultracompact exotic stars, *JCAP* **04**, p. 011 (2019).
16. W. A. Hiscock, Gravitational vacuum polarization around static spherical stars, *Phys. Rev. D* **37**, 2142 (Apr 1988).

Einstein anomaly with tensors of odd order in six dimensional curved space

Kohei Yamamoto* and Satoshi Yajima

Department of Physics, Kumamoto University,
2-39-1 Kurokami, Chuo-ku, Kumamoto 860-8555, Japan
* E-mail: 191d9021@st.kumamoto-u.ac.jp

By applying the covariant Taylor expansion method to the heat kernel, Einstein anomaly associated with the Weyl fermion of spin 1/2 interacting with tensor fields of 1 and 3 order in six dimensional curved space are given. From the relation between Einstein and Lorentz anomalies, which are the gravitational anomalies, all terms of the Einstein anomaly should form total derivatives.

Keywords: Einstein anomaly

1. Introduction

The gravitational anomalies are the Lorentz anomaly that appears from the local Lorentz transformation and the general coordinate anomaly that appears from the covariant general coordinate transformation, in the model for the Weyl fermion in even dimensional curved space. The Lorentz anomaly can be canceled by appropriately replacing the expectation value of the energy-momentum tensor, and then the general coordinate anomaly, called the Einstein anomaly, remains.

The Lagrangian in $N = 1$ supergravity coupled to supersymmetric Yang-Mills theory has some four-Fermi interactions, in addition to the minimal couplings of the fermion with the gravitational and gauge fields. The gravitino field with an irreducible element of spin $\frac{3}{2}$ exists in the supergravity. The kinetic part of the gravitino is treated as that for a fermion of spin $\frac{1}{2}$, fixing the field by a suitable gauge, and the spacetime index of the gravitino may be regarded as that of the representation matrix elements of a gauge group in vector and odd order tensor type couplings. Then the tensor may not commute with the vector.

2. Heat kernel

In this article, in order to apply for the above model, we consider the covariant gravitational anomalies for a Weyl fermion with spin $\frac{1}{2}$, interacting with both the vector field V_μ and the totally antisymmetric tensor $C_{\mu\alpha\beta}$, in even $2n$-dimensional Riemannian space. The concrete form of the anomalies may directly be calculated by using the heat kernel $K^{(2n)}(x, x'; t)$ for the fermion, which is defined as[1]

$$-\frac{\partial}{\partial t}K^{(2n)}(x, x'; t) = \slashed{D}^2 K^{(2n)}(x, x'; t),$$
$$K^{(2n)}(x, x'; 0) = \mathbf{1}|h(x)|^{-\frac{1}{2}}|h(x')|^{-\frac{1}{2}}\delta^{(2n)}(x - x'), \tag{1}$$

where **1** is the spinor unit matrix, $\delta^{(2n)}(x-x')$ denotes the delta function, and $h(x)$ stand for the determinant $\det h^m{}_\mu$ of a vielbein $h^m{}_\mu$. Note that the metric tensor is $g_{\mu\nu} = h^m{}_\mu h^n{}_\nu \eta_{mn}$ with $\eta_{mn} = -\delta_{mn}$ in flat tangent space. Moreover, the square of the Dirac operator $\not{D}$ for fermion ψ is written as follows,

$$\not{D}^2 = D_\mu D^\mu + X, \quad \not{D} = \gamma^\mu \nabla_\mu + Y, \quad D_\mu = \nabla_\mu + Q_\mu, \quad Q_\mu = \frac{1}{2}\{\gamma_\mu, Y\},$$

$$X = Z - \nabla_\mu Q^\mu - Q_\mu Q^\mu, \quad \nabla_\mu \psi = \partial_\mu \psi + \frac{1}{4}\gamma_{mn}\omega^{mn}{}_\mu \psi, \quad \gamma_{\mu_1\cdots\mu_n} = \gamma_{[\mu_1}\cdots\gamma_{\mu_n]},$$

$$Z = \frac{1}{2}\gamma^{\mu\nu}[\nabla_\mu, \nabla_\nu] + \gamma^\mu(\nabla_\mu Y) + Y^2, \quad [D_\mu, D_\nu]\psi = \Lambda_{\mu\nu}\psi,$$

$$Y = \gamma^\mu V_\mu + \gamma^\mu \gamma^{\alpha\beta} C_{\mu\alpha\beta}, \quad V_\mu \equiv V^a_\mu T^a, \quad C_{\mu\alpha\beta} \equiv C^a_{\mu\alpha\beta} T^a, \tag{2}$$

where $\omega^{mn}{}_\mu$ is the spin connection. The interaction term Y of the boson in $\not{D}$ is given by vector and tensor fields, and T^a is the matrix representation of the nonabelian gauge group. The γ-matrix valued Q_μ, X and $\Lambda_{\mu\nu}$ in (2) are rewritten in the following form,

$$Q_\mu = V_\mu + 3\gamma^{\alpha\beta}C_{\mu\alpha\beta}, \quad F_{\mu\nu} \equiv \partial_\mu V_\nu - \partial_\nu V_\mu + [V_\mu, V_\nu],$$

$$X = -\frac{1}{4}R + 12 C^{\alpha\beta\gamma} C_{\alpha\beta\gamma} + \gamma^{\mu\nu}\left(\frac{1}{2}F_{\mu\nu} + 18 C_\mu{}^{\alpha\beta} C_{\nu\alpha\beta}\right)$$

$$- \gamma^{\alpha\beta\gamma\delta}C_{\alpha\beta\gamma;\delta} + \gamma^{\mu\nu\alpha\beta\gamma\delta}C_{\mu\alpha\beta}C_{\nu\gamma\delta}, \tag{3}$$

$$\Lambda_{\mu\nu} = \frac{1}{4}\gamma^{\rho\sigma}R_{\rho\sigma\mu\nu} + F_{\mu\nu} - 18[C_\mu{}^{\alpha\beta}, C_{\nu\alpha\beta}] - \gamma^{\alpha\beta}(6C_{\alpha\beta[\mu;\nu]} + 72 C^\rho{}_{\alpha[\mu|} C_{\rho\beta|\nu]})$$

$$+ 18\gamma^{\alpha\beta\gamma\delta} C_{[\mu|\alpha\beta}C_{|\nu]\gamma\delta}, \quad \gamma_{2n+1} = i^n \gamma^1 \gamma^2 \cdots \gamma^{2n},$$

where the semi-colon ';μ' denotes the covariant differentiation $\nabla_\mu + V_\mu$ for the vector gauge transformation in curved space, $R_{\rho\sigma\mu\nu}$ is the Riemann curvature tensor, and $R = g^{\rho\mu}g^{\sigma\nu}R_{\rho\sigma\mu\nu}$. The antisymmetric product $\gamma^{\alpha\beta\gamma\delta}$ and $\gamma^{\mu\nu\alpha\beta\gamma\delta}$ of X can be replaced by $-\frac{i}{2}\gamma_7\gamma^{\rho\sigma}\epsilon_{\rho\sigma\alpha\beta\gamma\delta}$ and $i\gamma_7\epsilon^{\mu\nu\alpha\beta\gamma\delta}$ in 6 dimensions, respectively.

It is difficult to obtain the exact form of the heat kernel. In order to perform the concrete calculation, the following ansatz by DeWitt is applied to the heat kernel.[2]

$$K^{(2n)}(x,x';t) \sim \frac{\Delta^{\frac{1}{2}}(x,x')}{(4\pi t)^n}\exp\left\{\frac{\sigma(x,x')}{2t}\right\}\sum_{q=0}^\infty a_q(x,x')t^q, \tag{4}$$

where $\sigma(x,x')$ is half of the square of the geodesic distance between x and x', $\Delta(x,x') = |h(x)|^{-1}|h(x')|^{-1}\det\sigma_{;\mu\nu'}$, and $a_q(x,x')$ is a bispinor. The coincidence limit of a_n appears in formal expression of the anomaly, and is defined by $\lim_{x'\to x} a_n(x,x') \equiv [a_n](x)$.[3] The orthonormal bases $|n\rangle \equiv |\mu_1\cdots\mu_n\rangle$ being the eigenfunctions belonging to the eigenvalue n for $\sigma^\nu D_\nu$ consist of n products of $\sigma_{\mu'}(=\nabla_{\mu'}\sigma)$, and a_q can be expanded by the bases,

$$a_q = \sum_{n=0}^{\infty} |n\rangle\langle n|a_q\rangle = \sum_{n=0}^{\infty} \frac{(-1)^n}{n!} \sigma^{\mu'_1}\cdots\sigma^{\mu'_n} \lim_{x\to x'}[D_{(\mu_1}\cdots D_{\mu_n)}a_q], \tag{5}$$

$$\langle n|a_q\rangle = [a_{q!(\mu_1\cdots\mu_n)}] = \lim_{x\to x'}[D_{(\mu_1}\cdots D_{\mu_n)}a_q], \quad \langle 0|a_q\rangle = [a_q],$$

where the exclamation mark '!μ' means the covariant differentiation D_μ modified in (2).

3. Einstein anomaly

The formal forms of the general coordinate anomaly $\mathcal{A}_\nu^{(2n)}$ and the Lorentz anomaly $\mathcal{A}_{\mu\nu}^{(2n)}$ are obtained from the path integral measure of left-handed Weyl fermion in $2n$ dimensions, in Fujikawa's method,[4] and are expressed by the heat kernel after regularized by the Gaussian cut-off differential operator.

$$D^\mu \langle T_{\mu\nu}\rangle = \mathcal{A}_\nu^{(2n)}, \quad \langle T_{\mu\nu}\rangle_A \equiv \frac{1}{2}(\langle T_{\mu\nu}\rangle - \langle T_{\nu\mu}\rangle) = \mathcal{A}_{\mu\nu}^{(2n)},$$

$$\mathcal{A}_\nu^{(2n)}(x) = \frac{1}{2}\lim_{t\to 0}\lim_{x'\to x}\text{Tr}\left\{\gamma_{2n+1}(D_\nu - D_{\nu'})K^{(2n)}(x,x';t)\right\}, \tag{6}$$

$$\mathcal{A}_{\mu\nu}^{(2n)}(x) = \frac{1}{4}\lim_{t\to 0}\lim_{x'\to x}\text{Tr}\left\{\gamma_{2n+1}\gamma_{\mu\nu}K^{(2n)}(x,x';t)\right\},$$

where 'Tr' runs over both indices of γ-matrix and T^a. These anomalies seem to break the general covariance and the local Lorentz symmetry simultaneously, but one of the symmetries is restored by using the relation $2D^\mu\mathcal{A}_{\mu\nu}^{(2n)} = \mathcal{A}_\nu^{(2n)}$ and redefining the expectation value of the energy-momentum tensor.[5] Einstein anomaly $G_\nu^{(2n)}$ is given by $\langle T'_{\mu\nu}\rangle = \langle T_{\mu\nu}\rangle - \mathcal{A}_{\mu\nu}^{(2n)}$. Thus, the local Lorentz symmetry is preserved.

$$D^\mu \langle T'_{\mu\nu}\rangle_S = G_\nu^{(2n)} = D^\mu \mathcal{A}_{\mu\nu}^{(2n)} = \frac{1}{2}\mathcal{A}_\nu^{(2n)}, \quad \langle T'_{\mu\nu}\rangle_A = 0, \tag{7}$$

where $\langle T'_{\mu\nu}\rangle_S$ is the symmetric part of $\langle T'_{\mu\nu}\rangle$. From (7), it is expected that the concrete form of the Einstein anomaly becomes the total derivative of the Lorentz anomaly. Substituting (4) into (6), $G_\nu^{(2n)}$ is rewritten by the coincidence limit of a_n and its first order derivative in (5),

$$G_\nu^{(2n)}(x) = \frac{1}{4(4\pi)^n}\text{Tr}\left\{2\gamma_{2n+1}[a_{n!\nu}](x) - \gamma_{2n+1}[a_n]_{!\nu}(x)\right\}. \tag{8}$$

The tensorial form of the anomaly in 6 dimensions is obtained from

$$G_\nu^{(6)} = \frac{1}{256\pi^3} \text{Tr}\left\{\gamma_7 \left(2\left[a_{3!\nu}\right] - \left[a_3\right]_{!\nu}\right)\right\}$$

$$= \frac{1}{256\pi^3} \text{Tr}\left\{\gamma_7 \left[\frac{1}{6}\Lambda_{\mu\nu}\left(\frac{1}{6}R + X\right)^2 + \frac{1}{45}J_{[\mu}X_{!\nu]} - \frac{1}{60}J_{[\mu!\nu]}X\right.\right.$$

$$+ \frac{1}{15}\Lambda_{\mu\nu}X_{!\rho}{}^\rho + \frac{2}{45}\Lambda_{\mu\nu!\rho}X^{!\rho} + \frac{1}{40}\Lambda_{\mu\nu!\rho}{}^\rho X + \frac{1}{180}\left[\Lambda_{\mu\rho}, \Lambda_\nu{}^\rho\right]X$$

$$+ \frac{1}{180}R^\rho{}_{[\mu}\Lambda_{\nu]\rho}X + \frac{17}{360}R_{\mu\nu\rho\sigma}\Lambda^{\rho\sigma}X + \frac{1}{36}\Lambda_{\mu\nu}\Lambda_{\rho\sigma}\Lambda^{\rho\sigma}$$

$$\left.\left.+ \frac{1}{45}\Lambda_{[\mu}{}^\rho\Lambda_{\nu]}{}^\sigma\Lambda_{\rho\sigma} - \frac{1}{90}\Lambda_{\mu\nu!\rho}J^\rho - \frac{1}{45}\Lambda_{\rho[\mu}J_{\nu]}{}^{!\rho}\right]^{;\mu}\right\}, \qquad (9)$$

where $J_\mu \equiv \Lambda^\rho{}_{\mu!\rho}$. Since $\text{Tr}\gamma_7 X = \text{Tr}\{\gamma_7\Lambda_{\mu\nu}\} = 0$, terms containing X and $\Lambda_{\mu\nu}$ of one degree do not contribute to the anomaly. The concrete form of $G_\nu^{(6)}$ becomes some total derivatives before the trace operation of γ-matrices. Substituting (3) into (9) and performing the trace operation, $G_\nu^{(6)}$ yields many terms in tensorial form.

References

1. J. Schwinger, Phys. Rev. **82**, 664 (1951).
2. B. S. DeWitt, *Dynamical Theory of Groups and Fields* (Gordon and Breach, 1965).
3. I. G. Avramidi, Nucl. Phys. **B355**, 712 (1991).
4. K. Fujikawa, Phys. Rev. **D21**, 2848 (1980).
5. K. Fujikawa, M. Tomiya and O. Yasuda, Z. Phys. **28**, 289 (1985).

Quantum memory and BMS symmetries

Sanved Kolekar

Indian Institute of Astrophysics,
2nd Block, Koramangala, Bangalore 560034, India
E-mail: sanved.kolekar@iiap.res.in
www.iiap.res.in

Jorma Louko

School of Mathematical Sciences, University of Nottingham,
Nottingham NG7 2RD, UK
E-mail: jorma.louko@nottingham.ac.uk

In this talk, we discuss the effect of BMS symmetries on quantum entanglement and its implications in the context of the black hole information paradox. In particular, we illustrate the gravitational memory effect for linear uniformly accelerated observers in a physical process involving a BMS shock-wave without planar/spherical symmetry. This classical memory is accompanied by a quantum memory that modulates the quantum entanglement between the opposing Rindler wedges in quantum field theory. A corresponding phenomenon across the Schwarzschild black hole horizon suggests that the Negativity measure of entanglement between infalling and outgoing Hawking pair should be degraded due to an infalling BMS shockwave while there should be linear order generation of Negativity between two outgoing Hawking particles. Implications are discussed.

Keywords: Gravitational memory effect, BMS, Negativity

1. Introduction

Bondi-Metzner-Sachs (BMS) showed that asymptotically flat spacetimes possess an infinite number of symmetries now known as the BMS supertranslations.[1] These diffeomorphisms extend the symmetry group of the standard four global translations at the asymptotic boundary. The BMS supertranslations are related to the gravitational memory effect and also the Weinberg's soft theorems via the so called Universal triad relations.[4–8] Based on these relations Hawking et. al. conjectured that applying these relations to an asymptotically flat spacetime with a black hole in the interior would imply the existence of an infinite number of soft hairs[2,3] for the black hole which can have possible implications in the context of the black hole information paradox.

One can analyse the process of implanting soft hairs on a black hole through a physical process involving a BMS type shock wave without spherical symmetry infalling into the horizon.[3] In this talk, we consider a simplified and analogous setting consisting of the Rindler horizon and the linearly uniformly accelerated (LUA) observers, but, in the presence of a BMS type shock wave, having planar asymmetry, and impinging onto the Rindler horizon; so as to analyse the effect of Rindler BMS type supertranslations on LUA observers and on the Unruh thermal bath. The former constitutes the classical version of the gravitational memory effect on uniformly accelerated observers[9] while the effect on the latter is the quantum memory effect which modulates the quantum entanglement between the opposing Rindler wedges in quantum field theory.[10] A corresponding phenomenon across the Schwarzschild black hole horizon suggests that the Negativity measure of entanglement between infalling and outgoing Hawking pair should be degraded due to an infalling BMS shockwave while there should be linear order generation of Negativity between two outgoing Hawking particles. Implications are discussed.

2. Implanting supertranslational hair: Physical process

We work with the advanced Bondi-type co-ordinates (v, r, x, y) and write the metric of the Rindler spacetime as

$$ds^2 = -2\kappa r dv^2 + 2dvdr + \delta_{AB} dx^A dx^B \tag{1}$$

where $\kappa > 0$, $-\infty < v < \infty$ and $-\infty < r < \infty$. The BMS-type supertranslation diffeomorphism vector for the Rindler horizon which preserves the Bondi-type gauge and also the structure of the Rindler horizon is given by[11–15]

$$\Xi^a = \frac{1}{\kappa}[f(x,y), 0, -r\partial^A f(x,y)] \tag{2}$$

where $f(x,y)$ depends only on the transverse co-ordinates. The Rindler spacetime with a BMS type null shock wave at $v = v_0$ having non-planar symmetry infalling on the Rindler horizon at $r = 0$ is then defined to be[9]

$$ds^2 = -2\kappa r dv^2 + 2dvdr + 4rh(v-v_0)\partial_A f dv dx^A$$
$$+ \left(\delta_{AB} + 2h(v-v_0)\frac{r}{\kappa}\partial_A \partial_B f\right) dx^A dx^B \tag{3}$$

where $h(v - v_0)$ is the Heaviside step function. Essentially, the above metric is obtained by joining the Rindler supertranslated metric to the one described in Eq.(1) along the shock wave at $v = v_0$. The stress energy tensor including a surface energy term satisfying the null energy conditions is non zero along the shockwave at $v = v_0$ while it vanishes elsewhere for $v \neq v_0$.

3. Gravitational memory for LUA observers

The linearly uniformly accelerated (LUA) observers are the generalisation of the flat spacetime Rindler trajectories to the case of a curved background spacetime. As the name suggests, the LUA trajectories have constant magnitude of 4 vector acceleration and are also linear, in the sense of the Letaw-Frenet equations in a curved spacetime with vanishing torsion and hyper-torsion.[9] The linearity is essential since it guarantees that the LUA trajectory is locally hyperbolic in all local inertial frames at each point on the trajectory. Such trajectories satisfy the condition

$$u^b \nabla_b a^a = w^a = |a|^2 u^a \tag{4}$$

where u^i and a^i are the 4-velocity and the uniform magnitude 4-acceleration vectors respectively. The constraint in Eq.(4) guarantees that any change in the velocity and acceleration vectors lie in the same plane along the trajectory.

To address the question of finding the LUA trajectories for the case of infalling supertranslated BMS type shock wave on the Rindler horizon as described in section 2, we choose a representative family of orbits of the boost Killing vector $\bar{\xi}^a = \kappa^{-1}(1,0,0,0)$ in the advanced Bondi-type co-ordinates for $v < v_0$, the region before the wave. The worldline for such a family of trajectories is given by $x^a(\tau) = [\tau/\sqrt{2\kappa r_c}, r_c, x_c^A]$ where τ is the proper time and r_c, x_c^A are some fixed constants. These worldline can be extended over the BMS tyoe shock wave at $v = v_0$ by demanding that the constraint in Eq.(4) holds all along the trajectory. Working to linear order in the perturbation, the solution for the 4 velocity can be found to be

$$u^a = \left[\frac{1}{\sqrt{2\kappa r}}, 0, -h(v-v_0)\cosh[\kappa(v-v_0)]\frac{\sqrt{2\kappa r}}{\kappa}\partial^A f\right] \tag{5}$$

while the trajectories are found by integrating with respect to τ to be

$$x^a(\tau) = \left[\frac{\tau}{\sqrt{2\kappa r_c}}, r_c, x_c^A - h\left(\frac{\kappa(\tau-\tau_0)}{\sqrt{2\kappa r_c}}\right)\partial^A f(x_c^A) 2r_c \sinh\left(\frac{\kappa(\tau-\tau_0)}{\sqrt{2\kappa r_c}}\right)\right] \tag{6}$$

where τ_0 is the proper time at $v = v_0$. When the velocity vector in Eq.(5) is transformed to a set of standard Minkowski co-ordinates (T, X, Y^A), it takes the form

$$U^a = \left[\cosh\left(\frac{\kappa\tau}{\sqrt{2\kappa r_c}} - \frac{\log[\kappa r_c]}{2}\right), \sinh\left(\frac{\kappa\tau}{\sqrt{2\kappa r_c}} - \frac{\log[\kappa r_c]}{2}\right),\right.$$
$$\left. h\left(\frac{\kappa(\tau-\tau_0)}{\sqrt{2\kappa r_c}}\right)\alpha^A \cosh\left(\frac{\kappa\tau}{\sqrt{2\kappa r_c}} - \kappa v_0\right)\right] \tag{7}$$

where $\alpha^A = \frac{\sqrt{2\kappa r_c}}{\kappa}\partial^A f(x_c^A)$. Interestingly one can check that a trajectory with given r_c, x_c^A is an integral curve of a boost Killing vector that is obtained by applying to $\bar{\xi}^a$ the Lorentz boost

$$\Lambda^a{}_b = \begin{pmatrix} 1 & 0 & \alpha^Y \cosh\beta & \alpha^Z \cosh\beta \\ 0 & 1 & -\alpha^Y \sinh\beta & -\alpha^Z \sinh\beta \\ \alpha^Y \cosh\beta & \alpha^Y \sinh\beta & 1 & 0 \\ \alpha^Z \cosh\beta & \alpha^Z \sinh\beta & 0 & 1 \end{pmatrix} \tag{8}$$

where $\beta = (1/2)\log[\kappa r_c] - \kappa v_0$. Note that the magnitude and direction of the boost (8) depend on r_c and x_c^A. Hence, we can conclude that even though, before the wave, we started with a family of solutions with the same boost killing vector $\bar{\xi}^a$, after the wave, each trajectory is an orbit of a different boost Killing vector as determined by the Lorentz boost in Eq.(8); thus implanting a supertranslational hair on the Rindler horizon by the non-planar BMS type matter shock wave and boosting a family of Rindler trajectories in a way that differs from trajectory to trajectory through their initial conditions. The trajectory-dependence essentially carries a memory of the planar inhomogeneity of the wave and constitutes the gravitational memory effect for uniformly linearly accelerated observers.

4. Quantum memory

We consider a real massless Klein Gordon scalar field in the background of the shockwave metric of section 2. We only need to write down the solution of the perturbed Klein Gordon field upto the first order in the supertranslation field f. The Klein-Gordon field equation, $\nabla_a \nabla^a \phi = 0$ for the metric in Eq.(3), becomes

$$0 = 2\kappa r \partial_r^2 \phi + 2\partial_r \partial_v \phi + \partial_x^2 \phi + \partial_y^2 \phi + 2\kappa \partial_r \phi$$
$$- 4rh(\partial^A f)\partial_r \partial_A \phi - 2\kappa^{-1} rh(\partial^A \partial^B f)\partial_A \partial_B \phi - 2h(\partial^A f)\partial_A \phi$$
$$- 2\kappa^{-1} rh(\partial^A \partial_B \partial^B f)\partial_A \phi + \kappa^{-1} h(\partial_B \partial^B f)\partial_v \phi + \kappa^{-1} rh'(\partial_B \partial^B f)\partial_r \phi \,. \quad (9)$$

The solution before the wave can be written as a complete set for positive frequency with respect to $\bar{\xi}$ as

$$\phi^0_{\omega,\mathbf{k}} = \sqrt{\frac{\sinh(\pi\omega/\kappa)}{4\pi^4 \kappa}} e^{-i\omega v} \left(\frac{2k\sqrt{r}}{\sqrt{2\kappa}}\right)^{i\omega/\kappa} K_{i\omega/\kappa}\left(\frac{2k\sqrt{r}}{\sqrt{2\kappa}}\right) e^{ik_A x^A}, \quad (10)$$

where $\omega > 0$ and $\mathbf{k} = (k_x, k_y)$ and the mode functions satisfying the usual Klein Gordon inner product rules. For the $v > v_0$ region, we exploit the fact that the the metric in Eq.(3) is obtained as a diffeomorphism generated by the Rindler supertranslation vector field Ξ to obtain the solution in linear order of perturbation using the supertranslated vector as

$$\phi^1_{\omega,\mathbf{k}} = (1 - \Xi^a \partial_a) \phi^0_{\omega,\mathbf{k}}$$
$$= \left(1 + i\kappa^{-1}\omega f + i\kappa^{-1} r k_A \partial^A f\right) \phi^0_{\omega,\mathbf{k}} \,. \quad (11)$$

We can now expand the solution at $v > v_0$ in the basis $\left\{\phi^1_{\omega,\mathbf{k}}\right\}$ to get

$$\widehat{\phi}_{\omega,\mathbf{k}} = \begin{cases} \phi^0_{\omega,\mathbf{k}} & \text{for } v < v_0; \\ \int_0^\infty d\omega' \int d^2\mathbf{k}' \left(\alpha_{\omega,\mathbf{k};\omega',\mathbf{k}'} \phi^1_{\omega',\mathbf{k}'} + \beta_{\omega,\mathbf{k};\omega',\mathbf{k}'} \phi^{1*}_{\omega',\mathbf{k}'}\right) & \text{for } v > v_0, \end{cases} \quad (12)$$

where the αs and βs are the Bogoliubov coefficients between the $\left\{\phi^0_{\omega,\mathbf{k}}\right\}$ basis and the $\left\{\phi^1_{\omega,\mathbf{k}}\right\}$ basis. Imposing the proper the matching conditions at $v = v_0$, one can evaluate the Bogoliubov coefficients in a perturbation series, the linear order form of which is presented in.[10] The explicit form shall not be needed here except for one significant detail that both the Bogoliubov coefficients are non-vanishing. We can then quantise the field in the standard way which would then imply that the Rindler vacuum in the $v < v_0$ region before the wave is not same as the vacuum in the $v > v_0$ region, that is, the presence of the asymmetric supertranslated shock wave changes the background Rindler vacuum. We next address the question how the non-zero Bogoliubov coefficients affect the entanglement between the modes in the left and right Rindler wedge.

Before the shock wave we consider a two mode entangled state comprising of the left and right Rindler modes given by

$$|\Phi\rangle = |\phi_1\rangle \otimes |\phi_2\rangle , \qquad (13)$$

where

$$|\phi_1\rangle = \frac{1}{\sqrt{1+p^2}} \left(|0\rangle_A \otimes |0\rangle_B + p|1\rangle_A \otimes |1\rangle_B\right) , \qquad (14a)$$

$$|\phi_2\rangle = \frac{1}{\sqrt{1+q^2}} \left(|0\rangle_C \otimes |0\rangle_D + q|1\rangle_C \otimes |1\rangle_D\right) , \qquad (14b)$$

and p and q are real-valued parameters. We have labelled the two modes as 1 and 2 and their corresponding left and right mode pairs as (A, B) and (C, D). The choice of such a particular state is motivated from the form of low frequency expansion of the entanglement between left and right Rindler modes in the Minkowski vacuum state and hence is also related to the low energy Hawking spectra in Black holes. We use the entanglement monotone of Negativity[16–23] to quantify the entanglement between different pairs of modes. The initial nonvanishing negativities are

$$\mathcal{N}_{A\leftrightarrow B} = \frac{p}{1+p^2} , \qquad (15a)$$

$$\mathcal{N}_{C\leftrightarrow D} = \frac{q}{1+q^2} . \qquad (15b)$$

After the wave, One can compute the Negativity between the different pairs of particles using the Bogoliubov coefficients in terms of their perturbative orders to get

Negativity	Before wave	After wave
	$v < v_0$	$v > v_0$
A ↔ B	$\frac{p}{1+p^2}$	↓ $O(\lambda^2)$
B ↔ D	0	↑ $O(\lambda)$
B ↔ C	0	↑ $O(\lambda^2)$

The complete expressions are provided in.[10] One can observe from the above table that the negativity between the left and right modes A and B respectively is decreased by $O(\lambda^2)$ while there is linear order generation of Negativity between the right Rindler modes B and D. We have further checked that this is consistent with the quantum monogamy relation for Negativity.

5. Discussion

We have investigated the gravitational memory effect for the Rindler family of uniformly linearly accelerated observers using the BMS-type symmetries of the Rindler horizon. We described a physical process analogous to that proposed by HPS[3] that implants supertranslational hair on a Rindler horizon by a matter shock wave without planar symmetry. Before the wave, a family of observers are considered which are orbits of a single boost Killing vector. After the wave has passed, each observer satisfying the constraint of local hyperbolicity in Eq.(4) is found to be an orbit of a different boost Killing vector which differs from trajectory to trajectory. This is the classical memory effect for Rindler observers since the different boosts retains a memory of the planar inhomogeneity of the wave. The Classical memory is also accompanied by a supertranslation quantum memory which is found to modulate the entanglement between the opposing Rindler wedges in quantum field theory. A corresponding phenomenon across the Schwarzschild black hole horizon indicates that the Negativity measure of entanglement between infalling and outgoing Hawking pair should be degraded due to an infalling soft hair implanting shockwave while there should be linear order generation of Negativity between two outgoing Hawking particles Fig. 1.

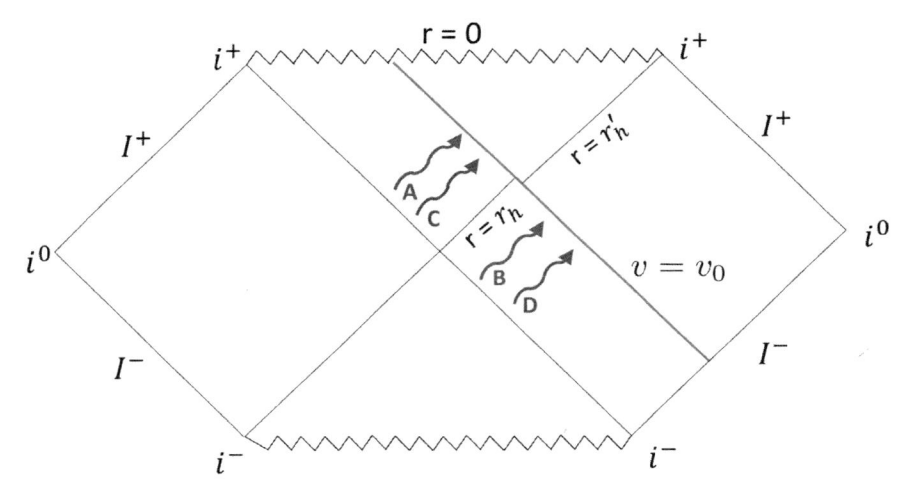

Fig. 1. The extended Schwarzschild spacetime with an infalling, supertranslation-implanting shock wave at $v = v_0$. Two Hawking pairs are shown, $A \leftrightarrow B$ (red) and $C \leftrightarrow D$ (blue).

References

1. H. Bondi, M. G. J. van der Burg and A. Metzner, Proc. Roy. Soc. Lond. **A269**, 21-52 (1962); R. Sachs, Proc. Roy. Soc. Lond. **A270**, 103-126 (1962); R. Sachs, Phys. Rev. **128**, 2851-2864 (1962).
2. S. W. Hawking, M. J. Perry and A. Strominger, Phys. Rev. Lett. **116**, 231301 (2016) [arXiv:1601.00921 [hep-th]].
3. S. W. Hawking, M. J. Perry and A. Strominger, JHEP **1705**, 161 (2017) [arXiv:1611.09175 [hep-th]].
4. A. Strominger, JHEP **1407**, 152 (2014) [arXiv:1312.2229].
5. T. He, V. Lysov, P. Mitra and A. Strominger, [arXiv:1401.7026 hep-th].

6. J. Winicour, Class. Quant. Grav. **31**, 205003 (2014) [arXiv:1407.0259].
7. A. Ashtekar, Surveys in Differential Geometry **20**, 99 (2015) [arXiv:1409.1800].
8. A. Strominger and A. Zhiboedov, JHEP **1601**, 086 (2016) [arXiv:1411.5745].
9. S. Kolekar and J. Louko, Phys. Rev. D **96**, 024054 (2017) [arXiv:1703.10619 [hep-th]].
10. S. Kolekar and J. Louko, Phys. Rev. D **97**, 085012 (2018) [arXiv:1709.07355 [hep-th]].
11. L. Donnay, G. Giribet, H. A. Gonzalez and M. Pino, Phys. Rev. Lett. **116**, 091101 (2016) [arXiv:1511.08687 [hep-th]].
12. L. Donnay, G. Giribet, H. A. Gonzalez and M. Pino, JHEP **1609**, 100 (2016) [arXiv:1607.05703 [hep-th]].
13. C. Eling and Y. Oz, JHEP **1607**, 065 (2016) [arXiv:1605.00183 [hep-th]].
14. R. G. Cai, S. M. Ruan and Y. L. Zhang, JHEP **1609**, 163 (2016) [arXiv:1609.01056 [gr-qc]].
15. M. Hotta, J. Trevison and K. Yamaguchi, Phys. Rev. D **94**, 083001 (2016) [arXiv:1606.02443 [gr-qc]].
16. A. Peres, Phys. Rev. Lett. **77**, 1413 (1996) [arXiv:quant-ph/9604005].
17. M. Horodecki, P. Horodecki and R. Horodecki, Phys. Lett. A **223**, 1 (1996) [arXiv:quant-ph/9605038].
18. G. Vidal and R. F. Werner, Phys. Rev. A **65**, 032314 (2002) [arXiv:quant-ph/0102117].
19. M. B. Plenio, Phys. Rev. Lett. **95**, 090503 (2005) [arXiv:quant-ph/0505071].
20. K. Audenaert, M. B. Plenio, and J. Eisert, Phys. Rev. Lett. **90**, 027901 (2003) [arXiv:quant-ph/0207146].
21. M. B. Plenio and S. Virmani, Quant. Inf. Comput. **7**, 1 (2007) [arXiv:quant-ph/0702059].
22. R. Simon, Phys. Rev. Lett. **84**, 2726 (2000).
23. G. Adesso and F. Illuminati, J. Phys. A **40**, 7821 (2007) [arXiv:quant-ph/0701221].

Gravitational singularities, scattering maps for bouncing, and structure-preserving algorithms

Philippe G. LeFloch

Laboratoire Jacques-Louis Lions and Centre National de la Recherche Scientifique Sorbonne Université, 4 Place Jussieu, 75252 Paris, France
Email: contact@philippelefloch.org. Blog: philippelefloch.org

This note emphasizes the role of multi-scale wave structures and junction conditions in many fields of physics, from the dynamics of fluids with non-convex equations of state to the study of gravitational singularities and bouncing cosmologies in general relativity. Concerning the definition and construction of bouncing spacetimes, we review the recent proposal in collaboration with B. Le Floch and G. Veneziano based on the notion of singularity scattering maps. We also present recent numerical investigations of small-scale phenomena arising in compressible fluid flows on FRLW or Kasner geometries for which we developed structure-preserving algorithms.

Keywords: Gravitational singularity; scattering map; small-scale phenomenon; structure-preserving algorithm.

1. Introduction

Recent advances on the mathematical modeling of complex fluid flows containing nonlinear waves and gravitational singularities lead to new challenges for numerical relativity. New ideas and techniques to analyze and compute the asymptotic behavior of multi-physics and multi-scale nonlinear waves have been introduced in the context of classical fluid dynamics but is relevant also for the dynamics of self-gravitating fluids. In this short note, we show some numerical results based on structure-preserving numerical algorithms for a few model problems describing multi-scale nonlinear waves on a fixed background. We also present a recent proposal for defining bouncing cosmologies, which is based on the notion of universal scattering maps for gravitational singularities.

This presentation uses material from joint collaborations, especially with B. Le Floch and G. Veneziano (scattering maps) and with F. Beyer (Fuchsian algorithm). It is based on a lecture entitled *"On the scattering laws of bouncing universes"* given at the *Sixteenth Marcel Grossmann Meeting* in July 2021. It is also based on a lecture entitled *"Gravitational singularities, massive fields, and asymptotic localization"* given at the Workshop *"Computational Challenges in Multi-Messenger Astrophysics"*, held at IPAM, University of California at Los Angeles, in October 2021.

Only few references are included in this short note and, for our motivations to study bouncing cosmologies and relativistic fluids with complex equation of state, we refer to the review papers by Ashtekar,[2] Blaschke,[7] Font,[11] as well as the recent papers by Ibánez et al.[10] and Wilson-Ewing.[23]

An outline is as follows. In Section 2 our standpoint concerning problems involving viscosity-capillarity waves and other multi-scale interfaces is discussed. In Section 3, numerical observations obtained with structure-preserving algorithms are overviewed for fluid problems in the vicinity of gravitational singularities. In Section 4, the scattering laws for gravitational singularities are presented and we distinguish between their universal and model-dependent properties.

2. Structure of multi-physics and multi-scale waves

2.1. Multi-scale wave phenomena

Systems of balance laws. The models of interest are formulated from first principles of continuum physics (that is, conservation laws or more generally balance laws) when suitable physics features are taken into account.

- Several parameters are often relevant in order to fully describe the fine dynamics of the fluid flows of interest: viscosity, surface tension, heat conduction, Hall effect, friction, etc. Various competitive effects take place, due to the presence of several very different scales in, both, the fluid unknowns and the geometry unknowns of the problem.
- These nonlinear systems of partial differential equations, in the course of the time evolution, exhibit a formation of interfaces, shocks, oscillating patterns, etc. Fluids, gases, plasmas, solid materials, etc. all exhibit fine structures that form dynamically. This is the case of liquid-vapor flows, thin liquid films, combustion wave problems, bores in shallow water, astrophysical flows, neutron stars, phase transformations (austenite-martensite), etc.
- Very often, a *fine-scale structure* (oscillations, turbulence) arises asymptotically (for instance in the vicinity of a singularity hypersurface) which is challenging to analyze mathematically and to compute numerically.

Asymptotic analysis. The ideas and techniques developed in the context of fluid dynamics are relevant for the modeling of the global dynamics of massive fields (Klein-Gordon), complex fluids, as well as models of modified gravity beyond Einstein gravity. In addition to the shock waves observed in fluid dynamics one must also encompass impulsive gravitational waves and cosmological singularities.

In order to understand the global dynamics of these *scale-sensitive nonlinear waves*, a novel perspective is required which is based on an asymptotic analysis of the physical models.

- We restrict attention to the regime where we can extract variables with well-defined limits, even though persistent oscillations in some other variables may be observed as the singularity is approached.

- We seek junction laws or scattering laws, which in the case of fluid take the form of jump laws for (subsonic) liquid-gas boundaries, for combustion waves, etc.
- The interfaces that require additional junction laws are typically *undercompressive waves* and turn out to enjoy (saddle) stability properties.

2.2. *Regime of small viscosity and capillarity*

Non-convex equation of state. One of the simplest partial differential equation that exhibits small-scale dependent interfaces is the following model in plane-symmetry formulated as a hyperbolic conservation law with non-convex equation of state $p(\rho) = \rho^3$

$$\frac{\partial}{\partial t}\rho + \frac{\partial}{\partial x}\rho^3 = \varepsilon \frac{\partial^2}{\partial x^2}\rho + \kappa \frac{\partial^3}{\partial x^3}\rho, \tag{1}$$

for a fluid density unknown $\rho = \rho(t,x)$ (with $t \geq 0$ and $x \in \mathbb{R}$, say). This equation describes certain phase transition phenomena, but also arises as a simplified model of magnetohydrodynamics. Here, a small viscosity coefficient $\varepsilon > 0$ and a surface tension/capillarity coefficient $\kappa > 0$ are given, the latter representing the intermolecular forces between a liquid and its surroundings.

The Riemann problem consists of an initial value problem associated with a single initial discontinuity (also called the dam breaking problem). Interestingly, in the limit of arbitrarily small $\varepsilon, \kappa \to 0$, the equation (1) exhibits complex wave patterns, which are more involved than the ones usually observed with (polytropic perfect, say) compressible fluids. See the illustration in Figure 1. Many scalar wave models exhibit the same features, for instance the so-called thin liquid film model and the so-called Benjamin–Bona–Mahony model. Let us for instance give here a class of fourth-order models (with $\varepsilon, \kappa, \lambda > 0$):

$$\frac{\partial}{\partial t}\rho + \frac{\partial}{\partial x}p(\rho) = \varepsilon \frac{\partial^2}{\partial x^2}\rho + \kappa \frac{\partial^3}{\partial x^3}\rho - \lambda \frac{\partial^4}{\partial x^4}\rho. \tag{2}$$

Three possible asymptotic regimes. In the limit $\varepsilon \to 0$ in (1), we should distinguish between three behaviors depending upon the capillarity parameter κ:

- $\kappa \ll \varepsilon^2$: the viscosity is then dominant, and no oscillations are observed while a single limit is reached. The solutions (sometimes referred to as classical weak solutions) are characterized by standard Rankine-Hugoniot relations and entropy criteria.
- $\kappa = \alpha \varepsilon^2$: this is the *balanced regime* of main interest in the present discussion. The numerical solutions converge in a strong sense, despite some mild oscillations in the limit. (See again Figure 1.) Interestingly, the limit (now sometimes referred to as a nonclassical weak solution) *depends upon the ratio* $\alpha = \kappa/\varepsilon^2$ of the viscosity and capillarity parameters. (See also Figure 3 for van der Waals fluids.)

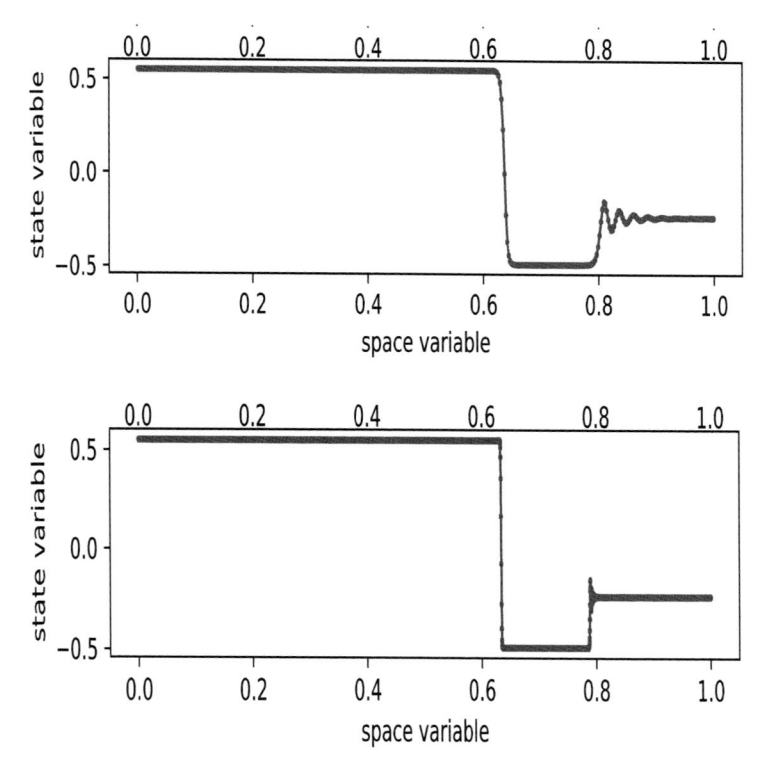

Fig. 1. The Riemann problem for a non-convex equation of state.

- $\kappa \gg \varepsilon^2$: in this regime, the effect of the surface tension is dominant and wild oscillations arise as $\varepsilon \to 0$. There is no well-defined limit, unless weak convergence techniques or a suitable turbulence-like theory are introduced.

Wave structure of van der Waals fluids. Let us provide a further illustration with the system of isothermal compressible fluids which is closest to the interest of the GR community. We consider a Van der Waals fluid, in a non-relativistic setup, whose dynamics is modeled by the following two conservation laws (continuity equation, conservation of momentum) :

$$\frac{\partial}{\partial t}\tau - \frac{\partial}{\partial x}u = 0, \qquad \frac{\partial}{\partial t}u + \frac{\partial}{\partial x}p(v) = \varepsilon \frac{\partial^2}{\partial x^2}u - \kappa \frac{\partial^3}{\partial x^3}\tau, \qquad (3)$$

in which $\tau = 1/\rho$ represents the specific volume and u denotes the velocity component for plane-symmetric solutions to the Euler equations. The viscosity parameter ε and the capillarity parameter κ are taken to be small. We assume that the temperature T remains constant (in a suitable approximation) and we model liquid-vapor phase transitions by the non-convex pressure law (after normalization)

$$p(\tau) = \frac{8T}{3\tau - 1} - \frac{3}{\tau^2}. \qquad (4)$$

The equations (3)-(4) are nonlinear hyperbolic when T is sufficiently large, but of mixed (hyperbolic-elliptic) type otherwise. The typical Riemann wave structure for van der Waal fluids is shown in Figure 2.

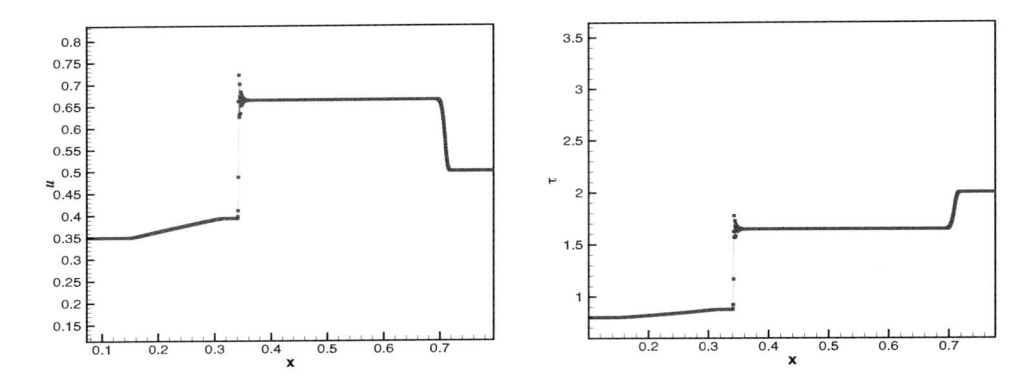

Fig. 2. Van der Waals fluids: velocity (left-hand) and specific volume (right-hand).

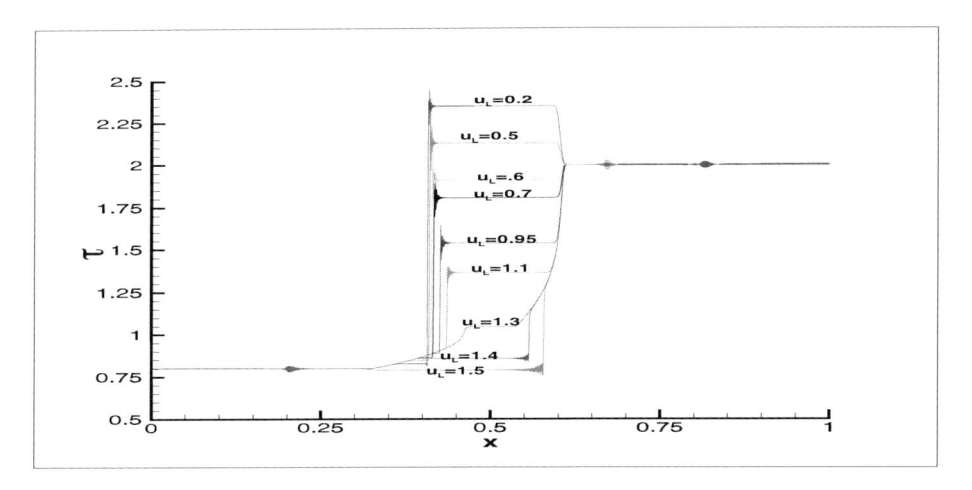

Fig. 3. Van der Waals fluids: specific volume for different ratios of the viscosity and capillarity.

Proposed standpoint: hidden junction conditions. Small-scale dependent, shock waves enjoy a structure that is not properly captured by the standard Rankine-Hugoniot junction conditions of fluid dynamics, even when a suitable entropy condition is enforced. Further analytical work is required which shows that the wave structure strongly depends upon varying the ratio surface tension/viscosity $\kappa = \alpha \varepsilon^2$ (in the balanced regime). (See again Figure 3 for van der Waals fluids.) Suitable rules for connecting left- and right-hand state values from both sides of the interface is necessary, beyond the standard Rankine-Hugoniot relations. These *scattering laws* take the form, in this context, of *kinetic functions for interfaces*. It is outside the scope of this short Note to explain this notion here, and we refer the reader to the textbook[13] and the lecture notes[12,14] and the historical references therein. Importantly, based on these scattering maps we need to design structure-preserving algorithms, which are typically of front tracking type, or of shock capturing type with well-controlled dissipation.[15] The algorithms are designed in order to *mimic analytical properties at the discrete level* and this requirement may take very different flavors: divergence form, spacelike decay, timelike decay shock-capturing, energy balance laws, asymptotics on singularities, etc.

3. Structure-preserving algorithms for fluids near gravitational singularities

3.1. *Preserving the asymptotic structure on a Kasner background: evolution from the singularity*

Evolution in the vicinity of a gravitational singularity. In a joint work with F. Beyer,[6] I have studied the evolution of a compressible fluid on a Kasner geometry, namely on a spatially homogeneous, anisotropic vacuum background described by the metric

$$g = t^{(K^2-)/2}\bigl(-dt^2 + dx^2 + t^{1-K}dy^2 + t^{1+K}dz^2\bigr), \qquad M = (0, +\infty) \times \mathbb{T}^3 \qquad (5)$$

Here, we set $t \in (0, \infty)$ and $x, y, z \in (0, 2\pi)$ and we introduce the parameter $K \in \mathbb{R}$ and the Kasner exponents

$$p_1 = \frac{K^2 - 1}{K^2 + 3}, \quad p_2 = \frac{2(1-K)}{K^2 + 3}, \quad p_3 = \frac{2(1+K)}{K^2 + 3}. \qquad (6)$$

The free parameter $K \in \mathbb{R}$ is sometimes referred to as the *asymptotic velocity*. Except for the three flat Kasner cases given by $K = 1$, $K = -1$, and (formally) $|K| \to \infty$, the Kasner metrics g have a curvature singularity in the limit $t \searrow 0$. We treat a compressible fluid flow with pressure law

$$p = (\gamma - 1)\rho \quad \text{with } \gamma \in (1, 2). \qquad (7)$$

Fuchsian analysis for the Euler equations of compressible fluids. In[6] we discovered a *characteristic fluid exponent* defined as

$$\Gamma = \frac{1}{4}\bigl(3\gamma - 2 - K^2(2-\gamma)\bigr) \in (0,1), \qquad (8)$$

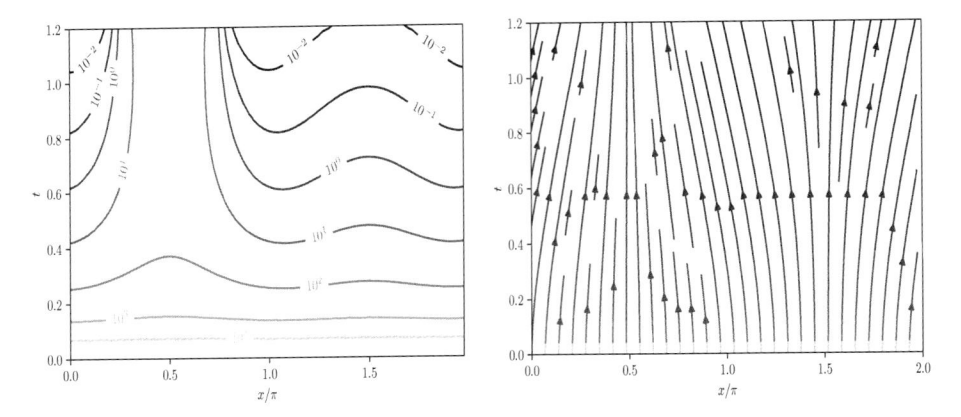

Fig. 4. Evolution of a compressible fluid *from* a gravitational singularity: Kasner background.

which compares the geometry and fluid behaviors:

- $\Gamma > 0$: this is a sub-critical regime which is dynamically stable.
- $\Gamma \leq 0$: this is a super-critical (or critical) regime which is dynamically unstable.

This (positivity/negativity) condition arises by plugging an expansion in power of t for the fluid unknown variables of the Euler equations, and attempting to validate this expansion in t via the Fuchsian method.

The Fuschian method concerns the evolution problem *from* the cosmological singularity $t = 0$ (rather than *towards* it). We formulate a singular initial value problem of the form

$$B^0(U,t,x)\frac{\partial}{\partial t}U + B^1(U,t,x)\frac{\partial}{\partial x}U = f(U,t,x) \qquad (9)$$

with suitable "singular initial data" prescribed at $t = 0$. Fuchsian-type expansions are then derived from an ODE approximation near the cosmological singularity. In the present work, we focus on the sufficiently regular, shock-free regime for the Euler equations.

Algorithm preserving the Fuchsian structure. We approximate the singular Cauchy problem of Fuchsian type by a sequence of regular Cauchy problems, which we next discretize by the pseudo-spectral method of lines, say $U(t,x) \simeq V(t) = (V_j(t))$ with

$$\partial_t V - AV = h(V,t). \qquad (10)$$

A high-order Runge-Kutta discretization is used in time. Importantly, we introduce *suitably rescaled variables* and next careful study of the numerical error. To this end, we take into account the Fuchsian expansion available near the singularity. We observe that there are two sources of approximation error, namely continuum and discrete.

Our proposal in order to get an efficient algorithm is to *keep the two error sources asymptotically in balance*. With this numerical strategy, we can demonstrate the *nonlinear stability of the flow* near the cosmological singularity in the sub-critical regime. See Figure 4 for a numerical simulation on a Kasner background for a typical evolution from the singularity. The fluid density is shown in contour plot while the normalized velocity field is shown in flow lines.

The density ρ unbounded as the time $t \to 0$, and we carefully checked the numerical error in order to produce quantitative error control. In turn we arrive at reliable and accurate algorithm, despite the solutions being *highly singular*.

3.2. *Preserving the asymptotic structure on an inhomogeneous FLRW background*

Evolution of fluid with shock waves. In a joint work[8,9] with Y. Cao and M. Ghazizadeh, I have considered the evolution of a compressible fluid *toward* a cosmological singularity. Therein, we consider the Cauchy problem i isothermal, relativistic compressible flow with linear pressure law $p(\rho) = k^2 \rho$. The background geometry is taken to be a contracting (or expanding) inhomogeneous background with torus topology $\mathbb{T}^2$, corresponding to a FLRW-type cosmological background with small inhomogeneities. For isothermal fluids, the Euler equations take the form of a system of two nonlinear hyperbolic balance laws, which we treat in one and in two space dimensions under symmetry assumptions. Let us focus here on the future-contracting direction ($t < 0$ with $t \to 0$) and we observe that the mass energy density $\rho \to +\infty$. The expanding direction is also treated in.[8,9] The challenge is to design a scheme that preserves the structure of the solutions as the singularity is approached and the unknown variables become singular.

We analyze the asymptotic behavior of the fluid variables toward the cosmological singularity, by rewriting first the equations as a nonlinear hyperbolic systems on a curved geometry, say

$$\partial_t U + \partial_x F(t, x, U) = H(t, x, U). \tag{11}$$

Two *competitive effects* take place in this problem which concern the contracting geometry and the shock propagation. The nonlinear wave interactions give rise to a small-scale structure, which in the present setup is simply driven by the background geometry. Yet, we can keep in mind the analogy with phase transition dynamics which involves multiple scales as explained in Section 2. Extensive numerical experiments were performed in one and in two space dimensions are performed in order to investigate the fine behavior of the solutions in the vicinity of the singularity.

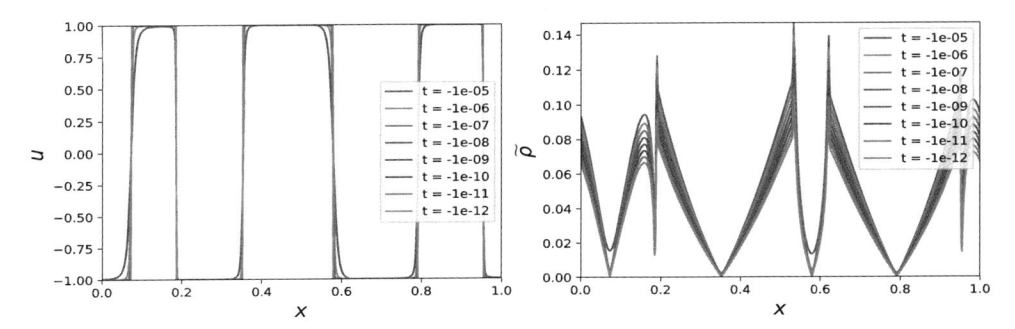

Fig. 5. Evolution of a compressible fluid **toward** a gravitational singularity. Left-hand: velocity scalar. Right-hand: rescaled mass energy density.

Structure-preserving methodology. We formulate a shock-capturing scheme in divergence form, based on the finite volume methodology. The shock-capturing property ensures that the shock waves will propagate with the correct speed given by the Rankine-Hugoniot condition. We require high accuracy and use a discretization which is 4th-order in time and 2nd-order in space, hence ensure that the numerical solution is oscillation-free. In order to guarantee the *well-balanced property* we proceed as follows:

- We introduce suitably *rescaled unknowns* which are directly motivated by a Fuchsian analysis of the problem.
- The discrete form of the balance laws is designed in order to enforce the correct *asymptotic state equations at the discrete level*.
- In turn , we enforce the *commutation property*

$$\lim_{t \to 0} \lim_{\Delta x \to 0} U = \lim_{\Delta x \to 0} \lim_{t \to 0} U \qquad (12)$$

relating the limits of the numerical solution $U_{\Delta x}(t, x)$

The typical behavior that we observed *toward* the cosmological singularity are sharp transitions with spikes, and these spikes turn out to be well capured by our numerical method in the asymptotic limit $t \to 0$. See the plots of the rescaled velocity component u and rescaled density $\widetilde{\rho}$. See Figure 5 for the evolution of a compressible fluid **toward** a gravitational singularity.

4. On the scattering laws of bouncing universes

4.1. *Seeking a formulation of bouncing laws*

Bouncing cosmologies. In a joint work in collaboration with B. Le Floch (Paris) and G. Veneziano (Geneva) I considered gravitational singularities in the context of the Einstein equations coupled to a self-gravitating scalar field. More generally, our ideas apply to a stiff fluid or a compressible fluid. We are interested in analyzing bouncing cosmologies involving a contracting phase and an expanding phase of evolution, connected across a singularity hypersurface. Our analysis takes place in the vicinity of such a singularity hypersurface, and we focus on the jump relations that should hold at that interface. Recall that in presence of strong fields or away from the near-Minkowski regime of evolution, Penrose and Hawking's singularity theorems (or incompleteness theorems) suggest that gravitational singularities (or other incompleteness phenomena) are expected to occur, although very little is known on the actual asymptotic behavior beyond the classical BKL conjecture.

Physics literature on bouncing. We build upon a large literature on bouncing cosmologies by Penrose, Tod, Lübbe, Turok, Barrow, and many others. We emphasize that existing proposals are based on the analysis of symmetric spacetimes and/or the formulation of special junctions. In order to define the bouncing, a large number of proposals are found in the literature, including the pre-Big Bang scenario (Gasperini, Veneziano, etc.), a variety of models of modified gravity-matter (Brandenberger, Chamseddine, Cotsakis, Mukhanov, Peter, Steinhardt, Turok, etc.), and the theory of loop quantum cosmology (Asthekar, de Cesare, Gupt, Pawlowski, Singh, Wilson-Ewing, etc.).

Proposed standpoint. Our aim is to propose a formulation of the problem of junction at singularities and to perform a systematic investigation of such junction conditions. This is motivated by the ideas discussed in Section 2. We expect to derive classes of physically meaningful junction conditions which depend upon certain (limited) degrees of freedom and constraints at the singularity. Interestingly, based on the scattering maps we propose we can also define and construct classes of cyclic spacetimes. Here, we only outline a selection of our results and refer the reader to[18–20] for the complete definitions and further material.

We study the class of (past, future) *singularity data* denoted by $(g^\pm, K^\pm, \phi_0^\pm, \phi_1^\pm)$ and defined after a suitable rescaling (see below). We then introduce a *singularity scattering map* $(g^-, K^-, \phi_0^-, \phi_1^-) \mapsto (g^+, K^+, \phi_0^+, \phi_1^+)$ in order to cross the singularity hypersurface. Our main contribution is a full classification of the possible bouncing conditions. We are able to distinguish between *universal* scattering laws and *model-dependent* scattering maps.

We thus provide a flexible framework and a classification which uncovers all possible classes of junctions that are geometrically and physically meaningful. We also exhibit several sub-classes of particular interest, namely the conformal/non-conformal maps, the spacelike/null/timelike maps, and we encompass different models of matter (scalar field, stiff fluid, compressible fluid). In the course of establishing our classification, we also discover three universal laws that put constrains on the macroscopic aspects of spacetime bounces, *regardless of their origin from different microscopic corrections*. Our classification provides one with a guide in order to uncover relevant structures, described by scattering maps associated with specific theories.

4.2. Proposed formulation of the bouncing problem

The field equations. We consider a local ADM formulation near a singularity hypersurface, based on a Gaussian foliation (local patch) $\mathcal{M}^{(4)} = \bigcup_{\tau \in [\tau_{-1}, \tau_1]} \mathcal{H}_\tau$ by spacelike hypersurfaces (diffeomorphic to $\mathcal{H}_0$). We write

$$g^{(4)} = (g^{(4)}_{\alpha\beta}) = -d\tau^2 + g(\tau) \qquad g(\tau) = g_{ij}(\tau) dx^i dx^j, \tag{13}$$

and we impose Einstein's evolution equations for the unknown metric g and the unknown extrinsic curvature K

$$\partial_\tau g_{ij} = -2\, K_{ij} \qquad \partial_\tau K^i_j = \mathbf{Tr}(K) K^i_j + R^i_j - 8\pi\, M^i_j. \tag{14}$$

Here, $M^i_j = \frac{1}{2}\rho g^i_j + T^i_j - \frac{1}{2}\mathbf{Tr}(T)g^i_j$ is the matter contribution. These equations are supplemented with Einstein's constraint equations

$$R + |K|^2 - \mathbf{Tr}(K^2) = 16\pi\rho \qquad \nabla_i K^i_j - \nabla_j(\mathbf{Tr} K) = 8\pi J_j, \tag{15}$$

which are nonlinear elliptic equations. Finally, we assume that the energy-momentum tensor is given by a massless scalar field ϕ whose evolution is given by the wave equation

$$\Box_{g^{(4)}} \phi = 0. \tag{16}$$

Near a singularity hypersurface, it is standard to rely on the Fuchsian method (Baouendi, Goulaouic, Rendall, Isenberg, Moncrief, etc.):

- We solve locally from $\tau = 0$ toward the past ($\tau < 0$) or the future ($\tau > 0$).
- We apply the so-called "velocity dominated" Ansatz, which tells us that in the gauge under consideration all spatial derivatives (except for the momentum equations) can be neglected.
- In turn, we must solve a system of nonlinear coupled differential equations in the time variable with nonlinear source-terms (containing spatial derivatives) and by a suitable iteration scheme we generate solutions to the full Einstein equations.

Singularity data and asymptotic profiles. A 3-manifold $\mathcal{H}$ is fixed throughout and represents the singularity hypersurface.

1. An **asymptotic profile** associated with data $(g^-, K^-, \phi_0^-, \phi_1^-) \in \mathbf{I}(\mathcal{H})$ is the flow on $\mathcal{H}$

$$\begin{aligned}
\tau \in (-\infty, 0) \mapsto (g^*, K^*, \phi^*)(\tau), & \qquad g^*(\tau) = |\tau|^{2K^-} g^-, \\
K^*(\tau) = \frac{-1}{\tau} K^-, & \qquad \phi^*(\tau) = \phi_0^- \log|\tau| + \phi_1^-,
\end{aligned} \tag{17}$$

in which $|\tau|^{2K^-}$ is defined by exponentiation.

2. A **singularity initial data set** $(g^-, K^-, \phi_0^-, \phi_1^-)$, consists of two tensor fields (rescaled metric and extrinsic curvature) and two scalar fields defined on $\mathcal{H}$.

3. The **asymptotic version of the Einstein constraints** reads as follows:

Riemannian metric	$g^- = (g_{ij}^-)$ on $\mathcal{H}$.
CMC symmetric $(1,1)$-tensor	$K^- = (K_i^{-j})$ with $\mathbf{Tr}(K^-) = 1$ on $\mathcal{H}$.
Hamiltonian constraint	$1 - |K^-|^2 = 8\pi (\phi_0^-)^2$ on $\mathcal{H}$.
momentum constraints	$\mathbf{Div}_{g^-}(K^-) = 8\pi \phi_0^- d\phi_1^-$ on $\mathcal{H}$.

(18)

We denote by $\mathbf{I}(\mathcal{H})$ the set of space of all singularity data.

Junction conditions. The notion of a *scattering map* arises naturally from earlier considerations about fluid interfaces. We think of a singularity hypersurface as a fluid-like interface between two "phases", across which the geometry and the matter field encounter a "jump". Small-scale physics phenomena are not directly modeled at this stage. We are only interested in the "average" effect rather than the detailed physics that may take place "within" this interface. This is a standard strategy in fluid dynamics and material science in presence of phase transition phenomena, especially when some (micro-scale) parameters (viscosity, surface tension, heat conduction, etc.,) can be neglected in the modeling. Macro-scale effects are captured by jump conditions such as Rankine-Hugoniot, kinetic relations, Dal Maso-LeFloch-Murat's paths, etc. For instance, kinetic relations in material science (martensite-austenite) and in two-phase liquid-vapor flows have been extensively studied. In this context, hypersurfaces are timelike; in the present discussion of gravitational singularities we focus our attention on spacelike hypersurfaces and refer the reader to[19] for the treatment of timelike singularity hypersurfaces.

Bounce based on a singularity scattering map. A (past-to-future) **singularity scattering map** on $\mathcal{H}$ is defined as a diffeomorphism-covariant map on $\mathbf{I}(\mathcal{H})$

$$\mathbf{S} : \mathbf{I}(\mathcal{H}) \ni (g^-, K^-, \phi_0^-, \phi_1^-) \mapsto (g^+, K^+, \phi_0^+, \phi_1^+) \in \mathbf{I}(\mathcal{H}) \tag{19}$$

satisfying the *ultra-locality property*: for all $x \in \mathcal{H}$

$$\mathbf{S}(g^-, K^-, \phi_0^-, \phi_1^-)(x) \text{ depends only on } (g^-, K^-, \phi_0^-, \phi_1^-)(x) \tag{20}$$

Thanks to the locality condition, it is natural to identify singularity scattering maps $\mathbf{S}$ on all 3-manifolds and suppress the dependence on $\mathcal{H}$.

The map $\mathbf{S}$ is said to be a **tame-preserving map** if it preserves positivity, in the sense that

$$\text{if } K^- > 0 \text{ then } K^+ > 0, \text{ where } K^+ \text{ is defined from the image of } \mathbf{S}. \tag{21}$$

It is said to be a **rigidly-conformal map** if

$$g^+ \text{ and } g^- \text{ only differ by a conformal factor.} \tag{22}$$

Observations. We emphasize that the asymptotic profiles with $K^-, K^+ > 0$ describe a "bounce" at which

- volume element decreases to zero as $\tau \to 0^-$, and
- then increases back to finite values for $\tau > 0$.

For further notions and constructions of *cyclic spacetimes* containing many singularity hypersurfaces, we refer to[19] and, in this short Note, we focus on the issue of defining a proper junction at the bouncing.

The regime of quiescent singularities $K > 0$ is motivated by the absence of BKL oscillations in this case (named after Belinsky, Khalatnikov, and Lifshitz). This quiescent regime exhibits a monotone behavior which has received a lot of attention by mathematicians in recent years (Rendall, Andersson, Lott, Fournodavlos, Luk, Rodnianksi, Speck, etc.).

4.3. Classification of bouncing laws

Rigidly conformal maps. We discover that *only two classes* of ultra-local spacelike and rigidly conformal, singularity scattering maps exist for self-gravitating scalar fields, namely:

- The maps describing **isotropic rigidly conformal bounces** $\mathbf{S}_{\lambda,\varphi}^{\text{iso, conf}}$:

$$g^+ = \lambda^2 g^-, \qquad K^+ = \delta/3, \qquad \phi_0^+ = 1/\sqrt{12\pi}, \qquad \phi_1^+ = \varphi, \qquad (23)$$

parametrized by a conformal factor $\lambda = \lambda(\phi_0^-, \phi_1^-, \det K^-) > 0$ and a constant φ.

- The maps describing **non-isotropic rigidly conformal bounces** $\mathbf{S}_{f,c}^{\text{ani, conf}}$:

$$g^+ = c^2 \mu^2 g^-, \qquad K^+ = \mu^{-3}(K^- - \delta/3) + \delta/3,$$
$$\phi_0^+ = \mu^{-3}\phi_0^-/F'(\phi_1^-), \qquad \phi_1^+ = F(\phi_1^-), \qquad (24)$$

parametrized by a constant $c > 0$ and a function $f: \mathbb{R} \to [0, +\infty)$:

$$\mu(\phi_0, \phi_1) = \left(1 + 12\pi(\phi_0)^2 f(\phi_1)\right)^{1/6}, \quad F(\phi_1) = \int_0^{\phi_1} (1 + f(\varphi))^{-1/2} d\varphi. \quad (25)$$

General classification. Only two classes of ultra-local spacelike singularity scattering maps exist for self-gravitating scalar fields, which we denote by $\mathbf{S}_{\lambda,\varphi}^{\text{iso}}$ (isotropic bounce) and $\mathbf{S}_{\Phi,c}^{\text{ani}}$ (non-isotropic bounce). Now, λ is a two-tensor, Φ a "canonical transformation", c a constant. For the detailed expressions we refer the reader to.[19]

Three universal laws of quiescent bouncing cosmology. Interestingly our conclusions can be restated in terms of universal laws obeyed by any ultra-local bounce, as follows.

- **First law. Scaling of Kasner exponents**:

  There exists a (dissipation) constant $\gamma \in \mathbb{R}$ such that
  $$|g^+|^{1/2} \mathring{K}^+ = -\gamma |g^-|^{1/2} \mathring{K}^- \qquad (26)$$

  for the spatial metric g in synchronous gauge with volume factor $|g|^{1/2}$, where $\mathring{K}$ denotes the traceless part of the extrinsic curvature (as a $(1,1)$ tensor).

- **Second law. Canonical transformation of matter:** by denoting the conjugate matter momentum by $\pi_\phi \sim \phi_0$,

  $$\begin{aligned} &\text{there exists a nonlinear map } \Phi\colon (\pi_\phi, \phi)^- \mapsto (\pi_\phi, \phi)^+ \\ &\text{preserving the volume form in the phase space } d\pi_\phi \wedge d\phi \\ &\text{and depending solely on the scalar invariant } \mathbf{det}(\mathring{K}_-). \end{aligned} \qquad (27)$$

- **Third law. Directional metric scaling:**
  $$g^+ = \exp(\sigma_0 + \sigma_1 K + \sigma_2 K^2) g^-, \qquad (28)$$
  which is a nonlinear scaling in each proper direction of K.

We have either $\gamma = 0$ in the isotropic scattering and no restriction $\sigma_0, \sigma_1, \sigma_2$, or else $\gamma \neq 0$ for non-isotropic scattering and explicit formulas are available in terms of Φ, γ.

4.4. *Ongoing work*

Our next task will be the derivation of scattering maps associated with specific theories taking small-scale physical modeling into account. Mathematical investigations as well as numerical investigations are required. We emphasize that our methodology is based on a class of *general* spacetimes without symmetry restrictions. Earlier approaches relied on classes of symmetric spacetimes or on special junction proposals, and therefore could not single out the three universal laws we have derived. The recent developments overviewed in the present Note suggest to perform numerical simulations of cyclic spacetimes with a bounce using some of the techniques discussed in Sections 2 and 3. We refer the reader to[18–20] and to.[17]

References

1. P. Amorim, C. Bernardi, and P.G. LeFloch, Computing Gowdy spacetimes via spectral evolution in future and past directions, *Class. Quantum Grav.* 26 (2009), 1–18.
2. A. Ashtekar, Singularity resolution in loop quantum cosmology: a brief overview, *J. Phys. Conf. Ser.* 189 (2009), 012003.
3. F. Beyer and P.G. LeFloch, Second–order hyperbolic Fuchsian systems and applications, *Class. Quantum Grav.* 27 (2010), 245012–245033.
4. F. Beyer and P.G. LeFloch, Second–order hyperbolic Fuchsian systems. Asymptotic behavior of geodesics in Gowdy spacetimes, *Phys. Rev. D.* 84 (2011), 084036.

5. F. Beyer and P.G. LeFloch, Dynamics of self–gravitating fluids in Gowdy-symmetric spacetimes near cosmological singularities, *Comm. Part. Diff. Equa.* 42 (2017), 1199–1248.
6. F. Beyer and P.G. LeFloch, A numerical algorithm for Fuchsian equations and fluid flows on cosmological spacetimes, *J. Comput. Phys.* 431 (2021), 110145.
7. D. Blaschke, D.E. Alvarez-Castillo, A. Ayriyan, H. Grigorian, N.K. Lagarni, and F. Weber, Astrophysical aspects of general relativistic mass twin stars, Chapter 1, Topics on Strong Gravity, 2019.
8. Y.-Y. Cao, M.A. Ghazizadeh, and P.G. LeFloch, Asymptotic structure of cosmological Burgers flows in one and two space dimensions: A numerical study, *Communications in Computational Physics* 29 (2021), 472–509.
9. Y.-Y. Cao, M.A. Ghazizadeh, and P.G. LeFloch, Asymptotic structure of cosmological fluid flows in one and two space dimensions: A numerical study, *Commun. Appl. Math. Comput. Sci.* (2021), submitted. See also ArXiv:1912.13439.
10. J.M. Ibánez, A. Marquina, S. Serna, and M.A. Aloy, Anomalous dynamics triggered by a non-convex equation of state in relativistic flows, *MNRAS* 000 (2018), 1–22.
11. J.A. Font, Numerical hydrodynamics and magnetohydrodynamics in general relativity, *Living Reviews in Relativity* 11 (2008).
12. P.G. LeFloch, An introduction to nonclassical shocks of systems of conservation laws, *Lect. Notes Comput. Eng.*, Vol. 5, Springer Verlag, 1999, pp. 28–72.
13. P.G. LeFloch, *Hyperbolic Systems of Conservation Laws. The theory of classical and nonclassical shock waves*, Lectures in Mathematics, ETH Zürich, Birkhäuser, 2002.
14. P.G. LeFloch, Kinetic relations for undercompressive shock waves. Physical, mathematical, and numerical issues, *Contemporary Mathematics,* vol. 526, Amer. Math. Soc., Providence, RI, 2010, pp. 237–272.
15. P.G. LeFloch, Structure-preserving shock-capturing methods: late-time asymptotics, curved geometry, small-scale dissipation, and nonconservative products, in *"Lecture Notes of the XV Jacques-Louis Lions Spanish-French School"*, Ed. C. Parès, C. Vázquez, and F. Coquel, Springer Verlag, Switzerland, 2014, pp. 179–222.
16. B. Le Floch and P.G. LeFloch, Compensated compactness and corrector stress tensor for the Einstein equations in T2 symmetry, *Portugaliae Math.* 77 (2020), 409–421.
17. B. Le Floch and P.G. LeFloch, On the global evolution of self-gravitating matter. Scattering maps for interfaces, in preparation.
18. B. Le Floch, P.G. LeFloch, and G. Veneziano, Universal scattering laws for quiescent bouncing cosmology, *Physical Rev. D.* 8 (2021), 083531. See also ArXiv:2006.08620.
19. B. Le Floch, P.G. LeFloch, and G. Veneziano, Cyclic spacetimes through singularity scattering maps. The laws of bouncing cosmology. Preprint ArXiv:2005.11324.
20. B. Le Floch, P.G. LeFloch, and G. Veneziano, Cyclic spacetimes through singularity scattering maps. Plane-symmetric gravitational collisions. Preprint ArXiv:2106.09666.
21. M. Mars and J.M. Senovilla, Geometry of general hypersurfaces in spacetime: Junction conditions, *Class. Quantum Grav.* 10 (1993), 1865–1897.
22. A.D. Rendall, *Partial differential equations in general relativity*, Oxford University Press, Oxford, 2008.
23. E. Wilson-Ewing, The loop quantum cosmology bounce as a Kasner transition, *Classical Quant. Grav.* 35 (2018), 065005.

Brane-world asymptotics in a nonlinear fluid bulk

I. Antoniadis

Laboratoire de Physique Théorique et Hautes Energies - LPTHE, Sorbonne Université, CNRS 4 Place Jussieu, 75005 Paris, France, and
Institute for Theoretical Physics, KU Leuven, Celestijnenlaan 200D, B-3001 Leuven, Belgium
E-mail: antoniad@lpthe.jussieu.fr

S. Cotsakis

Institute of Gravitation and Cosmology, RUDN University ul. Miklukho-Maklaya 6, Moscow 117198, Russia, and
Research Laboratory of Geometry, Dynamical Systems and Cosmology, University of the Aegean, Karlovassi 83200, Samos, Greece
E-mail: skot@aegean.gr

Ifigeneia Klaoudatou

Research Laboratory of Geometry, Dynamical Systems and Cosmology, University of the Aegean, Karlovassi 83200, Samos, Greece
E-mail: iklaoud@aegean.gr

We present recent results on the asymptotics of a brane-world that consists of a flat 3-brane embedded in a five-dimensional bulk. The bulk matter is modelled by a fluid that satisfies a nonlinear equation of state of the form $p = \gamma \rho^\lambda$, where p is the 'pressure' and ρ is the 'density' of the fluid. We show that for appropriate ranges of the parameters γ and λ, it is possible to construct a regular solution, compatible with energy conditions, that successfully localizes gravity on the brane. These results improve significantly previous findings of the study of a bulk fluid with a linear equation of state.

Keywords: Brane-worlds, singularities

1. Introduction

In this paper, we review very recent work, presented in,[1] on the asymptotic behaviors of a class of brane-worlds. The models consist of a flat 3-brane embedded in a five-dimensional bulk filled with a fluid that satisfies a nonlinear equation of state $p = \gamma \rho^\lambda$, where p is the 'pressure' and ρ is the 'density' of the fluid and γ, λ are constants.

Such an equation of state, has been studied in cosmology for its contribution in avoiding big-rip singularities during late time asymptotics,[2–4] in obtaining inflationary models with special properties,[5] in unifying models of dark energy and dark matter,[6,7] as well as in studies of singularities.[8–10]

Our goal in studying these brane-world models, is to find a solution that is regular and meets physical requirements set by energy conditions and localization of gravity on the brane. In our previous work in,[11–16] which extended work done in brane-worlds with scalar fields,[17-19] we studied a 3-brane (flat or curved) and a fluid with a linear equation of state $p = \gamma\rho$. We found that such a solution becomes possible only for the special value of $\gamma = -1$ and only for a flat brane. These results gave us the motivation to explore whether the generalization of the linear equation of state to a nonlinear one, could have a decisive impact in finding a solution with all required properties and valid for a wide range of γ and λ. This exploration turned out to be very fruitful, and we were able to find in[1] such solutions for a flat brane and a fluid with $\gamma < 0$ and $\lambda > 1$.

As the analysis of the nonlinear equation of state is quite complicated, for the most part of this paper, we will focus on the study of a specific value of $\lambda = 3/2$, which is simpler for illustration and offers important insight on the behavior of solutions for general $\lambda > 1$.

The structure of this paper is the following: In Section 2, we set up our model and derive the field equations. In Section 3, we formulate the null energy condition which we embody in our solutions later in Section 4. In Section 5, we derive a matching solution for the specific value of $\lambda = 3/2$ and based on this solution, we calculate, in Section 6, the four-dimensional Planck mass. Finally, in Section 7, we discuss briefly the asymptotic behaviors of solutions for general λ.

2. Setup of brane-world

To set up our model, we start by considering a flat 3-brane embedded in a five-dimensional bulk with a metric of the form,

$$g_5 = a^2(Y)g_4 + dY^2, \qquad (1)$$

where $a(Y)$ is the warp factor and g_4 is the four-dimensional flat metric, i.e.,

$$g_4 = -dt^2 + dx_1^2 + dx_2^2 + dx_3^2. \qquad (2)$$

The timelike coordinate is denoted by t and the spacelike ones by (x_1, x_2, x_3, Y). In our notation, Capital Latin indices are taken as $A, B, \cdots = 1, 2, 3, 4, 5$ while lowercase Greek indices range as $\alpha, \beta, \cdots = 1, 2, 3, 4$. The 5-dimensional Riemann tensor is defined by the formula,

$$R^A{}_{BCD} = \partial_C \Gamma^A{}_{BD} - \partial_D \Gamma^A{}_{BC} + \Gamma^M{}_{BD}\Gamma^A{}_{MC} - \Gamma^M{}_{BC}\Gamma^A{}_{MD} \qquad (3)$$

the Ricci tensor is the contraction,

$$R_{AB} = R^C{}_{ACB}, \qquad (4)$$

and the five-dimensional Einstein equations on the bulk space are given by,

$$G_{AB} = R_{AB} - \frac{1}{2}g_{AB}R = \kappa_5^2 T_{AB}. \qquad (5)$$

Next, we set up the bulk matter component by considering a bulk fluid with an energy-momentum tensor of the form,

$$T_{AB} = (\rho + p)u_A u_B - p g_{AB}, \qquad (6)$$

where p is the 'pressure' and ρ is the 'density' which we take as functions only of the extra dimension Y. In (6), the velocity vector field is $u_A = (0,0,0,0,1)$, that is $u_A = \partial/\partial Y$, parallel to the Y-dimension. We assume that the pressure and density are interconnected by the following nonlinear equation of state

$$p = \gamma \rho^\lambda, \tag{7}$$

with γ and λ constants.

The Einstein equations can be written as

$$\frac{a'^2}{a^2} = \frac{\kappa_5^2}{6}\rho, \tag{8}$$

$$\frac{a''}{a} = -\frac{\kappa_5^2}{6}(2\gamma\rho^\lambda + \rho), \tag{9}$$

with the prime (') denoting differentiation with respect to Y. The equation of energy-momentum conservation, on the other hand,

$$\nabla_A T^{AB} = 0,$$

becomes

$$\rho' + 4(\gamma\rho^\lambda + \rho)\frac{a'}{a} = 0. \tag{10}$$

At this point, it is useful to clarify the terminology that we use in what follows. We use the term *finite-distance singularities* to refer to the following singular behaviors of a, occurring within a finite distance Y_s:

- $a \to 0^+$, as $Y \to Y_s$ (collapse singularity),
- $a \to \infty$, as $Y \to Y_s$ (big-rip singularity).

With Y_s, we denote a finite value of Y designating the position of the singularity. The above behaviors may be accompanied, in general, by a divergence in the density, or, even in the pressure of the fluid. Note that, these singularities are not related to geodesic incompleteness as in standard cosmology, but rather on a pathological behavior of the warp factor. In the absence of finite-distance singularities, we call the solutions regular and include in this category the behaviors of the warp factor given above, provided that these occur *only* at infinite distance, *i.e* $Y \to \pm\infty$.

We are interested to see, if it is possible to find solutions of Eqs. (8)-(10) that rectify previous findings of solutions of brane-worlds with linear bulk fluids studied in.[11–16] As mentioned in the introduction, excepting the case of a flat brane and a fluid with $\gamma = -1$, the main problem that we faced in the study of a linear bulk fluid, is that regular solutions that exist in the case of curved branes, or even singular ones out of which we can construct a regular matching solution for both flat and curved branes, lead to a challenging compromise: they either satisfy energy conditions, or, localize gravity on the brane. Therefore, a solution arising from the consideration of this different and more complicated type of fluid would be preferable and worth examining in detail, if it has each one of the following characteristics:

- it is regular (no finite-distance singularities)
- it satisfies physical conditions, such as energy conditions
- it leads to a finite four-dimensional Planck mass, thus, it localizes gravity on the brane.

We can simplify the situation of finding such a solution, by incorporating, for example, the energy conditions a priori. As we show in the next Sections this is indeed possible. The regular nature as well as the requirement of a finite four-dimensional Planck mass can be checked as a subsequent step, since to accomplish that, we first need to find the exact form of the warp factor and density.

3. The null energy condition

We are going to derive the null energy condition for our type of nonlinear bulk fluid described by (6) and (7) and transform it to a condition imposed on the density ρ and parameters γ and λ of the equation of state.

To achieve this, we follow the technique analysed in.[14,16] We start by recalling that the metric (1) and the bulk fluid (6) and (7) depend only on the extra dimension Y and they are therefore static with respect to the time coordinate t. Such fluid can be viewed as an anisotropic one with energy-momentum tensor

$$T_{AB} = (\rho^0 + p^0) u_A^0 u_B^0 - p^0 g_{\alpha\beta} \delta_A^\alpha \delta_B^\beta - p_Y g_{55} \delta_A^5 \delta_B^5, \tag{11}$$

where $u_A^0 = (a(Y), 0, 0, 0, 0)$, $A, B = 1, 2, 3, 4, 5$ and $\alpha, \beta = 1, 2, 3, 4$. As a next step, we compare (6) with (11) and find that the following relations should hold

$$p_Y = -\rho \tag{12}$$

$$\rho^0 = -p \tag{13}$$

$$p^0 = p. \tag{14}$$

We note that once we combine the last two relations we get

$$p^0 = -\rho^0, \tag{15}$$

which means that this type of matter satisfies a cosmological constant-like equation of state. Substituting (12)-(15) in (11), we find that

$$T_{AB} = -p g_{\alpha\beta} \delta_A^\alpha \delta_B^\beta + \rho g_{55} \delta_A^5 \delta_B^5. \tag{16}$$

Here, we focus only on the null energy condition according to which, every future-directed null vector k^A should satisfy[20]

$$T_{AB} k^A k^B \geq 0. \tag{17}$$

This means that we should have

$$p + \rho \geq 0, \tag{18}$$

from which we find
$$\gamma\rho^\lambda + \rho \geq 0, \tag{19}$$
after inputting the equation of state $p = \gamma\rho^\lambda$. Now, Eq. (19) can be written as
$$\rho^\lambda(\gamma + \rho^{1-\lambda}) \geq 0 \tag{20}$$
and since $\rho \geq 0$ from Eq. (8), we arrive at the the final form of the null energy condition, which reads
$$\gamma + \rho^{1-\lambda} \geq 0. \tag{21}$$
In the next Section, we are going to incorporate this condition in the process of deriving our solutions.

4. Regular solution

We start solving the system of Eqs. (8)–(10), by first integrating the continuity equation (10) to find the relation between the warp factor and the density. In the integration process we arrive at a logarithmic term of the form $\ln|\gamma + \rho^{1-\lambda}|$. To incorporate from the beginning the null energy condition (21), we choose to ignore the absolute value and simply put this term equal to $\ln(\gamma + \rho^{1-\lambda})$. The resulting relation between ρ and a is
$$\rho = (-\gamma + c_1 a^{4(\lambda-1)})^{1/(1-\lambda)}, \tag{22}$$
where
$$c_1 = \frac{\gamma + \rho_0^{1-\lambda}}{a_0^{4(\lambda-1)}}, \tag{23}$$
with $\rho_0 = \rho(Y_0)$, $a_0 = a(Y_0)$ being the initial conditions. According to (21) this translates to $c_1 \geq 0$.

It is crucial to note that there is a singularity in the density ($\rho \to \infty$) for $\lambda > 1$ and
$$a^{4(\lambda-1)} = \frac{\gamma}{c_1}. \tag{24}$$
However, it is possible to avoid this singularity, by restricting the range of the parameter γ, only to negative values, which we do in the analysis that follows.

Substituting Eq. (22) in Eq. (8) and integrating, we obtain,
$$\int \frac{a}{(c_1 - \gamma a^{4(1-\lambda)})^{1/(2(1-\lambda))}}\, da = \pm \frac{\kappa_5}{\sqrt{6}} \int dY. \tag{25}$$
The complicated integral on the LHS of Eq. (25), can be greatly simplified for those values of λ that make $1/(2(1-\lambda))$ a negative integer. This is possible when $\lambda = (n+1)/n$, with $n = 2k$ and k a positive integer.

Clearly, the simplest case is for $n = 2$ which corresponds to $\lambda = 3/2$. Then $1/(2(1 - \lambda)) = -1$ and we can directly integrate Eq. (25) to get the solution in the following implicit form

$$\pm Y + c_2 = \frac{\sqrt{6}}{\kappa_5} \left(\frac{c_1}{2} a^2 - \gamma \ln a \right), \tag{26}$$

where c_2 is an integration constant. It is straightforward to see that this solution is regular: all possible singular behaviors of a, namely $a \to 0$ and $a \to \infty$ happen only for infinite values of Y with p and ρ either vanishing there, or, approaching finite nonzero values. In particular, we have

$$a \to \infty, \quad \rho \to 0, \quad p \to 0, \quad \text{as} \quad Y \to \pm\infty \tag{27}$$
$$a \to 0^+, \quad \rho \to 1/\gamma^2, \quad p \to -1/\gamma^2, \quad \text{as} \quad Y \to \pm\infty. \tag{28}$$

Summarizing, the solution for $\lambda = 3/2$ has already two out of the three good qualities mentioned in the previous Section: it is regular and at the same time satisfies the null energy condition. In the following section, we construct an appropriate matching solution out of this solution, which leads to a finite four-dimensional Planck mass, thus fitting perfectly the profile of a plausible solution.

As for the asymptotics for general values of λ, it is interesting to note here that even though the case of $\lambda = 3/2$ is the simplest possible one for the nonlinear fluid, further analysis performed in,[1] shows that this case is significant in the sense that it can act as a guide for the whole range of values of $\lambda > 1$. This follows from the fact that all of its good physical properties are, in a way, inherited to all cases with $\lambda > 1$.

5. Matching solution for $\lambda = 3/2$

For $\lambda = 3/2$, a matching solution that leads to a finite four-dimensional Planck mass, can be constructed in the following way: First, we write down the two different branches of solution of Eq. (26),

$$Y^+ = h_+(a) = \frac{\sqrt{6}}{\kappa_5} \left(\frac{c_1^+}{2} a^2 - \gamma \ln a \right) + C_2^+ \tag{29}$$

$$Y^- = h_-(a) = \frac{\sqrt{6}}{\kappa_5} \left(-\frac{c_1^-}{2} a^2 + \gamma \ln a \right) + C_2^-, \tag{30}$$

using the notation $Y^\pm$ to describe the solutions for the ($\pm$) choice of sign in Eq. (26). Similarly, the notation $c_1^\pm$, $C_2^\pm$ describes the values of c_1 and $\mp c_2$, respectively, on the ($\pm$) branch of Y.

Second, in order to gain a complete idea of the behavior of $h_+(a)$, we study the shape of the curve of $h_+(a)$ by calculating the first and second derivative of $h_+(a)$.

These read

$$h'_+(a) = \frac{\sqrt{6}}{\kappa_5}\left(\frac{c_1^+ a^2 - \gamma}{a}\right) \tag{31}$$

$$h''_+(a) = \frac{\sqrt{6}}{\kappa_5}\frac{c_1^+}{a^2}\left(a^2 + \frac{\gamma}{c_1^+}\right). \tag{32}$$

For our choice of integration constants and parameters, $c_1^+ > 0$ and $\gamma < 0$, Eq. (31) shows that h_+ is strictly increasing for all values of a. Also, Eq. (32) shows that the graph of h_+ changes from concave downward on $(0, \sqrt{-\gamma/c_1^+})$ to concave upward on $(\sqrt{-\gamma/c_1^+}, \infty)$, making the point $(\sqrt{-\gamma/c_1^+}, -\sqrt{6}/\kappa_5(\gamma/2+\gamma\ln\sqrt{-\gamma/c_1^+})+C_2^+)$, an inflection point of the graph of h_+.

On the other hand, the first two derivatives of $h_-(a)$ are exactly the opposites of the ones of h_+ given in Eq. (31) and Eq. (32). This means that h_- is strictly decreasing and the graph of h_- changes from concave upward on $(0, \sqrt{-\gamma/c_1^-})$ to concave downward on $(\sqrt{-\gamma/c_1^-}, \infty)$, with $(\sqrt{-\gamma/c_1^-}, \sqrt{6}/\kappa_5(\gamma/2+\gamma\ln\sqrt{-\gamma/c_1^-})+C_2^-)$ being an inflection point of the graph of h_-.

We can match the two branches at their common inflection point by making an appropriate choice of the constants $c_1^\pm$ and $C_2^\pm$. This is a third step in the matching process. Naturally, we assume that the warp factor is continuous

$$\sqrt{\frac{-\gamma}{c_1^+}} = \sqrt{\frac{-\gamma}{c_1^-}}, \quad \text{or,} \quad c_1^+ = c_1^- = c_1 \tag{33}$$

and that, of course, the inflection point has the same Y coordinate through the two branches, which leads to

$$h_+\left(\sqrt{\frac{-\gamma}{c_1}}\right) = h_-\left(\sqrt{\frac{-\gamma}{c_1}}\right) \tag{34}$$

and yields the following relation between C_2^+ and C_2^-,

$$-\frac{\sqrt{6}}{\kappa_5}\left(\frac{\gamma}{2}+\gamma\ln\sqrt{\frac{-\gamma}{c_1}}\right) + C_2^+ = \frac{\sqrt{6}}{\kappa_5}\left(\frac{\gamma}{2}+\gamma\ln\sqrt{\frac{-\gamma}{c_1}}\right) + C_2^-, \tag{35}$$

or,

$$C_2^+ = \frac{\sqrt{6}}{\kappa_5}\left(\gamma + 2\gamma\ln\sqrt{\frac{-\gamma}{c_1}}\right) + C_2^-. \tag{36}$$

There is an axis of symmetry at $Y = Y_s$, with Y_s given by

$$Y_s = h_\pm(\sqrt{-\gamma/c_1}) = -\frac{\sqrt{6}}{\kappa_5}\left(\frac{\gamma}{2}+\gamma\ln\sqrt{\frac{-\gamma}{c_1}}\right) + C_2^+ = \frac{\sqrt{6}}{\kappa_5}\left(\frac{\gamma}{2}+\gamma\ln\sqrt{\frac{-\gamma}{c_1}}\right) + C_2^-. \tag{37}$$

Since the embedding of the brane introduces a $Y \to -Y$ symmetry in the bulk, it is natural to position the brane at $Y = Y_s$. Without loss of generality and in order to simplify our expressions, we can place the brane at $Y = 0$, that is we take $Y_s = 0$ in (37). This will set the values of $C_2^{\pm}$ to

$$C_2^+ = \frac{\sqrt{6}}{\kappa_5}\left(\frac{\gamma}{2} + \gamma \ln \sqrt{\frac{-\gamma}{c_1}}\right) = -C_2^-. \tag{38}$$

The matching solution described by Eq. (29) and (30) that satisfies the above boundary condition can be written as

$$|Y| = \frac{\sqrt{6}}{\kappa_5}\left(-\frac{c_1}{2}a^2 + \gamma \ln a - \frac{\gamma}{2} - \gamma \ln \sqrt{\frac{-\gamma}{c_1}}\right), \quad 0 < a \leq \sqrt{\frac{-\gamma}{c_1}}. \tag{39}$$

It is essential that the density is well defined and continuous at the position of the brane $Y = 0$. Here, we find

$$\rho\left(\sqrt{\frac{-\gamma}{c_1}}\right) \equiv \rho(0) = \frac{1}{4\gamma^2}, \tag{40}$$

where $\rho(0)$ denotes $\rho(Y = 0)$ and it is an abbreviation of $\rho(h_{\pm}^{-1}(\sqrt{-\gamma/c_1}))$.

The graph of h_+ is depicted in Fig. 1 with a thick solid and dashed line, while the graph of h_-, in the same Figure, is depicted with a thin solid and dashed line. The matching solution is build up only from the solid parts of both graphs, as this is the only choice that leads to a solution with a finite four-dimensional Planck mass. In Fig. 2, we have rotated the axes of Fig. 1, for a more convenient view of the evolution of the warp factor as a function of Y.

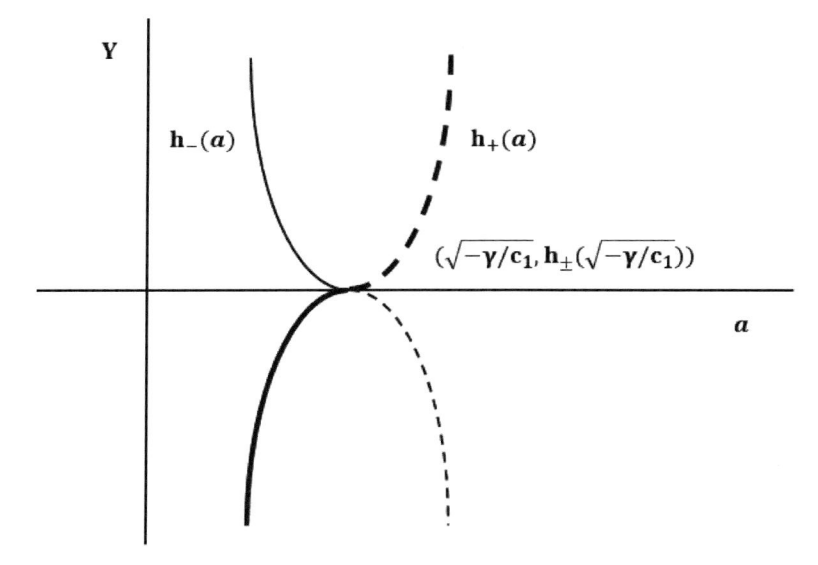

Fig. 1. Matching graphs of $h_{\pm}(a)$ for $\lambda = 3/2$.

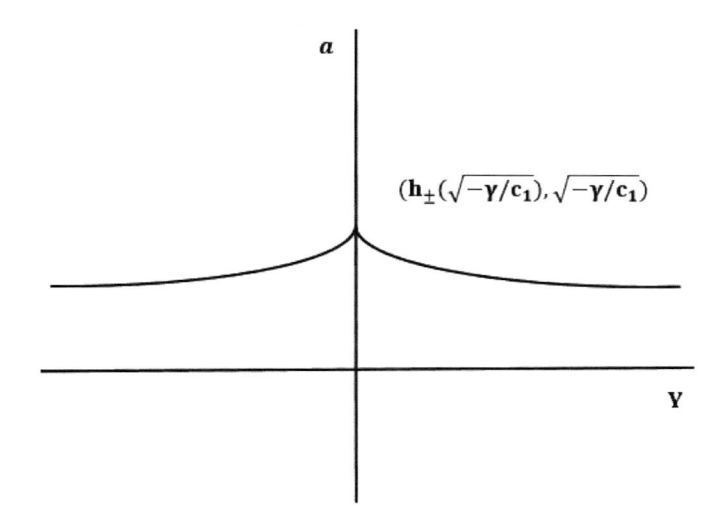

Fig. 2. Graph of $a(Y)$ for the matching solution for $\lambda = 3/2$.

Finally, we take into account the jump of the derivative of the warp factor across the brane and find, for our type of geometry, the following junction condition

$$a'(0^+) - a'(0^-) = 2a'(0^+) = -\kappa_5^2 \frac{f(\rho(0))a(0)}{3}, \qquad (41)$$

where $f(\rho(0))$ is the tension of the brane. Using Eq. (39) in the above equation we can deduce the form of the brane tension, this reads

$$f(\rho(0)) = -\frac{\sqrt{6}}{2\kappa_5\gamma} = \frac{\sqrt{6\rho(0)}}{\kappa_5}, \qquad (42)$$

where the last equality is derived by using Eq. (40).

This completes the construction of a viable matching solution for $\lambda = 3/2$. In the next Section, we are going to show that this solution also leads to a finite four-dimensional Planck mass.

6. Localization of gravity for $\lambda = 3/2$

To calculate the value of the four-dimensional Planck mass, $M_p^2 = 8\pi/\kappa$, we use the following integral (see[1, 14, 16, 21]),

$$\frac{\kappa_5^2}{\kappa} = \int_{-Y_c}^{Y_c} a^2(Y)dY. \qquad (43)$$

We can deduce the behaviour of a^2 as $Y \to -\infty$ from Eq. (39). We find

$$a^2 \sim e^{-(\sqrt{6}\kappa_5/(3\gamma))Y}, \qquad (44)$$

where the symbol $\sim$ is used to signify 'behaves according to', and using the symmetry of Eq. (39), we can write the above integral in the following form

$$\int_{-Y_c}^{Y_c} a^2 dY = 2 \int_{-Y_c}^{0} a^2 dY \sim 2 \int_{-Y_c}^{0} e^{-(\sqrt{6}\kappa_5/(3\gamma))Y} dY = -\sqrt{6}\frac{\gamma}{\kappa_5}(1 - e^{(\sqrt{6}\kappa_5/(3\gamma))Y_c}). \tag{45}$$

Taking $Y_c \to \infty$ and keeping in mind that $\gamma < 0$, it follows that the four-dimensional Planck mass remains finite and is proportional to

$$-\sqrt{6}\frac{\gamma}{\kappa_5}.$$

In conclusion, we have seen a specific example of the nonlinear equation of state $p = \gamma \rho^{3/2}$, for which it is possible to construct a regular matching solution compatible with the null condition and which also localizes gravity on the brane. In the discussion below, we outline what happens for extended ranges of values of λ.

7. Discussion

We briefly review in this Section, the behavior of solutions for general λ, a detailed analysis can be found in.[1]

The key factor that determines whether a solution of Eqs. (8)-(10), is regular, or, singular, is the ordering of λ with respect to the value one: for $\lambda < 1$, we encounter singular solutions, whereas, for $\lambda > 1$ the solutions are regular.

Before presenting the solutions for general λ, we emphasize that for $\lambda \neq 1 + 1/(2k)$, where k is a positive integer, the integral on the LHS of Eq. (25) cannot in general be calculated directly. However, we can still deduce the behaviors of solutions by expressing them in terms of the Gaussian hypergeometric function $_2F_1(\alpha, b, c; z)$.

In particular, for $\lambda < 1$, the solution is given implicitly in terms of a hypergeometric function and reads

$$\pm Y + c_2 = \frac{\sqrt{6}}{2\kappa_5} c_1^{1/(2(\lambda-1))} a^2 \,_2F_1\left(\frac{1}{2(1-\lambda)}, \frac{1}{2(1-\lambda)}, \frac{1}{2(1-\lambda)} + 1; \frac{\gamma}{c_1} a^{4(1-\lambda)}\right). \tag{46}$$

As shown in,[1] this solution has a finite-distance singularity at $Y \to \pm c_2$, with

$$a \to 0^+, \quad \rho \to \infty, \quad p \to 0, \quad \text{if} \quad \lambda < 0 \tag{47}$$
$$a \to 0^+, \quad \rho \to \infty, \quad p \to \infty, \quad \text{if} \quad 0 < \lambda < 1. \tag{48}$$

The behaviors of p and ρ above, have been deduced from Eq. (7) and Eq. (22).

For $\lambda > 1$, on the other hand, we have the following types of solution. First, we have the general form of solution for $\lambda = 1 + 1/(2k)$, with k a positive integer, which is

$$\pm Y + c_2 = \frac{\sqrt{6}}{\kappa_5}\left(\sum_{s=0}^{k-1} \frac{k!}{(k-s)!s!}\frac{c_1^{k-s}}{2-2s/k}a^{2-2s/k}(-\gamma)^s + (-\gamma)^k \ln a\right). \tag{49}$$

Second, for $\lambda > 3/2$ we have the following solution

$$\pm Y + c_2 = \frac{\sqrt{6}}{\kappa_5} \left(\frac{a^2}{2}(c_1 - \gamma a^{4(1-\lambda)})^{1/(2(\lambda-1))} - \frac{\gamma c_1^{(3-2\lambda)/(2(\lambda-1))}}{2(3-2\lambda)} a^{2(3-2\lambda)} \right.$$
$$\left. \times {}_2F_1\left(\frac{3-2\lambda}{2(1-\lambda)}, \frac{3-2\lambda}{2(1-\lambda)}, \frac{3-2\lambda}{2(1-\lambda)} + 1; \frac{\gamma}{c_1} a^{4(1-\lambda)} \right) \right), \qquad (50)$$

Finally, the case of $1 < \lambda < 3/2$ is more complicated: we have forms of solutions valid for $1 + 1/(2k) < \lambda < 1 + 1/2(k-1)$, with k a positive integer such that $k \geq 2$, and given by

$$\pm Y + c_2 = \frac{\sqrt{6}}{\kappa_5} \left(\sum_{s=0}^{n/2-1} \frac{(-\gamma)^s}{2(1-2s(\lambda-1))} \left(c_1 a^{4(\lambda-1)} - \gamma \right)^{1/(2(\lambda-1))-s} \right.$$
$$+ \frac{(-\gamma)^{n/2}(c_1)^{((n+1)-n\lambda)/(2(\lambda-1))}}{2((n+1)-n\lambda)} a^{2((n+1)-n\lambda)} \times$$
$$\left. \times {}_2F_1\left(\frac{(n+1)-n\lambda}{2(1-\lambda)}, \frac{(n+1)-n\lambda}{2(1-\lambda)}, \frac{(n+1)-n\lambda}{2(1-\lambda)} + 1; \frac{\gamma}{c_1} a^{4(1-\lambda)} \right) \right). \qquad (51)$$

All solutions for $\lambda > 1$ are free from finite-distance singularities, and their asymptotic behaviors are

$$a \to \infty, \quad \rho \to 0, \quad p \to 0, \quad \text{as} \quad Y \to \pm\infty \qquad (52)$$
$$a \to 0^+, \quad \rho \to (-\gamma)^{1/(1-\lambda)}, \quad p \to -(-\gamma)^{1/(1-\lambda)}, \quad \text{as} \quad Y \to \pm\infty. \qquad (53)$$

The procedure for deriving a matching solution with a finite four-dimensional Planck mass, presented in the previous Sections, can still be performed for all solutions with $\lambda > 1$ and can be found in.[1]

Summarizing, the effect of the nonlinear equation of state is catalytic in the process of creating a regular solution with essential physical properties and valid for a wide range of parameters. It is left to be seen from a physics point of view, what are the possible field realizations that could lead to such an equation of state.

Acknowledgments

Work partially performed by I.A. as International professor of the Francqui Foundation, Belgium.

References

1. I. Antoniadis, S. Cotsakis, I. Klaoudatou, Regular branewords with nonlinear bulk-fluids, *Eur. Phys. J. C* 81, (2021). [arXiv:2106.15669v2 [hep-th]].
2. S. K. Srivastava, Future Universe With $w < -1$ Without Big Smash, *Phys. Lett. B* 619, 1-4 (2005). [arXiv:0407048v4 [astro-ph]].

3. P. F. Gonzalez-Diaz, You need not be afraid of phantom energy, *Phys. Rev. D* 68, 021303 (2003). [arXiv:0305559 [astro-ph]].
4. A. V. Astashenok, S. Nojiri, S. D. Odintsov, A. V. Yurov. Phantom Cosmology without Big Rip Singularity, *Phys. Lett. B* 709, 396-403 (2012). [arXiv:1201.4056 [gr-qc]].
5. J. D. Barrow, Graduated inflationary universes, *Phys. Lett. B* 235, 40-43 (1990).
6. A. Y. Kamenshchik, U. Moschella, V. Pasquier, An alternative to quintessence, *Phys. Lett. B* 511, 265-268 (2001). [arXiv:0103004 [gr-qc]].
7. M. C. Bento, O. Bertolami, A. A. Sen., Generalized Chaplygin gas, accelerated expansion and dark energy-matter unification, *Phys. Rev. D* 66, 043507 (2002). [arXiv:0202064 [gr-qc]].
8. S. Cotsakis, I. Klaoudatou, Future Singularities of Isotropic Cosmologies, *J. Geom. Phys.* 55, 306-315 (2005). [arXiv:0409022 [gr-qc]].
9. S. Cotsakis, I. Klaoudatou, Cosmological Singularities and Bel-Robinson Energy, *J. Geom. Phys.* 57, 1303-1312 (2007). [arXiv:0604029 [gr-qc]].
10. S. Nojiri, S. D. Odintsov, S. Tsujikawa, Properties of singularities in (phantom) dark energy universe, *Phys. Rev. D* 71, 063004 (2005). [arXiv:0501025 [hep-th]].
11. I. Antoniadis, S. Cotsakis, I. Klaoudatou, Braneworld cosmological singularities, *Proceedings of the 11th Marcel Grossmann Meeting on General Relativity* 3, 2054-2056 (2007). [arXiv:0701033 [gr-qc]].
12. I. Antoniadis, S. Cotsakis, I. Klaoudatou, Brane singularities and their avoidance, *Class. Quant. Grav.* 27, 235018 (2010). [arXiv:1010.6175 [gr-qc]].
13. I. Antoniadis, S. Cotsakis, I. Klaoudatou, Brane singularities with mixtures in the bulk, *Fortschr. Phys.* 61, 20-49 (2013). [arXiv:1206.0090 [hep-th]].
14. I. Antoniadis, S. Cotsakis, I. Klaoudatou, Enveloping branes and braneworld singularities, *Eur. Phys. J. C* 74, 3192 (2014). [arXiv:1406.0611v2 [hep-th]].
15. I. Antoniadis, S. Cotsakis, I. Klaoudatou, Dynamics and asymptotics of brane-worlds, *Proceedings of the 13th Marcel Grossmann Meeting on General Relativity* 3, 1859-1861 (2015).
16. I. Antoniadis, S. Cotsakis, I. Klaoudatou, Curved branes with regular support, *Eur. Phys. J. C* 76, 511 (2016). [arXiv:1606.09453 [hep-th]].
17. N. Arkani-Hamed, S. Dimopoulos, N. Kaloper, R. Sundrum, A small cosmological constant from a large extra dimension, *Phys. Lett. B* 480, 193-199 (2000). [arXiv:0001197v2 [hep-th]].
18. S. Kachru, M. Schulz, E. Silverstein. Bounds on curved domain walls in 5d gravity, *Phys. Rev. D* 62, 085003 (2000). [arXiv:0002121 [hep-th]].
19. S. S. Gubser, Curvature singularities: The good, the bad, and the naked, *Adv. Theor. Math. Phys.* 4, 679-745 (2000). [arXiv:0002160 [hep-th]].
20. E. Poisson, *A Relativist's Toolkit* (Cambridge University Press, 2004).
21. S. Forste, H. P. Nilles and I. Zavala, Nontrivial Cosmological Constant in Brane Worlds with Unorthodox Lagrangians, *JCAP* 07, 007 (2011). [arXiv:1104.2570 [hep-th]].

Primordial synchronization of Mixmaster spatial points

Spiros Cotsakis

Institute of Gravitation and Cosmology, RUDN University
ul. Miklukho-Maklaya 6, Moscow 117198, Russia
and
Research Laboratory of Geometry, Dynamical Systems and Cosmology
University of the Aegean, Karlovassi 83200, Samos, Greece
E-mail: skot@aegean.gr

We review recent work on the possibility of primordial synchronization of different Mixmaster regions in generic inhomogeneous spacetime. It is shown that inhomogeneous domains undergoing chaotic oscillations may synchronize themselves exponentially fast and proceed in perfect symphony asymptotically in the past direction. Implications of this result for the structure and evolution of an early phase of the universe are briefly discussed.

Keywords: Nature of the cosmological singularity; structure of primordial states; chaotic synchronization

1. Introduction

Recently, we introduced a dynamical mechanism via chaotic synchronization of different spatial point of Mixmaster type as a new factor governing the global structure and evolution of primordial cosmology.[1] We have shown that a pair of spatial Mixmaster points in generic inhomogeneous spacetime coupled to each other and one of them ('the transmitter') communicating to the other ('the receiver') only part of the information necessary to determine its state, evolves in such a way that the receiver becomes able to completely reconstruct the remaining information and synchronize its chaotic evolution with that of the transmitter point.

This mechanism radically changes the structure of the early universe and provides a novel setting for the consideration of a number of fundamental issues in cosmology, such as the homogeneity ('horizon') problem, and the unexplained behaviour of the entropy in the early universe. In this contribution, we shall briefly recall the main features of the proposed cosmological sync mechanism.[1]

2. Evolution of inhomogeneous Mixmaster points

Our results concern the so-called G_0 cosmologies that admit no isometries and may be described in vacuum by the dimensionless state vector field X along the orbit of a fixed spatial point A. This is given by,[2]

$$X_A(\tau) = (\Sigma_+, \Sigma_-, N_1, N_2, N_3), \quad \Sigma_\pm = \frac{\sigma_\pm}{H}, \; N_\alpha = \frac{n_\alpha}{H}, \qquad (1)$$

where H denotes the Hubble scalar function equal to $1/3\Theta$ and is taken with respect to the fundamental 4-velocity timelike vector field $u^a, a = 0, 1, 2, 3$. The expansion scalar is defined by $\Theta = \nabla_a u^a$. Derivatives are taken with respect to the dimensionless τ-time related to the proper (clock) time by $dt/d\tau = 1/H$, the variables $\Sigma_\pm$ describe the anisotropy in the Hubble flow, while the N_α's are related to the spatial curvature and the Bianchi type of the isometry group associated with the evolution of the spatial point.

We assume that different spatial points evolve in the past direction as separate homogeneous Mixmaster universes coupled to each other in inhomogeneous spacetime. For any pair of spatial points A, B, we have a pair of dynamical equations, namely, for the point A we have equations for the (N, Σ) variables, and for the point B similar equations for the different (M, Π) variables as follows[3-5]:

System A:

$$N_1' = (q - 4\Sigma_+)N_1, \quad (2)$$

$$N_2' = (q + 2\Sigma_+ + 2\sqrt{3}\Sigma_-)N_2, \quad (3)$$

$$N_3' = (q + 2\Sigma_+ - 2\sqrt{3}\Sigma_-)N_3, \quad (4)$$

$$\Sigma_+' = -(2 - q)\Sigma_+ - 3S_+, \quad (5)$$

$$\Sigma_-' = -(2 - q)\Sigma_- - 3S_-, \quad (6)$$

with the constraint,

$$\Sigma_+^2 + \Sigma_-^2 + \frac{3}{2}\left(N_1^2 + N_2^2 + N_3^2 - 2(N_1 N_2 + N_2 N_3 + N_3 N_1)\right) = 1, \quad (7)$$

where,

$$q = 2(\Sigma_+^2 + \Sigma_-^2), \quad (8)$$

$$S_+ = \frac{1}{2}\left((N_2 - N_3)^2 - N_1(2N_1 - N_2 - N_3)\right), \quad (9)$$

$$S_- = \frac{\sqrt{3}}{2}(N_3 - N_2)(N_1 - N_2 - N_3), \quad (10)$$

and a prime denoting differentiation with respect to the τ-time.

System B: We have the unknowns $y = (M, \Pi)$, the variables $M = (M_1, M_2, M_3)$ satisfy similar equations to the Eqns. (2)-(4), and the shear variables $\Pi = (\Pi_+, \Pi_-)$ satisfy the system,

$$\Pi_+' = -(2 - p)\Pi_+ - 3Q_+, \quad (11)$$

$$\Pi_-' = -(2 - p)\Pi_- - 3Q_-, \quad (12)$$

with $p = 2(\Pi_+^2 + \Pi_-^2)$, the Q's are like the variables S's in the Eqns. (9), (10) but with the M's in the corresponding places of N's. The constraint is identical to (7) but with the (M, Π)'s in the places of the (N, Σ)'s.

3. The problem of cosmological sync

We shall be interested in the possibility that the spatial points A, B, with A in the causal past of B, can influence each other by sending signals from A to B and sync with each other in the past direction, while chaotically oscillating in inhomogeneous Mixmaster spacetime.

We imagine that the A-system in the form $x' = f(x)$ for the variables $x = (N, \Sigma)$, breaks into two 'subsystems', with the N variables satisfying the first three equations ('sys-1') and the Σ's the last two ('sys-2'), namely,

$$N' = g(N, \Sigma), \quad \Sigma' = h(N, \Sigma), \tag{13}$$

where $N = (N_1, N_2, N_3)$, $\Sigma = (\Sigma_+, \Sigma_-)$. We then set the B-system (receiver) variables M simply equal to the corresponding A-transmitter variables N (that is to those in sys-1). Then the B-system equations break into the pair consisting of the sys-1 equations, and those identical to sys-2 but for the Π variables, the 'sys-3' system:

$$M_i = N_i, \quad i = 1, 2, 3 \tag{14}$$

$$\Pi'_+ = -(2-p)\Pi_+ - 3S_+, \tag{15}$$

$$\Pi'_- = -(2-p)\Pi_- - 3S_-. \tag{16}$$

Following,[6,7] we introduce the synchronization (error) function $\Omega = (\Omega_+, \Omega_-)$, which in the present case we take it to be: $\Omega = \Sigma - \Pi$, that is,

$$\Omega_+ = \Sigma_+ - \Pi_+, \quad \Omega_- = \Sigma_- - \Pi_-. \tag{17}$$

Then we say that there is complete synchronization of the two Mixmaster oscillating spatial points (that is of systems A and B) provided we can show that,

$$\Omega \to (0, 0), \quad \text{as} \quad \tau \to -\infty. \tag{18}$$

If this happens, we say that system A is synchronized with system B. Otherwise, the two oscillating spatial points corresponding to systems A and B will evolve autonomously, out of sync.

In general, we expect the appearance of extra coupling terms in the dynamical equations which describe the evolution of the sync function Ω during the past evolution the Mixmaster oscillating spatial points, the latter evolution given by Eqns. (5), (6), and (11), (12). The question then arises as to whether or not a system of spatial points chaotically oscillating in the past direction may sync and evolve in unison thereafter.

This is the problem of cosmological sync for the case of spatial points satisfying Mixmaster-type evolution equations. As shown in,[1] there are indeed different types of sync possible in this problem depending on the form of the coupling between different spatial points.

4. Generic sync

Let us suppose that there is a linear in the sync function Ω coupling between the two spatial points. In this case, the evolution equations become,

$$\Sigma' = -(2-q)\Sigma - 3S + \alpha(\Pi - \Sigma) \tag{19}$$
$$\Pi' = -(2-p)\Pi - 3Q + \alpha(\Sigma - \Pi), \tag{20}$$

where Q is the analogous expression of S for the Π system, and α is some coupling between the two oscillators.

Then if the orbit Σ has Lyapunov exponent λ, we find that the associated Ω-evolution equation leads to the result,[1]

$$|\Omega| \leq Ce^{(\lambda - 2\alpha)\tau}, \tag{21}$$

with C an integration constant.

Therefore if we set $\alpha_c = \lambda/2$, for the critical coupling strength, we conclude that when $\alpha > \alpha_c$, we have complete synchronization of the Mixmaster oscillating regions.

A typical value of the Lyapunov exponents for Mixmaster orbits is (see, e.g.,[8]) $\lambda \sim 0.45$, so that when $\alpha > 0.225$, we have synchronization between the two spatial Mixmaster points A, B.

5. Lyapunov function sync

As is further shown in,[1] there is in fact a Lyapunov function for the dynamics of sync, for a general coupling $g(\Omega)$ satisfying a positivity condition, and under the further condition that,

$$\Omega' \cdot \nabla g \leq 0, \tag{22}$$

where Ω' is the orbital derivative of Ω. The Lyapunov function is given by,

$$V(\Omega_+, \Omega_-) = \frac{1}{2}\left(\Omega_+^2 + \Omega_-^2\right) + g(\Omega), \tag{23}$$

This implies that the state $\Omega = 0$ is asymptotically stable, making synced spatial regions globally asymptotically stable in the past direction.

As an example, consider the simplest, uncoupled, case. The sync equations of the dynamics take the form,

$$\Omega'_+ = -(2-q)\Omega_+ \tag{24}$$
$$\Omega'_- = -(2-q)\Omega_-. \tag{25}$$

Then the function,

$$V(\Omega_+, \Omega_-) = \frac{1}{2}\left(\Omega_+^2 + \Omega_-^2\right), \tag{26}$$

is a Lyapunov function for the dynamics and satisfies,

$$V \leq V_0 e^{-4\tau}. \tag{27}$$

where V_0 is a constant. We conclude that Mixmaster regions in inhomogeneous spacetime synchronize exponentially fast.

6. Phase sync

A different characterization of the possibility of cosmological sync in the assumed primordial chaotic state of the universe may be effected when considering any number of oscillating domains having their own frequencies. This leads to different dynamical evolution of their phases, and the question arises as to whether we can have phase sync between them in this situation.

This problem was shown to have an affirmative answer in two steps. In the first step,,[9] Barrow wrote down the equation describing the phase evolution of a spatial Mixmaster point as a response of the system in terms of the mean field amplitude and phase r, ψ respectively,

$$\theta' = \frac{3}{\rho}\sqrt{S_+^2 + S_-^2} \sin(\theta - \psi), \quad \tan\psi = S_-/S_+, \tag{28}$$

with ρ being the polar coordinate in the pair (ρ, θ) in the (Σ_+, Σ_-) plane. A further elaboration using these dynamical equations shows that sync is indeed possible.

It can be further shown[1] that this equation leads to a direct coupling between the oscillating domains, precisely given by a time-dependent Kuramoto-like coupling of spontaneous synchronization. For any partition of N regions, we can show that the i-th domain responds directly to the j-th domain in the partition via the equation,[1]

$$\theta'_i = \frac{3}{N\rho_i}\sqrt{S_+^2 + S_-^2} \sum_{j=1}^{N} \sin(\theta_j - \theta_i). \tag{29}$$

7. Physical meaning of sync

We are led to the following physical interpretation[1] of the process of sync in the present context. The spatial point B will synchronize with the point A lying in B's past after receiving a signal from A. This will be so because their sync function $\Omega \to 0$, and sync will become progressively apparent when their corresponding BKL[10-12] parameter u values for A and B become equal with each other in the sense that the numbers of Kasner epochs and eras for the two evolutions of the spatial points A, B become identical to each other exponentially fast. Thereafter the two points will start oscillating in perfect unison.

This process will lead to the simplest possible initial state of the universe, characterized by a perfect sync between its different but correlated spatial regions. This will be so because, according to the results reported here, every spatial point will continually send and receive signals from other spacetime points shifting their state of oscillation, adjusting them to that of the other points, and resetting their motion, until sync organizes them all in perfect harmony. In turn, this may have important implications some of which will be discussed elsewhere.

References

1. S. Cotsakis, *Onset of synchronization in coupled Mixmaster oscillators*, to appear in the Phil. Trans. Roy. Soc. A.; arXiv: 2010.00298.
2. C. Uggla, H. van Elst, J. Wainwright and G.F.R. Ellis, Phys. Rev. D 68 (2003) 103502; arXiv: gr-qc/0304002.
3. G. F. R. Ellis and M. MacCallum, Commun. Math. Phys. 12, 108 (1969).
4. J. Wainwright and L. Hsu, Class. Quantum Gravity 6, 1409 (1989).
5. J. Wainwright and G. F. R. Ellis, *Dynamical systems in cosmology* (CUP. 1993).
6. L. M. Pecora, T. L. Carroll, Phys. Rev. Lett. 64, 821 (1990).
7. L. M. Pecora, *et al*, Chaos 7, 520 (1997).
8. B. K. Berger, Gen. Rel. Grav. 23, 1385 (1991).
9. J. D. Barrow, Phys. Rev. D 102, 024017 (2020); arXiv: gr-qc/2006.01562.
10. V. A. Belinski, I. M. Khalatnikov, and E. M. Lifshitz, Adv. Phys. 12, 185 (1963).
11. V. A. Belinski, I. M. Khalatnikov, and E. M. Lifshitz, Adv. Phys. 19, 525 (1970).
12. V. A. Belinski, I. M. Khalatnikov, and E. M. Lifshitz, Adv. Phys. 31, 639 (1982).

Quintessential inflation from Lorentzian slow roll

David Benisty

DAMTP, Centre for Mathematical Sciences, University of Cambridge,
Wilberforce Road, Cambridge CB3 0WA, UK
Institute of Astronomy, University of Cambridge,
Madingley Road, Cambridge, CB3 0HA, UK

From the assumption that the slow roll parameter ϵ has a Lorentzian form as a function of the e-folds number N, a successful model of a quintessential inflation is obtained. The form corresponds to the vacuum energy both in the inflationary and in the dark energy epochs. The form satisfies the condition to climb from small values of ϵ to 1 at the end of the inflationary epoch. At the late universe ϵ becomes small again and this leads to the Dark Energy epoch. The observables that the models predicts fits with the latest Planck data: $r \sim 10^{-3}, n_s \approx 0.965$. Naturally a large dimensionless factor that exponentially amplifies the inflationary scale and exponentially suppresses the dark energy scale appears, producing a sort of *cosmological see saw mechanism*. We find the corresponding scalar Quintessential Inflationary potential with two flat regions - one inflationary and one as a dark energy with slow roll behavior.

Keywords: Dark Matter; Dark Energy

1. Introduction

The inflationary paradigm is considered as a necessary part of the standard model of cosmology, since it provides the solution to the fundamental puzzles of the old Big Bang theory, such as the horizon, the flatness, and the monopole problems.[1-9] It can be achieved through various mechanisms, for instance through the introduction of a scalar inflaton field.[10-25] Almost twenty years after the observational evidence of cosmic acceleration the cause of this phenomenon, labeled as dark energy", remains an open question which challenges the foundations of theoretical physics: why there is a large disagreement between the vacuum expectation value of the energy momentum tensor which comes from quantum field theory and the observable value of dark energy density.[26-28] One way to parametrize dynamical dark energy uses a scalar field, the so-called quintessence model for canonical scalar fields.[29-31] In such a way that the cosmological constant gets replaced by a dark energy fluid with a nearly constant density today.[32-36] For the slow roll approximation the scalar field behaves as an effective dark energy. The form of the potential is clearly unknown and many different potentials have been studied and confronted to observations.

These two regimes of accelerated expansion are treated independently. However, it is both tempting and economical to think that there is a unique cause responsible for a quintessential inflation[37-42,42-48] which refers to unification of both concepts

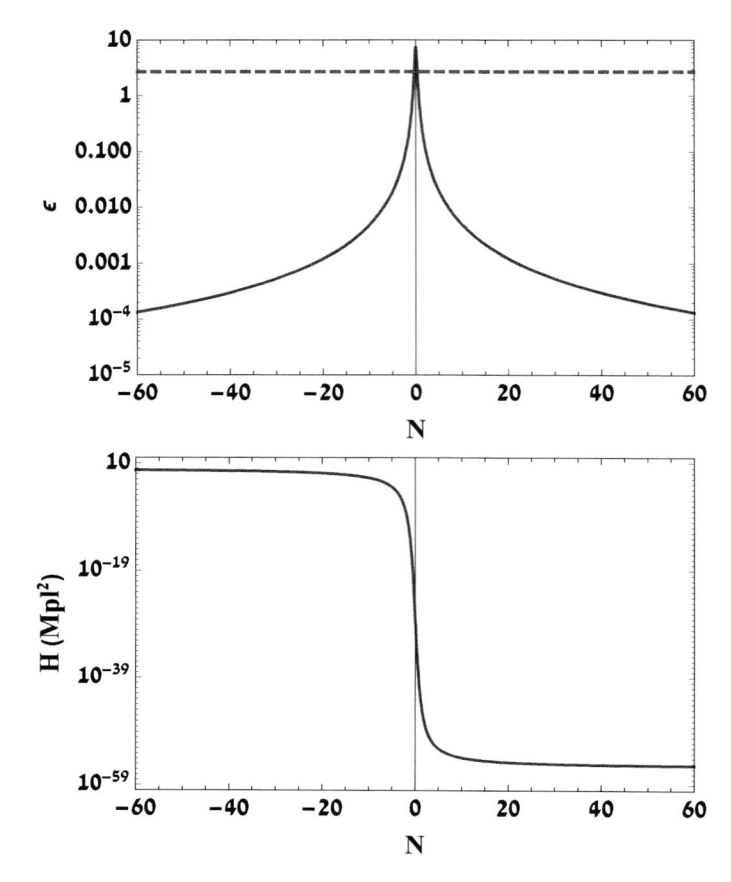

Fig. 1. The upper panel shows the slow roll parameter ϵ vs. the number of e-folds for the ansatz (1), in a logarithmic scale. The lower panel shows the corresponding Hubble function of the vacuum vs. the number of e-folds.

using a single scalar field. Consistency of the scenario demands that the new degree of freedom, namely the scalar field, should not interfere with the thermal history of the Universe, and thereby it should be "invisible" for the entire evolution and reappear only around the present epoch giving rise to late-time cosmic acceleration.

2. Lorentzian Ansatz

In order to formulate an ansatz for the Hubble function that treats symmetrically both the early and late times we use the Lorentzian function for the slow roll parameter:

$$\epsilon(N) = \frac{\xi}{\pi} \frac{\Gamma/2}{N^2 + (\Gamma/2)^2} \qquad (1)$$

as a function of the number of e-folds $N = \log(a/a_i)$, where a_i is the scale parameter at some time (which we may choose as the initial state of the inflationary phase). ξ is the amplitude of the Lorentzian, Γ is the width of the Lorentzian. In that way the ϵ parameter increases from the initial value to 1 at the end of inflation, then continues to increase, peak and then decreases until it gets down to the value 1 and this represents the beginning of a the new Dark Energy phase that will eventually dominate the late evolution of the Universe. The upper panel of Fig. 1 presents the qualitative shape of this behavior.

The strong energy condition yields another bound on the coefficients. The equation of states w is in the range $|w| \leq 1$. From the relation $\epsilon = \frac{3}{2}(w+1)$ we obtain the bound $0 \leq \epsilon \leq 3$. The ansatz for the vacuum energy evolution (1) positive always, hence the lower bound is preserved. The largest value of the ansatz (1) is $2\xi/\pi\Gamma$. From the the upper bound of ϵ we obtain the condition:

$$\Gamma < 2\xi/3\pi. \tag{2}$$

In general, the calculation of the above observables demands a detailed perturbation analysis. Nevertheless, one can obtain approximate expressions by imposing the slow-roll assumptions, under which all inflationary information is encoded in the slow-roll parameters. In particular, one first introduces[49]

$$\epsilon_{n+1} = \frac{d}{dN} \log |\epsilon_n|, \tag{3}$$

where $\epsilon_0 \equiv H_i/H$ and n a positive integer. The slow roll parameters read:

$$\epsilon \equiv \epsilon_1 = -\frac{H'}{H}, \quad \epsilon_2 = \frac{H''}{H'} - \frac{H'}{H},$$

and so on. From the first slow roll parameter definition with the ansatz (1), we obtain the solution:

$$H = \sqrt{\frac{\Lambda_0}{3}} \exp\left[-\frac{\xi}{\pi} \tan^{-1}\left(\frac{2N}{\Gamma}\right)\right], \tag{4}$$

where Λ_0 is an integration constant. The Hubble function interpolates from the inflationary values $H_{-\infty}$ to the dark energy value $H_{+\infty}$ that corresponds to:

$$H_\pm = \sqrt{\frac{\Lambda_0}{3}} \exp^{\mp \xi/2}. \tag{5}$$

The magnitude of the vacuum energy at the inflationary phase reads $10^{-8} Mpl^4$, while the magnitude of the vacuum energy at the present slowly accelerated phase of the universe is $10^{-120} Mpl^4$. From the Friedmann equations the values of the energy density is $3H^2$ in the Planck scale. Therefore, the coefficients of the model are:

$$\xi \approx 129, \quad \Lambda_0 = 1.7 \cdot 10^{-32} Mpl^4. \tag{6}$$

We calculate the other slow roll parameters using (3):
$$\epsilon_2 = -\frac{8N}{\Gamma^2 + 4N^2}, \quad \epsilon_3 = \frac{1}{N} - \frac{8N}{\Gamma^2 + 4N^2}. \tag{7}$$

For $\Gamma \to 0$ all of the slow roll parameters with $n \geq 3$ yields the value $-1/N$. However in the general case, all of the slow parameters have small values if the ϵ_2 is small.

As usual inflation ends at a scale factor a_f where $\epsilon_1(a_f) = 1$ and the slow-roll approximation breaks down. Therefore the end of inflation takes place when the number of e-folds reads:
$$N_f = \pm \sqrt{\frac{\Gamma}{4\pi}(2\xi - \pi\Gamma)}. \tag{8}$$

Notice that with the condition (2) it gets a definite value. In order to have an inflationary phase the condition $2\xi > \pi\Gamma$ must be satisfied. The negative value of N_f is the final state of the inflationary phase, while the positive value of N_f is the initial value of the slow rolling Dark Energy at the late universe. Therefore, in order to calculate the inflationary observables, we must take the minus sing of N_f. Consequently the initial N_i satisfies the condition: $N_f - N_i = \mathcal{N} \approx 50 - 60$, where we impose 60 e-folds for the inflationary phase. Hence, the initial state of the inflationary phase reads:
$$N_i = -\sqrt{\frac{\Gamma}{4\pi}(2\xi - \pi\Gamma)} - \mathcal{N}. \tag{9}$$

The inflationary observables are expressed as[49]
$$r \approx 16\epsilon_1, \quad n_s \approx 1 - 2\epsilon_1 - \epsilon_2, \quad \alpha_s \approx -2\epsilon_1\epsilon_2 - \epsilon_2\epsilon_3, \quad n_T \approx -2\epsilon_1, \tag{10}$$
where all quantities are calculated at N_i. Therefore the tensor to scalar ratio and the primordial tilt give:
$$r = \frac{32\Gamma\xi}{\pi\Gamma^2 + 4\pi N_i^2}, \quad n_s = \frac{\pi\left(\Gamma^2 + 4N_i(N_i+2)\right) - 4\Gamma\xi}{\pi\left(\Gamma^2 + 4N_i^2\right)}. \tag{11a}$$

For 60 e-folds and $\Gamma = 0.1$ the observables read:
$$r = 0.0076, \quad n_s = 0.961754. \tag{12}$$

These values in agreement with the latest 2018 Planck data[50,51]:
$$0.95 < n_s < 0.97, \quad r < 0.064. \tag{13}$$

Fig. 2 shows the predicted distribution of the observables.[52] We assume a uniform prior: $N \in [50; 70]$, $\xi \in [100; 200]$, $\Gamma \in [0; 1]$, with 10^7 Markov Chain Monte Carlo samples. We find the posterior yields:
$$r = 0.045^{+0.065}_{-0.053}, \tag{14}$$
$$n_s = 0.9624^{+0.0087}_{-0.011}, \tag{15}$$
$$\alpha_s = -\left(33^{+27}_{-30}\right) \cdot 10^{-5}, \tag{16}$$
in good agreement with the recent Planck values.

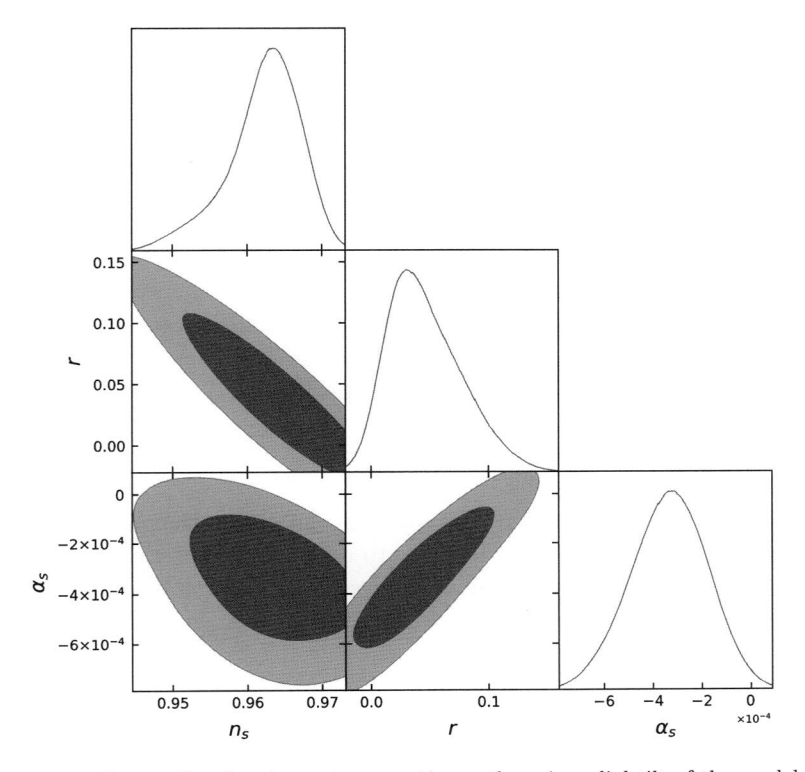

Fig. 2. The predicted scalar to tensor ratio vs. the primordial tilt of the model.

3. Scalar field dynamics

The above ansatz is of general applicability in any inflation realization, whether this is driven by a scalar field, or it arises effectively from modified gravity, or from any other mechanism. In order to provide a more transparent picture let us consider a realization of these ideas in the context of a canonical scalar field theory ϕ moving in a potential $V(\phi)$. The Friedmann equations are

$$H^2 = \frac{8\pi G}{3}\left[\frac{1}{2}\dot\phi^2 + V(\phi)\right], \quad \dot H = -4\pi G \dot\phi^2, \qquad (17)$$

while that for the scalar field is

$$\ddot\phi + 3H\dot\phi + V'(\phi) = 0. \qquad (18)$$

Let us apply the ansatz in order to reconstruct a physical scalar-field potential that can generate the desirable inflationary observables. From the Friedmann equation (17) that holds in every scalar-field inflation, we extract the following solutions

$$\phi = \int_0^N \sqrt{-2\frac{H'}{H}}\, dN, \quad V(\phi) = HH' + 3H^2, \qquad (19)$$

with $8\pi G = 1$. From the integration of the Hubble parameter we get:

$$N = \frac{\Gamma}{2}\sinh\left(\sqrt{\frac{\pi}{\xi\Gamma}}\phi\right), \quad V(N) = \Lambda_0 e^{-\frac{2\xi}{\pi}\tan^{-1}\left(\frac{2N}{\Gamma}\right)}\left(1 - \frac{2\Gamma\xi}{3\pi\Gamma^2 + 12\pi N^2}\right). \quad (20)$$

Relations (20) can be used in order to write V in terms of ϕ analytically

$$V(\phi) = \Lambda_0 e^{-\frac{2\xi}{\pi}\tan^{-1}(\sinh x)}\left(1 - \frac{2\xi}{3\pi\Gamma}\text{sech}^2 x\right), \quad (21)$$

with $x \equiv \sqrt{\pi/\Gamma\xi}\phi$. Fig. 3 shows the scalar potential $V(\phi)$. The universe in this picture begins with $\phi \to \infty$ with a slow roll behavior and goes to the left-hand side. After approaching the minimum the universe evolves with another slow roll behavior that corresponds to the dark energy epoch when $\phi \to -\infty$. The asymptotic values of the potential are:

$$V_{+\infty} = \Lambda_0 e^{\xi}, \quad V_{-\infty} = \Lambda_0 e^{-\xi}. \quad (22)$$

Notice that this represents a see saw cosmological effect, that is if Λ_0 represents an intermediate scale, we see that in order to make the inflationary scale big forces the present vacuum energy to be small. Λ_0 represents the geometric average of the inflationary vacuum energy and the present Dark Energy vacuum energies.

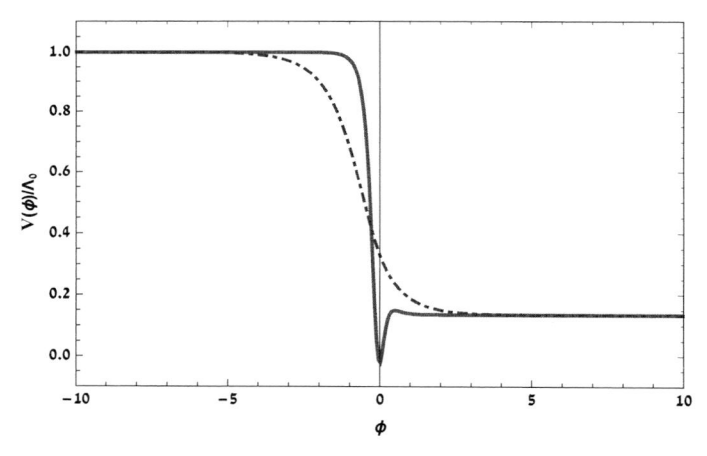

Fig. 3. The corresponding scalar field potential for the Lorenzian ansatz, with different values of Γ: 0.1 red smooth line, 1 blue dashed line.

4. Discussion

This essay introduces a model where we start with an ansatz for the slow roll parameter ϵ for the whole history of the Universe. We choose a Lorentzian form for ϵ, which peaks at some point and goes to zero for the early and late Universe, so these two epochs have an accelerated phase. The magnitude of the vacuum energies at the early and late Universe obeys a see saw mechanism: since the asymptotic values of the potential are $\Lambda_0 e^{\pm\xi}$ this represents a see saw cosmological effect, where the requirement that one scale (the inflationary scale) be large pushes the Dark Energy scale to be very low. See saw cosmological effects in modified measure theories with spontaneously broken scale invariance have been studied in.[53-55] For the situation presented in this paper to work, we must choose Λ_0 as an intermediate scale, and indeed then we see that in order to make the inflationary scale big, this forces the present vacuum energy to be small. Λ_0 represents the geometric average of the inflationary vacuum energy and the present Dark Energy vacuum energies.

The model formulates the vacuum energies both in the inflationary epoch and in the dark energy epoch. However to compare the basis of the model with the whole history of universe, we have to take into account particle creation models with temperature, as well as radiation production.

Acknowledgments

D.B. gratefully acknowledge the support the supports of the Blavatnik and the Rothschild fellowships. We have received partial support from European COST actions CA15117 and CA18108.

References

1. A. H. Guth, *Phys. Rev.* **D23** (1981) 347, [Adv. Ser. Astrophys. Cosmol.3,139(1987)].
2. A. H. Guth and S. Y. Pi, *Phys. Rev. Lett.* **49** (1982) 1110.
3. A. A. Starobinsky, *JETP Lett.* **30** (1979) 682 [767(1979)].
4. D. Kazanas, *Astrophys. J.* **241** (1980) L59.
5. A. A. Starobinsky, *Phys. Lett.* **91B** (1980) 99 [771(1980)].
6. A. D. Linde, *Phys. Lett.* **108B** (1982) 389, [Adv. Ser. Astrophys. Cosmol.3,149(1987)].
7. A. Albrecht and P. J. Steinhardt, *Phys. Rev. Lett.* **48** (1982) 1220, [Adv. Ser. Astrophys. Cosmol.3,158(1987)].
8. J. D. Barrow and A. C. Ottewill, *J. Phys.* **A16** (1983) 2757.
9. S. K. Blau, E. I. Guendelman and A. H. Guth, *Phys. Rev.* **D35** (1987) 1747.
10. J. D. Barrow and A. Paliathanasis, *Phys. Rev.* **D94** (2016) 083518, arXiv:1609.01126 [gr-qc].
11. J. D. Barrow and A. Paliathanasis, *Gen. Rel. Grav.* **50** (2018) 82, arXiv:1611.06680 [gr-qc].
12. K. A. Olive, *Phys. Rept.* **190** (1990) 307.
13. A. D. Linde, *Phys. Rev.* **D49** (1994) 748, arXiv:astro-ph/9307002 [astro-ph].
14. A. R. Liddle, P. Parsons and J. D. Barrow, *Phys. Rev.* **D50** (1994) 7222, arXiv:astro-ph/9408015 [astro-ph].
15. C. Germani and A. Kehagias, *Phys. Rev. Lett.* **105** (2010) 011302, arXiv:1003.2635 [hep-ph].
16. T. Kobayashi, M. Yamaguchi and J. Yokoyama, *Phys. Rev. Lett.* **105** (2010) 231302, arXiv:1008.0603 [hep-th].
17. C.-J. Feng, X.-Z. Li and E. N. Saridakis, *Phys. Rev.* **D82** (2010) 023526, arXiv:1004.1874 [astro-ph.CO].

18. C. Burrage, C. de Rham, D. Seery and A. J. Tolley, *JCAP* **1101** (2011) 014, arXiv:1009.2497 [hep-th].
19. T. Kobayashi, M. Yamaguchi and J. Yokoyama, *Prog. Theor. Phys.* **126** (2011) 511, arXiv:1105.5723 [hep-th].
20. J. Ohashi and S. Tsujikawa, *JCAP* **1210** (2012) 035, arXiv:1207.4879 [gr-qc].
21. Y.-F. Cai, J.-O. Gong, S. Pi, E. N. Saridakis and S.-Y. Wu, *Nucl. Phys.* **B900** (2015) 517, arXiv:1412.7241 [hep-th].
22. V. Kamali, S. Basilakos and A. Mehrabi, *Eur. Phys. J.* **C76** (2016) 525, arXiv:1604.05434 [gr-qc].
23. D. Benisty and E. I. Guendelman, *Int. J. Mod. Phys.* **A33** (2018) 1850119, arXiv:1710.10588 [gr-qc].
24. I. Dalianis, A. Kehagias and G. Tringas, *JCAP* **1901** (2019) 037, arXiv:1805.09483 [astro-ph.CO].
25. I. Dalianis and G. Tringas, *Phys. Rev.* **D100** (2019) 083512, arXiv:1905.01741 [astro-ph.CO].
26. S. Weinberg, *Rev. Mod. Phys.* **61** (1989) 1.
27. L. Lombriser, *Phys. Lett.* **B797** (2019) 134804, arXiv:1901.08588 [gr-qc].
28. D. Merritt, *Stud. Hist. Phil. Sci.* **B57** (2017) 41, arXiv:1703.02389 [physics.hist-ph].
29. B. Ratra and P. J. E. Peebles, *Phys. Rev.* **D37** (1988) 3406.
30. R. R. Caldwell, R. Dave and P. J. Steinhardt, *Phys. Rev. Lett.* **80** (1998) 1582, arXiv:astro-ph/9708069 [astro-ph].
31. D. Benisty and E. I. Guendelman, *Phys. Rev.* **D98** (2018) 023506, arXiv:1802.07981 [gr-qc].
32. I. Zlatev, L.-M. Wang and P. J. Steinhardt, *Phys. Rev. Lett.* **82** (1999) 896, arXiv:astro-ph/9807002 [astro-ph].
33. R. R. Caldwell, *Phys. Lett.* **B545** (2002) 23, arXiv:astro-ph/9908168 [astro-ph].
34. T. Chiba, T. Okabe and M. Yamaguchi, *Phys. Rev.* **D62** (2000) 023511, arXiv:astro-ph/9912463 [astro-ph].
35. M. C. Bento, O. Bertolami and A. A. Sen, *Phys. Rev.* **D66** (2002) 043507, arXiv:gr-qc/0202064 [gr-qc].
36. S. Tsujikawa, *Class. Quant. Grav.* **30** (2013) 214003, arXiv:1304.1961 [gr-qc].
37. C. Wetterich, *Phys. Rev.* **D89** (2014) 024005, arXiv:1308.1019 [astro-ph.CO].
38. M. W. Hossain, R. Myrzakulov, M. Sami and E. N. Saridakis, *Phys. Rev.* **D90** (2014) 023512, arXiv:1402.6661 [gr-qc].
39. E. Guendelman, E. Nissimov and S. Pacheva, *Bulg. J. Phys.* **44** (2017) 015, arXiv:1609.06915 [gr-qc].
40. E. Guendelman, E. Nissimov and S. Pacheva, *Bulg. J. Phys.* **45** (2018) 152, arXiv:1709.03786 [gr-qc].
41. E. Guendelman, E. Nissimov and S. Pacheva, *Bulg. J. Phys.* **42** (2015) 249, arXiv:1505.07680 [gr-qc].
42. M. W. Hossain, R. Myrzakulov, M. Sami and E. N. Saridakis, *Phys. Rev.* **D90** (2014) 023512, arXiv:1402.6661 [gr-qc].
43. M. W. Hossain, R. Myrzakulov, M. Sami and E. N. Saridakis, *Phys. Lett.* **B737** (2014) 191, arXiv:1405.7491 [gr-qc].
44. M. Wali Hossain, R. Myrzakulov, M. Sami and E. N. Saridakis, *Int. J. Mod. Phys.* **D24** (2015) 1530014, arXiv:1410.6100 [gr-qc].
45. C.-Q. Geng, M. W. Hossain, R. Myrzakulov, M. Sami and E. N. Saridakis, *Phys. Rev.* **D92** (2015) 023522, arXiv:1502.03597 [gr-qc].

46. C.-Q. Geng, C.-C. Lee, M. Sami, E. N. Saridakis and A. A. Starobinsky, *JCAP* **1706** (2017) 011, arXiv:1705.01329 [gr-qc].
47. A. B. Kaganovich, *Phys. Rev.* **D63** (2001) 025022, arXiv:hep-th/0007144 [hep-th].
48. M. W. Hossain, R. Myrzakulov, M. Sami and E. N. Saridakis, *Phys. Rev.* **D89** (2014) 123513, arXiv:1404.1445 [gr-qc].
49. J. Martin, C. Ringeval and V. Vennin, *Phys. Dark Univ.* **5-6** (2014) 75, arXiv:1303.3787 [astro-ph.CO].
50. Planck Collaboration (N. Aghanim *et al.*) (2018) arXiv:1807.06209 [astro-ph.CO].
51. Planck Collaboration (Y. Akrami *et al.*) (2018) arXiv:1807.06211 [astro-ph.CO].
52. A. Lewis (2019) arXiv:1910.13970 [astro-ph.IM].
53. E. I. Guendelman, *Mod. Phys. Lett.* **A14** (1999) 1397, arXiv:hep-th/0106084 [hep-th].
54. E. I. Guendelman, *Mod. Phys. Lett.* **A14** (1999) 1043, arXiv:gr-qc/9901017 [gr-qc].
55. E. Guendelman, R. Herrera, P. Labrana, E. Nissimov and S. Pacheva, *Gen. Rel. Grav.* **47** (2015) 10, arXiv:1408.5344 [gr-qc].

Condensed light, quantum black holes and L-CDM cosmology: Experimentally suggested and tested unified approach to dark matter, dark energy, cosmogenesis and two-stage inflation

Victor Borsevici

International Informatization Academy, branch Rep. of Moldova,
Chisinau, Rep. of Moldova
E-mail: borsevici@mail.ru

Based on the fundamental last discoveries (such as gravitational waves, Higgs field, gravitating Bose-Einstein photon condensates etc.), guided by the last A. Einstein's conjecture (about algebraic approach to the combined quantum and continuum description of reality) and directed by the J. Bekenstein-V. Mukhanov approach to the quantum black holes physics and astrophysics, the L. Susskind's "one photon – one bit" principle and V. Gribov-S. Hawking tunneling effect, one can easily find the simple but consistent algebraic relations and physical laws that govern birth and death of black holes in the Early Universe, its accretion and two-particle emitting (both outside black hole) accompanied with gravitational radiation.

From these basic relations in a natural way derive the Planck units system that confirm the theoretical consistence of presented approach and directly leads to the Planck Scale physics where standard models of the particle physics and cosmology are "blinded". Presented approach elucidates the physical background of dark matter (black holes), dark energy (gravitational waves), hot Big Bang and two-stage inflation of the Universe. Moreover, it solves many old unsolved problems, such as "cosmic censorship" conjecture, information loss paradox, black hole "end-point" problem, "cosmological constant" problem and so on.

The great importance for the validation of presented approach and it results had the comparison with "Planck-2018" data and other relevant information from the sources of observational cosmology, astrophysics, gravitational waves astronomy and numerical relativity.

Keywords: Planck scale physics, dark matter, dark energy, Bose–Einstein photon condensates, Cosmology.

To the blessed memory of Jacob Bekenstein
and Steven Weinberg

Introduction

"Raffiniert ist der HerrGott, aber boshaft ist er nicht."
(A. Einstein)

What "banged"? What is dark matter? What is dark energy? What caused two-stage inflation? *etc.* Such problematic questions that provoked a lot of troubles for L-CDM cosmology are a consequence of unsolved problems in physics. L. Smolin called this stagnant situation "Einstein's unfinished revolution" and the more critical theoreticist S. Hossenfelder called it "Lost in math".

But over the last decade, experimental physics and observational cosmology have made many fundamental discoveries: gravitational waves (LIGO), Higgs boson (LHC), photon condensates with rest energy and rest mass trapped in "mirror cavities" (Bonn University).[1,2]

Through these remarkable results, Nature suggests that at pressures and temperatures well above the Higgs field level (246 GeV), only the 2-d and 3-d photon condensates trapped in their own "gravitational cavities" should be unique sources of gravity during the Early Universe. Moreover, we conclude that the real *"prima materia"* at the "beginning of the times" was a 3-dimensional Planck photonic condensate as "explosive" accompanied by Planck fluctuations as "fuse". This unambiguously postulates the fundamental role of the laws of conservation of energy and momentum in cosmology, as well as reflect the decisive role of quantum fluctuation in the formation of the modern Universe (see V. Mukhanov-G. Chibisov and S. Hawking – B. Carr approaches).

Note that after the discovery of gravitational waves, the famous Nobel Prize winner P. W. Anderson, in his prophetic "Four Last Conjectures" (2018), argues that "dark energy" is gravitational radiation which causes irreversible loss of mass in the Universe.

It is quite clear that in the swift initial process of Hot Bing Bang we have only three kinds of "actors" at the Planck scale: the 2-d spherical self-gravitating photonic condensates (primordial quantum black holes as "dark matter"), free hot photons and gravitational waves (both acting as massless stretched "dark energy" forces). Note that only gravitational radiation represents one irreversible repulsive force. According to our calculations, only a part of relic gravitational waves with Planck energies E_p and $E_p/2$ make up 93.38% of the dark energy in the modern Universe. As you can see, S. Weinberg was absolutely right: only the energy of Hot Bing Bang causes the universal expansion process.

Moreover, the irreversibility of the gravitational radiation energy prohibits all kind of "big crunch" and "bouncing" (cyclic) cosmological theories, proving instead the Hot Big Bang approach to the cosmogenesis.

We must point out separately that at the end of the initial phase of the Hot Big Bang process (at about $50\pi \times 5.391 \times 10^{-44}$ sec), when the strongest inequality $\Omega_M \ll \Omega_\Lambda$ was reached and stage I of hyperinflation began, a part of the surviving primordial black holes became "seed" of the primordial Cosmic Web, in which baryogenesis occurs and all astrophysical objects are formed.

Where do these conclusions follow? Taking into account the quantum nature of the 2-d spherical photon condensates, trapped in their own gravitational fields, guided by the J. Bekenstein's fundamental dependence between the Compton wavelength and the gravitational radius,[3] L. Susskind's principle "one photon — one bit",[4] the V. Mukhanov's quantum black holes "degeneracy" principle[5] and the modified V. Gribov–S. Hawking tunneling effect,[6,7] one can easily find any exact and adequate laws that govern birth and death, rise and downfall, accretion of light and quantum two-particle emission (both outside black holes). All these processes are accompanied by the emission of gravitational waves.[8]

In what follows, we will demonstrate that the most important thing that distinguishes such natural black holes modelling from all other "membrane models" (see K. S. Thorne, F. Wilczek and M. Maggiore approaches) is that tremendous gravitational squeezed force is perfectly equilibrated by repulsive ("antigravitational") quantum-mechanical one.

Note that only the 2-d photon condensate "construct" with its tremendous "band" of possible wavelengths can explain the incredibly wide range of sizes, lifetimes and masses of black holes, ranging from the Planck scale to tens of Pluto orbits and tens of billions of masses of the Sun (see the quasar *TON 618*). We will demonstrate that this approach is free from the "cosmic censorship" principle, the "no hair" theorem and the information loss paradox.

Using this unified approach, we can calculate that at the end of the epoch of baryogenesis, when stage I of inflation ends, the rest energies of black holes (dark matter) and energy of gravitational waves (dark energy) are 28.62% and 66.42%, respectively. After this epoch, there came a non-accelerated expansion. But 6–8 billion years ago, the II stage of inflation began. Now, accordingly to "Planck-2018" data, we find the 26.57% and 68.47%, respectively. Comparison with the end of the stage I clearly shows that the increase in dark energy is caused by a decrease in the energy associated with dark matter. This leads to the unambiguous conclusion that stage II of inflation is provided by binary coalescences of black holes.

The greatest discoveries of L-CDM cosmologies are namely such epiphenomenons as "dark matter", "dark energy", "Hot Big Bang" and "two-stage inflation". It remains to find the deep physical background of these unsolved phenomenologies. The "Einstein's Unfinished Revolution" must be continued. However, it is quite clear that this is impossible without taking into account the new discoveries of modern physics and cosmology, including the self-gravitating Bose–Einstein photonic condensates. We must demonstrate the new approach to the Planck Scale Physics, where standard models of physics and cosmology was "blinded".

The new theoretical approach is consistent, when from it basic relations and equations directly derive any fundamental constants. In what follows, we will demonstrate that proposed basic equations generate the fundamental system of Planck units. This directly leads to the Terra Incognita of Planck Scale Physics and solves many puzzles of black hole physics, astrophysics and cosmology, such as "cosmic censorship" problem, information loss paradox, black hole "end-point" problem, "cosmological constant" problem, dark matter and dark energy problems and so on.

1. Principia

In 1916 A. Einstein wrote: "...das die Quantentheorie nicht nur die Maxwellische Elektrodynamik, ... auch die neue Gravitationstheorie wird modifizieren mussen".[9]

Already in those distant times, under the influence of Bohr's theory of hydrogen atom, he came to the conclusion that a spherical system should emit not only quanta of light, but also any portions of gravitational waves. This led him to believe that the new theory of gravity should be modified taking into account quantum electrodynamics.

Many years later, in 1954, in his last work, he wrote the closing lines that sound like a testament: "... a finite system with its finite energy can be described in full by a finite set of numbers (quantum numbers). Seemingly, it cannot be compliant with the continuum theory and requires a purely algebraic theory for a reality description. However now nobody knows, how to find a basis for such a theory".[10] Actually, A. Einstein explicitly clamed in his "last will" that just the algebraic approach must be the magistral way to unify quantum physics and continuum general relativity.

Only two decades later, it was the young Israeli physicist J. Bekenstein who turned out to be the "nobody" who found a way to do this. In his revolutionary work "Black Holes and Entropy"[3] he gave an amazing formula for the entropy of a black hole

$$S_s \text{ (Bekenstein)} = \frac{\ln 2}{8\pi} k c^3 \hbar^{-1} G^{-1} A_S ,$$

which unites all world constants: Boltzmann's constant (k), speed of light (c), reduced Plank constant ($\hbar$), gravitational constant (G), as well as the area of the Schwarzschild spherical singularity

$$A_S = 4\pi R_S^2 ,$$

where R_S is the Schwarzschild gravitational radius.

Bekenstein's formula was striking in that it linked together thermodynamics, quantum physics, the theory of gravity, and geometry. But the most surprising thing was that he connected all this within the framework of a unified information approach to the physics and astrophysics of black holes. In his famous formula, he associated the multiplier $\ln 2$ with Shannon's "bit". And this is not accidental, because he followed the famous principle of his great teacher J. A. Wheeler: "It from bit".

In 1986, the young Russian physicist V. Mukhanov, guided (as A. Einstein) by hydrogen atom analogy, came to the irrefutable conclusion that the emission mechanism of quantum black holes must obey the "degeneracy" principle.[11] He turns to J. Bekenstein and in 1995 their common outstanding work "Spectroscopy of the quantum black hole"[12] is published. In this work, it was shown that the true emission spectrum of quantum black holes *is discrete*.

With the advent of new fundamental experimental discoveries, this work of J. Bekenstein and V. Mukhanov began to acquire fundamental significance for physics and cosmology. Moreover, it turned out to be not just a "window" (as its authors was believed), but a whole "gateway" to *Terra Incognita* of Planck Scale Physics.

2. Basic Relations

With the discovery of 2-d photonic Bose-Einstein condensate[1] it became clear that the rejected Schwarzshild spherical singularity was becoming an obvious alternative to the black hole model in the form of a "point singularity" surrounded by an "event horizon" of Schwarzschild radius.

The biggest problem of all "membrane models" was their physical inconsistence. No one has been able to prove their resilience when facing the tremendous gravitational squeezed forces. From the "relativistic" point of view, this seemed to be an unsolvable problem. That is why, first of all, after justifying our approach, we will prove the strong equilibrium between squeezed gravitational forces and repulsive "antigravitational" quantum mechanical forces of quantum black hole. Note, that this strong equilibrium may be broken only by V. Mukhanov's "degeneracy" effect.

Based on the Bekenstein–Mukhanov approach, we will show how all these unsolved problems are solved in terms of the original basic system of equations for spherical 2-d photon condensates, trapped in their own gravitational field:

$$\begin{cases} \bar{\lambda}_{sm} = R_s \,, & (1) \\ \bar{\lambda}_{sm} = \dfrac{\hbar}{M_{sm}c} = \dfrac{\hbar c}{E_{sm}} \,, & (2) \\ R_s = \dfrac{2G}{c^2} M_s = \dfrac{2G}{c^4} E_s \,, & (3) \\ N_s = \dfrac{M_s}{M_{sm}} = \dfrac{E_s}{E_{sm}} \,, & (4) \\ N_s(min) = 2 \,. & (5) \end{cases}$$

Equations (1)–(3) bind together the reduced Compton wavelength, $\bar{\lambda}_{sm}$, which is associated to one photon with rest mass M_{sm} and rest energy E_{sm}, and Schwarzschild radius, R_s, which is expressed in terms of M_s (total rest mass of the condensate) and E_s (total rest energy).

Note that relation of the type of Eq. (1) was first time discovered by Bekenstein in his remarkable work Ref. 3 to determine the largest Compton wavelength of a particle absorbable by a black hole. In essence, general Eq. (1) can be called "Bekenstein relation". This is the only one equation known to us that organically interconnects Quantum Physics and General Relativity. In fact, it reflect the deepest equivalence between the "quantum wavelength geometry" ($\bar{\lambda}_{sm}$) and the "relativistic geometry" (R_s) that occurs in black holes as spherical 2-d photon condensates trapped in their own gravitational fields.

Equation (4) organically make links between the number of photons in the condensate, N_S, and the quantities expressing its "individual" rest mass, M_{sm}, and rest energy, E_{sm}, as well as with "total" rest mass, M_s, and rest energy, E_s. We note in particular that N_s is a natural integer, that reflect a quantum nature of black holes physics.

Equation (5) sets a natural limit on the minimum number of photons in the condensate, equal to two: $N_S(min) = 2$.

Note that for the evident lower boundary condition, system Eqs. (1)–(5) gives us (it is easy to verify) the following solutions:

$$M_s(min) = \sqrt{\frac{\hbar c}{G}} = M_p, \quad E_s(min) = \sqrt{\frac{\hbar c^5}{G}} = E_p, \quad R_s(min) = 2\sqrt{\frac{\hbar G}{c^3}} = 2l_p, \tag{6}$$

where M_p and E_p are the Planck mass and energy, respectively, l_p — Planck length.

It is striking that we unexpectedly found ourselves in the field of Planck Scale Physics and absolutely accurately described the Planck black hole without any preliminary assumptions, hypotheses and conjectures. We have used only the most basic information from Quantum Physics and General Relativity enclosed in the base system Eqs. (1)–(5).

Note that we do not use the "quantum gravity" approach based on the "gravitons" hypothesis because of the gravitational waves (the "ripples" of spacetime) radically differ from the quantum-mechanical waves (the "waves of probability").

3. Equilibrium

In order to make certain that a quantum black hole taken as spherical self-gravitating 2-d photon condensate is a quasi-stable astrophysical object, from all the solutions of the system Eqs. (1)--(5) we will pick the following one:

$$M_{sm} = \frac{\hbar}{cR_s} = \frac{\hbar c}{2GM_s} = \frac{M_p^2}{2M_s}, \tag{7}$$

$$E_{sm} = \frac{\hbar c}{\lambda_{sm}} = \frac{\hbar c}{R_s} = \frac{\hbar c^5}{2GE_s} = \frac{E_p^2}{2E_s}. \tag{8}$$

As we can see, according to Birkhoff's Theorem the attractive gravitational force for one photon with rest mass M_{sm} is equal to

$$F_{sm,\, gr} = \frac{2GM_{sm}M_s}{R_s^2} = \frac{\hbar c}{R_s^2}. \tag{9}$$

But this attractive gravitational force must be perfectly equilibrated by quantum-mechanical "antigravitational" force:

$$F_{sm,\, qu} = \frac{dE_{sm}(\bar\lambda_{sm})}{d\bar\lambda_{sm}} = \frac{d(\hbar c/R_s)}{dR_s} = -\frac{\hbar c}{R_s^2}. \tag{10}$$

4. Quantum Information and Entropy: The Downfall of the "Point-Centered" Model

In his remarkable book "The Cosmic Landscape",[4] L. Susskind convincingly demonstrates that every photon is a carrier of one bit of quantum information. The point is that a photon can be in two spin states, $|0\rangle$ or $|1\rangle$.

In the case of a quantum black hole consisting of N_s photons, this means that the power of the set of its possible quantum states is 2^{N_s}. From the point of view of information theory, a quantum black hole can be represented as a binary text consisting of N_s positions filled with symbols from the alphabet $\{|0\rangle, |1\rangle\}$. To each such text, θ_i, a probability, p_i, can be attributed. The maximum of C. E. Shannon's entropy is achieved for an uniform distribution $p_i = 2^{-N_s}$:

$$H_s \text{ (Shannon)}_{max} = -\sum_{i=1}^{2^{N_s}} 2^{-N_s} \log_2 2^{-N_s} = N_s \text{ (bit)} . \quad (11)$$

According to Shannon's approach, the maximum amount of quantum information, I_s, contained in a quantum black hole does not exceed this value. Moreover, it is equal to it:

$$I_s = H_s \text{ (Shannon)}_{max} = N_s \text{ (bit)} . \quad (12)$$

Now let's calculate the thermodynamic entropy of the black hole. To do this, we first need to calculate the temperature of the quantum black hole from the relation

$$E_{sm} = 2 \times kT_s , \quad (13)$$

where kT_s is the energy corresponding to vibrational freedom degree, 2 is the multiplier due to the two spin states, $|0\rangle$ and $|1\rangle$. From Eq. (13) directly follows the wanted relationship for the temperature

$$T_s = \frac{E_{sm}}{2k} = \frac{E_p^2}{4kE_s} = \frac{\hbar c^3}{4kGM_s} . \quad (14)$$

It is easy to see that we have obtained an expression very close to the one of S. Hawking:

$$T_s \text{ (Hawkinhg)} = \frac{1}{2\pi} T_s . \quad (15)$$

However, the essential difference lies in the fact that the temperature T_s (Hawkinhg) is the typical temperature of the black hole taken as a "black body", whereas we are dealing with a quantum black hole. On the other hand, this similitude of the results suggests that we are acting in the right direction.

From the Clausius relation $\mathrm{d}S = \mathrm{d}E/T$ and Eq. (14), by integration, we easily find the required expression for the thermodynamic entropy:

$$S_s = \int_0^{E_s} \frac{4k}{E_p^2} E \, \mathrm{d}E = k2\frac{E_s^2}{E_p^2} = kN_s . \quad (16)$$

In other words, we get a direct connection between the entropy of a black hole and the Shannon's entropy:

$$S_s = kH_s \text{ (Shannon)}_{max} = kN_s . \quad (17)$$

From Eqs. (3), (4) and (16) we can get another important relation:

$$S_s = kN_s = k\frac{R_s^2}{2l_p^2} = \frac{1}{8\pi} kc^3 \hbar^{-1} G^{-1} A_s , \quad (18)$$

where A_s is the area of the Schwarzschild spherical singularity. This immediately implies a connection with the cited above Bekenstein formula:

$$S_s \text{ (Bekenstein)} = \ln 2 \cdot S_s . \tag{19}$$

The remarkable physicist S. Hawking relied on a model of a black hole in the form of a "point-singularity" surrounded by a "event-horizon". Actually, this means that in the center of symmetry of any black hole there should be matter with the limiting Planck density. Only 3-d Planck photon condensate can have such a density. It is not difficult to calculate the amount of quantum information, I_{s*}, in this model:

$$I_{s*} = N_{s*} = \frac{M_s}{M_p} . \tag{20}$$

For a 2-d model, as we already know, this quantity will be equal to

$$I_s = N_s = 2M_s^2/M_p^2 .$$

Let's compare these amounts of quantum information for a black hole of solar mass $M_\odot$:

$$I_s/I_{s*} = 2M_\odot/M_p = 1.827 \times 10^{38} \text{ (sic!)} .$$

As we can see, in the light of modern discoveries, this difference in the amounts of quantum information, is simply monstrous. That clearly shows the invalidity of "point-model".

5. Natural Quantum Black Hole Description

We can continue J. Bekenstein–V. Mukhanov approach that in fact derive from the A. Einstein "testament" that was cited above.

From (4) and (5) we can conclude that the number of photons in quantum black hole taken as a spherical self-gravitating 2-d photon condensate must be presented in the following form:

$$N_s = 2n_s, \quad n_s = 1, 2, 3, \dots \tag{21}$$

where n_s is *the principal quantum number*.

Then it is easy to show that all our previous results can be represented as follows:

$$\bar\lambda_{sm} = R_s = 2l_p\sqrt{n_s} ; \tag{22}$$

$$M_s = M_p\sqrt{n_s} , \quad E_s = E_p\sqrt{n_s} ; \tag{23}$$

$$M_{sm} = M_p/2\sqrt{n_s} , \quad E_{sm} = E_p/2\sqrt{n_s} ; \tag{24}$$

$$\omega_{sm} \text{ (ciclic frequence)} = E_{sm}/\hbar = \omega_p/2\sqrt{n_s} , \tag{25}$$

where $\omega_p = 1/t_p$ is the Planck frequency, $t_p = \sqrt{\hbar G/c^5}$ is the Planck time;

$$A_s = 16\pi l_p^2 n_s ; \tag{26}$$

$$I_s = N_s = 2n_s \text{ (bit)} ; \tag{27}$$

$$S_s = kI_s = 2kn_s ; \tag{28}$$

$$T_s = E_p/4k\sqrt{n_s} = T_p/4\sqrt{n_s} , \tag{29}$$

where $T_p = E_p/k$ is the Planck temperature;

$$\rho_{sh}^I \text{ (surface information density)} = I_s/A_s = 1/8\pi l_p^2 = \frac{c}{\hbar \varkappa} \left(\frac{\text{bit}}{\text{m}^2}\right), \qquad (30)$$

where $\varkappa = 8\pi G/c^2$ is the Einstein constant;

$$g_{sh} \text{ (surface gravity)} = G\frac{M_s}{R_s^2} = a_p/4\sqrt{n_s}, \qquad (31)$$

$a_p = F_p/M_p = c/t_p$ is the Planck gravity *etc.*

Note, that this natural "emergence" of Planck Scale Physics, that was "automatically" arised from basics system Eqs. (1)–(5), clearly shows, that Planck Units System as such was organically and naturally emerge from experimental physics and observational cosmology. Moreover, as we see, the "great" unity between Quantum Physics and General Relativity was reached in natural way.

The famous physicist J. A. Wheeler once said: "Mass tells spacetime how to curve; spacetime tells mass how to move." Inspired by this example, we can coin a new one: "Light quanta tells spacetime how to quantize; spacetime tells light quanta how to curve."

6. Quantum Black Hole "Evaporation": Two-Particle Emission and Gravitational Waves Radiation

As shown above, quantum black hole has the property of strong equilibrium between squeezed gravitational force and repulsive ("antigravitational") quantum-mechanical force. This state of strong equilibrium can be broken only by the V. Mukhanov's degeneracy effect, which consists in spontaneous quantum jump from n_s state to $n_s - 1$ state. In our case this means that in all relations Eqs. (21)–(31) the argument n_s must be replaced by $n_s - 1$. It's obvious that quantum energy corresponding to the level $E_p\sqrt{n_s}$ must reduce to the one corresponding to the level $E_p\sqrt{n_s - 1}$. The difference

$$\Delta E_{s,s-1} = E_p\left(\sqrt{n_s} - \sqrt{n_s - 1}\right) = \frac{E_p}{2\sqrt{n_s}}\left(1 + \frac{1}{4n_s} + \frac{1}{8n_s^2} + ...\right) \qquad (32)$$

is equal to the sum of radiance energy of two-particle emission

$$\Delta E_{s,s-1\,qu} = \frac{E_p}{2\sqrt{n_s}}$$

and gravitational waves radiation energy

$$\Delta E_{s,s-1\,gr} = \Delta E_{s,s-1} - \Delta E_{s,s-1\,qu} = \frac{E_p}{2\sqrt{n_s}}\left(\frac{1}{4n_s} + \frac{1}{8n_s^2} + ...\right). \qquad (33)$$

Note that energy of the quadrupolar mode is represented by term:

$$\left|\frac{\hbar}{c}\frac{dg_{sh}(n_s)}{dn_s}\right| = \frac{E_p}{2\sqrt{n_s}} \times \frac{1}{4n_s}. \qquad (34)$$

From this result we easily understand that the next term $1/8n_s^2$ from the sequence in parentheses from Eq. (33) corresponds to octupolar mode and so on.

We come to the conclusion that in the parenthesis
$$\left(1 + \frac{1}{4n_s} + \frac{1}{8n_s^2} + ...\right)$$
of the main expansion of polynomial in Eq. (32), the first term refers to the dipolar mode, the second term — to the quadrupolar mode, the third — to the octupolar and so on. In other words, all the terms, except the first one, are directly related to the gravitational radiation of a quantum black hole. It only remains to find out the physical nature of the dipolar mode. For this, we turn to the data of experimental physics. In 2011, physicists from Chalmers University of Technology experimentally proved the existence of Casimir–Unruh dynamical effect in the squeezed vacuum excited by the "moving mirror" with frequency ω, that produce a pair of non-entangled photons with associated frequency $\omega/2$ each.[13]

By this experiment Nature suggests that in general case the energy $\Delta E_{s,s-1\,qu}$ of two-particle emission, $(X_s, \bar{X}_s)$, must be presented by the following form:
$$\Delta S_{s,s-1\,qu} = \hbar\omega_{sm} = \hbar\omega_{sx} + \hbar\omega_{s\bar{x}} = E(X_s) + E(\bar{X}_s), \tag{35}$$
where ω_{sm} is the cyclic frequency Eq. (36),
$$\omega_{sx} = \omega_{s\bar{x}} = {\omega_{sm}}/{2}, \qquad E(X_s) = E(\bar{X}_s) = {E_{sm}}/{2}, \tag{36}$$
where ω_{sx}, $\omega_{s\bar{x}}$ are the frequencies associated with emitted particles.

The following quantum black hole "degeneracy" diagram can illustrate all these results:
$$BH_s \longrightarrow BH_{s-1} + X_s + \bar{X}_s + \Gamma_s, \tag{37}$$
where Γ_s is the generated gravitational wave with energy Eq. (33).

Note that the pair $(X_s, \bar{X}_s)$ of non-entangled particles, depending on their energy, can be a pair of hot photons, this being especially important at energies well above the Higgs field level (246 GeV).

Remark 6.1. Using the expressions obtained above, it is easy to calculate the energy structure of quantum black hole at its "end-point" ($n_s = 1$):
$$BH_p \longrightarrow 2\gamma_{p,0} + \Gamma_{p,0} \tag{38}$$
with energies:
$$E(BH_p) = E_p\sqrt{1} = E_p, \qquad 2E(\gamma_{p,0}) = {E_p}/{2\sqrt{1}} = {E_p}/{2}, \tag{39}$$
$$E(\Gamma_{p,0}) = E_p\left(\sqrt{1} - \sqrt{1-1} - {1}/{2\sqrt{1}}\right) = {E_p}/{2}. \tag{40}$$

As it can be observed, at the "end-point" of the existence of any black hole, all ends with a spectacular explosion with emission of half of energy, $\left({E_p}/{2}\right)$, as quantum electromagnetic radiation and another half, $\left({E_p}/{2}\right)$ — as gravitational radiation. Note that these last two photons carry the last two bits of quantum information. As we can see, in the presented unified approach so called "end-point" problem is solved.

In general case we can find that the total energy radiated by a quantum black hole "evaporating" from the state n_s to its "end-point" is equal to

$$E_{s\,qu}\,(\text{rad}) = \sum_{n=1}^{n_s} E_p/2\sqrt{n}\,, \tag{41}$$

$$E_{s\,gr}\,(\text{rad}) = \sum_{n=1}^{n_s} E_p \left(\sqrt{n} - \sqrt{n-1} - \frac{1}{2\sqrt{n}}\right) = E_p\sqrt{n_s} - \sum_{n=1}^{n_s} \frac{E_p}{2\sqrt{n_s}}\,, \tag{42}$$

$$E_s\,(\text{total rad.}) = E_{s\,qu}\,(\text{rad}) + E_{s\,gr}\,(\text{rad}) = E\sqrt{n_s} = E_s\,. \tag{43}$$

Note that with increase of n_s the total gravitational radiation quickly tends to its maximal value E_p. As we see, the proportionality

$$E_{s\,gr}\,(\text{rad})\big/E_{s\,qu}\,(\text{rad}) = {}^1\!/_{4n_s} + {}^1\!/_{8n_s^2} + \ldots \tag{44}$$

clearly shows the great importance of gravitational radiance when the temperatures of black holes are near to Planckian scale.

7. Real Mechanism of Quantum-Gravitational Radiation and Removal of "Information Loss" Problem

Above we have showed that, in accordance with the V. Mukhanov's degeneracy effect, the strong equilibrium of quantum black hole can be broken by quantum jump from n_s state to the $n_s - 1$ one. We have found, in Eq. (36), that each of the two emitted particles have the energy equal to $E_{sm}/2$. From this, we can easily calculate their non-reduced Compton wavelength:

$$\lambda_c\,(X_s) = \lambda_c\,(\bar{X}_s) = \frac{2\pi\hbar c}{E_{sm}/2} = 4\pi R_s\,. \tag{45}$$

If we compare this value with quantum black hole gravitational radius R_s, we find that these two particles will immediately "escape" from tremendous gravitational "well" of quantum black hole via the V. Gribov–S. Hawking tunneling effect. However, the "breaking news" is: this quantum tunneling effect of two emitted particles is accompanied with radiation of gravitational waves that play an important role in the Planck Scale Physics. Note that quantum black hole radiates two bit of quantum information during "jumping" process:

$$\Delta I_{s,s-1\,qu} = I_s - I_{s-1} = 2n_s - 2(n_s - 1) = 2\,(\text{bit})\,, \tag{46}$$

and these two bits were carried away by two "escaped" particles.

As we see above Eq. (52), the last, "remnant" Planck hole collapsed emitting the last two photons carrying the last two bits of quantum information. These conclusions can represented by the strict mathematical relation:

$$I_s \text{ (radiated)} = \sum_{n=1}^{n_s} \Delta I_{n,n-1\,qu} = 2n_s = I_s\,, \tag{47}$$

that confirms the unitarity principle of quantum physics in the quantum black hole theory in the form of the law of quantum information conservation, that definitely solves the so-called "information loss" problem.

8. Entropy Production by Radiation

In conformity with Clausius relation, we can easily find the entropy production by quantum black hole radiation:

$$\Delta S_{s,s-1} = \frac{\Delta E_{s,s-1}}{T_s} = \frac{\Delta E_{s,s-1\,qu}}{T_s} + \frac{\Delta E_{s,s-1\,gr}}{T_s} = \\ = \Delta S_{s,s-1\,qu} + \Delta S_{s,s-1\,gr} = 2k + 2k\left(\frac{1}{4n_s} + \frac{1}{8n_s} + ...\right). \tag{48}$$

The quantum entropy term

$$\Delta S_{s,s-1\,qu} = 2k = k\Delta I_{s,s-1} \tag{49}$$

is closely connected with two bit of radiated information Eq. (46). But what represent the gravitational radiance term $\Delta S_{s,s-1\,gr}$? The form of the term

$$\Delta S_{s,s-1\,gr} = 2k\left(\frac{1}{4n_s} + \frac{1}{8n_s^2} + ...\right) \tag{50}$$

suggests that it is closely connected with quadrupolar, octupolar etc. modes of gravitational radiation that is the source of a dissipative and irreversible dark energy. We may call this term "gravitational waves entropy production".

It is interesting that famous physicist T. Jacobson in his important work "Non-equilibrium Thermodynamics of Spacetime" named a similar term "bulk viscosity entropy production term" and connected it with Ricci flow. But what is more fascinating: the famous mathematician Grisha Perelman presented his extraordinary work "The entropy formula for Ricci flow and its geometric application", in which argue that the entropy is an effective tool for mathematical investigation.

9. Dynamics: Radiance Power and Lifetime

Before the V. Mukhanov's "degeneracy" jump, quantum black hole must relax to gain the spherical form. Note that inside the 2-d photon condensate the "time flow" is the same as the "time flow" for external observer. This is not a deliberative assumption but a result of LIGO measurement in which the duration of ring-down phase is only a small part of a second. This is because in each point of the 2-d photon condensate all the tangential forces are equilibrated. The "stopped time-flow" effect take place only in the nearest vicinity, but not inside the "stretched horizon".

It is clear that the relaxation process needs a causal synchronism, which means that all the pairs of points located, one from another, at a distance of half a circle (πR_s) must be casually connected. This requires fulfillment of a lot of time at n_s state

$$\Delta t_s = \frac{\pi R_s}{c} = 2\pi t_p \sqrt{n_s} \, . \tag{51}$$

From this formula, we can easily calculate the lifetime of an "evaporated" quantum black hole:

$$\tau_s = \sum_{n=1}^{n_s} 2\pi t_p \sqrt{n} \, . \tag{52}$$

Using Bohr's correspondence principle, a very simple relation is found:

$$\tau_s = \int_0^{n_s} 2\pi t_p \sqrt{n} \, \mathrm{d}n = \frac{4\pi}{3} t_p n_s^{3/2} = \frac{4\pi}{3} t_p \left(\frac{E_s}{E_p}\right)^3 \, . \tag{53}$$

If we compare it with the S. Hawking's formula, we can see that

$$\tau_s = \frac{1}{3840} \tau_s \, (\text{Hawking}) \, . \tag{54}$$

This big difference appears because S. Hawking associated black hole radiation with the blackbody radiation and with the Stefan-Boltzmann law, which means a continuous thermal spectrum. In contrast to this, following J. Bekenstein and V. Mukhanov, we have showed that this spectrum is <u>discrete</u>. Hence such a strong difference occurs.

Let's find the radiance power:

$$P_s = \frac{\Delta E_{s,s-1}}{\Delta t_s} \cong \frac{E_p}{4\pi t_p n_s} = \frac{\hbar c^6}{4\pi G^2 M_s^2} \, . \tag{55}$$

Comparing this with the S. Hawking's result, we find, respectively

$$P_s = 3840 P_s \, (\text{Hawking}) \, . \tag{56}$$

The reason for such a large difference is the same.

We have a rare opportunity to qualitatively compare our results. It is known that the "baryonic epoch" lasted for about 400 thousand years. According to our calculations, in conformity with Eq. (53), the lifetime of the black hole, able of generating baryons, is about 240 thousand years, that quite "fits" into the mentioned interval of 400 thousand years. Whereas by S. Hawking model Eq. (54) it take as long as 920 millions (!) years, which is completely inconsistent with the data of observational cosmology. In what follows, we can find more details.

Moreover, such quantum black holes can produce pairs of ordinary neutrons via broken chiral symmetry that may solve the "old" problems of baryogenesis (followed by nucleosynthesis and leptogenesis) and matter–antimatter asymmetry in the Universe.

10. Dynamical Parameters of Particle Production

Whereas with him, the results obtained above can be easily extended to the processes of pair-production of any kind. To do this, it is enough to implement the condition for their generation

$$E_{s,s-1\,qu} \geqslant 2E_x \,, \tag{57}$$

where $E_x = m_x c^2$ is the rest energy of each particle, m_x being the rest mass. This condition is easily transformed into

$$E_s \leqslant \frac{E_p^2}{4E_x} \,. \tag{58}$$

The main result can be obtained by substituting Eq. (58) into Eq. (53):

$$\tau_s(x) \leqslant \frac{\pi}{48} t_p \left(\frac{E_p}{E_x}\right)^3 \,. \tag{59}$$

Condition Eq. (58) is easily modified into

$$M_s(x) \leqslant \frac{M_p^2}{4m_x} \,, \tag{60}$$

which determines the extremely large mass of a black hole able to produce a pair of particles $(X_s, \bar{X}_s)$ of a given type.

If it is known that, in the table of rest masses, a particle of type X_1 of mass m_{X1} is immediately followed by a particle of type X_2 of a larger mass m_{X2}, then we can determine the generation time of a particle of type X_1 by a black hole using the formula

$$\Delta \tau_1(X_1) = \tau_s(X_1) - \tau_s(X_2) \,, \tag{61}$$

whereas the total number of generated particles and antiparticles of the type X_1 is easily found from relation

$$N_s(X_1) = \frac{M_p^2}{8} \left(\frac{1}{m_{X1}^2} - \frac{1}{m_{X2}^2}\right) \,. \tag{62}$$

11. Birth and Rise of Quantum Black Holes at The Beginning of the Universe and at the Gravitational Collapse of Astrophysical Objects

> *"What I cannot create, I do not understand."*
> (R. Feynman)

The natural "suppression" of the Higgs field at the energies well above 246 GeV exclude all Feynman's diagrams that describe scattering processes in Standard Model. Even two photon scattering "box-diagram" do not work because it needs the presence of a non-zero Higgs field. Despite that quantum electromagnetic field do not depends on Higgs field, two-photon scattering require intermediate virtual particle-antiparticle pair that is impossible when Higgs field is suppressed by energies of photons. Note that photons do not interact directly. Only gravitational field may save this situation but photons are massless particles. With one notable exception: photons do have rest masses in 2-d and 3-d photon condensates.

With these arguments, we conclude that Planckian black hole may be created only through the mediation of the gravitational field that acted in the 3-d Planck photon condensate. Note that a minimal photon condensate is represented by binary Planck system, (γ_p, γ_p), with two Planck photons in a close contact. These distinct binary Planck systems were formed when local homogeneity and isotropy were broken through the Planckian fluctuations The distance between the "centers" of this "fuzzballs" is equal to Planck length l_p. The total mass of Planck binary system is $2M_p$ and its rest energy is $2E_p$. The initial internal gravitational force is equal to the Planckian one:

$$F(\gamma_p, \gamma_p) = G \frac{M_p M_p}{l_p^2} = F_p . \tag{63}$$

This tremendous gravitational force provokes coalescence of this binary Planckian system. This tremendous Planckian coalescence inevitably generates a Planckian gravitational wave Γ_p that break the continuity of spacetime and forms a two-photon spacetime "buble". The energy of this Planckian gravitational wave is equal to Planckian work W_p:

$$E(\Gamma_p) = W_p = F_p l_p = E_p . \tag{64}$$

But what is the rest energy of this "buble"? This rest energy is equal to difference between initial rest energy of binary Planck system and energy of radiated Planck gravitational wave:

$$E(\gamma_p, \gamma_p) - E(\Gamma_p) = 2E_p - E_p = E_p .$$

In Sec. "2. Basic Relations" we have found that a minimal spherical 2-d photon condensate with two photons have Planck rest mass M_p and Planck rest energy E_p, Eq. (6). Note that this result was obtained without any presumptions and hypotheses about the importance of the Planckian Units System. We may say that it emerged in natural way starting from basic system of relations Eqs. (1)–(5) for quantum black holes. This means that the produced spacetime "buble" is nothing but the Planck black hole BH_p.

Thus, we can write the following fundamental scheme (diagram) of the birth of Planck black hole accompanied by Planck gravitational wave:

$$(\gamma_p, \gamma_p) \longrightarrow BH_p + \Gamma_p \tag{65}$$

with

$$E(BH_p) = E(\gamma_p, \gamma_p) - E(\Gamma_p) = E_p . \tag{66}$$

Expressions Eqs. (65) and (66) represent the fundamental conditions for the nucleation of Planck black holes, which, through accretion, can reach very significant sizes.

A very important question arises: where and when conditions of formation of Planck binary systems (γ_p, γ_p) could exist?

There are only two mutually reinforcing answers to this question:

- at the Beginning of the Universe, when *primordial* quantum black holes were created;
- in the nuclei of gravitationally collapsed astrophysical objects, such as neutron stars, where did the *secondary* quantum black holes emerged from.

Let us define the natural condition for accretion in the general form

$$\lambda_\gamma \leqslant \lambda_{sm} = 2\pi R_s , \qquad (67)$$

which is equivalent to the condition

$$E_\gamma \geqslant E_{sm} . \qquad (68)$$

Here E_γ is the energy of the absorbed photon, γ, and λ_γ is its wavelength.

Note that the velocity of accretion can be well above velocity of emission because it depends only on the intensity of captured photons flow.

Note one more very important circumstance: black holes consist of light and "feed" only on light. A clear understanding of the function of accretion disks and jets accompanying black holes immediately follows from this. Accretion discs perform the function of "thermal extraction" of light from the ordinary matter, while jets perform the functions of "evacuators" of rested plasma as a sort of "production wast". The tremendous two jets from *Sagittarius A**, which is called "Fermi bubbles", are the good illustrations and demonstration of these statements.

12. Cosmogenesis: Hot Big Bang and Pre-Inflation Stage

According to the law of conservation of energy, it accounts for an energy equal to the value of the energy of the modern Universe of the order of $10^{61} E_p$. Since in the future we will operate with energy densities, the exact value of this quantity is not important for us, only important being the fact that the total number of Planck photons in this condensate is tremendous large and has a value of the order of 10^{61}, that allows us to use in the following the theory of probabilities and the law of large numbers. At the same time, we will consider our diagrams as probabilistic events which should be connected in the casual and energetical sense.

Remark 12.1. Considering primordial Planck photon condensate trapped in its gravitational field as a *"prima materia"* at the "beginning of times" we automatically remove the synchronization problem, since the speed of physical processes is the same in all domains of primordial condensate. Also, we are removing the homogeneity and isotropy problems due to the fact that the 3-d Planck condensate has the densest possible packing, close to the fuzzy spherical one, in which each Planck photon is densely "covered" by 12 other ones (interference is impossible due to the impossibility of exceeding the Planck energy density E_p/l_p^3). The "time flow" was homogenic and was determined by the Planckian time t_p. Note that it was this fact that caused the initial synchronization of all processes that occurred at the beginning of Hot Bing Bang.

Remark 12.2. The law of conservation of energy in the observable Universe guarantees us that it is the energy of primordial Planckian 3-d photon condensate trapped in its own gravitational field that cause all physical processes that occurred and will occur in the Universe.

Vacuum cannot serve as a *"perpetuum mobile"* of the Universe. All attempts to explain the so called "cosmology constant problem" by the cosmic vacuum energy was failed. However, it is the Planckian quantum fluctuations of vacuum in the primordial 3-d condensate that are the natural sources of "breaking" of its gravitational homogeneity and anisotropy.

We must consider one very important problem: not all Planckian photons in the primordial 3-d condensate can form the primordial binary Planckian systems (γ_p, γ_p). A part becames free.

The probability of such event to occur, due to its exceptional importance for cosmology, we will note as $\aleph$ (*alef*: "divine"). This probability can be computed using the relation

$$\aleph = (1 - \aleph)^{12} , \qquad (69)$$

where $(1 - \aleph)^{12}$ is the probability for all its twelve surrounding photons to become non-free, *i.e.* to take part at events of the type Eq. (65). Solving the Eq. (69) we obtain

$$\aleph = 0.14745\ldots . \qquad (70)$$

If we use the presented above diagrams Eq. (65) as events from the point of view of probability theory and laws of large numbers we can easily find the following numbers at the beginning of the Universe as a beginning of the Hot Big Bang:

$$\Omega_L = \aleph \cong 0.1474 , \qquad \Omega_{BH} = \Omega_{GR} = \frac{(1 - \aleph)}{2} \cong 0.4263 , \qquad (71)$$

where Ω_L — energy density of free light (free Planck photons, γ_p), Ω_{BH} — rest energy density of Planck black holes (BH_p), Ω_{GR} — energy density of Planck gravitational waves (Γ_p).

After about $50\pi t_p$ (*i.e.* $\sim 10^{-41}$ sec) the preinflation stage of Hot Big Bang is finished with following results:

$$\Omega_L = (7\aleph - 1)\sum_{n=1}^{7}\frac{1}{2\sqrt{n}} + (1 - 6\aleph)\sum_{n=1}^{9}\frac{1}{2\sqrt{n}} \cong 0.3358, \tag{72}$$

$$\Omega_{BH} \cong 0 \text{ (a very small value)}, \tag{73}$$

$$\Omega_{GR} = 1 - \Omega_L - \Omega_{BH} \cong 0.6642 \ (66.42\%). \tag{74}$$

Note that this irreversible density of energy (66.42%) remains practically unchanged till the beginning of II stage of inflation, when the binary collisions of black holes will become the source of the increase of this density (as we can see below).

From Eqs. (72)–(74) we find the strongest inequality

$$\Omega_{BH} \ll \Omega_L + \Omega_{GR}, \tag{75}$$

that denote the end of the pre-inflation stage of the Hot Big Bang and the beginning of the hyperinflation stage of the Universe.

The strong inequality Eq. (75) shows that at the end of the pre-inflation stage the weak energy of the squeezed gravitational forces were totally suppressed by the tremendous common energy of the quantum electromagnetic and gravitational radiation stretched forces (close to the whole energy of the Universe!).

Moreover, the very small value of Ω_{BH} is backed by the enormous absolute number of primordial black holes that were the "seeds" of the modern Cosmic Web.

As far as we know, all these results are the only physically substantiated confirmation of Hot Bing Bang and inflation theories.

In conformity with "Planck-2018" observational data[14] the energy density of dark energy Ω_Λ represents 0.6847 (68.47%) of the total energy of the Universe. This means that the relic gravitational waves emitted in the pre-inflation phases of Hot Big Bang represent

$$\frac{\Omega_{GR}}{\Omega_\Lambda} \times 100\% = \frac{0.6642}{0.6847} \times 100\% \cong 97\% \ (sic!) \tag{76}$$

of the nowadays dark energy.

Note that the only two kinds of primordial gravitational waves Γ_p and $\Gamma_{p,0}$ with E_p and $E_p/2$ energies that accompanied birth and death of Planck black holes taken together represents 93.39% of the nowadays dark energy.

These and others relic gravitational waves form the homogenic and anisotropic relic Cosmic Gravitational Waves Background (CGWsB) manifested only as the most of the irreversible and omnipresent dark energy shown in the "Planck-2018" data. Now these waves are of infinitesimal amplitudes and of frequency range of few kilohertz.

In fact, these results represent the veritable solutions of so called "cosmological constant problem",[15] dark matter and dark energy problems.

13. Two-stage Inflation

At the end of the baryogenesis, leptogenesis and nucleosynthesis epoch, when the stage I of inflation was ended, the remaining energy of ordinary matter reached the 4.96% of the total energy of the observable Universe (note that this value presented by "Planck-2018" data is unchanged in time). If we neglect the small energy density of light, we can determine the remaining energy density of black holes (dark matter) at the end of I-st stage of inflation:

$$\Omega_{BH}(\%) = 100\% - 4.96\% - 66.42\% = 28.62\% \, .$$

After this epoch, there came the non-accelerated stage of the expanse of the Universe. But 6–8 billions of years ago, the II-nd stage of small inflation began. Now, from "Planck-2018" data we know that the distribution of the energy in the nowadays Universe is roughly represented by the following numbers:

$$4.96\% \quad \text{(for baryonic matter)},$$
$$26.57\% \quad \text{(for dark matter)},$$
$$68.47\% \quad \text{(for dark energy)}.$$

As we can see, a comparison with the end of the I stage of inflation clearly shows that the increase in the dark energy is caused by the decrease of the energy associated to dark matter. This leads to the unambiguous conclusion that the stage II of inflation is provided by the binary coalescences of black holes.

Conclusions

Presented approach to the Planck scale physics that governed the cosmological processes at the beginning of the Universe is based on the simple but consistent algebraic relations and schemes (diagrams) with such specific terms as Planck binary systems (γ_p, γ_p) quantum black holes BH_s, gravitational waves Γ_s etc. These physico-mathematical tools work in the area where the tools of standard models of physics and cosmology do not work because of tremendous temperatures and pressures that blocked the Higgs field activity. In a such terrible environment only 3-d photon condensates and 2-d spherical photon condensates (quantum black holes) are unique sources of gravity at the beginning of the Universe.

As it was showed above, presented results elucidate the decisive role of primordial black holes (as a dominated part of dark matter) in the generation of gravitational waves (a dominant part of dark energy) and clearly explain the physical background of Hot Big Bang and two-stage inflation. Moreover, these results solve the "old" unsolved problem of physics and cosmology such as "cosmic censure" problem, information loss paradox, black hole "end-point" problem, so called "cosmological constant" problem and so on.

From the theoretical point of view, presented approach derive from the last A. Einstein's conjecture about algebraic combined quantum and continuum description of reality and from the deepest principles and conjectures of such distinguished physicists and cosmologists as J. Bekenstein, S. Weinberg, S. Hawking, V. Mukhanov, L. Susskind, G. 't Hooft, W. Unruh, T. Jacobson, K. S. Thorne, F. Wilczek, M. Maggiore., J. Peebles, B. Carr, P. W. Anderson, L. Smolin, C. Rovelly, F. Vidotto ("Planck Star" concept), A. Kashlinsky, S. Hossenfelder and many other eminent theorists. But the decisive role was played the theoretical consequences from the last fundamental discoveries of experimental physics and observational cosmology.

Acknowledgments

The author expresses his sincere gratitude to prof. Gr. Vereshchagin, prof. S. Ansoldi and prof. A. Pittelli for the opportunity to present these results at the "Early Universe" session of the 16-th Marcel Grossmann Meeting (Rome, 2021).

References

1. J. Klaers, J. Schmitt, F. Vewinger and M. Weitz, Bose-Einstein condensation of photons in an optical microcavity, *Nature* **468**, 545-548 (2010).
2. Eberhard E. Muller, Note on Bose-Einstein condensation of photons, *arXiv: 1801.05220 (quant-ph)*.
3. J. D. Bekenstein, Black Holes and Entropy, *Phys Rev* **D7 No. 8**, 2333 (1973).
4. L. Susskind, *The Cosmic Landscape* (Little, Brown and Co. NY, 2006).
5. V. Mukhanov, Quantum Black Holes, *arXiv:1810.03525 (physics)*.
6. L. V. Okun, "Vladimir Naumovich Gribov (1930-1991)", *Physics Today* **51, 3** 104 (1998). ("... Gribov insisted, long before Stephen Hawking proposal, that due to quantum tunneling, black holes must emit particles.")
7. S. W. Hawking, Particle creation by black holes, *Commun Math Phys* **43**, 199 (1975).
8. V. Borsevici, Black holes and Genesis of the Universe: Physics and Astrophysics of Spherical Photon Condensates in Their Own Gravitational Fields (Chisinau (Rep. Moldova): Stratum Plus, 2019), 179 p. (ISBN 978-9975-3198-5-0).
9. A. Einstein, Naherungsweise Integration der Feldgleichungen der Gravitation, *Sitzungsber preuss. Akad. Wiss* **1**, 688-696 (1916).
10. A. Einstein, *Relativistic Theory of the non-symmetric Field. The Meaning of Relativity.* 5th edn. (Princeton, 1955).
11. V. Mukhanov, Evaporation and Entropy of Quantized Black Hole, *Lebedev Institute preprint* **N 163** (1986).
12. J. D. Bekenstein, V. F. Mukhanov, Spectroscopy of the quantum black hole, *arXiv:gr-qc/9505012 (gr-qc)*.
13. C. M. Wilson, G. Johansson, A. Pourkabirian, M. Simoen, J. R. Johansson, T. Duty, F. Nori and P. Delsing, Observation of the dynamical Casimir effect in a superconducting circuit, *Nature* **479**, 376-379 (2011).
14. Planck 2018 results. VI. Cosmological parameters. *arXiv:1807.06209 (astro-ph)*.
15. S. Weinberg, The cosmological constant problem. *Reviews of Modern Physics* **Vol. 61, No. 1**, (January 1989).
16. L. Smolin, *The Trouble with Physics* (Houghton Mifflin, 2006).
17. S. Hossenfelder, *Lost in Math: How Beauty Leads Physics Astray*. (Basic Books, 2018).
18. A. Kashlinski *et al.*, Electromagnetic probes of primordial black holes as dark matter, *arXiv:1903.04424v2 (astro-ph.CO)*.

Helical magnetic fields lead to baryogenesis

Ashu Kushwaha and S. Shankaranarayanan

*Department of Physics, Indian Institute of Technology Bombay,
Mumbai 400076, India
E-mail: ashu712@iitb.ac.in, shanki@phy.iitb.ac.in*

The origin of primordial magnetic fields and baryon asymmetry of the Universe are still unresolved issues and require physics beyond the standard models of cosmology and particle physics. Since both require physics beyond the standard model, there is a possibility that the same new physics can solve both. In this talk, I will discuss our model, where non-minimal coupling to the Riemann tensor generates sufficient primordial helical magnetic fields at all observable scales during inflation. Interestingly, the generation of helical magnetic fields leads to baryogenesis, and the model predicts the observed amount of baryon asymmetry of the Universe for a range of reheating temperatures consistent with the observations.

Keywords: Helical magnetic fields, baryogenesis, based on the works[1,2]

1. Introduction

The present Universe contains only matter and no antimatter, except for the rare antiparticles produced by cosmic rays. This asymmetry between baryons and antibaryons, also known as Baryon Asymmetry of the Universe (BAU), is characterized by the parameter $\eta_B \sim 10^{-10}$. Yet, we still do not completely understand the genesis of this asymmetry. However, in a remarkable paper in 1967, Sakharov[4] pointed out that to have observed baryon asymmetry following conditions must be satisfied by any theory: (1) baryon number violation (2) charge (C) and charge parity (CP) violation and (3) departure from thermal equilibrium.[6]

Observations from Faraday rotation and synchrotron radiation show the presence of micro-Gauss strength magnetic fields in the galaxies and the clusters of galaxies.[8] While the magnetic field measurements from Faraday rotation and synchrotron radiation provide upper bounds of the magnetic fields, the FERMI measurement of gamma-rays emitted by blazars provides a lower bound of the order of 10^{-15} G in intergalactic voids.[9] The origin of the magnetic field in these regions is still an open problem in modern cosmology; there is no compelling theoretical model to explain the generation of these large-scale magnetic fields.

The origin of primordial magnetic fields and the origin of the baryon asymmetry of the Universe are the unresolved issues in modern cosmology and particle physics models. Both require physics beyond the standard model and pose an exciting question— are these processes cosmological or particle physics or both? It seems impossible to generate the observed amount of baryon asymmetry within the Standard Model of particle physics framework. Since both require physics beyond the standard model, there is a possibility that the same physics can solve both problems. This talk discusses a mechanism that leads to the generation of primordial helical magnetic fields and baryon asymmetry at the beginning of the radiation-dominated epoch.

The electromagnetic field has two transverse degrees of freedom, i.e., left and right circular polarization, associated with the left and right-handed helicity modes. Furthermore, modes with the same evolution (or dispersion relation) lead to the non-helical electromagnetic field. In contrast, differently propagating modes with non-zero net helicity imbalance give a helical magnetic field. In order to create this helicity imbalance we consider the following scenario: under parity transformation electric and magnetic fields transform as $\mathbf{E} \longrightarrow -\mathbf{E}, \mathbf{B} \longrightarrow \mathbf{B}$, since standard electromagnetic action, $F_{\mu\nu}F^{\mu\nu} = (B^2 - E^2)/2$ is parity invariant, but the Chern-Simon term $F_{\mu\nu}\tilde{F}^{\mu\nu} = -4\mathbf{E}\cdot\mathbf{B}$ is parity non-invariant. Therefore, introducing this term in the action will lead to the different evolution of the modes. There is an interesting quantity related to the $F_{\mu\nu}\tilde{F}^{\mu\nu}$ called magnetic helicity density, which in a given volume, is proportional to the difference between the number of left and right-handed photons, and is given by: $\mathcal{H}_M = \frac{1}{V}\int_V d^3x \mathbf{A}\cdot\mathbf{B}$, where $\mathbf{A}$ is electromagnetic vector potential. Helical magnetic fields are very interesting for the following reasons: (1) the decay rate to energy density and coherence length is slow for these fields, which differs from the non-helical, (2) helical magnetic fields leave a very distinct signature as they violate parity symmetry which leads to observable effects, for example, correlations between the anisotropies in the temperature and B-polarisation or the E- and the B-polarisations in the CMB, and (3) if we could measure helical magnetic fields, it would provide evidence of CP violation in the early Universe.

It is important to note that both kinds of magnetogenesis models, i.e., early time and late time models, have problems. Inflation provides a causal mechanism to generate the magnetic fields of large coherence length. The problem with magnetic field generation during inflation is that standard electromagnetic action is conformally flat. Hence, the inflationary mechanism can not amplify quantum fluctuations of electromagnetic fields. Therefore one needs to break the conformal symmetry of the action. In the literature, models breaking conformal invariance by introducing non-minimal coupling terms in the electromagnetic action are proposed or by the time-dependent coupling with the gauge field.[8] These models produce non-helical magnetic fields. On the other hand, the generation of helical magnetic fields baryogenesis in the early Universe requires a parity-violating source.

A more popular scenario of helical field generation (and baryogenesis) is by adding the interaction term $f(\phi)F_{\mu\nu}\tilde{F}^{\mu\nu}$ which is responsible for creating the imbalance between left-handed and right-handed photons.[10] However, these scalar field coupled models suffer from strong coupling and backreaction problems and sensitivity to the reheating dynamics. In this talk, I will discuss our model where the electromagnetic field is coupled to the Riemann curvature, which breaks the conformal invariance and parity symmetry of the theory and leads to the production of primordial helical fields at all length scales. Interestingly, as we will see that the same helical modes will give a non-zero contribution to Chern-Simon (CS) number density and hence lead to the baryogenesis.

1.1. *Baryogenesis in the presence of primordial helical magnetic field*

Almost two decades back, Davidson[3] pointed out some very interesting relation between primordial magnetic field and Sakharov's conditions of the baryon asymmetry of the Universe. The presence of background magnetic fields in the early Universe may break the $C, CP, SO(3)$ and thermal equilibrium. Specifically, she argued that there are symmetries that are broken due to the presence of magnetic field: (1) there should be some kind of out-of- thermal-equilibrium dynamics because in equilibrium, the photon distribution is thermal, and there are no particle currents to sustain a "long-range" field, (2) because **B** is odd (changes sign) under CP, the presence of magnetic field will lead to CP violation, (3) since the magnetic field is a vector quantity, it chooses a particular direction hence breaks the isotropy (rotational invariance). This implies that one could see the presence of a magnetic field to provide the CP violation and out of thermal equilibrium conditions required in baryogenesis models. However, Davidson's conditions are necessary but not sufficient. One key missing ingredient is the requirement of *primordial helical magnetic fields* which can provide evidence of CP violation in the early Universe if we could measure them. Interestingly, as we show next, the presence of primordial helical fields leads to the non-zero Chern-Simons number and, eventually, the change in the Fermion number.

In the early Universe, the generation of the non-zero primordial helical magnetic fields leads to a chiral anomaly resulting from the imbalance between left and right-handed fermions. In the presence of an electromagnetic field in curved space-time, the chiral anomaly is given by the following equation[5]:

$$\nabla_\mu J_A^\mu = -\frac{1}{384\pi^2} \epsilon^{\mu\nu\rho\sigma} R_{\mu\nu\alpha\beta} R^{\alpha\beta}{}_{\rho\sigma} + \frac{e^2}{16\pi^2} \epsilon^{\mu\nu\alpha\beta} F_{\mu\nu} F_{\alpha\beta} \qquad (1)$$

where J_A^μ is the chiral current, $R_{\rho\sigma}{}^{\alpha\beta}$ is the Riemann tensor and A_μ is the four-vector potential of the electromagnetic field, $F_{\mu\nu} = \nabla_\mu A_\nu - \nabla_\nu A_\mu$ and $\epsilon^{\mu\nu\rho\sigma} = \frac{1}{\sqrt{-g}} \eta^{\mu\nu\rho\sigma}$ is a fully antisymmetric tensor, and we set $\eta^{0123} = 1 = -\eta_{0123}$.

In the case of flat FRW background in conformal time (η):

$$ds^2 = a^2(\eta) \left(d\eta^2 - \delta_{ij} dx^i dx^j\right), \qquad (2)$$

the first non-zero contribution of the first term in the RHS of Eq. (1) comes only at second order and hence will not play any role in our analysis. However, due to the presence of the magnetic fields, the second term in the RHS of Eq.(1) is the non-zero only and hence leads to a net chiral current. Thus, if we consider only up to the first-order in perturbations, *only* the second term in the RHS of Eq. (1) contributes, and the chiral anomaly equation reduces to:

$$\partial_\mu \left(\sqrt{-g} J_A^\mu\right) = \frac{e^2}{4\pi^2} \partial_\mu \left(\sqrt{-g} K^\mu\right) \tag{3}$$

where

$$K^\mu = \frac{\eta^{\mu\nu\alpha\beta}}{\sqrt{-g}} A_\nu \partial_\alpha A_\beta$$

is the topological current. Using Eq. (6), the net baryon number density, $n_B = a(\eta)\langle 0|J_A^0|0\rangle$ is related to Chern-Simon number density $n_{CS} = \langle 0|K^0|0\rangle$ as,[7]

$$n_B \equiv \frac{e^2}{4\pi^2} a(\eta) n_{CS}, \tag{4}$$

where

$$n_{CS} = \frac{1}{a^4} \epsilon_{ijk} \langle 0|A_i \partial_j A_k|0\rangle = \frac{1}{a^4} \int_\mu^\Lambda \frac{dk}{k} \frac{k^4}{2\pi^2} \left(|A_+|^2 - |A_-|^2\right), \tag{5}$$

where Λ, and μ set the possible energy range (or epoch) of the baryogenesis after inflation, and $A_\pm$ refer to the positive and negative modes of the helical magnetic fields which are generated during inflation. Note that due to the absence of standard model particles $n_B = 0$ during inflation. As we can see from Eq.(8) that all the modes re-entering the horizon at the beginning of the radiation-dominated epoch contribute significantly, and hence the value of n_{CS} depends on the upper cut-off Λ. It is important to note that n_{CS} vanishes if the primordial magnetic fields are non-helical, i. e. $|A_+| = |A_-|$, and hence will not lead to baryogenesis. Thus, the key missing ingredient of Davidson's conditions is the requirement of helical magnetic fields. non-zero only and hence leads to a net chiral current. Thus, if we consider only up to the first-order in perturbations, *only* the second term in the RHS of Eq. (1) contributes, and the chiral anomaly equation reduces to:

$$\partial_\mu \left(\sqrt{-g} J_A^\mu\right) = \frac{e^2}{4\pi^2} \partial_\mu \left(\sqrt{-g} K^\mu\right) \tag{6}$$

where

$$K^\mu = \frac{\eta^{\mu\nu\alpha\beta}}{\sqrt{-g}} A_\nu \partial_\alpha A_\beta$$

is the topological current. Using Eq. (6), the net baryon number density, $n_B = a(\eta)\langle 0|J_A^0|0\rangle$ is related to Chern-Simon number density $n_{CS} = \langle 0|K^0|0\rangle$ as,[7]

$$n_B \equiv \frac{e^2}{4\pi^2} a(\eta) n_{CS}. \tag{7}$$

where

$$n_{CS} = \frac{1}{a^4} \epsilon_{ijk} \langle 0|A_i \partial_j A_k|0\rangle = \frac{1}{a^4} \int_\mu^\Lambda \frac{dk}{k} \frac{k^4}{2\pi^2} \left(|A_+|^2 - |A_-|^2\right), \tag{8}$$

where Λ, and μ set the possible energy range (or epoch) of the baryogenesis after inflation, and $A_\pm$ refer to the positive and negative modes of the helical magnetic fields which are generated during inflation. Note that due to the absence of standard model particles $n_B = 0$ during inflation. As we can see from Eq.(8) that all the modes re-entering the horizon at the beginning of the radiation-dominated epoch contribute significantly, and hence the value of n_{CS} depends on the upper cut-off Λ. It is important to note that n_{CS} vanishes if the primordial magnetic fields are non-helical, i. e. $|A_+| = |A_-|$, and hence will not lead to baryogenesis. Thus, the key missing ingredient of Davidson's conditions is the requirement of helical magnetic fields.

2. Generation and evolution of primordial helical magnetic field

We consider the following action:

$$S = -\frac{M_P^2}{2}\int d^4x\sqrt{-g}\,R + \int d^4x\sqrt{-g}\left[\frac{1}{2}\partial_\mu\phi\partial^\mu\phi - V(\phi)\right]$$
$$-\frac{1}{4}\int d^4x\sqrt{-g}\,F_{\mu\nu}F^{\mu\nu} - \frac{\sigma}{M^2}\int d^4x\sqrt{-g}\,R_{\rho\sigma}{}^{\alpha\beta}F_{\alpha\beta}\tilde{F}^{\rho\sigma} \quad (9)$$

where $R_{\rho\sigma}{}^{\alpha\beta}$ is the Riemann tensor, A_μ is the four-vector potential of the electromagnetic field, $F_{\mu\nu} = \nabla_\mu A_\nu - \nabla_\nu A_\mu$ and $\tilde{F}^{\rho\sigma} = \frac{1}{2}\epsilon^{\mu\nu\rho\sigma}F_{\mu\nu}$ is the dual of $F_{\mu\nu}$. $\epsilon^{\mu\nu\rho\sigma} = \frac{1}{\sqrt{-g}}\eta^{\mu\nu\rho\sigma}$ is fully antisymmetric tensor, $\eta^{\mu\nu\rho\sigma}$ is Levi-Civita symbol whose values are ± 1 and we set $\eta^{0123} = 1 = -\eta_{0123}$.

Note that in Eq. (9), the first three terms are the standard terms (the Einstein-Hilbert action, scalar field action, and standard electrodynamics, respectively). However, the presence of the Riemann tensor term breaks the conformal (and parity) invariance of the action. We assume that the scalar field (ϕ) dominates the energy density in the early Universe (during inflation) and leads to 60 − 70 e-foldings of inflation with $H \simeq 10^{14}$ GeV. M is the energy scale, which sets the scale for the breaking of conformal invariance. We assume that $10^{-3} \leq (H_{\text{Inf}}/M) \leq 1$ where $H_{\text{Inf}} \sim 10^{14}$ GeV is the Hubble scale during inflation. It is important to note that due to Riemann coupling, M appears as a time-dependent coupling in the FRW background i.e. $\frac{1}{M_{\text{eff}}} \sim \frac{1}{M}\frac{a'}{a^2} = \frac{H}{M}$. Using $H_0 \approx 10^{-44}$ GeV and $M \approx 10^{17}$ GeV, we can see that at current epcoh $\frac{H_0}{M} \sim 10^{-59}$. Therefore, the Riemann coupling is tiny, and the non-minimal coupling term in the electromagnetic action will have a significant contribution only in the early Universe.

Our model has the following salient features: First, our model does not require the coupling of the electromagnetic field with the scalar field. Hence, there are no extra degrees of freedom, which will not lead to a strong-coupling problem. Second, the conformal invariance is broken due to the coupling to the Riemann tensor. Since the curvature is significant in the early Universe, the coupling term will introduce non-trivial corrections to the electromagnetic action. However, as mentioned above, the Riemann coupling term will not contribute at late-times, and the model is identical to standard electrodynamics. Third, as we show explicitly, our model is free from backreaction for a range of scale-factor during inflation. This is different from other models where a specific coupling function is chosen to avoid any back-reaction.[10]

2.1. *Estimating the strength of the helical magnetic fields*

We estimate the total electromagnetic energy density at the horizon exit and to identify whether the modes lead to back-reaction on the metric, we define the quantity, $R = \frac{(\rho_B + \rho_E)|_{\mathcal{H} \sim k_*}}{6H^2 M_{\text{Pl}}}$, which is the ratio of the total energy density of the fluctuations at horizon exit and background energy density during inflation. Since $R << 1$ for any $\alpha \leq -\frac{1}{2}$ ($\alpha = -1/2$ corresponds to de-Sitter universe), the model does not have back-reaction.

α	ρ_{total} (in GeV^4)	R
$-\frac{1}{2} - \epsilon$	$\sim 10^{64}$	$\sim 10^{-4}$
$-\frac{3}{4}$	$\sim 10^{62}$	$\sim 10^{-6}$
-1	$\sim 10^{61}$	$\sim 10^{-7}$
-3	$\sim 10^{59}$	$\sim 10^{-9}$

To estimate the current value of the helical fields, we assume instantaneous reheating and the fact that Universe becomes radiation-dominated after inflation. Due to flux conservation, the magnetic energy density will decay as $1/a^4$, i.e. $\rho_B(0) = \rho_B^{(f)} \left(\frac{a_f}{a_0}\right)^4$ where a_0 is the present day scale-factor, $\rho_B^{(f)}$ and a_f refer to the magnetic energy density and the scale-factor at the end of inflation, respectively. Using the fact that the relevant modes exited Hubble radius around 30 e-foldings of inflation, with energy density $\rho_B \approx 10^{64}$ GeV^4, the primordial helical fields at GPc scales is: $B_0 \approx 10^{-20}$ G where we have used $1G = 1.95 \times 10^{-20}$ GeV^2. Our model predicts the following primordial helical fields that re-entered the horizon at two different epochs: $B|_{50 \text{ MPc}} \sim 10^{-18} \, G \, (z \sim 20)$ and $B|_{1 \text{ MPc}} \sim 10^{-14} \, G \, (z \sim 1000)$. Thus, the model generates sufficient primordial helical magnetic fields at all observable scales. Also, our model predicts the present-day helical magnetic field of strength 10^{-15}G on Mpc scales.

3. Baryon asymmetry of the Universe

Now, we compute the baryon asymmetry created by the helical modes generated during inflation. To do that, we need to obtain the ranges of Λ and μ. The largest scales observed in the CMB are produced around 40 - 60 e-foldings before the end of inflation, and hence we have considered these modes for the generation of the helical magnetic field. However, taking advantage that modes are generated at all length scales in our model, we focus on the helical fields that renter the horizon very early (at the beginning of the radiation-dominated epoch) to generate the required BAU. This means that the modes that left the horizon around the last 5 to 10 e-foldings of inflation are only relevant.

Since the entropy density per comoving volume is conserved, the quantity n_B/s is better suited for theoretical calculations. Assuming that there was no significant entropy production after reheating phase, entropy density in the radiation-dominated epoch is:

$$s \simeq \frac{2\pi^2}{45} g T_{\rm RH}^3, \qquad (10)$$

where $T_{\rm RH}$ is the reheating temperature and the effective relativistic degrees of freedom $g \sim 100$ at reheating. The BAU parameter is given by:

$$\eta_B = \frac{n_B}{s} \approx 10^{-29} |C|^2 \frac{\Lambda^3}{T_{\rm RH}^3} \approx 10^{-2} \left(\frac{M}{M_{\rm Pl}}\right)^3 \left(\frac{\Lambda}{T_{\rm RH}}\right)^3 \qquad (11)$$

where $|C| \approx \frac{M^{3/2} \eta_0}{\sqrt[4]{\eta_{end} 10^{45} GeV^3}}$ and $M_{\rm Pl} \approx 10^{19}$ GeV. Assuming the exit of inflation at 10^{14} GeV, and for the observed baryon asymmetry 10^{-10}, the reheating temperature $T_{\rm RH}$ is in the range 10^{12}—10^{14} GeV, which is is consistent with the constraints on the reheating temperature. This suggests that our model does not prefer a very low-energy reheating temperature

4. Conclusions

This talk focuses on a viable scenario for the generation of helical magnetic fields during inflation which lead to the baryogenesis in the early Universe. The model does not require coupling to the scalar field and hence does not lead to a strong coupling problem, and also, there is no backreaction on the background dynamics. The generation of the helical fields is due to the coupling of the electromagnetic fields with the dual of the Riemann tensor, which breaks the parity symmetry of the action. Interestingly, our model generates the present-day magnetic field of strength $10^{-15} G$ Mpc scales.

We have explicitly shown that Davidson's conditions are necessary *but not* sufficient. The key missing ingredient is the requirement of *primordial helical magnetic fields*. We have shown that the BAU parameter predicted by our model is independent of any specific inflation model and reheating dynamics; however, it depends on the scale at which inflation ends and reheating temperature. Furthermore, focussing on the modes that leave the horizon around 5 to 10 e-foldings the BAU parameter obtained in our model is inversely proportional to reheating temperature. Assuming the exit of inflation at 10^{14} GeV, for the observed amount of baryon asymmetry $\eta_B \sim 10^{-10}$, we obtained that the reheating temperature should be in the range $10^{12} - 10^{14}$ GeV, which is consistent with the constraints on the reheating temperature.

Acknowledgments

The MHRD fellowship at IIT Bombay financially supports AK. This work is supported by the ISRO-Respond grant.

References

1. Ashu Kushwaha and S. Shankaranarayanan. Helical magnetic fields from riemann coupling. *Phys. Rev. D*, 102:103528, Nov 2020.
2. Ashu Kushwaha and S. Shankaranarayanan. Helical magnetic fields from Riemann coupling lead to baryogenesis. *Phys. Rev. D*, 104(6):063502, 2021.
3. Sacha Davidson. Ingredients and equations for making a magnetic field in the early universe. *Phys. Lett. B*, 380:253–256, 1996.
4. A. D. Sakharov. Violation of CP Invariance, C asymmetry, and baryon asymmetry of the universe. *Sov. Phys. Usp.*, 34(5):392–393, 1991.
5. Leonard E. Parker and D. Toms. *Quantum Field Theory in Curved Spacetime: Quantized Field and Gravity*. Cambridge Monographs on Mathematical Physics. Cambridge University Press, 8 2009.
6. Antonio Riotto and Mark Trodden. Recent progress in baryogenesis. *Ann. Rev. Nucl. Part. Sci.*, 49:35–75, 1999.
7. Neil D. Barrie and Archil Kobakhidze. Inflationary Baryogenesis in a Model with Gauged Baryon Number. *JHEP*, 09:163, 2014.
8. Kandaswamy Subramanian. The origin, evolution and signatures of primordial magnetic fields. *Rept. Prog. Phys.*, 79(7):076901, 2016.
9. Andrii Neronov and Ievgen Vovk. Evidence for strong extragalactic magnetic fields from fermi observations of tev blazars. *Science*, 328(5974):73–75, 2010.
10. Ramkishor Sharma, Kandaswamy Subramanian, and T. R. Seshadri. Generation of helical magnetic field in a viable scenario of inflationary magnetogenesis. *Phy. Rev. D*, D97(8):083503, 2018.

Polymer Quantization of the Isotropic Universe: Comparison with the Bounce of Loop Quantum Cosmology

G. Barca*, E. Giovannetti and F. Mandini

Department of Physics, La Sapienza University of Rome, Rome, Italy
Speaker. E-mail: gabriele.barca@uniroma1.it

G. Montani

Department of Physics, La Sapienza University of Rome, Rome, 00185 Italy
Fusion and Nuclear Safety Department, ENEA, Frascati (RM), Italy

We implement Polymer Quantum Mechanics on the Hamiltonian formulation of the isotropic Universe in both the representations of the standard Ashtekar-Barbero-Immirzi connection and of a new generalized coordinate conjugate to the Universe volume. The resulting dynamics is a bouncing cosmology; when quantizing the volume-like variable the Big Bounce is an intrinsic cut-off on the cosmological dynamics, while when using the standard connection the Bounce density results to be dependent on the initial conditions of the prepared wave packet. Then we compare the nature of the resulting Bounce with what emerges in Loop Quantum Cosmology, where the dependence of the critical density on the initial conditions is present when the minimum area eigenvalue is implemented in a comoving representation instead of the physical one. We conclude that, if one hand the preferable scenario should be a Big Bounce whose density depends on initial conditions in view of the privileged $SU(2)$ character that the Ashtekar-Barbero-Immirzi connection possesses in the full Loop Quantum Gravity, on the other hand the equivalence demonstrated in the context of polymer cosmology can be a hint in favour of the viability of the improved scheme of Loop Quantum Cosmology even though it is not expressed through the privileged set of variables.

Keywords: Quantum Cosmology; Polymer Quantum Mechanics; Early Universe.

1. Introduction

Loop Quantum Cosmology (LQC)[1–5] is the implementation of Loop Quantum Gravity (LQG)[6] in the symmetry-reduced cosmological minisuperspaces. It predicts the emergence of a Bouncing scenario that removes the classical singularity, but has the intrinsic limitation that the $SU(2)$ symmetry of LQG is lost.

Here we address the nature of the Bounce through the implementation of Polymer Quantum Mechanics (PQM)[7] on the flat isotropic Friedmann-Lemaître-Robertson-Walker (FLRW) model in two different representations: the Ashtekar-Barbero-Immirzi variables (the basic $SU(2)$ variables of LQG and LQC) and the volume variables.[8] Then, we compare our results with LQC in order to gain some insight on both frameworks. A more detailed analysis is presented in Ref. 9.

This work is organized as follows: in section 2 we introduce the framework of PQM; then we implement PQM on the FLRW model firstly expressed in the Ashtekar variables in section 3, and then in the volume variables in section 4; in section 5 we compare our results with LQC; finally in section 6 we summarize our work. We use the natural units $\hbar = c = 8\pi G = 1$.

2. Polymer Quantum Mechanics

PQM[7] is an alternative representation that is non-unitarily connected to the standard Schrödinger representation. It implements a fundamental scale in the Hilbert space through the introduction of a lattice structure. Its aim is to reproduce effects similar to those of LQG through an independent framework that allows for more freedom in the choice of the preferred configurational variable and that is easily and reliably applicable to many Hamiltonian systems.

Let us consider a generic Hamiltonian system with canonical variables (Q, P). The kinematical framework of PQM consists in assigning to one of the variables, usually the position Q, a discrete character. As a consequence, in the quantization procedure, the conjugate momentum P cannot be promoted to a well-defined operator because the translational operator $\hat{T}(\lambda) = e^{i\lambda P}$ is not weakly continuous.

The procedure to regularize the momentum P and to construct a well-defined operator consists in the introduction of a lattice on position Q with constant spacing $\beta_0 \in \mathbb{R}$. The Hilbert space is then constructed as the one that contains all those states $|\psi\rangle = \sum_i b_i |\beta_n\rangle$, with $\beta_n = n\beta_0$ and $\sum_i |b_i|^2 < \infty$. Now the translational operator must be restricted to act only by discrete steps to remain on γ_{β_0}: this is achieved simply by setting $\zeta = \beta_0$ in order to obtain $\hat{T}(\beta_0) |\beta_n\rangle = |\beta_{n+1}\rangle$.

When the condition $P\beta_0 \ll 1$ is satisfied, we can approximate P with a sine function, so that the regulated momentum operator can be constructed as the incremental ratio of the translational operator on the lattice:

$$P \approx \frac{\sin(\beta_0 P)}{\beta_0} = \frac{e^{i\beta_0 P} - e^{-i\beta_0 P}}{2i\beta_0}, \tag{1a}$$

$$\widehat{P_{\beta_0}} |\beta_n\rangle = \frac{\hat{T}(\beta_0) - \hat{T}(-\beta_0)}{2i\beta_0} |\beta_n\rangle = \frac{|\beta_{n+1}\rangle - |\beta_{n-1}\rangle}{2i\beta_0}. \tag{1b}$$

For the squared momentum operator there are infinitely many approximations, but they usually amount to just a rescaling of the lattice parameter β_0; the simplest one in order to avoid discrepancies is obtained by composing the operator (1b) with itself, corresponding to the approximation $P^2 \approx \sin^2(\beta_0 P)/\beta_0^2$.

When performing the quantization of a system using the momentum polarization of the polymer representation, the regulated momentum operator must be used together with the differential coordinate operator. Alternatively, it is possible to perform a semiclassical analysis by using the formal substitution (1a) in the classical Hamiltonian, thus including quantum modifications in the classical dynamics.[8, 10, 11]

3. Polymer FLRW Dynamics in Ashtekar Variables

We will now show the dynamics of the flat isotropic FLRW model expressed in the Ashtekar variables. Given the symmetries of the model, the connection and the triads reduce to a very simple form: $A_a^i \to c = \gamma \dot{a}$, $E_i^a \to p$, with $|p| = a^2$, $\{c, p\} = \gamma/3$, where $a = a(t)$ is the scale factor of the Universe, the dot represents a derivative with respect to time t and γ is the Immirzi parameter.

3.1. *Semiclassical Dynamics*

We consider the FLRW model filled with a free massless scalar field ϕ; we discretize the area p, so we use the sine substitution (1a) on the connection c. We have a four-dimensional phase space $(c, p; \phi, P_\phi)$, where P_ϕ is the momentum conjugate to the scalar field. The modified Hamiltonian constraint for this model is

$$\mathcal{C}_{\text{poly}} = -\frac{3}{\gamma^2 \beta_0^2} \sqrt{p} \sin^2(\beta_0 c) + \rho_\phi \, p^{\frac{3}{2}} = 0. \tag{2}$$

Then the dynamics is derived through the standard Hamilton's equations.

Through the constraint, we obtain a modified Friedmann equation:

$$H^2 = \left(\frac{\dot{a}}{a}\right)^2 = \left(\frac{\dot{p}}{2p}\right)^2 = \frac{\rho_\phi}{3}\left(1 - \frac{\rho_\phi}{\rho_\beta}\right), \quad \rho_\beta = \frac{3}{\gamma^2 \beta_0^2 p}; \tag{3}$$

the correction factor in parentheses contains a regularizing density ρ_β that depends on time through p; the minus sign introduces a critical point for the dynamics.

Since P_ϕ is a constant of motion, it is possible to use the scalar field as internal time; this makes the Friedmann equation easily solvable, and its solution $p(\phi)$ is

$$p(\phi) = \frac{\gamma \beta_0 P_\phi}{\sqrt{6}} \cosh\left(\sqrt{\frac{2}{3}}\, \phi\right). \tag{4}$$

The hyperbolic cosine has a non-zero minimum: the singularity is avoided and the Big Bang is replaced by a Big Bounce. However, the critical density, i.e. the energy density at the Bounce, is $\rho_{\text{crit}} = \rho_\beta(p|_{\phi_B}) = 3^{\frac{3}{2}} \sqrt{2}/P_\phi \gamma \beta_0$: it is dependent on the constant of motion P_ϕ that must be therefore set through initial conditions.

3.2. *Quantum Dynamics*

In the quantum picture, the fundamental variables are promoted to operators so that the quantum Hamiltonian constraint yields a Wheeler–De Witt (WDW) equation:

$$\hat{c} = \frac{\sin(\beta_0 c)}{\beta_0}, \quad \hat{p} = -i\frac{\gamma}{3}\frac{\mathrm{d}}{\mathrm{d}c}, \quad \widehat{P_\phi} = -i\frac{\mathrm{d}}{\mathrm{d}\phi}, \tag{5a}$$

$$\hat{\mathcal{C}}_{\text{poly}} \Psi(c, \phi) = \left[-\frac{2}{3\beta_0^2}\left(\sin(\beta_0 c)\frac{\mathrm{d}}{\mathrm{d}c}\right)^2 + \frac{\mathrm{d}^2}{\mathrm{d}\phi^2}\right] \Psi(c, \phi) = 0; \tag{5b}$$

through a substitution, the latter is recast as a Klein-Gordon-like (KG) equation:

$$x = \sqrt{\frac{3}{2}} \ln\left[\tan\left(\frac{\beta_0 c}{2}\right)\right] + x_0 \quad \Longrightarrow \quad \frac{\mathrm{d}^2}{\mathrm{d}x^2}\Psi(x, \phi) = \frac{\mathrm{d}^2}{\mathrm{d}\phi^2}\Psi(x, \phi). \tag{6}$$

We construct its solution as a Gaussian-like wavepacket over eigenvalues k_ϕ of $\hat{P}_\phi$:

$$\Psi(x,\phi) = \int_0^\infty \frac{\mathrm{d}k_\phi}{\sqrt{4\pi\sigma}} e^{-\frac{(k_\phi - \bar{k}_\phi)^2}{2\sigma^2}} k_\phi\, e^{ik_\phi x}\, e^{ik_\phi \phi}; \tag{7}$$

then we evolve it backwards in time, and study the behaviour of the expectation value of the energy density operator through a KG scalar product of the form

$$\langle \widehat{\rho_\phi} \rangle = \int_{-\infty}^\infty \mathrm{d}x \left(\Psi^* \partial_\phi (\widehat{\rho_\phi} \Psi) - (\widehat{\rho_\phi} \Psi) \partial_\phi \Psi^* \right), \quad \widehat{\rho_\phi} = \frac{\hat{P}_\phi^2}{2|\hat{p}|^3}. \tag{8}$$

The result is a function of time ϕ. Figure 1 shows the energy density increasing towards the singularity, reaching a finite maximum and then decreasing again; in view of its scalar nature, this behaviour confirms the presence of a Big Bounce also at the quantum level. However, the critical density at the Bounce (i.e. the value of the peak) is dependent on the initial condition $\bar{k}_\phi$, as in the semiclassical dynamics.

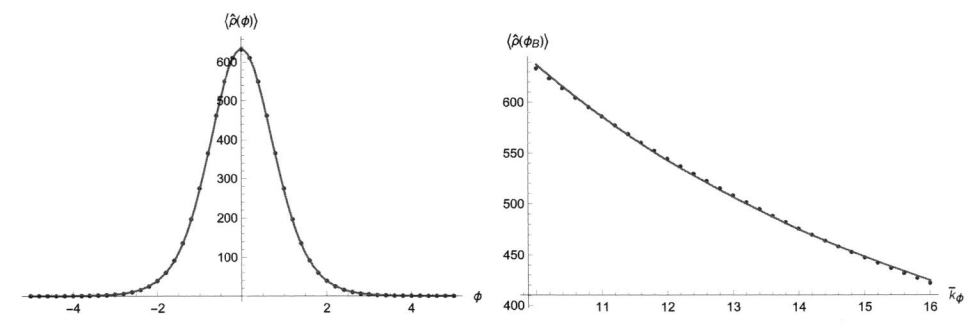

Fig. 1. Behaviour of the expected value of the energy density operator $\langle \widehat{\rho_\phi} \rangle$ as function of time ϕ (left panel) and dependence of the value of the energy density at the Bounce $\langle \widehat{\rho_\phi} \rangle |_{\phi_B}$ on the initial condition for the wavepacket $\bar{k}_\phi$ (right panel). The blue dots are the quantum expectation values, fitted with red continuous functions in accordance with semiclassical evolution.

4. Polymer FLRW Dynamics in Volume Variables

4.1. *Specialization of Polymer Cosmology*

In order to find the suitable variable to obtain a fixed Bounce density,[8] we perform a canonical transformation on the classical Hamiltonian to a generic function F of the scale factor: $p \to F(a)$, $c \to P_F = 2\sqrt{p}\, c/F'(a)$ with $F'(a) = \partial F / \partial a$. By using the polymer substitution (1a) on the new momentum P_F, we obtain a modified Hamiltonian constraint and a corresponding modified Friedmann equation:

$$\mathcal{C}_{\text{poly}} = -\frac{3}{4\gamma^2 \beta_0^2} \frac{\left(F'(a)\right)^2}{\sqrt{p}} \sin^2(\beta_0 P_F) + \rho_\phi\, p^{\frac{3}{2}} = 0, \quad \rho_\phi = \frac{P_\phi^2}{2p^3}, \tag{9a}$$

$$H^2 = \frac{\rho_\phi}{3}\left(1 - \frac{\rho_\phi}{\tilde{\rho}_\beta}\right), \quad \tilde{\rho}_\beta = \frac{3}{4\gamma^2\beta_0^2}\frac{\left(F'(a)\right)^2}{p^2} \propto \left(\frac{F'(a)}{p}\right)^2. \tag{9b}$$

To obtain a universal regularizing density $\tilde{\rho}_\beta$, we must have $F(a) \propto a^3$; we choose to use as new fundamental variables $v = a^3$ and $\tilde{c} = 2c/3\sqrt{p} \propto \dot{a}/a$.

4.2. Semiclassical Dynamics

We implement PQM on the system by considering v as discrete and using the formal substitution (1a) on the new generalized coordinate $\tilde{c}$:

$$\mathcal{C}_{\text{poly}} = -\frac{27}{4\gamma^2\beta_0^2} v \sin^2(\beta_0\tilde{c}) + \rho_\phi v = 0, \quad \rho_\phi = \frac{P_\phi^2}{2v^2}. \tag{10}$$

This new representation yields a modified Friedmann equation with a fixed regularizing density, as expected:

$$H^2 = \left(\frac{\dot{a}}{a}\right)^2 = \left(\frac{\dot{v}}{3v}\right)^2 = \frac{\rho_\phi}{3}\left(1 - \frac{\rho_\phi}{\tilde{\rho}_\beta}\right), \quad \tilde{\rho}_\beta = \frac{27}{4\gamma^2\beta_0^2} = \tilde{\rho}_{\text{crit}}. \tag{11}$$

The quantity $\tilde{\rho}_\beta = \tilde{\rho}_{\text{crit}}$ depends only on fundamental constants and the Immirzi parameter, and can therefore be already considered a critical density. Using ϕ as time, the new modified Friedmann equation is easily solvable for $v(\phi)$:

$$v(\phi) = \frac{2\gamma\beta_0}{\sqrt{54}} P_\phi \cosh\left(\sqrt{\frac{3}{2}}\,\phi\right). \tag{12}$$

We still have a hyperbolic cosine, indicating a Bounce that replaces the Big Bang, but this time the value of the energy density at which this happens is universal.

4.3. Quantum Dynamics

In the quantization procedure the fundamental variables are promoted to operators and the quantum Hamiltonian constraint yields a WDW equation:

$$\hat{v} = -i\frac{d}{d\tilde{c}}, \quad \hat{\tilde{c}} = \frac{\sin(\beta_0\tilde{c})}{\beta_0}, \quad \hat{P}_\phi = -i\frac{d}{d\phi}; \tag{13}$$

$$\hat{\mathcal{C}}_{\text{poly}}\Psi(\tilde{c},\phi) = \left[-\frac{3}{2\beta_0^2}\left(\sin(\beta_0\tilde{c})\frac{d}{d\tilde{c}}\right)^2 + \frac{d^2}{d\phi^2}\right]\Psi(\tilde{c},\phi) = 0. \tag{14}$$

Through a suitable substitution, the latter is recast as a KG-like equation in the variable $\tilde{x}$ where ϕ plays the role of time:

$$\tilde{x} = \sqrt{\frac{2}{3}}\ln\left[\tan\left(\frac{\beta_0\tilde{c}}{2}\right)\right] + \tilde{x}_0 \quad \Longrightarrow \quad \frac{d^2}{d\tilde{x}^2}\Psi(\tilde{x},\phi) = \frac{d^2}{d\phi^2}\Psi(\tilde{x},\phi). \tag{15}$$

We construct the solution as a Gaussian-like wavepacket of the form

$$\Psi(\tilde{x},\phi) = \int_0^\infty \frac{dk_\phi}{\sqrt{4\pi\sigma}} e^{-\frac{(k_\phi - \bar{k}_\phi)^2}{2\sigma^2}} k_\phi\, e^{ik_\phi\tilde{x}}\, e^{ik_\phi\phi}. \tag{16}$$

Finally, we evolve it backwards in time and study the behaviour of the expected value of relevant operators (the volume $\hat{V} = \hat{v}$ and the energy density $\widehat{\rho_\phi} = \hat{P}_\phi^2/2\hat{v}^2$) through the same KG scalar product (8) in terms of $\tilde{x}$. The Bounce is present also

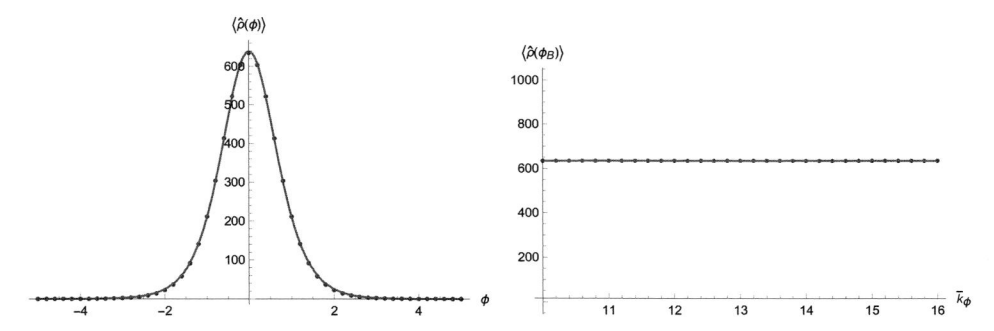

Fig. 2. Expected value of the energy density operator as function of time ϕ (left panel) and dependence of the critical density (the value of the energy density at the Bounce) on the initial condition for the wavepacket $\bar{k}_\phi$. The blue dots are the quantum expectation values that have been fitted with red continuous functions in accordance with semiclassical evolution.

in this quantum setting; however in this case the energy density, depicted in the left panel of figure 2, has a value at the Bounce that is constant and independent on $\bar{k}_\phi$, as shown in the right panel of the same figure.

5. Discussion of the Results

5.1. *The Nature of the Bounce in Polymer Cosmology*

The quantization procedure of PQM implements on a Hamiltonian system a lattice that has a constant step by construction. Therefore the canonical changes of variables must be performed on the classical Hamiltonian constraint before discretization. The nature of the resulting Bounce in the two pictures is not the same, and the two dynamics are inequivalent.

To recover the equivalence, we can perform the canonical transformation *after* the implementation of the lattice. We consider the system with the discretized volume and change the variables to Ashtekar ones; the canonical transformation must preserve the Poisson brackets and therefore must satisfy the condition $\beta_0 \tilde{c} = \beta' c$. We obtain a discretized system in the variables (c, p) that has a new lattice spacing β' dependent on the variable p. The new equation of motion for p is mapped to the original equation of motion in the Ashtekar variables, but the lattice parameter β_0 is replaced by the new one β'; the resulting dynamics is a Big Bounce scenario with a fixed, universal critical density, the same obtained by discretizing the volume with a constant lattice. Thus we conclude that the nature of the Bounce is decided by the variable to which a constant lattice spacing is assigned.

We stress that this result can be demonstrated only at a semiclassical level; on the quantum level this comparison is impossible, because a quantization procedure with a non-constant translational parameter has not been developed yet.

5.2. *Comparison with Loop Quantum Cosmology*

One of the most important results of LQG is the quantization of the kinematical geometrical operators of area and volume,[12] with the Area Gap Δ being the smallest non-zero area eigenvalue. In the construction of the quantum Hamiltonian constraint of LQC, the area gap is introduced from the full theory somewhat ad hoc, and the character of its implementation defines different schemes of LQC. In the first formulation, the area gap was implemented as a kinematical feature (as in full LQG) on the comoving area: this is equivalent to introducing a fixed lattice and yields the original μ_0 scheme of LQC, a scenario very similar to our polymer cosmology with the Ashtekar variables of section 3, that presents a Big Bounce dependent on initial conditions.[2,3] Then, in the improved dynamics, the area gap is implemented as a dynamical feature on the physical area, i.e. rescaled by the squared scale factor; this leads to a lattice with a non-constant spacing $\bar{\mu}(p)$, and prevents quantization. Therefore a change of basis is performed to a volume-like variable $\nu \propto v$ to make the lattice parameter constant (note how this is the inverse change of variables that we performed above). Now the quantization can be completed, and the resulting dynamics is a Big Bounce with a critical density that is a universal feature.[4,5] This scenario, dubbed $\bar{\mu}$ scheme, is analogous to the polymer FLRW cosmology in volume variables presented here in section 4.

The improved scheme avoids the dependence of quantum gravitational effects on initial conditions, a feature that does not have a very clear physical interpretation, and therefore seems to be more appealing than the original formulation. One criticism is that the new $\bar{\mu}$ scenario takes LQC further away from LQG because it does not use the Ashtekar variables anymore, that are privileged in the full theory in view of their $SU(2)$ character. However the dynamical similarities of PQM and LQC may justify the change of variables: at least on a semiclassical effective level, the dynamics of the model expressed in volume variables with a constant spacing is equivalent to that of the same model expressed in Ashtekar variables with a p-dependent lattice step.

6. Summary and Conclusions

We have shown how the implementation of PQM on the flat isotropic model solves the singularity by replacing the Big Bang with a Big Bounce, but its nature depends on the fundamental variable used to describe the model: with the area p from the Ashtekar variables the energy density at the Bounce is dependent on the initial conditions, while if the volume $v = a^3$ is used instead, the Bounce is a universal feature with a fixed energy density; therefore the two pictures yield two different and inequivalent dynamics. A possibility to recover the equivalence is to perform the canonical transformation after the implementation of the lattice and to allow for a non-constant step; this does not affect the dynamics, meaning that the nature of the Bounce is decided by the variable that has a lattice with constant spacing.

In LQC two analogous pictures emerge: the original μ_0 scheme yields a Bounce dependent on initial conditions, while the improved $\bar{\mu}$ scheme prevents this feature through a change of basis and presents a universal Bounce. These similarities with polymer cosmology may be used to gain insight into the validity of the two scenarios: if on one hand the improved scheme, although physically more appealing, can be criticized for not using the privileged $SU(2)$ variables of LQG, on the other hand the parallelism with the minisuperspace implementation of PQM justifies the $\bar{\mu}$ scenario in view of the equivalence demonstrated in semiclassical polymer cosmology.

References

1. M. Bojowald, Loop Quantum Cosmology, *Living Reviews in Relativity* **8** (Dec 2005).
2. A. Ashtekar, T. Pawlowski and P. Singh, Quantum nature of the Big Bang, *Physical Review Letters* **96** (Apr 2006).
3. A. Ashtekar, T. Pawlowski and P. Singh, Quantum nature of the Big Bang: An analytical and numerical investigation, *Physical Review D* **73** (Jun 2006).
4. A. Ashtekar, T. Pawlowski and P. Singh, Quantum nature of the Big Bang: Improved dynamics, *Physical Review D* **74** (Oct 2006).
5. A. Ashtekar, A. Corichi and P. Singh, Robustness of key features of Loop Quantum Cosmology, *Physical Review D* **77** (Jan 2008).
6. C. Rovelli and L. Smolin, Loop space representation of quantum General Relativity, *Nuclear Physics B* **331**, 80 (1990).
7. A. Corichi, T. Vukašinac and J. A. Zapata, Polymer Quantum Mechanics and its continuum limit, *Physical Review D* **76** (Aug 2007).
8. G. Montani, C. Mantero, F. Bombacigno, F. Cianfrani and G. Barca, Semiclassical and quantum analysis of the isotropic Universe in the polymer paradigm, *Physical Review D* **99** (Mar 2019).
9. F. Mandini, G. Barca, E. Giovannetti and G. Montani, Polymer quantum dynamics of the isotropic Universe in the Ashtekar-Barbero-Immirzi and in the volume variables (2021).
10. R. Moriconi and G. Montani, Behavior of the Universe anisotropy in a Big Bounce cosmology, *Physical Review D* **95** (Jun 2017).
11. S. Antonini and G. Montani, Singularity-free and non-chaotic inhomogeneous Mixmaster in polymer representation for the volume of the Universe, *Physics Letters B* **790**, p. 475–483 (Mar 2019).
12. C. Rovelli and L. Smolin, Discreteness of area and volume in quantum gravity, *Nuclear Physics B* **442**, 593 (1995).

General relativistic evolution equations for density perturbations in open, flat and closed FLRW universes and the problem of structure formation

Pieter G. Miedema

Independent Scientist
Breda, The Netherlands
E-mail: PG.Miedema@ProtonMail.com

Due to the general covariance of the Einstein equations and conservation laws, the linearized equations have solutions which are gauge-dependent and have, therefore, no physical significance.

In this contribution I will show that the decomposition theorems for symmetric second-rank tensors of the maximally symmetric subspaces of constant time imply that there are exactly two, unique, gauge-invariant quantities which describe the true, physical perturbations to the energy density and particle number density. In the limit of zero spatial fluid velocity, and hence zero pressure, the set of linearized Einstein equations and conservation laws, combined with the new gauge-invariant quantities reduce to the Poisson equation of the Newtonian Theory of Gravity and the energy-mass relation of the Special Theory of Relativity. The relativistic gauge transformation reduces to the Newtonian gauge transformation in which time and space are decoupled.

The cosmological perturbation theory for open, flat and closed Friedmann-Lemaître-Robertson-Walker (FLRW) universes consists of a second-order ordinary differential equation (with source term entropy perturbations) which describes the evolution of perturbations in the total energy density, and a first-order ordinary differential equation which describes the evolution of entropy perturbations.

The cosmological perturbation theory is applied to a flat FLRW universe. For large-scale perturbations the outcome is in accordance with treatments in the literature. In the radiation-dominated era small-scale perturbations grew proportional to the square root of time and perturbations in the CDM particle number density were, due to gravitation, coupled to perturbations in the total energy density. Therefore, structure formation could have begun successfully only after decoupling of matter and radiation. After decoupling density perturbations exchanged heat with their environment. This heat exchange may have enhanced the growth rate of their mass sufficiently to explain structure formation in the early universe, a phenomenon which cannot be understood from adiabatic density perturbations.

Keywords: Cosmology; Perturbation Theory; Structure Formation.

1. Introduction

The theory related to the linearized Einstein equations and conservation laws is important in cosmology because it describes the growth of all kinds of structures in the expanding universe, such as stars, galaxies and microwave background fluctuations. Lifshitz[1] and Lifshitz and Khalatnikov[2] were the first researchers to derive a cosmological perturbation theory. They encountered the problem that the solutions of the linearized Einstein equations and conservation laws have no physical significance. Due to the linearity of the equations, the solutions can be changed by a linear coordinate transformation, i.e., a gauge transformation. Therefore, the solutions are *gauge-dependent*. This is the well-known *gauge problem of cosmology* which is up till now not solved.

In this contribution I outline the solution of the gauge problem. Next, I briefly give the derivation of a new perturbation theory for cosmological perturbations in open, flat and closed FLRW universes. The perturbation theory is applied to a flat FLRW universe to study the evolution of density perturbations. The derivation of the perturbation theory is given in full detail in Ref. 3, whereas the problem of structure formation in a flat FLRW universe is discussed in detail in Ref. 4.

2. Cosmological Perturbation Theory

We consider FLRW universes filled with a perfect fluid. The energy momentum tensor is then given by

$$T^{\mu\nu} = (\varepsilon + p)u^\mu u^\nu - pg^{\mu\nu}. \tag{1}$$

From thermodynamics it is known that both the energy density ε and the pressure p depend on the particle number density n and the absolute temperature T, i.e.,

$$\varepsilon = \varepsilon(n, T), \quad p = p(n, T). \tag{2}$$

Since T can, in principle, be eliminated from these equations of state, a computationally more convenient equation of state for the pressure is used, namely

$$p = p(n, \varepsilon). \tag{3}$$

Using (1) and (3) one can write down the Einstein equations and conservation laws into a set of background equations

$$G^{\mu\nu}_{(0)} = \kappa T^{\mu\nu}_{(0)}, \quad T^{\mu\nu}_{(0);\nu} = 0, \tag{4}$$

which govern the *global* evolution of FLRW universes, and a system of perturbation equations

$$G^{\mu\nu}_{(1)} = \kappa T^{\mu\nu}_{(1)}, \quad T^{\mu\nu}_{(1);\nu} = 0. \tag{5}$$

These equations govern the evolution of *local* perturbations in FLRW universes.

2.1. *General Covariance*

It is well-known that the General Theory of Relativity is invariant under general coordinate transformations $x^\mu \to x'^\mu(x^\nu)$. In particular, the linearized Einstein equations and conservation laws are invariant under a general linear coordinate transformation, i.e., a gauge transformation

$$x^\mu \to x'^\mu = x^\mu - \xi^\mu(t, \boldsymbol{x}), \tag{6}$$

where $\xi^\mu(t, \boldsymbol{x})$ are four arbitrary infinitesimal functions of time, $x^0 = ct$, and space, $\boldsymbol{x} = (x^1, x^2, x^3)$, coordinates, the so-called gauge functions. As a consequence, there are no preferred coordinate systems (see Weinberg,[5] Appendix B), so that one may choose any system of reference which makes the calculations tractable.

However, because of the linearity of the perturbation equations and conservation laws, the so-called gauge problem of cosmology emerges.

2.2. *Gauge Problem of Cosmology*

Consider a closed, flat or open FLRW universe filled with a perfect fluid, with an equation of state for the pressure (3). The evolution of the energy density $\varepsilon_{(0)}$, the particle number density $n_{(0)}$ and the expansion scalar $\theta_{(0)} = 3H$ of the background universe are governed by the usual Einstein equations and conservation laws for a FLRW universe

$$3H^2 = \tfrac{1}{2}R_{(0)} + \kappa\varepsilon_{(0)} + \Lambda, \quad \kappa = 8\pi G_{\mathrm{N}}/c^4, \tag{7a}$$

$$\dot{R}_{(0)} = -2HR_{(0)}, \tag{7b}$$

$$\dot{\varepsilon}_{(0)} = -3H\varepsilon_{(0)}(1+w), \quad w := p_{(0)}/\varepsilon_{(0)}, \tag{7c}$$

$$\dot{n}_{(0)} = -3Hn_{(0)}. \tag{7d}$$

From this system of equations it follows that the evolution of FLRW universes is characterized by the three scalars $\varepsilon_{(0)}$, $n_{(0)}$ and $\theta_{(0)}$.

The general solution of the linearized Einstein equations and conservation laws contain, among other quantities, the perturbed quantities $\varepsilon_{(1)}$, $n_{(1)}$ and $\theta_{(1)}$. Since the linearized equations are invariant under linear coordinate transformations (6) one can generate new, equivalent, solutions $\varepsilon'_{(1)}$, $n'_{(1)}$ and $\theta'_{(1)}$, i.e.,

$$\varepsilon'_{(1)} = \varepsilon_{(1)} + \xi^0\dot{\varepsilon}_{(0)}, \quad n'_{(1)} = n_{(1)} + \xi^0\dot{n}_{(0)}, \quad \theta'_{(1)} = \theta_{(1)} + \xi^0\dot{\theta}_{(0)} \tag{8}$$

where $\xi^0\dot{\varepsilon}_{(0)}$, $\xi^0\dot{n}_{(0)}$ and $\xi^0\dot{\theta}_{(0)}$ are the so-called gauge modes. Therefore, $\varepsilon_{(1)}$, $n_{(1)}$ and $\theta_{(1)}$ are *gauge-dependent* and have, as a consequence, no physical significance.

3. Previous Attempts to Solve the Gauge Problem of Cosmology

Bardeen[6] was the first to demonstrate that, using gauge-invariant quantities, one can recast the linearized Einstein equations and conservation laws into a new set of evolution equations that are free of non-physical gauge modes. Bardeen's definition of a gauge-invariant density perturbation is such that it becomes equal to the gauge-dependent density perturbation in the limit of small scales. The underlying assumption is that on small scales the gauge modes vanish so that gauge-dependent quantities become gauge-independent. However, the physical quantities $\varepsilon_{(1)}^{\mathrm{phys}}$, $n_{(1)}^{\mathrm{phys}}$ and $\theta_{(1)}^{\mathrm{phys}}$ do not become equal to the gauge-dependent quantities $\varepsilon_{(1)}$, $n_{(1)}$ and $\theta_{(1)}$ in the non-relativistic limit, since the gauge modes $\hat{\varepsilon}_{(1)}$, $\hat{n}_{(1)}$ and $\hat{\theta}_{(1)}$ never become zero. This is a direct consequence of the facts that the universe is not static in the non-relativistic limit and that the relativistic space-time gauge transformations reduce in the non-relativistic limit to Newtonian gauge transformations with space and time decoupled. Consequently, the quantities defined by Bardeen are not equal to the real physical energy density perturbation.

The article of Bardeen has inspired the pioneering works of Ellis et al.,[7–9] Mukhanov et al.[10,11] and Bruni et al.[12] These researchers proposed alternative perturbation theories using gauge-invariant quantities which differ from the ones used by Bardeen. The theory proposed by Mukhanov et al.[10,11] yields the Poisson equation of the Newtonian Theory of Gravity only if the Hubble function, i.e., the expansion scalar, vanishes. This, however, violates the background Friedmann equation. In fact, the background Friedmann equation is needed to derive the Poisson equation from the linearized Friedmann equation in the non-relativistic limit. Consequently, the gauge-invariant quantities defined in Refs. 10 and 11 are not equal to the true physical perturbations.

In the approach in Refs. 7–9 a density perturbation is defined using gradients, i.e., a gauge-invariant and covariant function is defined which 'closely corresponds to the intention of the usual gauge-dependent density contrast function'. However, a perturbation theory based on this definition does not yield the Poisson equation in the non-relativistic limit.

The above mentioned pioneering treatments caused an abundance of other important works, e.g., Refs. 13–18. In his review article, Ellis[19] discusses the work of Lifshitz and Khalatnikov, and also provides an overview of other research on the subject. From the vast literature on cosmological density perturbations, it must be concluded that there is still no agreement on which gauge-invariant quantities are the true energy density perturbation and particle number density perturbation. None of the cosmological perturbation theories in the literature has a correct non-relativistic limit, so that there is still no solution to the gauge problem of cosmology.

4. Real, Measurable Density Perturbations

In contrast to the gauge-dependent quantities $\varepsilon_{(1)}$, $n_{(1)}$ and $\theta_{(1)}$ the real, measurable density perturbations $\varepsilon_{(1)}^{\text{phys}}$, $n_{(1)}^{\text{phys}}$ and $\theta_{(1)}^{\text{phys}}$ are independent of the choice of a coordinate system, i.e., are *gauge-invariant*. The physics of density perturbations is hidden in the general solution of the linearized Einstein equations and conservation laws. Therefore, the physical quantities $\varepsilon_{(1)}^{\text{phys}}$, $n_{(1)}^{\text{phys}}$ and $\theta_{(1)}^{\text{phys}}$ can be expressed as linear combinations, with time-dependent coefficients, of gauge-dependent solutions of these equations, such that the gauge modes are eliminated. Furthermore, $\varepsilon_{(1)}^{\text{phys}}$ and $n_{(1)}^{\text{phys}}$ have the property that in the non-relativistic limit the linearized Einstein equations and conservation laws combined with expressions for $\varepsilon_{(1)}^{\text{phys}}$ and $n_{(1)}^{\text{phys}}$ reduce, in a *non-static* flat FLRW universe, to the time-independent Poisson equation with $\varepsilon_{(1)}^{\text{phys}}$ as source term, and the well-known Einstein mass-energy relation $\varepsilon_{(1)}^{\text{phys}} = n_{(1)}^{\text{phys}} mc^2$ of the Special Theory of Relativity. Finally, the relativistic gauge transformation (6) reduces in the non-relativistic limit to the Newtonian gauge transformation. Consequently, the gauge problem is, in fact, the problem of finding expressions for $\varepsilon_{(1)}^{\text{phys}}$, $n_{(1)}^{\text{phys}}$ and $\theta_{(1)}^{\text{phys}}$.

5. Solution of the Gauge Problem

The gauge-dependent quantities $\varepsilon_{(1)}$, $n_{(1)}$ and $\theta_{(1)}$ transform under the gauge transformation (6) in exactly the same way, namely as (8). Therefore, one can combine two of these quantities such that the gauge modes are eliminated. We have three choices and in each choice one of the gauge-invariant quantities vanishes. The obvious, non-trivial choice is

$$\varepsilon_{(1)}^{\text{phys}} := \varepsilon_{(1)} - \frac{\dot{\varepsilon}_{(0)}}{\dot{\theta}_{(0)}}\theta_{(1)}, \quad n_{(1)}^{\text{phys}} := n_{(1)} - \frac{\dot{n}_{(0)}}{\dot{\theta}_{(0)}}\theta_{(1)}, \quad \theta_{(1)}^{\text{phys}} := \theta_{(1)} - \frac{\dot{\theta}_{(0)}}{\dot{\theta}_{(0)}}\theta_{(1)} = 0, \quad (9)$$

where $\theta_{(1)}^{\text{phys}} = 0$ implies that local density perturbations have no influence on the global expansion $\theta_{(0)} = 3H$ of the universe.

Now, the question arises, are $\varepsilon_{(1)}^{\text{phys}}$, $n_{(1)}^{\text{phys}}$ and $\theta_{(1)}^{\text{phys}}$ the real, measurable perturbations? Since the linear combinations (9) are the only possible ones, it is plausible that this is indeed the case. However, to be sure, we have to study the quantities (9) together with the background equations (4) and the perturbation equations (5) in the non-relativistic limit. This is the subject of Sec. 8. To that end, we have to rewrite the linearized Einstein equations and conservation laws (5) into a more convenient form. This will be done in Sec. 7 with the help of the decomposition theorems in the next section.

6. Decomposition Theorems of Symmetric Second-rank 3-tensors

Since the General Theory of Relativity is invariant under coordinate transformations, we may choose our coordinates such that the calculations are tractable.

We choose a synchronous system of reference, since this facilitates the non-relativistic limit: in the Newtonian Theory of Gravity all coordinate systems are synchronous. A second reason is that in synchronous coordinates, the decomposition theorems in Refs. 20–22 for symmetric second rank tensors of the maximally symmetric three-spaces of constant time can be used.

In synchronous coordinates the metric tensor $g_{\mu\nu}(t, \boldsymbol{x})$ of FLRW universes has the form

$$g_{00} = 1, \quad g_{0i} = 0, \quad g_{ij} = -a^2(t)\tilde{g}_{ij}(\boldsymbol{x}), \quad (10)$$

where $a(t)$ is the scale factor of the universe, $g_{00} = 1$ indicates that coordinate time is equal to proper time, $g_{0i} = 0$ is the global synchronicity condition (see the textbook of Landau and Lifshitz,[23] § 84) and $\tilde{g}_{ij}$ is the metric tensor of the three-dimensional maximally symmetric sub-spaces of constant time[a]. From the Killing equations $\xi_{\mu;\nu} + \xi_{\nu;\mu} = 0$ and (10) it follows that the functions $\xi^\mu(t, \boldsymbol{x})$ in (6) become

$$\xi^0 = \psi(\boldsymbol{x}), \quad \xi^i = \tilde{g}^{ik}(\boldsymbol{x})\frac{\partial \psi(\boldsymbol{x})}{\partial x^k}\int^{ct}\frac{\mathrm{d}\tau}{a^2(\tau)} + \chi^i(\boldsymbol{x}), \quad (11)$$

---

[a]Quantities with a tilde, i.e., $\tilde{q}$, belong to the three-dimensional maximally symmetric subspaces of constant time.

if only transformations between synchronous coordinates are allowed. The four functions $\psi(\boldsymbol{x})$ and $\chi^i(\boldsymbol{x})$ cannot be fixed since the four coordinate conditions $g_{00} = 1$ and $g_{0i} = 0$ have already exhausted all four degrees of freedom (see Weinberg,[24] Section 7.4 on coordinate conditions).

In Refs. 20–22 it is shown that *any* symmetric second-rank three-tensor, and hence the perturbed metric tensor h_{ij} and the perturbed Ricci tensor $R_{(1)ij}$, can uniquely be decomposed into three parts. For the perturbed metric tensor, one has

$$h^i{}_j = h^i{}_{\|j} + h^i{}_{\perp j} + h^i{}_{*j}, \qquad h^k{}_{\perp k} = 0, \quad h^k{}_{*k} = 0, \quad h^k{}_{*i|k} = 0, \tag{12}$$

where tensor, vector and scalar perturbations are denoted by $*$, $\perp$ and $\|$, respectively. The perturbed Ricci tensor, $R_{(1)ij}$, being a symmetric second-rank three-tensor, can in the same way be decomposed

$$R^i{}_{(1)j} = R^i{}_{(1)\|j} + R^i{}_{(1)\perp j} + R^i{}_{(1)*j}, \qquad R^k{}_{(1)\perp k} = 0, \quad R^k{}_{(1)*k} = 0, \quad R^k{}_{(1)*i|k} = 0. \tag{13}$$

Finally, York and Stewart demonstrated that the components $h^i{}_{\|j}$ can be written in terms of two independent potentials $\phi(t,\boldsymbol{x})$ and $\zeta(t,\boldsymbol{x})$, namely

$$h^i{}_{\|j} = \frac{2}{c^2}(\phi \delta^i{}_j + \zeta^{|i}{}_{|j}). \tag{14}$$

The decompositions (12) and (13) and the expression (14) imply that the decomposition of the spatial part $\boldsymbol{u}_{(1)} = (u^1_{(1)}, u^2_{(1)}, u^3_{(1)})$ of the perturbed fluid four-velocity

$$\boldsymbol{u}_{(1)} = \boldsymbol{u}_{(1)\|} + \boldsymbol{u}_{(1)\perp}, \tag{15}$$

where the components $\boldsymbol{u}_{(1)\|}$ and $\boldsymbol{u}_{(1)\perp}$ have the properties

$$\tilde{\boldsymbol{\nabla}} \cdot \boldsymbol{u}_{(1)} = \tilde{\boldsymbol{\nabla}} \cdot \boldsymbol{u}_{(1)\|}, \quad \tilde{\boldsymbol{\nabla}} \times \boldsymbol{u}_{(1)} = \tilde{\boldsymbol{\nabla}} \times \boldsymbol{u}_{(1)\perp}, \tag{16}$$

is consistent with the three linearized momentum constraint equations $G^{0i}_{(1)} = \kappa T^{0i}_{(1)}$. In expressions (16) $\tilde{\boldsymbol{\nabla}}$ is the generalized vector differential operator, defined by $\tilde{\nabla}_i v^k := v^k{}_{|i}$.

7. Evolution Equations for Scalar Perturbations

The general solution of the linearized Einstein equations and conservation laws (5) is a linear combination of scalar, vector and tensor perturbations. From the decomposition theorems it follows that only the scalar perturbations are coupled to density perturbations. Therefore, in the linearized equations (5) we may replace $h^i{}_j$ by $h^i{}_{\|j}$ and $u^i_{(1)}$ by $u^i_{(1)\|}$, to obtain perturbation equations which exclusively describe the evolution of scalar perturbations. For the Ricci tensor we find $R^i{}_{(1)j} \to R^i{}_{(1)\|j}$, so that the local perturbation to the global spatial curvature $R_{(0)}$ due to local density perturbations is given by

$$R_{(1)} := R^k{}_{(1)k} = g^{ij}_{(0)}(h^k{}_{k|i|j} - h^k{}_{i|k|j}) + \tfrac{1}{3} R_{(0)} h^k{}_k. \tag{17}$$

Since the rotational part of the local spatial fluid velocity is not coupled to scalar perturbations we may for scalar perturbations replace the three components of the fluid velocity by its divergence, i.e.,

$$\vartheta_{(1)} := u^k_{(1)|k}. \tag{18}$$

Finally, the perturbation to the expansion is given by

$$\theta_{(1)} = \vartheta_{(1)} - \tfrac{1}{2}\dot{h}^k{}_k. \tag{19}$$

Using the substitutions given above, we can rewrite the full set of perturbed Einstein equations and conservation laws (5) in the form

$$2H(\theta_{(1)} - \vartheta_{(1)}) = \tfrac{1}{2}R_{(1)} + \kappa\varepsilon_{(1)}, \tag{20a}$$

$$\dot{R}_{(1)} = -2HR_{(1)} + 2\kappa\varepsilon_{(0)}(1+w)\vartheta_{(1)} - \tfrac{2}{3}R_{(0)}(\theta_{(1)} - \vartheta_{(1)}), \tag{20b}$$

$$\dot{\varepsilon}_{(1)} = -3H(\varepsilon_{(1)} + p_{(1)}) - \varepsilon_{(0)}(1+w)\theta_{(1)}, \tag{20c}$$

$$\dot{\vartheta}_{(1)} = -H(2 - 3\beta^2)\vartheta_{(1)} - \frac{1}{\varepsilon_{(0)}(1+w)}\frac{\tilde{\nabla}^2 p_{(1)}}{a^2}, \quad \beta^2 := \frac{\dot{p}_{(0)}}{\dot{\varepsilon}_{(0)}}, \tag{20d}$$

$$\dot{n}_{(1)} = -3Hn_{(1)} - n_{(0)}\theta_{(1)}, \tag{20e}$$

which describe exclusively scalar perturbations. The system (20) consists of the energy density constraint equation or linearized Friedmann equation (20a), the momentum constraint equation (20b), the energy density conservation law (20c), the momentum conservation law (20d) and the particle number density conservation law (20e). These equations are the perturbed counterparts of Eqs. (7). Since the system of equations (20) includes all constraint equations and conservation laws, the *dynamical* equations $G^{ij}_{(1)} = \kappa T^{ij}_{(1)}$ are automatically satisfied by the solution of the system (20).

The background equations (7) combined with the system (20) determines the evolution of $\varepsilon^{\text{phys}}_{(1)}$ and $n^{\text{phys}}_{(1)}$ given by (9). However, the system (20) has also gauge modes as solution, i.e.,

$$\hat{\varepsilon}_{(1)} = \psi\dot{\varepsilon}_{(0)}, \quad \hat{n}_{(1)} = \psi\dot{n}_{(0)}, \quad \hat{\theta}_{(1)} = \psi\dot{\theta}_{(0)}, \tag{21a}$$

$$\hat{\vartheta}_{(1)} = -\frac{\tilde{\nabla}^2\psi}{a^2}, \quad \hat{R}_{(1)} = 4H\left[\frac{\tilde{\nabla}^2\psi}{a^2} - \tfrac{1}{2}R_{(0)}\psi\right], \tag{21b}$$

where $\xi^0 = \psi(\boldsymbol{x})$ in synchronous coordinates, see (11). Therefore, I have derived a new system of equations which is free from the gauge modes and determines exclusively the evolution of $\varepsilon^{\text{phys}}_{(1)}$ and $n^{\text{phys}}_{(1)}$. This will be the subject of Sec. 9. First, we show in the next section that $\varepsilon^{\text{phys}}_{(1)}$ and $n^{\text{phys}}_{(1)}$ are the real, measurable density perturbations.

8. Non-relativistic Limit

The standard non-relativistic limit is defined by four requirements, see, e.g., the textbook of Carroll,[25] page 153:

(1) The gravitational field should be weak, i.e., can be considered as a perturbation of a flat, i.e., $R_{(0)} = 0$, FLRW universe.

(2) The particles are moving slowly with respect to the speed of light.

(3) The transformation (6) with (11) is reduced to transformations for which the Newtonian Theory of Gravity is invariant.

(4) The gravitational field of a density perturbation should be static, i.e., it does not change with time.

Requirement (3), which is not used in the literature, is needed because we have to deal with gauge transformations (6) with (11) in an expanding universe.

In the Newtonian Theory of Gravity space is flat. Therefore, we consider a flat, $R_{(0)} = 0$, FLRW universe, so that spatial covariant derivatives reduce to ordinary derivatives. Combining expressions (14) and (17), we get

$$R_{(1)} = \frac{4}{c^2}\phi^{|k}{}_{|k} = -\frac{4}{c^2}\frac{\nabla^2\phi}{a^2}, \tag{22}$$

where ∇^2 is the usual Laplace operator.

The non-relativistic limit follows from

$$u^i_{(1)\mathrm{phys}} \to 0, \quad \Leftrightarrow \quad p^{\mathrm{phys}}_{(1)} \to 0, \tag{23}$$

i.e., the *physical* part of the fluid velocity is small with respect to the speed of light. Note that non-zero pressure differences imply fluid flow and vice versa. Using the background equations (7), the quantities (9) and the perturbation equations (20) we can draw the following conclusions:

(1) The momentum constraint equation (20b) implies with (22) and (23) that $\dot\phi = 0$, i.e., in the non-relativistic limit the potential ϕ is independent of time.

(2) The perturbed Friedmann equation (20a) and the time-derivative of the background Friedmann equation (7a) imply the Poisson equation

$$\nabla^2\varphi(\boldsymbol{x}) = \frac{4\pi G_{\mathrm{N}}}{c^2}\varepsilon^{\mathrm{phys}}_{(1)}(\boldsymbol{x}), \tag{24}$$

where $\varphi(\boldsymbol{x}) := \phi(\boldsymbol{x})/a^2(t_0)$.

(3) In the limit (23) the masses of the particles in a density perturbation are equal to their rest masses, so that the definitions (9) imply with (20c) and (20e)

$$n^{\mathrm{gi}}_{(1)}(\boldsymbol{x}) = \frac{\varepsilon^{\mathrm{gi}}_{(1)}(\boldsymbol{x})}{mc^2}, \tag{25}$$

which is the well-known energy mass relation of the Special Theory of Relativity.

(4) The relativistic gauge transformation (6) reduces in the non-relativistic limit to the Newtonian gauge transformation

$$x^0 \to x'^0 = x^0 - C, \quad x^i \to x'^i = x^i - \chi^i(\boldsymbol{x}), \tag{26}$$

where $\chi^i(\boldsymbol{x})$ are three arbitrary functions of the spatial coordinates and C is an arbitrary constant. Thus, in the non-relativistic limit time and space transformations are decoupled: time coordinates may be shifted and spatial coordinates may be chosen arbitrarily.

(5) Finally, the perturbed conservation laws (20c) and (20e) have only the gauge modes as solutions. Therefore, these equations have no physical significance and need not be considered anymore.

We can now draw the conclusion that $\varepsilon^{\text{phys}}_{(1)}$, $n^{\text{phys}}_{(1)}$ and $\theta^{\text{phys}}_{(1)} = 0$ defined by the expressions (9) are the unique, measurable, physical perturbations to the energy density, the particle number density and the global expansion, respectively.

9. Evolution Equations for Density Perturbations

I have used the computer algebra system to rewrite the system (20) into a new system of equations for the density contrast functions $\delta_\varepsilon := \varepsilon^{\text{phys}}_{(1)}/\varepsilon_{(0)}$ and $\delta_n := n^{\text{phys}}_{(1)}/n_{(0)}$. The result is the system of evolution equations for density perturbations in an open, flat and closed FLRW universe:

$$\ddot{\delta}_\varepsilon + b_1 \dot{\delta}_\varepsilon + b_2 \delta_\varepsilon = b_3 \left[\delta_n - \frac{\delta_\varepsilon}{1+w} \right], \tag{27a}$$

$$\frac{1}{c}\frac{\mathrm{d}}{\mathrm{d}t}\left[\delta_n - \frac{\delta_\varepsilon}{1+w}\right] = \frac{3Hn_{(0)}p_n}{\varepsilon_{(0)}(1+w)}\left[\delta_n - \frac{\delta_\varepsilon}{1+w}\right], \tag{27b}$$

where the coefficients b_1, b_2 and b_3 are determined by the background equations (7) and the equation of state for the pressure $p = p(n, \varepsilon)$.

9.1. *Diabatic Perturbations*

Density perturbations are diabatic ('non-adiabatic') if and only if the equation of state for the pressure depends on both the particle number density n and the energy density ε.

The combined First and Second Law of Thermodynamics is given by

$$T_{(0)}s^{\text{phys}}_{(1)} = -\frac{\varepsilon_{(0)}(1+w)}{n_{(0)}}\left[\delta_n - \frac{\delta_\varepsilon}{1+w}\right]. \tag{28}$$

Thus, the evolution of density perturbations is determined by both their internal gravity and heat exchange with their environment.

For diabatic perturbations the pressure perturbation is given by

$$p^{\text{phys}}_{(1)} = \beta^2 \varepsilon_{(0)} \delta_\varepsilon + n_{(0)} p_n \left[\delta_n - \frac{\delta_\varepsilon}{1+w}\right], \tag{29}$$

where the first term is the *adiabatic* part of the pressure perturbation and the second term is the *diabatic* part.

9.2. Adiabatic Perturbations

For barotropic equations of state, i.e., $p = p(\varepsilon)$, we have $p_n := (\partial p/\partial n)_\varepsilon = 0$, implying that $b_3 = 0$. In this case Eq. (27a) is a homogeneous equation and, as a consequence, describes adiabatic perturbations. Since for adiabatic perturbations $T_{(0)} s_{(1)}^{\text{phys}} = 0$, Eq. (27b) reduces in this case to an algebraic equation

$$\delta_n - \frac{\delta_\varepsilon}{1+w} = 0, \tag{30}$$

so that for adiabatic perturbations the perturbations in the energy density are coupled to perturbations in the particle number density. Adiabatic perturbations evolve only through their internal gravity.

10. Structure Formation in a Flat FLRW Universe

In this section we consider a flat FLRW universe. The coefficients of Eq. (27a) are in this case given by

$$b_1 = H(1 - 3w - 3\beta^2) - 2\frac{\dot{\beta}}{\beta}, \tag{31a}$$

$$b_2 = \kappa\varepsilon_{(0)}\left[2\beta^2(2+3w) - \tfrac{1}{6}(1+18w+9w^2)\right] + 2H\frac{\dot{\beta}}{\beta}(1+3w) - \beta^2\frac{\nabla^2}{a^2}, \tag{31b}$$

$$b_3 = \left\{\frac{-2}{1+w}\left[\varepsilon_{(0)}p_{\varepsilon n}(1+w) + \frac{2p_n}{3H}\frac{\dot{\beta}}{\beta} + p_n(p_\varepsilon - \beta^2) + n_{(0)}p_{nn}\right] + p_n\right\}\frac{n_{(0)}}{\varepsilon_{(0)}}\frac{\nabla^2}{a^2}, \tag{31c}$$

where the partial derivatives of the equation of state for the pressure $p(n,\varepsilon)$ are given by

$$p_n := \left(\frac{\partial p}{\partial n}\right)_\varepsilon, \quad p_\varepsilon := \left(\frac{\partial p}{\partial \varepsilon}\right)_n, \quad p_{\varepsilon n} := \frac{\partial^2 p}{\partial \varepsilon\, \partial n}, \quad p_{nn} := \frac{\partial^2 p}{\partial n^2}. \tag{32}$$

The symbol ∇^2 denotes the Laplace operator. The quantity $\beta(t)$ is defined by $\beta^2 := \dot{p}_{(0)}/\dot{\varepsilon}_{(0)}$. Using that $\dot{p}_{(0)} = p_n \dot{n}_{(0)} + p_\varepsilon \dot{\varepsilon}_{(0)}$ and the conservation laws (7c) and (7d) one gets

$$\beta^2 = p_\varepsilon + \frac{n_{(0)} p_n}{\varepsilon_{(0)}(1+w)}. \tag{33}$$

From the definitions $w := p_{(0)}/\varepsilon_{(0)}$ and $\beta^2 := \dot{p}_{(0)}/\dot{\varepsilon}_{(0)}$ and the energy conservation law (7c), one finds for the time-derivative of w

$$\dot{w} = 3H(1+w)(w - \beta^2). \tag{34}$$

This expression holds true *independent* of the precise form of the equation of state.

10.1. Radiation Dominated Universe

In this era the primordial fluid can be treated as radiation-dominated with equations of state

$$\varepsilon = a_B T_\gamma^4, \quad p = \tfrac{1}{3} a_B T_\gamma^4, \tag{35}$$

where a_B is the black body constant and T_γ the radiation temperature. The equations of state (35) imply the equation of state for the pressure $p = \tfrac{1}{3}\varepsilon$, so that, with (32),

$$p_n = 0, \quad p_\varepsilon = \tfrac{1}{3}. \tag{36}$$

Therefore, one has from (33),

$$\beta^2 = w = \tfrac{1}{3}. \tag{37}$$

Using (36) and (37), the perturbation equations (27) reduce to

$$\ddot{\delta}_\varepsilon - H\dot{\delta}_\varepsilon - \left[\frac{1}{3}\frac{\nabla^2}{a^2} - \tfrac{2}{3}\kappa\varepsilon_{(0)}\right]\delta_\varepsilon = 0, \tag{38a}$$

$$\delta_n - \tfrac{3}{4}\delta_\varepsilon = 0. \tag{38b}$$

Using the solutions of the background equations (7) and using that $\delta_\varepsilon(t,\boldsymbol{x}) = \delta_\varepsilon(t,\boldsymbol{q})\exp(i\boldsymbol{q}\cdot\boldsymbol{x})$, with $|\boldsymbol{q}| = 2\pi/\lambda$, Eq. (38a) can be written in the form

$$\delta_\varepsilon'' - \frac{1}{2\tau}\delta_\varepsilon' + \left[\frac{\mu_r^2}{4\tau} + \frac{1}{2\tau^2}\right]\delta_\varepsilon = 0, \quad \mu_r := \frac{2\pi}{\lambda_0}\frac{1}{H(t_0)}\frac{1}{\sqrt{3}}, \quad \lambda_0 := \lambda a(t_0), \tag{39}$$

where a prime denotes differentiation with respect to the dimensionless time $\tau := t/t_0 \geq 1$. The general solution of Eq. (39) is

$$\delta_\varepsilon(\tau,\boldsymbol{q}) = \Big[A_1(\boldsymbol{q})\sin\big(\mu_r\sqrt{\tau}\big) + A_2(\boldsymbol{q})\cos\big(\mu_r\sqrt{\tau}\big)\Big]\sqrt{\tau}, \tag{40}$$

where $A_1(\boldsymbol{q})$ and $A_2(\boldsymbol{q})$ are the 'constants' of integration. For large-scale ($\lambda \to \infty$) perturbations, we find from Eq. (40) the well-known[2, 26–29] solution

$$\delta_\varepsilon = c_1\tau + c_2\tau^{1/2}. \tag{41}$$

We can now draw the following conclusions. From Eq. (40) it follows that density perturbations oscillate. However, in contrast to the outcome of the standard perturbation theory in the literature, density perturbations oscillate with an *increasing* amplitude. Moreover, baryons were tightly coupled to radiation through Thomson scattering, i.e., baryons obey $\delta_{n,\text{baryon}} = \tfrac{3}{4}\delta_\varepsilon$. Thus, for baryons (38b) is identically satisfied. In contrast to baryons, CDM is *not* coupled to radiation through Thomson scattering. However, equation (38b) follows from the General Theory of Relativity. As a consequence, equation (38b) should be obeyed by *all* kinds of particles that interact through gravitation. In other words, equation (38b) holds true for baryons as well as CDM. Since CDM interacts only via gravity with baryons and radiation, the fluctuations in CDM are coupled through gravitation to fluctuations in the energy density.

10.2. Era after Decoupling of Matter and Radiation

Once protons and electrons combined to yield hydrogen, the radiation pressure was negligible, and the equations of state have become those of a non-relativistic monatomic perfect gas with three degrees of freedom

$$\varepsilon(n,T) = nmc^2 + \tfrac{3}{2}nk_\text{B}T, \quad p(n,T) = nk_\text{B}T, \tag{42}$$

where k_B is Boltzmann's constant, m the mean particle mass, and T the temperature of the matter. Eliminating T from (42) yields the equation of state for the pressure

$$p(n,\varepsilon) = \tfrac{2}{3}(\varepsilon - nmc^2), \tag{43}$$

so that with (32) one has

$$p_n = -\tfrac{2}{3}mc^2, \quad p_\varepsilon = \tfrac{2}{3}. \tag{44}$$

Substituting p_n, p_ε, and ε given by (42) into (33) on finds, using that $mc^2 \gg k_\text{B}T$,

$$\beta \approx \frac{v_\text{s}}{c} = \sqrt{\frac{5}{3}\frac{k_\text{B}T_{(0)}}{mc^2}}, \quad w \approx \frac{k_\text{B}T_{(0)}}{mc^2} \lesssim 2.7 \times 10^{-10}, \tag{45}$$

with v_s the adiabatic speed of sound and $T_{(0)}$ the matter temperature. Using that $\beta^2 \approx \tfrac{5}{3}w$ and $w \ll 1$, expression (34) reduces to $\dot{w} \approx -2Hw$, so that with $H := \dot{a}/a$ one has $w \propto a^{-2}$. This implies with (45) that the matter temperature decays as

$$T_{(0)} \propto a^{-2}. \tag{46}$$

This, in turn, implies with (45) that $\dot{\beta}/\beta = -H$. The system (27) can now be rewritten as

$$\ddot{\delta}_\varepsilon + 3H\dot{\delta}_\varepsilon - \left[\beta^2\frac{\nabla^2}{a^2} + \tfrac{5}{6}\kappa\varepsilon_{(0)}\right]\delta_\varepsilon = -\frac{2}{3}\frac{\nabla^2}{a^2}(\delta_n - \delta_\varepsilon), \tag{47a}$$

$$\frac{1}{c}\frac{\text{d}}{\text{d}t}(\delta_n - \delta_\varepsilon) = -2H(\delta_n - \delta_\varepsilon), \tag{47b}$$

where $w \ll 1$ and $\beta^2 \ll 1$ have been neglected with respect to constants of order unity. From equation (47b) it follows with $H := \dot{a}/a$ that

$$\delta_n - \delta_\varepsilon \propto a^{-2}. \tag{48}$$

Combining (46) and (48) it follows that the fluctuation in the kinetic energy density is given by

$$\delta_\text{kin}(t,\boldsymbol{x}) \approx \delta_\varepsilon(t,\boldsymbol{x}) - \delta_n(t,\boldsymbol{x}) \approx \frac{3}{2}\frac{k_\text{B}T_{(0)}(t)}{mc^2}\delta_T(t_\text{dec},\boldsymbol{x}), \tag{49}$$

where $\delta_T(t_\text{dec},\boldsymbol{x})$ is a constant, i.e., a free parameter of the perturbation theory and t_dec is the time of decoupling of matter and radiation. Moreover, it is found for the entropy perturbation and the fluctuation in the pressure, respectively,

$$s_{(1)}^\text{phys} \approx \tfrac{3}{2}k_\text{B}\delta_T, \quad \delta_p \approx \tfrac{5}{3}\delta_\varepsilon + \delta_T, \tag{50}$$

as follows from (28), (29) and (42).

Using that $\delta_\varepsilon(t,\boldsymbol{x}) = \delta_\varepsilon(t,\boldsymbol{q})\exp(i\boldsymbol{q}\cdot\boldsymbol{x})$, $\delta_n(t,\boldsymbol{x}) = \delta_n(t,\boldsymbol{q})\exp(i\boldsymbol{q}\cdot\boldsymbol{x})$ with $|\boldsymbol{q}| = 2\pi/\lambda$ and the solutions of the background equations (7), the system (47) can be rewritten as one ordinary differential equation

$$\delta_\varepsilon'' + \frac{2}{\tau}\delta_\varepsilon' + \left[\frac{4}{9}\frac{\mu_m^2}{\tau^{8/3}} - \frac{10}{9\tau^2}\right]\delta_\varepsilon = -\frac{4}{15}\frac{\mu_m^2}{\tau^{8/3}}\delta_T(t_{\rm dec},\boldsymbol{q}), \quad \tau \geq 1, \tag{51}$$

where a prime denotes differentiation with respect to the dimensionless time $\tau := t/t_{\rm dec}$. The parameter μ_m is expressed in observable quantities at the present time t_p

$$\mu_m = \frac{2\pi}{\lambda_{\rm dec}}\frac{1}{cH(t_p)}\frac{1}{[z(t_{\rm dec})+1]}\sqrt{\frac{5}{3}\frac{k_B T_{(0)\gamma}(t_p)}{m}} = \frac{16.48}{\lambda_{\rm dec}}, \tag{52}$$

where $\lambda_{\rm dec}$ is expressed in parsec.

For large scales $\lambda_{\rm dec} \to \infty$, the solution of Eq. (51) is given by

$$\delta_\varepsilon = c_1 \tau^{2/3} + c_2 \tau^{-5/3}. \tag{53}$$

The first term is a well-known solution, whereas the gauge mode τ^{-1} is absent.

In order to solve Eq. (51) for all finite scales $\lambda_{\rm dec}$, we have to specify the initial values $\delta(t_{\rm dec},\boldsymbol{q})$ and its derivative $\delta'(t_{\rm dec},\boldsymbol{q})$. From measurements of the Planck satellite[30] it is found that for $\tau = 1$, i.e., at $t = t_{\rm dec}$,

$$|\delta_\varepsilon(t_{\rm dec},\boldsymbol{q})| \lesssim 10^{-5}. \tag{54}$$

The initial growth rate is unknown. Therefore, we assume that there is initially no growth at all, i.e., we take

$$\delta_\varepsilon'(t_{\rm dec},\boldsymbol{q}) \approx 0. \tag{55}$$

The initial value of the entropy perturbation (50) is a random variable and depends on how a density perturbation undergoes the very fast transition from a very high pressure epoch just before decoupling to the very low pressure era just after decoupling. Some small areas end up with positive entropy perturbations and others with negative entropy perturbations. In fact, it is found that

(1) $s_{(1)}^{\rm phys} \approx \frac{3}{2}k_B\delta_T > 0 \Rightarrow$ large voids
(2) $s_{(1)}^{\rm phys} \approx \frac{3}{2}k_B\delta_T < 0 \Rightarrow$ structure formation

The results of the integration of Eq. (51) are depicted in Fig. 1. The curves are labeled by the diabatic pressure perturbation δ_T (50). Density perturbations start to grow at the time of decoupling. Each curve shows the time (or, equivalently, the redshift) when a density perturbation becomes non-linear, i.e., $\delta_\varepsilon = 1$. The growth of density perturbations is governed by both gravity and heat exchange. At a scale of $6.5\,{\rm pc} = 21\,{\rm ly}$ (the peak value) gravity and heat exchange work perfectly together, resulting in very early star formation. Because of the steepness of the curves to the left of the peak, I will refer to this value as the *relativistic* Jeans scale. The corresponding relativistic Jeans mass is $4.3 \times 10^3\,M_\odot$. For scales larger than the relativistic Jeans scale, gravity is strong but heat exchange is low because of the large

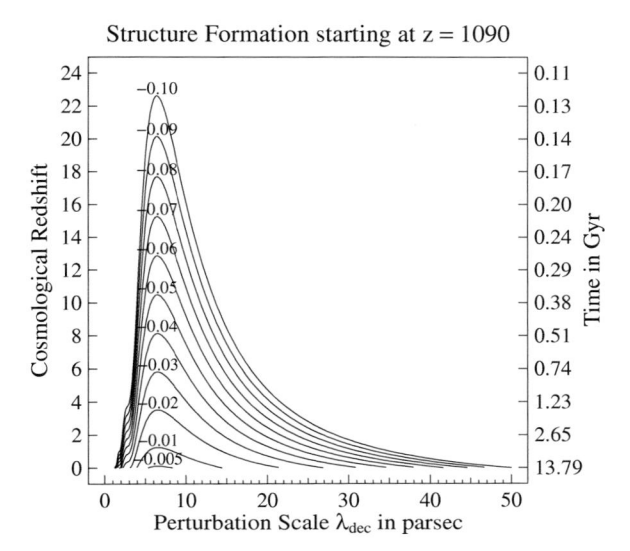

Fig. 1. The curves give the redshift and time, as a function of λ_{dec}, when a linear perturbation in the energy density with initial values $\delta_\varepsilon(t_{\text{dec}}, \boldsymbol{q}) \lesssim 10^{-5}$ and $\delta'_\varepsilon(t_{\text{dec}}, \boldsymbol{q}) \approx 0$ starting to grow at an initial redshift of $z(t_{\text{dec}}) = 1090$ has become non-linear, i.e., $\delta_\varepsilon(t, \boldsymbol{q}) = 1$. The curves are labeled with the initial values of the relative perturbations $\delta_T(t_{\text{dec}}, \boldsymbol{q})$ in the diabatic part of the pressure. For each curve, the Jeans scale, i.e., the peak value, is at 6.5 pc.

scale, resulting in a later collapse time. The larger the scale, the later the collapse time. For very large scales the collapse time is proportional to $\tau^{2/3}$, the classic result for adiabatic density perturbations. On the other hand, for scales smaller than the relativistic Jeans scale, gravity becomes rapidly very weak, resulting also in a much later collapse time.

Figure 2 shows the growth rates of density perturbations as a function of their initial scale λ_{dec} at decoupling. The fastest growth occurs within the first 16 Myr. Density perturbations at the relativistic Jeans scale of 6.5 pc grow fast until non-linearity. Density perturbations with initial scale 4.1 pc grow initially faster than perturbations at the relativistic Jeans scale. Eventually, the rapid growth slows down and the perturbations grow slowly into the non-linear phase. Density perturbations which are initially smaller than 4.1 pc oscillate towards non-linearity. Finally, perturbations smaller than approximately 1 pc and larger than 50 pc do not become non-linear within the age of the universe.

11. Standard Perturbation Theory

The standard equation which is supposed to describe the evolution of density perturbations $\delta := \varepsilon_{(1)}/\varepsilon_{(0)}$ and which is ubiquitous in the literature reads

$$\ddot{\delta} + 2H\dot{\delta} - \left[\beta^2 \frac{\nabla^2}{a^2} + \tfrac{1}{2}\kappa\varepsilon_{(0)}(1+w)(1+3w)\right]\delta = 0. \tag{56}$$

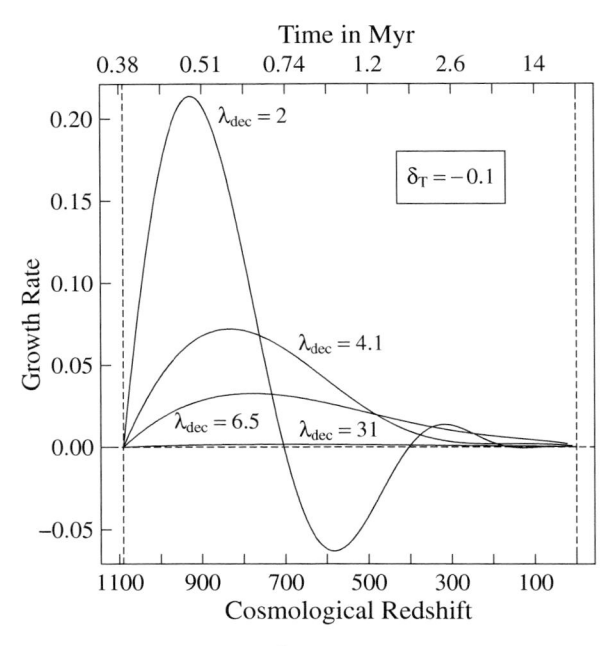

Fig. 2. The curves give the growth rates δ'_ε, as function of the redshift z, or time in million of years. The evolution of perturbations started at $z = 1090$. The initial dimensions λ_{dec} of the perturbations are measured in parsec.

See, for example, the classic article of Bonnor.[31] In this equation $\beta^2 = w = \frac{1}{3}$, (37), in the radiation-dominated universe, whereas $\beta = v_s/c$ and $w = 0$, (45), after decoupling of matter and radiation. The standard equation (56) differs substantially from the new equations (38) and (47), since the latter two equations determine the evolution of the true, measurable energy density fluctuation $\delta_\varepsilon := \varepsilon^{\text{phys}}_{(1)}/\varepsilon_{(0)}$. In this section we briefly explain why the standard equation differs from the new equations.

Since equations (38) and (47) are derived from the system (20), we try to derive Eq. (56) also from the system of equations (20), this time not using the definitions (9). In this procedure Eq. (20e) is not needed, since the equation of state for the pressure in Eq. (56) is of the form $p = p(\varepsilon)$.

11.1. Radiation-dominated Universe

The result for the radiation-dominated era is

$$\ddot{\delta} + 2H\dot{\delta} - \left[\frac{1}{3}\frac{\nabla^2}{a^2} + \tfrac{4}{3}\kappa\varepsilon_{(0)}\right]\delta = -\tfrac{4}{3}H\vartheta_{(1)}, \tag{57a}$$

$$\dot{\vartheta}_{(1)} + H\vartheta_{(1)} + \frac{1}{4}\frac{\nabla^2\delta}{a^2} = 0. \tag{57b}$$

The problem with this system is that it admits, next to physical solutions, also the gauge modes

$$\hat{\delta}(t,\boldsymbol{x}) := -4H(t)\psi(\boldsymbol{x}), \quad \hat{\vartheta}(t,\boldsymbol{x}) := -\frac{\nabla^2 \psi(\boldsymbol{x})}{a^2(t)}. \tag{58}$$

Since these solutions have no physical significance, one cannot impose *physical* initial conditions to solve the system (57) since that would imply that the arbitrary gauge function $\psi(\boldsymbol{x})$ could be fixed by physical conditions, which is impossible. Furthermore, the gauge modes displace the divergence $\vartheta_{(1)}$ of the fluid velocity to the right-hand side, Eq. (57a). Since $\vartheta_{(1)}$ is an intrinsic property of an evolving density perturbation, it should be incorporated in the left-hand side of the evolution equation, as is the case for Eq. (38a). That is why Eq. (38a) predicts oscillating density perturbations with an *increasing* amplitude, whereas the standard equation (56) yields oscillating perturbations with a *constant* amplitude. Because of the presence of gauge modes in its solution, the system (57) is inadequate to study the evolution of density perturbations in the universe. In contrast to the system (57) the standard equation (56) lacks the divergence $\vartheta_{(1)}$. Since, in addition, the gauge mode $\hat{\delta}$ is a solution of Equation (56), the standard equation is simply useless.

11.2. *Era after Decoupling of Matter and Radiation*

In the era after decoupling we find

$$\ddot{\delta} + 2H\dot{\delta} - \left[\beta^2 \frac{\nabla^2}{a^2} + \tfrac{1}{2}\kappa\varepsilon_{(0)}\right]\delta = -3H\beta^2 \vartheta_{(1)}, \tag{59a}$$

$$\dot{\vartheta}_{(1)} + 2H\vartheta_{(1)} + \beta^2 \frac{\nabla^2 \delta}{a^2} = 0. \tag{59b}$$

In this case the gauge function $\psi(\boldsymbol{x})$ reduces to a constant C, (26), in accordance with the fact that after decoupling the cosmological fluid is described by a non-relativistic fluid (42). Therefore, the only surviving gauge mode is given by

$$\hat{\delta}(t,\boldsymbol{x}) := -3H(t)C, \tag{60}$$

and $\vartheta_{(1)} = \vartheta_{(1)}^{\text{phys}}$ is a physical quantity. Due to the presence of a gauge mode, the system (59) is still inadequate to study the evolution of density perturbations.

Finally, we consider a pressure-less fluid, also known as 'dust'. Substituting $p = 0$, i.e., $\beta = 0$, into the system (59) we find

$$\ddot{\delta} + 2H\dot{\delta} - \tfrac{1}{2}\kappa\varepsilon_{(0)}\delta = 0, \tag{61a}$$

$$\dot{\vartheta}_{(1)} + 2H\vartheta_{(1)} = 0. \tag{61b}$$

These equations are decoupled, implying that the divergence of the fluid velocity has no influence whatsoever on the growth of a perturbation. However, if there are no pressure differences in a fluid, then there is no fluid flow, $\vartheta_{(1)}^{\text{phys}} = 0$, so that density perturbations do not evolve. Since Eq. (61b) has only the gauge mode $\hat{\vartheta}_{(1)}$ as solution this equation is not needed anymore.

Equation (61a) follows also from the Newtonian Theory of Gravity if one takes the expansion into account. Since it has next to the gauge mode $\propto t^{-1}$ also a physical solution $\propto t^{2/3}$ regardless of the fact that there is no fluid flow, it should be clear that the Newtonian perturbation theory is inadequate to describe the evolution of density perturbations in the universe.

12. Conclusion

In this article I have sketched the derivation of a perturbation theory for open, flat and closed FLRW universes filled with perfect fluid described by a non-barotropic equation of state for the pressure $p(n,\varepsilon)$. The new theory has a Newtonian limit in a non-static universe. As a consequence, the gauge problem of cosmology is finally solved. The new perturbation theory consists of a second-order ordinary differential equation for the density contrast $\delta_\varepsilon := \varepsilon_{(1)}^{\text{phys}}/\varepsilon_{(0)}$, and a first-order ordinary differential equation for $\delta_n - \delta_\varepsilon/(1+w)$, where the latter expression is proportional to entropy perturbations. A first conclusion that can be drawn from the new perturbation theory is that local density perturbations do not affect the global expansion of the universe.

The new perturbation theory has been applied to a flat FLRW universe. The results are as follows. In the radiation-dominated universe density perturbations oscillate with an amplitude which is proportional to the square root of time. Both CDM as well as ordinary matter are coupled to perturbations in the radiation. As a consequence, structure formation can start only after decoupling of matter and radiation. After decoupling the growth of structure depends on both its internal gravity and its heat exchange with its environment. Heat exchange depends on the initial value of the entropy perturbation as well as the initial scale of a density perturbation. The entropy perturbation is a free parameter of the perturbation theory and can, therefore, take on random values. For sufficiently large negative values of the entropy perturbation I have found that the first stars are formed at $z \approx 24$–12, or, equivalently 110–300 Myr after the Big Bang. The relativistic Jeans scale is 6.5 pc $\approx$ 21 ly, and the corresponding relativistic Jeans mass is $4.3 \times 10^3\, M_\odot$.

The research in Refs. 3 and 4 has revealed that the General Relativistic perturbation theory explains structure formation in the early universe, without the need of CDM. The standard equation (56) of cosmology should not be used anymore.

References

1. E. M. Lifshitz, On the Gravitational Stability of the Expanding Universe, *J. Phys.* **X**, 116 (1946).
2. E. M. Lifshitz and I. M. Khalatnikov, Investigations in Relativistic Cosmology, *Adv. Phys.* **12**, 185 (1963).
3. P. G. Miedema, General Relativistic Evolution Equations for Density Perturbations in Closed, Flat and Open FLRW Universes, *eprint arXiv:1410.211* (2014).
4. P. G. Miedema, Structure Formation in the Early Universe, *ArXiv e-prints* (January 2016).

5. S. Weinberg, *Cosmology*, first edn. (Oxford University Press Inc., New York, 2008).
6. J. M. Bardeen, Gauge-invariant Cosmological Perturbations, *Phys. Rev.* **D22**, 1882 (1980).
7. G. F. R. Ellis and M. Bruni, Covariant and Gauge-invariant Approach to Cosmological Density Fluctuations, *Phys. Rev. D* **40**, 1804 (1989).
8. G. F. R. Ellis, J. Hwang and M. Bruni, Covariant and Gauge-independent Perfect-Fluid Robertson-Walker Perturbations, *Phys. Rev. D* **40**, 1819 (1989).
9. G. F. R. Ellis and H. van Elst, Cosmological Models (Cargèse lectures 1998) (1998).
10. V. F. Mukhanov, H. A. Feldman and R. H. Brandenberger, Theory of Cosmological Perturbations, *Phys. Rep.* **215**, 203 (1992).
11. V. Mukhanov, *Physical Foundations of Cosmology* (Cambridge University Press, 2005).
12. M. Bruni, P. K. Dunsby and G. F. Ellis, Cosmological perturbations and the physical meaning of gauge invariant variables, *Astrophys.J.* **395**, 34 (1992).
13. K. A. Malik and D. Wands, Cosmological Perturbations, *Phys.Rept.* **475**, 1 (2009).
14. C. Knobel, An Introduction into the Theory of Cosmological Structure Formation, *eprint arXiv:1208.5931* (2012).
15. P. Peter, Cosmological Perturbation Theory, *eprint 1303.2509* (2013).
16. K. A. Malik and D. R. Matravers, Comments on gauge-invariance in cosmology, *General Relativity and Gravitation* **45**, 1989 (October 2013).
17. H. Kodama and M. Sasaki, Cosmological Perturbation Theory, *Progress of Theoretical Physics Supplements* **78**, 1 (1984).
18. C.-P. Ma and E. Bertschinger, Cosmological perturbation theory in the synchronous and conformal newtonian gauges, *Astrophys. J.* **455**, 7 (December 1995).
19. G. F. R. Ellis, Editorial note to: E. lifshitz, On the gravitational stability of the expanding universe, *General Relativity and Gravitation* **49** (2017).
20. J. W. York, jr., Covariant Decomposition of symmetric Tensors in the Theory of Gravitation, *Annales de l' Institut Henry Poincaré - Section A: Physique théorique* **XXI**, 319 (1974).
21. J. M. Stewart and M. Walker, Perturbations of Space-times in General Relativity, *Proc. R. Soc. London* **A 341**, 49 (1974).
22. J. M. Stewart, Perturbations of Friedmann-Robertson-Walker Cosmological Models, *Class. Quantum Grav.* **7**, 1169 (1990).
23. L. D. Landau and E. M. Lifshitz, *The Classical Theory of Fields*, Course of Theoretical Physics, Vol. 2, 4 edn. (Oxford: Butterworth-Heinemann (Elsevier), 2010).
24. S. Weinberg, *Gravitation and Cosmology: Principles and Applications of the General Theory of Relativity* (John Wiley & Sons, Inc. New York, 1972).
25. S. M. Carroll, *Space Time and Geometry*, first edn. (Benjamin Cummings, 2003).
26. P. J. Adams and V. Canuto, Exact Solution of the Lifshitz Equations Governing the Growth of Fluctuations in Cosmology, *Physical Review D* **12**, 3793 (1975).
27. D. W. Olson, Density Perturbations in Cosmological Models, *Physical Review D* **14**, 327 (1976).
28. E. W. Kolb and M. S. Turner, *The Early Universe* (Westview Press, 1994).
29. W. H. Press and E. T. Vishniac, Tenacious Myths about Cosmological Perturbations larger than the Horizon Size, *The Astrophysical Journal* **239**, 1 (July 1980).
30. Planck Collaboration, Planck 2018 results. VI. Cosmological parameters, *A&A* **641**, p. A6 (September 2020).
31. W. B. Bonnor, Jeans' Formula for Gravitational Instability, *Monthly Notices of the Royal Astronomical Society* **117**, 104 (02 1957).

Constraining beyond ΛCDM models with 21cm intensity mapping forecast observations combined with latest CMB data

M. Berti

SISSA – International School for Advanced Studies,
Via Bonomea 265, Trieste, 34136, Italy
INFN – National Institute for Nuclear Physics,
Via Valerio 2, Trieste, 34127, Italy
IFPU – Institute for Fundamental Physics of the Universe,
Via Beirut 2, Trieste, 34151, Italy
E-mail: mberti@sissa.it
https://www.sissa.it/

Observations of the 21cm signal through intensity mapping techniques are expected in the near future. This new observable will allow probing the evolution of the Universe in a very wide redshift range, from the dark ages, through the epoch of reionization up to the present time. We constrain cosmological parameters from forecast measurements of the 21 cm signal power spectrum $P_{21}(k,z)$ combined with the latest CMB data from Planck 2018 observations. In the same framework, we test also modified gravity models to unveil beyond ΛCDM features coupling information from primordial probes, such as the CMB, to lower redshift ones. We extend the codes EFTCAMB/EFTCosmoMC to compute the likelihood function for $P_{21}(k,z)$ and we construct a mock data set of forecast intensity mapping observations. At the time being, we are bound by the experimental state-of-the-art to consider the redshift bin $z = 0.39$. However, in the future, it may be possible to study also wider redshift ranges. We describe our likelihood implementation and present the results we obtained from the statistical Monte-Carlo Markov-Chain analysis we conducted.

Keywords: Cosmology; 21cm Intensity Mapping; Dark Energy; Modified Gravity; Forecast constraints.

1. Introduction

According to the Standard Model of Cosmology, the Λ - Cold Dark Matter (ΛCDM) model, the Universe we live in is currently going to a phase of accelerated expansion. The cause of acceleration is assigned to an enigmatic component, called Dark Energy (DE), which constitutes $\sim 70\%$ of the Universe. From the birth of the precision cosmology era, the ΛCDM model has been extensively tested and it proved to be in remarkable agreement with several, independent observations.[1-4] Despite its success, tensions on cosmological parameters[5-8] and open theoretical problems, regarding the nature of the Cosmological Constant (Λ),[9-11] motivated the emergence of a plethora of models alternative to ΛCDM.[12,13]

At the state-of-the-art, constraints on Modified Gravity (MG) or DE models are all broadly compatible with ΛCDM. However, observations from future experiments, such as Euclid[a] and the Square Kilometer Array Observatory (SKAO),[b] are expected to be crucial in the quest for selecting the correct model.

In this work, we test the effect of the detection on the 21cm signal on beyond ΛCDM models, i.e. $P_{21}(k)$. We forecast intensity mapping observations of $P_{21}(k)$, as it will be measured by the MeerKAT radio-telescope,[c] the SKAO precursor and pathfinder in South Africa.[14–16] We build a realistic mock data set for $P_{21}(k)$ at redshift $z = 0.39$ and conduct a Monte Carlo Markov Chain (MCMC) analysis to constrain beyond ΛCDM theories. We adopt a model-independent approach by studying MG/DE within the Effective Field Theory (EFT) formalism for Cosmic Acceleration.[17,18] To this end we modify the codes **EFTCAMB/EFTCosmoMC**,[19–21] to include a new module for the $P_{21}(k)$ likelihood computation. We compute constraints on cosmological and EFT parameters from $P_{21}(k)$ alone and combined with the latest Planck 2018 CMB data.[1]

This work is intended as an introduction to a more extensive analysis, that can be found in Ref.[22]. The structure of the paper is the following. First, we review general aspects of the theoretical and experimental framework in section 1.1. We outline the main aspects of our methodology in section 2. Results are presented in section 3 and summarized in section 4.

1.1. *Theoretical and experimental framework*

The Effective Field Theory (EFT) technique was first used in a cosmological scenario to describe inflation[23,24] and then applied to the description of Cosmic Acceleration.[17,18] The idea behind EFT for DE is to construct the most general action to be *effective*, i.e. easily interfaced with data, and *unifying*, in order to include as many DE/MG models as special cases. Up to second order in perturbation theory and in the Jordan frame, the resulting action is

$$S = \int d^4x \sqrt{-g} \Biggl\{ \frac{m_0^2}{2} \left[1 + \Omega^{\text{EFT}}(\tau)\right] R + \Lambda(\tau) - c(\tau) a^2 \delta g^{00} \\
+ \frac{M_2^4(\tau)}{2} \left(a^2 \delta g^{00}\right)^2 - \frac{\bar{M}_1^3(\tau)}{2} a^2 \delta g^{00} \delta K \\
- \frac{\bar{M}_2^2(\tau)}{2} (\delta K)^2 - \frac{\bar{M}_3^2(\tau)}{2} \delta K_\nu^\mu \delta K_\mu^\nu \\
+ m_2^2(\tau)(g^{\mu\nu} + n^\mu n^\nu) \partial_\mu \left(a^2 g^{00}\right) \partial_\nu \left(a^2 g^{00}\right) \\
+ \frac{\hat{M}^2(\tau)}{2} a^2 \delta g^{00} \delta R^{(3)} + \ldots \Biggr\} + S_m,$$

(1)

where the nine functions of the conformal time τ, $\{\Omega^{\text{EFT}}, \Lambda, c\}$ and $\{M_2^4, \bar{M}_1^3, \bar{M}_2^2, \bar{M}_3^2, m_2^2, \hat{M}^2\}$, are referred to as EFT functions. We recover the

---

[a]See https://sci.esa.int/web/euclid.
[b]See https://www.skatelescope.org/.
[c]See https://www.sarao.ac.za/gallery/meerkat/.

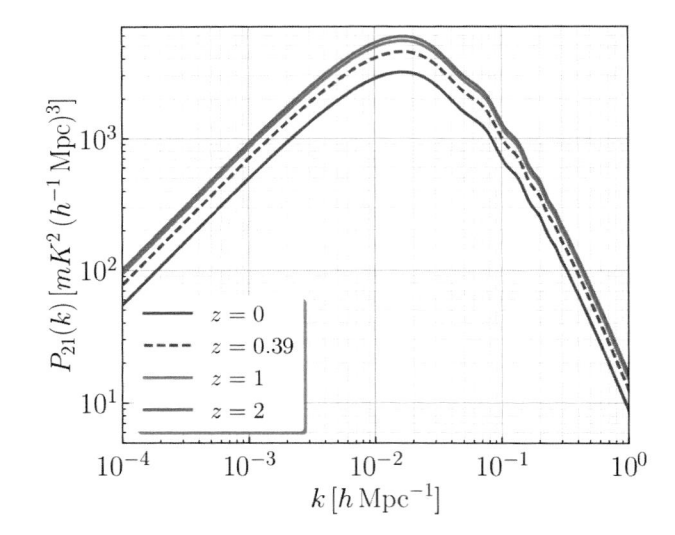

Fig. 1. Linear power spectra for the 21cm signal at different redshifts. Results are computed with the model in Eq. (2) for a ΛCDM fiducial cosmology, i.e. Planck 2018 best fit results.[1]

ΛCDM limit when all the EFT functions are set to zero. By choosing the evolution of each EFT function one can either test the specific effect of the single operators on observables (*pure* EFT approach) or map the EFT functions into well known DE/MG models. We will adopt the *pure* EFT approach and we will study a subset of models described by the functions $\{\Omega^{\text{EFT}}, \Lambda, c\}$ on a ΛCDM background.

EFT models can be studied numerically by means of the Einstein-Boltzmann solver EFTCAMB,[19,21] an extension of the code CAMB,[25] and the MCMC sampler EFTCosmoMC,[20] an extension of CosmoMC.[26,27] *Pure* EFT models have been studied in the literature,[1,20,28] however, at the state-of-the-art, all the models are compatible with ΛCDM. For a complete review on EFT for DE and the latest constraints, we refer to Ref.[29].

Although no significant proof supporting a specific beyond ΛCDM model has yet been found, in this work we quantify the impact of future observations on EFT models. We focus on the 21cm signal detection through line intensity mapping techniques, which allows sampling the neutral hydrogen (HI) distribution in a wide redshift range.[30–35] These observations will open an important window on DE/MG theories.[36–42] Currently, several purpose-built radio-telescopes, such as the Canadian Hydrogen Intensity Mapping Experiment (CHIME),[d] the Hydrogen Intensity and Real-Time Analysis experiment (HIRAX),[e] the Five-hundred-meter Aperture Spherical Telescope (FAST),[f] are already taking data or are under construction.

---

[d]See https://chime-experiment.ca/en.
[e]See https://hirax.ukzn.ac.za/.
[f]See https://fast.bao.ac.cn/.

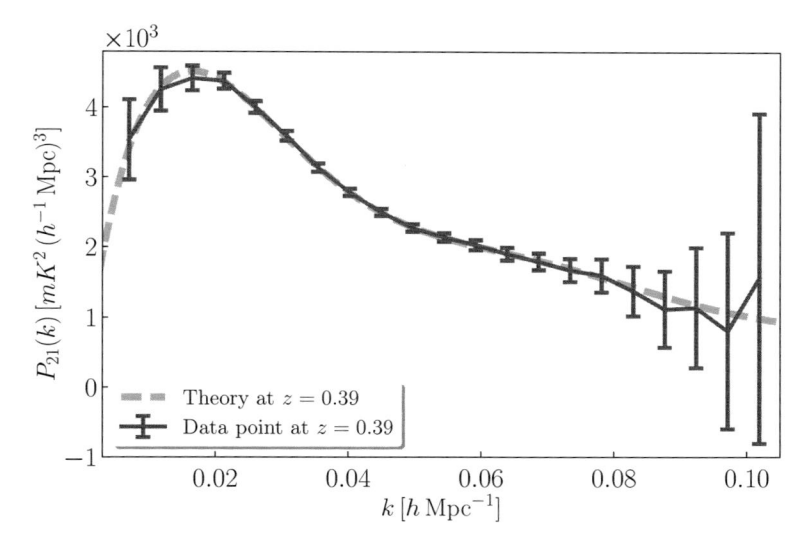

Fig. 2. Mock data set observations and theory prediction at $z = 0.39$ for the 21cm signal power spectrum. Error bars are generated considering a realistic intensity mapping survey with the MeerKAT telescope. Central values are instead obtained from points predicted by the theory for ΛCDM and the fiducial cosmology we assume. Each point from the theory is then displaced randomly according to a gaussian distribution with a fifth of the error on that point as standard deviation.

Moreover, radio cosmology and the study of DE/MG theories is one of the main science goals of the world's largest interferometer, the Square Kilometer Array Observatory (SKAO),[g] in particular with intensity mapping techniques.[43]

The MeerKAT telescope,[h] the SKAO precursor in South Africa, can be successfully exploited for 21cm intensity mapping[14,15] and has attained encouraging results.[16] In this work, we mimick observations with the MeerKAT telescope, which operates at an interesting redshift range for DE and for which real data will be available in the near future.

2. Likelihood implementation

To compute the likelihood function $\mathcal{L}(D|\boldsymbol{\alpha})$, which we assume to be a multivariate Gaussian, we need the theoretical expectations for the set of parameters $\boldsymbol{\alpha}$, describing the considered model, and the observed set of data D. To compute $\boldsymbol{\alpha}$ we extend the codes EFCAMB/ETCosmoMC and model the linear power spectrum of the 21cm signal as[35,43,44]

$$P_{21}(z, k) = \bar{T}_b^2(z)(b_{\rm HI}(z) + f(z))^2 P_{\rm m}(z, k), \qquad (2)$$

---

[g]See https://www.skatelescope.org/.
[h]See https://www.sarao.ac.za/gallery/meerkat/.

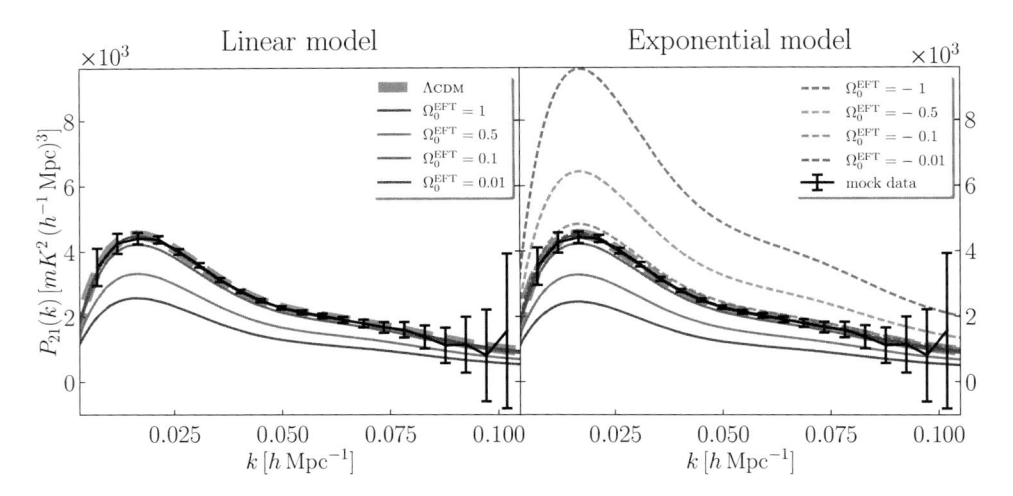

Fig. 3. Linear power spectra for the 21cm signal for ΛCDM and several *pure* EFT models, described by different values of the parameter Ω_0^{EFT}. We show theoretical predictions at redshift $z = 0.39$ for a linear (left panel) and an exponential (right panel) evolution of the function Ω_0^{EFT}. For the linear case we consider $\Omega_0^{\text{EFT}} = 0.01, 0.1, 0.5, 1$, while for the exponential $\Omega_0^{\text{EFT}} = \pm 0.01, \pm 0.1, \pm 0.5, \pm 1$. Black points with errorbars are the mock data set we construct in this work, as described in Sec. 2.

where T_b is the brightness temperature, b_{HI} is the HI bias, f is the linear growth rate and P_m is the linear matter power spectrum. We stress that the model dependence here enters through f and P_m. Our predictions for $P_{21}(z, k)$ at different redshifts are shown in Fig. 1.

Given that real data are not available yet, we construct a mock data set of forecast observations of $P_{21}(k)$. We model the errors taking into account the technical specifications of the MeerKAT telescope, while we generate central points from the theory. Our mock data set is presented in Fig. 2. Here we focus on the redshift bin $z = 0.39$, which will be measured by MeerKAT. We explore also the effects of tomography in Ref.[22].

3. Results

In this section, we present our main results. We begin by studying a ΛCDM reference scenario. Then, we study a *pure* EFT model on a ΛCDM background, where the function $\Omega^{\text{EFT}}(a)$ evolves as a linear function of the scale factor a, i.e. $\Omega^{\text{EFT}}(a) = \Omega_0^{\text{EFT}} a$. In Fig. 3, we compare theoretical predictions of $P_{21}(k)$ for different values of Ω_0^{EFT} with the mock data set we constructed. One can see that the $P_{21}(k)$ observable is sensitive to variations in Ω_0^{EFT}, thus we expect that the $P_{21}(k)$ likelihood could help in constraining such model. However, we anticipate that this single data set alone is still not powerful enough to constrain Ω^{EFT} alone. When combined with CMB data, instead, Ω_0^{EFT} is already constrained by CMB to be < 0.1 (green line),

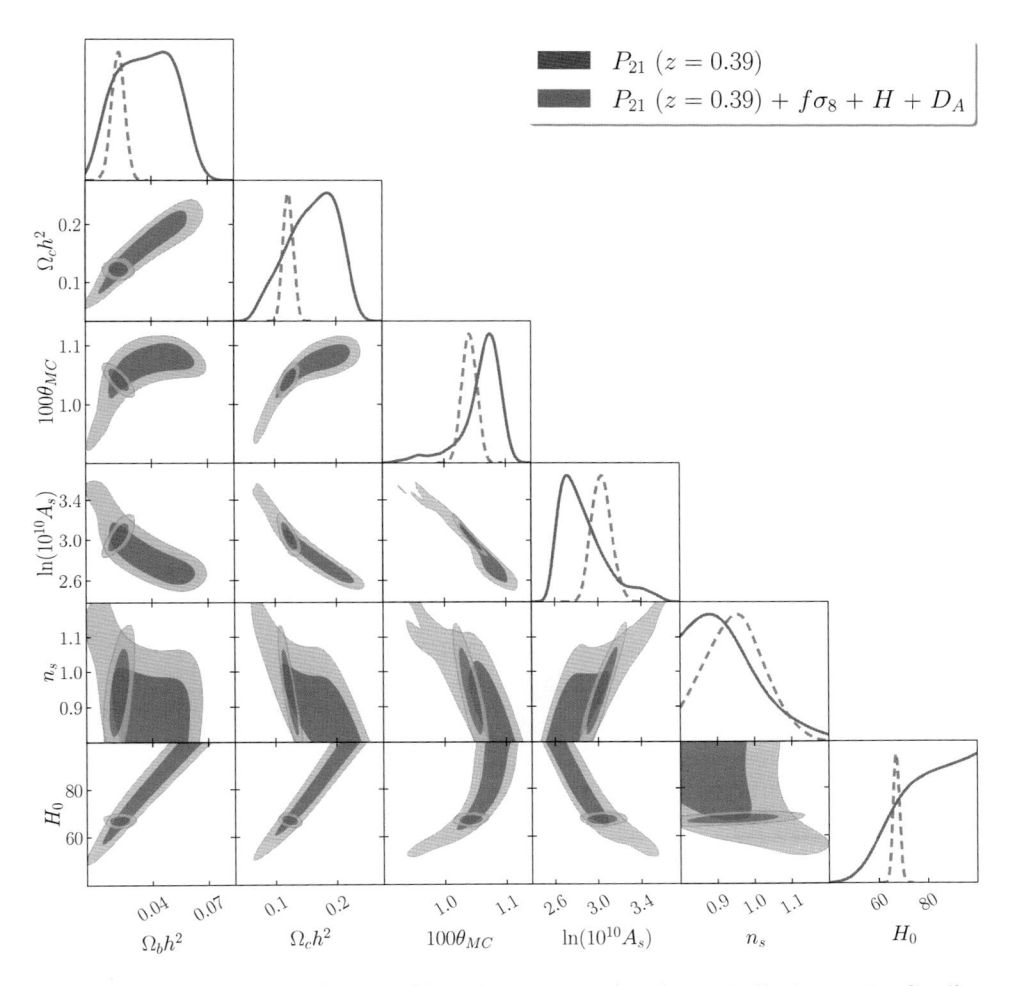

Fig. 4. Joint constraints (68% and 95% confidence regions) and marginalized posterior distributions on cosmological parameters for a ΛCDM model. Here the label $P_{21}(z = 0.39)$ stands for the 21cm power spectrum likelihood at redshift $z = 0.39$, while $f\sigma_8 + H + D_A$ represents the additional *background* likelihood computed at the same redshift $z = 0.39$. We consider the parameter τ fixed to a Planck 2018 fiducial cosmology value,[1] i.e. $\tau = 0.0543$.

therefore we will observe a small improvement in the constraining power when adding $P_{21}(k)$.

We analyse the effect of the $P_{21}(k)$ likelihood both alone and combined with CMB data. We consider the following data sets:

- *Planck 2018*: CMB data from Ref.[1], i.e. TT, TE, EE power spectra + low polarization (lowE) data + lensing;[i]

---

[i]See http://pla.esac.esa.int/pla/\#home.

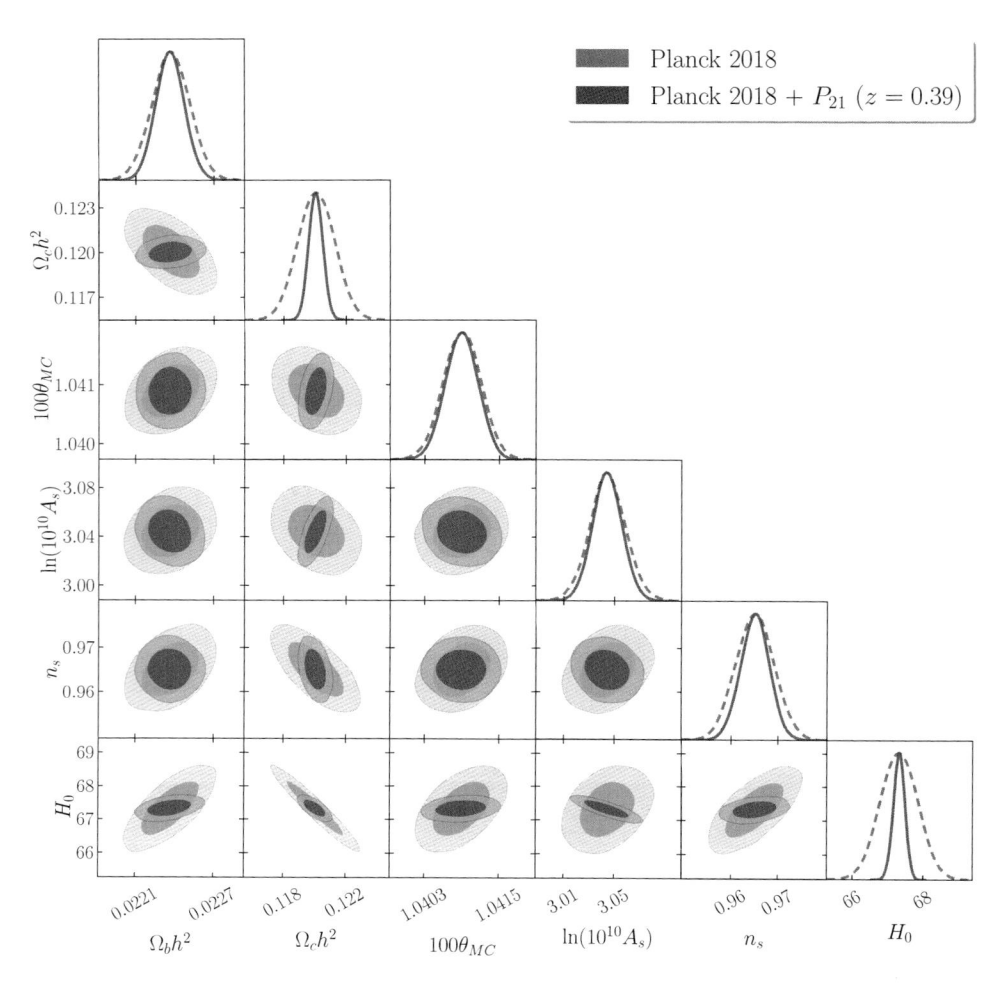

Fig. 5. Joint constraints (68% and 95% confidence regions) and marginalized posterior distributions on cosmological parameters for a ΛCDM model. Here the label Planck 2018 stands for TT, TE, EE + lowE + lensing while the label $P_{21}(z = 0.39)$ stands for the 21cm power spectrum likelihood at redshift $z = 0.39$.

Table 1. Marginalized constraints on cosmological parameters at the 68% confidence level for a ΛCDM model. Deviations in the error with respect to Planck 2018 results are shown in brackets.

Parameter	Planck 2018	+ $P_{21}(z = 0.39)$	$P_{21}(z = 0.39)$	+ $f\sigma_8 + H + D_A$
$\Omega_b h^2$	0.02237 ± 0.00014	$0.02236 \pm 0.00011\ (-24\%)$	0.038 ± 0.015	0.0226 ± 0.0035
$\Omega_c h^2$	0.1201 ± 0.0012	$0.12004 \pm 0.00046\ (-61\%)$	$0.162^{+0.050}_{-0.033}$	0.1227 ± 0.0081
n_s	0.9650 ± 0.0041	$0.9651 \pm 0.0031\ (-25\%)$	< 0.959	$0.951^{+0.072}_{-0.085}$
H_0	67.32 ± 0.53	$67.32 \pm 0.16 (-69\%)$	> 73.6	67.1 ± 1.3

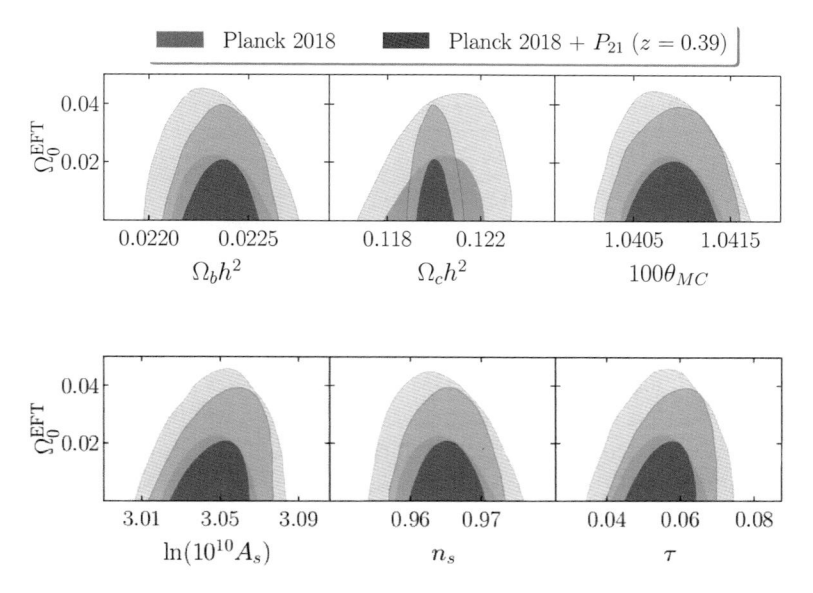

Fig. 6. Joint constraints (68% and 95% confidence regions) on cosmological and EFT parameters for a *pure* linear EFT model on a ΛCDM background. Here the label Planck 2018 stands for TT, TE, EE + lowE + lensing while the label $P_{21}(z = 0.39)$ stands for the 21cm power spectrum likelihood at redshift $z = 0.39$.

- $P_{21}(k)(z = 0.39)$: mock data set of MeerKAT forecast observations at redshift $z = 0.39$, constructed as described in Sec. 2;
- *background*: additional background and structure formation mock data sets for $f\sigma_8$, H, D_A at $z = 0.39$, inferred from higher redshift intensity mapping forecasts.[45]

For the ΛCDM case, we observe that the $P_{21}(k)$ likelihood alone has a weak constraining power on the cosmological parameters, as shown in Fig. 4. We find a strong correlation between H_0 and $\Omega_c h^2$, a feature that results to be pivotal when combining the 21cm signal data set with CMB data. The constraining power is significantly improved when we add the *background* data set. With $P_{21}(k)$ + *background* we are able to constrain the Hubble constant to $H_0 = 67.1 \pm 1.3$ km s^{-1}Mpc^{-1}, with a competitive error compared with results from other probes.[8] Combining CMB data with $P_{21}(k)$, we obtain an improvement on the errors on the cosmological parameters, as shown in Fig. 5 and Table 1. The effect is maximized for H_0 and $\Omega_c h^2$, for which we obtain a reduction on the error with respect to Planck estimate at the level of $\sim 60-70\%$. The correlation between H_0 and $\Omega_c h^2$ obtained with CMB data alone is perpendicular to the one found with $P_{21}(k)$. Therefore, combining the two data sets removes the correlation almost completely, thus significantly improving the constraints on H_0 and $\Omega_c h^2$.

Table 2. Marginalized constraints on cosmological parameters at the 68% confidence level for a *pure* linear EFT model on a ΛCDM background. Deviations in the error with respect to Planck 2018 results are shown in brackets.

Parameter	Planck 2018	$+ P_{21}(z = 0.39)$
$\Omega_b h^2$	0.02234 ± 0.00015	0.02237 ± 0.00011 (-26%)
$\Omega_c h^2$	0.1203 ± 0.0012	0.12003 ± 0.00046 (-63%)
H_0	67.21 ± 0.55	67.33 ± 0.17 (-70%)
$\Omega_0^{\rm EFT}$	< 0.0147	< 0.0135 (-11%)

As anticipated, for the beyond ΛCDM case, we find that $P_{21}(k)$ alone has a weak constraining power on the EFT parameters. Thus, here we discuss only the results for $P_{21}(k)$ combined with CMB data, which are presented in Fig. 6 and Table 2. We find that adding $P_{21}(k)$ to CMB data reduces the error on the EFT parameter $\Omega_0^{\rm EFT}$ at the level of 11%. From the 2D contours, we observe that $P_{21}(k)$ also helps in removing some of the correlation between $\Omega_0^{\rm EFT}$ and the other cosmological parameters. Moreover, the constraints we obtain are comparable with results in the literature.[20,28] We stress that opening the parameter space to EFT models does not spoil the results on the cosmological parameters described above.

4. Conclusions

In this work we extended the `EFTCAMB/EFTCosmoMC` codes by implementing a new likelihood module fully integrated with original codes, to test forecast 21cm Intensity Mapping observations. We constructed a realistic data set at $z = 0.39$ from future MeerKAT-like observation settings. We tested the impact of the $P_{21}(k)$ likelihood on DE/MG models in the EFT framework.

We find a significant improvement on the $\Omega_c h^2$, H_0 constraints, from P_{21} combined with Early Universe probes, i.e. Planck 2018 CMB data.[1] The impact of $P_{21}(k)$ on beyond ΛCDM models is at the level of 11%. Thus, from this analysis, we conclude that 21cm power spectrum observations could help in increasing our knowledge of DE. However, we believe that adding tomographic data set of $P_{21}(k)$ observations could significantly improve the constraining power on EFT parameters. We investigate this claim and further expand this analysis in Ref.[22].

Acknowledgments

The author would like to thank her supervisor Prof. Matteo Viel and her collaborators Marta Spinelli, Sandeep B. Haridasu, and Alessandra Silvestri. We thank José Fonseca, for his valuable help in the construction of the MeerKAT-like $P_{21}(k)$ mock data, and Marco Raveri for useful discussions and technical help. This work is supported by the INFN INDARK grant.

References

1. Planck 2018 results, Vi. cosmological parameters, *Astron. Astrophys.* **641**, p. A6 (2020).
2. T. M. C. Abbott *et al.*, Dark Energy Survey Year 1 Results: Constraints on Extended Cosmological Models from Galaxy Clustering and Weak Lensing, *Phys. Rev. D* **99**, p. 123505 (2019).
3. H. Hildebrandt *et al.*, KiDS-450: Cosmological parameter constraints from tomographic weak gravitational lensing, *Mon. Not. Roy. Astron. Soc.* **465**, p. 1454 (2017).
4. A. G. Riess *et al.*, Milky Way Cepheid Standards for Measuring Cosmic Distances and Application to Gaia DR2: Implications for the Hubble Constant, *Astrophys. J.* **861**, p. 126 (2018).
5. A. G. Riess, S. Casertano, W. Yuan, L. M. Macri and D. Scolnic, Large Magellanic Cloud Cepheid Standards Provide a 1% Foundation for the Determination of the Hubble Constant and Stronger Evidence for Physics beyond ΛCDM, *Astrophys. J.* **876**, p. 85 (2019).
6. K. C. Wong *et al.*, H0LiCOW – XIII. A 2.4 per cent measurement of H0 from lensed quasars: 5.3σ tension between early- and late-Universe probes, *Mon. Not. Roy. Astron. Soc.* **498**, 1420 (2020).
7. W. L. Freedman *et al.*, The Carnegie-Chicago Hubble Program. VIII. An Independent Determination of the Hubble Constant Based on the Tip of the Red Giant Branch (7 2019).
8. L. Verde, T. Treu and A. G. Riess, Tensions between the Early and the Late Universe, *Nature Astron.* **3**, p. 891 (7 2019).
9. S. M. Carroll, The Cosmological Constant, *Living Rev. Rel.* **4**, p. 1 (2001).
10. S. Weinberg, The Cosmological Constant Problem, *Rev. Mod. Phys.* **61**, 1 (1989).
11. P. Bull *et al.*, Beyond ΛCDM: Problems, solutions, and the road ahead, *Phys. Dark Univ.* **12**, 56 (2016).
12. P. G. Ferreira, Cosmological Tests of Gravity, *Ann. Rev. Astron. Astrophys.* **57**, 335 (2019).
13. M. Ishak, Testing General Relativity in Cosmology, *Living Rev. Rel.* **22**, p. 1 (2019).
14. M. G. Santos *et al.*, Cosmology from a SKA HI intensity mapping survey, *PoS* **AASKA14**, p. 019 (2015).
15. M. G. Santos *et al.*, MeerKLASS: MeerKAT Large Area Synoptic Survey (9 2017).
16. J. Wang *et al.*, HI intensity mapping with MeerKAT: Calibration pipeline for multi-dish autocorrelation observations (11 2020).
17. G. Gubitosi, F. Piazza and F. Vernizzi, The Effective Field Theory of Dark Energy, *JCAP* **02**, p. 032 (2013).
18. J. Bloomfield, É. É. Flanagan, M. Park and S. Watson, Dark energy or modified gravity? An effective field theory approach, *Journal of Cosmology and Astro-Particle Physics* **2013**, p. 010 (Aug 2013).
19. B. Hu, M. Raveri, N. Frusciante and A. Silvestri, *Effective Field Theory of Cosmic Acceleration: An implementation in CAMB*, *Phys. Rev. D* **89**, p. 103530 (2014).
20. M. Raveri, B. Hu, N. Frusciante and A. Silvestri, *Effective Field Theory of Cosmic Acceleration: Constraining dark energy with CMB data*, *Phys. Rev. D* **90**, p. 043513 (2014).
21. B. Hu, M. Raveri, N. Frusciante and A. Silvestri, *EFTCAMB/EFTCosmoMC: Numerical Notes v3.0* (5 2014).
22. M. Berti, M. Spinelli, B. S. Haridasu, M. Viel and A. Silvestri, Constraining beyond ΛCDM models with 21cm intensity mapping forecast observations combined with latest CMB data (9 2021).

23. P. Creminelli, M. A. Luty, A. Nicolis and L. Senatore, Starting the Universe: Stable Violation of the Null Energy Condition and Non-standard Cosmologies, *JHEP* **12**, p. 080 (2006).
24. C. Cheung, P. Creminelli, A. L. Fitzpatrick, J. Kaplan and L. Senatore, The Effective Field Theory of Inflation, *JHEP* **03**, p. 014 (2008).
25. A. Lewis, A. Challinor and A. Lasenby, *Efficient computation of CMB anisotropies in closed FRW models*, Astrophys. J. **538**, 473 (2000).
26. A. Lewis and S. Bridle, *Cosmological parameters from CMB and other data: A Monte Carlo approach*, Phys. Rev. D **66**, p. 103511 (2002).
27. A. Lewis, Efficient sampling of fast and slow cosmological parameters, *Phys. Rev. D* **87**, p. 103529 (2013).
28. P. . results, XIV. Dark energy and modified gravity, *Astron. Astrophys.* **594**, p. A14 (2016).
29. N. Frusciante and L. Perenon, Effective field theory of dark energy: A review, *Phys. Rept.* **857**, 1 (2020).
30. S. Bharadwaj, B. B. Nath, B. B. Nath and S. K. Sethi, Using HI to probe large scale structures at z $\sim$ 3, *J. Astrophys. Astron.* **22**, p. 21 (2001).
31. S. Bharadwaj and S. K. Sethi, HI Fluctuations at Large Redshifts. 1. Visibility correlation, *J. Astrophys. Astron.* **22**, p. 293 (2001).
32. R. A. Battye, R. D. Davies and J. Weller, Neutral hydrogen surveys for high redshift galaxy clusters and proto-clusters, *Mon. Not. Roy. Astron. Soc.* **355**, 1339 (2004).
33. M. McQuinn, O. Zahn, M. Zaldarriaga, L. Hernquist and S. R. Furlanetto, Cosmological parameter estimation using 21 cm radiation from the epoch of reionization, *Astrophys. J.* **653**, 815 (2006).
34. E. D. Kovetz et al., Line-Intensity Mapping: 2017 Status Report (9 2017).
35. F. Villaescusa-Navarro et al., *Ingredients for 21 cm Intensity Mapping*, Astrophys. J. **866**, p. 135 (2018).
36. T.-C. Chang, U.-L. Pen, J. B. Peterson and P. McDonald, Baryon Acoustic Oscillation Intensity Mapping as a Test of Dark Energy, *Phys. Rev. Lett.* **100**, p. 091303 (2008).
37. A. Hall, C. Bonvin and A. Challinor, Testing General Relativity with 21-cm intensity mapping, *Phys. Rev. D* **87**, p. 064026 (2013).
38. N. A. Lima, V. Smer-Barreto and L. Lombriser, Constraints on decaying early modified gravity from cosmological observations, *Phys. Rev. D* **94**, p. 083507 (2016).
39. P. Brax, S. Clesse and A.-C. Davis, Signatures of Modified Gravity on the 21-cm Power Spectrum at Reionisation, *JCAP* **01**, p. 003 (2013).
40. G. Zhao, D. Bacon, R. Maartens, M. Santos and A. Raccanelli, Model-independent constraints on dark energy and modified gravity with the SKA, *PoS* **AASKA14**, p. 165 (2015).
41. C. Heneka and L. Amendola, General Modified Gravity With 21cm Intensity Mapping: Simulations and Forecast, *JCAP* **10**, p. 004 (2018).
42. C. B. V. Dash and T. G. Sarkar, Constraining dark energy using the cross correlations of weak lensing with post-reionization probes of neutral hydrogen, *JCAP* **02**, p. 016 (2021).
43. S. C. SWG, *Cosmology with Phase 1 of the Square Kilometre Array: Red Book 2018: Technical specifications and performance forecasts*, Publ. Astron. Soc. Austral. **37**, p. e007 (2020).
44. N. Kaiser, *Clustering in real space and in redshift space*, Mon. Not. Roy. Astron. Soc. **227**, 1 (1987).
45. A. Obuljen, E. Castorina, F. Villaescusa-Navarro and M. Viel, High-redshift post-reionization cosmology with 21cm intensity mapping, *JCAP* **05**, p. 004 (2018).

Entropy and irreversible processes in gravity and cosmology

Llorenç Espinosa-Portalés* and Juan García-Bellido[†]

Instituto de Física Teórica UAM-CSIC, Universidad Autónoma de Madrid
Cantoblanco, 28049 Madrid, Spain
* E-mail: llorenc.espinosa@uam.es
[†] E-mail: juan.garciabellido@uam.es

General Relativity is *a priori* a theory invariant under time reversal. Its integration with the laws of thermodynamics allows for a formulation of non-equilibrium phenomena in gravity and the introduction of an arrow of time, i.e. the the breaking of such invariance. Even though most of the evolution of the universe takes place in local thermal equilibrium, the effects of irreversible processes on the expansion via entropic forces may be phenomenologically relevant. We review our previous work on the covariant formulation of non-equilibrium thermodynamics in General Relativity and the proposal to explain the recent cosmic acceleration from it.

Keywords: General Relativity, thermodynamics, non-equilibrium phenomena, entropic forces, cosmic acceleration.

1. Introduction

General Relativity is an extremely successful physical theory. More than a century after its formulation, its predictions continue to be valid at all probed scales, albeit an extension at short scales will be required in order to obtain a UV-complete quantum theory of gravity and resolve space-time singularities.

Thermodynamics is an even older discipline. Its fundamental laws seem to resist the passage of time and are still of great relevance today. On the one hand, thermodynamics may help in building the bridge between classical and quantum gravity, as the laws of black hole thermodynamics point towards the existence of a microphysical description of gravity yet to be understood.

On the other hand, the second law of thermodynamics, i.e. the growth of entropy, dictates the sign of the arrow of time. Physical laws are usually invariant under time inversion. The increase in entropy with time in out-of-equilibrium phenomena, however, allows one to distinguish the future-directed from the past directed description of a physical process.

There lacks a consistent and rigorous integration between General Relativity and the laws of thermodynamics. Understanding the very notion of the arrow of time is of particular interest for cosmology. In section 2 we argue for the need of going beyond reversible cosmology. This can be achieved for any space-time metric using variational techniques.[1] We review our main results in this new approach to non-equilibrium thermodynamics in General Relativity and present them in sections 3 to 6.

The growth of entropy associated to the causal horizon in open inflation scenarios may explain the current accelerated expansion of the universe within the general relativistic entropic acceleration (GREA) theory.[2] We briefly describe how this mechanism works in section 7 and finish with our conclusions.

2. Reversible cosmology

Let us begin the study of the problem of reversibility in gravity and cosmology by reviewing a prototypic case of reversible gravitational system: a homogeneous and isotropic universe. It is described by the Friedmann-Lemaître-Robertson-Walker (FLRW) metric

$$ds^2 = -dt^2 + a(t)^2 \left(\frac{dr^2}{1-kr^2} + r^2 d\Omega_2^2 \right), \tag{1}$$

where $a(t)$ is the scale factor, $k = -1, 0, 1$ is the curvature parameter corresponding to, respectively, an open, flat and closed universe; and $d\Omega_2^2$ is the solid angle element. This space-time is filled with a perfect fluid, described by the stress-energy tensor

$$T_{\mu\nu} = (\rho + p) u_\mu u_\nu + p g_{\mu\nu}, \tag{2}$$

where ρ and p are, respectively, the density and pressure of the fluid. The Einstein field equations for this metric and matter content deliver the dynamics for the scale factor, the well-known Friedmann equations

$$H^2 + \frac{k}{a^2} = \frac{8\pi G}{3} \rho, \quad \frac{\ddot{a}}{a} = -\frac{4\pi G}{3} (\rho + 3p), \tag{3}$$

where $H = \dot{a}/a$ is the Hubble parameter. There is a constraint on the stress-energy tensor due to the Einstein field equations and the Bianchi identities, namely its covariant conservation $D_\mu T^{\mu\nu} = 0$. From this constraint one can derive the continuity equation

$$\dot{\rho} + 3H(\rho + p) = 0. \tag{4}$$

However, one can also derive this equation from the second law of thermodynamics. Indeed, changes in entropy are related to changes in internal energy and work $TdS = \delta U + \delta W$. If we apply this to a region of fixed comoving volume $a(t)^3$ we get

$$T \frac{dS}{dt} = \frac{d}{dt}(\rho a^3) + p \frac{d}{dt}(a^3). \tag{5}$$

If the expansion of the universe is reversible, we can set the LHS to 0 and recover the continuity equation. However, this is only true in thermodynamical equilibrium and, in general, entropy is a monotonically increasing function of time. Most of the expansion history of the universe is indeed adiabatic. However, it is out-of-equilibrium at certain key points such as (p)reheating, phase transitions or gravitational collapse. Allowing for a time-varying entropy implies the addition of a term in the continuity equation

$$\dot{\rho} + 3H(\rho + p) = \frac{T\dot{S}}{a^3}. \tag{6}$$

Combining this with the first Friedmann equation we obtain a modified, non-equilibrium second Friedmann equation

$$\frac{\ddot{a}}{a} = -\frac{4\pi G}{3}\left(\rho + 3p - \frac{T\dot{S}}{a^3 H}\right).\tag{7}$$

In principle, this evolution equation does not seem to be compatible with the Einstein field equations. In order to achieve that, the laws of thermodynamics need to be rigorously incorporated into the computation of the equations of motion. This can be achieved by applying the variational formalism of non-equilibrium thermodynamics, developed in another context by Gay-Balmaz and Yoshimura,[3,4] to General Relativity.

3. Entropic forces in mechanics and field theory

Entropic forces emerge naturally in any physical system out of equilibrium. They are a consequence of the coarse-graining of physical degrees of freedom and the laws of thermodynamics, which impose entropy to be a monotonically increasing function of time. This breaks time reversibility.

The dynamics of the coarse-grained degrees of freedom is unknown or ignored and so they do not appear in the action of the physical system. It would seem that a variational treatment of an out-of-equilibrium system is not possible. However, both the extremal-action principle and the second law of thermodynamics can be merged consistently by imposing the latter as a constrain on the variational problem defined by the action.[3,4] On the other hand, the first law of thermodynamics is obtained from the symmetries of the problem.

3.1. *Entropic forces in mechanics*

Let us start by reviewing the emergence of entropic forces in a mechanical system. Consider the action

$$\mathcal{S} = \int dt\, L(q, \dot{q}, S),\tag{8}$$

where the Lagrangian depends on the generalized coordinate $q(t)$, its time derivative $\dot{q}(t)$ and the entropy $S(t)$. The variation of the action gives

$$\delta\mathcal{S} = \int dt \left(\frac{\delta L}{\delta q}\delta q + \frac{\partial L}{\partial S}\delta S\right).\tag{9}$$

Setting $\delta\mathcal{S} = 0$ defines the variational problem. In order to enforce the second law of thermodynamics, we need to impose the variational constraint

$$\frac{\partial L}{\partial S}\delta S = f\delta q,\tag{10}$$

which simply states the relationship between variations of the entropy and the generalized coordinate. If we plug this in the variation of the action, then we can readily obtain the equations of motion

$$\frac{\delta L}{\delta q} = \frac{\partial L}{\partial q} - \frac{d}{dt}\left(\frac{\partial L}{\partial \dot{q}}\right) = -f, \qquad (11)$$

which is the Euler-Lagrange equation modified by the addition of the entropic force f. In order to know its precise form, we need to impose as well the phenomenological constraint, which is obtained by formally replacing the variations with time derivatives

$$\frac{\partial L}{\partial S}\dot{S} = f\dot{q}. \qquad (12)$$

Note that usually temperature can be introduced as

$$T = -\frac{\partial L}{\partial S} > 0 \qquad (13)$$

providing a clearer meaning to the variational and phenomenological constraint.

The imposition of the constraints and the emergence of an entropic force break the symmetry under time inversion. First, note that formally the Euler-Lagrange equation is invariant under the $t \to -t$ transformation, even with a non-vanishing entropic force. Next, the positiveness of the temperature and the change of entropy imposes $f\dot{q} < 0$. The entropic force has qualities of a generalized friction, as it opposes the coordinate velocity. Now, if one performs time inversion, this sign constraint becomes $f\dot{q} > 0$, as the temperature remains positive but entropy decreases with time. Before solving the equations of motion, $\dot{q}$ is still a degree of freedom and, thus, one must conclude a flip in the sign of f, which flips the overall sign of the Euler-Lagrange equation. Hence, one concludes that the emergence of an entropic force breaks symmetry under time reversal. The evolution of the system becomes irreversible.

3.2. *Entropic forces in classical field theory*

The extension of the variational formalism of non-equilibrium thermodynamics to the continuum is somewhat involved. We present a short-cut derivation that relies on the introduction of an additional constraint. We refer the reader to the appendix of Ref. 1 to check its equivalence with the full variational derivation originally presented in Ref. 4.

The action of a scalar field on Minkowski space-time contains now a dependency on a scalar function $s(t, \vec{x})$ that encodes information related to coarse-grained degrees of freedom

$$\mathcal{S} = \int d^4x \, \mathcal{L}\left(\phi, \partial_\mu \phi, s\right). \qquad (14)$$

In a similar fashion as before, the extremal-action principle needs to be supplemented by a variational constraint

$$\frac{\partial \mathcal{L}}{\partial s}\delta s = f\delta\phi, \qquad (15)$$

so that the equation of motion becomes

$$\frac{\delta \mathcal{L}}{\delta \phi} = \frac{\partial \mathcal{L}}{\partial \phi} - \partial_\mu \frac{\partial \mathcal{L}}{\partial \partial_\mu \phi} = -f, \tag{16}$$

which is nothing but the Euler-Lagrange equation of a scalar field with a new term of entropic origin. As before, one can usually introduce a temperature as

$$T = -\frac{\partial \mathcal{L}}{\partial s} > 0 \tag{17}$$

and we would like to interpret s as the entropy density. However, due to spatial fluxes entropy does not need to necessarily increase locally and, thus, the constraint would not have a fixed sign. Before proceeding, we inspect the corresponding phenomenological constraint

$$\frac{\partial \mathcal{L}}{\partial s} \partial_0 s = f \partial_0 \phi. \tag{18}$$

Instead, we interpret δs and $\partial_0 s$ as local entropy production and introduce a new function s_{tot} which is the actual entropy density and whose changes δs_{tot} and $\partial_0 s_{\text{tot}}$ are indeed total local changes of the entropy density. Both are related as

$$\partial_0 s = \partial_0 s_{\text{tot}} - \partial_i j_s^i, \tag{19}$$

where j_s^i is the entropy flux. This latter equation is an additional constraint we impose for the variational formalism to be consistent. Now one can check that $f \partial_0 \phi < 0$ and time reversibility is broken by the same argument used in the mechanics example.

3.3. *Entropic forces in presence of additional symmetries*

The generalization of the above formalism to higher order tensors or to representations of some internal symmetry group is straightforward. Let us consider a field tensor z of contravariant rank r, which is also in some representation of an internal symmetry labelled by an index A. Then one builds the variational constraint as

$$\frac{\partial \mathcal{L}}{\partial s} \delta s = f_{A;\mu_1,\ldots \mu_r} \delta z_A^{\mu_1,\ldots \mu_r}, \tag{20}$$

which delivers the equation of motion

$$\frac{\delta \mathcal{L}}{\delta z_A^{\mu_1,\ldots \mu_r}} = -f_{A;\mu_1,\ldots \mu_r}. \tag{21}$$

4. Entropic forces in General Relativity

The previous discussion makes us ready to study entropic forces in General Relativity. However, with the introduction of a dynamical space-time the very notion of time evolution becomes non-trivial. As we will see shortly, it is possible to obtain a modification of entropic origin to Einstein's field equation in the Lagrangian formulation of General Relativity. Its proper interpretation will require, nevertheless, the use of the Hamiltonian formalism.

4.1. Lagrangian formulation

Let us consider the Einstein-Hilbert action plus a matter term

$$\mathcal{S} = \frac{1}{2\kappa} \int d^4x \sqrt{-g} R + \int d^4x \mathcal{L}_m(g_{\mu\nu}, s), \tag{22}$$

where $\kappa = 8\pi G$ is the gravitational coupling and we allow for the dependence of the matter Lagrangian on a function $s(t, \vec{x})$, which will have a similar interpretation to the one presented in the previous section. The extremal-action principle is supplemented by the variational constraint.

$$\frac{\partial \mathcal{L}_m}{\partial s} = \frac{1}{2}\sqrt{-g} f_{\mu\nu} \delta g^{\mu\nu}. \tag{23}$$

From the extremal-action principle and the variational constraint we obtain the modified Einstein's field equations

$$R_{\mu\nu} - \frac{1}{2} g_{\mu\nu} R = \kappa \left(T_{\mu\nu} - f_{\mu\nu} \right), \tag{24}$$

where there is an additional term $f_{\mu\nu}$ of entropic origin. In order to obtain an expression for this term and to check the breaking of symmetry under time inversion we need to work in the Hamiltonian formulation of General Relativity.

4.2. Hamiltonian formulation

General Relativity admits a Hamiltonian formulation in the Arnowitt-Deser-Misner (ADM) formalism. Space-time is foliated in constant time hypersurfaces with normal unit vector n^μ, being the 4-metric split as

$$g_{\mu\nu} = h_{\mu\nu} - n_\mu n_\nu, \tag{25}$$

where $h_{\mu\nu}$ is the 3-metric induced on the hypersurfaces. Analogously, one can parametrize the 4-metric in terms of the 3-metric h_{ij} and the lapse and shift functions N and N^i

$$ds^2 = -(N dt)^2 + h_{ij}(dx^i + N^i dt)(dx^j + N^j dt). \tag{26}$$

Greek indices run from 0 to 3, while Latin ones do from 1 to 3 and are raised and lowered by h_{ij}. The normal vector can be written as

$$n_\mu = (-N, 0, 0, 0). \tag{27}$$

Note that h_{ij} is the purely spatial part of $h_{\mu\nu}$ and is also the pull-back of $g_{\mu\nu}$ onto the hypersurface.

The Einstein-Hilbert action for this parametrization of the metric is given by the following gravitational Lagrangian:

$$\mathcal{L}_G = \sqrt{-g} R = \frac{1}{2\kappa} N \sqrt{h} \left({}^{(3)}R + K_{ij} K^{ij} - K^2 \right), \tag{28}$$

where K_{ij} is the extrinsic curvature of the 3-hypersurface Σ and is given by the Lie derivative along the normal vector n

$$K_{ij} = \frac{1}{2} \pounds_n h_{ij} = \frac{1}{2N} \left(\partial_0 h_{ij} - \nabla_i N_j - \nabla_j N_i \right), \tag{29}$$

where ∇ denotes the covariant derivative on Σ with respect to the 3-metric h_{ij}. Its trace and traceless part are:

$$\begin{aligned} K &= h^{ij} K_{ij} = \frac{1}{N} \left(\partial_0 \ln \sqrt{h} - \nabla_i N^i \right) \\ \bar{K}_{ij} &= K_{ij} - \frac{1}{3} K h_{ij} . \end{aligned} \tag{30}$$

Unlike the intrinsic curvature, described by the Riemann tensor $R^\rho_{\mu\nu\lambda}$ and its contractions, the extrinsic curvature is a quantity that depends on the embedding of a surface in a larger manifold.

We are now ready to introduce the Hamiltonian formulation of the theory. Note that the only quantity whose time derivative appears in the gravitational Lagrangian is the 3-spatial metric h_{ij} and, thus, it is the only dynamical or propagating d.o.f. Correspondingly, one defines its conjugate momentum as:

$$\Pi^{ij} = \frac{\partial \mathcal{L}_G}{\partial \dot{h}_{ij}} = \sqrt{h} \left(K^{ij} - K h^{ij} \right) . \tag{31}$$

With this, the gravitational Lagrangian can be rewritten as

$$\begin{aligned} \mathcal{L}_G &= N \sqrt{h} \, {}^{(3)}R - \frac{N}{\sqrt{h}} \left(\Pi_{ij} \Pi^{ij} - \frac{1}{2} \Pi^2 \right) - 2 \Pi^{ij} \nabla_i N_j \\ &= \Pi^{ij} \dot{h}_{ij} - N \mathcal{H} - N_i \mathcal{H}^i - 2 \nabla_i \left(\Pi^{ij} N_j \right) , \end{aligned} \tag{32}$$

where $\Pi = h_{ij} \Pi^{ij}$ and we introduced the functions:

$$\begin{aligned} \mathcal{H} &= -\sqrt{h} \, {}^{(3)}R + \frac{1}{\sqrt{h}} \left(\Pi_{ij} \Pi^{ij} - \frac{1}{2} \Pi^2 \right) \\ \mathcal{H}^i &= -2 \nabla_j \left(h^{-1/2} \Pi^{ij} \right) . \end{aligned} \tag{33}$$

Since N and N_i are not dynamical variables, they merely enter the gravitational Lagrangian as Lagrange multipliers. One defines the gravitational Hamiltonian as:

$$\begin{aligned} \mathcal{H}_G &= \Pi^{ij} \dot{h}_{ij} - \mathcal{L}_G \\ &= N \mathcal{H} + N_i \mathcal{H}^i + \nabla_i \left(\Pi^{ij} N_j \right) , \end{aligned} \tag{34}$$

with the Hamiltonian and momentum constraints:

$$\begin{aligned} \frac{\delta \mathcal{H}_G}{\delta N} &= \mathcal{H} = 0 \\ \frac{\delta \mathcal{H}_G}{\delta N_i} &= \mathcal{H}^i = 0 . \end{aligned} \tag{35}$$

The Hamiltonian evolution equations are obtained from the variations of the action with respect to the metric and conjugate momentum

$$\delta \mathcal{S} = \int d^4x \left[\left(-\dot{\Pi}^{ij} - \frac{\delta \mathcal{H}_G}{\delta h_{ij}} - \kappa N \sqrt{h} \tilde{f}^{ij} + 2\kappa \frac{\partial \mathcal{L}_m}{\partial h_{ij}} \right) \delta h_{ij} + \left(\dot{h}_{ij} - \frac{\delta \mathcal{H}_G}{\delta \Pi^{ij}} \right) \delta \Pi^{ij} \right], \tag{36}$$

where the variational constraint

$$\frac{\partial \mathcal{L}_m}{\partial s} \delta s = -\frac{1}{2} N \sqrt{h} \tilde{f}^{ij} \delta h_{ij} \tag{37}$$

was already implemented. Note that the minus sign arises from

$$\frac{\partial h_{ij}}{\partial h^{kl}} = -\frac{1}{2} \left(h_{ik} h_{jl} + h_{il} h_{jk} \right) \tag{38}$$

and that $\tilde{f}_{ij}$ is the pull-back of $f_{\mu\nu}$ onto the hypersurfaces. By setting the variation to 0 we obtain the two Hamilton equations

$$\begin{aligned} \frac{\delta \mathcal{H}_G}{\delta h_{ij}} &= -\dot{\Pi}^{ij} - \kappa N \sqrt{h} f^{ij} + 2\kappa \frac{\partial \mathcal{L}_m}{\partial h_{ij}} \\ \frac{\delta \mathcal{H}_G}{\delta \Pi^{ij}} &= \dot{h}_{ij}, \end{aligned} \tag{39}$$

which completes the derivation of the entropic modification to the gravitational equations of motion in the Hamiltonian formulation.

The tensor $\tilde{f}_{ij}$ can be obtained from the phenomenological constraint, which can now be stated rigorously. In the ADM formalism, a well-defined notion of time evolution is given by the flow along the normal vector n^μ. Hence, the time derivative is generalized to the Lie derivative along n^μ. Then the phenomenological constraint is given by

$$\frac{\partial \mathcal{L}}{\partial s} \pounds_n s = \frac{1}{2} N \sqrt{h} \tilde{f}_{ij} \pounds_n h^{ij}, \tag{40}$$

where growth in entropy by local processes is related to total entropy density growth by

$$\pounds_n s = \pounds_n s^{tot} - \nabla_i j_s^i. \tag{41}$$

Entropy produced locally is expected to grow over time, i.e. with the flow along the hypersurfaces, in compliance with the second law of thermodynamics. This completes the variational formulation of entropic forces in General Relativity.

4.3. *The Raychauduri equation*

Let us explore an immediate dynamical consequence of the inclusion of entropic forces, namely its effect on a congruence of worldlines with tangent vector n^μ. The congruence is then characterized by the tensor

$$\Theta_{\mu\nu} = D_\nu n_\mu = \frac{1}{3} \Theta h_{\mu\nu} + \sigma_{\mu\nu} + \omega_{\mu\nu} - a_\mu n_\nu, \tag{42}$$

where θ is the expansion rate of the congruence, $\sigma_{\mu\nu}$ is its shear or symmetric traceless part and $\omega_{\mu\nu}$ is its vorticity or antisymmetric part. If the worldline is not a geodesic, then the congruence suffers an acceleration given by:

$$a_\mu = n^\nu D_\nu n_\mu \,. \tag{43}$$

One can compute the Lie derivative of the expansion of the congruence along its tangent vector and find the Raychauduri equation[5]:

$$\pounds_n \Theta = -\frac{1}{3}\Theta^2 - \sigma_{\mu\nu}\sigma^{\mu\nu} + \omega_{\mu\nu}\omega^{\mu\nu} - R_{\mu\nu}n^\mu n^\nu + D_\mu a^\mu \,. \tag{44}$$

Let us perform the standard analysis of the sign of this equation. It is clear that $\sigma_{\mu\nu}\sigma^{\mu\nu} > 0$ and $\Theta^2 > 0$. On the other hand, if the congruence is chosen to be orthogonal to the spatial hypersurfaces, as we have been considering, then the vorticity vanishes $\omega_{\mu\nu} = 0$. Lastly, it is left to consider the term $R_{\mu\nu}n^\nu n^\nu$, which we can rewrite with the help of the field equations:

$$R_{\mu\nu}n^\mu n^\nu = 8\pi G \left(T_{\mu\nu}n^\mu n^\nu + \frac{1}{2}T - f_{\mu\nu}n^\mu n^\nu - \frac{1}{2}f \right) \,. \tag{45}$$

If the strong energy condition is satisfied, then

$$T_{\mu\nu}n^\mu n^\nu \geq -\frac{1}{2}T \tag{46}$$

and, in the absence of intrinsic acceleration, $a_\mu = 0$, we can establish the bound:

$$\pounds_n \Theta + \frac{1}{3}\Theta^2 \leq 8\pi G \left(f_{\mu\nu}n^\mu n^\nu + \frac{1}{2}f \right) \,. \tag{47}$$

For a vanishing entropic force $f_{\mu\nu} = 0$, this means that an expanding congruence cannot indefinitely sustain its divergence and will eventually recollapse. On the contrary, a positive and sufficiently large entropic contribution can avoid such recollapse. This may become relevant for an expanding universe, but also to generic gravitational collapse and the singularity theorems.[6–8]

5. Sources of entropy

A main ingredient in the variational formulation of non-equilibrium thermodynamics in General Relativity is the inclusion of entropy at the Lagrangian level and the derivation of a notion of temperature from it. In this section we present two relevant examples: hydrodynamical matter, which is a prototypical case, and horizons.

5.1. *Entropy from hydrodynamical matter*

A classical fluid is the simplest matter content that can be considered in General Relativity and it is of particular relevance in Cosmology. Without paying attention to microphysical details, the Lagrangian of hydrodynamical matter can be written as

$$\mathcal{L}_m = -\sqrt{-g}\rho(g_{\mu\nu}, s) \,, \tag{48}$$

the temperature being then simply given by

$$T = -\frac{1}{\sqrt{-g}}\frac{\partial \mathcal{L}_m}{\partial s} = \frac{\partial \rho}{\partial s}. \tag{49}$$

This is analogous to the case of a mechanical system, where the Lagrangian is generically given by a kinetic and a potential energy

$$L = E_K(q, \dot{q}) - U(q, S) \tag{50}$$

and temperature can be defined as

$$T = \frac{\partial L}{\partial S} = -\frac{\partial U}{\partial S}. \tag{51}$$

Thus, the energy density of a fluid can be readily interpreted as the thermodynamic internal energy.

5.2. *Entropy from gravity and horizons*

Gravity itself has thermodynamical features. It is known since the discovery of the laws of black hole mechanics and their promotion to laws of black hole thermodynamics, allowed by the introduction of Bekenstein entropy and Hawking temperature. We propose to include the entropy associated with a horizon $\mathcal{H}$ by extending the Einstein-Hilbert actions with surface terms of Gibbons-Hawking-York (GHY) type

$$S_{GHY} = \frac{1}{8\pi G}\int_{\mathcal{H}} d^3 y \sqrt{h}\, K\,, \tag{52}$$

where h is the determinant of the induced 3-metric on the horizon and K is the trace of its extrinsic curvature. Definitions are analogous to the ones used in the ADM formalism, but we stress that here the hypersurface of interest is a horizon and not constant-time hypersurfaces.

From the thermodynamic point of view, the GHY term contributes to the internal energy of the system. Hence, it can be rewritten as a function of the temperature and entropy of the horizon

$$S_{GHY} = -\int dt\, N(t)\, TS\,. \tag{53}$$

We have kept the lapse function $N(t)$, to indicate that the variation of the total action with respect to it will generate a Hamiltonian constraint with an entropy term together with the ordinary matter/energy terms. In order to illustrate this, let us now compute the GHY for the event horizon of a Schwarzschild black hole.

The space-time of a Schwarzschild black hole of mass M is described by the static metric

$$ds^2 = -\left(1 - \frac{2GM}{r}\right)dt^2 + \left(1 - \frac{2GM}{r}\right)^{-1}dr^2 + r^2 d\Omega_2^2\,. \tag{54}$$

We foliate it with spherical hypersurfaces, i.e. their intersection with constant time hypersurfaces is a 2-sphere around the origin of coordinates. The corresponding normal vector is

$$n = -\sqrt{1 - \frac{2GM}{r}}\partial_r\,. \tag{55}$$

With this, the trace of the extrinsic curvature for such a sphere scaled by the metric determinant is

$$\sqrt{h}K = (3GM - 2r)\sin\theta\,. \tag{56}$$

Integrating over the angular coordinates and setting the 2-sphere at the event horizon, i.e. $r = 2GM$, and restoring for a moment $\hbar$ and c, the GHY becomes

$$S_{GHY} = -\frac{1}{2}\int dt\, Mc^2 = -\int dt\, T_{BH}S_{BH}\,, \tag{57}$$

where T_{BH} is the Hawking temperature and S_{BH} is the Bekenstein entropy of the Schwarzschild black hole:

$$T_{BH} = \frac{\hbar c^3}{8\pi GM}\,, \quad S_{BH} = \frac{Ac^3}{4G\hbar} = \frac{4\pi GM^2}{\hbar c}\,. \tag{58}$$

This favors the interpretation of the GHY term of a horizon as a contribution to the internal energy in the thermodynamic sense.

6. Irreversible cosmology

We derived in section 4 a powerful, generic tool to describe non-equilibrium thermodynamic effects in gravity. In the Hamiltonian formulation of General Relativity it is possible to obtain the modified equations of motion and rigorously impose the time-evolution of the entropy as dictated by the second law of thermodynamics.

In section 2 we motivated the study of these phenomena by our interest in understanding the dynamics of irreversible cosmology and justifying its equations of motion. One can obtain them using the Hamilton equations.[1] Here, however, we present a slightly different approach. Due to the symmetries of the FLRW universe, homogeneity and isotropy, there is a preferred slicing and time evolution is well-defined even at the Lagrangian level. Therefore, we can obtain the equations of non-equilibrium cosmology by imposing these symmetries, i.e. making an ansatz for the metric

$$ds^2 = -N(t)^2 dt^2 + a(t)^2\left(\frac{dr^2}{1-kr^2} + r^2 d\Omega_2^2\right)\,, \tag{59}$$

where the lapse function $N(t)$ accounts for the freedom in choosing the time coordinate, i.e. the symmetry under $t \to f(t)$. The Ricci scalar associated to this metric is

$$R = \frac{6}{a^2}\left(\frac{a\ddot{a}}{N^2} + \frac{\dot{a}^2}{N^2} + k\right)\,. \tag{60}$$

Let us stress that this result is imposed by symmetry, not dynamics. Without loss of generality, we can restrict the action to a region of comoving volume 1 and write it as

$$S = \int dt\, L = \frac{3}{8\pi G} \int dt\, Na \left(\frac{a\ddot{a}}{N^2} + \frac{\dot{a}^2}{N^2} + k \right) + \int dt\, Na^3 \mathcal{L}_m(N, a, S). \tag{61}$$

Effectively, this action describes a mechanical system, for the scale factor $a(t)$ has no spatial dependency and we got rid of the integral over spatial coordinates. The first term can be rewritten using integration by parts in order to get only terms with at most the first derivative of a

$$S = \frac{3}{8\pi G} \int dt\, Na \left(-\frac{\dot{a}^2}{N^2} + k \right) + \int dt\, Na^3 \mathcal{L}_m(N, a, S). \tag{62}$$

The variational constraint is here given by the usual expression for a mechanical system

$$\frac{\partial L}{\partial S} \delta S = f \delta a. \tag{63}$$

The Hamiltonian of the system is

$$H = \dot{a}\frac{\partial L}{\partial \dot{a}} - L = \frac{3}{8\pi G} \left(-\frac{\dot{a}^2 a}{N} - kaN \right) - Na^3 \mathcal{L}_m. \tag{64}$$

For an arbitrary lapse function $N(t)$ this can be rewritten as

$$H = N^2 a^3 \frac{\partial \mathcal{L}_m}{\partial N}, \tag{65}$$

which gives the Hamiltonian constraint of the system. On the other hand, the dynamics is obtained from the equation of motion for a

$$\frac{\delta L}{\delta a} = -f. \tag{66}$$

Let us now consider the matter Lagrangian to be that of a perfect fluid, i.e.

$$\mathcal{L}_m = -\rho(a, S). \tag{67}$$

Its stress-energy tensor is given in terms of the density ρ and pressure p by

$$T^{\mu\nu} = (\rho + p)u^{\mu\nu} + pg^{\mu\nu} \tag{68}$$

and $u^m u = (N, 0, 0, 0)$ is the unit vector tangent to a comoving observer. Pressure is then obtained as

$$p = \frac{a^2}{3} T^{ij} \delta_{ij} = -\frac{1}{2a^4} \frac{\partial a^3 \rho}{\partial a}. \tag{69}$$

Using the expressions for ρ and p and rearranging the terms in the Hamiltonian constraint and the equation of motion for $a(t)$ we arrive at the modified Friedmann equations

$$\left(\frac{\dot{a}}{a}\right)^2 + \frac{k}{a^2} = \frac{8\pi G}{3}\rho$$
$$\frac{\ddot{a}}{a} = -\frac{4\pi G}{3}\left(\rho + 3p + \frac{f}{a^2}\right).$$
(70)

The expression for the entropic force F is obtained from the phenomenological constraint

$$\left(\frac{\partial L}{\partial S}\right)\dot{S} = -T\dot{S} = f\dot{a} < 0,$$
(71)

which determines the sign $f < 0$ whenever dealing with an expanding universe $\dot{a} > 0$. We express finally the second Friedmann equation as

$$\frac{\ddot{a}}{a} = -\frac{4\pi G}{3}\left(\rho + 3p - \frac{T\dot{S}}{a^2\dot{a}}\right).$$
(72)

From this equation we can conclude that entropic forces generally drive an acceleration of the expansion of the universe. Whether this can dominate the dynamics of the scale factor will depend on the particular thermodynamic process. Most of the expansion history of the universe takes place in equilibrium. Out of equilibrium processes, such as (p)reheating, phase transitions or gravitational collapse are short-lived. Should their associated entropic force dominate, we still only expect a short period of accelerated expansion.

Symmetry under time inversion is broken by the same arguments presented in section 3. Hence, the Friedmann equations together with the phenomenological constraint, i.e. the second law of thermodynamics, describe cosmic irreversible dynamics.

We currently live in a universe that is undergoing an accelerated expansion. The possibility of explaining this by means of an entropic force is fascinating. In the next section we review our proposal to achieve this by means of the sustained growth of the entropy associated to a causal horizon.

7. Cosmic acceleration as an entropic force

The growth of entropy associated to the cosmic horizon may be responsible for the current observed accelerated expansion of the universe. The choice of horizon is in principle not unique. The only available one which can be defined locally in time is the cosmic apparent horizon, but it fails to significantly affect the expansion.[2]

There is another option in the framework of eternal inflation, according to which we live in an open universe nucleated by quantum tunneling from a false to a true vacuum. After nucleation the bubble universe undergoes its own inflationary era, which renders the local metric almost flat. However, due to the presence of the bubble wall, the true causal horizon is located at a finite distance. It induces an entropic fluid via GHY term with energy density

$$\rho_H\, a^2 = \frac{T_H S_H}{a} = \frac{x_0}{2G}\sinh(2a_0 H_0 \eta)\,, \quad x_0 \equiv \frac{1-\Omega_0}{\Omega_0} = e^{-2N}\left(\frac{T_{\rm rh}}{T_{\rm eq}}\right)^2 (1+z_{\rm eq})\,, \tag{73}$$

where η is the conformal time, Ω_0 is the density parameter, $T_{\rm rh}$ is the reheating temperature, $T_{\rm eq}$ and $z_{\rm eq}$ are, respectively, the temperature and redshift at matter-radiation equality. Introducing $\tau = a_0 H_0 \eta$ one can write the second Friedmann equation in conformal time as

$$\left(\frac{a'}{a_0}\right)^2 = \Omega_M\left(\frac{a}{a_0}\right) + \Omega_K \left(\frac{a}{a_0}\right)^2 + \frac{4\pi}{3}\Omega_K\left(\frac{a}{a_0}\right)^2 \sinh(2\tau)\,, \tag{74}$$

where Ω_M is the matter density paremeter and Ω_K is the curvature parameter. We call this the general relatvistic entropic acceleration (GREA) theory.

By solving this equation with cosmological parameters consistent with the CMB values (Planck 2018: $\Omega_M \simeq 0.31$, $\Omega_K \simeq 0.0006$, $h_0 \simeq 0.68$) and initial conditions deep in the matter era, $a_i(\tau) = a_0\, \Omega_M \tau^2/4$, we find generic accelerating behaviour beyond the scale factor $a \sim 1/2$ (i.e. $z \sim 1$), see Fig. 1. This is consistent with the current observed acceleration of the universe and may even resolve the Hubble tension,[9] providing a way to obtain from the CMB a present value of H_0 that is consistent with late-universe observations, see Fig. 2.

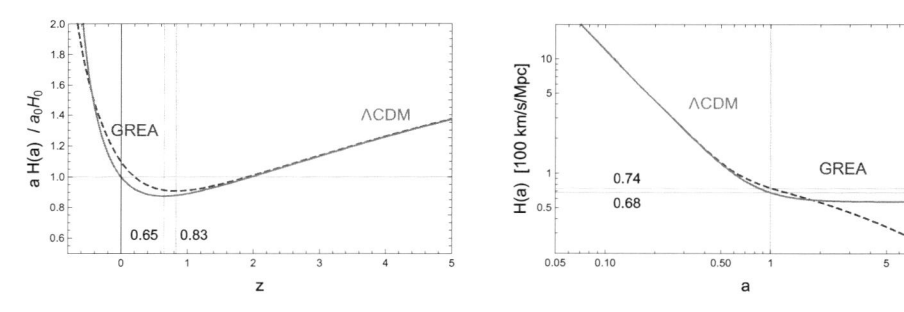

Fig. 1. The left plot shows the evolution of the inverse comoving horizon with the coasting point for each model, at $z \simeq 0.65$ for ΛCDM (in green) and $z \simeq 0.83$ for GREA (in red). The right plot shows the evolution of the rate of expansion. For GREA the present rate of expansion is approximately 74 km/s/Mpc, compared with the value of 68 km/s/Mpc predicted by ΛCDM, in agreement with the asymptotic value at the CMB.

8. Conclusions

The consistent inclusion of non-equilibrium phenomena in General Relativity leads to the modification of the Einstein field equations, as can be checked both in the Lagrangian and Hamiltonian formulations of the theory. This breaks symmetry under time inversion and allows for the introduction of an arrow of time.

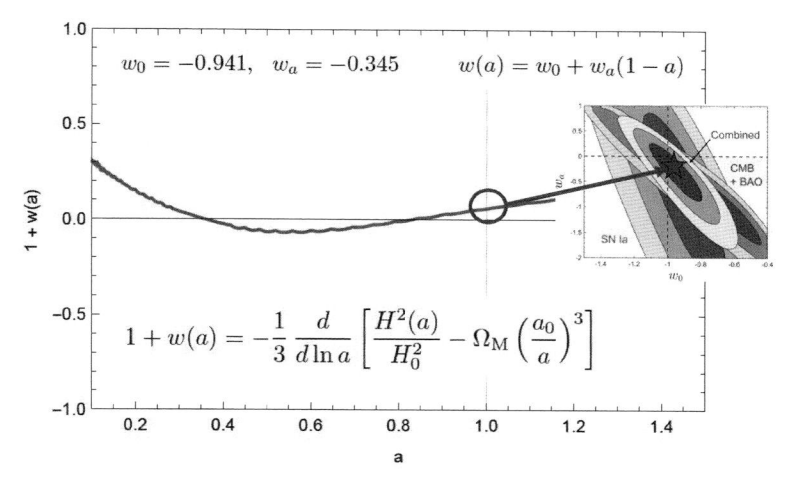

Fig. 2. The effective equation of state of the non-matter component of the GREA theory, as a function of thee sale factor. Note that the predicted effective PCL parameters (w_o, w_a) agree remarkably well with present observations.

In cosmology this implies the appearance of a term of entropic origin in the second Friedmann equation, which tends to accelerate the expansion of the universe as a result of the increase in entropy. Some physical processes such as (p)reheating, phase transitions or gravitational collapse may lead to phenomenologically relevant applications of this formalism. We look forward to further developments.

The sustained entropy growth associated to a causal horizon in the open universe scenario leads to an acceleration consistent with current observations and it may even solve the H_0 tension. Further research will be required to establish the full viability of the GREA theory.

Acknowledgments

The authors acknowledge support from the Spanish Research Project PGC2018-094773-B-C32 (MINECO-FEDER) and the Centro de Excelencia Severo Ochoa Program SEV-2016-0597. The work of LEP is funded by a fellowship from "La Caixa" Foundation (ID 100010434) with fellowship code LCF/BQ/IN18/11660041 and the European Union Horizon 2020 research and innovation programme under the Marie Sklodowska-Curie grant agreement No. 713673.

References

1. L. Espinosa-Portales and J. Garcia-Bellido, Covariant formulation of non-equilibrium thermodynamics in General Relativity, *Phys. Dark Univ.* **34**, p. 100893 (2021).
2. J. García-Bellido and L. Espinosa-Portales, Cosmic acceleration from first principles, *Phys. Dark Univ.* **34**, p. 100892 (2021).

3. F. Gay-Balmaz and H. Yoshimura, A lagrangian variational formulation for nonequilibrium thermodynamics. part i: Discrete systems, *Journal of Geometry and Physics* **111**, 169 (2017).
4. F. Gay-Balmaz and H. Yoshimura, A lagrangian variational formulation for nonequilibrium thermodynamics. part ii: Continuum systems, *Journal of Geometry and Physics* **111**, 194 (2017).
5. R. M. Wald, *General Relativity* (Chicago Univ. Pr., Chicago, USA, 1984).
6. R. Penrose, Gravitational collapse and space-time singularities, *Phys. Rev. Lett.* **14**, 57 (1965).
7. R. Penrose, Gravitational collapse: The role of general relativity, *Riv. Nuovo Cim.* **1**, 252 (1969).
8. S. W. Hawking and R. Penrose, The Singularities of gravitational collapse and cosmology, *Proc. Roy. Soc. Lond. A* **314**, 529 (1970).
9. A. G. Riess, The Expansion of the Universe is Faster than Expected, *Nature Rev. Phys.* **2**, 10 (2019).

Experimental detection of the CNO cycle

B. Caccianiga[1], N. Rossi[2], G. Testera[3]

M. Agostini, K. Altenmüller, S. Appel, V. Atroshchenko, Z. Bagdasarian, D. Basilico, G. Bellini,
J. Benziger, R. Biondi, D. Bravo, B. Caccianiga, F. Calaprice, P. Cavalcante, A. Chepurnov,
D. D'Angelo, S. Davini, A. Derbin, A. Di Giacinto, V. Di Marcello, X.F. Ding, A. Di Ludovico,
L. Di Noto, I. Drachnev, A. Formozov, D. Franco, C. Galbiati, C. Ghiano, M. Giammarchi,
A. Goretti, A.S. Göttel, M. Gromov, D. Guffanti, Aldo Ianni, Andrea Ianni, A. Jany, D. Jeschke,
V. Kobychev, G. Korga, S. Kumaran, M. Laubenstein, E. Litvinovich, P. Lombardi, I. Lomskaya,
L. Ludhova, G. Lukyanchenko, L. Lukyanchenko, I. Machulin, J. Martyn, E. Meroni, M. Meyer,
L. Miramonti, M. Misiaszek, V. Muratova, B. Neumair, M. Nieslony, R. Nugmanov, L. Oberauer,
V. Orekhov, F. Ortica, M. Pallavicini, L. Papp, L. Pelicci, Ö. Penek, L. Pietrofaccia,
N. Pilipenko, A. Pocar, G. Raikov, M.T. Ranalli, G. Ranucci, A. Razeto, A. Re, M. Redchuk,
A. Romani, N. Rossi, S. Schönert, D. Semenov, G. Settanta, M. Skorokhvatov, A. Singhal,
O. Smirnov, A. Sotnikov, Y. Suvorov, R. Tartaglia, G. Testera, J. Thurn, E. Unzhakov,
F. Villante, A. Vishneva, R.B. Vogelaar, F. von Feilitzsch, M. Wojcik, M. Wurm, S. Zavatarelli,
K. Zuber, and G. Zuzel

[1] *Dipartimento di Fisica, Università degli Studi e INFN, 20133 Milano, Italy*

[2] *INFN Laboratori Nazionali del Gran Sasso, 67010 Assergi (AQ), Italy*

[3] *Dipartimento di Fisica, Università degli Studi e INFN, 16146 Genova, Italy*

The Borexino has recently reported the first experimental evidence of neutrinos from the CNO cycle. Since this process accounts only for about 1% of the total energy production in the Sun, the associated neutrino flux is extremely low as compared with the one from the pp-chain, the dominant process of hydrogen burning. This experimental evidence of the CNO neutrinos was obtained using the highly radio-pure liquid scintillator of Borexino. Improvements in the thermal stabilization of the detector over the last five years enabled us to exploit a method to constrain the rate of ^{210}Bi background. Since the CNO cycle is dominant in massive stars, this result gives the first experimental proof of the primary mechanism for stellar conversion of hydrogen into helium in the Universe.

Keywords: Solar neutrinos, CNO cycle, Liquid organic scintillators, solar models

Introduction

Stars are fuelled by nuclear fusion of light elements with a release of an enormous amount of energy. In particular the *pp* chain and the CNO cycle, active also in the Sun, produces a rich spectrum of electron-flavour neutrinos detectable on the Earth.[1,2] Those two mechanisms basically converts four hydrogen nuclei into a helium nucleus: the first using direct process throughout a big variety of branches, while the second using a closed loop starting and ending with ^{12}C acting as catalyst.

The contribution of these two mechanisms in the energy production is related to mass, and then to the core temperature, of the stars and to abundance of elements heavier than helium in the core (in jargon, "metallicity").

For stars heavier than 1.3 $M_\odot$ the CNO cycle is the dominant process of hydrogen fusion,[3] while in the Sun, with a core temperature of about 15×10^6K, the CNO accounts only for 1% of the total luminosity, with a large uncertainty related to poorly known metallicity.[4] The Borexino experiment, starting from mid-2007, has published a comprehensive study of the neutrino from the pp chain[5] and recently has reported the first direct detection of the CNO.[26] The CNO quest, started by Borexino, could in principle create a situation that makes it possible the solution of the long standing "solar metallicity problem",[2] i.e. the disagreement between the metallicity predicted by solar models using updated (low) metal abundances from spectroscopy (SSM-LZ)[6] and the one obtained from the helioseismology, which foresees a higher metal content (SSM-HZ).

In Sec. 1 a description of the detector and the main physics results of Borexino are reported. At the end of the section the hardware improvement for the CNO detection in Phase-III is also reported. In Sec. 2 the main strategy for the CNO detection is described and in Sec. 3 the independent constraint of the ^{210}Bi (the main background for the CNO neutrino interaction rate) is largely detailed. Finally, in Sec. 4 the spectral analysis for the extraction of the CNO rate in Borexino is presented.

1. The Borexino detector

Borexino experiment is the only experiment capable to detect solar neutrinos with a threshold as low as about 150 keV and to reconstruct the position and the energy of each event in real-time.

Borexino is located in the Hall C of Laboratori Nazionali Gran Sasso (INFN).[12] The detector is made of concentric shells with increasing radiopurity (see e.g. Ref.[13]): the innermost core, enclosed in a 125 μm thick ultra-pure nylon vessel of radius 4.25 m, is made of 300 tons of liquid scintillator (1,2,4-Trimethylbenzene with 1.5 g/l of PPO wavelength shifter). The active core is contained by a stainless steel sphere filled up with $\sim$ 1000 of buffer liquid (1,2,4-Trimethylbenzene with DMP quencher), whose internal surface is instrumented with more than 2000 PMTs for detecting the scintillation light. Finally, the SSS is located inside a 2000 ton water Cherenkov detector, equipped with about 200 PMTs. In Fig. 1 all the parts described above are represented in a graphical scheme. Thanks to an intense calibration campaign carried out in 2010, the Borexino detector is able to reconstruct the event position with an accuracy of $\sim$ 10 (at 1 MeV) and with energy resolution of about $\sigma(E)/E = 5\%/\sqrt{(E/[MeV])}$.

The Borexino data-set is traditionally divided in three Phases, determined by the hardware milestones: Phase-I, from mid-2007 to beginning of 2010, ended with the calibration campaign, in which the first measurement of the ^{7}Be solar neutrino interaction rate[8–10] was performed; Phase-II, from the-beginning of 2012 to mid-2016, started after an intense purification campaign, based on water extraction, with unprecedented suppression of the radioactive contaminants, in which the first

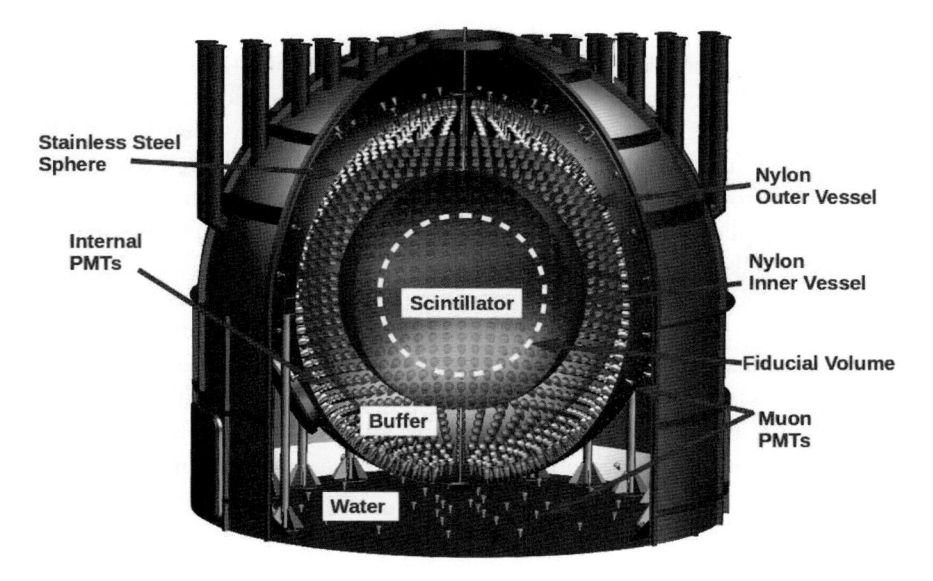

Fig. 1. Scheme of the Borexino detector.

evidence of the *pep* neutrinos[15] and a 10% measurement of the *pp* neutrinos[16] were published, later updated in the solar neutrino comprehensive analysis;[17–19] Phase-III, from mid-2016 to 2021 (still in progress), after the thermal insulation program, in which the first detection of the CNO neutrinos[11] discussed here was performed. Table 1 summarizes the most important results concerning solar neutrinos interaction rates measured by Borexino. Thanks to its unprecedented radio-purity, Borexino has also set a lot of limits on rare processes (see e.g.,[20–24] and performed other neutrino physics studies, as e.g. geo-neutrino detection (for review, see e.g.[25])

The CNO detection has required, as it is explained in Sec. 2, an independent constraint of the ^{210}Bi contaminant from the ^{210}Po through the secular equilibrium starting from the out-of-equilibrium parent ^{210}Pb, present in the liquid scintillator

Table 1. Solar neutrino interaction rates and fluxes measured by Borexino. Rates are reported in cpd/100t, while fluxes are reported in cm^{-2}s^{-1}.

Species	Rate [cpd/100t]	Flux [cm^{-2} s^{-1}]
pp	$(134 \pm 10)^{+6}_{-10}$	$(6.1 \pm 0.5)^{+0.3}_{-0.5} \times 10^{10}$
^{7}Be	$(48.3 \pm 1.1)^{+0.4}_{-0.7}$	$(4.99 \pm 0.11)^{+0.06}_{-0.08} \times 10^9$
pep (HZ)	$(2.7 \pm 0.4)^{+0.1}_{-0.2}$	$(1.3 \pm 0.3)^{+0.1}_{0.1} \times 10^8$
^{8}B(> 3 MeV)	$0.223^{+0.021}_{-0.022}$	$5.68^{+0.42}_{-0.44} \times 10^6$
CNO	$7.2^{+3.0}_{-1.7}$	$7.0^{+3.0}_{-2.0} \times 10^8$
hep	< 0.002 (90% CL)	$< 1.8 \times 10^5$ (90% CL)

after the purification carried out at the end of Phase-I. That constraint required the contaminants, and then the whole scintillator, to be stable against the the convective motions activated by the seasonal variation of the temperature in the experimental hall hosting the detector. In mid-2014 Borexino was equipped with a detailed temperature mapping. In mid-2015 the detector was covered with a thermal insulation and, from the beginning of 2016, a series of active temperature control system were installed around the water tank and at the end on the experimental hall. See for details Ref.[26].

The thermal insulation program was aimed at the realization of a vertical temperature gradient from the cold floor, made of constant temperature rock with a huge thermal capacitance, and the detector top, warmed up by the air flushed into the underground laboratory coming from the external environment out of the Gran Sasso mountain. This challenging enterprise was successful and the strongest convective motions, mixing the liquid scintillator and then the contaminants from the outermost regions into the center, were actually stopped and the conditions for the ^{210}Bi-^{210}Po link, described in Sec. 3 were finally met. Figure 2 shows the ^{210}Po contaminant evolution during the thermal insulation program in 59 small cubes enumerated from the bottom to the top inside a radius of 3 m from the center of the Inner Vessel. The red superimposed curve represents the average temperature in the same region. The dashed vertical lines show the most important milestones of the temperature stabilisation program: 1. Beginning of insulation; 2. Turning off of the water recirculation system in the Water Tank; 3. First operation of the active temperature control system; 4. Change of the active control set point; 5. Installation and commissioning of the Hall C temperature control system. The white vertical bands represent different technical DAQ breaks. The ^{210}Po shown in the figure is a

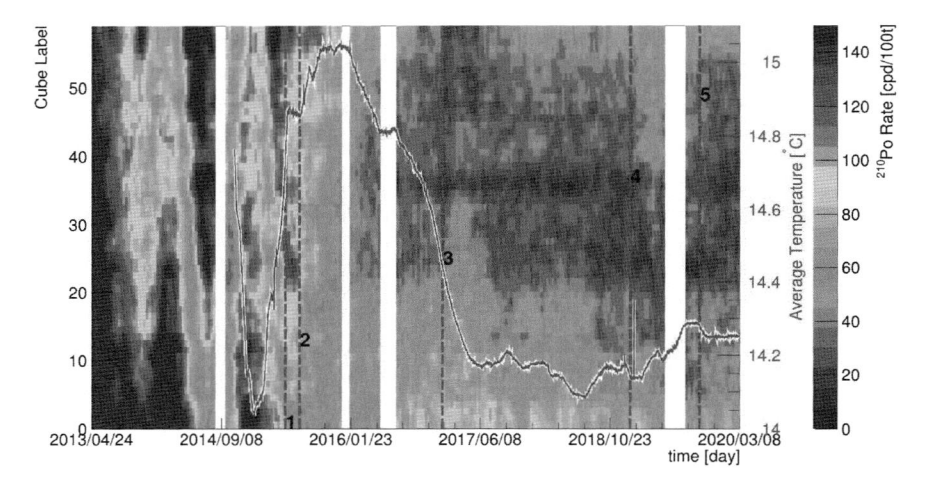

Fig. 2. Evolution of the ^{210}Po contamination during the thermal insulation program.

tracker of the convective motions, that are drastically damped as a consequence of the insulation program.

2. CNO detection strategy

Neutrinos emitted in the CNO cycle, see Fig. 3, have a continuous spectrum with a maximum energy of 1.74 MeV (see Fig. 4, left). In the Sun, the flux of CNO neutrinos is two orders of magnitude smaller than the one due to proton-proton neutrinos: this makes the expected rate in Borexino very low, of the order of few counts per day. Besides the low rate, the main difficulty in detecting CNO neutrinos with Borexino is the presence of two radioactive backgrounds which produce signal in approximately the same energy region: ^{11}C and ^{210}Bi. Furthermore, also solar neutrinos from the *pep* reaction are a significant background for the CNO analysis.

Fig. 4 (right) shows a MonteCarlo simulation of the energy spectrum of electrons scattered by neutrinos from the CNO cycle (red line) in comparison with the signal induced by the radioactive decay of ^{11}C (purple line) and ^{210}Bi (green line). The blue line is the *pep* signal. The relative proportion of the four contributions is approximately the one expected in reality. From this plot the difficulty of extracting the CNO signal from the background becomes evident: it is like looking for a needle in a haystack!

The cosmogenic ^{11}C is an isotope produced by residual muons crossing the scintillator which decays emitting a positron with a lifetime of approximately 30 minutes. It can be very effectively tagged by the Three Fold Coincidence (TFC) method described in,[27] which looks for the triple coincidence of the parent muon, the cosmogenic neutron produced together with ^{11}C and the positron emitted in the ^{11}C decay. This tagging method allows us to divide the data-set in two complementary parts, one rich and the other depleted in ^{11}C which are then simultaneously fitted in the multivariate analysis described in Section 4. This is a powerful tool to help the fit isolate the ^{11}C signal contribution, breaking the correlation with the CNO neutrino signal.

Separating the CNO signal from the ^{210}Bi and *pep* one is more tricky since their spectral shapes are quite similar and the multivariate fit has trouble in distinguishing between them, if no additional external contraints are imposed.

For what concerns *pep* neutrinos, we exploited the external and independent information coming from the available solar neutrino data, solar luminosity and the most recent oscillation parameters to put a constraint to their rate in the fit with a 1.4% uncertainty.

The remaining obstacle to the CNO neutrino detection is the contamination from ^{210}Bi. This isotope belongs to the ^{210}Pb chain, which in turn is the last segment of the ^{238}U chain. In Borexino, we found the ^{210}Pb chain to be out of equilibrium with respect to the ^{238}U chain and with a significantly higher activity, of the order of tens of counts per day per 100 tons of scintillator.

The ^{210}Pb chain is composed of three isotopes: the long lived ^{210}Pb father of the chain ($\tau \sim 32$ y), ^{210}Bi which has a relatively short lifetime ($\tau \sim 7.23$ d) and ^{210}Po which decays into ^{206}Pb (stable) emitting an alpha particle ($\tau \sim 199.1$ d). If secular equilibrium holds, the activities of ^{210}Bi and ^{210}Po are the same (apart for negligible corrections due to the finite ^{210}Pb lifetime). Measuring the ^{210}Po rate is in principle straightforward since an alpha peak is clearly separable from the continuous beta-like background underneath. Furthermore, alpha/beta discrimination techniques provide a powerful additional tool to isolate the ^{210}Po events.

Based on these premises, our strategy for the CNO detection relies on the ^{210}Bi-^{210}Po link to determine independently the ^{210}Bi content from ^{210}Po and constrain it in the multivariate fit. The next Section will describe in details the difficulties we encountered to apply this technique and how we were able of overcoming them.

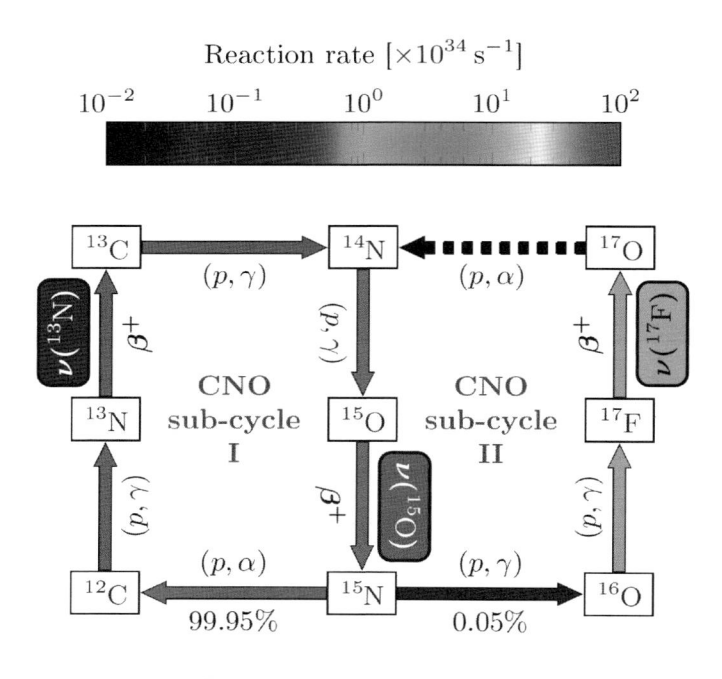

Fig. 3. Neutrinos in CNO cycle.

3. The ^{210}Bi–^{210}Po link

In order to exploit the ^{210}Bi–^{210}Po link to obtain an external constraint on the ^{210}Bi rate, we carefully studied the evolution in time and the spatial distribution

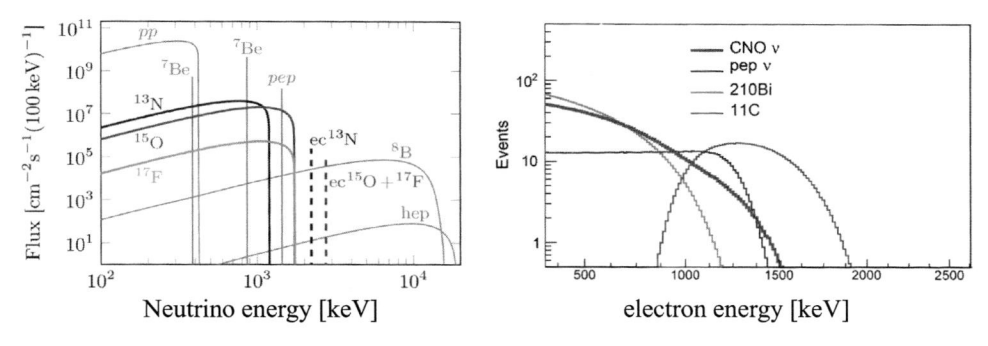

Fig. 4. (Left): Energy spectrum of neutrinos emitted in the CNO cycle (colored lines); (right): energy spectrum in Borexino for events of CNO (red), pep (blue), ^{210}Bi (geen) and ^{11}C (purple) obtained from MonteCarlo simulations.

of the polonium contamination in the detector during the Borexino data-taking. We soon realized that the ^{210}Po present in the fiducial region used in the analysis (an innermost subset of the scintillator volume) is actually the sum of two contributions: ^{210}Po from the intrinsic ^{210}Pb scintillator contamination (in equilibrium with ^{210}Bi); ^{210}Po from the nylon vessel containing the scintillator. This last contribution was found to be changing in time and highly correlated with variations of the temperature gradient in the detector, which induce convective motions strong enough to bring ^{210}Po from the vessel surface into the fiducial region. In order to reduce these convective motions, we thermally insulated the detector, as discussed in Section 1.

After the completion of the thermal insulation (2016), the temperature of the detector has become very stable and the convective currents inside the scintillator have significantly reduced. This has favoured the formation of an innermost region of the detector, called Low Polonium Field (LPoF), where the contribution to the ^{210}Po rate coming from the vessel is very small. A pictorial view of this region is shown in Fig. 5. This region exhibits an effective migration profile with a minimum in the ^{210}Po rate above the detector equator (dark blue region). The qualitative shape and approximate position of the LPoF is reproduced by fluid dynamical numerical simulations reported in.[28]

Assuming azimuthal symmetry around the detector z-axis (which was confirmed by a 3D analysis), the ^{210}Po minimum activity is determined by fitting LPoF with a 2D paraboloidal function:

$$\frac{d^2 R(^{210}\text{Po})}{d(\rho^2)dz} = \left[R(^{210}\text{Po}_{\text{min}})\epsilon_E \epsilon_{\text{MLP}} + R_\beta\right] \times \\ \times \left(1 + \frac{\rho^2}{a^2} + \frac{(z-z_0)^2}{b^2}\right), \quad (1)$$

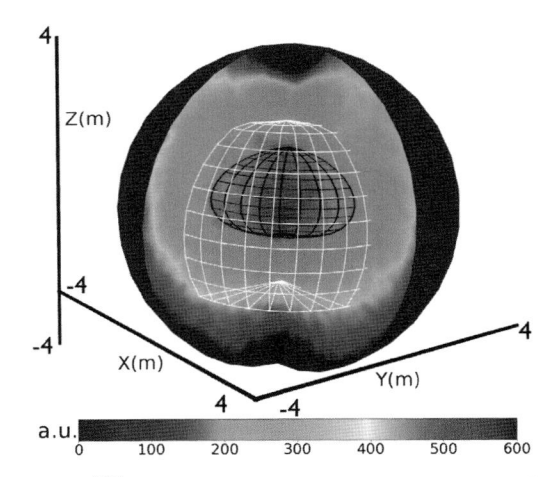

Fig. 5. Pictorial view of the ^{210}Po activity in the Borexino scintillator. The color scale goes from red (highest activity) to blue (lowest activity). The LPoF is the innermost blue region where the contribution of ^{210}Po from the vessel is the smallest (black grid). The white grid indicates the software defined fiducial volume used for the analysis to extract the CNO neutrinos.

Here, $\rho^2 = x^2 + y^2$, a and b are the paraboloid axes, z_0 is the position of the minimum along the z axis, ϵ_E and ϵ_{MLP} are the efficiencies of the cuts used to select ^{210}Po events, and R_β is the residual rate of β events after the selection. First, we performed the fit integrating data from 2 months (compatible results are obtained also changing the time bins) and we found that the minimum position slowly moves along the z direction by less than 20 cm per month. In order to perform a better estimation of the ^{210}Po minimum, we finally sum up all the time bins after aligning the 3D distributions with respect to z_0.

From this fit we extract the ^{210}Po minimum. This value might still have a small contribution from the vessel component, therefore this method provides only an upper limit for the ^{210}Bi rate. In order to cross-check the results, we performed the fit in different ways: adopting a standard likelihood fit with ROOT or a Bayesian tool called MultiNest. In addition to the 2D paraboloidal fit, we also performed the fit with a 3D ellipsoidal function or alternatively with a cubic spline. The differences in the results were included in the systematic error associated to the upper limit on ^{210}Bi. In the analysis to extract the CNO neutrino rate which will be described in Section 4, we would like to costraint the value of the ^{210}Bi to the upper limit found in the low polonium field region, extrapolating the results to the whole fiducial volume. In order to do so, we need to verify that ^{210}Bi is uniform in this volume during the time period over which the estimation is performed. For this reason, we studied the spatial distribution of β-like events in an energy window where the bismuth contribution is maximized. This distribution was found to be uniform within errors: we include in the systematic error budget a contribution of 0.78 cpd/100t accounting for residual non uniformity.

The final upper limit on ^{210}Bi including statistical and systematical errors added in quadrature is:

$$\text{Rate}(^{210}\text{Bi}) \leq (11.5 \pm 1.3)\,\text{cpd}/100\text{t}$$

4. Spectral analysis

We performed a multivariate analysis, simultaneously fitting the energy spectra in the window between 320 keV and 2640 keV and the radial distribution of the selected events, using the data collected from June 2016 to February 2020 (Borexino Phase-III). The fiducial volume (FV) is defined as r<2.8 m and z in the interval (-1.8 m, 2.2 m) (r and z being the reconstructed radial and vertical position, respectively). The total exposure corresponds to 1072 days · 71.3 tonnes. Free parameters in the fit procedure are: the interaction rate of CNO neutrinos, ^{85}Kr, ^{11}C, internal and external ^{40}K, external ^{208}Tl and ^{214}Bi, and ^{7}Be neutrinos. The pep neutrino rate is constrained to to 2.74 ± 0.04 cpd per 100 t by multiplying the standard likelihood with a symmetric Gaussian term. The upper limit to the ^{210}Bi rate is the one reported in previous section. It is enforced asymmetrically by multiplying the likelihood with a half-Gaussian term, i.e., leaving the ^{214}Bi rate unconstrained between 0 and 11.5 cpd per 100 t .

The reference spectral and radial distributions of each signal and background species are obtained with a complete GEANT4-based Monte Carlo simulation which models all physics processes occurring in the scintillator, including energy deposition, photon emission, propagation, and detection, generation and processing of the electronic signal. The simulation takes into account the evolution in time of the detector response and produces data that are reconstructed and selected following the same pipeline of real data. The results of the simultaneous multivariate fit of the energy spectra are given in Fig. 6, showing the TFC subtracted and TFC-tagged data. The fit is performed in the energy estimator N_{hits} (defined as the sum of all photons triggering a PMT, normalized to 2000 active PMTs) and the results are reported also in keV. The p-value of the fit is 0.3, demonstrating fair agreement between data and the underlying fit model. The fit clearly prefers a non-zero CNO neutrino rate as also shown in a detailed study of log-likelihood profile.

The best fit value of the CNO neutrinos interaction rate is 7.2 cpd per 100 t with an asymmetric confidence interval of -1.7 cpd per 100 t and +2.9 cpd per 100 t (68% C.L.), considering the statistical error only. The many details of the analysis, including the list and evaluation of the systematic effects are reported in.[26] Folding the systematic uncertainty over the log-likelihood profile we determine the final CNO interaction rate to be $7.2^{+3}_{-1.7}$ cpd per 100 t. The rate can be converted to of CNO neutrinos on Earth of $7.2^{+3.0}_{-2.0} \cdot 10^8$ cm^{-2} s^{-1} assuming MSW conversion in matter and a density of electrons in the scintillator of $(3.307 \pm 0.015) \cdot 10^{31}$ e$^-$ per 100 t.

In order to evaluate the significance of our result in rejecting the no-CNO hypothesis, we performed a frequentist hypothesis test using the profile likelihood.

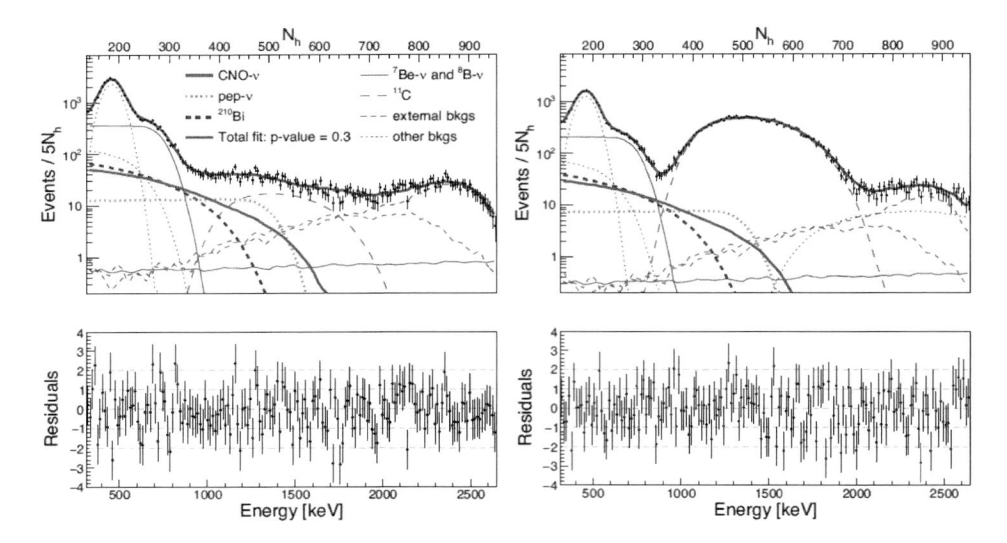

Fig. 6. Energy distributions from a multivariate fit of the Borexino data. Full multivariate fit results for the TFC-subtracted (left) and the TFC-tagged (right) energy spectra with corresponding residuals. In both graphs the magenta lines represent the resulting fit function, the red line is the CNO neutrino electron recoil spectrum, the green dotted line is the pep neutrino electron recoil spectrum, the dashed blue line is the $^{210}\beta$ spectrum, and in grey we report the remaining background (bkgs) contributions.

We defined a test statistics q, as the ratio between the maximum likelihood obtained by keeping the CNO rate fixed to zero or free. Figure 7 shows the q distribution obtained from 13.8 millions of pseudo-data sets simulated with deformed PDFs to include systematics effects, and no-CNO injected (q_0, grey curve). In the same plot, the theoretical q_0 distribution in case of no PDF deformation is shown (blue curve). The result on data obtained from the fit is the black line ($q_{data} = 30.05$). The results reported in Figure 7 allow us to reject the CNO = 0 hypothesis with a significance better than 5.0σ at 99.0% C.L. In the figure we also provide as reference the q distribution (red) obtained with one million pseudo-data sets including systematic deformations and injected CNO rate equal to 7.2 cpd per 100 t, i.e., our best fit value.

The results of the analysis based on the fit are also confirmed by that obtained with a nearly independent method (counting analysis), in which we simply count events in an optimized energy window (region of interest, ROI) and subtract the contributions due to known backgrounds. This method reveals a non zero CNO signal and its consistency with the multivariate analysis is remarkable. This method is simpler, albeit less powerful, with respect to the multivariate fit and is less prone to possible correlations between different species. However, while the multivariate analysis implicitly checks the validity of the background model by the goodness of the fit, the counting analysis relies completely on the assumption that there are no unknown backgrounds contributing to the ROI.

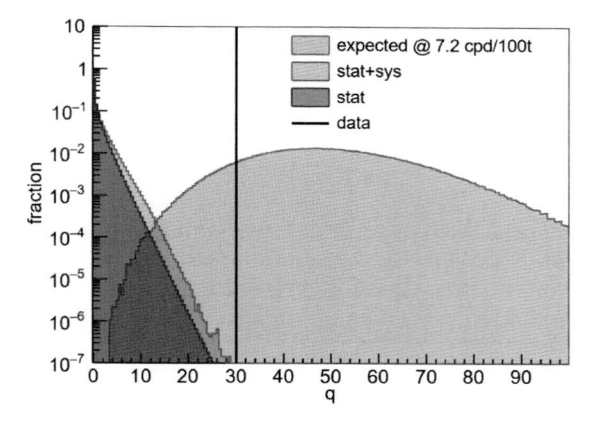

Fig. 7. Distribution of the test statistic q, as discussed in the text.

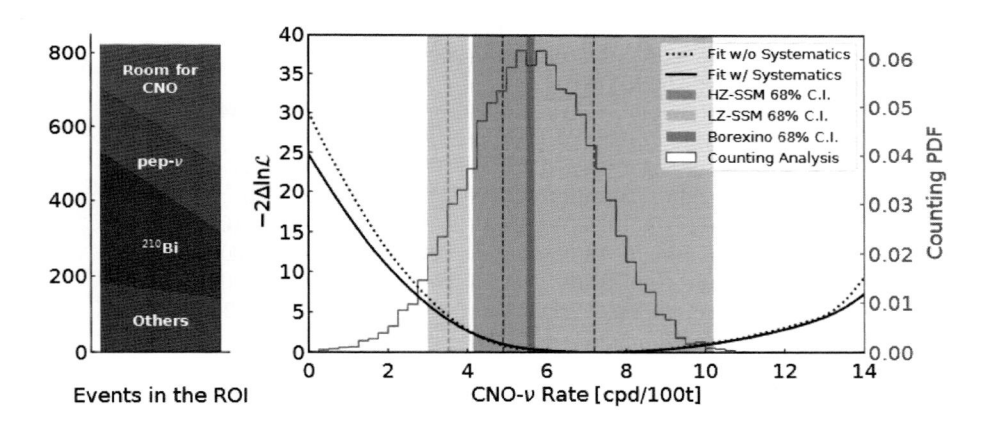

Fig. 8. Results of the CNO counting and spectral analyses. Left. Counting analysis bar chart. The height represents the number of events allowed by the data for CNO neutrinos and backgrounds in the ROI; on the left, the CNO signal is minimum and backgrounds are maximum, while on the right, CNO is maximum and backgrounds are minimum. It is clear from this figure that CNO cannot be zero. Right. CNO neutrinos rate negative log-likelihood profile directly from the multivariate fit (dashed black line) and after folding in the systematic uncertainties (black solid line). Histogram in red: CNO neutrino rate obtained from the counting analysis. Finally, the blue, violet, and grey vertical bands show 68% confidence intervals (C.I.) for the SSM-LZ (3.52±0.52 cpd per 100 t) and SSM-HZ (4.92±0.78 cpd per 100 t) predictions and the Borexino result (corresponding to black solid-line log-likelihood pro- file), respectively.

Conclusions

We have reported the results about the first direct detection of neutrinos from the CNO cycle in the Sun. This result proves the occurrence of the primary mechanism for the stellar conversion of hydrogen into helium in the Universe. The observation of CNO neutrinos experimentally confirms the overall solar picture and shows that a direct measurement of the metallicity of the Sun's core is within reach of an improved, future measurement.

References

1. J. N. Bahcall, Neutrino Astrophysics, *Cambridge University Press*, 1989.
2. N. Vinyoles, A.M. Serenelli, F.L. Villante, S. Basu, J. Bergström, M.C. Gonzalez-Garcia, M. Maltoni, C. Peña-Garay, and N. Song, *Astrophys. J.*, **835**(2):202, 2017.
3. M. Salaris and S. Cassisi, Evolution of Stars and Stellar Populations, *John Wiley & Sons Ltd.*, 2005.
4. C. Angulo et al., *Nuclear Physics A*, **656**(1):3–183, 1999.
5. M. Agostini et al. (Borexino Collaboration), *Nature*, **562**(7728):505–510, 2018.
6. A. M. Serenelli, W. C. Haxton, and C. Peña-Garay, *The Astrophysical Journal*, **743**(1):24, 2011.
7. G. Bellini et al. [Borexino], Phys. Rev. D **89** (2014).
8. C. Arpesella et al. [Borexino], Phys. Lett. B **658** (2008), 101-108.
9. C. Arpesella et al. [Borexino], Phys. Rev. Lett. **101**(2008), 091302.
10. G. Bellini, et al. [Bore ino], Phys. Rev. Lett. **107** (2011), 141302.
11. M. Agostini et al. [Borexino], Nature **587** (2020), 577-582.
12. Website: https://www.lngs.infn.it
13. G. Alimonti et al. [Borexino], Astropart. Phys. **16** (2002), 205-234.
14. H. Back et al. [Borexino], JINST **7** (2012), P10018.
15. G. Bellini et al. [Borexino], Phys. Rev. Lett. **108** (2012), 051302.
16. G. Bellini et al. [Borexino], Nature **512** (2014) no.7515, 383-386.
17. M. Agostini et al. [Borexino], Nature **562** (2018) no.7728, 505-510.
18. M. Agostini et al. [Borexino], Phys. Rev. D **100** (2019) no.8, 082004.
19. M. Agostini et al. [Borexino], Phys. Rev. D **101** (2020) no.6, 062001.
20. A. Vishneva et al. [Borexino], J. Phys. Conf. Ser. **888** (2017), 012193.
21. S. K. Agarwalla et al. [Borexino], JHEP **02** (2020), 038.
22. M. Agostini et al. [Borexino], Astropart. Phys. **125** (2021), 102509.
23. M. Agostini et al. [Borexino], Phys. Rev. D **96** (2017), 091103.
24. G. Bellini et al. [Borexino], Phys. Rev. D **88** (2013), 072010.
25. M. Agostini et al. [Borexino], Phys. Rev. D **101** (2020), 012009.
26. The Borexino Collaboration, *Nature* **587**, 577 (2020).
27. The Borexino Collaboration, *arXiV:2106.1097*. Submitted for publication on *EPJ C*.
28. V. Di Marcello *et al*, *Nucl. Instrum. Meth. A*, **964**, 163801 (2020).

Borexino detector performances

A. Caminata*, M. Agostini, K. Altenmüller, S. Appel, V. Atroshchenko, Z. Bagdasarian,
D. Basilico, G. Bellini, J. Benziger, R. Biondi, D. Bravo, B. Caccianiga, F. Calaprice,
P. Cavalcante, A. Chepurnov, D. D'Angelo, S. Davini, A. Derbin, A. Di Giacinto,
V. Di Marcello, X.F. Ding, A. Di Ludovico, L. Di Noto, I. Drachnev, A. Formozov, D. Franco,
C. Galbiati, C. Ghiano, M. Giammarchi, A. Goretti, A.S. Göttel, M. Gromov, D. Guffanti,
Aldo Ianni, Andrea Ianni, A. Jany, D. Jeschke, V. Kobychev, G. Korga, S. Kumaran,
M. Laubenstein, E. Litvinovich, P. Lombardi, I. Lomskaya, L. Ludhova, G. Lukyanchenko,
L. Lukyanchenko, I. Machulin, J. Martyn, E. Meroni, M. Meyer, L. Miramonti, M. Misiaszek,
V. Muratova, B. Neumair, M. Nieslony, R. Nugmanov, L. Oberauer, V. Orekhov, F. Ortica,
M. Pallavicini, L. Papp, L. Pelicci, Ö. Penek, L. Pietrofaccia, N. Pilipenko, A. Pocar, G. Raikov,
M.T. Ranalli, G. Ranucci, A. Razeto, A. Re, M. Redchuk, A. Romani, N. Rossi, S. Schönert,
D. Semenov, G. Settanta, M. Skorokhvatov, A. Singhal, O. Smirnov, A. Sotnikov, Y. Suvorov,
R. Tartaglia, G. Testera, J. Thurn, E. Unzhakov, F. Villante, A. Vishneva, R.B. Vogelaar,
F. von Feilitzsch, M. Wojcik, M. Wurm, S. Zavatarelli, K. Zuber, and G. Zuzel

*INFN Sezione di Genova,
Genova, 16146, Italy

Borexino, a large volume detector for low energy neutrino spectroscopy, is currently taking data underground since 2007 at the Laboratori Nazionali del Gran Sasso, Italy. The main goal of the experiment is the real-time measurement of solar neutrinos, especially the low energy part of the spectrum. Neutrinos are detected via neutrino-electron scattering in an ultra-pure organic liquid scintillator. The light generated by the interaction is detected by 2212 phototubes. During many years of data taking the experiment provided several remarkable results as the first evidence of pep neutrinos, the real-time detection of the pp neutrinos, the evidence of CNO neutrinos, and the detection of antineutrinos from the Earth. All these results are based on an accurate modelling of the detector's response and performances. The contribution shows the design, the modelling of the detector's response, and the performances. Moreover it will be discussed how the performances and the response were studied by means of extensive calibration campaigns.

Keywords: Borexino; Neutrino; Solar neutrinos; calibrations

1. The Borexino detector

Borexino is a liquid-scintillator experiment at the hall C of the Laboratori Nazionali del Gran Sasso in Italy. Borexino looks for solar neutrinos scattering off electrons in its active volume. Given the tiny cross-section of neutrino interactions with electrons ($\sigma \sim 10^{-44}\,cm^2$ to $10^{-45}\,cm^2$ for the solar-neutrino energy range), the rates expected in Borexino are small, ranging from less than one to a few tens of counts per day per 100 tons for different solar-neutrino components. To cope with such a low event rate, Borexino has a large target mass (about 300 t) and it is housed deep underground, under 3,800 m water equivalent of dolomitic rock that suppresses the flux of cosmic radiation by a factor of approximately one million. The active core of the detector consists of about 300 t of pseudocumene (1,2,4-trimethylbenzene) doped with 1.5 g per litre of PPO (2,5-diphenyloxazole) and contained in a spherical nylon inner vessel (radius R = 4.25 m). The scintillator is surrounded by a non-scintillating pseudocumene-based buffer liquid which serves as a passive shield against external radioactivity (see Figure 1). The scintillator fluorescence light is collected by 2,212 photomultiplier tubes mounted on the Stainless Steel Sphere (radius R = 6.9 m). The entire detector is enclosed in a domed, cylindrical tank filled with high-purity water, equipped with 208 photomultiplier tubes, which provides extra shielding against external radioactivity (photons and neutrons), and also serves as an active water Cherenkov veto against residual cosmic muons.[1] Together with the lack of directionality information from the scintillation light, the low rate demands a high detector radiopurity, a deep understanding of the backgrounds, and an accurate modeling of the detector response.

To achieve the extreme sensitivity required by the experiment, very stringent procedures of material selection and cleaning were adopted to limit radioactive background in the experiment. Since usual materials are contaminated at the order of Bq/kg, material selection played a key role in the success of the experiment. One example is the choice of oil coming from deep wells to produce pseudocumene. In this way a low content of ^{14}C is achieved in the detector. Several cycles of scintillation purification were performed during the years achieving the unprecedented contamination of $^{238}U < 9.4 \cdot 10^{-20}$ g/g (95% C.L.) and $^{232}Th < 5.7 \cdot 10^{-19}$ g/g (95% C.L.). Further details on the purification strategy can be found here.[2]

The position and pulse-shape of each event are reconstructed by exploiting the number of detected photons and their detection times. The information about the event energy is carried by the number of detected photoelectrons or just the number of hit PMTs, as in our energy range the PMTs mainly work in a single photoelectron regime. Moreover, from the time distribution of the emitted light it is possible to statistically discriminate between α and β^- events[3] and between β^+ and β^- events.[4]

Due to a small leak in the nylon vessel, the vessel shape changes with time. At analysis stage it is updated every three weeks looking at radioactive decays happening on in (mostly due to ^{210}Bi, ^{40}K, ^{208}Tl) as shown by Figure 2. This method enables to reconstruct the vessel shape with a ±5 cm uncertainty.

2. The Borexino calibration campaign

Calibrations in Borexino are performed inserting radioactive sources inside the liquid scintillator (internal calibrations) and placing a ^{232}Th source close to the stainless steel sphere (external calibrations). The former is used to map the detector's response while the latter is used to better understand and modeling the backgrounds that are coming from the construction materials. To insert sources inside the detector, a complex system of rods and cameras is exploited. This ensures knowing the position of the source at ~cm level.[6] Table 1 shows the used sources and their purpose.

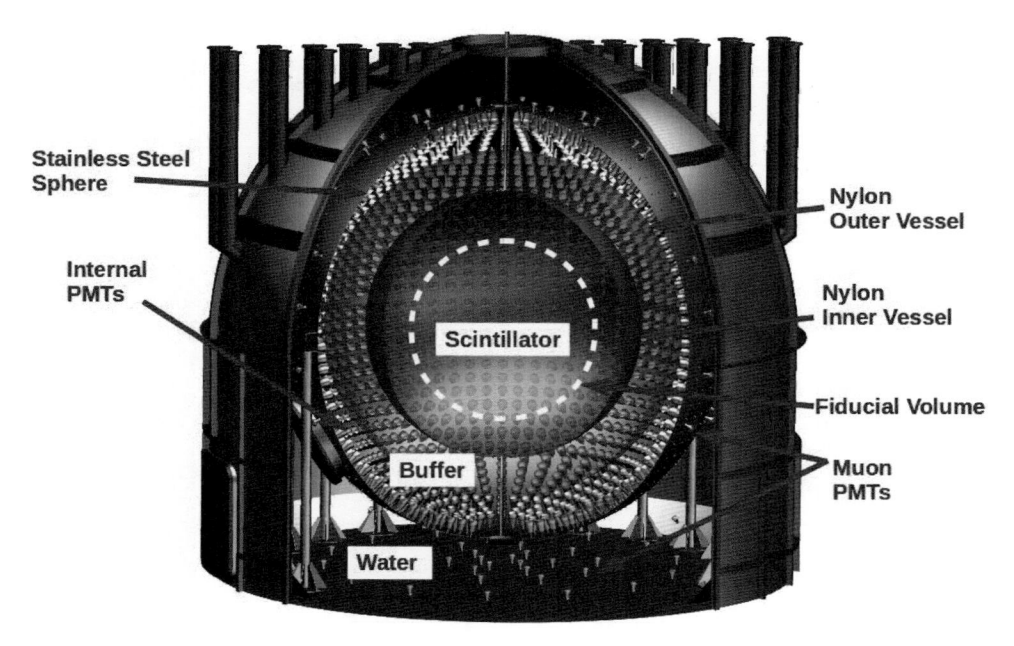

Fig. 1. The Borexino detector: Schematic view of the structure of the Borexino apparatus. From inside to outside: the liquid scintillator, the buffer liquid, the stainless steel sphere with the photomultipliers, and the water tank.[5]

Table 1. Used sources and placement during the internal calibration campaign.[6]

Source	Type	E [MeV]	Position	Motivations
^{57}Co	γ	0.122	in IV volume	Energy scale
^{139}Ce	γ	0.165	in IV volume	Energy scale
^{203}Hg	γ	0.279	in IV volume	Energy scale
^{85}Sr	γ	0.514	z-axis + sphere R=3 m	Energy scale + FV
^{54}Mn	γ	0.834	along z-axis	Energy scale
^{65}Zn	γ	1.115	along z-axis	Energy scale
^{60}Co	γ	1.173, 1.332	along z-axis	Energy scale
^{40}K	γ	1.460	along z-axis	Energy scale
^{222}Rn+^{14}C	β,γ	0-3.20	in IV volume	FV+uniformity
	α	5.5, 6.0, 7.4	in IV volume	FV+uniformity
^{241}Am^{9}Be	n	0-9	sphere R=4 m	Energy scale + FV
394 nm laser	light	-	center	PMT equalization

The position of an event is calculated by the time of arrival of the first photon on photomultipliers corrected by the hit multiplicity and minimizing a proper likelihood function. Figure 3 shows the resolution as function of the energy of the event. The reconstruction of calibration events and their comparison with the know source position shows a bias of maximum 4 cm in the vertical direction for events in the

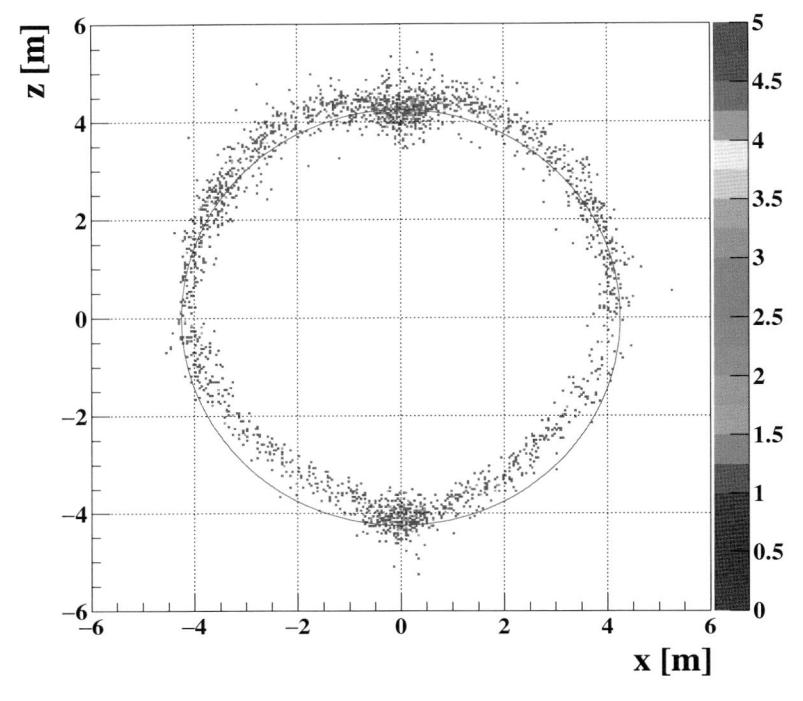

Fig. 2. A cross section (z-x plane, $|y| < 0.5\,\text{m}$) view of the distribution of 2478 events, acquired during a 3 week period, and selected for the IV shape reconstruction. The color axis represents the number of events per cubic pixel of 0.04 m of size. This distribution reveals the IV shift and deformation with respect to its nominal spherical position shown in solid black line.[3]

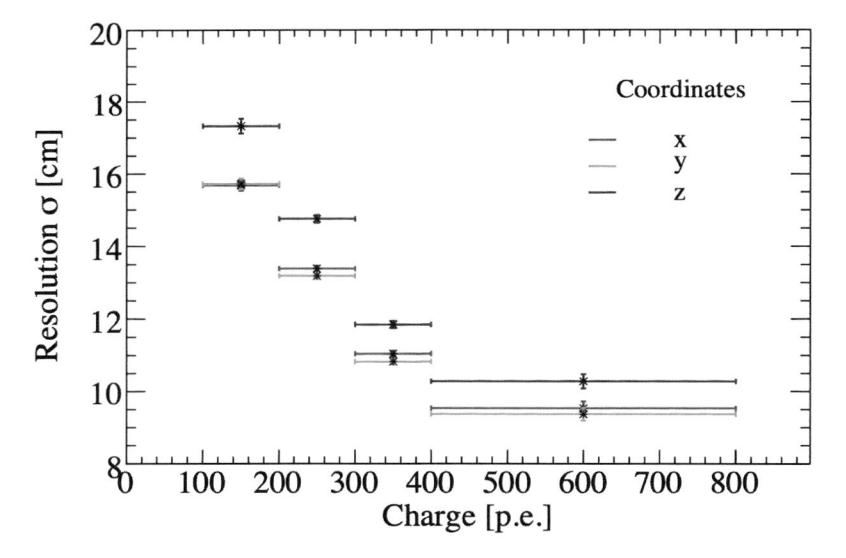

Fig. 3. Position resolution in Borexino as function of event energy.[6]

center. This bias has a small (less than 0.2%) impact on the fiducial volume determination. Since Borexino is a self triggering experiment, calibrations with laser and radioactive sources were performed to test the triggering efficiency, which is 100% at the energies of interest for solar neutrino detection.[7]

3. Modeling the detector response

The collaboration developed two independent approaches for modeling the detector's response. One is based on a particle physics simulation,[8] the other on an analytical model.[4]

The MC code developed for Borexino is a customized Geant4-based simulation package, which can simulate all processes following the interaction of a particle in the detector (energy loss including ionization quenching in the scintillator; scintillation and Cherenkov light production; optical photon propagation and interaction in the scintillator modelling absorption and re-emission, Rayleigh scattering, interaction of the optical photons with the surface of the materials; photon detection on the PMTs, and response of the electronics chain) including all known characteristics of the apparatus (geometry, properties of the materials, variable number of the working channels over the duration of the experiment as in the real data) and their evolution in time. The code thus produces a fully simulated detector response function because it provides a simulated version of all the measured physical variables. All the MC input parameters have been chosen or optimized using samples of data independent from the specific analysis (laboratory measurements and Borexino calibrations with radioactive sources.

In the analytical approach, a PDF for the energy estimator under consideration and analytical expressions for its mean value and variance are introduced. This PDF describes the detector's energy response function to monoenergetic events and, in brief, it is mainly influenced by the number of scintillation and Cherenkov photons and effects due to the nonuniformity of the light collection. The energy spectra of each species are transformed into the corresponding distributions of the energy estimators. Effects like the ionization quenching in the scintillator, the contribution of the Cherenkov light, the spatial dependence of the reconstructed energy and its resolution are accounted for through some parameters, part of which are fixed, while others are free to vary during the fit on the dataset.

4. Conclusion

Borexino is a neutrino detector able to measure the flux of all the neutrinos emitted by the Sun and the existence of antineutrinos emitted by the Earth.[3-5,9] Thanks to a wide calibration campaign the performances of the detector were assessed: for a 1 MeV event the energy resolution is $\sim 50\,\text{keV}$ and the position resolution is $\sim 10\,\text{cm}$. The triggering efficiency is 100% for energies typical of solar neutrinos events. Moreover the Monte Carlo and analytical models were tested on calibration data with agreement better than 1%.

References

1. G. Alimonti, C. Arpesella, H. Back, M. Balata, D. Bartolomei, A. de Bellefon, G. Bellini, J. Benziger, A. Bevilacqua, D. Bondi, S. Bonetti, A. Brigatti, B. Caccianiga, L. Cadonati, F. Calaprice, C. Carraro, G. Cecchet, R. Cereseto, A. Chavarria, M. Chen, A. Chepurnov, A. Cubaiu, W. Czech, D. D'Angelo, F. Dalnoki-Veress, A. De Bari, E. De Haas, A. Derbin, M. Deutsch, A. Di Credico, A. Di Ludovico, G. Di Pietro, R. Eisenstein, F. Elisei, A. Etenko, F. von Feilitzsch, R. Fernholz, K. Fomenko, R. Ford, D. Franco, B. Freudiger, N. Gaertner, C. Galbiati, F. Gatti, S. Gazzana, V. Gehman, M. Giammarchi, D. Giugni, M. Goeger-Neff, T. Goldbrunner, A. Golubchikov, A. Goretti, C. Grieb, C. Hagner, T. Hagner, W. Hampel, E. Harding, S. Hardy, F. Hartmann, R. von Hentig, T. Hertrich, G. Heusser, M. Hult, A. Ianni, A. Ianni, L. Ioannucci, K. Jaenner, M. Joyce, H. de Kerret, S. Kidner, J. Kiko, T. Kirsten, V. Kobychev, G. Korga, G. Korschinek, Y. Kozlov, D. Kryn, P. La Marche, V. Lagomarsino, M. Laubenstein, C. Lendvai, M. Leung, T. Lewke, E. Litvinovich, B. Loer, F. Loeser, P. Lombardi, L. Ludhova, I. Machulin, S. Malvezzi, A. Manco, J. Maneira, W. Maneschg, I. Manno, D. Manuzio, G. Manuzio, M. Marchelli, A. Martemianov, F. Masetti, U. Mazzucato, K. McCarty, D. McKinsey, Q. Meindl, E. Meroni, L. Miramonti, M. Misiaszek, D. Montanari, M. Monzani, V. Muratova, P. Musico, H. Neder, A. Nelson, L. Niedermeier, S. Nisi, L. Oberauer, M. Obolensky, M. Orsini, F. Ortica, M. Pallavicini, L. Papp, R. Parcells, S. Parmeggiano, M. Parodi, N. Pelliccia, L. Perasso, A. Pocar, R. Raghavan, G. Ranucci, W. Rau, A. Razeto, E. Resconi, P. Risso, A. Romani, D. Rountree, A. Sabelnikov, P. Saggese, R. Saldhana, C. Salvo, R. Scardaoni, D. Schimizzi, S. Schönert, K. Schubeck, T. Shutt, F. Siccardi, H. Simgen, M. Skorokhvatov, O. Smirnov, A. Sonnenschein, F. Soricelli, A. Sotnikov, S. Sukhotin, C. Sule, Y. Suvorov, V. Tarasenkov, R. Tartaglia, G. Testera, D. Vignaud, S. Vitale, R. Vogelaar, V. Vyrodov, B. Williams, M. Wojcik, R. Wordel, M. Wurm, O. Zaimidoroga, S. Zavatarelli and G. Zuzel, The borexino detector at the laboratori nazionali del gran sasso, *Nuclear Instruments and Methods in Physics Research Section A: Accelerators, Spectrometers, Detectors and Associated Equipment* **600**, 568 (2009).
2. J. Benziger, L. Cadonati, F. Calaprice, M. Chen, A. Corsi, F. Dalnoki-Veress, R. Fernholz, R. Ford, C. Galbiati, A. Goretti, E. Harding, A. Ianni, A. Ianni, S. Kidner, M. Leung, F. Loeser, K. McCarty, D. McKinsey, A. Nelson, A. Pocar, C. Salvo, D. Schimizzi, T. Shutt and A. Sonnenschein, A scintillator purification system for the borexino solar neutrino detector, *Nuclear Instruments and Methods in Physics Research Section A: Accelerators, Spectrometers, Detectors and Associated Equipment* **587**, 277 (2008).
3. M. Agostini, K. Altenmüller, S. Appel, V. Atroshchenko, Z. Bagdasarian, D. Basilico, G. Bellini, J. Benziger, D. Bick, G. Bonfini, D. Bravo, B. Caccianiga, F. Calaprice, A. Caminata, L. Cappelli, P. Cavalcante, F. Cavanna, A. Chepurnov, K. Choi, D. D'Angelo, S. Davini, A. Derbin, A. Di Giacinto, V. Di Marcello, X. F. Ding, A. Di Ludovico, L. Di Noto, I. Drachnev, G. Fiorentini, A. Formozov, D. Franco, F. Gabriele, C. Galbiati, M. Gschwender, C. Ghiano, M. Giammarchi, A. Goretti, M. Gromov, D. Guffanti, C. Hagner, E. Hungerford, A. Ianni, A. Ianni, A. Jany, D. Jeschke, S. Kumaran, V. Kobychev, G. Korga, T. Lachenmaier, T. Lasserre, M. Laubenstein, E. Litvinovich, P. Lombardi, I. Lomskaya, L. Ludhova, G. Lukyanchenko, L. Lukyanchenko, I. Machulin, F. Mantovani, G. Manuzio, S. Marcocci, J. Maricic, J. Martyn, E. Meroni, M. Meyer, L. Miramonti, M. Misiaszek, M. Montuschi, V. Muratova, B. Neumair, M. Nieslony, L. Oberauer, A. Onillon, V. Orekhov, F. Ortica, M. Pallavicini, L. Papp, O. Penek, L. Pietrofaccia, N. Pilipenko, A. Pocar, G. Raikov, M. T. Ranalli, G. Ranucci,

A. Razeto, A. Re, M. Redchuk, B. Ricci, A. Romani, N. Rossi, S. Rottenanger, S. Schönert, D. Semenov, M. Skorokhvatov, O. Smirnov, A. Sotnikov, V. Strati, Y. Suvorov, R. Tartaglia, G. Testera, J. Thurn, E. Unzhakov, A. Vishneva, M. Vivier, R. B. Vogelaar, F. von Feilitzsch, M. Wojcik, M. Wurm, O. Zaimidoroga, S. Zavatarelli, K. Zuber and G. Zuzel, Comprehensive geoneutrino analysis with borexino, *Phys. Rev. D* **101**, p. 012009 (Jan 2020).

4. M. Agostini, K. Altenmüller, S. Appel, V. Atroshchenko, Z. Bagdasarian, D. Basilico, G. Bellini, J. Benziger, D. Bick, G. Bonfini, D. Bravo, B. Caccianiga, F. Calaprice, A. Caminata, S. Caprioli, M. Carlini, P. Cavalcante, A. Chepurnov, K. Choi, L. Collica, D. D'Angelo, S. Davini, A. Derbin, X. F. Ding, A. Di Ludovico, L. Di Noto, I. Drachnev, K. Fomenko, A. Formozov, D. Franco, F. Gabriele, C. Galbiati, C. Ghiano, M. Giammarchi, A. Goretti, M. Gromov, D. Guffanti, C. Hagner, T. Houdy, E. Hungerford, A. Ianni, A. Ianni, A. Jany, D. Jeschke, V. Kobychev, D. Korablev, G. Korga, D. Kryn, M. Laubenstein, E. Litvinovich, F. Lombardi, P. Lombardi, L. Ludhova, G. Lukyanchenko, L. Lukyanchenko, I. Machulin, G. Manuzio, S. Marcocci, J. Martyn, E. Meroni, M. Meyer, L. Miramonti, M. Misiaszek, V. Muratova, B. Neumair, L. Oberauer, B. Opitz, V. Orekhov, F. Ortica, M. Pallavicini, L. Papp, Ö. Penek, N. Pilipenko, A. Pocar, A. Porcelli, G. Raikov, G. Ranucci, A. Razeto, A. Re, M. Redchuk, A. Romani, R. Roncin, N. Rossi, S. Schönert, D. Semenov, M. Skorokhvatov, O. Smirnov, A. Sotnikov, L. F. F. Stokes, Y. Suvorov, R. Tartaglia, G. Testera, J. Thurn, M. Toropova, E. Unzhakov, F. L. Villante, A. Vishneva, R. B. Vogelaar, F. von Feilitzsch, H. Wang, S. Weinz, M. Wojcik, M. Wurm, Z. Yokley, O. Zaimidoroga, S. Zavatarelli, K. Zuber, G. Zuzel and T. B. Collaboration, Comprehensive measurement of pp-chain solar neutrinos, *Nature* **562**, 505 (2018).

5. M. Agostini, K. Altenmüller, S. Appel, V. Atroshchenko, Z. Bagdasarian, D. Basilico, G. Bellini, J. Benziger, R. Biondi, D. Bravo, B. Caccianiga, F. Calaprice, A. Caminata, P. Cavalcante, A. Chepurnov, D. D'Angelo, S. Davini, A. Derbin, A. Di Giacinto, V. Di Marcello, X. F. Ding, A. Di Ludovico, L. Di Noto, I. Drachnev, A. Formozov, D. Franco, C. Galbiati, C. Ghiano, M. Giammarchi, A. Goretti, A. S. Göttel, M. Gromov, D. Guffanti, A. Ianni, A. Ianni, A. Jany, D. Jeschke, V. Kobychev, G. Korga, S. Kumaran, M. Laubenstein, E. Litvinovich, P. Lombardi, I. Lomskaya, L. Ludhova, G. Lukyanchenko, L. Lukyanchenko, I. Machulin, J. Martyn, E. Meroni, M. Meyer, L. Miramonti, M. Misiaszek, V. Muratova, B. Neumair, M. Nieslony, R. Nugmanov, L. Oberauer, V. Orekhov, F. Ortica, M. Pallavicini, L. Papp, L. Pelicci, Ö. Penek, L. Pietrofaccia, N. Pilipenko, A. Pocar, G. Raikov, M. T. Ranalli, G. Ranucci, A. Razeto, A. Re, M. Redchuk, A. Romani, N. Rossi, S. Schönert, D. Semenov, G. Settanta, M. Skorokhvatov, A. Singhal, O. Smirnov, A. Sotnikov, Y. Suvorov, R. Tartaglia, G. Testera, J. Thurn, E. Unzhakov, F. L. Villante, A. Vishneva, R. B. Vogelaar, F. von Feilitzsch, M. Wojcik, M. Wurm, S. Zavatarelli, K. Zuber, G. Zuzel and T. B. Collaboration, Experimental evidence of neutrinos produced in the cno fusion cycle in the sun, *Nature* **587**, 577 (2020).

6. H. Back, G. Bellini, J. Benziger, D. Bick, G. Bonfini, D. Bravo, M. B. Avanzini, B. Caccianiga, L. Cadonati, F. Calaprice, C. Carraro, P. Cavalcante, A. Chavarria, A. Chepurnov, D. D. Angelo, S. Davini, A. Derbin, A. Etenko, F. von Feilitzsch, G. Fernandes, K. Fomenko, D. Franco, C. Galbiati, S. Gazzana, C. Ghiano, M. Giammarchi, M. Goeger-Neff, A. Goretti, L. Grandi, E. Guardincerri, S. Hardy, A. Ianni, A. Ianni, A. Kayunov, S. Kidner, V. Kobychev, D. Korablev, G. Korga, Y. Koshio, D. Kryn, M. Laubenstein, T. Lewke, E. Litvinovich, B. Loer, F. Lombardi, P. Lombardi, L. Ludhova, I. Machulin, S. Manecki, W. Maneschg, G. Manuzio, Q. Meindl,

E. Meroni, L. Miramonti, M. Misiaszek, D. Montanari, P. Mosteiro, V. Muratova, L. Oberauer, M. Obolensky, F. Ortica, K. Otis, M. Pallavicini, L. Papp, L. Perasso, S. Perasso, A. Pocar, R. S. Raghavan, G. Ranucci, A. Razeto, A. Re, A. Romani, N. Rossi, D. Rountree, A. Sabelnikov, R. Saldanha, C. Salvo, S. Schönert, H. Simgen, M. Skorokhvatov, O. Smirnov, A. Sotnikov, S. Sukhotin, Y. Suvorov, R. Tartaglia, G. Testera, D. Vignaud, R. B. Vogelaar, J. Winter, M. Wojcik, A. Wright, M. Wurm, J. Xu, O. Zaimidoroga, S. Zavatarelli and G. Zuzel, Borexino calibrations: hardware, methods, and results, *Journal of Instrumentation* **7**, P10018 (oct 2012).

7. G. Bellini, J. Benziger, D. Bick, G. Bonfini, D. Bravo, M. Buizza Avanzini, B. Caccianiga, L. Cadonati, F. Calaprice, P. Cavalcante, A. Chavarria, A. Chepurnov, D. D'Angelo, S. Davini, A. Derbin, A. Empl, A. Etenko, K. Fomenko, D. Franco, F. Gabriele, C. Galbiati, S. Gazzana, C. Ghiano, M. Giammarchi, M. Göger-Neff, A. Goretti, L. Grandi, M. Gromov, C. Hagner, E. Hungerford, A. Ianni, A. Ianni, V. Kobychev, D. Korablev, G. Korga, D. Kryn, M. Laubenstein, T. Lewke, E. Litvinovich, B. Loer, F. Lombardi, P. Lombardi, L. Ludhova, G. Lukyanchenko, I. Machulin, S. Manecki, W. Maneschg, G. Manuzio, Q. Meindl, E. Meroni, L. Miramonti, M. Misiaszek, M. Montuschi, P. Mosteiro, V. Muratova, L. Oberauer, M. Obolensky, F. Ortica, K. Otis, M. Pallavicini, L. Papp, C. Pena-Garay, L. Perasso, S. Perasso, A. Pocar, G. Ranucci, A. Razeto, A. Re, A. Romani, N. Rossi, R. Saldanha, C. Salvo, S. Schönert, H. Simgen, M. Skorokhvatov, O. Smirnov, A. Sotnikov, S. Sukhotin, Y. Suvorov, R. Tartaglia, G. Testera, D. Vignaud, R. B. Vogelaar, F. von Feilitzsch, J. Winter, M. Wojcik, A. Wright, M. Wurm, J. Xu, O. Zaimidoroga, S. Zavatarelli and G. Zuzel, Final results of borexino phase-i on low-energy solar neutrino spectroscopy, *Phys. Rev. D* **89**, p. 112007 (Jun 2014).

8. M. Agostini, K. Altenmüller, S. Appel, V. Atroshchenko, Z. Bagdasarian, D. Basilico, G. Bellini, J. Benziger, D. Bick, G. Bonfini, L. Borodikhina, D. Bravo, B. Caccianiga, F. Calaprice, A. Caminata, M. Canepa, S. Caprioli, M. Carlini, P. Cavalcante, A. Chepurnov, K. Choi, D. D'Angelo, S. Davini, A. Derbin, X. Ding, L. Di Noto, I. Drachnev, K. Fomenko, A. Formozov, D. Franco, F. Froborg, F. Gabriele, C. Galbiati, C. Ghiano, M. Giammarchi, M. Goeger-Neff, A. Goretti, M. Gromov, C. Hagner, T. Houdy, E. Hungerford, A. Ianni, A. Ianni, A. Jany, D. Jeschke, V. Kobychev, D. Korablev, G. Korga, D. Kryn, M. Laubenstein, E. Litvinovich, F. Lombardi, P. Lombardi, L. Ludhova, G. Lukyanchenko, I. Machulin, M. Magnozzi, G. Manuzio, S. Marcocci, J. Martyn, E. Meroni, M. Meyer, L. Miramonti, M. Misiaszek, V. Muratova, B. Neumair, L. Oberauer, B. Opitz, F. Ortica, M. Pallavicini, L. Papp, A. Pocar, G. Ranucci, A. Razeto, A. Re, A. Romani, R. Roncin, N. Rossi, S. Schönert, D. Semenov, P. Shakina, M. Skorokhvatov, O. Smirnov, A. Sotnikov, L. Stokes, Y. Suvorov, R. Tartaglia, G. Testera, J. Thurn, M. Toropova, E. Unzhakov, A. Vishneva, R. Vogelaar, F. von Feilitzsch, H. Wang, S. Weinz, M. Wojcik, M. Wurm, Z. Yokley, O. Zaimidoroga, S. Zavatarelli, K. Zuber and G. Zuzel, The monte carlo simulation of the borexino detector, *Astroparticle Physics* **97**, 136 (2018).

9. G. Bellini, J. Benziger, D. Bick, G. Bonfini, D. Bravo, B. Caccianiga, L. Cadonati, F. Calaprice, A. Caminata, P. Cavalcante, A. Chavarria, A. Chepurnov, D. D'Angelo, S. Davini, A. Derbin, A. Empl, A. Etenko, K. Fomenko, D. Franco, F. Gabriele, C. Galbiati, S. Gazzana, C. Ghiano, M. Giammarchi, M. Göger-Neff, A. Goretti, M. Gromov, C. Hagner, E. Hungerford, A. Ianni, A. Ianni, V. Kobychev, D. Korablev, G. Korga, D. Kryn, M. Laubenstein, B. Lehnert, T. Lewke, E. Litvinovich, F. Lombardi, P. Lombardi, L. Ludhova, G. Lukyanchenko, I. Machulin, S. Manecki, W. Maneschg,

S. Marcocci, Q. Meindl, E. Meroni, M. Meyer, L. Miramonti, M. Misiaszek, M. Montuschi, P. Mosteiro, V. Muratova, L. Oberauer, M. Obolensky, F. Ortica, K. Otis, M. Pallavicini, L. Papp, L. Perasso, A. Pocar, G. Ranucci, A. Razeto, A. Re, A. Romani, N. Rossi, R. Saldanha, C. Salvo, S. Schönert, H. Simgen, M. Skorokhvatov, O. Smirnov, A. Sotnikov, S. Sukhotin, Y. Suvorov, R. Tartaglia, G. Testera, D. Vignaud, R. B. Vogelaar, F. von Feilitzsch, H. Wang, J. Winter, M. Wojcik, A. Wright, M. Wurm, O. Zaimidoroga, S. Zavatarelli, K. Zuber, G. Zuzel and B. Collaboration, Neutrinos from the primary proton–proton fusion process in the sun, *Nature* **512**, 383 (2014).

Study of antineutrinos from the Earth and the Cosmos with the Borexino detector

Sandra Zavatarelli*, M. Agostini, K. Altenmuller, S. Appel, V. Atroshchenko, Z. Bagdasarian, D. Basilico, G. Bellini, J. Benziger, R. Biondi, D. Bravo, B. Caccianiga, A. Caminata, F. Calaprice, P. Cavalcante, A. Chepurnov, D. D'Angelo, S. Davini, A. Derbin, A. Di Giacinto, V. Di Marcello, X.F. Ding, A. Di Ludovico, L. Di Noto, I. Drachnev, A. Formozov, D. Franco, C. Galbiati, C. Ghiano, M. Giammarchi, A. Goretti, A.S. Gottel, M. Gromov, D. Guffanti, Aldo Ianni, Andrea Ianni, A. Jany, D. Jeschke, V. Kobychev, G. Korga, S. Kumaran, M. Laubenstein, E. Litvinovich, P. Lombardi, I. Lomskaya, L. Ludhova, G. Lukyanchenko, L. Lukyanchenko, I. Machulin, J. Martyn, E. Meroni, M. Meyer, L. Miramonti, M. Misiaszek, V. Muratova, B. Neumair, M. Nieslony, R. Nugmanov, L. Oberauer, V. Orekhov, F. Ortica, M. Pallavicini, L. Papp, L. Pelicci, O Penek, L. Pietrofaccia, N. Pilipenko, A. Pocar, G. Raikov, M.T. Ranalli, G. Ranucci, A. Razeto, A. Re, M. Redchuk, A. Romani, N. Rossi, S. Schonert, D. Semenov, G. Settanta, M. Skorokhvatov, A. Singhal, O. Smirnov, A. Sotnikov, Y. Suvorov, R. Tartaglia, G. Testera, J. Thurn, E. Unzhakov, F. Villante, A. Vishneva, R.B. Vogelaar, F. von Feilitzsch, M. Wojcik, M. Wurm, S. Zavatarelli, K. Zuber, and G. Zuzel (Borexino Collaboration)

*Istituto Nazionale di Fisica Nucleare - Sezione di Genova,
Via Dodecaneso 33, 16146 Genoa, Italy
E-mail: sandra.zavatarelli@ge.infn.it*

The largest amount of antineutrinos detected about the Earth is emitted by the natural radioactive decays of ^{232}Th and ^{238}U chains isotopes and of ^{40}K. Other flux components are yielded by cosmic rays interactions in the atmosphere or by possible extra-terrestrial sources such as supernovae explosions, gamma ray bursts, GW events and solar flares. This contribution is aimed to summarise the results obtained by the Borexino experiment about antineutrinos from the Earth and from extraterrestrial sources.

Keywords: Antineutrinos; Geonetrinos; solar flares; diffuse supernovae background.

1. Introduction

Large underground ultrapure liquid scintillators are very suitable to antineutrinos studies. Low energy neutrinos such as solar neutrinos are in general detected through the elastic scattering process on electrons but for electron antineutrinos a specific interaction channel can be exploited, the Inverse Beta-Decay (IBD) mechanism on the free proton:

$$\bar{\nu}_e + p \rightarrow n + e^+ \quad (1)$$

The emitted positron deposits its kinetic energy and annihilates almost immediately, inducing a prompt signal whose visible energy E_{prompt} is directly correlated with the incident antineutrino energy $E_{\bar{\nu}_e}$:

$$E_{prompt} = E_{\bar{\nu}_e} - 0.784 \, \text{MeV}. \quad (2)$$

The neutron thermalizes and is captured by a proton with the mean capture time: $\sim \tau = 254.5 \pm 1.8 \mu s$.[1] The IBD cross section is on average a factor ~ 100 higher than elastic scattering at few MeV. Moreover the fast time coincidence between the positron annihilation and the neutron capture provides an almost background free signature, that allows to investigate also tiny flux components. By exploiting this detection mechanism, Borexino[2] has robustly detected the geo-neutrino signal and begun to place constraints on the amount of radiogenic heating in the Earth's interior: the null-hypothesis of observing a geoneutrino signal from the mantle has been excluded at a 99.0% C.L. and the overall production of radiogenic heat constrained to $38.2^{+13.6}_{-12.7}$ TW.[3] The extreme radiopurity of the Borexino detector has also allowed to set new limits on diffuse supernova antineutrino background for in the previously unexplored energy region below 8 MeV,[4] and to obtain the best upper limits on all flavor antineutrino fluences in the few MeV energy range from solar flares,[4] gamma-ray bursts[5] and from gravitational wave events.[6] In the following sections we detail the analysis procedures and the results obtained by Borexino about geoneutrinos, diffuse supernovae background and possible time correlated signals with solar flares.

2. Geo-neutrinos

Geoneutrinos are electron antineutrinos ($\bar{\nu}_e$) emitted in the β decays of long-lived isotopes, which are present in the Earth, such as ^{40}K and the ^{238}U and ^{232}Th chain unstable isotopes.[11] The decay schemes and the released heat are summarised in the following equations:

$$^{238}\text{U} \rightarrow\ ^{206}\text{Pb} + 8\alpha + 8e^- + 6\bar{\nu}_e + 51.7 \quad \text{MeV} \tag{3}$$

$$^{235}\text{U} \rightarrow\ ^{207}\text{Pb} + 7\alpha + 4e^- + 4\bar{\nu}_e + 46.4 \text{ MeV} \tag{4}$$

$$^{232}\text{Th} \rightarrow\ ^{208}\text{Pb} + 6\alpha + 4e^- + 4\bar{\nu}_e + 42.7 \text{ MeV} \tag{5}$$

$$^{40}\text{K} \rightarrow\ ^{40}\text{Ca} + e^- + \bar{\nu}_e + 1.31 \text{ MeV } (89.3\%) \tag{6}$$

$$^{40}\text{K} + e \rightarrow\ ^{40}\text{Ar} + \nu_e + 1.505 \text{ MeV} \quad (10.7\%) \tag{7}$$

Since the present-day isotopic abundance of ^{235}U is small (0.7%), the overall contribution of ^{238}U, ^{232}Th, and ^{40}K is largely predominant. Information about the deep Earth's composition is mainly based on indirect probes: seismologic data constrains the density profile, while geochemistry provides predictions based on chemical compositions of upper Earth's rocks, chondritic meteorites, and the Sun photosphere. The surface of the Earth is emitting an heat flow at an estimated rate of 47 ± 2 TW.[12] This result is based on $\sim 40,000$ observations of heat conduction in surface rocks and corrected for hydrothermal circulation and volcanism. Measurements of Th, U and K in the continental crust rocks prove that at least ~ 8 TW of this heat is from radiogenic decays but is not at all known what proportion of the overall surface heat flow comes from radioactive decays and how much is from primordial sources such as the gravitational energy released after core formation or the kinetic energy of accretion bombardment.

Geo-neutrinos give us a way of measuring the amount of this radiogenic heat directly: the heat released is in a well fixed ratio with the total mass of Heat Producing Elements (HPE's) inside the Earth. Thus, it is possible to extract from the measured geo-neutrino fluxes several geological information unreachable by other means. The idea of studying geo-neutrinos dates back to the sixties[7,8] but only in 1998 it was proposed the idea of using solar neutrino and reactor neutrino detectors[9,10]: presently, two large-volume, liquid-scintillator neutrino experiments, KamLAND in Japan[13–15] and Borexino in Italy,[3,16–18] have been able to measure the geo-neutrino signal. The typical fluxes are of the order of 10^6 cm^{-2}s^{-1} and with cross section values of 10^{-43} cm^{-2} only a hand-full number of interactions, few tens per year are expected with the current-size detectors. This means, underground laboratories are crucial to shield the detector from cosmic radiation and make possible their measurement. Since the inverse beta decay (IBD) on protons has a threshold of 1.8 MeV (Eq. 1) and both the ^{40}K and ^{235}U geo-neutrinos spectra are below (Fig. 1), they cannot be detected by this process. However, the elemental abundances ratios are much better known than the absolute abundances. Therefore, by measuring the absolute content of ^{238}U and ^{232}Th, also the overall amount of ^{40}K and ^{235}U can be inferred with an improved precision.

Geo-neutrino spectrum extends up to 3.26 MeV and the ^{238}U and ^{232}Th contributions can be distinguished according to their different end-points (Fig. 1).

The most recent Borexino analysis is based on 3263 days of data taking in the period December 2007 - April 2019.

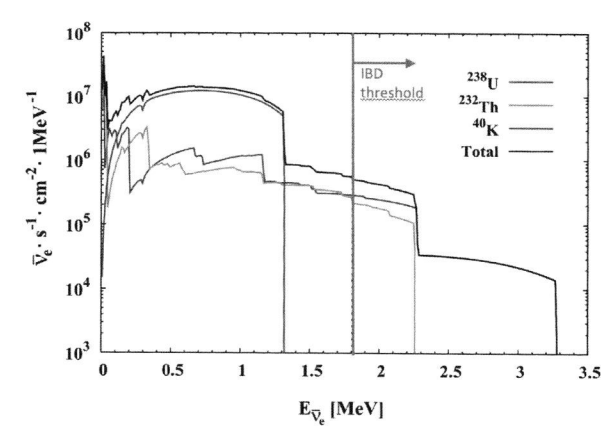

Fig. 1. Geoneutrino fluxes[3] from different isotopes and the overall signal at LNGS calculated with geophysical and geochemical inputs from[24] for the far-field lithosphere and from[23] for the local crust.

To select the $\bar{\nu}_e$ candidates we apply the following criteria: we discard events occurring within 2 ms of every muon crossing the outer detector to reject cosmogenic neutrons. In case of muons crossing the inner detector long-lived cosmogenic nuclides such a ^{9}Li may be produced: to reduce this possible background a different veto ranging from 0.2 to 2 s is applied after the muon depending on the deposited energy, the track reconstruction quality and the eventually associated neutrons. Independently from a detected muon, we ask that selected events are neither preceded or followed by neutron-like events within a 2 ms window. The coincidences are searched for at a distance between the reconstructed positions $\Delta r < 1.3$ m, that accounts for the uncertainty of the spatial reconstruction algorithm and the free path of the 2.2 MeV γ's and with Δt in the range 20–1280 μs ($\sim$5 neutron capture time) for single events, and 2.5–12.5 μs for double cluster events. We remind that if a decay triggering the Borexino DAQ is followed within 16.5 μs by other decays, it is classified as a unique event with multiple clusters. To reduce the external γ background from radioactive decays in the detector materials, we accept only candidates having the prompt event position reconstructed inside the inner detector at distance larger than 10 cm with respect to the the time-varying IV surface: $D_{IV,prompt} > 10\,cm$. The energy of the prompt event is required to be above the value corresponding to the IBD threshold, considering the energy resolution ($N_{p.e.,prompt} > 408$ p.e.), while for the delayed event, the energy cut was tuned to cover the gamma peak from neutron capture on proton and on carbon ($700 < N_{p.e.,delayed} < 3000$ p.e.). The lower limit is justified because photons at the edge of the scintillator can escape, depositing only a fraction of their total energy. This limit was increased to 860 p.e. during the detector purifications in 2010-2011 to remove the time-correlated $\beta + (\alpha + \gamma)$ decays of ^{214}Bi-^{214}Po, having a time constant close to the neutron capture time. Such background was relevant only during the purifications as a consequence of the increased radon contamination. Finally a pulse shape $\alpha - \beta$ discrimination is applied based on a trained MultiLayerPerceptron binary classifier [3] : MLP$_D > 0.8$ for delayed signals.

The combined efficiency of the cuts is determined by Monte Carlo to be $(85\pm1.0)\%$. The total efficiency-corrected exposure for the data set is $(1.29 \pm 0.05) \times 10^{32}$ protons $\times$ year with an increase by a factor of two over the previous Borexino analysis reported in 2015. We have identified 154 candidates passing all the selection cuts. The estimated background, that mimics $\bar{\nu}_e$ candidates, amounts to 8.28 ± 1.01 events, mainly due to random coincidences, residual ^{9}Li decays and ^{13}C$(\alpha,n)^{16}$O reactions in the scintillator.

Antineutrinos from nuclear reactor power plants are the main background to the geo-neutrino measurements. The $\bar{\nu}_e$ flux comes primarily from the beta decays of neutron-rich fragments produced in the fission of four isotopes: ^{235}U, ^{238}U, ^{239}Pu, and ^{241}Pu. The expected fluxes can be estimated from the knowledge of the monthly energy production at each reactor site, including the neutrino propagation effects. At present, there are about 440 nuclear power reactors in the world, providing, nominally, a total amount of about 1200 Thermal GW, corresponding to about 400 Electrical GW. Since there are no nuclear power plants close by, the Gran Sasso laboratory is well suited for geo-neutrino studies. According to a detailed computation[22] based on the information retrieved by the International Atomic Energy Agency database[19] we expect 91-98 events in our sample whereas the main source of uncertainty in the prediction comes from the knowledge of the energy spectrum for each fuel component at the source. The lowest value (91.9 ± 1.6) is obtained when the spectra are normalised to the measurements of reactor neutrino experiments[20,21] and they include also the so called "5 MeV excess".

A smaller background can also be induced by atmospheric neutrinos. Because of the uncertainty of the relevant fluxes and cross sections, this contribution is poorly constrained: we have estimated 9.2 ± 4.6 event in our sample.

Both reactor and atmospheric $\bar{\nu}_e$ are more energetic respect to the geo-neutrino; therefore they can be experimentally disentangled thanks to a fit of prompt event energies. An unbinned likelihood fit of the energy spectrum of selected prompt events has been performed.

In Fig. 2 the selected candidates and the fit results are shown. Using the value ratio for the masses of Th and U, m(Th)/m(U)=3.9, suggested by the chondritic metheorithes, our best fit yield $N_{geo} = 52.6^{+9.4}_{-8.6}(stat)^{+2.7}_{-2.1}(sys)$ events, with 18% precision. A compatible result was found when contributions from ^{238}U and ^{232}Th were both fit as free parameters. Antineutrino background from reactors is fit unconstrained and found compatible with the expectations. The measured geo-neutrino signal corresponds to fluxes at the detector from decays in the U and Th chains of $\Phi_U = 2.8^{+0.6}_{-0.4} \cdot 10^6$ cm^{-2}s^{-1} and $\Phi_{Th} = 2.6^{+0.6}_{-0.4} \cdot 10^6$ cm^{-2}s^{-1} respectively.

To connect the number of geo-neutrinos detected by an experiment with the overall radioactivity in the crust and in the mantle, we have to rely on our knowledge

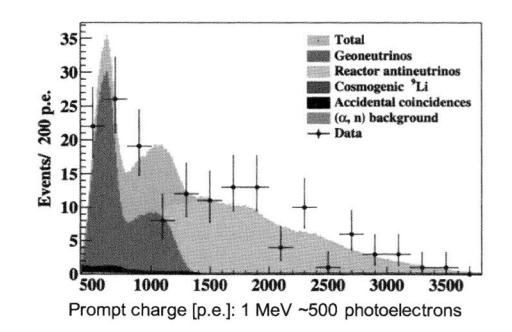

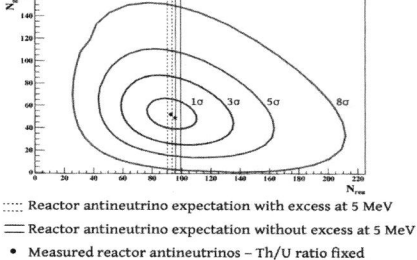

Fig. 2. (**Left**) Spectral fit of the data (black points assuming the chondritic Th/U ratio. Geoneutrinos (blue) and reactor antineutrinos (yellow) were kept as free fit parameters. Other non antineutrino backgrounds were constrained in the fit. (**Right**) The best fit point (black dot) and the 2D coverage contours for N_{geo} vs N_{rea}.

of the local geological conditions. Geoscientist developed models of the crust close to the Borexino site, based on geological surveys and on 3D models of all the layers up to the mantle boundary.[23,24] Both U and Th are lithophile i.e. "rock-loving" elements so they are believed to be concentrated in the crust and mantle and absent in the iron-made core. According to these studies 28.8 ± 5.6 events should have been induced by the crust radioactivity among the 154 candidates: we have therefore repeated the fit with separate contribution of mantle and crust geoneutrinos, the latter being constrained to the expectations within the error. A small difference in the relative amount of U and Th fraction in the two signals has been introduced according to geological predictions. The fit returns $N_{geo} = 23.7^{+10.7}_{-10.0}(stat)^{+1.2}_{-1.0}(sys)$ events: with a sensitivity study the null-hypothesis of observing geoneutrino signal from the mantle is excluded at a 99.0% C.L..

It is possible to extract from the measured geo-neutrino signal, the Earth's radiogenic heat power that is a fundamental question for understanding the plate tectonics and mantle convection. The uncertain distribution of HPE's in the deep Earth has to be included: two rather extreme cases are represented by the homogeneous mantle or by the assumption that all the U and Th are placed at the mantle core boundary. By following this conservative approach one can demonstrate that our measured mantle signal corresponds to the production of a radiogenic heat of 24.6 ± 11.1 TW (68% interval) from ^{238}U and ^{232}Th in the mantle. Assuming 18% contribution of ^{40}K in the mantle and 8.1 ± 1.9 TW of total radiogenic heat of the lithosphere, the Borexino estimate of the total radiogenic heat of the Earth is 38.2 ± 13.6 TW, which corresponds to ∼81% of the overall Earth's heat flux (47 TW). These values are compatible with different geological predictions, in the particular with the geodynamical BSE models,[25] however there is a ∼2.4σ tension with those Earth models which predict the lowest concentration of heat-producing elements in the mantle, such as cosmochemical ones.[25] In addition, by constraining the number of expected reactor antineutrino events, the existence of a hypothetical georeactor at the center of the Earth having power greater than 2.4 TW is excluded at 95% C.L..[26,27] In conclusion, Borexino confirms the feasibility of geoneutrino measurements as well as the validity of different geological models predicting the U and Th abundances in the Earth. This is an enormous success of both neutrino physics and geosciences. The next generation of large volume liquid scintillator detectors (such as JUNO and SNO+) has a strong potential to provide fundamental information about our planet and geoneutrinos may be the key tool to support the new discoveries about the deep Earth.

3. Diffuse supernovae neutrino background

The Diffuse Supernova Neutrino Background (DSNB) is formed by the stars that collapsed during the evolution of the Universe and it is made of neutrinos and antineutrinos of all flavours. The flux spectrum at the Earth can be parametrised as[28]:

$$\frac{d\phi_\nu}{dE_\nu} = \frac{c}{H_0} \int_0^{z_{max}} \frac{dN_\nu(E'_\nu)}{dE'_\nu} \frac{R_{SN}(z)dz}{\sqrt{\Omega_m(1+z)^3 + \Omega_\Lambda}}, \qquad (8)$$

where c is the speed of light, z is the red shift, H_0 is Hubble constant, $R_{SN}(z)$ is the supernova rate at the distance z to the observer $\frac{dN_\nu(E'_\nu)}{dE'_\nu}$ is the neutrino emission spectrum for individual supernova, Ω_m and Ω_Λ are the relative densities of matter and dark energy in the Universe. The spectrum is sensitive to particular cosmological model through Ω_m and Ω_Λ and reflects the expansion of the Universe through the dependence on H_0.

The possible signal due to tiny, still undisclosed, extraterrestrial $\bar{\nu}_e$ fluxes, such as supernovae relic neutrinos, can be put in evidence as an excess of events with respect to the backgrounds and the known sources of $\bar{\nu}_e$. Borexino made a search for this possible signal, based on the data collected between December 2007–October 2017. The events selection is based on an approach similar to the one adopted in the geo-neutrino analysis, the only differences being more conservative muon and FV cuts. In detail we applied a veto of 2 s after each muon crossing the inner detector and we asked for a prompt event distance from the inner vessel larger than 25 cm: in the overall statistics we have selected 101 candidates.

As outlined in the previous sections, the most relevant sources of $\bar{\nu}_e$ events below 10 MeV are the Earth's radioactive isotopes and the nuclear reactors, while at higher energies the atmospheric neutrino background dominates the energy spectrum. Borexino made a comprehensive study of geo-neutrinos but the achieved precision, in particular on the mantle signal is still poor ($\sim 40\%$), With the aim to quote conservative limits, the minimal expected number of events for each background has been considered. For the geoneutrino signal we have therefore chosen the Minimal Radiogenic Earth model, which only includes the radioactivity from the crust and that, in our case, corresponds to 17.9 ± 2.1 events in our data sample.

The spectrum of reactor $\bar{\nu}_e$ is significant till ~ 10 MeV. As discussed before, the flux calculation that includes the normalisation to reactor neutrino experiments data provides the lowest signal. We have taken this option being the most conservative: 61.1 ± 1.7 events among our candidates have been attributed to reactor $\bar{\nu}_e$. Finally the most serious background to the detection of DSNB fluxes at energies above 10 MeV is induced by the atmospheric neutrinos, i.e., the ν's and $\bar{\nu}$'s generated in the decay of secondary particles produced in the interactions of primary cosmic rays with Earth's atmosphere. After the simulation of detector response and by applying the same selection cuts as for real data, we have estimated 6.5 ± 3.2 IBD-like events in the present analysis statistics and in the equivalent $\bar{\nu}_e$ energy window 1.8–16.8 MeV. In the light of the large uncertainty on this background source, a conservative choice would be to not consider it at all in the upper limit calculations: this is the approach followed in Fig. 3. The model-independent limit for electron antineutrino flux ($\Phi_{\bar{\nu}_e}$) in each energy bin (i) have been computed according to the equation:

$$\Phi_{\bar{\nu}_e,i} = \frac{N_{90,i}}{<\sigma> \cdot \varepsilon \cdot N_p \cdot T} \tag{9}$$

where N_{90} is the 90% C.L. upper limit for the number of antineutrino interactions obtained by following the Feldman-Cousins approach,[29] $<\sigma>$ is the mean cross-section of Inverse Beta Decay calculated according to[30] for each energy bin, $\varepsilon = (0.850 \pm 0.015)$ is the average detection efficiency, $N_p = (1.32 \pm 0.06) \times 10^{31}$ is the number of protons in the Borexino average fiducial volume mass and $T = 2485$ days is the total live-time. The other limits existing in literature are quoted on the same plot.

Borexino limits are the only existing below 8 MeV, thanks to the high energy resolution, the low intrinsic backgrounds, and the small reactor $\bar{\nu}_e$ flux at the Gran Sasso site.

4. Search for time correlated signals with solar flares

Solar flares are induced by the rearrangement of the solar magnetic field which also bring to the acceleration of charged particles. Pions, eventually produced in the flare's region by pp- and $p\alpha$-collisions, could then decay by emitting neutrinos with a mean neutrino energy expected around ~ 10 MeV.[35]

In the eighties R. Davis[36,37] advanced for the first time the possibility of neutrino emissions correlated with solar flares as an explanation for the excess of events in several runs of the Homestake Cl-Ar experiment. In general the production of $\bar{\nu}_e$ is expected to be smaller respect to ν_e due to the higher threshold of π^- generation in pp-collisions: for this reason we have searched for ν_x and $\bar{\nu}_x$ ($x = e, \mu, \tau$)

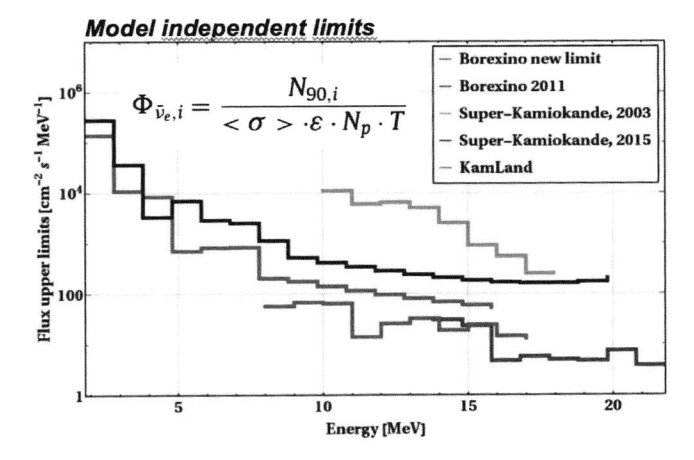

Fig. 3. Borexino model-independent limits on electron $\bar{\nu}_e$ fluxes from unknown sources compared with the results of other experiments (Super-Kamiokande,[31,32] KamLAND[33]) and older Borexino limits.[34]

signals correlated with solar flares by looking their elastic scattering on electrons in the Borexino scintillator. According to the assumption that the neutrino flux is proportional to the flare's intensity, we have only considered the most intense flares of M and X classes according to the GOES database.[38]

The analysis is based on the statistics collected between November 2009 and October 2017 : data acquired both by the primary and the FADC DAQ systems have been used in the energy interval of 1–15 MeV, while in the interval 0.25 – 1 MeV only the primary DAQ data have been considered. After removing muons and muon daughters, single events are selected without any fiducial volume cut in the interval of 1–15 MeV, while at lower energies a fiducial volume cut of 145 tons (75 cm from the IV) is applied to reduce the external radioactivity. In our study, an excess of single events above the measured background at the time of a flare is searched for. For the flare signal we choose a time window equal to the flare's duration according to the database, while the background is calculated in a time window of the same length but opened before the flare time. By requiring at least 95% of Borexino's up time for both windows we restrict our analysis to a 472 flares sample. No statistically significant excess of events is observed in correlation with the flares. The fluence limit for neutrinos of energy E_ν is calculated according to the equation:

$$\Phi_\nu(E_\nu) = \frac{N_{90}(E_\nu)}{N_e \sigma_{\text{eff}}(E_\nu)}, \qquad (10)$$

where N_e is the number of electrons in the Borexino scintillator, that is, $N_e = 9.2 \cdot 10^{31}$ for the whole IV and $N_e = 4.8 \cdot 10^{31}$ for the 145 tons FV. The scattering of monoenergetic neutrinos with energy E_ν off electrons leads to recoil electrons with a Compton-like continuous energy spectrum with maximum energy $T_\nu^{max} = 2E_\nu^2/(m_e + 2E_\nu)$. For each neutrino energy bin, a corresponding recoiled electrons energy interval is computed by considering the cross section and the detector response function.

In order to set the fluence limits for flare-correlated neutrinos (antineutrinos) of electron and $(\mu + \tau)$ flavors individually, the corresponding cross section in Eq. 10 was set to σ_{ν_e} ($\sigma_{\bar{\nu}_e}$) and $\sigma_{\nu_{\mu,\tau}}$ ($\sigma_{\bar{\nu}_{\mu,\tau}}$), respectively. Figure 4 quotes Borexino limits obtained from the primary DAQ ($E_\nu < 3.5$ MeV) and the FADC DAQ ($E_\nu > 3.5$ MeV).

Limits for ν_e quoted by SNO[39] and an allowed band for the neutrino fluence that would have explained the Homestake run 117 excess of events are also shown for comparison.

As of today, Borexino sets the strongest limits on fluences of all neutrino flavors from the solar flares below 3–7 MeV. Under the hyphothesis that neutrino flux is proportional to the flare's intensity, Borexino's data excludes an intense solar flare occurred during run 117 of the Cl-Ar Homestake experiment as a possible source for the observed excess of events.

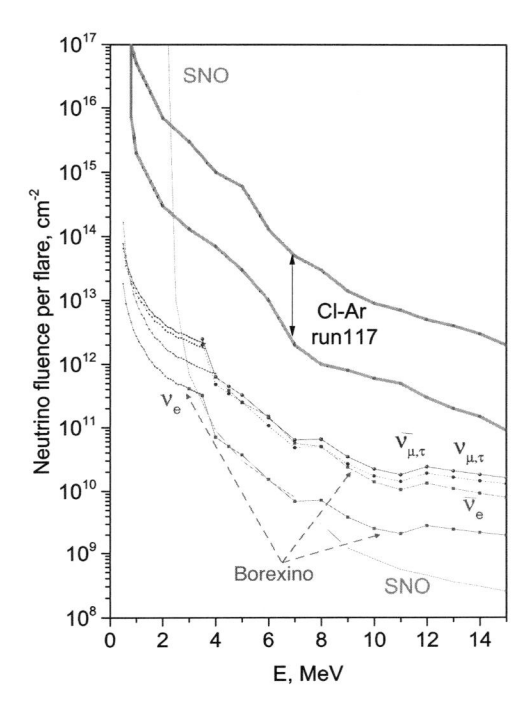

Fig. 4. Borexino 90% C.L. fluence upper limits obtained through elastic scattering for ν_e, $\bar{\nu}_e$, $\nu_{\mu,\tau}$, and $\bar{\nu}_{\mu,\tau}$. The limits by SNO[39] for ν_e are reported and the fluences that would have explained the Cl-Ar Homestake excess in run 117.

5. Conclusions

Large ultrapure liquid scintillators in underground laboratories have a strong potential for the comprehension of our planet energetics and in the various fields of experimental neutrino astronomy. Collecting more data in the incoming years with a network of detectors will be crucial to probe the very foundations of our understanding of the Universe and of our planet.

References

1. G. Bellini et al. (Borexino Collaboration), *J. Instrum.* **6**, P05005 (2011).
2. G. Alimonti et al. (Borexino Collaboration), *Nucl. Instr. and Meth. A* **600**, 58 (2009).
3. M. Agostini et al. (Borexino Collaboration), *Phys. Rev. D* **101**, 012009 (2020).
4. M. Agostini et al. (Borexino Collaboration), *Astropart. Phys.* **125**, 102509 (2021).
5. M. Agostini et al. (Borexino Collaboration), *Astropart. Phys.* **86**, 11 (2017).
6. M. Agostini et al. (Borexino Collaboration), *Ap. J.* **850**, 21 (2017).
7. G. Eder, *Nucl. Phys.* **78** (1966)
8. G. Marx, *Czech J. Phys. B* **19** (1969).
9. R. S. Raghavan et al., *Phys. Rev. Lett.* **80**, 635 (1998).
10. C. G. Rotschild, et al., *Geo. Res. Lett.* **25**, 1083 (1998).

11. G. Fiorentini, M. Lissia, and F. Mantovani, *Phys. Rep.* **453**, 117 (2007).
12. J. H. Davies and D. R. Davies, *Solid Earth* **1**, 5 (2010).
13. T. Araki et al. (KamLAND Collaboration), *Nature* **436**, 499 (2005).
14. S. Abe et al. (KamLAND Collaboration), *Phys. Rev. Lett.* **100**, 221803 (2008).
15. A. Gando et al. (KamLAND Collaboration), *Phys. Rev. D* **88**, 033001 (2013).
16. G. Bellini et al. (Borexino Collaboration), *Phys. Lett. B* **687**, 299 (2010).
17. G. Bellini et al. (Borexino Collaboration), *Phys. Lett. B* **722**, 295 (2013).
18. M. Agostini et al. (Borexino Collaboration), *Phys. Rev. D* **92**, 031101 (2015).
19. Nuclear Power Engineering Section, IAEA-PRIS database, http://www.iaea.org/pris/
20. F. P. An et al. (Daya Bay Collaboration), *Phys. Rev. Lett.* **116**, 061801 (2016).
21. F. P. An et al. (Daya Bay Collaboration), *Phys. Rev. Lett.* **118**, 099902(E) (2017).
22. M. Baldoncini, I. Callegari, G. Fiorentini, F. Mantovani, B. Ricci, V. Strati, and G. Xhixha, *Phys. Rev. D* **91**, 065002 (2015).
23. M. Coltorti et al., *Earth Planet. Sci. Lett.* **293**, 259 (2010).
24. Y. Huang, V. Chubakov, F. Manotavani, R. L. Rudnick, and W. F. McDonough, *Geochemistry, Geophysics, Geosystems* **14**, 2003 (2013).
25. O. Sramek, W. F. McDonough, E. S. Kite, V. Lekic, S. T. Dye, and S. Zhong, *Earth and Planet. Sci. Lett.* **361**, 356 (2013).
26. J. M. Herndon, *Proc. Natl. Acad. Sci. U.S.A.* **93(2)**, 646 (1996).
27. J. M. Herndon and D. A. Edgerley, *arXiv:hep-ph/0501216*.
28. S. Ando and K. Sato, *New J. Phys* **6**, 170 (2004).
29. G. J. Feldman, R. D. Cousins, *Phys. Rev. D* **57**, 3873(1998).
30. A. Strumia, F. Vissani, *Phys. Lett. B* **564**, 42 (2003).
31. Y. Gando, et al. (Super-Kamiokande Collaboration), *Phys. Rev. Lett.* **90**, 171302 (2003).
32. H. Zhang, et al. (Super-Kamiokande Collaboration), *Astropart. Phys.* **60**, 41 (2015).
33. A. Gando, et al. (KamLAND Collaboration), *Astroph. J.* **745**, 193 (2012).
34. G. Bellini, et al. (Borexino Collaboration), *Phys. Lett. B* **696**, 191 (2011).
35. G. E. Kocharov, G. A. Kovaltsov, I. G. Usoskin, *Il nuovo cimento* **14 C**, 417 (1991).
36. R. Davis Jr., *Prog. Part. Nucl. Phys.* **32**, 13 (1994).
37. R. Davis Jr., *Nucl. Phys. Proc. Suppl.* **48**, 284 (1996).
38. GOES Database: https://hesperia.gsfc.nasa.gov/goes/goeseventlistings
39. B. Aharmim et al. (SNO Collaboration), *Astropart. Phys.* **551137**, 1 (2014).

Unveiling the engine of the Sun: Measurements of the pp-chain solar neutrinos with Borexino

D. Guffanti[1,†], A.C. Re[2], O. Smirnov[3]

[1] *Institute of Physics and Excellence Cluster PRISMA+,
Johannes Gutenberg-Universität Mainz, 55099, Mainz, Germany*
daniele.guffanti@uni-mainz.de

[2] *Dipartimento di Fisica "A. Pontremoli", Università degli Studi and INFN Milano,
20133 Milano, Italy*
alessandra.re@mi.infn.it

[3] *Joint Institute for Nuclear Research, 141980 Dubna, Russia*
oleg.smirnov@lngs.infn.it

on behalf of the Borexino Collaboration:
M. Agostini, K. Altenmüller, S. Appel, V. Atroshchenko, Z. Bagdasarian,
D. Basilico, G. Bellini, J. Benziger, R. Biondi, D. Bravo, B. Caccianiga,
F. Calaprice, A. Caminata, P. Cavalcante, A. Chepurnov, D. D'Angelo,
S. Davini, A. Derbin, A. Di Giacinto, V. Di Marcello, X.F. Ding, A. Di
Ludovico, L. Di Noto, I. Drachnev, A. Formozov, D. Franco, C. Galbiati,
C. Ghiano, M. Giammarchi, A. Goretti, A.S. Göttel, M. Gromov, Aldo Ianni,
Andrea Ianni, A. Jany, D. Jeschke, V. Kobychev, G. Korga, S. Kumaran,
M. Laubenstein, E. Litvinovich, P. Lombardi, I. Lomskaya, L. Ludhova,
G. Lukyanchenko, L. Lukyanchenko, I. Machulin, J. Martyn, E. Meroni,
M. Meyer, L. Miramonti, M. Misiaszek, V. Muratova, B. Neumair,
M. Nieslony, R. Nugmanov, L. Oberauer, V. Orekhov, F. Ortica,
M. Pallavicini, L. Papp, L. Pelicci, Ö. Penek, L. Pietrofaccia, N. Pilipenko,
A. Pocar, G. Raikov, M.T. Ranalli, G. Ranucci, A. Razeto, M. Redchuk,
A. Romani, N. Rossi, S. Schönert, D. Semenov, G. Settanta,
M. Skorokhvatov, A. Singhal, A. Sotnikov, Y. Suvorov, R. Tartaglia,
G. Testera, J. Thurn, E. Unzhakov, F. Villante, A. Vishneva, R.B. Vogelaar,
F. von Feilitzsch, M. Wojcik, M. Wurm, S. Zavatarelli, K. Zuber,
and G. Zuzel.

About 99% of solar energy is produced through sequences of nuclear processes that convert Hydrogen into Helium in the so-called pp-chain. The neutrinos emitted in five of these reactions represent a unique probe of the Sun's internal working and, at the same time, offer an intense natural neutrino beam for fundamental physics research.

The Borexino experiment consists of a large-volume liquid-scintillator detector designed and constructed for real-time detection of low energy solar neutrinos. It is installed at the underground INFN Laboratori Nazionali del Gran Sasso (L'Aquila, Italy) and started taking data in May 2007. Borexino has been the only experiment so far capable of performing a complete study of the pp-chain by directly measuring the neutrino-electron

---
[†]Current address: Dipartimento di Fisica "G. Occhialini", Università degli Studi and INFN Milano Bicocca, 20126 Milano, Italy.

elastic scattering rates for the neutrinos produced in four of its reactions: the initial proton–proton (pp) fusion, the electron capture of Beryllium-7, the proton–electron–proton (pep) fusion, and the Boron-8 β^+ decay. A limit on the neutrino flux produced in the helium-proton fusion (hep) was also set. This set of measurements further probes the solar fusion mechanism via the direct determination of the relative intensity of the two primary terminations of the pp-chain, and the computation of the solar neutrino luminosity. Moreover, the Beryllium-7 and Boron-8 fluxes are indicative of the Sun's core temperature, and their measurement shows a mild preference for the higher temperature expected from the high-metallicity Standard Solar Model scenario. Finally, the experimental survival probability of these solar electron neutrinos allows to simultaneously probe the MSW neutrino flavor conversion paradigm, both in vacuum and in matter-dominated regimes, at different energies.

The details of the strategy adopted by the Borexino collaboration for successfully isolating the spectral components of the pp-chain neutrinos signal from residual backgrounds in the total energy spectrum will be presented.

Keywords: Solar neutrinos, proton-proton chain, Borexino

1. Introduction

The study of neutrinos generated by nuclear processes in the Sun has been producing outstanding scientific results for more than 50 years in both the fields of astrophysics and particle physics. The measurements of solar neutrinos provided the first direct evidence of the nuclear origin of stars' luminosity, as well as the first indication of flavour transition in the neutrino sector. In the years, solar neutrino experiments have progressively improved their accuracy, bringing new insights on the functioning of the Sun and on the properties of neutrinos.

The Borexino experiment is a key player in this field, being the most sensitive detector so-far for low-energy solar neutrinos. One of the milestones of the Borexino physics program, which significantly exceeded the expected physics reach, is the (almost) complete investigation of neutrinos produced throughout the entire proton-proton fusion chain, the sequence of nuclear reactions responsible for $\approx 99\%$ of the Sun luminosity. This fundamental result, partially achieved already during the first phase of the experiment (2007-2010), has been further improved in the phase II (2011-2016) and made it possible to test our knowledge of the Sun and to constrain exotic properties of neutrinos.

We present in this contribution the latest results of Borexino regarding solar neutrinos emitted throughout the pp-chain and we discuss their implications for both neutrino and solar physics. Section 2 describes the proton-proton fusion chain and the neutrinos produced therein, while the Borexino detector is presented in Sec. 3. The spectrum of solar neutrinos spans across a wide energy range extended up to 19 MeV and their fluxes vary of several orders of magnitude, therefore we setup two separate analyses targeting the low- and high-energy region of the solar neutrino spectrum that are described in Secs. 4 and 5 respectively along with the main results of Borexino.

2. Solar neutrinos from the pp-chain

The Sun, as most of other stars, produces energy by fusing four protons into a helium nucleus. This idea, originally hypothesized by Perrin and Eddington,[1,2] was later formalized by Bethe and Critchfield and independently by Weizsäcker who proposed two mechanisms for the hydrogen burning, known as the proton-proton chain[3] (pp-chain) and the Carbon-Nitrogen-Oxygen (CNO) cycle.[4-6] The relative efficiency of these two processes depends heavily on the features of the star under consideration, specifically on its core temperature and on its chemical composition. While the CNO-cycle was initially believed to be the dominant energy-production mechanism in the Sun, in light of a more accurate estimate of the Sun core temperature it became clear that the pp-chain drives the energy production in the Sun. The relative weight of the two mechanisms is estimated by a detailed model of the Sun, also known as Standard Solar Model (SSM), which -provided an accurate description of all the physical processes driving the evolution of a star- is able to produce a comprehensive snapshot of the Sun by forcing the modelled star to match the current solar mass, radius, luminosity and surface composition. The most recent update of the SSM[7] indicates that only $\approx 1\%$ of the Sun energy is produced through the CNO-cycle, while the real "engine" of the Sun is the pp-chain, accounting for $\approx 99\%$ of the Sun luminosity.

$$p + p \to {}^2\mathrm{H} + e^+ + \boxed{\nu_e} \qquad p + e^- + p \to {}^2\mathrm{H} + \boxed{\nu_e}$$

99.76% | 0.24%

$${}^2\mathrm{H} + p \to {}^3\mathrm{He} + \gamma$$

84.6% | 15.4% | $2.5 \times 10^{-5}\%$

$${}^3\mathrm{He} + {}^3\mathrm{He} \to {}^4\mathrm{He} + 2p \qquad {}^3\mathrm{He} + {}^4\mathrm{He} \to {}^7\mathrm{Be} + \gamma \qquad \boxed{\text{hep } \nu}$$

99.89% | 0.11%

$${}^7\mathrm{Be} + e^- \to {}^7\mathrm{Li} + \boxed{\nu_e} \qquad {}^7\mathrm{Be} + p \to {}^8\mathrm{B} + \gamma$$

$${}^7\mathrm{Li} + p \to 2\mathrm{He}^4 \qquad {}^8\mathrm{B} \to {}^8\mathrm{Be}^* + e^+ + \boxed{\nu_e}$$

$${}^8\mathrm{Be} \to 2\,{}^4\mathrm{He}$$

ppI   **ppII**   **ppIII**   hep

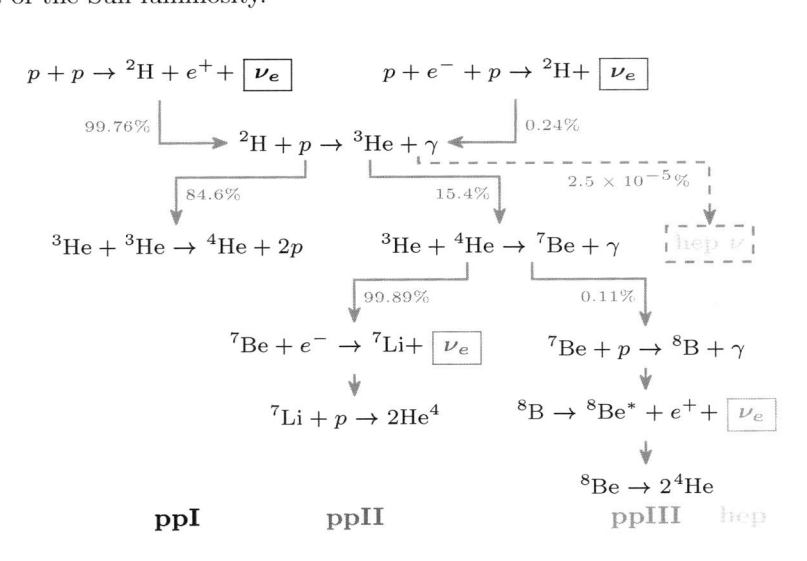

Fig. 1. The sequence of reactions composing the proton-proton fusion chain.

The sequence of reactions composing the pp-chain is shown in Fig. 1. Neutrinos are emitted in five of such processes, starting with the fusion of two protons into a deuteron which begins the chain (pp neutrinos). An alternative way of producing a deuteron, although ≈ 400 times less likely than the proton-proton fusion, consists in the reaction between two protons and an electron, which releases a 1.44 MeV monoenergetic neutrino (*pep* neutrino). The *pp*-chain can progress into different branches, namely ppI, ppII, ppIII and hep. Depending on the evolution of the chain, different neutrinos can be emitted: while the most prominent branch (ppI) terminates the chain without releasing any additional neutrino, the ppII branch is characterized by monoenergetic neutrinos produced by electron-capture onto ^{7}Be, with energy of 0.86 MeV (branching ratio 89.5%) or 0.38 MeV (B.R. 10.5%) depending if the ^{7}Li nucleus in the final state is produced at its ground state or on the first excited state. The high-energy neutrinos emitted in the decay of ^{8}B (*Q*-value 15.5 MeV) tag the ppIII branch, and the faintest branch of all, the helium-proton fusion (hep) branch, produces neutrinos up to an energy of 19.8 MeV. The expected solar neutrino spectrum is shown in Fig. 2.

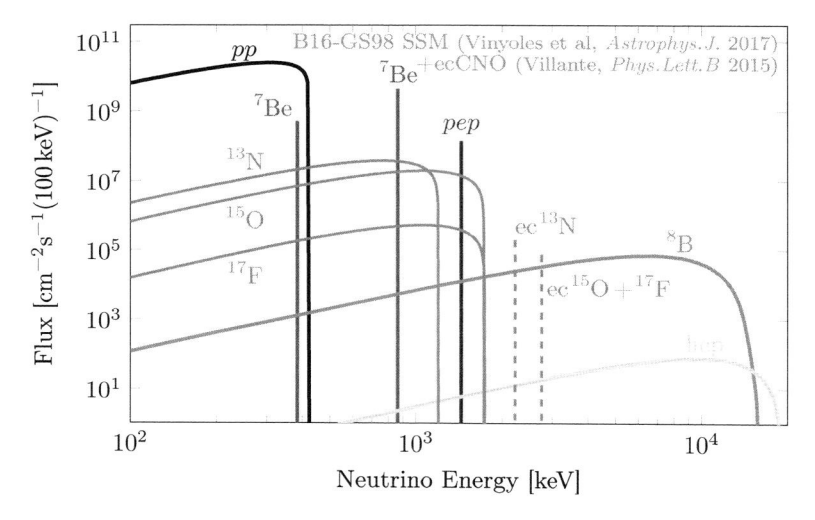

Fig. 2. Expected solar neutrino spectrum, with the neutrinos originating from the *pp*-chain shown with coloured lines and those produced in the CNO-cycle in grey. The fluxes are taken from[7,8] (note that the flux of monoenergetic neutrinos is reported in cm^{-2} s^{-1}).

The fluxes of *pp*-chain solar neutrinos depends on the abundance of heavy elements in the Sun, which is currently not fully understood and affects the temperature profile thus impacting on the *pp*-chain nuclear reactions rate. Recent estimates of the photosphere composition[9] (AGSS09met) show a consistent reduction of the metallicity respect to previous studies[10] (GS98), but this new "low-metallicity" (LZ) SSM shows a worst agreement with observation of the sound speed profile as inferred by helioseismology measurements respect to the old "high-metallicity" (HZ) predictions.[7] The precision measurement of solar neutrino fluxes from the *pp*-chain and the CNO-cycle is a promising way to solve the controversy about solar metallicity and the impact of Borexino results in this connection is discussed in Sec. 6.

3. The Borexino experiment

The Borexino experiment can detect solar neutrinos which interact via elastic scattering with the electrons of a liquid scintillator (LS). This detection technique, which provides a low-energy threshold and a good energy resolution, makes it possible to separate the different components of the solar neutrino flux exploiting their specific signature in the energy spectrum, but requires an extremely careful strategy to reduce the indistinguishable radioactive background since the expected interaction rate is ≈ 9 orders of magnitude smaller than the average activity of ordinary water.

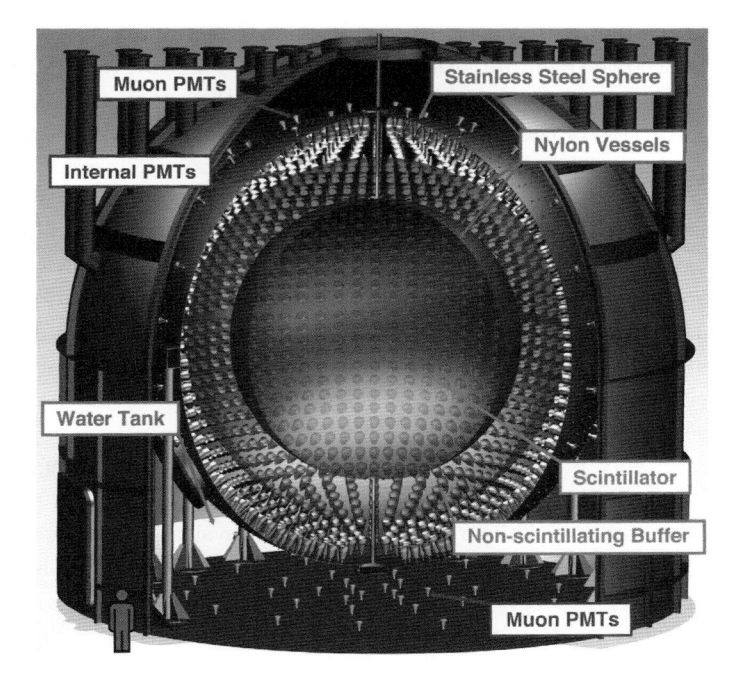

Fig. 3. Schematic view of the Borexino detector. Figure from.[11]

A cutaway of the detector is shown in Fig. 3. The experiment[12] is located in the INFN Gran Sasso National Laboratories, under the Gran Sasso massif in L'Aquila (Italy). The underground laboratories are shielded from cosmic radiation by 1400 m or rock (3800 m.w.e.), which attenuates the cosmic-ray flux by 6 orders of magnitude. Residual muons still reaching the experimental hall[13] ($3.432 \pm 0.003\,\mathrm{cm^{-2}\,s^{-1}}$) are tagged using a water Cherenkov detector equipped with 208 PMTs which surrounds the entire inner detector also providing an effective shielding against environmental neutrons and γ-rays. The detector active volume consists of ≈ 300 ton of pseudocumene mixed with 1.5 g/l of (PPO) as a wavelength shifter and is contained into a 125 µm-thick, 4.25 m radius spherical nylon vessel (Inner Vessel, IV). The light produced by the energy deposition of charged particles is detected by 2212 8 in PMTs (1800 of which are equipped with a light collector cone) mounted onto a 6.85 m radius Stainless Steel Sphere. The space between the IV and the PMTs is filled with quenched LS in order to shield the active volume from the radiation coming from radioactive contamination in the PMTs' glass and in the steel of the support structure.

With the underground location and shielding strategies fighting the external background, the key of Borexino results has been the successful suppression of internal background, *i.e.* those radioactive contamination of the detector itself. This has been achieved thanks to a careful selection of materials and to the implementation of effective purification methods for the LS (primarily distillation and water extraction) which reduced the contamination of ^{238}U and ^{232}Th down to $< 9.5 \times 10^{-20}$ g/g and $< 7.2 \times 10^{-19}$ g/g respectively in the Phase II of the experiment.[14]

The reconstruction of the solar neutrino interaction rate and its separation from the residual background is based primarily (although not exclusively) on the signatures in the visible energy spectrum reconstructed from the scintillation light, therefore the understanding of the detector energy response is fundamental. The energy released in the detector is reconstructed by measuring the isotropic scintillation light produced by recoiling electrons in the LS; the information about the detected light is expressed using three different energy observable that are used in the analysis: the number of hit PMTs in a 230(400) time window ($N_p^{dt_{1(2)}}$), the number of reconstructed hits (N_h) and the total charge measured at the PMTs anode, *i.e.* the number of detected photoelectrons (N_{pe}).

Borexino can rely on two different methods to model the detector response function: the first is based on a full Monte Carlo (MC) simulation of the entire experimental apparatus,[15] which reproduces all the physical processes following the interaction of a particle in the detector (including the electronic chain response) and keeps track of evolution of the detector properties in time, such as the number of operating channels. The simulation has been tuned using both lab measurements and data collected in an extensive calibration campaign,[16] resulting in a sub-percent accuracy for the variables of interest for solar neutrino analysis.[15] An alternative method for modelling the detector energy response consists in an analytical model encapsulating the effect of ionization quenching, the contribution of Cherenkov light as well as the spatial dependence of the reconstructed energy and of the energy resolution.[14] With such model it is possible to reproduce the observed energy spectrum of a given signal by computing the convolution of the visible energy spectrum with the detector response function. More details about this procedure can be found in.[14]

The performance of the detector and the reliability of the response models have been carefully studied during the calibration campaign[16] and are constantly monitored using some known background (such as the ^{14}C, cosmogenic ^{11}C or the characteristic peak of ^{210}Po, see Sec. 4). During the Phase II of Borexino data taking, the energy resolution for 1 MeV deposited energy was close to 50 keV, while the position of the event –reconstructed via a time-of-flight method– had an accuracy of $\approx 10\,\mathrm{cm}$

4. Low-Energy solar neutrino spectroscopy

The observation of low-energy solar neutrinos has been one of the main goal of the experiment, given their fundamental importance for both neutrino- and solar physics. Differently from the previous generation of low-energy solar neutrino experiments, which were able to measure the integrated neutrino flux over a given energy threshold, the key advantage of Borexino is the possibility to separate the individual contribution of neutrinos produced in different reactions thanks to their specific signature in the visible energy spectrum.

Already during the first phase[17] of the experiment Borexino was able to measure the interaction rate of ^{7}Be, ^{8}B and *pep* neutrinos,[18–20] while imposing an upper limit to the rate of CNO neutrinos.[20] We present in this section the result obtained from the analysis of low-energy neutrinos obtained in the second phase of the Borexino data taking, started in 2011 following a very successful purification campaign which further reduced the already low contamination level in the liquid scintillator. In Sec. 4.1 we discuss the measurement of *pp*-chain low-energy neutrinos reported in,[11,14] while in 4.2 we show the evidence of the time modulation of solar neutrinos interaction rate expected from the Earth's orbit eccentricity. In the second part of this section we report the search of exotic properties of neutrinos performed using low-energy solar neutrinos: in particular Sec. 4.3 presents a limit on the neutrino magnetic moment, while we discuss in Sec. 4.4 the search for neutrino non-standard interactions.

Given their low-flux and different energy scale, neutrinos from the ^{8}B decay require a separate analysis, which is presented in Sec. 5.

4.1. *Simultaneous measurement of low-energy solar neutrino fluxes*

The latest measurements of low-energy solar neutrinos produced by the *pp*-chain performed by Borexino is based on a dataset collected between December 14th, 2011 and May 21st, 2016 (1291.51 days). The increased exposure ($\approx$ 1.6 times larger than Phase I), combined with the lower contamination background and the improved understanding of the detector made it possible to simultaneously extract all the interaction rates of the low-energy components of the *pp*-chain in a single fit over a large portion of the energy spectrum (0.19–2.93 MeV), differently from previous Borexino results where the different solar neutrino species were studied separately optimising the choice of the energy window.

Data recorded by the detector are filtered to remove residual cosmic muons and short-living cosmogenic isotopes by applying a 300 ms veto.[14] In order to remove "external" γ-ray background generated in the material surrounding the liquid scintillator (especially in the PMTs and in the nylon of the inner vessel) we select only those events reconstructed in a 71.3 tonnes fiducial volume defined in the innermost part of the detector.[14]

The reconstruction of solar neutrinos interaction rates from the energy spectrum is made more challenging by the presence of multiple backgrounds that still contaminates the dataset even after the successful purification of the scintillator and the data selection outlined above: in particular, the sensitivity of Borexino in the low-energy part of the spectrum is limited by the presence of ^{14}C in the LS molecules (β^-, $Q = 0.16$ MeV), which decay in the detector at an much higher rate than solar neutrino interactions. Other contamination affecting the energy window are ^{85}Kr (β^-, $Q = 0.69$ MeV), ^{210}Po (α, $E_\alpha = 5.3$ MeV, light quenched by a factor ≈ 10 in LS) and ^{210}Bi (β^-, $Q = 1.16$ MeV). At higher energies, the relevant background is mostly due to residual "external" γ-rays and to cosmogenic ^{11}C (β^+, $Q = 0.96$ MeV). The latter can be efficiently tagged by exploiting the fact that it is often produced together with one or more neutrons following muon spallation onto ^{12}C, therefore one can evaluate the likelihood for an event to be a ^{11}C decay on the basis of a set of observables such as the distance and time interval from a crossing muon, the distance of a detected neutron capture and the muon energy deposition profile.[21] Using this selection it has been possible to tag $(92 \pm 4)\%$ of ^{11}C events retaining $(64.28 \pm 0.01)\%$ of the total exposure, and those events classified as likely to be ^{11}C decays are used to build a separate, ^{11}C-tagged dataset that is analysed jointly with ^{11}C suppressed one.

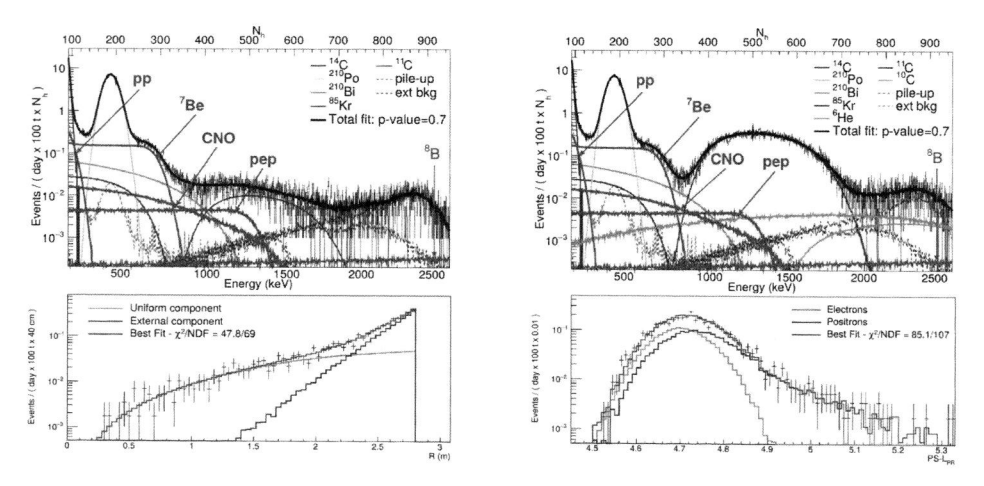

Fig. 4. Result of the simultaneous measurement of low-energy pp-chain solar neutrinos. *Top panel*: visible energy spectra in the ^{11}C-subtracted (left) and -tagged datasets. *Bottom left*: Distribution of the events distance from the detector centre. *Bottom right*: Distribution of the pulse shape parameter. All figures from.[14]

To help constraining some of these backgrounds, in some specific cases it is possible to rely on some distinctive features of the signal or on some independent measurements: this is the case of the rate of ^{14}C, which has been measured using a separate dataset to be 40 ± 1 Bq/100 t and that was constrained in the analysis together with the rate of random coincidences of ^{14}C decays. Differently, the signal from external γ-rays shows a clear exponential decrease towards the detector centre due to the shielding effect of LS, while energy release of positrons emitted in the β^+ decay of ^{11}C and its subsequent annihilation results in a slightly different time profile, that we used to define a Pulse Shape (PS) parameter[14] that improves the separation between β^+ and β^- events. In order to take into account these features, we implemented a multivariate analysis which include the events' distance from the detector centre and pulse shape parameter in addition to the energy observables in the region where they can help the analysis.

The analysis procedure has been tested running a detailed sensitivity study[14] based on simulated experiments. This study showed a significant correlation between the reconstructed rates of pep, CNO end ^{210}Bi events, which led to a reduced sensitivity for such parameters. For this reason, we decided to constrain in the analysis the rate of CNO neutrinos to the value expected from the prediction of the SSM (both HZ and LZ). The results of the fit[11,14] are reported in Tab. 1 next to the expectations from the SSM,[7] assuming the MSW-LMA oscillation parameters.[22] Similarly, the lower part of Tab. 1 reports the fluxes of solar netrinos inferred from Borexino measurements assuming the MSW-LMA solution. Figure 4 shows the different contributions of solar neutrinos and backgrounds to the energy spectrum as well as to the radial distance and pulse shape distributions.

Systematic uncertainties in the measurement account for possible deviations of the computed exposure, uncertainties in the detector response model as well as specific effects of the analysis methods.[11,14]

The results in Tab. 1 represents the most accurate experimental measurements of low-energy solar neutrinos from the pp-chain, improving Borexino previous findings: in particular, the interaction rate of ^{7}Be neutrinos is constrained at the 3 % level, twice as accurate as the expectation of the SSM, while the absence of pep neutrinos is disfavoured with a 5σ significance.

4.2. *Time modulations of neutrino signal*

The solar neutrino signal should follow the annual variations of the Sun-to-Earth distance, the effect appears as a 6.7% peak-to-peak seasonal amplitude modulation, with a maximum at the perihelion. The observation of seasonal variation would confirm the solar origin of the signal. Another possible modulation could be induced due to the Earth matter: neutrino are passing through the dense matter in the night and this could cause flavour regeneration with probability dependent on

Table 1. Results of Borexino-Phase II on the pp, ^{7}Be and pep solar neutrinos interaction rate. The first term of the associated uncertainty represents the statistical error obtained with a likelihood profile under the Wilk's approximation, while the second indicates the systematic uncertainty. The pep neutrino rate depends on the different SSM used to constrain the CNO neutrino flux, and therefore two results are quoted. The fluxes reported in the lower part of the table are computed assuming the MSW-LMA oscillation parameters[22]

Solar ν	**Borexino results** Rate (cpd/100 t)	**HZ SSM** Rate (cpd/100 t)	**LZ SSM** Rate (cpd/100 t)
pp	$134 \pm 10^{+6}_{-10}$	131.0 ± 2.4	132.1 ± 2.3
^{7}Be	$48.3 \pm 1.1^{+0.4}_{-0.7}$	47.8 ± 2.9	43.7 ± 2.6
pep (HZ)	$2.43 \pm 0.36^{+0.15}_{-0.22}$	2.74 ± 0.05	2.78 ± 0.05
pep (LZ)	$2.65 \pm 0.36^{+0.15}_{-0.24}$		
	Flux cm^{-2}s^{-1}	Flux cm^{-2}s^{-1}	Flux cm^{-2}s^{-1}
pp	$(6.1 \pm 0.5^{+0.3}_{-0.5}) \times 10^{10}$	$5.98(1 \pm 0.006) \times 10^{10}$	$6.03(1 \pm 0.005) \times 10^{10}$
^{7}Be	$(4.99 \pm 0.13^{+0.07}_{-0.10}) \times 10^9$	$4.93(1 \pm 0.06) \times 10^9$	$4.50(1 \pm 0.06) \times 10^9$
pep (HZ)	$(1.27 \pm 0.19^{+0.08}_{-0.12}) \times 10^8$	$1.44(1 \pm 0.009) \times 10^8$	$1.46(1 \pm 0.009) \times 10^8$
pep (LZ)	$(1.39 \pm 0.19^{+0.08}_{-0.13}) \times 10^8$		

the oscillation parameters. The fact of observation or non-observation of diurnal modulation can be used to restrict the neutrino oscillation parameters.

The seasonal modulation of the ^{7}Be neutrino signal was studied by Borexino collaboration in,[17,23] The earlier work was performed with Borexino Phase-I data acquired from May 2007 to May 2010; the period and phase were found to be consistent with a solar origin of the signal. More advanced analysis of 1456 astronomical days of Phase-II data can be found in more recent paper.[23] The analysis of neutrino signal variations on the many years time-scale is complicated by the presence of time-dependent background components. Three methods have been used to extract the time modulations: the analytical fit to event rate, and two more elaborated techniques: Lomb-Scargle and the Empirical Mode Decomposition. The results obtained with these methods are in excellent agreement. The duration of astronomical year measured with neutrino by using fit to the event rate is 367 ± 10 days with phase shift of $T_0 = 14 \pm 22$ days, i.e. in good agreement with the expected values. Also, the observe eccentricity $\epsilon = 0.0174 \pm 0.0045$ corresponds to the modulation amplitude of $(7.1 \pm 1.9)\%$.

In contrast to the annual signal modulation, no variation of day/night solar neutrino signal at the level of 1% is observed in Borexino data.[24] The measured asymmetry $A_{dn} = 0.001 \pm 0.012(stat) \pm 0.007(syst)$ agrees with the prediction of LMA solution for MSW mechanism. Moreover, this result disfavours MSW oscillations with mixing parameters in the LOW region at more than 8.5σ. The LOW solution was previously excluded by using the reactor antineutrino data, which involves the assumption of CPT symmetry.

4.3. *Neutrino magnetic moment*

One of the explanation of recent puzzling result of the XENON1T collaboration at few keV electronic recoils could be due to the scattering of solar neutrinos with large Majorana transition magnetic moments[25] (MM). The required transition MM strengths lie within the range that can be probed by current or near future experiments.

Borexino is spectroscopic detector with a relatively good energy resolution at low energies of about 5% at 1 MeV. The spectroscopic feature provides a good possibility to search for the deviations from the standard shape of recoils electrons scattered off monoenergetic ^{7}Be neutrinos. The manifestation of the large neutrino magnetic moment in the electron recoils spectrum would be an additional term in the cross section with a characteristic $1/T_e$ (T is electron recoil kinetic energy) signature. A sensitive search for the deviations of the electron recoil spectra from the predicted by the Standard Model was performed using Borexino Phase-II data in.[26] A model-independent limit on the effective moment of the solar neutrino of $\mu_{\text{eff}} < 2.8 10^{-11} \mu_B$ at 90% C.L. was obtained. This could be compared to the best direct limit on the magnetic moment of electron antineutrino $\mu_{\text{eff}} < 2.9 10^{-11} \mu_B$ at 90% C.L. obtained using Ge detectors in the most sensitive reactor experiment GEMMA.[27] The Borexino limit is free from uncertainties associated with predictions of the SSM neutrino flux and with the detector's fiducial volume, and is obtained by constraining the sum of the solar neutrino fluxes using the results from radiochemical (gallium) experiments.

Since neutrinos are a mixture of mass eigenstates the effective magnetic moment for neutrino-electron scattering is:

$$\mu_{\text{eff}}^2 = \sum_j |\sum_k \mu_{kj} A_k(E_\nu, L)|^2, \qquad (1)$$

where μ_{jk} is an element of the neutrino electromagnetic moments matrix and $A_k(E_\nu, L)$ is the amplitude of the k-mass state at the point of scattering. For the Majorana neutrino, only the transition moments are nonzero, while the diagonal elements of the matrix are equal to zero due to CPT-conservation. For the Dirac neutrino, all matrix elements may have nonzero values. The effective magnetic moment can be expanded both in terms of the mass eigenstates or the flavor eigenstates.

In the general case the expression for the effective magnetic moment in the mass eigenstate basis will have a complex form consisting of interference terms $\propto \mu_{jk}\mu_{ik}$. Without significant omissions the solar neutrinos arriving at the Earth can be considered as an incoherent mixture of mass eigenstates. In the case of Dirac neutrinos assuming that only diagonal magnetic moments μ_{ii} are nonvanishing:

$$\mu_{\text{eff}}^2 = P_{e1}^{3\nu}\mu_{11}^2 + P_{e2}^{3\nu}\mu_{22}^2 + P_{e3}^{3\nu}\mu_{33}^2 \qquad (2)$$

where $P_{ei}^{3\nu} = |A_i(E,L)|^2$ is the probability of observing the i-mass state at the scattering point for an initial electron flavor.

In the case of Majorana transition magnetic moments the effective moment is:

$$\mu_{\text{eff}}^2 = P_{e1}^{3\nu}(\mu_{12}^2 + \mu_{13}^2) + P_{e2}^{3\nu}(\mu_{21}^2 + \mu_{23}^2) + P_{e3}^{3\nu}(\mu_{31}^2 + \mu_{32}^2) \qquad (3)$$

For the well-known approximation of three- to two- neutrino oscillation probabilities for solar neutrinos: $P_{e1}^{3\nu} = \cos^2\theta_{13} P_{e1}^{2\nu}$, $P_{e2}^{3\nu} = \cos^2\theta_{13} P_{e2}^{2\nu}$ and $P_{e3}^{3\nu} = \sin^2\theta_{13}$ – one can get the effective magnetic moment expressed in well-established oscillation parameters in the mass eigenstate basis. Equation (2) can be rewritten as:

$$\mu_{\text{eff}}^2 = C_{13}^2 P_{e1}^{2\nu}\mu_{11}^2 + C_{13}^2 P_{e2}^{2\nu}\mu_{22}^2 + S_{13}^2 \mu_{33}^2 \qquad (4)$$

where $C_{13}^2 \equiv \cos^2\theta_{13}$ and $S_{13}^2 \equiv \sin^2\theta_{13}$, and $P_{e1}^{2\nu} + P_{e2}^{2\nu} = 1$. Similarly, assuming CPT-conservation ($\mu_{jk} = \mu_{kj}$) relation (3) for the transition moments can be rewritten as:

$$\mu_{\text{eff}}^2 = C_{13}^2 P_{e1}^{2\nu}\mu_{12}^2 + (1 - C_{13}^2 P_{e2}^{2\nu})\mu_{13}^2 + (1 - C_{13}^2 P_{e1}^{2\nu})\mu_{23}^2 \qquad (5)$$

In general, $P_{e1}^{2\nu}$ and $P_{e2}^{2\nu}$ (and $P_{ee}^{2\nu}$) depend on the neutrino energy, but in the energy region below 1 MeV the probabilities can be assumed constant.

Since μ_{eff}^2 is the sum of positively defined quantities, one can constrain any term in (4) and (5). By using the most probable values of $P_{ee}^{2\nu}$, θ_{12} and θ_{13} one can obtain the following limits from the relation $\mu_{\text{eff}} \leq 2.8 \times 10^{-11} \mu_B$:

$$|\mu_{11}| \leq 3.4; \quad |\mu_{22}| \leq 5.1; \quad |\mu_{33}| \leq 18.7; \qquad (6)$$

$$|\mu_{12}| \leq 2.8; \quad |\mu_{13}| \leq 3.4; \quad |\mu_{23}| \leq 5.0; \qquad (7)$$

all measured in units of $10^{-11}\mu_B$ and for 90% C.L.

The effective magnetic moment for the LMA-MSW solution in flavour basis assuming the survival probability of pp and ^{7}Be solar neutrinos is the same:

$$\mu_{\text{eff}}^2 = P^{3\nu}\mu_e^2 + (1 - P^{3\nu})(\cos^2\theta_{23} \cdot \mu_\mu^2 + \sin^2\theta_{23} \cdot \mu_\tau^2), \qquad (8)$$

where $P^{3\nu} = \sin^4\theta_{13} + \cos^4\theta_{13} P^{2\nu}$ is the probability that ν_e is detected in its original flavor (survival probability), with $P^{2\nu}$ calculated in the "standard" 2-neutrino scheme, θ_{13} and θ_{23} are the corresponding mixing angles. Though $P^{2\nu}$ depends on E_ν, the difference between $P^{2\nu}(400) = 0.57$ for a neutrino energy close to the pp-neutrino spectrum end point of 420 keV (only a small fraction of the total pp-neutrino spectrum close to the end point contributes to the sensitive region in analysis) and $P^{2\nu}(862) = 0.55$ for ^{7}Be-neutrinos (higher energy line) is negligible. An estimate of $P^{2\nu} = 0.55$ was used in calculations.

The limits on the flavor magnetic moment can be obtained from (8) because individual contributions are positive. With $\mu_{\text{eff}} < 2.8 \cdot 10^{-11} \mu_B$ and for $\sin^2 \theta_{13} = 0.0210 \pm 0.0011$ and $\sin^2 \theta_{23} = 0.51 \pm 0.04$ for normal hierarchy (or $\sin^2 \theta_{23} = 0.50 \pm 0.04$ for inverted hierarchy) the following limits were obtained: $\mu_e < 3.9 \cdot 10^{-11} \mu_B$, $\mu_\mu < 5.8 \cdot 10^{-11} \mu_B$ and $\mu_\tau < 5.8 \cdot 10^{-11} \mu_B$, all at 90% C.L.

The values above were calculated for the choice of hierarchy providing a more conservative limit.

In another paper[28] the Borexino collaboration performed a search for the hidden antineutrino sources in the data. The presence of antineutrinos in original neutrino fluxes can be a consequence of neutrino electromagnetic interactions induced by the non-zero neutrino magnetic moment. The limit derived for solar antineutrino flux is 384 cm^{-2} s^{-1} (90% C.L.), assuming an undistorted solar ^{8}B neutrinos energy spectrum, corresponding to a neutrino-antineutrino transition probability $P_{\nu \to \bar{\nu}} < 7.2 \times 10^{-5}$ (90% C.L.) for E_ν above inverse beta-decay threshold of 1.8 MeV. Based on the upper limit of the antineutrino admixture in the Solar neutrino flux the following limit on the magnetic moment was obtained:

$$\mu_\nu < 6.0 \cdot 10^{-9} B_\perp [\text{kG}] \cdot \mu_B \quad (90\% \text{ CL}) \qquad (9)$$

where $B_\perp$ is transverse component of the strength of the solar magnetic field. The estimates of B in the solar core varies by some orders of magnitude ranging from $B < 600$ G to $B < 7$ MG. These estimations correspond to upper limits of the neutrino magnetic moment between $1.0 \cdot 10^{-8} \mu_B$ and $8.5 \cdot 10^{-13} \mu_B$ (90% C.L.). The latter value is stronger than the current limit from astrophysical observations while the former limit is overlaid by other measurements.

4.4. *Neutrino non-standard interactions*

The observed neutrino contribution in Borexino spectra are determined by the fraction of the electron neutrino in the total neutrino flux at the surface of the Earth (or electron neutrino survival probability $P_{ee}(E)$), and the neutrino-electron scattering cross section defined by the chiral couplings of the neutrino and electron. Some theories beyond the Standard Model postulate the existence of Non-Standard Interactions (NSI's) which can modify the chiral couplings and P_{ee}. Phenomenologically, NSI's of the neutral current (NC) type are described by the Lagrangian density

$$\mathcal{L}_{\text{NSI}} = -2\sqrt{2} G_F \varepsilon_{\alpha\beta}^{ff'C} (\bar{\nu}_\alpha \gamma^\mu \nu_\beta)(\bar{f} \gamma_\mu C f')$$

where $\alpha, \beta = e, \mu, \tau$ label the neutrino flavor, f and f' are leptons or quarks of the same charge but not necessarily the same flavor, C is the chirality of the ff' current (L or R), and $\varepsilon_{\alpha\beta}^{ff'C}$ is a dimensionless coupling constant parametrizing the strength of the NSI interaction normalized to G_F. In the Borexino data analysis the attention was paid to the flavor-diagonal case $f = f' = e$ and $\alpha = \beta$, so it is convenient to denote $\varepsilon_{\alpha\beta}^{fC}$ as ε_{α}^{C}. Borexino, relying on neutrino-electron elastic scattering, is particularly sensitive to this type.

At detection, ε_α shifts the coupling constants that appear in the expression for the differential cross section for the weak interactions

$$g_\alpha^C \to \tilde{g}_\alpha^C = g_\alpha^C + \varepsilon_{\alpha\beta}^C$$

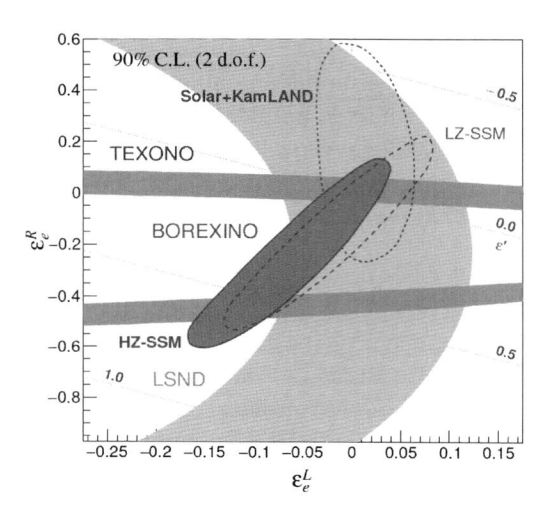

Fig. 5. Allowed region for NSI parameters in $\varepsilon_e^{L/R}$ plane obtained in.[29] The parameters $\varepsilon_\tau^{L/R}$ are fixed at zero. Both HZ- (filled red) and LZ- (dashed red) SSM's were considered. The bounds from the LSND and TEXONO experiments are provided for comparison. Besides, the contour obtained from the global analysis of solar neutrino experiments is presented by dashed black line,[30] NSI's are included in detection and propagation. All contours correspond to 90% C.L. (2 d.o.f.). The dotted gray lines represent the corresponding range of ε' parameter, relevant for NSI's at propagation.

The Borexino Phase II data data were used for the search of the flavor-diagonal neutral current interactions responsible for the ν_{ee} and and $\nu_{\tau e}$ couplings not excluded by other experiments. The solar luminosity constraints were implied to improve the sensitivity to the effects under study, both high- and low-metallicity (HZ and LZ) Standard Solar Model (SSM) predictions of the solar neutrino fluxes were considered. No indications of new physics were found at the level of sensitivity of the detector. The constraints on the parameters of the NSI's were obtained[29] compatible with or better than the existing ones. The results for $\varepsilon_e^{L/R}$ and $\varepsilon_\tau^{L/R}$ parameters are shown in Fig. 5 and Fig. 6 correspondingly.

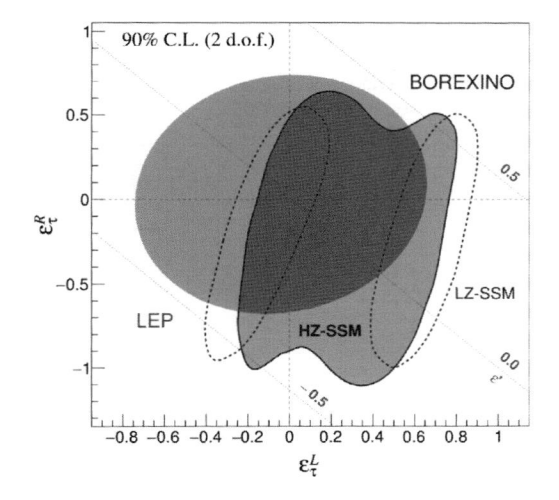

Fig. 6. Allowed region for NSI parameters in $\varepsilon_\tau^{L/R}$ plane obtained in.[29] The $\varepsilon_e^{L/R}$ are fixed at zero. Both HZ- (filled dark blue) and LZ- (dashed dark blue) SSM'sare considered. The contour from LEP experiment is provided for comparison. Both contours correspond to 90% C.L. (2 d.o.f.). The dotted gray lines represent the corresponding range of ε' parameter, relevant for NSI's at propagation.

5. High-energy solar neutrinos in Borexino

As already discussed, Borexino's original goal was the measurement of low energy solar neutrinos and this objective was fully centered. However, through the years, Borexino turned out to be a quite versatile experiment and the collaboration succeeded in measuring also neutrinos belonging to the above-MeV part of the solar neutrino spectrum. In particular, in 2020, Borexino presented a refinement of the measurement of the ^{8}B solar neutrino interaction rate,[31] also setting a new limit on the interaction rate of solar *hep* neutrinos.

The High-Energy Region (HER) work is based on 2062.4 live days of data, collected between January 2008 and December 2016 (detector's purifications and calibrations period excluded). In order to better handling the backgrounds, the analysis is performed with MonteCarlo radial fits, independently performed on two energy subranges: the HER-I (1650, 2950 p.e., roughly 3.2-5 MeV) and the HER-II (2950, 8500 p.e., roughly 5-16 MeV). The HER-I sector includes events originated from natural radioactivity while the HER-II sector is characterized by intense external γ rays following the neutron capture processes that happens on the Stainless Steel Sphere. In Borexino, the energy depositions of natural radioactivity never exceeds 5 MeV (Q-value of the ^{208}Tl β decay) since the α scintillation signals are strongly quenched and end below this analysis threshold. As of 2020, the ^{8}B neutrinos are detected via their elastic scattering off electrons on a fiducial mass of 300 t of liquid scintillator (the entire Borexino active mass) resulting in a total exposure of

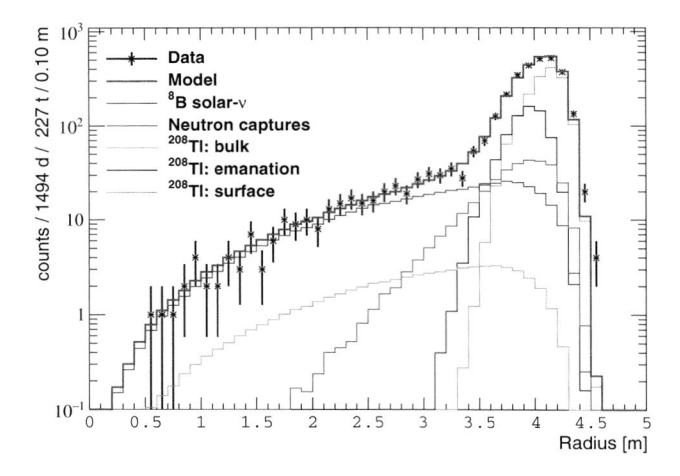

Fig. 7. Fit of the event radial distribution in the HER-I range[31] [1650,2950]p.e.

1.5 ktonne x year: an impressive 11.5-fold increase with respect to the previous Borexino ^{8}B measurement.[19]

In the HER analysis, the selection of data is performed via software cuts that tag/remove the primary/secondary backgrounds associated with the interaction of cosmic muons in the detector. The identification of the ^{8}B neutrino signal is then based on its different radial distribution with respect to that of background: neutrino events are expected to be uniformly distributed in the active volume while the remaining background event distribution is strongly radial dependent (Fig. 7).

The radial fit estimator is a binned likelihood and the χ^2/dof of the radial fits are 31.3/36 (HER-I), and 30.4/35 (HER-II) excluding empty bins. The best-fit rates for the ^{8}B solar neutrinos are found to be:

$$R_{\text{HER}-\text{I}} = 0.136 ^{+0.013}_{-0.013} \text{(stat)} ^{+0.003}_{-0.003} \text{(syst)} \text{ cpd}/ 100 \text{ t}$$

$$R_{\text{HER}-\text{II}} = 0.087 ^{+0.080}_{-0.010} \text{(stat)} ^{+0.005}_{-0.005} \text{(syst)} \text{ cpd}/ 100 \text{ t}$$

$$R_{\text{HER}} = 0.223 ^{+0.015}_{-0.016} \text{(stat)} ^{+0.006}_{-0.006} \text{(syst)} \text{ cpd}/ 100 \text{ t}$$

The precision of the HER ^{8}B rate analysis is then about 8% and it improves more than a factor 2 our previous result.[19] The equivalent ^{8}B neutrino flux inferred from the HER analysis[31] is $\Phi(^8\text{B}) = 2.57 ^{+0.17}_{-0.18} \text{(stat)} ^{+0.07}_{-0.07} \text{(syst)} \times 10^6 \text{ cm}^{-2}\text{s}^{-1}$ well in agreement with the previous Borexino result[19] and with the high-precision measurement performed by Super Kamiokande.[32] The B16 HZ-SSM[7] expected ^{8}B neutrino flux is $5.46 \pm 0.66 \times 10^6 \text{ cm}^{-2}\text{s}^{-1}$ but the apparently missing flux is fully compatible the MSW-LMA neutrino oscillation scenario.

The Borexino experiment is not optimized for a clear detection of neutrino fluxes as low as those predicted by the SSM for the *hep* neutrinos ($\sim 10^3 \text{ cm}^{-2}\text{s}^{-1}$). Nevertheless, this elusive type of neutrinos is searched via their elastic scattering on electrons as well as via their neutral current-mediated inelastic scattering on Carbon nuclei. The Borexino collaboration was able to set a limit on the number of expected *hep* events of 4.37 (90% C.L.), corresponding to a limit on the flux of $< 1.8 \times 10^5$ cm^{-2} s^{-1} which is about 1.2 times stronger than the one we previously reported in 2018.[11]

6. Conclusion and discussion

Solar neutrinos are an essential tool to understand stellar physics, being able at the same time to reveal some of their fundamental properties. The Borexino experiment, with its 14-years-long data taking, has been one of the key players in the investigation of these particles. Thanks to its outstanding radiopurity and to the deep understanding of the detector behaviour, Borexino has been able to overcome the intrinsic limitations of the previous generations of radiochemical experiments and to provide a precision measurement of all the components of the solar neutrino spectrum with the only exception of the very low flux of neutrinos from the Helium-proton fusion for which an upper limit has been set. In particular, in this contribution we report the Borexino results on neutrinos produced in the proton-proton fusion chain, which is by far the main energy production mechanism in our star. With a separate analysis of the low- and high-energy region of the energy spectrum, the individual fluxes of *pp*, *pep*, ^{7}Be and ^{8}B neutrinos were directly measured for the first time by a single experiment.

This result has significant implications for solar and particle physics: by measuring the flux of *pp* neutrinos with a 11% accuracy and the ^{7}Be flux with an unprecedented 3% precision, we could compute the luminosity of the Sun using neutrinos,[11] finding an excellent agreement with the photon-inferred result ($L_\odot^{\text{ph}} = (3.846 \pm 0.015) \times 10^{33}$ erg s^{-1} vs $L_\odot^\nu = (3.89^{+0.35}_{-0.42}) \times 10^{33}$ erg s^{-1}), thus confirming the nuclear origin of the solar power and the thermodynamical equilibrium of the Sun over the timescale required for radiation to flow from the core to the surface of the Sun, which is in the order of 10^5 years. Using the measurements of *pp* and ^{7}Be neutrino fluxes we could also study the relative weight of the two main terminations of the *pp*-chain (ppI and ppII in Fig. 1), which is the ratio $R_{\text{I/II}}$ between the ^{3}He–^{4}He and ^{3}He–^{3}He fusion rates. Neglecting the small contribution of the ppIII branch and assuming the local kinetic equilibrium of ^{2}H and ^{3}He, we find $R_{\text{I/II}} = 0.178^{+0.027}_{-0.023}$, in good agreement with the predictions of both the HZ and LZ SSM[11] ($R_{\text{I/II}}^{\text{HZ}} = 0.180 \pm 0.011$, $R_{\text{I/II}}^{\text{LZ}} = 0.161 \pm 0.010$). Furthermore, we could exploit the strong dependence of ^{7}Be and ^{8}B fluxes upon the Sun core temperature to test the predictions of the SSM implementing a different chemical composition. Changes in the Sun metallicity will indeed lead to different expectations of the temperature profile, affecting the expected neutrino fluxes. Borexino *pp*-chain results are compatible with the predictions of both HZ and LZ SSM,[11] but an hypothesis test show a mild preference for the higher core temperature expected from the HZ SSM.[11]

In its long scientific life, Borexino exceeded the expectations of its physics reach and is now among the leading solar neutrino experiments. This extraordinary journey recently culminated with the first observation of solar neutrinos from the CNO-cycle,[33] adding a new fundamental piece to our understanding of the Sun and of all stars.

Acknowledgements

The Borexino collaboration acknowledges the hospitality and support of the Laboratori Nazionali del Gran Sasso (Italy). The Borexino program is made possible by funding from Istituto Nazionale di Fisica Nucleare (INFN) (Italy), National Science Foundation (NSF) (USA), Deutsche Forschungsgemeinschaft (DFG) and Helmholtz-Gemeinschaft (HGF) (Germany), Russian Science Foundation (RSF) (grant number 21-12-00063), and Narodowe Centrum Nauki (NCN) (grant number UMO 2017/26/M/ST2/00915) (Poland).

References

1. A. Eddington, The Internal Constitution of the Stars, *Nature* **106** (1920).
2. A. Eddington, The internal constitution of the stars, *Observatory* **43** (1920).
3. H. Bethe and C. Critchfield, The Formation of Deuterons by Proton Combination, *Phys. Rev.* **54** (1938).
4. H. Bethe, Energy Production in Stars, *Phys. Rev.* **55** (1939).
5. C. von Weizsäcker, Über Elementumwandlungen in Innern der Sterne I, *Phys. Z.* (1937).
6. C. von Weizsäcker, Über Elementumwandlungen in Innern der Sterne II, *Phys. Z.* (1938).
7. N. Vinyoles, A. M. Serenelli, F. L. Villante, S. Basu, J. Bergström, M. C. Gonzalez-Garcia, M. Maltoni, C. Peña Garay and N. Song, A new Generation of Standard Solar Models, *Astrophys. J.* **835**, p. 202 (2017).
8. F. L. Villante, ecCNO Solar Neutrinos: A Challenge for Gigantic Ultra-Pure Liquid Scintillator Detectors, *Phys. Lett. B* **742**, 279 (2015).
9. M. Asplund, A. Grevesse, N.and Sauval and P. Scott, The chemical composition of the sun, *Annu. Rev. Astron. Astrophys.* **47** (2009).
10. N. Grevesse and A. Sauval, Standard solar composition, *Space Sci. Rev.* **85** (1998).
11. M. Agostini *et al.*, Comprehensive measurement of *pp*-chain solar neutrinos, *Nature* **562**, 505 (2018).
12. G. Alimonti *et al.*, The Borexino detector at the Laboratori Nazionali del Gran Sasso, *Nucl. Instrum. Meth. A* **600**, 568 (2009).
13. M. Agostini *et al.*, Modulations of the Cosmic Muon Signal in Ten Years of Borexino Data, *JCAP* **02**, p. 046 (2019).
14. M. Agostini *et al.*, First Simultaneous Precision Spectroscopy of *pp*, ^{7}Be, and *pep* Solar Neutrinos with Borexino Phase-II, *Phys. Rev. D* **100**, p. 082004 (2019).
15. M. Agostini *et al.*, The Monte Carlo simulation of the Borexino detector, *Astropart. Phys.* **97**, 136 (2018).
16. H. Back *et al.*, Borexino calibrations: Hardware, Methods, and Results, *JINST* **7**, p. P10018 (2012).

17. G. Bellini et al., Final results of Borexino Phase-I on low-energy solar neutrino spectroscopy, *Phys. Rev. D* **89**, p. 112007 (Jun 2014).
18. C. Arpesella et al., Direct Measurement of the Be-7 Solar Neutrino Flux with 192 Days of Borexino Data, *Phys. Rev. Lett.* **101**, p. 091302 (2008).
19. G. Bellini et al., Measurement of the solar 8B neutrino rate with a liquid scintillator target and 3 MeV energy threshold in the Borexino detector, *Phys. Rev. D* **82**, p. 033006 (2010).
20. G. Bellini et al., First evidence of *pep* solar neutrinos by direct detection in Borexino, *Phys. Rev. Lett.* **108**, p. 051302 (2012).
21. M. Agostini et al., Identification of the cosmogenic ^{11}C background in large volumes of liquid scintillators with Borexino (6 2021).
22. I. Esteban, M. C. Gonzalez-Garcia, M. Maltoni, I. Martinez-Soler and T. Schwetz, Updated fit to three neutrino mixing: Exploring the accelerator-reactor complementarity, *JHEP* **01**, p. 087 (2017).
23. M. Agostini et al., Seasonal modulation of the ^{7}Be solar neutrino rate in Borexino, *Astropart. Phys.* **92**, 21 (2017).
24. G. Bellini et al., Absence of a day–night asymmetry in the ^{7}Be solar neutrino rate in Borexino, *Phys. Lett. B* **707**, 22 (2012).
25. E. Aprile et al., Excess electronic recoil events in XENON1T, *Phys. Rev. D* **102**, p. 072004 (Oct 2020).
26. M. Agostini et al., Limiting neutrino magnetic moments with Borexino Phase-II solar neutrino data, *Phys. Rev. D* **96**, p. 091103 (Nov 2017).
27. A. G. Beda et al., Gemma experiment: The results of neutrino magnetic moment search, *Physics of Particles and Nuclei Letters* **10**, 139 (2013).
28. M. Agostini et al., Search for low-energy neutrinos from astrophysical sources with borexino, *Astroparticle Physics* **125**, p. 102509 (2021).
29. M. Agostini et al., Constraints on flavor-diagonal non-standard neutrino interactions from Borexino Phase-II, *J. High Energ. Phys.* **38** (2020).
30. A. Bolaños, O. G. Miranda, A. Palazzo, M. A. Tórtola and J. W. F. Valle, Probing nonstandard neutrino-electron interactions with solar and reactor neutrinos, *Phys. Rev. D* **79**, p. 113012 (Jun 2009).
31. M. Agostini et al., Improved measurement of ^{8}B solar neutrinos with 1.5kty of Borexino exposure, *Phys. Rev. D* **101**, p. 062001 (2020).
32. K. Abe et al., Solar neutrino measurements in Super-Kamiokande-IV, *Phys. Rev. D* **94**, p. 052010 (Sep 2016).
33. M. Agostini et al., Experimental evidence of neutrinos produced in the CNO fusion cycle in the Sun, *Nature* **587**, 577 (2020).

Electron neutrino survival probability in the energy range 200 keV–15 MeV

Marco Pallavicini

Dipartimento di Fisica - Università degli Studi di Genova
and
INFN - Istituto Nazionale di Fisica Nucleare, Sezione di Genova
Via Dodecaneso 33, 16146 Genova - Italy
E-mail: marco.pallavicini@unige.it

on behalf of the Borexino Collaboration:
M. Agostini K. Altenmüller S. Appel V. Atroshchenko Z. Bagdasarian D. Basilico G. Bellini J. Benziger R. Biondi D. Bravo B. Caccianiga F. Calaprice A. Caminata P. Cavalcante A. Chepurnov D. D'Angelo S. Davini A. Derbin A. Di Giacinto V. Di Marcello X.F. Ding A. Di Ludovico L. Di Noto I. Drachnev A. Formozov D. Franco C. Galbiati C. Ghiano M. Giammarchi A. Goretti A.S. Göttel M. Gromov D. Guffanti Aldo Ianni Andrea Ianni A. Jany D. Jeschke V. Kobychev G. Korga S. Kumaran M. Laubenstein E. Litvinovich P. Lombardi I. Lomskaya L. Ludhova G. Lukyanchenko L. Lukyanchenko I. Machulin J. Martyn E. Meroni M. Meyer L. Miramonti M. Misiaszek V. Muratova B. Neumair M. Nieslony R. Nugmanov L. Oberauer V. Orekhov F. Ortica M. Pallavicini L. Papp L. Pelicci Ö. Penek L. Pietrofaccia N. Pilipenko A. Pocar G. Raikov M.T. Ranalli G. Ranucci A. Razeto A. Re M. Redchuk A. Romani N. Rossi S. Schönert D. Semenov G. Settanta M. Skorokhvatov A. Singhal O. Smirnov A. Sotnikov Y. Suvorov R. Tartaglia G. Testera J. Thurn E. Unzhakov F. Villante A. Vishneva R.B. Vogelaar F. von Feilitzsch M. Wojcik M. Wurm S. Zavatarelli K. Zuber G. Zuzel

The Borexino experiment, located at the Laboratori Nazionali del Gran Sasso in Italy, has been the first and so far unique experiment capable to measure the interaction rate of all solar neutrino components produced by the Sun through the so called *pp*-chain and CNO-cycle fusion mechanisms. Particularly, Borexino has measured the rate of *pp*, ^{7}Be, *pep* and ^{8}B neutrinos, which span a wide energy range from a few hundreds keV up to almost 15 MeV. This capability offered Borexino the unique opportunity to experimentally test the expected electron neutrino survival probability predicted by the theory. The paper briefly summarises this important achievement and discusses possible future developments.

Keywords: Solar neutrinos; electron neutrino survival probability; neutrino oscillations; LMA-MSW effect

1. Introduction

The Sun is a powerful source of low energy neutrinos that are a unique tool to test the solar theory and to probe neutrino physics. A remarkable set of discoveries have been made by means of solar neutrinos, among which the most important is the discovery electron neutrino oscillations into muon and tau neutrinos made by the SNO[1,2] experiment, which led to the Nobel prize of Art McDonald in 2015.[3]

It is quite well known that the stellar theory has long predicted two mechanisms for hydrogen fusion into helium in the Sun, known as the *pp*-chain and the

CNO cycle.[4] Both mechanism are based on a sequence of nuclear reactions, some of which produce electron neutrinos. The *pp*-chain is initiated by the fusion of two protons and produce neutrinos through four detectable mechanisms[a]. The CNO cycle bears this name because carbon, nitrogen and oxygen act as catalysers and produce neutrinos as well.[4] Fig. 1 shows the electron neutrino spectrum predicted by[4] without any neutrino oscillation effect.

The two fusion reactions occur in the Sun's core, and because of the relatively low solar temperature, they contribute very unequally to energy production: about 99% of the solar luminosity is due to the *pp*-chain, while the rest is due to the CNO cycle. The CNO cycle is dominant for more massive stars.

Borexino is the first experiment that was able to measure directly all individual solar neutrino components emitted by the *pp*-chain reactions[5] and by the CNO cycle in the Sun.[6] This fact is by itself a remarkable experimental achievement, which was obtained thanks to almost 30 years of activity.[7] It has also the consequence that the

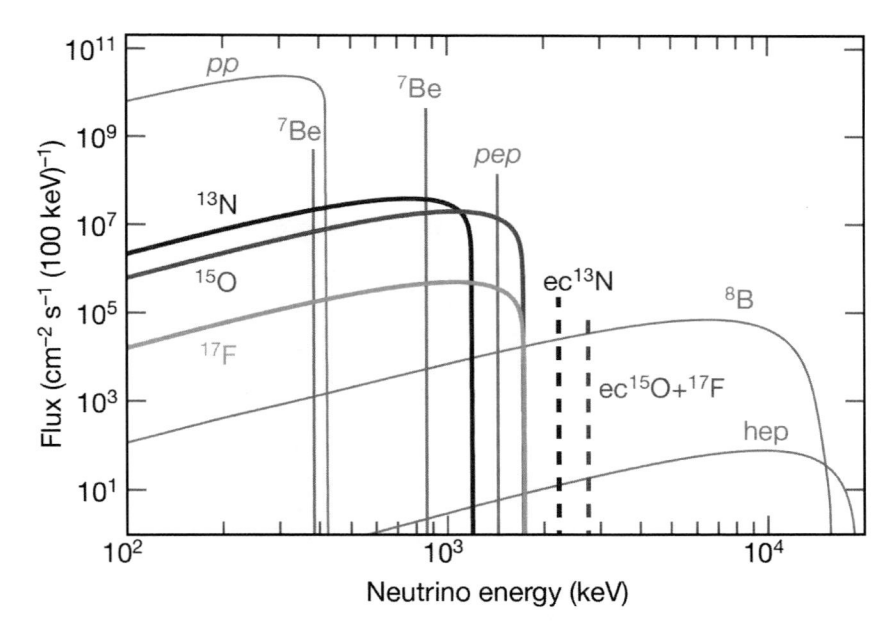

Fig. 1. The spectrum of solar neutrinos as predicted by Vinyoles et al. Hep neutrinos, while at high energy, have a flux that is too low to be detected by current generation experiments. All other components have been measured directly by Borexino through spectral analysis, exploiting the very low radioactive background, the low energy threshold and the good energy resolution of the liquid scintillator detector. Borexino has been so far the only experiment being able to perform such a comprehensive spectral measurement.

---

[a]A fifth mechanism due to the fusion of ^{3}He with a proton (hep neutrinos) is too small to be detected.

experiment was able to measure the survival probability of neutrinos as a function of the energy and to test directly the LMA-MSW[8] theory of neutrino oscillations. LMA refers to Large Mixing Angle solution, while MSW to the Mikheyev-Smirnov-Wolfenstein mechanism.[9–11]

According to MSW theory, at energy above a few MeV the different refractive index affecting the propagation of electron neutrinos with respect to that affecting the muon and tau neutrinos propagation introduce an additional phase shift that can change the survival probability of electron neutrinos from the central core to the Earth. At some energies the effect can be very large because of a resonance.[10,11] As a consequence, the LMA-MSW theory predicts that solar neutrino oscillations are strongly energy dependent and particularly are dominated by the matter effects above above a few MeV. Vacuum oscillations are dominant at lower energies.

When the LMA-MSW theory is taken into account, the neutrino fluxes predicted by the Standard Solar Model[4] are translated into a well defined prediction of the neutrino interaction rate in Borexino, which depends both on the total electron neutrino flux and on the fraction of electron neutrinos and other neutrino types reaching the Earth.

In this paper we show how the precision measurement pp, ^{7}Be, pep and ^{8}B neutrino rate made by Borexino translates into the first direct measurement of the electron neutrino survival probability as a function of the neutrino energy.

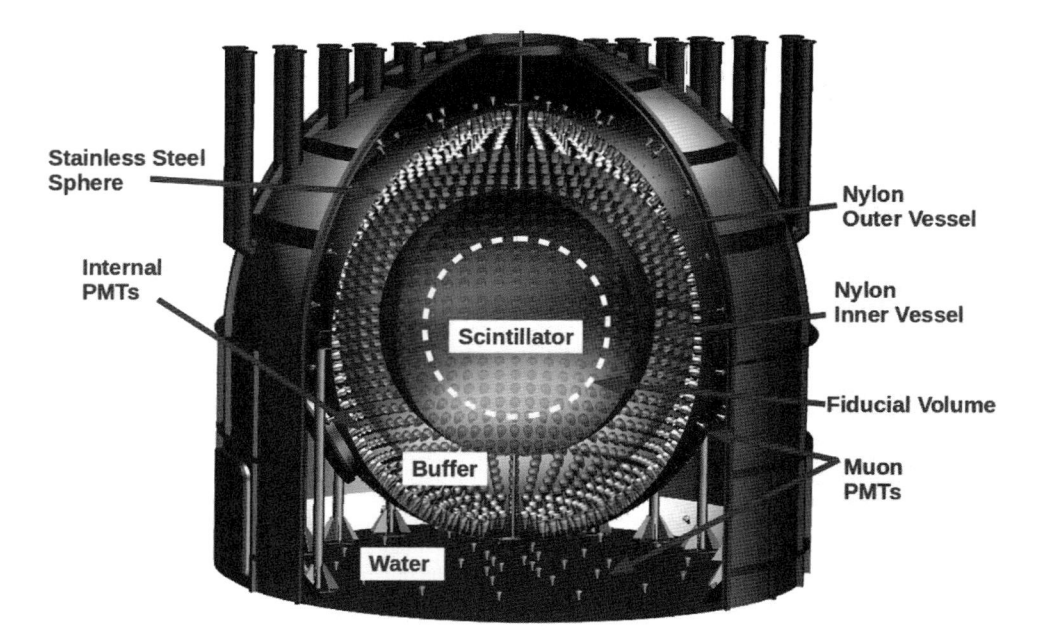

Fig. 2. Drawing of the Borexino detector. The various components are labelled in the picture. To give a feeling of the size, we quote the diameter of the Stainless Steel Sphere, which is 13.7 m.

2. The Borexino experimental setup

Borexino is a very pure liquid scintillator detector[12–15] designed for the real–time observation of low energy solar neutrinos. It is located in Italy deep underground ($\simeq$3800 meters of water equivalent, m w.e.) in the Hall C of the Laboratori Nazionali del Gran Sasso, where the muon flux is suppressed by a factor of $\approx 10^6$ with respect to sea level.

The detector is schematically depicted in Fig. 2. The inner part is an unsegmented stainless steel sphere (SSS) that is both the container of the scintillator and the mechanical support of the photomultipliers. Within this sphere, two nylon vessels separate the scintillator volume in three shells of radii 4.25 m, 5.50 m and 6.85 m, the latter being the radius of the SSS itself. The inner nylon vessel (IV) contains the liquid scintillator solution, namely PC (pseudocumene, 1,2,4-trimethylbenzene $C_6H_3(CH_3)_3$) as a solvent and the fluor PPO (2,5-diphenyloxazole, $C_{15}H_{11}NO$) as a solute at a concentration of approximately 1.5 g/l (0.17 % by weight). The second and the third shell contain PC with a small amount (few g/l) of DMP (dimethylphthalate, $C_6H_4(COOCH_3)_2$) that is added as a light quencher in order to further reduce the scintillation yield of pure PC.[12]

The Inner Vessel is made of 125 μm thick Nylon-6 carefully selected and handled in order to achieve maximum radio–purity. Since the PC/PPO solution is slightly lighter (about 0.4 %) than the PC/DMP solution, the Inner Vessel is anchored to the bottom (south pole of the SSS) with a set of nylon strings. The outer nylon vessel (OV) has a diameter of 11 m and is built with the same material as the inner one. The OV is a barrier that prevents ^{222}Rn emanated from the external materials (steel, glass, photomultiplier materials) to di?use into the fiducial volume.

The buffer fluid between the Inner Nylon Vessel and the SSS (PC/DMP solution) is the last shielding against external backgrounds. The use of PC as a buffer is convenient because it matches both the density and the refractive index of the scintillator, thus reducing the buoyancy force for the nylon vessel and avoiding optics aberrations that would spoil the spatial resolution.

The addition of the DMP quenches the scintillation yield of the buffer fluid by a factor of 20. This is important in order to avoid the unacceptable trigger rate due to the radioactivity of the photomultipliers.

The scintillation light is collected by nominally 2212 photomutipliers (PMTs) that are uniformly attached to the inner surface of the SSS. All but 384 photomultipliers are equipped with light concentrators that are designed to reject photons not coming from the active scintillator volume, thus reducing the background due to radioactive decays originating in the buffer liquid or γ's from the PMTs. The PMTs without concentrators are used to measure this background, and to help identify muons that cross the buffer, but not the Inner Vessel.

The number of active PMTs has changed over time during the almost 15 years of data taking, so that collection efficiency is a function of time and run–dependent.

The SSS is supported by 20 steel legs and enclosed within a large tank that is filled with ultra-pure water. The tank has a cylindrical base with a diameter of 18 m and a hemispherical top with a maximum height of 16.9 m. The Water Tank (WT) is a powerful shielding against external background (γ rays and neutrons from the rock) and is also used as a Cherenkov muon counter and muon tracker. The muon flux, although reduced by a factor of 10^6 by the 3800 m w.e. depth of the Gran Sasso Laboratory, is of the order of 1 m^{-2} h^{-1}, corresponding to about 4000 muons per day crossing the detector. This flux is well above Borexino requirements and a strong additional reduction factor (about 10^4) is necessary and was indeed achieved[13] by the combined use of WT signal and inner detector signal. More details on the detector can be found in.[12,13]

3. Neutrino detection

Low energy neutrinos of all flavours are detected by means of their elas- tic scattering off electrons or, in the case of electron anti–neutrinos, by means of their inverse beta decay on protons or carbon nuclei. The electron (positron) recoil energy is converted into scintillation light, which is then collected by a set of pho- tomultipliers. Neutron detection is often possible as well, through its capture on proton and emission of energetic gamma. A tiny amount of Cherenkov light is also produced, though it is mostly absorbed and re–emitted.

Scintillation light offers several advantages with respect to both the water Cherenkov detectors and the older radiochemical detectors used before Borexino in solar neutrino experiments. Water Cherenkov detectors, in fact, can not effectively detect solar neutrinos whose energy is below approximately 3.5 MeV, both because the Cherenkov light yield is low and because the intrinsic radioactive background cannot be pushed down to sufficiently low levels. On the other hand, radiochemical experiments cannot intrinsically perform spectral measurements and do not detect events in real time. Cherenkov detector, however, can efficiently detect the direction of the scattered electron and therefore of the incoming neutrino, which is not possible yet in liquid scintillators.

A liquid scintillator, on the other hand, solves these problems: the detection of low energy neutrino becomes possible possible because the light yield is high, offering an energy threshold as low as a few tens ofkeV[b]; the organic nature of the scintillator, and its liquid form at ambient temperature, provide very low solubility of ions and metal impurities, and yield the technical possibility to purify the material as required. However, no measurement of the direction of the incoming neutrino is possible[c] and, even more importantly, the neutrino induced events are intrinsically

---

[b]However, the unavoidable contamination of ^{14}C that is present in any organic liquid practically limits the "neutrino window" above ?200 keV
[c]Very recently Borexino has shown that some of this prompt Cherenkov light can be detected and identified. Future detector might be able to make useful use of this additional information.

indistinguishable from β and γ radioactivity, posing formidable requirements in terms of radio–purity of the scintillator and of the detector materials.

The total number of detected photons and their arrival times are used to reconstruct the electron recoil energy and the interaction point in the detector, respectively. The energy and spatial resolution of Borexino is not constant because it has slowly deteriorated over time owing to the steady loss of photomultiplier tubes (on average 1238 channels were active during the recent CNO analysis, with larger numbers available at the time of pp-chain analysis), with current values of $\sigma_E/E \approx 6\%$ and $\sigma_{x;y;z} \approx 11$ cm for 1 MeV events at the centre of the detector. The time profile of the scintillation light provides also a powerful way to distinguish between different particle types α, β and β^+ via pulse-shape discrimination methods.[16,17]

The final radio–purity levels achieved by Borexino on ^{238}U and ^{232}Th chains, and on several other radioactive contaminants, are many orders of magnitude lower than those either set as design goals or achieved by any other low–background experiment. In this short paper it is simply not possible to give an account of the amount of work done, nor a detailed description of the final numbers obtained. We invite the interested reader to look at the bibliography and particularly to[16,17] and references therein.

The total cross section of electron neutrinos on electrons depends on both charged and neutral currents weak interactions, while that of muon and tau neutrinos is induced by neutral currents only. The interaction rate depends therefore on the neutrino type at the target, a fact that makes the experiment sensitive to neutrino oscillations occurring along the path from the production site in the Sun's up to the detector. This is the key element that allows the direct measurement of the energy dependence of the flavour conversion probability through the Sun induced by the LMA-MSW effect.

The extraction of the survival probability can be obtained from the measured rate using the total fluxes predicted by the Standard Solar Model through the formula:

$$R_x(E) = \Phi_x \left[P_{ee}(E)\sigma_e + (1 - P_{ee}(E))\sigma_\mu \right] \quad (1)$$

where R_x is the measured rate of the x neutrino component with average energy E (x can be pp, ^{7}Be, pep, ^{8}B), Φ_x is the predicted electron neutrino flux of the x component at the Sun's core, P_{ee} is the electron neutrino survival probability, and σ_e and σ_μ are the neutrino-electron total cross sections for electron and muon neutrinos respectively. It is clear from the equation above that for any given measured rate the corresponding value of P_{ee} can be directly measured using as inputs the very well known standard model cross sections (which introduce a negligible uncertainty) and the solar model predictions, which drive most of the uncertainty beside experimental errors.

At the time of the proposal, the main goal of Borexino was the precise measurement of the rate induced by the monochromatic electron neutrinos (0.862 keV)

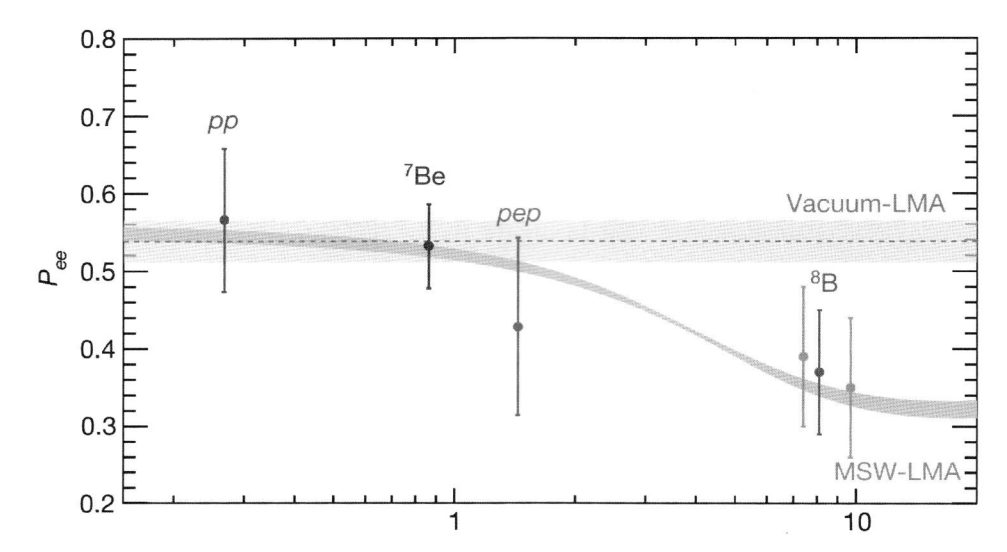

Fig. 3. The measured survival probability for the four neutrino components of the pp-chain. The pink band is the theoretical prediction of the P_{ee} with its uncertainty. The error on each value of P_{ee} depends on both theoretical errors and experimental error. See text for more details.

produced by the electron capture decay of ^{7}Be in the Sun. However, the very high radio purity of the scintillator offered new unexpected results, such as a clear evidence of the pep solar neutrinos,[18] a low energy threshold (3 MeV) detection of ^{8}B neutrinos,[19] the first direct measurement of pp neutrinos,[20] an unambiguous detection of geo-neutrinos,[21–23] and, last but definitely not least, the first prove of the existence of the CNO cycle in the Sun.[6]

After a careful detector calibration with internal sources[15] and an extensive purification campaign performed in 2010-2011, the complete pp-chain has been studied. This chain includes four reactions that emit four electron neutrino components of quite different energies: the pp neutrinos, whose average energy is around 200 keV, the ^{7}Be neutrinos, which offer a monochromatic line at 0.862 keV, the pep neutrinos, which offer another monochromatic line at 1.44 MeV, and ^{8}B neutrinos, which have a broad β^+ energy spectrum reaching about 15 MeV. These four neutrino components have very different survival probabilities in the Sun matter because of MSW effect, as we will see in the next section.

Although not relevant for LMA-MSW measurement, it is worth recalling that Borexino, after a substantial effort devoted to the thermal stabilisation of the detector developed in 2016-2018, has been able to measure the small and diffcult CNO neutrino signal.

In next section we focus on the complete measurement of the pp-chain neutrinos and on the consequence of these measurements to the knowledge of LMA-MSW effect in the Sun.

4. Electron neutrino survival probability measurement

The neutrinos produced in the *pp*-chain fusion reactions are all electron neutrinos because they originate from reactions with either an electron in the initial state (^{7}Be and *pep*) or with a positron in the final state (^{8}B and *pp*). However, neutrinos may undergo flavour transitions through the propagation inside solar matter, in the vacuum between the Sun and the Earth and, in the case of ^{8}B neutrinos, also while propagating at night through the Earth itself.

Without matter effects the conversion probability would be just a constant that depends on the vacuum mixing angle θ_{12}, with very little dependence on the other mixing angles and no dependence at all on mass splittings, because for solar neutrinos quantum coherence is completely lost. Indeed, coherence is washed out by the fact that the core of the Sun (diameter approximately 200.000 km) is comparable to the wavelength induced by mass-splitting at solar energies ($2\pi\ E/(1.27 \cdot \delta m_{12}^2) \simeq (2\pi\ 1\ MeV)/(1.27 \cdot 7.\ 10^{-5}\ eV^2) \simeq 70.000$ km) and also because the relative high temperature inside the Sun induce full decoherence of the neutrino beam ($k_B T \gg \delta m_{12}$).

However, since the late '80s and early '90s it was noticed that neutrino flavour oscillations may explain the solar neutrino problem only by assuming that the survival probability is energy dependent, chiefly because the neutrino deficit observed by Gallex[24] and SAGE[25] was different from that observed by Homestake[26] and also from that observed by the SuperKamiokande experiment.[27] The LMA-MSW effect provides an elegant mechanism to recover the energy dependence of the survival probability and Borexino is the first experiment which has been able to test it directly by measuring the survival probability of several neutrino components of various energies.

The LMA-MSW theory predicts a very well defined value of P_{ee} which is shown in Fig. 3 as a pink band whose thickness corresponds to the theoretical error. The same figure also shows the result of the P_{ee} computed using Borexino data using the measurements of *pp*, ^{7}Be, *pep* and ^{8}B neutrinos by means of formula (2). Neutrinos from *pp* initial fusion into deuteron are very low energy and their flavour conversion is dominated by vacuum oscillations. The grey band labelled as Vacuum-LMA corresponds to:

$$P_{ee}^{vac} = 1 - \frac{1}{2}\sin^2 2\theta_{12}, \qquad (2)$$

which is the expected value for vacuum oscillations in case of completely incoherent propagation.

The neutrinos produced by ^{7}Be electron capture and *pep* three body fusion are mono–chromatic, so they bear no uncertainty in horizontal axis. *pep* is well within the transition region and shows a hint of that, with a large statistical uncertainty. ^{7}Be energy is still in the vacuum regime region and its corresponding P_{ee} is well consistent with that. Finally, ^{8}B neutrinos, on the other side, are well within the matter dominated LMA-MSW regime. Being a broad β^+ spectrum it is possible

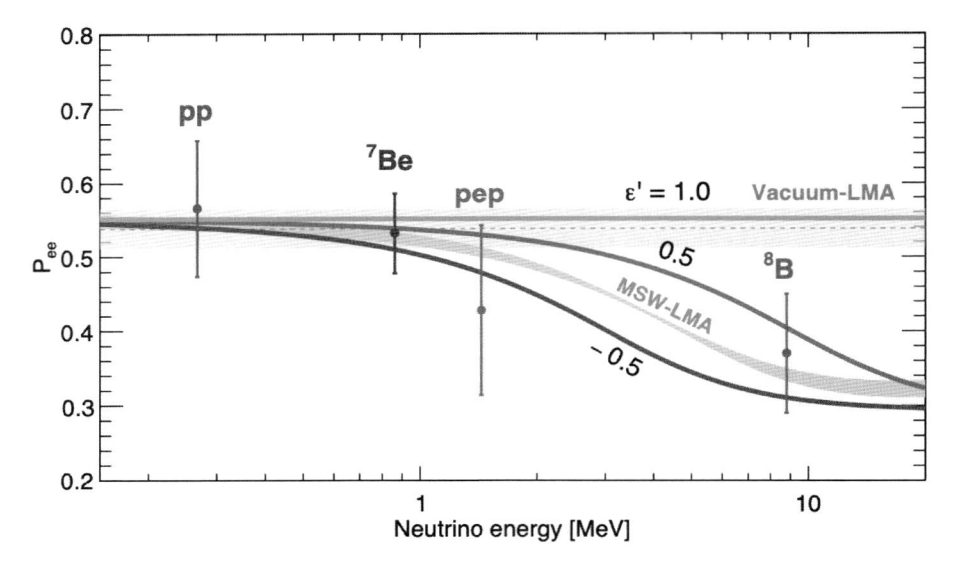

Fig. 4. Electron neutrino survival probability P_{ee} as a function of neutrino energy in LMA-MSW solution with uncertainties of oscillation parameters taken into account (pink band), and LMA-MSW + NSI solutions for $\epsilon'=$ -0.5, 0.5, 1.0 and average values of oscillation parameters. Vacuum oscillations scenario with LMA-MSW parameters is also shown (grey band). The definition of the non–standard interaction parameter is that of reference.[28]

to bin in energy, offering the data points shown in grey, while the green one is the average value. The error are too large, however, to show any hint of the expected rise of P_{ee} at lower energies (the slight uprise of the points has no real statistical significance, though consistent).

Globally, Borexino data clearly are well consistent with the theoretical expectation, confirming LMA-MSW effect, though the error are still large. Unfortunately, there is no room for Borexino to improve further.

In order to improve the result significantly two elements are important, depending on the energy. The ^{7}Be point has an error dominated by the theoretical uncertainty on the expected flux, while other points have also a relevant error coming from the rate measurement. Therefore, a better test of LMA-MSW theory requires an improvement in the Standard Solar Model predictions. For a discussion of the main sources of uncertainties see.[5]

The result obtained on the P_{ee} can be used to test the existence of low energy non–standard neutrino interactions beyond those predicted by the Standard Model. We have carefully studied this opportunity, parametrising the effect of non–standard interactions in terms of a single parameter ϵ'.[28] Fig. 4 shows that with the current theoretical and experimental uncertainties there is still quite a lot of room for new physics and that the future better measurement of this curve might be worth pursuing.

5. Conclusions

Borexino is the first and sole experiment able to measure all neutrino components from pp-chain reactions in the Sun and probe the electron neutrino survival probability as a function of energy.

The results confirm the LMA-MSW scenario with nice agreement with Standard Model physics. The precision is still low and room for new physics exists.

Borexino has opened the era of precise solar neutrino spectroscopy, but even better experiments are desirable to complete the job.

Acknowledgements

I thank the organisers of the Sixteenth Marcel Grossman meeting for the beautiful conference and for offering me the opportunity to give this talk. I am also grateful to the whole Borexino Collaboration for the long and beautiful journey we made all together. Finally, I warmly thank the Laboratori Nazionali del Gran Sasso for the continual support given to Borexino over a period of more than thirty years.

References

1. Q. R. Ahmad et al., Direct evidence for neutrino flavor transformation from neutral current interactions in the Sudbury Neutrino Observatory, *Phys. Rev. Lett.* **89**, p. 011301 (2002).
2. Q. R. Ahmad et al., Measurement of the rate of $\nu_e + d \to p + p + e^-$ interactions produced by ^{8}B solar neutrinos at the Sudbury Neutrino Observatory, *Phys. Rev. Lett.* **87**, p. 071301 (2001).
3. A. B. McDonald, Nobel Lecture: The Sudbury Neutrino Observatory: Observation of flavor change for solar neutrinos, *Rev. Mod. Phys.* **88**, p. 030502 (2016).
4. N. Vinyoles, A. M. Serenelli, F. L. Villante, S. Basu, J. Bergström, M. C. Gonzalez-Garcia, M. Maltoni, C. Peña Garay and N. Song, A new Generation of Standard Solar Models, *Astrophys. J.* **835**, p. 202 (2017).
5. M. Agostini et al., Comprehensive measurement of pp-chain solar neutrinos, *Nature* **562**, 505 (2018).
6. M. Agostini et al., Experimental evidence of neutrinos produced in the CNO fusion cycle in the Sun, *Nature* **587**, 577 (2020).
7. G. Alimonti et al., Science and technology of BOREXINO: A Real time detector for low-energy solar neutrinos, *Astropart. Phys.* **16**, 205 (2002).
8. G. L. Fogli, E. Lisi, A. Marrone, D. Montanino, A. Palazzo and A. M. Rotunno, Global analysis of neutrino masses, mixings and phases: entering the era of leptonic CP violation searches, *Phys. Rev. D* **86**, p. 013012 (2012).
9. L. Wolfenstein, Neutrino Oscillations in Matter, *Phys. Rev. D* **17**, 2369 (1978).
10. S. P. Mikheev and A. Y. Smirnov, Resonant amplification of neutrino oscillations in matter and solar neutrino spectroscopy, *Nuovo Cim. C* **9**, 17 (1986).
11. S. P. Mikheyev and A. Y. Smirnov, Resonance Amplification of Oscillations in Matter and Spectroscopy of Solar Neutrinos, *Sov. J. Nucl. Phys.* **42**, 913 (1985).
12. G. Alimonti et al., The Borexino detector at the Laboratori Nazionali del Gran Sasso, *Nucl. Instrum. Meth. A* **600**, 568 (2009).
13. G. Bellini et al., Muon and Cosmogenic Neutron Detection in Borexino, *JINST* **6**, p. P05005 (2011).

14. G. Alimonti et al., The liquid handling systems for the Borexino solar neutrino detector, *Nucl. Instrum. Meth. A* **609**, 58 (2009).
15. M. Agostini et al., The Monte Carlo simulation of the Borexino detector, *Astropart. Phys.* **97**, 136 (2018).
16. G. Bellini et al., Final results of Borexino Phase-I on low energy solar neutrino spectroscopy, *Phys. Rev. D* **89**, p. 112007 (2014).
17. M. Agostini et al., First Simultaneous Precision Spectroscopy of pp, ^{7}Be, and pep Solar Neutrinos with Borexino Phase-II, *Phys. Rev. D* **100**, p. 082004 (2019).
18. G. Bellini et al., First evidence of pep solar neutrinos by direct detection in Borexino, *Phys. Rev. Lett.* **108**, p. 051302 (2012).
19. G. Bellini et al., Measurement of the solar 8B neutrino rate with a liquid scintillator target and 3 MeV energy threshold in the Borexino detector, *Phys. Rev. D* **82**, p. 033006 (2010).
20. G. Bellini et al., Neutrinos from the primary proton–proton fusion process in the Sun, *Nature* **512**, 383 (2014).
21. G. Bellini et al., Observation of Geo-Neutrinos, *Phys. Lett. B* **687**, 299 (2010).
22. G. Bellini et al., Measurement of geo-neutrinos from 1353 days of Borexino, *Phys. Lett. B* **722**, 295 (2013).
23. M. Agostini et al., Spectroscopy of geoneutrinos from 2056 days of Borexino data, *Phys. Rev. D* **92**, p. 031101 (2015).
24. W. Hampel et al., GALLEX solar neutrino observations: Results for GALLEX IV, *Phys. Lett. B* **447**, 127 (1999).
25. J. N. Abdurashitov et al., Solar neutrino flux measurements by the Soviet-American Gallium Experiment (SAGE) for half the 22 year solar cycle, *J. Exp. Theor. Phys.* **95**, 181 (2002).
26. B. T. Cleveland, T. Daily, R. Davis, Jr., J. R. Distel, K. Lande, C. K. Lee, P. S. Wildenhain and J. Ullman, Measurement of the solar electron neutrino flux with the Homestake chlorine detector, *Astrophys. J.* **496**, 505 (1998).
27. S. Fukuda et al., Determination of solar neutrino oscillation parameters using 1496 days of Super-Kamiokande I data, *Phys. Lett. B* **539**, 179 (2002).
28. S. K. Agarwalla et al., Constraints on flavor-diagonal non-standard neutrino interactions from Borexino Phase-II, *JHEP* **02**, p. 038 (2020).

The relevance of pp-chain and CNO-cycle neutrino measurements for solar physics

F. L. Villante[1,2]

[1]*Dipartimento di Scienze Fisiche e Chimiche,*
Universitá degli Studi dell'Aquila,
Via Vetoio, L'Aquila, I-67100, Italy

[2]*Laboratori Nazionali del Gran Sasso (LNGS),*
Istituto Nazionale di Fisica Nucleare (INFN),
Via G. Acitelli 22, Assergi (AQ), I-67100, Italy

E-mail: villante@lngs.infn.it

A. M. Serenelli[3,4]

[3]*Institute of Space Sciences (ICE, CSIC),*
Carrer de Can Magrans s/n, Cerdanyola del Valles, E-08193, Spain

[4]*Institut d'Estudis Espacials de Catalunya,*
Carrer Gran Capita 2.4, Barcelona, E-08034, Spain

E-mail: a.serenelli@csic.es

We discuss the present status of Standard Solar Models in order to provide the scientific framework to fully understand the relevance of the latest solar neutrino flux measurements performed by Borexino. After reviewing recent Standard Solar Model calculations, we discuss the solar abundance problem and the composition-opacity degeneracy. We then focus on hydrogen burning and neutrino production in Sun, discussing an analytical model that helps understanding the dependence of neutrino fluxes on solar core temperature and composition and the possibility they offer for determining physical characteristics of the solar interior.

Keywords: Solar neutrino fluxes, solar physics, solar models

1. Introduction

Being the closest star to us, the Sun can be investigated by a variety of different approaches/messengers. We can e.g. study the electromagnetic radiation that is emitted from its photosphere, determining its luminosity $L_\odot$, surface temperature $T_{\rm eff}$ and radius $R_\odot$. By looking at the absorption lines that are formed in the solar atmosphere, we are also able to infer the surface composition through spectroscopic techniques, more precisely the present-day abundance of chemical elements relative to hydrogen, usually summarized in the metal-to-hydrogen ratio $(Z/X)_\odot$. At the same time, the properties of the solar core, in particular its temperature and composition, can be probed by measuring the fluxes of neutrinos produced by nuclear reactions responsible for hydrogen burning. Finally, the properties of the solar interior, namely the sound speed stratification and the depth and helium abundance of the external convective envelope, can be inferred with high accuracy by helioseismology, i.e. by looking at non-radial oscillations of the solar surface. As a result of these observations, we have a redundancy of experimental information that make the Sun an over-constrained system. This allows us to use the Sun as a laboratory for fundamental physics and a benchmark for stellar astrophysics.

As a remarkable example, the development of increasingly more precise Standard Solar Models[1,2] (SSMs), i.e. self calibrated theoretical models of the solar interior that automatically implements the observational values of $L_\odot$, $R_\odot$ and $(Z/X)_\odot$ and have no free parameters, and the fact that they were able to successfully reproduce the tight constraints imposed by helioseismology,[3] suggested that solution of the solar neutrino problem had to be found outside the realm of astrophysics, as had originally been suggested a few years earlier.[4] Simultaneously, Super-Kamiokande[5,6] led to the precise measurement of ^{8}B neutrino flux which, in combination with the results of radiochemical experiments Homestake,[7] Gallex[8] and SAGE[9] strongly hinted at the existence of solar neutrino oscillations, result confirmed just a few years later by SNO results.[10,11]

The discovery of neutrino oscillations and the accurate and precise determination of neutrino fluxes from individual reactions changed the focus of interest of solar physics. Starting from 2007, Borexino has obtained an almost complete characterization of the spectrum of neutrinos from the pp-chain.[12,13] Together with the very precise measurement of the ^{8}B flux from SNO[14] and Super-Kamiokande,[15] we have come full circle and results from solar neutrino experiments can now be used to learn about the properties of the Sun. This is timely. There is a lingering dispute about which is the detailed chemical composition of the Sun, the solar abundance problem, that is intimately linked to the uncertainties in our knowledge of radiative opacities in the solar interior. Solar neutrino data can in principle be used to disentangle this problem,[16–18] in particular if the promising results by Borexino on solar CN neutrinos[19] can be further improved.

The goal of this work is to discuss the present status of SSMs and to provide the scientific framework to fully understand the relevance of the recent solar neutrino flux measurements performed by Borexino. After reviewing recent SSM calculations (Sect. 2), we discuss the solar abundance problem (Sect. 3) and the composition-opacity degeneracy (Sect. 4). We then focus on hydrogen burning (Sect. 5) and solar neutrino production (Sect. 6), discussing an analytical model (Sect. 7) that helps understanding the dependence of neutrino fluxes on solar core temperature, composition and nuclear cross sections, and the possibility they offer for determining physical characteristics of the solar interior (Sect. 8).

2. Standard solar models

SSMs are a snapshot in the evolution of a $1\,M_\odot$ star, calibrated to match present-day surface properties of the Sun. Two basic assumptions in SSM calculations are: 1) after the phase of star formation the Sun was chemically homogenized as a result of the fully convective phase during its contraction along the Hayashi track and before nuclear reactions start altering its initial composition and, 2) at all moments during its evolution up to the present solar age $\tau_\odot = 4.57\,\mathrm{Gyr}$ mass loss is negligible. The calibration is done by adjusting the mixing length parameter (α_{MLT}) and the initial helium and metal mass fractions (Y_{ini} and Z_{ini} respectively) in order to satisfy the constraints imposed by the present-day solar luminosity $L_\odot = 3.8418 \times 10^{33}\,\mathrm{erg\,s^{-1}}$, radius $R_\odot = 6.9598 \times 10^{10}\,\mathrm{cm}$,[20] and surface metal to hydrogen abundance ratio $(Z/X)_\odot$, see sect.3. As a result of this procedure, SSM has no free parameters and completely determines the physical properties of the Sun. It can be then validated (or falsified) by other observational constraints, in particular by those provided by solar neutrino fluxes measurements and helioseismic frequencies determinations.

The physics input in the SSM is rather simple and it accounts for: convective and radiative transport of energy, chemical evolution driven by nuclear reactions, microscopic diffusion of elements which comprises different processes but among which gravitational settling dominates. For over more than 25 years, since the modern version of the SSM was established with the inclusion of microscopic diffusion,[21,22] the continuous improvement of the constitutive physics has brought about the changes and the evolution of SSMs. In particular, a lot of effort has gone into experimental and theoretical work on nuclear reaction rates. But changes in radiative opacities and the equation of state were also relevant. We take here as a reference the results of recent SSM calculations,[23] the so-called Barcelona 2016 (B16, for short) SSMs, which are based on the following state of the art ingredients. The equation of state is calculated consistently for each of the compositions used in the solar calibrations by using FreeEOS.[24] Atomic radiative opacities are from the Opacity Project (OP),[25] complemented at low temperatures with molecular opacities from Ref. 26. Nuclear reaction rates for the pp-chain and CNO-bicycle are from the Solar Fusion II compilation[27] with important updates for the rates of $\mathrm{p}(\mathrm{p},e^+\nu_e)\mathrm{d}$, $^7\mathrm{Be}(\mathrm{p},\gamma)^8\mathrm{B}$ and $^{14}\mathrm{N}(\mathrm{p},\gamma)^{15}\mathrm{O}$ reactions, see Refs. 28–32. Microscopic diffusion coefficients are computed as described in Ref. 33. Convection is treated according to the mixing length theory.[34] The atmosphere is grey and modeled according to a Krishna-Swamy $T - \tau$ relationship.[35]

3. The solar composition problem

The solar surface composition, determined with spectroscopic techniques, is a fundamental input in the construction of SSMs. The development of three dimensional hydrodynamic models of the solar atmosphere, of techniques to study line formation under non-local thermodynamic conditions and the improvement in atomic properties (e.g. transition strengths) have led since 2001 to a complete revision of solar abundances. Table 1 lists the abundances determined by different authors for the most relevant metals in solar modeling: GN93,[36] GS98,[37] AGSS09,[38] C11,[39] AGSS15,[40–42] and AAG20.[43]

Table 1. Solar photospheric composition through time and authors for most relevant metals in solar modeling. Abundances are given in the standard astronomical scale $\epsilon_i = \log_{10}(n_i/n_H) + 12$, where n_i is the number density of a given atomic species.

El.	GN93	GS98	AGSS09	C11	AGSS15	AAG20
C	8.55	8.52	8.43	8.50	—	8.46
N	7.97	7.92	7.83	7.86	—	7.83
O	8.87	8.83	8.69	8.76	—	8.69
Ne	8.08	8.08	7.93	8.05	7.93	8.06
Mg	7.58	7.58	7.60	7.54	7.59	7.55
Si	7.55	7.55	7.51	7.52	7.51	7.51
S	7.33	7.33	7.13	7.16	7.13	7.12
Fe	7.50	7.50	7.50	7.52	7.47	7.46
$(Z/X)_\odot$	0.0245	0.0230	0.0180	0.0209	—	0.0187

Note that only abundances relative to hydrogen can be obtained from spectroscopy because the intensity of spectroscopic lines is measured relative to a continuum that is determined by the hydrogen abundance in the solar atmosphere. The last row in the table gives the total photospheric present-day metal-to-hydrogen ratio $(Z/X)_\odot$ and it is the quantity used as observational constraint to construct a solar model. In fact, the solar composition set used in solar models determines not only $(Z/X)_\odot$ but also the relative abundances of metals in the models. In this sense, $Z_{\rm ini}$ acts as a normalization factor that, together with $Y_{\rm ini}$ and the relation $X_{\rm ini} + Y_{\rm ini} + Z_{\rm ini} = 1$, determines completely the initial composition of the model.

There is no complete agreement among authors, and some controversy still remains as to what the best values for the new spectroscopic abundances are. See in particular recent work on solar oxygen,[44] based on the same 3D atmosphere models as used by the Asplund group, but improved atomic data and methods, leads to $\epsilon_O = 8.75 \pm 0.03$, i.e. very close to the C11 value. However, at the moment there seems to be consensus in that all determinations of the solar metallicity based on the new generation of spectroscopic studies yield a solar metallicity lower than older spectroscopic results,[36,37] in particular for the volatile and most abundant C, N, and O. For refractories elements, like Fe, Si, Mg and S that have important role in solar modeling being important contributors to the radiative opacity, meteorites offer a very valuable alternative method (see e.g. Ref. 45) and, in fact, elemental abundances determined from meteorites have been historically more robust than spectroscopic ones.

Considering that uncertainties of element abundances are difficult to quantify, it has become customary to consider two canonical sets of abundances to which we refer to as high metallicity (HZ) and low metallicity (LZ) solar admixtures as reference assumptions for SSM calculations. These are obtained by using the photospheric (volatiles) + meteoritic (refractories) abundances from GS98 and AGSS09 respectively, and are reported in Table 2. In the last column, we give the fractional differences $\delta z_i \equiv z_i^{\rm HZ}/z_i^{\rm LZ} - 1$ where $z_i \equiv Z_i/X$ is the ratio of the i-element

Table 2. The two canonical HZ and LZ solar mixtures given as $\epsilon_i = \log_{10}(n_i/n_H) + 12$. The two compilations are obtained by using the photospheric (volatiles) + meteoritic (refractories) abundances from GS98 and AGSS09 respectively, and correpond to the admixture labelled as GS98 and AGSS09met in Ref. 23.

El.	High-Z (HZ)	Low-Z (LZ)	δz_i
C	8.52 ± 0.06	8.43 ± 0.05	0.23
N	7.92 ± 0.06	7.83 ± 0.05	0.23
O	8.83 ± 0.06	8.69 ± 0.05	0.38
Ne	8.08 ± 0.06	7.93 ± 0.10	0.41
Mg	7.58 ± 0.01	7.53 ± 0.01	0.12
Si	7.56 ± 0.01	7.51 ± 0.01	0.12
S	7.20 ± 0.06	7.15 ± 0.02	0.12
Ar	6.40 ± 0.06	6.40 ± 0.13	0.00
Fe	7.50 ± 0.01	7.45 ± 0.01	0.12
$(Z/X)_\odot$	0.02292	0.01780	0.29

abundance with that of hydrogen, to facilitate comparison among the two admixtures. Even if GS98 abundances are presumably surpassed by the more recent determinations, they are still considered as a valid option to construct solar models because they lead to a temperature stratification that well reproduces the helioseismic constraints.

This can be better appreciated by considering Tab. 3 and Fig. 1 where we compare theoretical predictions of SSMs implementing HZ and LZ surface composition with helioseismic determinations of the surface helium abundance Y_s, of the convective envelope depth R_{CZ} and the solar sound speed $c_\odot(r)$. We see that solar models implementing the LZ abundances fail to reproduce all helioseismic probes of solar properties. This disagreement constitutes the so-called *solar abundance problem*[46–48] that has defied a complete solution. All proposed modifications to physical processes in SSMs offer, at best, only partial improvements in some helioseismic probes (e.g.[49–53]). An alternative possibility is to consider modifications to the physical inputs of SSMs at the level of the constitutive physics, radiative opacities in particular (see next section).

4. The opacity-composition degeneracy

The interpretation of the solar abundance problem is complicated by the degeneracy between effects produced by a modification of the radiative opacity $\kappa(\rho, T, Y, Z_i)$ and effects induced by a change of the heavy element admixture $\{z_i\}$, expressed here in terms of the quantities $z_i \equiv Z_i/X$ where Z_i is the surface abundance of the i-element and X is that of hydrogen.

This degeneracy was discussed in quantitative terms in Ref. 55 by using the linear solar model (LSM) approach introduced in Ref. 56. By neglecting the role of

Table 3. Main characteristics of SSMs with different surface composition.[23] The observational values for Y_s and R_{CZ} are taken from Ref. 46 and 54, respectively. The quantity $\delta c/c = (c_\odot - c_{mod})/c_{mod}$ is the fractional difference between sound speed helioseismic determination and model prediction.

Qnt.	B16-HZ	B16-LZ	Solar
Y_s	0.2426 ± 0.0059	0.2317 ± 0.0059	0.2485 ± 0.0035
$R_{CZ}/R_\odot$	0.7116 ± 0.0048	0.7223 ± 0.0053	0.713 ± 0.001
$\langle \delta c/c \rangle$	$0.0005^{+0.0006}_{-0.0002}$	0.0021 ± 0.001	-
α_{MLT}	2.18 ± 0.05	2.11 ± 0.05	-
Y_{ini}	0.2718 ± 0.0056	0.2613 ± 0.0055	-
Z_{ini}	0.0187 ± 0.0013	0.0149 ± 0.0009	-
Z_s	0.0170 ± 0.0012	0.0134 ± 0.0008	-
Y_c	0.6328 ± 0.0053	0.6217 ± 0.0062	-
Z_c	0.0200 ± 0.0014	0.0159 ± 0.0010	-

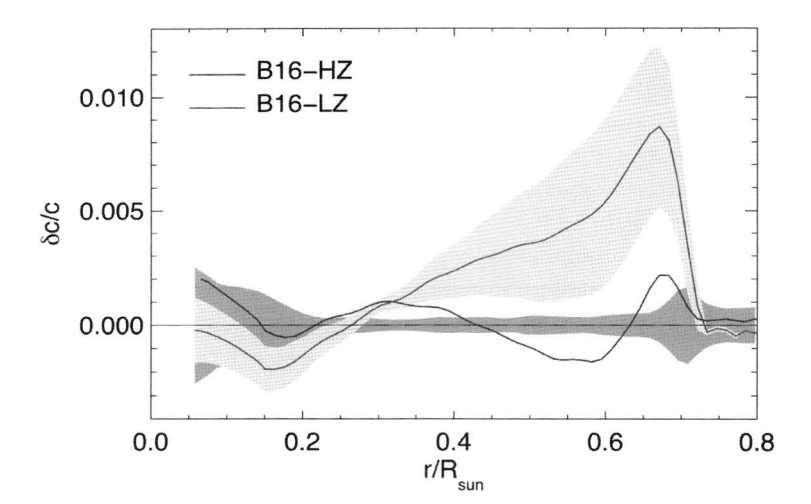

Fig. 1. Fractional sound speed difference in the sense $\delta c/c = (c_\odot - c_{mod})/c_{mod}$. Grey shaded regions corresponds to errors from helioseismic inversion procedure. Red shaded region corresponds to uncertainties in SSM predictions which we chose to plot around the B16-LZ central value (solid red line). An equivalent relative error band holds around the central value of the B16-HZ central value (solid blue line) which we do not plot for the sake of clarity.

metals in the equation of state and in the energy generation coefficient, it was shown that the source term $\delta\kappa(r)$ that drives the modification of the solar properties and that can be constrained by observational data can be written as the sum of two contributions:

$$\delta\kappa(r) = \delta\kappa_I(r) + \delta\kappa_Z(r) \tag{1}$$

The first term $\delta\kappa_{\rm I}(r)$, which we refer to as *intrinsic* opacity change, represents the fractional variation of the opacity along the solar profile and it is given by:

$$\delta\kappa_{\rm I}(r) = \frac{\kappa(\overline{\rho}(r),\overline{T}(r),\overline{Y}(r),\overline{Z}_i(r))}{\overline{\kappa}(\overline{\rho}(r),\overline{T}(r),\overline{Y}(r),\overline{Z}_i(r))} - 1 \qquad (2)$$

where the notation $\overline{Q}$ indicates, here and in the following, the value for the generic quantity Q in reference SSM calculation. The second term $\delta\kappa_{\rm Z}(r)$, which we refer to as *composition* opacity change, describes the effects of a variation of $\{z_i\}$. It takes into account that a modification of the photospheric admixture implies a different distribution of metals inside the Sun and, thus, a different opacity profile, even if the function $\kappa(\rho,T,Y,Z_i)$ is unchanged. The contribution $\delta\kappa_{\rm Z}(r)$ is given by:

$$\delta\kappa_{\rm Z}(r) = \frac{\overline{\kappa}(\overline{\rho}(r),\overline{T}(r),\overline{Y}(r),Z_i(r))}{\overline{\kappa}(\overline{\rho}(r),\overline{T}(r),\overline{Y}(r),\overline{Z}_i(r))} - 1 \qquad (3)$$

where $Z_i(r) \simeq \overline{Z}_i(r)\,(z_i/\overline{z}_i)$ and can be calculated as:

$$\delta\kappa_{\rm Z}(r) \simeq \sum_i \left.\frac{\partial \ln \overline{\kappa}}{\partial \ln Z_i}\right|_{\rm SSM} \delta z_i \qquad (4)$$

where δz_i represents the fractional variation of z_i and the symbol $|_{\rm SSM}$ indicates that we calculate the derivatives along the density, temperature and chemical composition profiles predicted by the reference SSM. Equation (1), although being approximate, is quite useful because it makes explicit the connection (and the degeneracy) between the effects produced by a modification of the radiative opacity and of those produced by a modification of the heavy element admixture.

Early works[57,58] suggested that a localized increase in opacities could solve or, at least, alleviate the disagreement of low-Z solar models with helioseismology. Refs. 59 and 55 have concluded that a tilted increase in radiative opacities, with a few percent increase in the solar core and a larger (15-20%) increase at the base of the convective envelope could lead to low-Z SSMs that would satisfy helioseismic probes equally as well as SSMs based on the older, higher, metallicities. Incidentally, the above conclusion is confirmed by the analysis presented in Ref. 18 where helioseismic and solar neutrino data are used to infer the optimal composition of the Sun (see their Fig. 10).

Recent years have seen a surge of activity in theoretical calculations of atomic radiative opacities. Updated calculations[25] by the Opacity Project have led the way, followed by OPAS,[60,61] STAR[62] and a new version of OPLIB, the opacities from Los Alamos.[63] For conditions in solar interiors, all theoretical opacities agree with each other within few %. Interestingly, Ref. 64 have presented the first ever measurement of opacity under conditions close to those present in the solar interior. Four measurements were carried out to measure the iron opacity, each at different temperature and electron densities. The most extreme conditions used in the experiment approach those at the base of the solar convective envelope. While the experiment has been carried out only for iron, their conclusion is that all theoretical calculations predict a too low Rosseland mean opacity, at a level of $7 \pm 4\%$, for the temperature and density combinations realized in the experiment. Further experimental work on chromium and nickel opacities[65] helps to evaluate discrepancies between experimental and theoretical results on iron opacity. Results point towards shortcomings that affect models, particularly in the case of open electronic L-shell configurations such as is present in iron at the base of the convective envelope. Also, the disagreement between theoretical and measured line shapes for the three elements indicates shortcomings in the theoretical understanding of atomic interaction with the plasma. On the other hand, the results also indicate that the quasicontinuum opacity determined experimentally agrees well with the chromium and nickel experiments, contrary to results from the iron experiment. However, the chromium and nickel experiments were carried out at lower temperatures than those used in the extreme conditions of the original iron experiment, which suggests that the problem of missing quasicontinuum opacity might have an unknown temperature dependence, or that a systematic error affected the high temperature iron measurements. Moreover,[66] in a recent theoretical analysis of line broadening modeling in opacity calculations, have found that uncertainties linked to this are larger at the base of the convective envelope than in the core. These arguments suggest that opacity calculations are more accurate in the solar core than in the region around the base of the convective envelope.

5. Hydrogen burning in the Sun

The Sun is powered by nuclear reactions that transform hydrogen into helium-4. The overall effect of these reactions is the conversion:

$$4\,\mathrm{p} + 2\,e^- \to {}^4\mathrm{He} + 2\,\nu_e \qquad (5)$$

with the production of a fixed amount of energy $Q = 4\,m_\mathrm{p} + 2m_\mathrm{e} - m_{^4\mathrm{He}} = 26.7\,\mathrm{MeV}$ per synthesized ^{4}He nucleus. Most of this energy is released in the solar plasma and slowly diffuses toward the solar surface supporting the radiative luminosity of the Sun. A small fraction of it, that depends on the specific channel by which hydrogen burning proceeds, is emitted in neutrinos. According to SSM calculations, the two neutrinos carry away about 0.6 MeV on the average.

The SSM predicts that most of the solar energy ($> 99\%$) is produced by the pp-chain, i.e. the hydrogen fusion reaction chain displayed in the left panel of Fig. 2. The pp-chain is is mostly initiated by p(p, $e^+\nu_e$)d reaction and, to a minor extent, by electron capture reaction p(pe^-, ν_e)d and has several possible terminations that depend on the specific mechanism by which helium-3 nuclei, which are produced by d(p, γ)^{3}He reaction, are converted to heavier elements. In the Sun, the dominant mechanism is ^{3}He(^{3}He, $2p$)^{4}He that corresponds to the so-called pp-I termination of the pp-chain. Alternatively, helium-3 can lead to production of ^{7}Be through the reaction ^{3}He(^{4}He, γ)^{7}Be. Depending on the destiny of ^{7}Be, that can be processed either by the electron capture ^{7}Be(e^-, ν_e)^{7}Li or by the (largely sub-dominant)

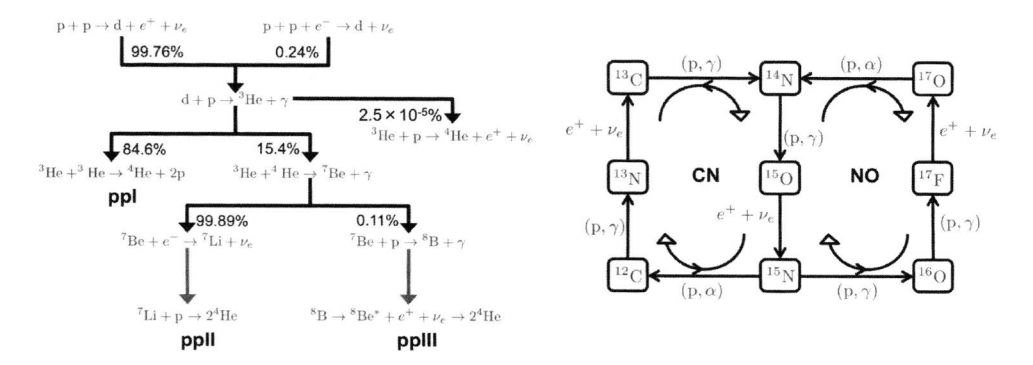

Fig. 2. Left Panel: The pp-chain; Right Panel: The CNO-bicycle.

proton capture reaction ^{7}Be$(p,\gamma)^8$B, one obtains the pp-II or the pp-III terminations of the chain. Finally, a very small amount of helium-4 nuclei is produced by ^{3}He$(p,e^+\nu_e)^4$He reaction. The relative importance of the different branches of the pp-chain depends primarily on the core temperature of the Sun and on the cross section of specific reactions, as will be discussed in next section. The numbers given in Fig. 2 show the branching ratios in the present Sun.

An alternative hydrogen burning mechanism is provided by the CNO-bicycle that is displayed in the right panel of Fig. 2. The CNO-bicycle uses carbon, nitrogen and oxygen nuclei that are present in the core of the Sun as catalysts for hydrogen fusion. It is composed by two different branches, i.e. the CN-cycle and the NO-cycle, whose relative importance depends on the outcome of proton capture reaction on ^{15}N. In the Sun, the ^{15}N$(p,\alpha)^{12}$C channel is largely dominant and so, in practice, the CNO-bicycle is reduced to the CN-cycle with a marginal contribution by the NO-cycle. Note that the CN-cycle conserves the total number of C and N nuclei in the core of the Sun, but alters their distribution as it burns into equilibrium, eventually achieving equilibrium abundances proportional to the inverse of the respective rates. The reactions controlling conversion of ^{12}C and ^{14}N in the solar core and the approach to equilibrium are ^{12}C$(p,\gamma)^{13}$N and ^{14}N$(p,\gamma)^{15}$O: these are the next-to-slowest and slowest rates in the CN-cycle, respectively. The temperature above which the ^{12}C burning time through ^{12}C$(p,\gamma)^{13}$N is smaller than the Sun's lifetime is $T \sim 10^7$ K. In the SSM, the entire energy-producing core, $r \lesssim 0.2 R_\odot$ and $m \lesssim 0.3 M_\odot$ is at temperature larger than this value, so that nearly all of the core's ^{12}C is converted to ^{14}N. The slower ^{14}N$(p,\gamma)^{15}$O reaction determines whether equilibrium is achieved. The ^{14}N burning time is shorter than the age of the Sun for $T \gtrsim 1.3 \times 10^7$ K. Therefore equilibrium for the CN cycle is reached only for $R \lesssim 0.1 R_\odot$, corresponding to the central 7% of the Sun by mass. Consequently, over a significant portion of the outer core, ^{12}C is converted to ^{14}N, but further reactions are inhibited by the ^{14}N$(p,\gamma)^{15}$O bottleneck.

Table 4. Solar neutrino fluxes predicted by SSMs with different surface composition.[23] Units are: 10^{10} (pp), 10^9 (^{7}Be), 10^8 (pep, ^{13}N, ^{15}O), 10^6 (^{8}B, ^{17}F), 10^5 (eN, eO) and 10^3 (hep, eF) cm^{-2}s^{-1}.

Flux	B16-HZ	B16-LZ
Φ(pp)	$5.98(1 \pm 0.006)$	$6.03(1 \pm 0.005)$
Φ(pep)	$1.44(1 \pm 0.01)$	$1.46(1 \pm 0.009)$
Φ(hep)	$7.98(1 \pm 0.30)$	$8.25(1 \pm 0.30)$
Φ(^{7}Be)	$4.93(1 \pm 0.06)$	$4.50(1 \pm 0.06)$
Φ(^{8}B)	$5.46(1 \pm 0.12)$	$4.50(1 \pm 0.12)$
Φ(^{13}N)	$2.78(1 \pm 0.15)$	$2.04(1 \pm 0.14)$
Φ(^{15}O)	$2.05(1 \pm 0.17)$	$1.44(1 \pm 0.16)$
Φ(^{17}F)	$5.29(1 \pm 0.20)$	$3.26(1 \pm 0.18)$
Φ(eN)	$2.20(1 \pm 0.15)$	$1.61(1 \pm 0.14)$
Φ(eO)	$0.81(1 \pm 0.17)$	$0.57(1 \pm 0.16)$
Φ(eF)	$3.11(1 \pm 0.20)$	$1.91(1 \pm 0.18)$

6. Solar neutrinos

A very effective tool to investigate the properties of the Sun is provided by neutrinos which are necessarily produced along with ^{4}He nuclei during hydrogen burning, in order to satisfy lepton number conservation. Neutrinos free stream in the solar plasma and reach the Earth in about 8 minutes where they can be detected by solar neutrino experiments. While the total amount of neutrinos produced in the Sun can be easily estimated from the solar luminosity constraint (see below), the evaluation of their spectrum requires the knowledge of the individual rates of neutrino producing reactions and thus the construction of a complete solar model. We report in Fig. 3 and Tab. 4, the SSM predictions for the different components of the solar neutrino flux, named according to the specific reaction by which they are produced.[23] We also include, for completeness, ecCNO neutrinos, i.e. neutrinos produced by electron capture reaction in the CNO-bicycle (in addition to the "standard" CNO neutrinos produced by β decays of ^{13}N, ^{15}O and ^{17}F) that were originally calculated in Refs. 67 and 68 and recently reevaluated in Ref. 69[a]. The two columns "B16-HZ" and "B16-LZ" reported in Tab. 4 are obtained by considering two different options for the solar surface composition, as it discussed in Sect. 3. During the last few decades, solar neutrino experiments have allowed us to determine with great accuracy most of the components of the solar flux. As an example, ^{7}Be and ^{8}B neutrino fluxes are measured with accuracy better than $\sim 3\%$ by Borexino,[13] Super-Kamiokande[15] and SNO.[14] The pp and pep-neutrino flux can be determined

---

[a]In order to take into account the new inputs in B16-SSM calculations, the ecCNO fluxes given in Tab. 4 have been scaled with respect to the values quoted in Ref. 69 proportionally to the corresponding β-decay fluxes. This follows from the assumption that the ratio of electron capture and beta decay processes in the Sun is equal to what evaluated in Ref. 69

with $\lesssim 1\%$ accuracy by assuming the solar luminosity constraint, see e.g. Ref. 70. These fluxes, however, have been also directly measured by Borexino[13,71,72] with $\sim 10\%$ and $\sim 17\%$ accuracy, respectively. Finally, Borexino has recently obtained the experimental identification of CNO neutrinos,[19] providing the first direct evidence that CNO-bicycle is active in the Sun.

The solar luminosity constraint
SSM calculations predict that the Sun is very close to thermal equilibrium and that evolutionary timescales are much longer than the heat diffusion time across the solar structure. In this case, the amount of energy which is produced (in unit time) by nuclear reactions in the solar core almost exactly counterbalance the luminosity radiated at the surface of the Sun, with the contribution of gravothermal energy to the solar luminosity being $< 0.1\%$. Since a fixed amount of energy Q and two electron neutrinos are produced for synthesized ^{4}He nucleus, and neglecting the small gravothermal contribution, this argument implies a relationship between the measured solar luminosity and the solar neutrino fluxes that can be expressed as

$$\frac{L_\odot}{4\pi D^2} = \sum_i \left(\frac{Q}{2} - \langle E_\nu \rangle_i \right) \Phi(i) \qquad (6)$$

where the index i indicates the different components of the neutrino flux and the quantity $\langle E_\nu \rangle_i$ is the average energy of neutrinos produced by a specific reaction. This argument was illustrated and discussed e.g. in Ref. 73, 74 and has been recently reviewed in Refs. 75, 76.

It is clearly important to experimentally confirm the validity of the solar luminosity constraint because this represents a test of fundamental assumptions in the SSM paradigm, e.g. that the Sun is stable on timescales much longer than the heat diffusion time ($\sim 10^5$y), and that the are no additional energy losses or production mechanisms besides those normally included in solar model calculations. The recent Borexino direct identification of the pp-neutrino flux,[13] which provides the dominant term in the r.h.s of Eq. (6), has finally made this test possible, confirming the energy balance employed by SSMs at the $\sim 10\%$ level. Future more accurate measurements will be important to further constrain non standard scenarios.

7. The dependence of neutrino fluxes on the central temperature of the Sun

Even a small modification of the central temperature of the Sun reflects into large variations of solar neutrino fluxes. The dependence of solar neutrino fluxes on the core temperature of the Sun was recently re-analyzed in Ref. 77 (see also Refs. 78 and 74 for previous discussions on the subject) where an analytical model that helps understanding the possibility they offer for determining physical characteristics of the solar interior was also provided. We summarize the main results of Ref. 77.

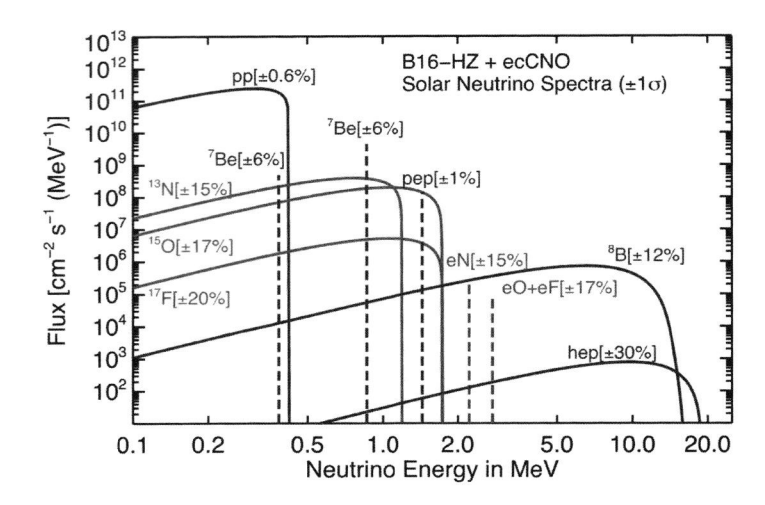

Fig. 3. The solar neutrino spectrum.

The pp-neutrino flux:
The flux $\Phi(\text{pp})$ is basically fixed by the solar luminosity constraint and it is expected to be mildly dependent on the central temperature of the Sun and nuclear reaction cross sections. By taking into account that the two largest contributions to the r.h.s of Eq. 6 are provided by pp and ^{7}Be-neutrinos, one arrives at the conclusions that $\delta\Phi(\text{pp}) \simeq -\eta\,\delta\Phi(^7\text{Be})$, where $\delta\Phi(i)$ represent the fractional variation of the i-neutrino flux and $\eta \equiv \Phi(^7\text{Be})/\Phi(\text{pp}) \simeq 0.08$. By considering the dependence of $\Phi(^7\text{Be})$ on solar central temperature and nuclear cross sections (discussed below), one obtains the following relationship

$$\delta\Phi(\text{pp}) = -\eta\,\delta S_{34} - \frac{\eta}{2}(\delta S_{11} - \delta S_{33}) + \beta_{\text{pp}}\,\delta T_c \quad (7)$$

where $\beta_{\text{pp}} = -\eta\beta_{\text{Be}} \simeq -0.9$, δT_c is the fractional variation of the core temperature and δS_{ij} indicates the fractional variations of the astrophysical factor S_{ij}.

The pep-neutrino flux:
The pep-neutrinos are produced by electron capture reaction $p(pe^-,\nu_e)d$ which is linked to the β-decay process $p(p,e^+\nu_e)d$ by well-known nuclear physics. The ratio between their rates is roughly proportional to $T_c^{-1/2}\,n_e$ (see e.g. Ref. 27 for a review). We can thus assume $\Phi(\text{pep}) \propto T_c^{1/2}\,\Phi(\text{pp})$, allowing us to conclude:

$$\delta\Phi(\text{pep}) = -\eta\,\delta S_{34} - \frac{\eta}{2}(\delta S_{11} - \delta S_{33}) + \beta_{\text{pep}}\,\delta T_c \quad (8)$$

where $\beta_{\text{pep}} = \beta_{\text{pp}} - 1/2 \simeq -1.4$.

The ^{7}Be-neutrino flux:
The Be-neutrino flux is linked to the rate of the $^3\text{He}(^4\text{He},\gamma)^7\text{Be}$ reaction, since the electron capture reaction $^7\text{Be}(e^-,\nu_e)^7\text{Li}$ largely dominates over the competing

proton-capture reaction. By considering that ^{3}He abundance in a large part of the solar core can be estimated by using the equilibrium condition $X_3 \simeq X_{3,\mathrm{eq}} \propto (\langle\sigma v\rangle_{11}/\langle\sigma v\rangle_{33})^{1/2}$, one obtains the expression:

$$\delta\Phi(^7\mathrm{Be}) = \delta S_{34} + \frac{1}{2}(\delta S_{11} - \delta S_{33}) + \beta_{\mathrm{Be}}\,\delta T_{\mathrm{c}} \qquad (9)$$

where $\beta_{\mathrm{Be}} = \gamma_{34} + (\gamma_{11} - \gamma_{33})/2 \sim 11$ and we considered that $\langle\sigma v\rangle_{ij} \propto S_{ij}\,T_{\mathrm{c}}^{\gamma_{ij}}$.

The ^{8}B-neutrino flux:
The ^{8}B neutrinos constitute a largely subdominant component of the solar flux which is produced when ^{7}Be nuclei capture a proton (instead of an electron) producing ^{8}B (instead of ^{7}Li). The ^{8}B-neutrino flux is thus given by $\Phi(^8\mathrm{B}) = r\,\Phi(^7\mathrm{Be})$ where r is the ratio between proton and electron capture rates on ^{7}Be. The parameter r scales as $r \propto (S_{17}/S_{e7}) \cdot T_{\mathrm{c}}^{\alpha}$ where $\alpha = \gamma_{17} + (1/2)$ and we have considered that $\langle\sigma v\rangle_{e7} \propto S_{e7}\,T_{\mathrm{c}}^{-1/2}$ for electron capture reaction. Taking this into account, we obtain the following equation:

$$\delta\Phi(^8\mathrm{B}) = (\delta S_{17} - \delta S_{e7}) + \delta S_{34} + \frac{1}{2}(\delta S_{11} - \delta S_{33}) + \beta_{\mathrm{B}}\,\delta T_{\mathrm{c}} \qquad (10)$$

with $\beta_{\mathrm{B}} = \beta_{\mathrm{Be}} + \gamma_{17} + 1/2 \simeq 24$. The large value of β_{B} indicates that ^{8}B neutrinos are a very sensitive probe of the core temperature of the Sun.

The CNO neutrino fluxes:
The neutrino fluxes produced in the CN-cycle by β-decay (and electron capture reactions) of ^{13}N and ^{15}O nuclei, besides depending on the solar central temperature, are approximately proportional to the stellar-core number abundance of CN elements. This dependence is extremely important because, as it is discussed in Refs. 16, 17, 79, it permits us to use CNO neutrinos, in combination with other neutrino fluxes, to directly probe the chemical composition of the Sun. By considering an analytical model to calculate the abundance of carbon and nitrogen in the core of the Sun, Ref. 77 obtained the following expressions;

$$\delta\Phi(^{15}\mathrm{O}) = \beta_{\mathrm{O}}\,\delta T_{\mathrm{c}} + (1-a)\,\delta X_{12,\mathrm{s}} + a\,\delta X_{14,\mathrm{s}} + b\left(\Delta^{(\mathrm{cs})} - 0.16\right) + \delta S_{114} \qquad (11)$$

$$\delta\Phi(^{13}\mathrm{N}) = \beta_{\mathrm{N}}\,\delta T_{\mathrm{c}} + (1-a')\,\delta X_{12,\mathrm{s}} + a'\,\delta X_{14,\mathrm{s}} + b\left(\Delta^{(\mathrm{cs})} - 0.16\right) + f\,\delta S_{114}$$

with $\beta_{\mathrm{O}} = \gamma_{114} \simeq 20$, $f = \Phi(^{15}\mathrm{O})/\Phi(^{13}\mathrm{N}) = 0.74$, $a = 6\xi/(6\xi + 7) \simeq 0.20$ and $\xi = (X_{14,\mathrm{s}}/X_{12,\mathrm{s}}) \simeq 0.30$, $b = 0.86$, $\beta_{\mathrm{N}} \equiv f\,\beta_{\mathrm{O}} = 15$ and $a' \equiv f a = 0.15$. In the previous relations, $\delta X_{12,\mathrm{s}}$ and $\delta X_{14,\mathrm{s}}$ are the fractional variations of the carbon-12 and nitrogen-14 surface abundances. The quantity $\Delta^{(\mathrm{cs})}$ takes into account the effects of elemental diffusion that enhances heavy element abundances in the solar core with respect to surface. It is defined by:

$$\mathcal{N}_{\mathrm{c}} = \mathcal{N}_{\mathrm{s}}\left[1 + \Delta^{(\mathrm{cs})}\right] \qquad (12)$$

where $\mathcal{N}_c$ ($\mathcal{N}_s$) is the central (surface) value of the total number abundance of CN nuclei defined as $\mathcal{N} \equiv X_{12}/12 + X_{13}/13 + X_{14}/14$. Reference SSM calculations[23] gives $\Delta^{(cs)} = 0.16$ but this value can be different in non standard scenarios and/or if diffusion coefficients are modified.

8. Using CNO neutrinos to probe the solar core composition

In Refs. 16 and 17, it was suggested to combine the CN-neutrino fluxes with the boron neutrino flux that, due to the exquisite precision of current experimental results and the large temperature sensitivity can be efficiently used as solar thermometer. As can be understood by considering Eqs.(10) and (12), the following combinations can be formed:

$$\delta\Phi(^{15}\text{O}) - x\,\delta\Phi(^{8}\text{B}) = (1-a)\,\delta X_{12,\,s} + a\,\delta X_{14,\,s} + b\left(\Delta^{(cs)} - 0.16\right)$$
$$+ \delta S_{114} - x\left(\frac{\delta S_{11}}{2} - \frac{\delta S_{33}}{2} + \delta S_{34} + \delta S_{17} - \delta S_{e7}\right) \quad (13)$$

$$\delta\Phi(^{13}\text{N}) - x'\,\delta\Phi(^{8}\text{B}) = (1-a')\,\delta X_{12,\,s} + a'\,\delta X_{14,\,s} + b\left(\Delta^{(cs)} - 0.16\right)$$
$$+ \delta S_{114} - x'\left(\frac{\delta S_{11}}{2} - \frac{\delta S_{33}}{2} + \delta S_{34} + \delta S_{17} - \delta S_{e7}\right) \quad (14)$$

where $x = \beta_O/\beta_B \simeq 0.8$ and $x' = fx \simeq 0.6$, that are independent from δT_c. This possibility is extremely important because it allows us to cancels out the dependence on the radiative opacity (implicit in δT_c). The uncertainty of available opacity calculations is indeed not easily quantified and may be potentially underestimated. Moreover, it breaks the degeneracy between composition and opacity effects on solar observable properties. Indeed, the considered flux combinations only depend on the carbon and nitrogen abundance in the solar core allowing us to test the chemical composition and evolution of the Sun. The first two terms in the r.h.s. of Eqs. (13,14) quantify the effects of a variation of the surface C and N abundances. A change of the diffusion efficiency is instead described in terms of a variation of $\Delta^{(cs)}$ from the SSM value, i.e. by assuming $\Delta^{(cs)} - 0.016 \neq 0$. It should be remarked that the ability to probe solar composition by using this approach is only limited by experimental accuracy of flux determinations and by nuclear cross section uncertainties.

While the above relationships are based on the simplified arguments discussed in the previous section, the optimal combinations $\delta\Phi(\nu_1) - x_{12}\delta\Phi(\nu_2)$, or equivalently weighted ratios $\Phi(\nu_1)/\Phi(\nu_2)^{x_{12}}$, can be determined by using the power-law coefficients $\alpha(\nu, I)$ given in Ref. 23. The parameter x_{12} is obtained by minimizing the residual

$$\rho = \sum_{I=1}^{N} \left[\alpha(\nu_1, I) - x_{12}\,\alpha(\nu_1, I)\right]^2 \sigma_I^2 \quad (15)$$

where the sum extends to the N input parameters whose dependence we want to cancel out and σ_I are the corresponding uncertainties. The minimal value for ρ gives the intrinsic error in the considered approach. This method, originally proposed by Refs. 16 and 17, has been recently adapted to Borexino in Ref. 80. By taking into account that the measured CNO neutrino signal in Borexino is basically probing $\delta\phi_{\rm CNO}^{\rm BX} \equiv \xi\,\delta\Phi(^{15}{\rm O}) + (1-\xi)\,\delta\Phi(^{13}{\rm N})$ with $\xi = 0.764$, it was concluded that the surface composition of the Sun can be probed by the combination:

$$\delta R_{\rm CNO}^{\rm BX} - 0.716\,\delta\Phi(^8{\rm B}) = 0.814\,\delta X_{12,\,{\rm s}} + 0.191\,\delta X_{14,\,{\rm s}}$$
$$\pm\,0.5\%\,({\rm env}) \pm 9.1\%\,({\rm nucl}) \pm 2.8\%\,({\rm diff}) \qquad (16)$$

where $\delta R_{\rm CNO}^{\rm BX}$ is the fractional difference of the observed CNO signal with respect to SSM expectations and the quoted uncertainties are obtained by propagating errors of SSM input parameters. The error budget is presently dominated by the uncertainty of the CNO signal Borexino measurement. However, a relevant error ($\sim 10\%$) is also provided by nuclear reactions, with the largest contributions coming from S_{114} (7.6%), S_{34} (3.4%), and S_{17} (3.5%). In the perspective of future improvements of the CNO signal determination, it is evidently important to have reliable and accurate determinations of these cross sections.

9. Final remarks

The standard solar model establishes a well-defined framework for studying solar interior physics. Despite all its success, still faces difficulties, mainly the solar abundance problem, as diagnosed by helioseismic constraints. The advancements in solar neutrino experiments, and in particular those by Borexino in the last 10 years, have added solar neutrinos as an independent probe of the solar interior properties, complementary to helioseismology. In addition to the now seemingly routine accurate measurement of the ^{7}Be flux, Borexino has opened up the possibilities of quantitative and model independent tests of the origin of solar luminosity and has detected solar CN-neutrinos for the first time (the first direct experimental evidence of the CN-cycle operating in stars). Future improvements in the CN flux measurement by Borexino might help in the quest for the solar abundances, a fundamental open problem in solar physics. This is a prerequisite for developing robust and physically sound solar models beyond the standard model paradigm. Non-standard solar physics requires unfortunately the introduction of free parameters (e.g. to treat non-standard mixing processes) that can be calibrated robustly only once the standard solar model is set on firmer grounds.

Finally, we would like to express that the value of Borexino for solar physics does not only lie in the direct results obtained by the experiment, but also in the development of experimental techniques, which represent a very valuable legacy for future neutrino experiments.

References

1. J. N. Bahcall, M. H. Pinsonneault and G. J. Wasserburg, Solar models with helium and heavy-element diffusion, *Reviews of Modern Physics* **67**, 781 (October 1995).

2. J. Christensen-Dalsgaard, W. Dappen, S. V. Ajukov, E. R. Anderson, H. M. Antia, S. Basu, V. A. Baturin, G. Berthomieu, B. Chaboyer, S. M. Chitre, A. N. Cox, P. Demarque, J. Donatowicz, W. A. Dziembowski, M. Gabriel, D. O. Gough, D. B. Guenther, J. A. Guzik, J. W. Harvey, F. Hill, G. Houdek, C. A. Iglesias, A. G. Kosovichev, J. W. Leibacher, P. Morel, C. R. Proffitt, J. Provost, J. Reiter, J. Rhodes, E. J., F. J. Rogers, I. W. Roxburgh, M. J. Thompson and R. K. Ulrich, The Current State of Solar Modeling, *Science* **272**, 1286 (May 1996).
3. D. O. Gough, A. G. Kosovichev, J. Toomre, E. Anderson, H. M. Antia, S. Basu, B. Chaboyer, S. M. Chitre, J. Christensen-Dalsgaard, W. A. Dziembowski, A. Eff-Darwich, J. R. Elliott, P. M. Giles, P. R. Goode, J. A. Guzik, J. W. Harvey, F. Hill, J. W. Leibacher, M. J. P. F. G. Monteiro, O. Richard, T. Sekii, H. Shibahashi, M. Takata, M. J. Thompson, S. Vauclair and S. V. Vorontsov, The Seismic Structure of the Sun, *Science* **272**, 1296 (May 1996).
4. Y. Elsworth, R. Howe, G. R. Isaak, C. P. McLeod and R. New, Evidence from solar seismology against non-standard solar-core models, *Nature* **347**, 536 (October 1990).
5. Y. Fukuda *et al.*, Measurements of the solar neutrino flux from Super-Kamiokande's first 300 days, *Phys. Rev. Lett.* **81**, 1158 (1998), [Erratum: Phys.Rev.Lett. 81, 4279 (1998)].
6. S. Fukuda *et al.*, Solar B-8 and hep neutrino measurements from 1258 days of Super-Kamiokande data, *Phys. Rev. Lett.* **86**, 5651 (2001).
7. B. Cleveland, T. Daily, J. Davis, Raymond, J. R. Distel, K. Lande, C. Lee, P. S. Wildenhain and J. Ullman, Measurement of the solar electron neutrino flux with the Homestake chlorine detector, *Astrophys. J.* **496**, 505 (1998).
8. W. Hampel *et al.*, GALLEX solar neutrino observations: Results for GALLEX IV, *Phys. Lett. B* **447**, 127 (1999).
9. J. N. Abdurashitov, V. N. Gavrin, S. V. Girin, V. V. Gorbachev, T. V. Ibragimova, A. V. Kalikhov, N. G. Khairnasov, T. V. Knodel, I. N. Mirmov, A. A. Shikhin, E. P. Veretenkin, V. M. Vermul, V. E. Yants, G. T. Zatsepin, T. J. Bowles, W. A. Teasdale, D. L. Wark, M. L. Cherry, J. S. Nico, B. T. Cleveland, R. Davis, K. Lande, P. S. Wildenhain, S. R. Elliott and J. F. Wilkerson, Measurement of the solar neutrino capture rate with gallium metal, *Phys. Rev. C* **60**, p. 055801 (1999).
10. Q. R. Ahmad *et al.*, Measurement of the rate of $\nu_e + d \to p + p + e^-$ interactions produced by ^{8}B solar neutrinos at the Sudbury Neutrino Observatory, *Phys. Rev. Lett.* **87**, p. 071301 (2001).
11. Q. R. Ahmad *et al.*, Direct evidence for neutrino flavor transformation from neutral current interactions in the Sudbury Neutrino Observatory, *Phys. Rev. Lett.* **89**, p. 011301 (2002).
12. C. Arpesella *et al.*, Direct Measurement of the Be-7 Solar Neutrino Flux with 192 Days of Borexino Data, *Phys. Rev. Lett.* **101**, p. 091302 (2008).
13. M. Agostini *et al.*, Comprehensive measurement of pp-chain solar neutrinos, *Nature* **562**, 505 (2018).
14. B. Aharmim *et al.*, Combined Analysis of all Three Phases of Solar Neutrino Data from the Sudbury Neutrino Observatory, *Phys. Rev. C* **88**, p. 025501 (2013).
15. K. Abe *et al.*, Solar Neutrino Measurements in Super-Kamiokande-IV, *Phys. Rev. D* **94**, p. 052010 (2016).
16. W. C. Haxton and A. M. Serenelli, CN-Cycle Solar Neutrinos and Sun's Primordial Core Metallicity, *Astrophys. J.* **687**, 678 (2008).
17. A. Serenelli, C. Peña-Garay and W. C. Haxton, Using the standard solar model to constrain solar composition and nuclear reaction S factors, *Phys. Rev.* **D87**, p. 043001 (2013).

18. F. L. Villante, A. M. Serenelli, F. Delahaye and M. H. Pinsonneault, The chemical composition of the Sun from helioseismic and solar neutrino data, *Astrophys. J.* **787**, p. 13 (2014).
19. M. Agostini *et al.*, Experimental evidence of neutrinos produced in the CNO fusion cycle in the Sun, *Nature* **587**, 577 (2020).
20. J. N. Bahcall, A. M. Serenelli and S. Basu, 10,000 standard solar models: A Monte Carlo simulation, *Astrophys. J. Suppl.* **165**, 400 (2006).
21. J. N. Bahcall and M. H. Pinsonneault, Standard solar models, with and without helium diffusion, and the solar neutrino problem, *Reviews of Modern Physics* **64**, 885 (October 1992).
22. J. Christensen-Dalsgaard, C. R. Proffitt and M. J. Thompson, Effects of Diffusion on Solar Models and Their Oscillation Frequencies, *Astrophysical Journal Letters* **403**, p. L75 (February 1993).
23. N. Vinyoles, A. M. Serenelli, F. L. Villante, S. Basu, J. Bergström, M. C. Gonzalez-Garcia, M. Maltoni, C. Peña-Garay and N. Song, A new Generation of Standard Solar Models, *Astrophys. J.* **835**, p. 202 (2017).
24. S. Cassisi, M. Salaris and A. W. Irwin, The initial helium content of galactic globular cluster stars from the r-parameter: Comparison with the cmb constraint, *Astrophys. J.* **588**, p. 862 (2003).
25. N. R. Badnell, M. A. Bautista, K. Butler, F. Delahaye, C. Mendoza, P. Palmeri, C. J. Zeippen and M. J. Seaton, Up-dated opacities from the Opacity Project, *Mon. Not. Roy. Astron. Soc.* **360**, 458 (2005).
26. J. W. Ferguson, D. R. Alexander, F. Allard, T. Barman, J. G. Bodnarik, P. H. Hauschildt, A. Heffner-Wong and A. Tamanai, Low temperature opacities, *Astrophys. J.* **623**, 585 (2005).
27. E. G. Adelberger, A. García, R. G. H. Robertson, K. A. Snover, A. B. Balantekin, K. Heeger, M. J. Ramsey-Musolf, D. Bemmerer, A. Junghans, C. A. Bertulani, J. W. Chen, H. Costantini, P. Prati, M. Couder, E. Uberseder, M. Wiescher, R. Cyburt, B. Davids, S. J. Freedman, M. Gai, D. Gazit, L. Gialanella, G. Imbriani, U. Greife, M. Hass, W. C. Haxton, T. Itahashi, K. Kubodera, K. Langanke, D. Leitner, M. Leitner, P. Vetter, L. Winslow, L. E. Marcucci, T. Motobayashi, A. Mukhamedzhanov, R. E. Tribble, K. M. Nollett, F. M. Nunes, T. S. Park, P. D. Parker, R. Schiavilla, E. C. Simpson, C. Spitaleri, F. Strieder, H. P. Trautvetter, K. Suemmerer and S. Typel, Solar fusion cross sections II: The pp chain and CNO cycles, *Rev. Mod. Phys.* **83**, p. 195 (2011).
28. L. E. Marcucci, R. Schiavilla and M. Viviani, Proton-Proton Weak Capture in Chiral Effective Field Theory, *Phys. Rev. Lett.* **110**, p. 192503 (2013).
29. E. Tognelli, S. Degl'Innocenti, L. E. Marcucci and P. G. Prada Moroni, Astrophysical implications of the proton–proton cross section updates, *Phys. Lett.* **B742**, 189 (2015).
30. B. Acharya, B. D. Carlsson, A. Ekström, C. Forssén and L. Platter, Uncertainty quantification for proton–proton fusion in chiral effective field theory, *Phys. Lett.* **B760**, 584 (2016).
31. X. Zhang, K. M. Nollett and D. R. Phillips, Halo effective field theory constrains the solar ^{7}Be + p → ^{8}B + gamma rate, *Phys. Lett.* **B751**, 535 (2015).
32. M. Marta, A. Formicola, D. Bemmerer, C. Broggini, A. Caciolli, P. Corvisiero, H. Costantini, Z. Elekes, Z. Fülöp, G. Gervino, A. Guglielmetti, C. Gustavino, G. Gyürky, G. Imbriani, M. Junker, A. Lemut, B. Limata, C. Mazzocchi, R. Menegazzo, P. Prati, V. Roca, C. Rolfs, C. Rossi Alvarez, E. Somorjai, O. Straniero, F. Strieder, F. Terrasi, H. P. Trautvetter and A. Vomiero, The ^{14}N$(p,\gamma)^{15}$O reaction studied with a composite germanium detector, *Phys. Rev.* **C83**, p. 045804 (2011).

33. A. A. Thoul, J. N. Bahcall and A. Loeb, Element diffusion in the solar interior, *Astrophys. J.* **421**, 828 (1994).
34. R. Kippenhahn and A. Weigert, *Stellar Structure and Evolution* 1990.
35. K. S. Krishna Swamy, Profiles of Strong Lines in K-Dwarfs, *Astrophys. J.* **145**, p. 174 (July 1966).
36. N. Grevesse and A. Noels, Cosmic abundances of the elements., in *Origin and Evolution of the Elements*, eds. N. Prantzos, E. Vangioni-Flam and M. Casse, 1993.
37. N. Grevesse and A. J. Sauval, Standard Solar Composition, *Space Sci. Rev.* **85**, 161 (1998).
38. M. Asplund, N. Grevesse, A. J. Sauval and P. Scott, The chemical composition of the Sun, *Ann. Rev. Astron. Astrophys.* **47**, 481 (2009).
39. E. Caffau, H.-G. Ludwig, M. Steffen, B. Freytag and P. Bonifacio, Solar Chemical Abundances Determined with a CO5BOLD 3D Model Atmosphere, *Solar Phys.* **268**, p. 255 (2011).
40. P. Scott, N. Grevesse, M. Asplund, A. J. Sauval, K. Lind, Y. Takeda, R. Collet, R. Trampedach and W. Hayek, The elemental composition of the Sun I. The intermediate mass elements Na to Ca, *Astron. Astrophys.* **573**, p. A25 (2015).
41. P. Scott, M. Asplund, N. Grevesse, M. Bergemann and A. J. Sauval, The elemental composition of the Sun II. The iron group elements Sc to Ni, *Astron. Astrophys.* **573**, p. A26 (2015).
42. N. Grevesse, P. Scott, M. Asplund and A. J. Sauval, The elemental composition of the Sun III. The heavy elements Cu to Th, *Astron. Astrophys.* **573**, p. A27 (2015).
43. M. Asplund, A. M. Amarsi and N. Grevesse, The chemical make-up of the Sun: A 2020 vision, *Astronomy & Astrophysics* **653**, p. A141 (September 2021).
44. M. Bergemann, R. Hoppe, E. Semenova, M. Carlsson, S. A. Yakovleva, Y. V. Voronov, M. Bautista, A. Nemer, A. K. Belyaev, J. Leenaarts, L. Mashonkina, A. Reiners and M. Ellwarth, Solar oxygen abundance, *Monthly Notices of the Royal Astronomical Society* **508**, 2236 (December 2021).
45. K. Lodders, H. Palme and H.-P. Gail, Abundances of the Elements in the Solar System, *Landolt Börnstein*, p. 712 (2009).
46. S. Basu and H. M. Antia, Constraining solar abundances using helioseismology, *Astrophys. J.* **606**, p. L85 (2004).
47. J. N. Bahcall, S. Basu, M. Pinsonneault and A. M. Serenelli, Helioseismological implications of recent solar abundance determinations, *Astrophys. J.* **618**, 1049 (2005).
48. F. Delahaye and M. Pinsonneault, The solar heavy element abundances. 1. Constraints from stellar interiors, *Astrophys. J.* **649**, 529 (2006).
49. J. A. Guzik, L. Watson and A. N. Cox, Can enhanced diffusion improve helioseismic agreement for solar models with revised abundances?, *Astrophys. J.* **627**, 1049 (2005).
50. M. Castro, S. Vauclair and O. Richard, Low abundances of heavy elements in the solar outer layers: Comparisons of solar models with helioseismic inversions, *Astron. Astrophys.* **463**, 755 (2007).
51. S. Basu and H. M. Antia, Helioseismology and Solar Abundances, *Phys. Rept.* **457**, 217 (2008).
52. J. A. Guzik and K. Mussack, Exploring mass loss, low-Z accretion, and convective overshoot in solar models to mitigate the solar abundance problem, *Astrophys. J.* **713**, 1108 (2010).
53. A. M. Serenelli, W. C. Haxton and C. Pena-Garay, Solar models with accretion. I. Application to the solar abundance problem, *Astrophys. J.* **743**, p. 24 (2011).
54. S. Basu and H. M. Antia, Seismic measurement of the depth of the solar convection zone, *Mon. Not. Roy. Astron. Soc.* **287**, 189 (May 1997).

55. F. L. Villante, Constraints on the opacity profile of the sun from helioseismic observables and solar neutrino flux measurements, *Astrophys. J.* **724**, 98 (2010).
56. F. L. Villante and B. Ricci, Linear Solar Models, *Astrophys. J.* **714**, 944 (2010).
57. J. N. Bahcall, A. M. Serenelli and S. Basu, New solar opacities, abundances, helioseismology, and neutrino fluxes, *Astrophys. J. Lett.* **621**, L85 (2005).
58. J. Montalban, A. Miglio, A. Noels, N. Grevesse and M. Di Mauro, Solar model with CNO revised abundances, *ESA Spec. Publ.* **559**, p. 574 (2004).
59. J. Christensen-Dalsgaard, M. P. Di Mauro, G. Houdek and F. Pijpers, On the opacity change required to compensate for the revised solar composition, *Astron. Astrophys.* **494**, p. 205 (2009).
60. C. Blancard, P. Cossé and G. Faussurier, Solar Mixture Opacity Calculations Using Detailed Configuration and Level Accounting Treatments, *Astrophys. J.* **745**, p. 10 (January 2012).
61. G. Mondet, C. Blancard, P. Cossé and G. Faussurier, Opacity Calculations for Solar Mixtures, *Astrophys. J. Supp.* **220**, p. 2 (September 2015).
62. M. Krief, A. Feigel and D. Gazit, Solar opacity calculations using the super-transition-array method, *Astrophys. J.* **821**, p. 45 (2016).
63. J. Colgan, D. P. Kilcrease, N. H. Magee, M. E. Sherrill, J. Abdallah, J., P. Hakel, C. J. Fontes, J. A. Guzik and K. A. Mussack, A New Generation of Los Alamos Opacity Tables, *Astrophys. J.* **817**, p. 116 (February 2016).
64. J. E. Bailey, T. Nagayama, G. P. Loisel, G. A. Rochau, C. Blancard, J. Colgan, P. Cosse, G. Faussurier, C. J. Fontes, F. Gilleron, I. Golovkin, S. B. Hansen, C. A. Iglesias, D. P. Kilcrease, J. J. Macfarlane, R. C. Mancini, S. N. Nahar, C. Orban, J.-C. Pain, A. K. Pradhan, M. Sherrill and B. G. Wilson, A higher-than-predicted measurement of iron opacity at solar interior temperatures, *Nature* **517**, 56 (January 2015).
65. T. Nagayama, J. E. Bailey, G. P. Loisel, G. S. Dunham, G. A. Rochau, C. Blancard, J. Colgan, P. Cossé, G. Faussurier, C. J. Fontes, F. Gilleron, S. B. Hansen, C. A. Iglesias, I. E. Golovkin, D. P. Kilcrease, J. J. MacFarlane, R. C. Mancini, R. M. More, C. Orban, J. C. Pain, M. E. Sherrill and B. G. Wilson, Systematic Study of L-Shell Opacity at Stellar Interior Temperatures, *Physics Review Letters* **122**, p. 235001 (June 2019).
66. M. Krief, A. Feigel and D. Gazit, Line Broadening and the Solar Opacity Problem, *Astrophys. J.* **824**, p. 98 (June 2016).
67. J. N. Bahcall, Line versus continuum solar neutrinos, *Phys. Rev.* **D41**, p. 2964 (1990).
68. L. C. Stonehill, J. A. Formaggio and R. G. H. Robertson, Solar neutrinos from CNO electron capture, *Phys. Rev.* **C69**, p. 015801 (2004).
69. F. L. Villante, ecCNO Solar Neutrinos: A Challenge for Gigantic Ultra-Pure Liquid Scintillator Detectors, *Phys. Lett.* **B742**, 279 (2015).
70. J. Bergstrom, M. C. Gonzalez-Garcia, M. Maltoni, C. Pena-Garay, A. M. Serenelli and N. Song, Updated determination of the solar neutrino fluxes from solar neutrino data, *JHEP* **03**, p. 132 (2016).
71. G. Bellini *et al.*, First evidence of pep solar neutrinos by direct detection in Borexino, *Phys. Rev. Lett.* **108**, p. 051302 (2012).
72. G. Bellini *et al.*, Neutrinos from the primary proton–proton fusion process in the Sun, *Nature* **512**, 383 (2014).
73. J. N. Bahcall, The Luminosity constraint on solar neutrino fluxes, *Phys. Rev.* **C65**, p. 025801 (2002).
74. S. Degl'Innocenti, W. A. Dziembowski, G. Fiorentini and B. Ricci, Helioseismology and standard solar models, *Astropart. Phys.* **7**, 77 (1997).

75. F. Vissani, Luminosity constraint and entangled solar neutrino signals, in *5th International Solar Neutrino Conference*, 2019.
76. D. Vescovi, C. Mascaretti, F. Vissani, L. Piersanti and O. Straniero, The luminosity constraint in the era of precision solar physics, *J. Phys. G* **48**, p. 015201 (2020).
77. F. L. Villante and A. Serenelli, The relevance of nuclear reactions for Standard Solar Models construction, *Front. Astron. Space Sci.* **7**, p. 112 (2021).
78. J. N. Bahcall and A. Ulmer, The Temperature dependence of solar neutrino fluxes, *Phys. Rev.* **D53**, 4202 (1996).
79. W. C. Haxton, R. G. Hamish Robertson and A. M. Serenelli, Solar Neutrinos: Status and Prospects, *Ann. Rev. Astron. Astrophys.* **51**, 21 (2013).
80. M. Agostini *et al.*, Sensitivity to neutrinos from the solar CNO cycle in Borexino, *Eur. Phys. J. C* **80**, p. 1091 (2020).

Role of the CNO cycles in stars

A. Ianni

I.N.F.N. Laboratori Nazionali del Gran Sasso,
Via Giovanni Acitelli 22,
67100 Assergi (AQ), Italy
E-mail: aldo.ianni@lngs.infn.it

Borexino has recently observed CNO solar neutrinos. This measurement confirms an energy production mechanism in stars predicted about a century ago. The CNO cycle in the Sun is sub-dominant with respect to the pp-chain energy production. However, it is definitely important in more massive stars. We describe the main characteristics of the CNO cycle in the Sun and in massive stars.

Keywords: Solar neutrinos; CNO cycle; stars; energy production in stars.

1. Energy production in stars and the role of the CNO bi-cycle

The fundamental paradigm for energy production in the Sun and similar stars is the transformation of hydrogen into helium through the process: $4p \to {}^4He + 2e^+ + 2\nu_e + 26.73$ MeV.[1] This mechanism makes electron neutrinos of mainly sub-MeV energy. Due to the fact that neutrinos can travel through matter affected only by weak interactions, the observation of solar neutrinos allows to probe the interior of the Sun. Therefore, the Sun becomes a laboratory to understand the physics in stars. Solar neutrino measurements have been carried out since 1968.[2]

The main source of energy in the Sun is the so-called pp-chain shown in Figure 1. The pp-chain has three terminations. Each termination produces 26.2 MeV effective thermal energy and it burns 3.7×10^{38} hydrogen/sec, which corresponds to 612 ton/sec. Therefore, assuming 10% of solar mass involved in energy production, the timescale of the pp-chain for the Sun is of the order of 10^{10} years. This mechanism is dominant in first generation stars. In second or third generation stars a different mechanism is also at work. This latter involves light elements, such as carbon and nitrogen, generated after the production of helium. The idea of a second energy production mechanism was independently introduced by von Weizsaker and Bethe between 1937[3] and 1939.[4] Second and third generation stars contain some "heavy" elements, such as nitrogen and carbon. These elements allow the transformation of hydrogen into helium. The process can start from the reaction $p + {}^{12}_{6}C \to {}^{13}_{7}N + \gamma$, which is followed by the beta decay of ${}^{13}_{7}N$ to ${}^{13}_{6}C$ accompanied with the emission of an electron neutrino of maximum energy equal to 1.2 MeV. Afterward ${}^{14}_{7}N$ is formed by $p + {}^{13}_{6}C \to {}^{14}_{7}N + \gamma$. ${}^{14}_{7}N$ allows the production of ${}^{15}_{8}O$, which decays beta to ${}^{15}_{7}N$ with the emission of another electron neutrino of maximum energy equal to 1.7 MeV. At this point ${}^{15}_{7}N$ allows the production of ${}^{12}_{6}C$ through the process

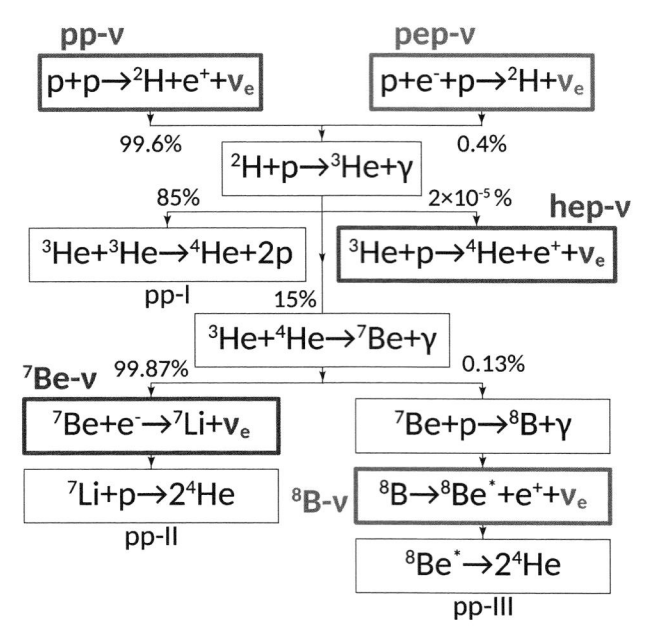

Fig. 1. Set of reactions in the pp-chain, which is the main source of energy in the Sun and in low mass H-burning stars with mass smaller than $1.3 M_\odot$.

$p + {}^{15}_{7}\text{N} \to {}^{12}_{6}\text{C} + \alpha$. With ${}^{12}_{6}\text{C}$ the sequence of reactions can start over again. This so-called CN cycle is shown in Figure 2. ${}^{12}_{6}\text{C}$ is used as a catalyst. This cycle produces two electron neutrinos, helium, and the same amount of energy produced by the pp-chain. The CN cycle till 1950 was considered the main source of energy in the Sun. The slowest reaction in the CN cycle is ${}^{14}_{7}\text{N}(p,\gamma){}^{15}_{8}\text{O}$, which has the highest Coulomb barrier.

The CN cycle might develop into a CNO bi-cycle as show in Figure 2. As a matter of fact, with a probability of order 10^{-3}, ${}^{16}_{8}\text{O}$ can be produced by ${}^{15}_{7}\text{N}(p,\gamma){}^{16}_{8}\text{O}$. This second branch produces ${}^{17}_{9}\text{F}$, which decays beta with the emission of an electron neutrino with maximum energy equal to 1.74 MeV. The CNO bi-cycle produces three electron neutrinos from beta decays of ${}^{13}\text{N}$, ${}^{15}\text{O}$ and ${}^{17}\text{F}$. These are the so-called CNO solar neutrinos. The flux of these neutrinos is related to the abundance of these elements in the Sun's core. Therefore, a measurement of CNO solar neutrinos is a probe of the Sun's metallicity.

Measurements of stellar interaction rates have shown that the CN cycle is not dominant in the Sun. This information is used by the Solar Standard Model (SSM),[1] which is the theoretical framework to describe the evolution of the Sun. According to the SSM the CNO bi-cycle in the Sun is responsible for only 1% of the energy production. The CNO bi-cycle is important for the nucleosynthesis of ${}^{16}_{8}\text{O}$, ${}^{17}_{8}\text{O}$, and other light elements. The CNO bi-cycle is also referred to as the "cold" CNO cycle[5] with respect to the "hot" cycle which is discussed in the next Section.

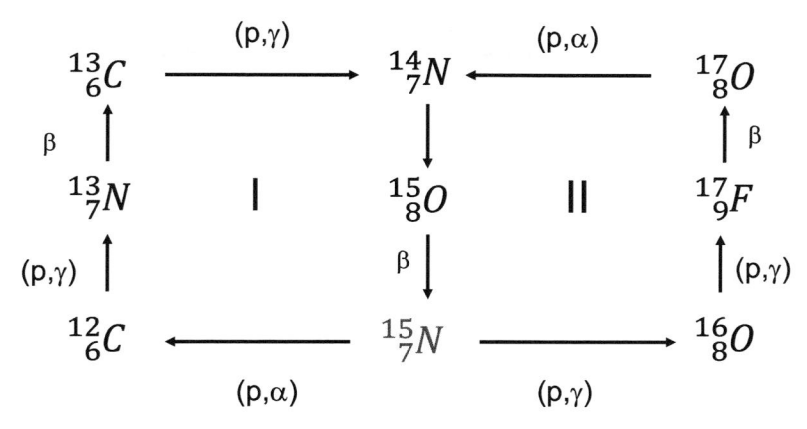

Fig. 2. The CNO bi-cycle divided in its two sub-cycles. The dominant one in the Sun is the CN cycle on the left side.

2. The CNO cycle in massive stars

The Sun's core temperature is 15×10^6 K, which we write as $15T_6$. As predicted by the SSM at this temperature the energy production for the pp-chain and the CNO bi-cycle scales as $\propto T^4$ and $\propto T^8$, respectively. For stellar masses smaller than $1.3 M_\odot$, the pp-chain dominates the energy production. In more massive stars with a higher core temperature, the CNO cycle is by far the dominant source of energy. In this case one has to take into account two competing processes, namely $^{17}_{8}O(p, \alpha)^{14}_{7}N$ and $^{17}_{8}O(p, \gamma)^{18}_{9}F$. For some temperature ranges the reaction rates for these processes are comparable.[6] In this case the CNO cycle is tri-cycling as shown in Figure 3.[7] In addition, for temperature ranging up to 10^{10} K the interaction rate for $^{18}_{8}O(p, \alpha)^{15}_{7}N$ and $^{18}_{8}O(p, \gamma)^{19}_{9}F$ is of order 100 with a flat minimum between T_9 and $7T_9$.[5] Therefore, with a probability of order 1% a fourth CNO cycle can develop. This fourth cycle is also shown in Figure 3. The third and fourth CNO cycles are referred to as the "hot" CNO cycles. It turns out that when $^{19}_{9}F(p, \gamma)^{20}_{10}Ne$ is dominat the CNO catalytic cycling stops.

One fundamental empirical properties of stars is the relationship between their total mass and surface luminosity:[8] $L/L_\odot = (M/M_\odot)^\alpha$, with $3 \lesssim \alpha \lesssim 4$[9] and $L_\odot$ and $M_\odot$ the solar surface luminosity and mass, respectively. This property is confirmed by basic stellar theory. One can make some general arguments for the role of the CNO cycle in stars in the rage of masses $[1, 10]M_\odot$. In this range it turns out that the luminosity scales as $\propto M^{\sim 4}$.[9] This implies that more massive stars have a smaller lifetime, for the lifetime scales as $\propto M^{-3}$. In addition, considering that the stars number density scales as $\propto M^{-2.5}$,[10] the energy production in a given bin of mass $[M_i, M_{i+1}]$ is written as:

$$\epsilon \propto \int_{M_i}^{M_{i+1}} M^{1.5} dM \qquad (1)$$

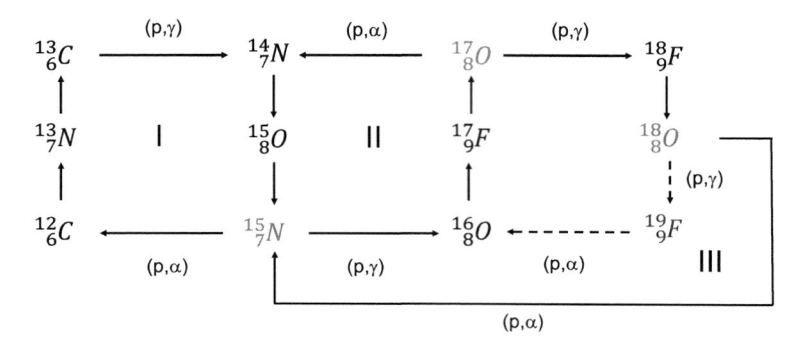

Fig. 3. The CNO tri-cycle in massive stars.

This implies that stars where the CNO energy production is dominant, namely $M > 1.3 M_\odot$, are producing about 100 times more energy in a much shorter timescale.

3. The role of Borexino

In 2020 Borexino has reported the first ever observation of CNO neutrinos from the Sun.[11] The null hypothesis (no CNO neutrinos) has been rejected at 5σ level. Indeed, Borexino has shown that this energy production mechanism predicted about a century ago is at work in stars. Although the accuracy of the measurement at present is still large ($\sim 35\%$), this measurement allows to probe the SSM in terms of neutrino emission, metallicity, and energy production. The solar luminosity, $L_\odot$ can be related to the solar neutrino fluxes:[12,13]

$$\frac{L_\odot}{4\pi AU^2} = \sum_i \alpha_i \phi_i \qquad (2)$$

where AU is one astronomical unit, ϕ_i are the neutrino fluxes, and α_i are coefficients related to the energy production in the reactions taking place in the pp-chain and CNO bi-cycle, respectively. The Borexino measurement implies that:

$$\frac{L_{CNO}}{L_\odot} = 1.0^{+0.4}_{-0.3}\% \qquad (3)$$

This is an important confirmation of the SSM prediction. Previously Borexino had measured all the main neutrinos produced by the pp-chain,[14] proving that this mechanism is the main energy production in the Sun with an experimental accuracy of the order of 10%. Therefore, at present, solar neutrino observations have demonstrated that the pp-chain and the CNO bi-cycle are producing energy in stars as it was predicted about a century ago.

References

1. J. N. Bahcall (1989). Neutrino Astrophysics. Cambridge University Press.
2. L. Oberauer, A. Ianni, A. Serenelli (2020). Solar Neutrino Physics. The interplay between particle physics and astronomy. Wiley-VCH

3. C. F. Weizsacker, On Elementary Transmutations in the Interior of Stars: Paper II, Physik. Zeit., (38), 1937.
4. H. A. Bethe., Energy production in stars, Physical Review, 55(5): 434-456, 1939.
5. M. Wiescher et al., Annu. Rev. Nucl. Part. Sci. 2010, 60: 381-404.
6. C. Rolfs and W. S. Rodney, Astrophys. J. 194: L63-L66, 1974.
7. J. J. Cowan and W. K. Rose, Astrophys. J. 201: L45-L48, 1975.
8. M. Salaris and S. Cassisi, Evolution of Stars and Stellar Populations, John Wiley and Sons, Ltd, 2005.
9. M. Harwit, Astrophysical Concepts, 2nd Ed., Springer, 1988.
10. G. Srinivasan, Neutron Stars and Black Holes (Lecture 02: White Dwarf Stars).
11. Borexino collaboration, Nature 587 (2020) 577-582.
12. J. N. Bahcall, 2002 Phy. Rev. C 65 025801.
13. D. Vescovi et al., J. Phys. G 48 (2020) 1, 015201.
14. Borexino collaboration, Nature 562 (2018) 7728, 505-510.

Geoneutrino observation

Tadao Mitsui

Research Center for Neutrino Science,
Tohoku University,
Sendai 980-8578, Japan
E-mail: mitsui@awa.tohoku.ac.jp

for the KamLAND Collaboration

Neutrinos from the Earth's interior "geoneutrinos" have been observed to reveal Earth's composition, heat budget, and the origin of the Earth. Observations by KamLAND and Borexino experiments for 15 years are reviewed.

Keywords: Neutrino; Geoneutrino

1. Geoneutrino

Recent progress on the research about "why and how the sun and the stars shine" is quite notable, which has been summarized in this parallel session. Here I would like to review neutrinos from another familiar celestial body, the Earth. Neutrinos from the Earth ("geoneutrinos") are low-energy electron antineutrinos ($\bar{\nu}_e$) emitted in the decay chains of uranium (U), thorium (Th), and potassium (K) in the Earth's interior. Geoneutrino is expected as a probe of Earth's chemical composition. Also the decay of those radioactive elements contributes to the Earth's heat production. Then geoneutrino is a tool to reveal the Earth's energy budget. Although the existence of geoneutrino is predicted more than 50 years ago[1–3] experimental research has been difficult. Since Borexino and KamLAND experiments were planned, they have been hoped as the first experimental research of geoneutrinos.

With those liquid scintillator detectors, geoneutrinos (geo-$\bar{\nu}_e$'s) are detected via "inverse β decay" mode: $\bar{\nu}_e + p \to e^+ + n$. Considering the difference of masses of neutron (m_n) and proton (m_p), $m_n - m_p = 1.3$ MeV, the mass of positron ($m_e = 0.5$ MeV), and neglecting the small neutron recoil, the threshold of this reaction is $E_{th} \simeq m_n - m_p + m_e = 1.8$ MeV, above which neutrino energy E_ν and positron energy E_{e^+} (the kinetic energy of the positron plus the electron-positron annihilation energy) are related as $E_\nu \simeq E_{e^+} + E_{th} - 2m_e = E_{e^+} + 0.8$ MeV. The potassium neutrino is below E_{th}, so liquid scintillator detectors observe only uranium and thorium neutrinos. With energy spectrum (E_{e^+} spectrum which reflects E_ν spectrum), uranium (U) and thorium (Th) neutrinos can be separately measured. To obtain total geoneutrino flux with less statistical uncertainty, the relative abundance of U and Th is sometimes assumed to be Th/U = 3.9, based on geological consideration.

As Borexino and KamLAND plans started, calculation of expected flux of geoneutrinos, and expected signals of these detectors have also been performed. One of the examples is Ref. 4, in which expected "peaks" of geoneutrinos around $E_{e^+} \simeq 1$ to 3 MeV are shown. Also shown are the expected background spectra of nuclear reactor $\bar{\nu}_e$, showing that reactor $\bar{\nu}_e$ of Borexino is much less than that of KamLAND.

2. Experimental Research

In 2005, the first experimental research of geoneutrinos has been done,[5] in which KamLAND measured low-energy spectrum of $\bar{\nu}_e$ and fitted it to geoneutrino, reactor neutrino and other background spectra. As shown in Fig. 1, geoneutirno contribution is indicated although the statistical power is limited.

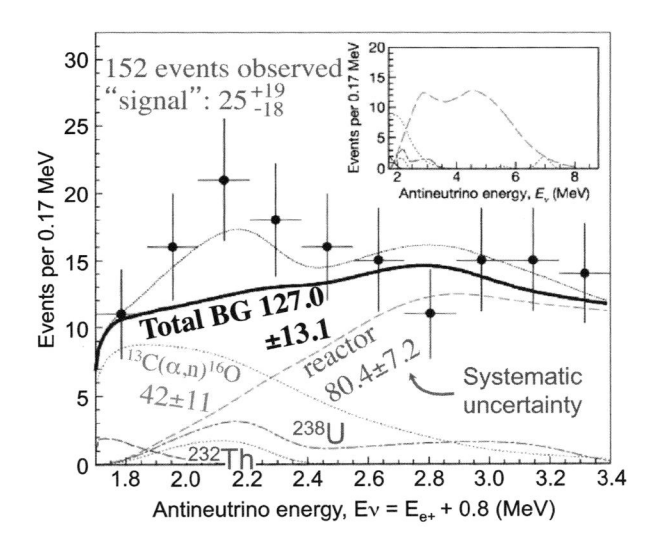

Fig. 1. First experimental research of geoneutrinos. Points are data, lines with labels and numbers are estimated background (thin line around 1.8 MeV is random coincidence). Lines labeled as ^{238}U and ^{232}Th are best-fit geoneutrino signals. Thick black line is the estimated total background, and thin black line is that with the best-fit signals added.

In 2010, Borexino collaboration reported their first result of geoneutrino observation,[6] with which the observation with two detectors on the Earth started. Borexino is an ultra pure detector and reactor neutrino flux is much less than KamLAND site. Thanks to those low background environment, the existence of geoneutrino was confirmed at 4.2 σ confidence level.

In an updated result of KamLAND,[7] it has been shown that the radiogenic heat source inferred from geoneutrino flux is significantly less than the total heat flow from the Earth's interior. With this result they concluded that there is contribution of secular cooling of the Earth to the total heat source of the Earth.

In the updated result of Borexino[8] released in 2013, the signal of geoneutrino became clearer and the probability for null geoneutrino measurement was shown to be 6×10^{-6}. The latest data of KamLAND was also shown[9] in 2013, which included the data of the period with most of Japanese nuclear reactors off. With these data, low background observation of geoneutrino was done also with KamLAND. The reactor $\bar{\nu}_e$ background was also unambiguously estimated using reactor on and off data. In those reports in 2013,[8,9] existence of mantle geoneutrino contribution was indicated by using both data in a cooperating way because crust contributions are different between KamLAND and Borexino sites.

In 2015, Borexino collaboration released new result[10] and reported that the probability for null geoneutrino measurement is 3.6×10^{-9} corresponding to 5.9 σ confidence level. This should be a conclusive result for geoneutrino existence. The latest result of Borexino was shonw in Ref. 11. This comprehensive report includes all the aspects of geoneutrino research, i.e., physics, geology, experiment, and data analysis of geoneutrino. All the researchers involved in geoneutrino study are recommended to read it carefully so that they are stimulated for new research. Also in this report, multiple Earth models are carefully tested with their latest data, including cosmochemical, geochemical, and geodynamical models.

3. Research in Geology and Theory

With those experimental data, research in geology and theory also became active. Combined analysis of KamLAND and Borexino data has been done by theorists. Ref. 12 is one of combined analysis, in which common and independent uncertainties of KamLAND and Borexino are treated properly and carefully with considering correlation.

New calculations of geoneutrino flux have also been done using up-to-date data and more precise and refined method of calculation. For example, such up-to-date "reference models" are reviewed in Refs. 11–13.

4. Futre Experiments

Although the observation with two detectors has lasted for more than 10 years, new detectors will be ready and expected to start their observations. SNO+[14] is a large liquid scintillator detector in Canada to search for neutrinoless double beta decay. It can also observe geoneutrinos. Large flux of geoneutrino is expected from the continent crust. In April 2021, SNO+ completed liquid scintillator filling. We have to stay tuned.

JUNO[15] is a multipurpose neutrino detector planned to be constructed in China. Their main purpose is to measure reactor neutrino oscillation to further improve Daya Bay achievements. When completed it will be the largest liquid scintillator detector (20 kton) in the world. The construction already started.

Jinping Neutrino Experiment[16] is planned in China. When completed, it will be the deepest detector in the world, with 2400 m overburden of rocks. It aims at observing large flux of geoneutrinos from Himalaya, which is a part of one of the largest continental crust of the present-day Earth.

For more research, especially for mantle geoneutrino detection, large liquid scintillator in the deep ocean[17] is one possibility. Directional measurement of electron antineutrinos is another future possibility in order to get more information about geoneutrino source distribution. Although the directional measurement was done by Chooz experiment,[18] application for large detector is not easy and under development. Considering the observation at a lot of points are essentially important, design of cheap detector[19] may be useful to construct as many detector as possible.

Acknowledgments

The author thanks organizers for their kind hospitality under the current unusual situation. The KamLAND experiment is supported by JSPS KAKENHI, the World Premier International Research Center Initiative (WPI Initiative), MEXT Japan, Netherlands Organization for Scientific Research (NWO), the U.S. Department of Energy (DOE), and the National Science Foundation (NSF). The Kamioka Mining and Smelting Company has provided service for activities in the mine. We acknowledge the support of NII for SINET4.

References

1. G. Eder, Terrestrial neutrinos, *Nucl. Phys.* **78** 657 (1966).
2. G. Marx, Geophysics by neutrinos, *Czech. J. Phys. B* **19** 1471 (1969).
3. G. Gamow, Letter to F. Reines (1953).
4. R. S. Raghavan *et al.*, Measuring the global radioactivity in the Earth by multidetector antineutrino spectroscopy, *Phys. Rev. Lett.* **80** 635 (1998).
5. T. Araki *et al.* (KamLAND Collab.), Experimental investigation of geologically produced antineutrinos with KamLAND, *Nature* **436** 499 (2005).
6. Borexino Collab. (G. Bellini *et al.*), Observation of geo-neutrinos, *Phys. Let. B* **687** 299 (2010).
7. KamLAND Collab. (A. Gando *et al.*), Partial radiogenic heat model for Earth revealed by geoneutrino measurements, *Nature Geosci.* **4** 647 (2011).
8. Borexino Collab. (G. Bellini *et al.*), Measurement of geo-neutrinos from 1353 days of Borexino, *Phys. Let. B* **722** 295 (2013).
9. A. Gando *et al.* (KamLAND Collab.), Reactor on-off antineutrino measurement with KamLAND, *Phys. Rev. D* **88** 033001 (2013).
10. M. Agostini *et al.* (Borexino Collab.), Spectroscopy of geoneutrinos from 2056 days of Borexino data *Phys. Rev. D* **92** 031101(R) (2015).
11. M. Agostini *et al.* (Borexino Collab.), Comprehensive geoneutrino analysis with Borexino, *Phys. Rev. D* **101** 012009 (2020).
12. G. L. Fogli, E. Lisi, A. Palazzo, and A. M. Rotunno, Combined analysis of KamLAND and Borexino neutrino signals from Th and U decays in the Earth's interior, *Phys. Rev. D* **82** 093006 (2010).
13. O. Šrámek, W. F. McDonough, J. G. Learned, Geoneutrinos, *Adv. High Energy Phys.* **2012** 235686 (2012).
14. The SNO+ experiment, https://snoplus.phy.queensu.ca/.

15. JUNO, http://juno.ihep.cas.cn/.
16. Jinping Neutrino Experiment, http://jinping.hep.tsinghua.edu.cn/.
17. J. G. Learned, S. T. Dye, S. Pakvasa, Hanohano: A deep ocean anti-neutrino detector for unique neutrino physics and geophysics studies, in *Proc. 12th Int. Workshop on Neutrino Telescopes*, (Venice, Italy, 2007), https://arxiv.org/abs/0810.4975.
18. M. Apollonio *et al.*, Determination of neutrino incoming direction in the CHOOZ experiment and its application to supernova explosion location by scintillator detectors, *Phys. Rev. D* **61** 012001 (1999).
19. T. Mitsui, Neutron background and possibility for shallow experiments, *Earth, Moon, and Planets* **99** 265 (2006).

Synthesis of the session: Why and how the Sun and the stars shine

Gianpaolo Bellini

Physics Department, Università degli Studi and Istituto Nazionale di Fisica Nucleare
Milano, via Celoria 16, 20133, Italy
E-mail: gianpaolo.bellini@mi.infn.it

This article is the synthesis of the MG16 session "Why and how the Sun and the stars shine". A brief scientific history of the Borexino experiment and its discoveries are traced.

Keywords: Solar neutrinos, neutrinos physics, geo-neutrinos

In this session the technical and scientific results obtained with the Borexino experiment have been presented. In 1989 we began a feat that seemed absolutely impossible, that is to build a detector able to study, in real time, solar neutrinos from few tens of keV of energy by measuring separately the fluxes produced by the various nuclear fusion reactions that take place in the Sun. The difficulty was the natural radioactivity present in any material as well as the emissions from the rocks of the underground laboratory, the Gran Sasso lab., where it was decided to install the detector. Just owing to the natural radioactivity, the experiments before Borexino set a threshold between 4 and 5 MeV, then measuring only a tail towards the largest energies of the neutrino energy spectrum, corresponding to about 0.01% of the total flux.

The activity for Borexino started in 1990 and the first five years (1990-1995) were spent to develop innovative methods that would be able to break down the radioactivity of liquids up to ultra-traces. In order to measure the reached level of radio-purity and to understand if it was satisfying the very high level requested by the project, a special detector was needed; therefore a reduced and simplified version of Borexino has been constructed, the Counting Test Facility, which functioned as a bench mark. At 1995 this detector was able to demonstrate that our methods were able to reduce the radioactivity up to about 10^{-16} g of contaminants/g of pure material, as per project requests.

The construction, installation and tuning of the detector took a long time and only in 2007 we started the data taking; this time has been necessary because nothing is standard in Borexino: all the materials were carefully selected, all the parts of the detector and the components were developed on purpose also in collaboration with external companies, most of the activities were carried out in clean room, the detector itself has been equipped as a 10,000 level clean room. All these special cares were aimed to an exceptional suppression of the radioactive background.

Borexino is designed like an onion: the more internal a shell, the greater the radiopurity. At the center, a 125 micron-thick nylon vessel -IV, with a 4.5 m radius, contains about 100 t of scintillator, with pseudocumene as solvent and PPO as solute. It is enclosed in a 6.75 m radius stainless steel sphere, SSS, which supports 2212 photomultipliers: the space between IV and SSS is filled with about 1000 t of pseudocumene added a quencher. A 5.50 m-radius nylon balloon functions as a barrier against to ^{222}Rn emitted by the SSS steel and the photomultipliers. All is inside a water tank (radius 9 m, height 16.9 m), which contains 2800 t of highly purified water and 208 PMTs, which, by means of the Cherenkov light, signal the muons crossing the detector. The water shields the IV from rocks and environment γs and ns.

The radio purification effort was very successful: for ^{238}U and ^{232}Th and their progeny the radiopurity reached some 10^{-20} and 10^{-19} g/g, respectively, and per the ubiquitous ^{222}Rn, < 1 count per day for 100 t of scintillator. Borexino is the unique detector which until now reached this unprecedented radiopurity.

With these premises, Borexino was able to identify the fusion reactions of the pp chain emitting neutrinos via the separate measurement of their fluxes. The problem of this analysis is to disentangle solar neutrinos signals from the residues of radio-contaminants, that survived the radio-purification. In addition, a software strategy had to be developed against the ^{11}C, which cannot be purified because it is continuously produced in the scintillator by the muons which survived the crossing of the Gran Sasso overburden (1.2 $\mu/m^2 h$). The results are summarized in the attached table where the measured rates and fluxes are compared with the SSM predictions for high and low metallicity: the comparison shows a good agreement.

The pp chain produces 99% of the entire solar energy; therefore the solar luminosity measured through solar neutrinos can be compared to the luminosity measured via photons: the good agreement found between them demonstrates that the Sun is in thermodynamic equilibrium over 10^4 years scale because, while neutrinos take a few seconds to leave the Sun, photons need more than 100,000 years.

reaction	Borexino rates (cpd/100t)	Borexino fluxes ($cm^{-2}s^{-1}$)	SSM HZ Fluxes ($cm^{-2}s^{-1}$)	SSM LZ Fluxes ($cm^{-2}s^{1}$)	Global fit Fluxes ($cm^{-2}s^{1}$)
pp	$134 \pm 10^{+6}_{-10}$	$(6.1 \pm 0.5^{+0.3}_{-0.5}) \times 10^{10}$	$5.98(1 \pm 0\text{-}006) \times 10^{10}$	$6.03(1 \pm 0.005) \times 10^{10}$	$5.97^{+0.037}_{-0.033} \times 10^{10}$
^{7}Be	$48.3 \pm 1.1^{+0.4}_{-0.7}$	$(4.99 \pm 0.11^{+0.06}_{-0.12}) \times 10^9$	$4.93 (1 \pm 0.06) \times 10^9$	$4.50(1 \pm 0.06) \times 10^9$	$4.80^{+0.24}_{-0.22} \times 10^9$
pep (HZ)	$2.43 \pm 0.36^{+0.15}_{-0.22}$	$(1.27 \pm 0.19^{+0.08}_{-0.12}) \times 10^8$	$1.44 (1 \pm 0.009) \times 10^8$	$1.46 (1 \pm 0.009) \times 10^8$	$1.448 \pm 0.08 \times 10^8$
Pep (LZ)	$2.65 \pm 0.36^{+0.15}_{-0.24}$	$(1.39 \pm 0.19^{+0.08}_{-0.13}) \times 10^8$	$1.44 (1 \pm 0.009) \times 10^8$	$1.46 (1 \pm 0.009) \times 10^8$	
^{8}B	$0.220^{+0.015}_{-0.016}{}^{+0.006}_{-0.006}$	$5.68^{+0.39}_{-0.41}{}^{+0.03}_{-0.03}$	$5.46 (1 \pm 0.12) \times 10^6$	$4.50 (1 \pm 0.12) \times 10^6$	$5.16^{+0.13}_{-0.09} \times 10^6$
hep	<0.002 (90% C.L.)	< 1.8 x 10^5 (90% C.L.)	$7.98 (1 \pm 0.30) \times 10^3$	$8.25(1 \pm 0.12) \times 10^3$	

Fig. 1. SSM-HZ and SSM-LZ fluxes: from Aldo Serenelli, F.Villante et al.. Global fit fluxes from J. Bergstroem et al.

The measurement of the various neutrino fluxes emitted by the pp chain nuclear fusions allows to determine the electron-neutrino survival probability in an energy range from a few tens of keV up to about 15 MeV, that is, according to the MSW model, from vacuum regime up to the matter enhanced oscillation. The experimental results are in agreement with the MSW-LMA predictions within the experimental and the Standard Solar Model uncertainties.

In the Sun the pp chain produces a temperature able to avoid its implosion caused by the gravitational forces acting among the solar matter. In massive stars, with a mass at least 30% greater that the Sun, a higher temperature is required to avoid implosion. Already in the '30s of the last century, Bethe and Von Weizsäcker hypothesized the existence of a cycle (CNO) dominating the massive stars where it reaches a core temperature of a few x 10^8 K; this hypothesis before Borexino never has been tested and demonstrated experimentally.

Fortunately, the CNO cycle is present in the Sun and produces 1% of its energy, and then Borexino was able to study the CNO cycle undertaking the analysis of the solar neutrinos produced by this cycle. The faced difficulties are due to the presence of CNO, pep and a residue of ^{210}Bi in the same energy window and to the tagging lack of the CNO energy spectrum. pep is not a problem because its shape and its rate are very well known, while to extract the CNO neutrinos flux, a strong constraint on the ^{210}Bi rate is needed. An important tool to this end is the presence of ^{210}Po in the scintillator and its secular equilibrium with ^{210}Bi.

Two components contribute to the ^{210}Po rate in the scintillator, one in secular equilibrium and one out of equilibrium: the latter decays with a half-life of 138.376 days and then, after a proper time, reaches a plateau corresponding to the ^{210}Po continuous production through the chain: ^{210}Pb- ^{210}Bi-^{210}Po and finally the stable ^{208}Pb. However, this plateau is not stable, but shows minor oscillations, due to convective currents in the scintillator which carry ^{210}Po nuclides, present on the IV walls, in the fiducial volume. Then a temperature stabilization is needed and it has been reached with a precision of 0.07 °C by thermally insulating the water tank and installing heating copper coils under the insulation.

As a result, the ^{210}Po and then the ^{210}Bi rates have been obtained, and, through a multivariate fit, the CNO neutrinos flux results to be:

$7.2^{+0.3}_{-1.7} \cdot 10^8 cm^{-2} s^{-1}$ (the uncertainty includes statistical and systematic errors), with no CNO hypothesis disfavored at 5σ C.L. In this way Borexino provided the direct experimental proof of the CNO cycle existence.

Borexino also observed with 5σ statistical significance the geoneutrinos, antineutrinos from the Earth interior. Unlike the solar neutrinos, Borexino is not the only experiment capable of making this measurement, because even the Japanese Kamland has studied geoneutrinos, with greater statistics and with greater background. This study allowed to investigate the presence of radioactive nuclides in the Earth's mantle, the contribution of radiogenic origin to the terrestrial heat and to obtain Earth's geo-physical and geo-chemical information.

The author thanks Lino Miramonti for his editing help.

The internal rotation of low-mass stars from solar and stellar seismology

G. Buldgen* and P. Eggenberger

Astronomy Department, University of Geneva,
Versoix, 1290, Switzerland
* E-mail: Gael.Buldgen@unige.ch

The possibility of measuring the internal rotation of the Sun and stars thanks to helio- and asteroseismology offers tremendous constraints on hydro- and magnetohydrodynamical processes acting in stellar interiors. Understanding the processes responsible for the transport of angular momentum in stellar interiors is crucial as they will also influence the transport of chemicals and thus the evolution of stars. Here we present some of the key results obtained in both fields and how detailed seismic analyses can provide stringent constraints on the physics of angular momentum transport in the interior of low mass stars and potentially rule out some candidates.

Keywords: Stellar physics; Stellar evolution; Helioseismology; Asteroseismology

1. Introduction

Low mass stars ($\approx 1 M_\odot$) are mostly characterized by the presence in their structure of an outer convective envelope during their main-sequence. As a result, they will exhibit efficient braking through the effect of magnetised winds and they will most often exhibit long rotation periods of a few days. As a result of their low mass, they exhibit long evolutionary timescales of typically a few Gy on the main sequence. This implies that, if a given dynamical process is at work in stellar interiors, it will have time to leave a durable imprint on the evolution of the star, even if its characteristic timescale is relatively long. A good example of such a process is microscopic diffusion, that plays a key role in both solar and stellar modelling.

Another consequence of the existence of an outer convective envelope in low mass stars is that they will exhibit solar-like oscillations. These oscillations are global acoustic modes of the star that have been measured in both the solar case,[1] giving birth to the field of helioseismology, and in the stellar case,[2–4] paving the way for the field of asteroseismology of solar-like oscillators. With the advent of space-based photometry missions, the field of asteroseismology experienced an exponential growth, with the detection of global acoustic oscillations in thousands of stars.

Moreover, the quality of the observations enabled to perform similar analysis to those of the Sun, but on distant stars, increasing the sample of objects for which the internal rotation could be measured. The detection of mixed oscillation modes also gave access to the deep core rotation of evolved stars, providing laboratories for angular momentum transport process at various evolutionary stages.

In addition, the fact that most solar-like oscillators exhibited slow rotation of their surface allowed modellers to use perturbative approaches applied in helioseismology.

These measurements proved to be very challenging to explain using classical self-consistent rotating models including the effects of meridional circulation and shear-induced turbulence. While there exists multiple candidates to explain the internal rotation of low-mass stars on the main-sequence, the internal rotation of post-main sequence stars is still impossible to fully reproduce. Behind these difficulties hide the limitations of stellar models, emphasizing the need to improve our physical representation of stellar interiors.

In this brief review, we will discuss how the internal rotation of low mass stars is measured using a perturbative formalism in the fields of helio- and asteroseismology in Section 2. We will discuss the implications for angular momentum transport of the seismic constraints obtained on the main-sequence and will discuss the link with the transport of chemicals in Section 3. We will focus here on the constraints from acoustic oscillations only. More complete reviews, discussing also the results of massive gravity mode pulsators can also be found in the litterature[5] and classical textbooks also provide a more detailed view and additional references.[6] In Section 4, we will briefly present the main results using the mixed oscillation modes observed in post-main sequence stars and briefly discuss in Section 5 the implications for the main candidates foreseen as the "missing angular momentum transport process".

2. Measuring the internal rotation of low mass stars

The surface rotation of stars is accessible in photometry through the observations of spots on the stellar surface, or in spectroscopy through the determination of the rotational broadening of spectral lines. This allows us to test for example the formalisms used for the magnetic braking of low mass stars or the correlation between the depletion of light elements such as lithium or beryllium and the rotation period of stars in clusters. However, to study the internal rotation of stars, the only method available is by using the constraints derived from global oscillation modes. Indeed, their properties are intimately linked to the internal structure and dynamics of stellar interiors.

In the case of a non-rotating, non-magnetic, isolated star, the global oscillation modes will exhibit spherical symmetry and their angular dependencies can be decomposed on the basis of spherical harmonics. The eigenfunction of an oscillation mode, denoted $\vec{\xi}$, will thus be written in spherical coordinates as

$$\vec{\xi} = a(r)Y_{\ell,m}(\theta,\phi)\vec{e}_r + b(r)\left[\frac{\partial Y_{\ell,m}(\theta,\phi)}{\partial \theta}\vec{e}_\theta + \frac{imY_{\ell,m}(\theta,\phi)}{\sin\theta}\vec{e}_\phi\right], \quad (1)$$

with r, θ and ϕ the radial and angular coordinates of the system, with their respective unit vectors $\vec{e}_r$, $\vec{e}_\theta$ and $\vec{e}_\phi$, $Y_{\ell,m}$ is the spherical harmonic of degrees ℓ and m, and $a(r)$ and $b(r)$ are the functions expressing the radial dependencies of the radial and angular components of the eigenfunctions.

There exists actually a degeneracy in the quantum numbers describing the eigenvalues, as they are identified by three quantum numbers, ℓ, the spherical degree, n, the radial order and m, the azimuthal degree in the general case, but only two are needed to describe the eigenvalue in the non-rotating case.

In the case of low-mass stars, we can assume that we are studying a slow rotator. Consequently, the effects of rotation will thus be treated as a perturbation of the operator describing the global acoustic modes, in a similar fashion to the treatment of a weak magnetic field in the case of the hydrogen atom in quantum mechanics. Just as the degeneracy in some eigenstates is lifted by the presence of the magnetic field in the hydrogen atom, the addition of rotation to the eigenvalue problem of stellar oscillations lifts the degeneracy of the eigenvalues, namely the oscillation frequencies of the star. They appear now as multiplets in the oscillation spectrum defined by their three quantum numbers, this time with m taking values between $-\ell$ and ℓ. This breaking of symmetry stems from the fact that adding rotation to the problem leads to the definition of an equator to the star and that one can now differentiates between the lines of the eigenfunction crossing the equator and those parallel to the equator, that define the quantum numbers ℓ and m in the base of spherical harmonics.

In other words, the eigenvalues will now be described as

$$\nu_{n,\ell,m} = \nu_{n,\ell,0} + \delta\nu_{n,\ell,m} \quad (2)$$

Mathematically, the perturbative approach applied to the stellar oscillation problem leads to a simple integral relation linking the so-called rotational splittings to the internal rotation as function of the radial position r and the latitude θ[7]

$$\delta\nu_{n,\ell,m} = m \int_0^R \int_0^\pi K_{n,\ell,m}(r,\theta) \Omega(r,\theta) dr d\theta \quad (3)$$

with $\delta\nu_{n,\ell,m}$ the rotational splitting, $\Omega(r,\theta)$ the internal rotation profile and $K_{n,\ell,m}(r,\theta)$ the so-called kernel function, depending on the internal structure and the eigenfunction of the oscillation mode.

This integral relation can be solved for the internal rotation profile, using specific numerical techniques (see e.g.[8]). Given that the linear perturbative approach is valid, the internal rotation profile can be determined independently from the stellar model used to perform the inversion. In other words, a non-rotating stellar model is sufficient to perform an analysis of the internal rotation of the star, if rotation is slow enough to be treated as a perturbation.

Equation 3 gives the general $2D$ form of the perturbative relations, but the ability to carry out $2D$ inversions is limited to a few exceptionnal targets, and was only possible for the Sun until very recently. In most seismic analyses, the hypothesis of spherical symmetry will be made and the rotation profile will be inferred as a function of r only. The rotation kernels are then a function of r only and show no explicit dependency in m, as shown for example in classical textbooks.[9] Moreover, the availability of only low ℓ modes for asteroseismic targets will also limit the resolution of the inferences. The positions at which the rotational profile can be inferred are intrinsically bound to the physical nature of the observed oscillation modes and the behaviour of their kernel functions.

3. Results on the main sequence

Main-sequence low mass stars are known to exhibit purely acoustic modes called solar-like oscillations. As indicated by their name, these oscillations have been observed for the first time in the Sun. The main feature of these modes is that they have a much higher amplitude in the outer layers, as indicated in Fig 1 by the $1D$ rotational kernels computed here for a standard solar model.

Consequently, most of the inferences we will have for all main-sequence solar-like oscillators will focus on the upper radiative layers and the outer convective envelope. The inner 20% of the star will not be accessible to the pressure modes and thus will not be constrained by the inversion procedure. This statement is also true for the Sun, despite the wealth of seismic data accumulated in the last 30 years and has motivated the search for the elusive solar gravity modes.

3.1. *The solar case*

In the solar case, thousands of oscillation modes with degrees ranging from $\ell = 0$ to $\ell = 1000$ have been observed.[10–12] This tremendous amount of data has allowed a full scan of the internal solar rotation profile, down to $\approx 0.2 R_\odot$ (see e.g[13]).

The obtained rotation profile exhibits three main features. First, approximately solid-body rotation in the inner radiative layers of the Sun. Second, latitudinal differential rotation in the outer convective zone. Third, these two zones are connected by a narrow region, the so-called tachocline,[14,15] where the transition between the two rotation profiles occur.

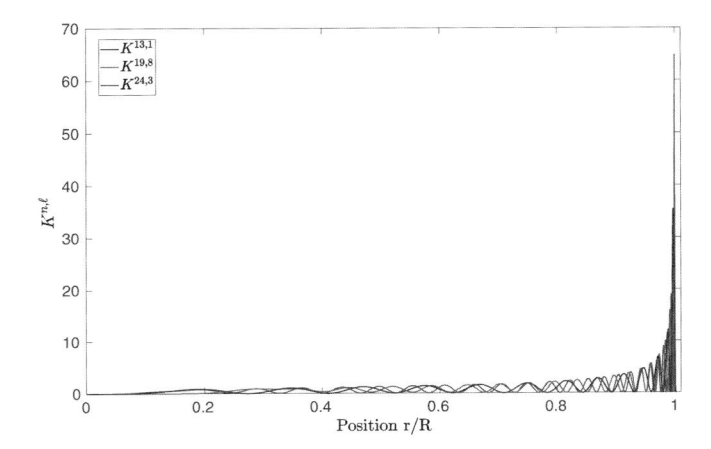

Fig. 1. $1D$ rotational kernels for various acoustic oscillaton modes of a standard solar model.

Here, we will focus mostly on the properties of the rotation profile in the inner solar radiative zone. The observed nearly uniform rotation of the inner solar layers is actually in complete contradiction with rotating models taking into account the effects of meridional circulation and shear-induced turbulence. Despite attempts at revising the prescriptions for these hydrodynamical processes,[16] it appears that their efficiency is too low to prevent the appearance of the characteristic strong differential rotation observed in these models.

Such a strong differential rotation is in disagreement with observations of the internal rotation of low-mass stars and also leads to a transport of chemicals by the shear-instability in disagreement with helioseismic inversions of the structure of the Sun and the depletion of light elements in low-mass stars. Therefore, additional processes have to be invoked to explain the discrepancies between rotating models and observations. The transport process involved should be very efficient at transporting angular momentum, but not chemical elements.

The first candidate is a large scale fossil magnetic field,[17] the second one are magnetic instabilities[18–20] and the third one are internal gravity waves.[21] We will further discuss the properties of these candidates in Section 5. They remain, to this day, the main suspects to explain the efficient angular momentum transport in stellar interiors.

3.2. *Results for Kepler and CoRoT targets*

With the advent of the CoRoT and *Kepler* missions, inferences on the internal rotation of main sequence stars could be carried out for a small sample of the best asteroseismic targets. Various authors[22–24] have shown that in the case of solar-like oscillators, the measurement of the average rotation seen by acoustic modes was consistent with the surface rotation derived from spots or spectroscopic measurements. In other words, no significant degree of differential rotation was found inside solar-like stars. This again accredited the existence of a very efficient transport of angular momentum acting in these stars, allowing to flatten their internal rotation profile.

However, a word of caution is required when stating that solar-like stars rotate as "solid-bodies". The constraints derived from asteroseismic data are not able to fully resolve the internal rotation of distant stars, but rather provide an average measurement of their internal rotation. Just as for the solar case, the purely acoustic oscillations observed for main-sequence solar-like oscillators do not allow to probe the deep core of these objects. As we will see in Section 5, this has important consequences to select one of the three candidates for additional transport mentioned above[a]. Recently, two studies[25,26] have also shown that solar-like oscillators also exhibited latitudinal differential rotation in their convective envelopes.

---

[a]We note that a similar situation is present also in more massive main-sequence stars such as γ Doradus stars, where the observed gravity modes only constrain the near core region, but not the convective core itself, as they do not propagate in these regions. Getting constraints on this region requires the analysis of inertial modes, recently observed.

3.3. Link with the transport of chemicals

An important consequence of the presence of an efficient angular momentum transport mechanism is its potential impact on the transport of chemical elements inside the star. For example, the effects of shear-induced instability in the presence of strong radial differential rotation in the radiative layers will be to erase the effects of microscopic diffusion and inhibit the settling of heavier elements from the convective layers to the deep interior.[27,28] While this effect should be limited as a result of the very low amplitude of rotation gradient in stellar radiative zones, it might not be fully negligible. In addition, a certain degree of additional mixing is required to reproduce the lithium abundance of the Sun[29] and solar-like stars.[30–33]

This is illustrated in Fig. 2 for the solar case and young solar-like stars.[34] The results show that mixing by the shear instability and the effects of magnetic instabilities will lead to a certain degree of mixing at the base of the convective zone thus changing both the helium and lithium abundances.

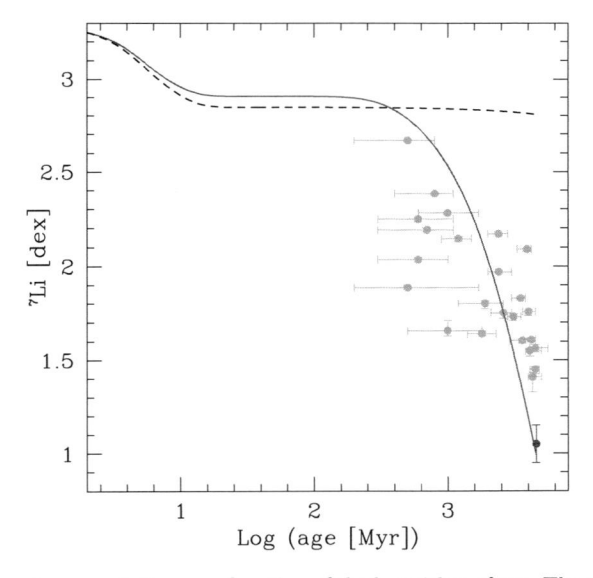

Fig. 2. Lithium abundance evolution as a function of the logarithm of age. The red dot correspond to the solar Lithium abundance[35] and the grey dots correspond to the abundance of solar-like stars.[34] The dashed line indicates the evolution of the surface Li abundance for a standard solar model, while the continuous red line corresponds to a model with hydrodynamic and magnetic instabilities.

Some of the stars observed by the *Kepler* satellite offer excellent testbeds for such effects, as for example the 16Cyg binary system,[36–39] where the binarity also allows to test the effects of planetary formation on the abundances of light elements. Moreover, seismic analyses of the helium abundance in the envelope of other *Kepler* targets[40] have shown the need for a mecanism reducing the efficiency of microscopic diffusion, that could be due to the effects of small rotation gradients.

4. Results for evolved stars

The determination of the internal rotation of subgiant and red giant stars[41–44] has been one of the main successes of the space-based photometry missions. These results have been achievable thanks to the observation of so-called mixed oscillation modes. The peculiarity of these modes is that they are of double nature and have high amplitudes both in the deep core and in the outer layers of post-main sequence solar-like oscillators. They exhibit a gravity-like character in the core and an acoustic nature in the envelope. Therefore they can be easily detected and carry information on the deepest layers of evolved stars, regions that are even unaccessible in the Sun due to the purely acoustic nature of the observed oscillations, despite the quality of helioseismic data.

From the analysis of these oscillation modes, it has been shown that subgiant and red giant stars exhibited radial differential rotation.[41–44] Namely, that their cores rotated faster than their outer layers. While this was expected, as a result of the contraction of the core and the expansion of the convective envelope undergone as the star leaves the main sequence, the degree of differential rotation observed is far lower than what is predicted by theoretical models.[45–47]

Recent results[48] have also indicated that young subgiant stars seem to exhibit almost solid-body rotation. Later on in the subgiant phase, they show some degree of differential rotation that develops but it appears that on the red giant phase, the stellar core does not spin up with the evolution.[49,50] In later stages of evolution such as the red clump or the secondary clump, similar conclusions are drawn regarding the need for a very efficient transport process.

A crucial point to note here is that to study the efficiency of the missing angular momentum transport process, core rotation is not entirely sufficient, and a measurement of the surface rotation is also required. This is available for a few targets, either from seismology, or from spot modulations. However in the latter case, it seems that the sample is biased towards active, fast rotators, who could perhaps not be quite representative of the bulk of red giants.

The main issue posed by the results obtained for post-main sequence stars is that there is, to this day, no single mechanism capable of explaining all the observations. Analyses of the average efficiency of the missing transport process[51,52] have shown that it should exhibit a drop in efficiency during the subgiant phase but reincrease as the star ascends the red giant branch. This could possibly point at either a change of regime in the transport process or at multiple transport processes acting at different evolutionary stages. For example, it has been shown that mixed modes themselves would lead to an efficient transport of angular momentum on the upper red giant branch and could potentially take over at stages where another process sees its efficiency reducing.[53]

5. Transport mechanism candidates

Apart from the transport by mixed modes, the main suspects under investigation are the processes already invoked to explain the solar rotation profile. Namely, these are large scale fossil magnetic fields, internal gravity waves and magnetic instabilities.

However, all of them needed to be revised to explain the results observed in post-main sequence stars. We will here briefly summarize the main results and remaining issues with each of these processes.

5.1. *Fossil magnetic fields*

The first candidate introduced to explain solar rotation is a large-scale fossil field present in the radiative zone of the Sun.[17] It was demonstrated that the field, if properly confined, could lead to a rigid rotation profile in the interior of the Sun.

The main difficulty for the fossil field solution in the solar case is indeed linked to the confinement of the field, as it should not extent in the solar convective zone where differential rotation in latitude is observed. This requires the field to reach a very specific configuration for which simulations give conflictual results regarding its confinement to the radiative zone.[54–57] In addition, recent work[58] has shown that, in addition to the confinement problem, simulations required a significant increase in the viscosity of the plasma to avoid a dead zone of the field where the profile would not reproduce at all the observed data.

Nevertheless, a second issue with the fossil field configuration used to explain the solar rotation profile is that it enforces a strictly solid-body rotation in radiative zones. As shown before, this is not what is found in later evolutionary stages and thus another configuration, or another physical process, is required to explain asteroseismic data. One possible configuration for red giants is to have a solid-body rotation profile in radiative zones, combined to a profile in the power law of the radius in convective zones,[59,60] of the form $\Omega(r) \propto r^{-\alpha}$, with $\alpha \in [1.0, 1.5]$. These studies[59,60] showed that such a rotation profile could explain the core rotation rate of red giant branch stars inferred from seismic data.[49,50]

However, these results are in contradiction with recent studies[61–63] who seem to indicate that the transition from the slow rotating envelope to the fast rotating core in red giant stars seems to be located in the radiative zone, close to the hydrogen burning shell. A detailed analysis of the case of Kepler 56 was recently performed,[64] including a full dedicated modelling of the internal structure of the star and an MCMC analysis of the rotational splittings using simple parametric profiles, including the power law solution provided by large scale fossil fields. Their results show that such a rotation profile cannot be used to explain the individual rotational splittings unless α is allowed to reach higher values of the order of 3.5, in contradiction with theoretical values.[59] This suggests that fossil magnetic fields are not the explanation for the efficient angular momentum transport process acting in evolved stars, and other processes must also be invoked.

5.2. Internal gravity waves

The effect of internal gravity waves has been studied already early on as being of potential interest to the modelling of stellar interiors and applied to the solar case.[21,65]

Later studies[66,67] indicated that the process was not efficient enough to actually flatten the solar rotation profile and pointed that the effect of waves excited by Reynold's stresses would leave a strong imprint of the wavefront on the internal solar rotation profile that is incompatible with observations. When applied to later evolutionary stages, the gravity wave model used on the main-sequence[21] is also found to be not efficient enough to reproduce the internal rotation of subgiants and red giant stars.[68]

However, hydrodynamical simulations[69] underlined the importance of the effects of convective plumes in the generation of gravity waves. These effects were later studied, showing that gravity waves induced by the impact of convective plumes could be much more efficient at transporting angular momentum both in the Sun and subgiant stars.[70,71] They also showed that it would likely not be able to operate efficiently on the red giant branch, where another process would then be needed. It would then be particularly interesting to compute full evolutionary models with plume-induced gravity waves to investigate their effects on the rotation profile of solar-type and subgiant stars.

5.3. Magnetic instabilities

The last main candidate to explain the efficient transport of angular momentum in stellar radiatives zone are magnetic instabilities. Work by H. Spruit[72] showed that the first instability likely set in stellar conditions would be the Tayler instability. In the presence of a differentially rotating fluid, the winding up of a seed magnetic field together with the Tayler instability has been shown to lead to an efficient angular momentum transport mechanism, the so-called Tayler-Spruit dynamo.[73] This transport mechanism has been shown to be able to reproduce the internal solar rotation profile.[19,20]

While a promising candidate, numerical simulations have shown contrasting results about the apparition of the Tayler-Spruit dynamo.[74,75] The main difficulty with such conclusions is that such simulations are never in fully realistic stellar conditions.

Nevertheless, in its original form, the Tayler-Spruit dynamo still proves not efficient enough to counteract the spin up of the core at the end of the main-sequence. Models computed taking it into account still predict faster core rotation rates than the seismically inferred values.[76,77]

Recently, a modification of the Tayler-Spruit instability was proposed that led to a more efficient braking of the stellar cores.[78] Further analyses[79] showed however that this variant could not reproduce all the observational constraints. Namely, it was found to be too efficient for subgiants if one wished to reproduce the red giant cores, or not efficient enough for red giants if the calibration parameter was set to reproduce subgiants, as shown in Fig 3. This calibration parameter, denoted α has to be varied from 0.5 to 1.5 to reproduce respectively the subgiants and the red giants. However, as it is set to the third power in the revised formalism, such a variation is far from anecdotic. A similar issue was found for secondary clump stars and white dwarfs.[80]

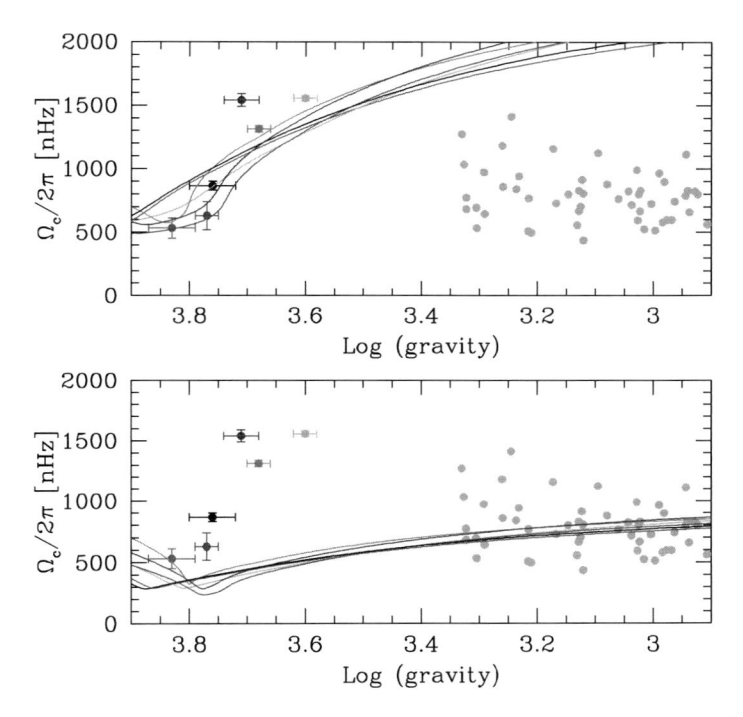

Fig. 3. Core rotation of subgiant and red giant stars as a function of the logarithm of the surface gravity. The colored points correspond to subgiant stars[43] and the grey dots to red giant stars.[49] In the upper and lower panels, the calibration parameter α in the revised version of the Tayler-Spruit dynamo is set to 0.5 and 1.5, respectively.

6. Conclusion

In this brief review, we have described the current state of the vision solar and stellar seismology brought on the internal rotation of low-mass stars in various evolutionary stages. We have focussed on the inferences brought by acoustic and mixed oscillations modes only, trying to provide a complete vision of the current issues at hand regarding the missing angular momentum transport mechanism found to act in stellar radiative zones.

The formalism for seismic inferences within the first-order perturbative formalism has been introduced in Section 2, while results for the main-sequence and post-main sequence stars have been discussed in Sections 3 and 4. We have also briefly introduced the three main candidates currently under extensive investigations in Section 5.

The main conclusion to be drawn from the current situation is a sort of stalemate between multiple processes, none of them providing a unifying satisfactory solution. In that respect, further investigations on the effiency of the missing transport process are required, analysing its dependencies with stellar properties such as mass and metallicity. To this end, better characterizing the location of rotation gradients inside stars is crucial, as well as providing both surface and core rotation measurements from a consistent seismic inference technique to fully constrain the efficiency of the transport process.

It should also be noted that the potential strong influence of chemical composition gradients in the development and efficiency of instabilities (magnetic or hydrodynamic) also calls for a better depiction of the chemical structure of stars. Therefore, the potential solution to the angular momentum transport problem is also tightly linked to the reliability of our vision of the internal structure of stars, that also relies on improving seismic inference techniques. At stakes is likely the recipe for a new generation of solar and stellar models, which would take into account both the effects of rotation, the depletion of light elements and better reproduce seismic and spectroscopic constraints. Moreover, while a unifying solution is tempting, the variations seen at different evolutionary stages might be pointing at various processes taking over during the evolution. To provide a clearer picture, further efforts must be made in the improvement of seismic inference techniques and in the exploitation of the current and future datasets from the CoRoT,[81] *Kepler*,[82] TESS[83] and Plato[84] missions.

References

1. R. B. Leighton, R. W. Noyes and G. W. Simon, Velocity Fields in the Solar Atmosphere. I. Preliminary Report., *ApJ* **135**, p. 474 (March 1962).
2. H. Kjeldsen, T. R. Bedding, M. Viskum and S. Frandsen, Solarlike Oscillations in eta Boo, *AJ* **109**, p. 1313 (March 1995).
3. M. Martić, J. Schmitt, J. C. Lebrun, C. Barban, P. Connes, F. Bouchy, E. Michel, A. Baglin, T. Appourchaux and J. L. Bertaux, Evidence for global pressure oscillations on Procyon, *A&A* **351**, 993 (November 1999).
4. F. Bouchy and F. Carrier, The acoustic spectrum of alpha Cen A, *A&A* **390**, 205 (July 2002).
5. C. Aerts, S. Mathis and T. M. Rogers, Angular Momentum Transport in Stellar Interiors, *Annu. Rev. Astron. Astrophys.* **57**, 35 (August 2019).
6. A. Maeder, *Physics, Formation and Evolution of Rotating Stars* 2009.
7. P. Ledoux, The Nonradial Oscillations of Gaseous Stars and the Problem of Beta Canis Majoris., *ApJ* **114**, p. 373 (November 1951).
8. J. Schou, H. M. Antia, S. Basu, R. S. Bogart, R. I. Bush, S. M. Chitre, J. Christensen-Dalsgaard, M. P. Di Mauro, W. A. Dziembowski, A. Eff-Darwich, D. O. Gough, D. A. Haber, J. T. Hoeksema, R. Howe, S. G. Korzennik, A. G. Kosovichev, R. M. Larsen, F. P. Pijpers, P. H. Scherrer, T. Sekii, T. D. Tarbell, A. M. Title, M. J. Thompson

and J. Toomre, Helioseismic Studies of Differential Rotation in the Solar Envelope by the Solar Oscillations Investigation Using the Michelson Doppler Imager, *ApJ* **505**, 390 (September 1998).
9. W. Unno, Y. Osaki, H. Ando, H. Saio and H. Shibahashi, *Nonradial oscillations of stars* 1989.
10. S. G. Korzennik, M. C. Rabello-Soares, J. Schou and T. P. Larson, Accurate Characterization of High-degree Modes Using MDI Observations, *ApJ* **772**, p. 87 (August 2013).
11. T. P. Larson and J. Schou, Global-Mode Analysis of Full-Disk Data from the Michelson Doppler Imager and the Helioseismic and Magnetic Imager, *Solar Physics* **293**, p. 29 (February 2018).
12. J. Reiter, J. Rhodes, E. J., A. G. Kosovichev, P. H. Scherrer, T. P. Larson and I., S. F. Pinkerton, A Method for the Estimation of f- and p-mode Parameters and Rotational Splitting Coefficients from Un-averaged Solar Oscillation Power Spectra, *ApJ* **894**, p. 80 (May 2020).
13. M. J. Thompson, J. Toomre, E. R. Anderson, H. M. Antia, G. Berthomieu, D. Burtonclay, S. M. Chitre, J. Christensen-Dalsgaard, T. Corbard, M. De Rosa, C. R. Genovese, D. O. Gough, D. A. Haber, J. W. Harvey, F. Hill, R. Howe, S. G. Korzennik, A. G. Kosovichev, J. W. Leibacher, F. P. Pijpers, J. Provost, J. Rhodes, E. J., J. Schou, T. Sekii, P. B. Stark and P. R. Wilson, Differential Rotation and Dynamics of the Solar Interior, *Science* **272**, 1300 (May 1996).
14. E. A. Spiegel and J.-P. Zahn, The solar tachocline, *A&Ap* **265**, 106 (November 1992).
15. D. W. Hughes, R. Rosner and N. O. Weiss, *The Solar Tachocline* May 2007.
16. S. Mathis, V. Prat, L. Amard, C. Charbonnel, A. Palacios, N. Lagarde and P. Eggenberger, Anisotropic turbulent transport in stably stratified rotating stellar radiation zones, *A&A* **620**, p. A22 (December 2018).
17. D. O. Gough and M. E. McIntyre, Inevitability of a magnetic field in the Sun's radiative interior, *Nature* **394**, 755 (August 1998).
18. H. C. Spruit, Dynamo action by differential rotation in a stably stratified stellar interior, *A&A* **381**, 923 (January 2002).
19. P. Eggenberger, A. Maeder and G. Meynet, Stellar evolution with rotation and magnetic fields. IV. The solar rotation profile, *A&A* **440**, L9 (September 2005).
20. P. Eggenberger, G. Buldgen and S. J. A. J. Salmon, Rotation rate of the solar core as a key constraint to magnetic angular momentum transport in stellar interiors, *A&A* **626**, p. L1 (Jun 2019).
21. C. Charbonnel and S. Talon, Influence of Gravity Waves on the Internal Rotation and Li Abundance of Solar-Type Stars, *Science* **309**, 2189 (September 2005).
22. M. N. Lund, M. S. Miesch and J. Christensen-Dalsgaard, Differential Rotation in Main-sequence Solar-like Stars: Qualitative Inference from Asteroseismic Data, *ApJ* **790**, p. 121 (August 2014).
23. O. Benomar, M. Takata, H. Shibahashi, T. Ceillier and R. A. García, Nearly uniform internal rotation of solar-like main-sequence stars revealed by space-based asteroseismology and spectroscopic measurements, *MNRAS* **452**, 2654 (September 2015).
24. M. B. Nielsen, H. Schunker, L. Gizon and W. H. Ball, Constraining differential rotation of Sun-like stars from asteroseismic and starspot rotation periods, *A&A* **582**, p. A10 (October 2015).
25. O. Benomar, M. Bazot, M. B. Nielsen, L. Gizon, T. Sekii, M. Takata, H. Hotta, S. Hanasoge, K. R. Sreenivasan and J. Christensen-Dalsgaard, Asteroseismic detection of latitudinal differential rotation in 13 Sun-like stars, *Science* **361**, 1231 (September 2018).

26. M. Bazot, O. Benomar, J. Christensen-Dalsgaard, L. Gizon, S. Hanasoge, M. Nielsen, P. Petit and K. R. Sreenivasan, Latitudinal differential rotation in the solar analogues 16 Cygni A and B, *A&A* **623**, p. A125 (March 2019).
27. P. Eggenberger, G. Meynet, A. Maeder, A. Miglio, J. Montalban, F. Carrier, S. Mathis, C. Charbonnel and S. Talon, Effects of rotational mixing on the asteroseismic properties of solar-type stars, *A&A* **519**, p. A116 (September 2010).
28. M. Deal, M. J. Goupil, J. P. Marques, D. R. Reese and Y. Lebreton, Chemical mixing in low mass stars. I. Rotation against atomic diffusion including radiative acceleration, *A&A* **633**, p. A23 (January 2020).
29. O. Richard, S. Vauclair, C. Charbonnel and W. A. Dziembowski, New solar models including helioseismological constraints and light-element depletion., *A&Ap* **312**, 1000 (August 1996).
30. S. Talon, C. Charbonnel, The Li dip: A probe of angular momentum transport in low mass stars, *A&A*, **335**, p. 959 to 968 (1998).
31. P. Eggenberger, A. Maeder and G. Meynet, Effects of rotation and magnetic fields on the lithium abundance and asteroseismic properties of exoplanet-host stars, *A&A* **519**, p. L2 (September 2010).
32. F. Thévenin, A. V. Oreshina, V. A. Baturin, A. B. Gorshkov, P. Morel and J. Provost, Evolution of lithium abundance in the Sun and solar twins, *A&A* **598**, p. A64 (February 2017).
33. M. Carlos, J. Meléndez, L. Spina, L. A. dos Santos, M. Bedell, I. Ramirez, M. Asplund, J. L. Bean, D. Yong, J. Yana Galarza and A. Alves-Brito, The Li-age correlation: The Sun is unusually Li deficient for its age, *MNRAS* **485**, 4052 (May 2019).
34. M. Carlos, J. Meléndez, L. Spina, L. A. dos Santos, M. Bedell, I. Ramirez, M. Asplund, J. L. Bean, D. Yong, J. Yana Galarza and A. Alves-Brito, The Li-age correlation: The Sun is unusually Li deficient for its age, *MNRAS* **485**, 4052 (May 2019).
35. M. Asplund, N. Grevesse, A. J. Sauval and P. Scott, The Chemical Composition of the Sun, *ARA&A* **47**, 481 (September 2009).
36. M. Deal, O. Richard and S. Vauclair, Accretion of planetary matter and the lithium problem in the 16 Cygni stellar system, *A&A* **584**, p. A105 (December 2015).
37. G. Buldgen, D. R. Reese and M. A. Dupret, Constraints on the structure of 16 Cygni A and 16 Cygni B using inversion techniques, *A&A* **585**, p. A109 (January 2016).
38. G. Buldgen, S. J. A. J. Salmon, D. R. Reese and M. A. Dupret, In-depth study of 16CygB using inversion techniques, *A&A* **596**, p. A73 (December 2016).
39. M. Bazot, Uncertainties and biases in modelling 16 Cygni A and B, *A&A* **635**, p. A26 (March 2020).
40. K. Verma and V. Silva Aguirre, Helium settling in F stars: Constraining turbulent mixing using observed helium glitch signature, *MNRAS* **489**, 1850 (October 2019).
41. P. G. Beck, J. Montalban, T. Kallinger, J. De Ridder, C. Aerts, R. A. García, S. Hekker, M.-A. Dupret, B. Mosser, P. Eggenberger, D. Stello, Y. Elsworth, S. Frandsen, F. Carrier, M. Hillen, M. Gruberbauer, J. Christensen-Dalsgaard, A. Miglio, M. Valentini, T. R. Bedding, H. Kjeldsen, F. R. Girouard, J. R. Hall and K. A. Ibrahim, Fast core rotation in red-giant stars as revealed by gravity-dominated mixed modes, *Nature* **481**, 55 (January 2012).
42. S. Deheuvels, R. A. García, W. J. Chaplin, S. Basu, H. M. Antia, T. Appourchaux, O. Benomar, G. R. Davies, Y. Elsworth, L. Gizon, M. J. Goupil, D. R. Reese, C. Regulo, J. Schou, T. Stahn, L. Casagrande, J. Christensen-Dalsgaard, D. Fischer, S. Hekker, H. Kjeldsen, S. Mathur, B. Mosser, M. Pinsonneault, J. Valenti, J. L. Christiansen, K. Kinemuchi and F. Mullally, Seismic Evidence for a Rapidly Rotating Core in a Lower-giant-branch Star Observed with Kepler, *ApJ* **756**, p. 19 (September 2012).

43. S. Deheuvels, G. Doğan, M. J. Goupil, T. Appourchaux, O. Benomar, H. Bruntt, T. L. Campante, L. Casagrande, T. Ceillier, G. R. Davies, P. De Cat, J. N. Fu, R. A. García, A. Lobel, B. Mosser, D. R. Reese, C. Regulo, J. Schou, T. Stahn, A. O. Thygesen, X. H. Yang, W. J. Chaplin, J. Christensen-Dalsgaard, P. Eggenberger, L. Gizon, S. Mathis, J. Molenda-Żakowicz and M. Pinsonneault, Seismic constraints on the radial dependence of the internal rotation profiles of six Kepler subgiants and young red giants, *A&A* **564**, p. A27 (April 2014).
44. S. Deheuvels, J. Ballot, P. G. Beck, B. Mosser, R. Østensen, R. A. García and M. J. Goupil, Seismic evidence for a weak radial differential rotation in intermediate-mass core helium burning stars, *A&A* **580**, p. A96 (August 2015).
45. P. Eggenberger, J. Montalbán and A. Miglio, Angular momentum transport in stellar interiors constrained by rotational splittings of mixed modes in red giants, *A&A* **544**, p. L4 (August 2012).
46. J. P. Marques, M. J. Goupil, Y. Lebreton, S. Talon, A. Palacios, K. Belkacem, R.-M. Ouazzani, B. Mosser, A. Moya, P. Morel, B. Pichon, S. Mathis, J.-P. Zahn, S. Turck-Chièze and P. A. P. Nghiem, Seismic diagnostics for transport of angular momentum in stars. I. Rotational splittings from the pre-main sequence to the red-giant branch, *A&A* **549**, p. A74 (January 2013).
47. T. Ceillier, P. Eggenberger, R. A. García and S. Mathis, Understanding angular momentum transport in red giants: The case of KIC 7341231, *A&A* **555**, p. A54 (July 2013).
48. S. Deheuvels, J. Ballot, P. Eggenberger, F. Spada, A. Noll and J. W. den Hartogh, Seismic evidence for near solid-body rotation in two Kepler subgiants and implications for angular momentum transport, *A&A* **641**, p. A117 (September 2020).
49. B. Mosser, M. J. Goupil, K. Belkacem, J. P. Marques, P. G. Beck, S. Bloemen, J. De Ridder, C. Barban, S. Deheuvels, Y. Elsworth, S. Hekker, T. Kallinger, R. M. Ouazzani, M. Pinsonneault, R. Samadi, D. Stello, R. A. García, T. C. Klaus, J. Li, S. Mathur and R. L. Morris, Spin down of the core rotation in red giants, *A&A* **548**, p. A10 (December 2012).
50. C. Gehan, B. Mosser, E. Michel, R. Samadi and T. Kallinger, Core rotation braking on the red giant branch for various mass ranges, *A&A* **616**, p. A24 (Aug 2018).
51. P. Eggenberger, N. Lagarde, A. Miglio, J. Montalbán, S. Ekström, C. Georgy, G. Meynet, S. Salmon, T. Ceillier, R. A. García, S. Mathis, S. Deheuvels, A. Maeder, J. W. den Hartogh and R. Hirschi, Constraining the efficiency of angular momentum transport with asteroseismology of red giants: The effect of stellar mass, *A&A* **599**, p. A18 (March 2017).
52. P. Eggenberger, S. Deheuvels, A. Miglio, S. Ekström, C. Georgy, G. Meynet, N. Lagarde, S. Salmon, G. Buldgen, J. Montalbán, F. Spada and J. Ballot, Asteroseismology of evolved stars to constrain the internal transport of angular momentum. I. Efficiency of transport during the subgiant phase, *A&A* **621**, p. A66 (January 2019).
53. K. Belkacem, J. P. Marques, M. J. Goupil, B. Mosser, T. Sonoi, R. M. Ouazzani, M. A. Dupret, S. Mathis and M. Grosjean, Angular momentum redistribution by mixed modes in evolved low-mass stars. II. Spin-down of the core of red giants induced by mixed modes, *A&A* **579**, p. A31 (July 2015).
54. A. S. Brun and J.-P. Zahn, Magnetic confinement of the solar tachocline, *A&A* **457**, 665 (October 2006).
55. A. Strugarek, A. S. Brun and J.-P. Zahn, Magnetic confinement of the solar tachocline: II. Coupling to a convection zone, *A&A* **532**, p. A34 (August 2011).

56. L. A. Acevedo-Arreguin, P. Garaud and T. S. Wood, Dynamics of the solar tachocline - III. Numerical solutions of the Gough and McIntyre model, *MNRAS* **434**, 720 (September 2013).
57. T. S. Wood and N. H. Brummell, A Self-consistent Model of the Solar Tachocline, *ApJ* **853**, p. 97 (February 2018).
58. F. Spada, A. C. Lanzafame and A. F. Lanza, A semi-analytic approach to angular momentum transport in stellar radiative interiors, *MNRAS* **404**, 641 (May 2010).
59. Y. Kissin and C. Thompson, Rotation of Giant Stars, *ApJ* **808**, p. 35 (July 2015).
60. K. Takahashi and N. Langer, Modeling of magneto-rotational stellar evolution. I. Method and first applications, *A&A* **646**, p. A19 (February 2021).
61. M. P. Di Mauro, R. Ventura, D. Cardini, D. Stello, J. Christensen-Dalsgaard, W. A. Dziembowski, L. Paternò, P. G. Beck, S. Bloemen, G. R. Davies, K. De Smedt, Y. Elsworth, R. A. García, S. Hekker, B. Mosser and A. Tkachenko, Internal Rotation of the Red-giant Star KIC 4448777 by Means of Asteroseismic Inversion, *ApJ* **817**, p. 65 (January 2016).
62. H. Klion and E. Quataert, A diagnostic for localizing red giant differential rotation, *MNRAS* **464**, L16 (January 2017).
63. M. P. Di Mauro, R. Ventura, E. Corsaro and B. Lustosa De Moura, The Rotational Shear Layer inside the Early Red-giant Star KIC 4448777, *ApJ* **862**, p. 9 (July 2018).
64. L. Fellay, G. Buldgen, P. Eggenberger, S. Khan, S. J. A. J. Salmon, A. Miglio and J. Montalbán, Asteroseismology of evolved stars to constrain the internal transport of angular momentum. IV. Internal rotation of Kepler 56 from an MCMC analysis of the rotational splittings, *arXiv e-prints*, p. arXiv:2108.02670 (August 2021).
65. S. Talon, P. Kumar and J.-P. Zahn, Angular Momentum Extraction by Gravity Waves in the Sun, *ApJL* **574**, L175 (August 2002).
66. T. M. Rogers, Numerical Simulations of Gravity Wave Driven Shear Flows in the Solar Tachocline, in *Unsolved Problems in Stellar Physics: A Conference in Honor of Douglas Gough*, eds. R. J. Stancliffe, G. Houdek, R. G. Martin and C. A. Tout, American Institute of Physics Conference Series, Vol. 948November 2007.
67. P. A. Denissenkov, M. Pinsonneault and K. B. MacGregor, What Prevents Internal Gravity Waves from Disturbing the Solar Uniform Rotation?, *ApJ* **684**, 757 (September 2008).
68. J. Fuller, D. Lecoanet, M. Cantiello and B. Brown, Angular Momentum Transport via Internal Gravity Waves in Evolving Stars, *ApJ* **796**, p. 17 (November 2014).
69. T. M. Rogers and G. A. Glatzmaier, Angular Momentum Transport by Gravity Waves in the Solar Interior, *ApJ* **653**, 756 (December 2006).
70. C. Pinçon, K. Belkacem and M. J. Goupil, Generation of internal gravity waves by penetrative convection, *A&A* **588**, p. A122 (April 2016).
71. C. Pinçon, K. Belkacem, M. J. Goupil and J. P. Marques, Can plume-induced internal gravity waves regulate the core rotation of subgiant stars?, *A&A* **605**, p. A31 (September 2017).
72. H. C. Spruit, Differential rotation and magnetic fields in stellar interiors, *A&A* **349**, 189 (September 1999).
73. H. C. Spruit, Dynamo action by differential rotation in a stably stratified stellar interior, *A&A* **381**, 923 (January 2002).
74. J. Zahn, A. S. Brun and S. Mathis, On magnetic instabilities and dynamo action in stellar radiation zones, *A&A* **474**, 145 (October 2007).
75. J. Braithwaite and H. C. Spruit, Magnetic fields in non-convective regions of stars, *Royal Society Open Science* **4**, p. 160271 (February 2017).

76. M. Cantiello, C. Mankovich, L. Bildsten, J. Christensen-Dalsgaard and B. Paxton, Angular Momentum Transport within Evolved Low-mass Stars, *ApJ* **788**, p. 93 (June 2014).
77. J. W. den Hartogh, P. Eggenberger and R. Hirschi, Constraining transport of angular momentum in stars. Combining asteroseismic observations of core helium burning stars and white dwarfs, *A&A* **622**, p. A187 (February 2019).
78. J. Fuller, A. L. Piro and A. S. Jermyn, Slowing the spins of stellar cores, *MNRAS* **485**, 3661 (May 2019).
79. P. Eggenberger, J. W. den Hartogh, G. Buldgen, G. Meynet, S. J. A. J. Salmon and S. Deheuvels, Asteroseismology of evolved stars to constrain the internal transport of angular momentum. II. Test of a revised prescription for transport by the Tayler instability, *A&A* **631**, p. L6 (November 2019).
80. J. W. den Hartogh, P. Eggenberger and S. Deheuvels, Asteroseismology of evolved stars to constrain the internal transport of angular momentum. III. Using the rotation rates of intermediate-mass stars to test the Fuller-formalism, *A&A* **634**, p. L16 (February 2020).
81. A. Baglin, M. Auvergne, L. Boisnard, T. Lam-Trong, P. Barge, C. Catala, M. Deleuil, E. Michel and W. Weiss, CoRoT: A high precision photometer for stellar ecolution and exoplanet finding, in *36th COSPAR Scientific Assembly*, COSPAR Meeting Vol. 362006.
82. W. J. Borucki, D. Koch, G. Basri, N. Batalha, T. Brown, D. Caldwell, J. Caldwell, J. Christensen-Dalsgaard, W. D. Cochran, E. DeVore, E. W. Dunham, A. K. Dupree, T. N. Gautier, J. C. Geary, R. Gilliland, A. Gould, S. B. Howell, J. M. Jenkins, Y. Kondo, D. W. Latham, G. W. Marcy, S. Meibom, H. Kjeldsen, J. J. Lissauer, D. G. Monet, D. Morrison, D. Sasselov, J. Tarter, A. Boss, D. Brownlee, T. Owen, D. Buzasi, D. Charbonneau, L. Doyle, J. Fortney, E. B. Ford, M. J. Holman, S. Seager, J. H. Steffen, W. F. Welsh, J. Rowe, H. Anderson, L. Buchhave, D. Ciardi, L. Walkowicz, W. Sherry, E. Horch, H. Isaacson, M. E. Everett, D. Fischer, G. Torres, J. A. Johnson, M. Endl, P. MacQueen, S. T. Bryson, J. Dotson, M. Haas, J. Kolodziejczak, J. Van Cleve, H. Chandrasekaran, J. D. Twicken, E. V. Quintana, B. D. Clarke, C. Allen, J. Li, H. Wu, P. Tenenbaum, E. Verner, F. Bruhweiler, J. Barnes and A. Prsa, Kepler Planet-Detection Mission: Introduction and First Results, *Science* **327**, 977 (February 2010).
83. G. R. Ricker, J. N. Winn, R. Vanderspek, D. W. Latham, G. Á. Bakos, J. L. Bean, Z. K. Berta-Thompson, T. M. Brown, L. Buchhave, N. R. Butler, R. P. Butler, W. J. Chaplin, D. Charbonneau, J. Christensen-Dalsgaard, M. Clampin, D. Deming, J. Doty, N. De Lee, C. Dressing, E. W. Dunham, M. Endl, F. Fressin, J. Ge, T. Henning, M. J. Holman, A. W. Howard, S. Ida, J. M. Jenkins, G. Jernigan, J. A. Johnson, L. Kaltenegger, N. Kawai, H. Kjeldsen, G. Laughlin, A. M. Levine, D. Lin, J. J. Lissauer, P. MacQueen, G. Marcy, P. R. McCullough, T. D. Morton, N. Narita, M. Paegert, E. Palle, F. Pepe, J. Pepper, A. Quirrenbach, S. A. Rinehart, D. Sasselov, B. Sato, S. Seager, A. Sozzetti, K. G. Stassun, P. Sullivan, A. Szentgyorgyi, G. Torres, S. Udry and J. Villasenor, Transiting Exoplanet Survey Satellite (TESS), *Journal of Astronomical Telescopes, Instruments, and Systems* **1**, p. 014003 (January 2015).
84. H. Rauer, C. Catala, C. Aerts, T. Appourchaux, W. Benz, A. Brandeker, J. Christensen-Dalsgaard, M. Deleuil, L. Gizon, M. J. Goupil, M. Güdel, E. Janot-Pacheco, M. Mas-Hesse, I. Pagano, G. Piotto, D. Pollacco, Ċ. Santos, A. Smith, J. C. Suárez, R. Szabó, S. Udry, V. Adibekyan, Y. Alibert, J. M. Almenara, P. Amaro-Seoane, M. A.-v. Eiff, M. Asplund, E. Antonello, S. Barnes, F. Baudin, K. Belkacem, M. Bergemann, G. Bihain, A. C. Birch, X. Bonfils, I. Boisse, A. S. Bonomo,

F. Borsa, I. M. Brandão, E. Brocato, S. Brun, M. Burleigh, R. Burston, J. Cabrera, S. Cassisi, W. Chaplin, S. Charpinet, C. Chiappini, R. P. Church, S. Csizmadia, M. Cunha, M. Damasso, M. B. Davies, H. J. Deeg, R. F. Díaz, S. Dreizler, C. Dreyer, P. Eggenberger, D. Ehrenreich, P. Eigmüller, A. Erikson, R. Farmer, S. Feltzing, F. de Oliveira Fialho, P. Figueira, T. Forveille, M. Fridlund, R. A. García, P. Giommi, G. Giuffrida, M. Godolt, J. Gomes da Silva, T. Granzer, J. L. Grenfell, A. Grotsch-Noels, E. Günther, C. A. Haswell, A. P. Hatzes, G. Hébrard, S. Hekker, R. Helled, K. Heng, J. M. Jenkins, A. Johansen, M. L. Khodachenko, K. G. Kislyakova, W. Kley, U. Kolb, N. Krivova, F. Kupka, H. Lammer, A. F. Lanza, Y. Lebreton, D. Magrin, P. Marcos-Arenal, P. M. Marrese, J. P. Marques, J. Martins, S. Mathis, S. Mathur, S. Messina, A. Miglio, J. Montalban, M. Montalto, M. J. P. F. G. Monteiro, H. Moradi, E. Moravveji, C. Mordasini, T. Morel, A. Mortier, V. Nascimbeni, R. P. Nelson, M. B. Nielsen, L. Noack, A. J. Norton, A. Ofir, M. Oshagh, R. M. Ouazzani, P. Pápics, V. C. Parro, P. Petit, B. Plez, E. Poretti, A. Quirrenbach, R. Ragazzoni, G. Raimondo, M. Rainer, D. R. Reese, R. Redmer, S. Reffert, B. Rojas-Ayala, I. W. Roxburgh, S. Salmon, A. Santerne, J. Schneider, J. Schou, S. Schuh, H. Schunker, A. Silva-Valio, R. Silvotti, I. Skillen, I. Snellen, F. Sohl, S. G. Sousa, A. Sozzetti, D. Stello, K. G. Strassmeier, M. Švanda, G. M. Szabó, A. Tkachenko, D. Valencia, V. Van Grootel, S. D. Vauclair, P. Ventura, F. W. Wagner, N. A. Walton, J. Weingrill, S. C. Werner, P. J. Wheatley and K. Zwintz, The PLATO 2.0 mission, *Experimental Astronomy* **38**, 249 (November 2014).

The rotation of supermassive stars

L. Haemmerlé

Département d'Astronomie, Université de Genève, chemin des Maillettes 51,
CH-1290 Versoix, Switzerland
E-mail: lionel.haemmerle@unige.ch

Supermassive stars (SMSs), with masses $> 10^5$ M$_\odot$, have been proposed as the possible progenitors of the most extreme supermassive black holes observed at redshifts $z > 6-7$. In this scenario ('direct collapse'), a SMS **accretes** at rates > 0.1 M$_\odot$ yr^{-1} until it collapses to a black hole via the general-relativistic (GR) instability. Rotation plays a crucial role in the formation of such supermassive black hole seeds. The centrifugal barrier appears as particularly strong in this extreme case of star formation. Moreover, rotation impacts sensitively the stability of SMSs against GR, as well as the subsequent collapse. In particular, it might allow for gravitational wave emission and ultra-long gamma-ray bursts at black hole formation, which represents currently the main observational signatures proposed in the literature for the existence of such objects. Here, I present the latest models of SMSs accounting for accretion and rotation, and discuss some of the open questions and future prospects in this research line.

Keywords: Stars: massive – stars: rotation – stars: black holes

1. Introduction

Supermassive stars (SMSs), with masses $\gtrsim 10^5$ M$_\odot$, were originally invoked to explain the high luminosity of quasars,[1,2] later understood as a consequence of accretion in the deep potential well of supermassive black holes (SMBHs).[3] The formation of these SMBHs remains, however, one of the main open problems in galaxy formation, and SMSs have been proposed as their possible progenitors.[4,5] In the last decade, a number of quasars powered by SMBHs with masses $10^9 - 10^{10}$ M$_\odot$ have been detected at redshifts 6 – 7. The most extreme case known to date is J0313-1806 a quasar at $z = 7.6$ that hosts a SMBH with mass $1-2\times 10^9$ M$_\odot$.[6] At redshifts 6 – 7, the age of the Universe is a fraction of a Gyr, so that objects of $10^9 - 10^{10}$ M$_\odot$ that exist at these redshifts must have accumulated their mass at average rates $\dot M \gtrsim 10$ M$_\odot$ yr^{-1}. The direct formation of SMBHs during the process of galaxy formation ('direct collapse' black holes) provides the most rapid pathway to form SMBHs with masses $\gtrsim 10^9$ M$_\odot$.[5,6] In this scenario, the direct progenitor of the SMBH is a SMS undergoing accretion at rates $\dot M \gtrsim 0.1$ M$_\odot$ yr^{-1}, until it collapses due to the general-relativistic (GR) instability.[7,8]

The direct collapse of $\sim 10^9$ M$_\odot$ into a compact object requires special conditions. Fragmentation is inhibited in primordial gas due to the absence of heavy elements, but the cooling by molecular hydrogen remains efficient enough to maintain temperatures 100 – 1000 K, which is thought to result in the formation of a cluster of stars with individual masses $M \lesssim 100$ M$_\odot$.[9] Black hole seeds formed from the collapse of such primordial clusters remain $\lesssim 1000$ M$_\odot$, and hardly explain the large masses of the earliest quasars.[6,10] Only in the presence of a strong Lyman-Werner flux the molecular hydrogen of primordial gas can be dissociated, which leads to temperatures $\sim 10^4$ K set by atomic cooling.[11] Primordial, atomically cooled halos are found to collapse isothermally with inflows $0.01 - 1$ M$_\odot$ yr^{-1} sustained down to sub-parsec scales, allowing for the direct formation of a supermassive compact object in a dynamical time.[12,13] However, this scenario implies tight synchronisation between halo pairs, since only star formation in a neighbouring halo can provide the required Lyman-Werner flux.[14] Another channel of direct collapse is provided by the merger of the most massive galaxies expected to have formed at redshifts 8 – 10, with masses $\sim 10^{12}$ M$_\odot$.[15] The merger is found to trigger inflows of $\sim 10^4 - 10^5$ M$_\odot$ yr^{-1} down to a fraction of a parsec, which allows to accumulate several 10^9 M$_\odot$ in a few tens of kyr. No special chemical composition is required, since the collapse is too rapid for star formation and radiative feedback to start, and metallicities up to solar are expected in these galaxies. However, SMBH formation by direct collapse in metal-rich gas requires a SMS with mass $M \gtrsim 10^6$ M$_\odot$ in order to avoid thermonuclear explosion.[16]

The strong contraction that characterises a gravitationnal collapse leads in general to rapidly rotating structures, by a simple argument of angular momentum conservation. In fact, star formation by accretion requires strong mechanisms to remove angular momentum from the collapsing gas in order to circumvent the centrifugal barrier.[17] This angular momentum problem represents one of the main bottleneck in models of massive star formation[18–20] and plays naturally a critical role in the context of SMS and SMBH formation.[21,22] Here, I review the latest theoretical results concerning SMSs in the context of SMBH formation, focusing on the importance of rotation. In Section 2, I review the main properties of SMSs formed by accretion; I discuss the angular momentum problem in section 3; section 4 focuses on the GR instability and the maximum mass of rotating SMSs; the implication for SMBH formation by direct collapse are discussed in section 5. A summary is given in section 6.

2. Rotation in rapidly accreting SMSs

The evolution of SMSs under rapid accretion has been addressed with analytical and numerical models in the last decade.[23–25] SMSs are always close to the Eddington limit, which implies that their H-burning time is of the order of the Myr, independently of their mass. Thus, forming a SMS of mass $M \gtrsim 10^5$ M$_\odot$ by accretion before fuel exhaustion requires rates $\dot M \gtrsim 0.1$ M$_\odot$ yr^{-1}. Under such accretion rates, SMSs are found to evolve as 'red supergiant protostars',[24] following upwards the Hayashi limit in the Hertzsprung-Russel diagram. An example is shown in figure 1, with numerical models of Population III (Pop III) SMSs computed with the stellar evolution code GENEC.[25] The effective temperature on the Hayashi limit remains $\lesssim 10^4$ K,

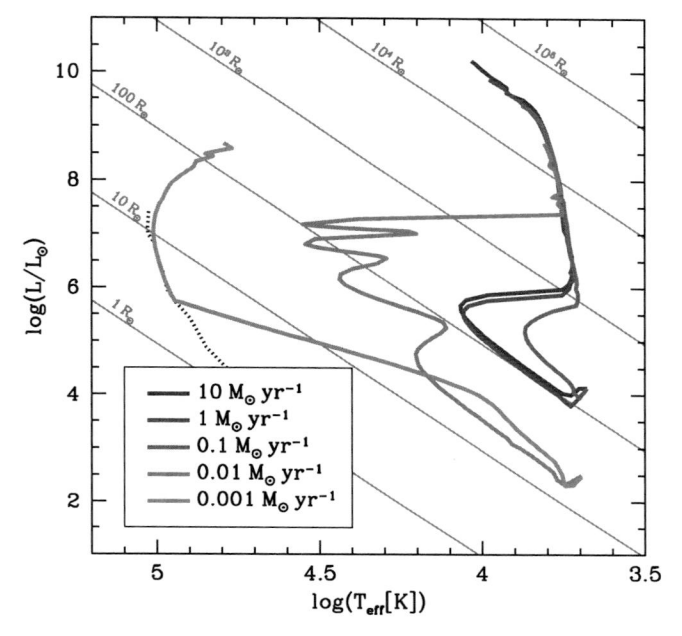

Fig. 1. Hertzsprung-Russel diagram of the GENEC models of Pop III, rapidly accreting SMSs. (Figure from.[25])

which implies negligible ionising feedback and allows for continuous accretion up to at least $M \sim 10^5$ $M_\odot$. As a consequence of the evolution along both the Eddington and the Hayashi limits, the mass-radius relation of rapidly accreting SMSs can be approximated by a simple power-law:

$$R = 260 \, R_\odot \left(\frac{M}{M_\odot}\right)^{1/2} \qquad (1)$$

The increase of the radius with the growing mass results from the fact that, at rates $\gtrsim 0.01$ $M_\odot \, \mathrm{yr}^{-1}$, the entropy advected by an element of mass ΔM at accretion cannot be radiated efficiently in the corresponding accretion time $\Delta M/\dot{M}$. Thus, the Kelvin-Helmholtz contraction of the stellar interior is too slow compared to the increase in radius that results from the accretion of new mass. As a consequence, most of the stellar interior is not thermally relaxed and maintains an outwards positive entropy gradient that stabilises the gas against convection. This is illustrated in figure 2 with the entropy profiles of the Pop III GENEC models at $\dot{M} = 1 - 100$ $M_\odot \, \mathrm{yr}^{-1}$, taken at successive stages of the evolution. The highly centralised energy production by H-burning drives convection in a core of $\sim 10\%$ of the stellar mass, that stays isentropic. An **outer** envelope is also convective (non-adiabatic), due to the high opacities at the low temperatures of the Hayashi limit. This **outer** envelope contains negligible mass ($\sim 1\% M$), but represents a significant fraction of the stellar radius. For accretion rates $\dot{M} \gtrsim 10$ $M_\odot \, \mathrm{yr}^{-1}$, the evolutionary timescale becomes so short that the radiative envelope contracts adiabatically, compressed by the weight of the layers newly accreted.[26] In this regime, the entropy profile converges towards a simple power-law of the mass-coordinates ('hylotrope'[23]):

$$s \propto M_r^{1/2} \tag{2}$$

This power-law is shown by a grey dotted line in figures 2.

For stars near the Eddington limit, the maximum rotation velocity consistent with hydrostatic equilibrium is given by the $\Omega\Gamma$-limit, that accounts for the role of radiation pressure:[28]

$$\Omega_\Gamma \simeq \Omega_K \sqrt{1-\Gamma} \tag{3}$$

where Ω_K is the Keplerian angular velocity and Γ the Eddington factor. SMSs have $\Gamma \sim 0.99$, which implies rotation velocities of $\lesssim 10\% \, \Omega_K$; in other words, SMSs must be slow rotators.[22] The maximum rotation velocity set by the $\Omega\Gamma$-limit is shown in figure 3 as a function of the SMS's mass. The ratio of centrifugal to gravitational forces in the star, which is of the same order as the ratio of rotational to gravitational energies, can be estimated by

$$\frac{\Omega^2}{\Omega_K^2} \sim 1 - \Gamma \lesssim 1\% \tag{4}$$

For such slow rotations, the deformation of the star by the anisotropic centrifugal force remains negligible. Moreover, due to the short evolutionary timescales, meridional currents and shear diffusion have no significant impact on the angular momentum distribution. Thus, the radiative layers contract with local angular momentum conservation, which translates into highly differential rotation, with a rotation frequency several orders of magnitude larger in the core than at the surface.[22] The break-up velocity is not reached in the core, thanks to the large Keplerian velocity in the densest regions.

3. The angular momentum problem

Because of the slow rotations imposed by the $\Omega\Gamma$-limit, SMS formation by accretion implies low angular momentum in the accreted gas. This is illustrated in figure 4, that shows the evolution of a Pop III SMS accreting at $\dot{M} = 1 \, \text{M}_\odot \, \text{yr}^{-1}$ under the assumption of maximal rotation. Rotation is post-processed from the non-rotating GENEC structures shown in the upper panel. Angular momentum is advected at accretion in order to satisfy the constraint from the $\Omega\Gamma$-limit (third panel) at each time-step, and the resulting angular momentum accretion history is shown in the fifth panel as a blue line. It remains 2 – 3 orders of magnitude below the Keplerian angular momentum (grey line), which means that, for the $\Omega\Gamma$-limit to be satisfied all along the accretion phase, the angular momentum advected at accretion cannot exceed a fraction $f \sim 0.1 - 1\%$ of the Keplerian angular momentum. In other

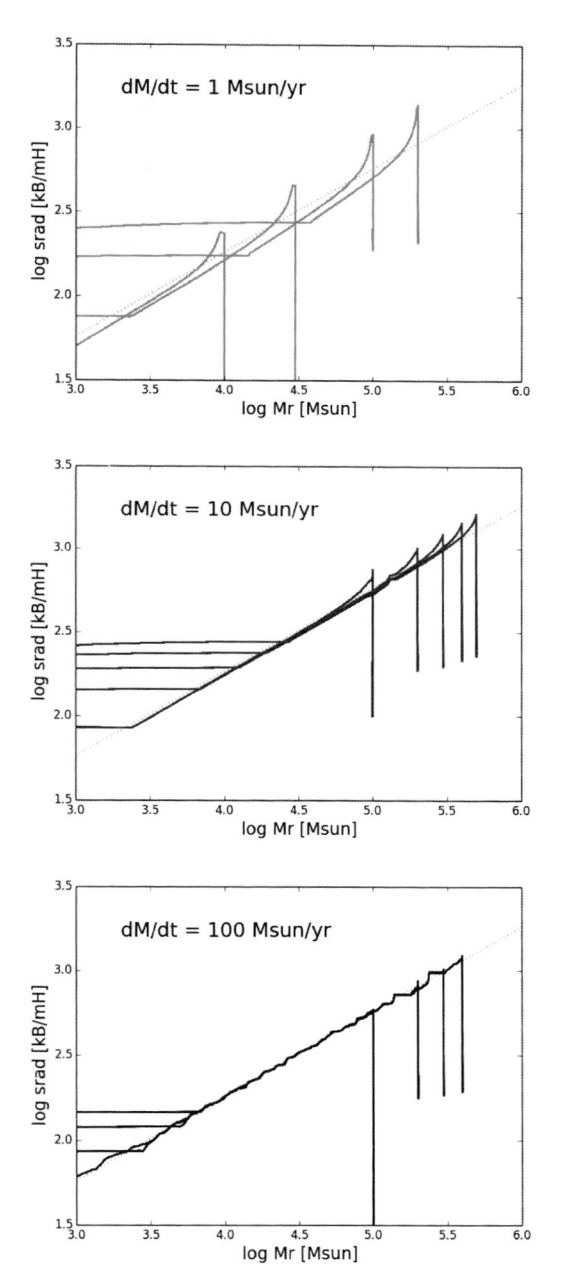

Fig. 2. Entropy profiles of the GENEC models of Pop III SMSs accreting at $\dot{M} = 1-100$ $M_\odot$ yr^{-1}. The grey dotted line indicates the power-law (2). (Figure from.[27])

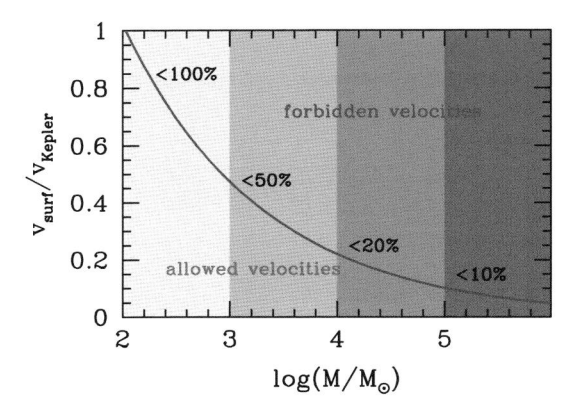

Fig. 3. Maximum rotation velocity of SMSs as a function of their mass (figure from[22]).

words, SMS formation by accretion from a Keplerian disc requires mechanisms efficient enough to remove more than 99% of the angular momentum from the disc. Notice that the fraction f is 1 – 2 orders of magnitude smaller than the ratio Ω/Ω_K imposed by the $\Omega\Gamma$-limit, which reflects the instantaneous redistribution of angular momentum in the **outer** convective envelope visible in the upper panel of figure 4. **Indeed, without convection, the ratio Ω/Ω_K in the surface layer would be simply given by the fraction f of angular momentum advected by this layer. But here, the surface velocity is given by the angular momentum accreted plus that received by convection from the deeper layers of the envelope. Thus, a given constraint on the ratio Ω/Ω_K (e.g. $\lesssim 10\%$) translates into a tighter constraint on the ratio f (e.g. $\lesssim 0.1 - 1\%$).**

The angular momentum problem is general to star formation.[17] For low-mass stars, the problem is easily solved by the magnetic coupling of the star with its disc and winds, thanks to the convective dynamo in the stellar envelope. But the problem becomes more difficult for massive stars, since these stars have no convective envelope, and only a few percent of them have detected magnetic fields, thought to be fossil fields.[30] The most efficient processes to extract angular momentum in the context of massive star formation rely on the gravitationnal instabilities that develop in massive accretion discs.[31] Since these gravitationnal instabilities are enhanced by high densities, their efficiency increases when the centrifugal barrier is reached, as gas accumulates in the vicinity of the star. Thus, these processes allow for a self-regulated, efficient angular momentum transport all along the collapse.

In the case of rapidly accreting, maximally rotating SMSs, the surface magnetic field required to remove the angular momentum excess at accretion from a Keplerian disc by star-winds coupling is of the order of 10 kG, as shown in the bottom panel of figure 4. The corresponding Alfvén radius is shown as a red dashed line in the top panel. According to estimates based on the Rossby number, a convective dynamo in the envelope of the SMS cannot produce a field larger than 1 G. Only fossil

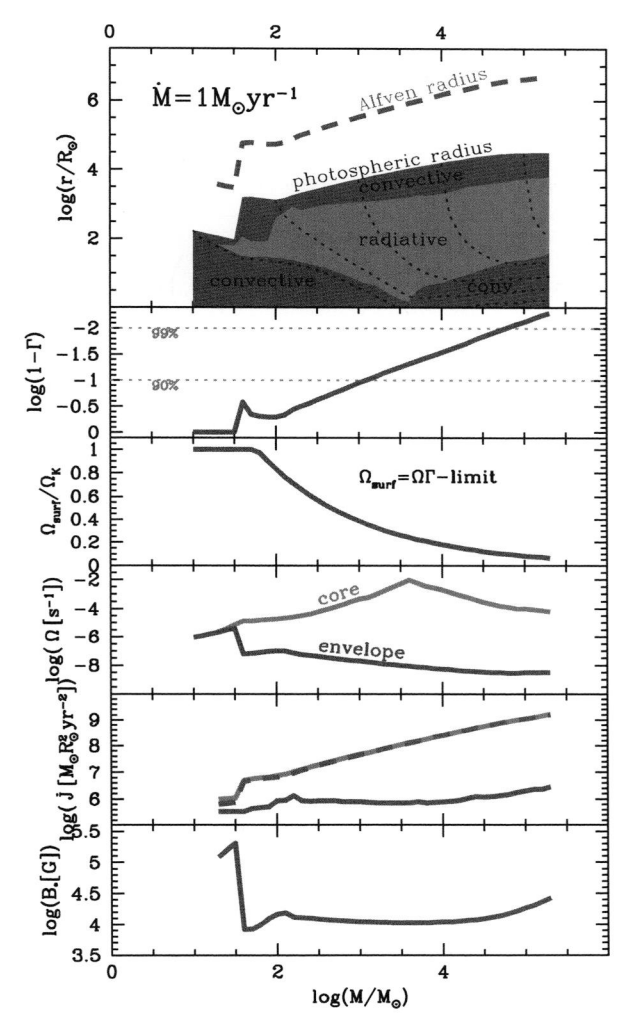

Fig. 4. GENEC model of a maximally rotating Pop III SMS accreting at $\dot{M} = 1\ M_\odot\ \mathrm{yr}^{-1}$. The horizontal axis represents the stellar mass, which is a time coordinate in case of constant accretion. The first four panels show the stellar structure in radial coordinates, the Eddington factor, the ratio of the surface velocity to the Keplerian velocity, and the angular velocity in the core and the envelope. The fifth panel shows the accreted angular momentum (in blue), compared to the Keplerian angular momentun (in grey). The difference is shown by the red dashed curve. The bottom panel shows the surface magnetic field required to remove this difference of angular momentum by star-wind coupling. (Figure from.[29])

fields from primordial origin could reach the required values. On the other hand, gravitational instabilities are particularly strong in the massive accretion discs of SMSs, and are thought to be efficient enough to circumvent the centrifugal barrier in the context of SMBH formation.[21,32]

4. GR instability

The formation of a SMBH by direct collapse occurs when the progenitor SMS becomes dynamically unstable. SMSs are expected to collapse via the GR instability,[33] which is a pulsation instability that arises from the GR corrections to the equation of radial momentum. For a non-rotating post-Newtonian SMS, the eigenfrequency ω of adiabatic pulsations can be obtained with[34]

$$\omega^2 I = \int \beta P dV - \int \left(\frac{2GM_r}{rc^2} + \frac{8}{3} \frac{P}{\rho c^2} \right) \frac{GM_r}{r} dM_r \tag{5}$$

where r is the radial distance from the stellar centre, M_r the mass-coordinates (i.e. the mass contained in all the layers below r), ρ the mass density, P the pressure, β the ratio of gas pressure to total pressure, I the moment of inertia, V the volume of the sphere r, G the gravitational constant and c the speed of light. Notice that in the post-Newtonian approximation, distinctions between rest-mass and relativistic-mass are irrelevant.

The GR instability is reached when ω becomes imaginary, which implies that exponentials are solutions to the equations of motion. Equation (5) expresses this condition in terms of the two integrals at the right-hand side. The first one is Newtonian and positive, and scales with β, that is with the departures from the Eddington limit, at which all the pressure support is provided by radiation. As the SMS grows in mass, it approaches the Eddington limit asymptotically with $\beta \to 0$, but $\beta > 0$. Thus, without any additional term, equation (5) would imply that the star remains always stable. However, the second term, that scales with the GR corrections $2GM_r/rc^2$ and $P/\rho c^2$, is negative. As the SMS grows in mass, these corrections grow until the sum of the integrals become negative. At this point, the star is dynamically unstable, which leads in general to the direct formation of a SMBH in a dynamical time.[35,36]

The exact mass at which the SMS reaches the GR instability depends on its structure, in particular on the mass of its convective core. The maximum masses of non-rotating Pop III SMSs as a function of the mass of their convective core are shown in figure 5. The black-blue-cyan tracks are the evolutionary models of Pop III SMSs computed with GENEC under accretion at the indicated rates.[25,26] These models were computed under the assumption of hydrostatic equilibrium, which makes them insensitive to dynamical instabilities, and the ends of the runs are arbitrary, imposed by the numerical stability of the models. The onset of the GR instability on these hydrostatic models, determined with equation (5), is indicated by star-like symbols. It is reached before the end of the run only for rates 1 and 10 $M_\odot$ yr^{-1}. The limitations due to the numerical instability of hydrostatic models with rapid accretion can be circumvented with the use of semi-analytical models built on the hylotropic law of equation (2).[23] With these structures, the limit of stability in the (M_{core}, M)-diagram is uniquely given by the central temperature of the star and its chemical composition. The central temperature of SMSs is well constrained

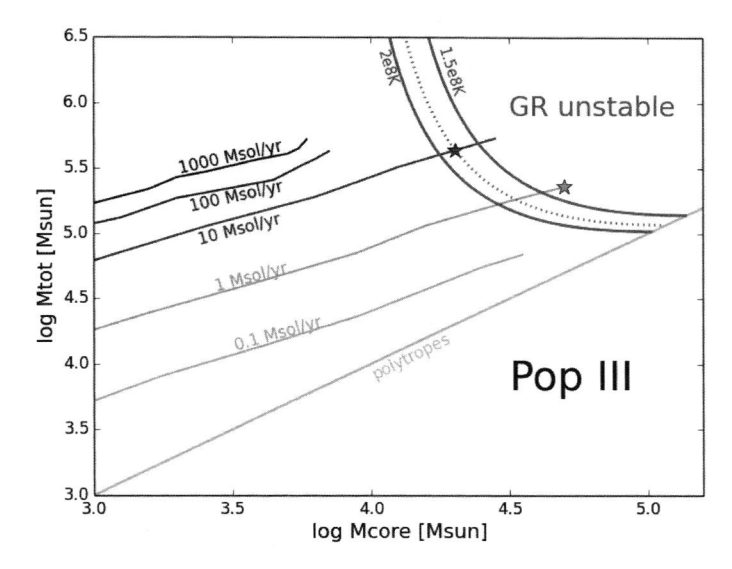

Fig. 5. Maximum masses of non-rotating Pop III SMSs consistent with GR stability, as a function of the mass of their convective core. The red curves show the limit of stability derived from hylotropic structures with the indicated central temperatures. The black-blue-cyan tracks are Pop III GENEC models computed with the indicated accretion rates. The star-like symbols indicate the point of GR instability of these models, when it is reached. (Figure from.[27])

by numerical models, and remains in a narrow range due to the thermostatic effect of H-burning ($T_c = 1.5 - 2 \times 10^8$ K for Pop III SMSs; $T_c = 0.6 - 0.9 \times 10^8$ K for Pop I SMSs). The limits of stability for Pop III SMSs derived from the hylotropic models are shown as red curves in figure 5. The dotted red curve is the stability limit for the exact central temperature of the last stable model of the GENEC track at $\dot{M} = 10$ M$_\odot$ yr^{-1}. We see that the hylotropic limit is already very precise for this rate, in spite of the small departures from the hylotropic profiles visible in figure 2. The entropy profile in the inner part, where the density is high and GR corrections are significant, is already well approximated by the hylotropic law (2) for this rate. Only for rates $\lesssim 1$ M$_\odot$ yr^{-1} the GENEC models departs significantly from the hyloptropic law. But even in this case the discrepancies in the final mass remains of ~ 0.1 dex, that is ~ 20 %. Thus, the limit of stability given by the hylotropic models remains a good approximation for any accretion rate. Moreover, the numerical simplicity of these models allows for a broader view of the parameter space. In particular, we see that for the central temperatures set by H-burning the GR instability cannot be reached if the stellar mass does not exceed $\gtrsim 10^5$ M$_\odot$. Moreover, the GR instability always requires the convective core to contain a mass $\gtrsim 10^4$ M$_\odot$.

Rotation plays a prominent role in the stability of SMSs. Near the GR instability, the dimensionless ratios β, $2GM_r/rc^2$ and $P/\rho c^2$ are all of the order of a percent.

It implies that the positive and negative integrals at the right-hand side of equation (5) represent typically a percent of the total internal and gravitational energies of the star, respectively. Thus, other small effects, that have negligible impact on the hydrostatic structure of SMSs, can play a critical role on the dynamical stability of these structures. This is the case for rotation: the slow rotation velocities ($\sim 0.1\ \Omega_K$) consistent with the $\Omega\Gamma$-limit correspond to rotational energies of the order of $\Omega^2/\Omega_K^2 \sim 1\%$ of the gravitational energy of the star (equation 4). The rotational corrections to equation (5) are thus of the same order as the β- and GR-terms. For these slow rotations and small GR corrections, however, the relativistic rotation terms are expected to be of second order, and can be neglected in the determination of the stability limit. Including the Newtonian rotation term to equation (5), we obtain[34]

$$\omega^2 I = \int \beta P \mathrm{d}V + \frac{4}{9}\int \frac{\Omega^2}{\Omega_K^2}\frac{GM_r}{r}\mathrm{d}M_r - \int\left(\frac{2GM_r}{rc^2} + \frac{8}{3}\frac{P}{\rho c^2}\right)\frac{GM_r}{r}\mathrm{d}M_r \quad (6)$$

The positive rotation term contributes to the stability of the star, and allows it to increase its mass by orders of magnitude beyond the non-rotating limit.[34, 37]

The limits of stability for rotating Pop III and Pop I SMSs are shown in figures 6 and 7, respectively.[34] The limits have been derived from hylotropic structures, on which rotation profiles are defined by local angular momentum conservation in the radiative envelope and solid rotation in the convective core. Each layer of the radiative envelope is assumed to keep the angular momentum it advected at accretion, defined as a faction f of the Keplerian angular momentum at the accretion radius given by equation (1). The angular momentum of the core is then given by that advected from the envelope. We see that the limits start to be shifted by rotation as soon as $f \gtrsim 0.1\%$, while for $f \sim 1\%$ they are already shifted by 3 orders of magnitudes towards larger masses. The lower central temperatures of the Pop I models allows for slightly larger masses when $f \sim 0.1\%$, but when $f \sim 1\%$ the limits do not depend anymore on the thermal properties of the star, and are uniquely given by f. In this regime, indicated by the red areas on the diagrams, the gas term in equation (6) becomes negligible compared to the rotation and GR terms, which means that rotation becomes the main stabilising agent against the destabilising GR corrections. An interesting consequence is that the profile of the spin parameter at the onset of the instability, which is key regarding black hole formation, becomes 'universal', that is, uniquely given by the mass-fraction of the convective core.

For typical conditions of atomically cooled halos (Pop III, $\dot{M} \lesssim 1\ \mathrm{M_\odot\ yr^{-1}}$), the $\Omega\Gamma$-limit imposes $f \lesssim 0.1 - 0.2\%$ (figure 4). In this case, rotation can increase the final stellar mass by up to a factor ~ 2, which does not allow to exceed $10^6\ \mathrm{M_\odot}$. As mentioned in section 3, this low value of f results from the instantaneous angular momentum transport in the deep convective envelope. Interestingly, the depth of the envelope decreases significantly for larger rates, and values $f \sim 1\%$ appear consistent with the conditions of merger-driven direct collapse. In this formation channel, masses up to $10^8 - 10^9\ \mathrm{M_\odot}$ could be reached before the GR instability.

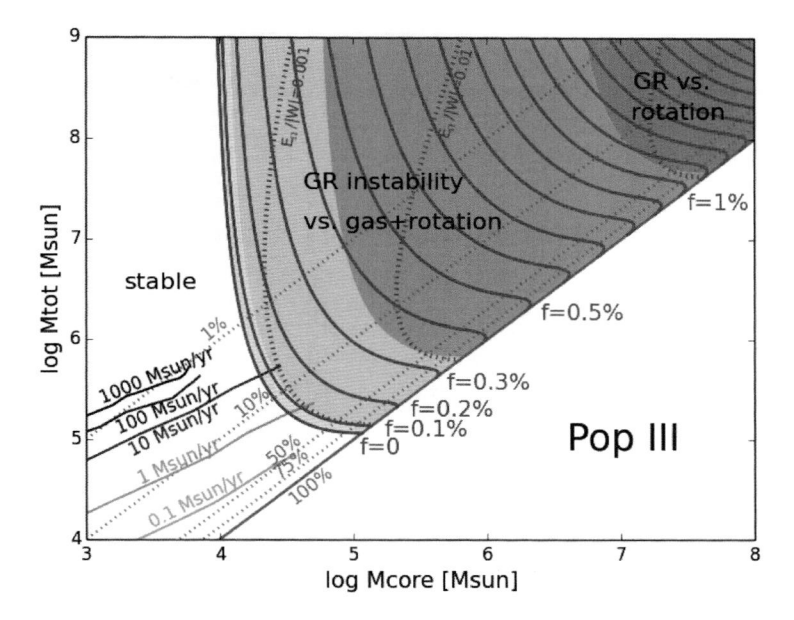

Fig. 6. Limits of GR stability for rotating Pop III SMSs, derived from the hylotropic models with $T_c = 1.8 \times 10^8$ K. The diagram represents the mass of the SMS as a function of the mass of its convective core. The various limits are obtained with the indicated values of the fraction f of accreted angular momentum over the Keplerian angular momentum (solid red lines). The limits are also shown for constant ratios of rotational to gravitational energies (dotted red lines). The coloured areas denote the relative importance of the β term (gas term) and the rotation term in the stability of the star (equation 6). The black-blue-cyan tracks are the same GENEC models as in figure 5. (Figure from.[34])

Since masses $> 10^6$ M$_\odot$ are required for SMBH formation in the Pop I case, the black hole seeds in merger-driven direct collapse must have masses $10^6 - 10^9$ M$_\odot$, which implies that the different channels of direct collapse lead to distinct ranges of seed's mass.

5. SMBH formation and observational signatures of direct collapse

The final collapse of SMSs has been followed with a large number of GR magnetohydrodynamical simulations.[16,35,36] In the Pop III case, the collapse is found to lead to the direct formation of a SMBH, that contains $\gtrsim 90\%$ of the total stellar mass. A fraction $\sim 1 - 10$ % of the mass can remain in orbit outside the horizon at the formation of the black hole, provided rapid enough rotation. This gas further collapses through the horizon, with possible gravitational wave emission detectable by future space-based observatories. Moreover, in the presence of magnetic fields, relativistic jets could be launched and trigger ultra-long gamma-ray bursts. Thus, the final collapse of SMSs provides the most promising possibilities for observational signatures of direct collapse and the existence of SMSs.

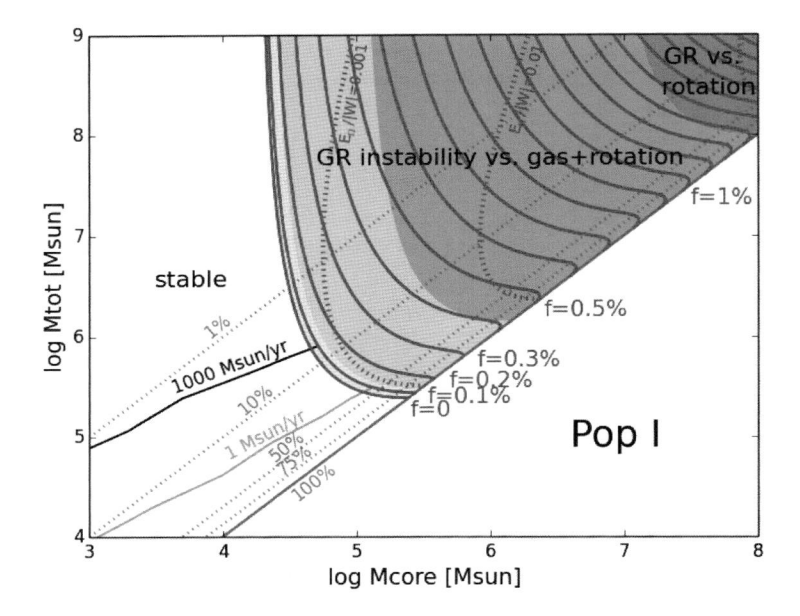

Fig. 7. Same as figure 6 for the Pop I case ($T_c = 0.85 \times 10^8$ K). (Figure from.[34])

Rotation is key since only the centrifugal barrier allows for the survival of a slowly decaying torus, and prevents the direct engulfment of the whole stellar mass by the black hole in a dynamical time. Figures 8 and 9 show the profiles of the spin parameter cJ_r/GM_r^2 (where J_r is the angular momentum of the mass M_r) for the hylotropic models of figures 6 and 7, taken at the onset of the instability. They correspond to typical conditions of atomically cooled halos and merger-driven direct collapse, respectively. In each case, the profiles are shown for three different core mass. The convective core is recognisable as the only region where the profiles departs from each other, as a result of the angular momentum transport by convection. In contrast, the profiles match each other in the radiative envelope, reflecting the angular momentum accretion law. We see that the solid rotation of the core maintains the angular momentum distribution decentralised. Notice that the profiles of figure 9 correspond to the 'universal' profiles obtained when rotation becomes the dominant stabilising agent.

From these rotation profiles, the fraction of the **outer** mass that has enough angular momentum to remain in orbit at the formation of the black hole can be estimated analytically by comparison with the angular momentum of the innermost stable circular orbits (ISCOs).[38] It is found to be significant only for the conditions of merger-driven direct collapse, and for fully convective SMSs, as indicated by the red squares in figures 8 and 9. The low angular momentum ($f \sim 0.2\%$) required in the context of atomically cooled halos prevents the formation of an orbiting structure, and even for $f \sim 1\%$ convection is required in the whole stellar interior for the

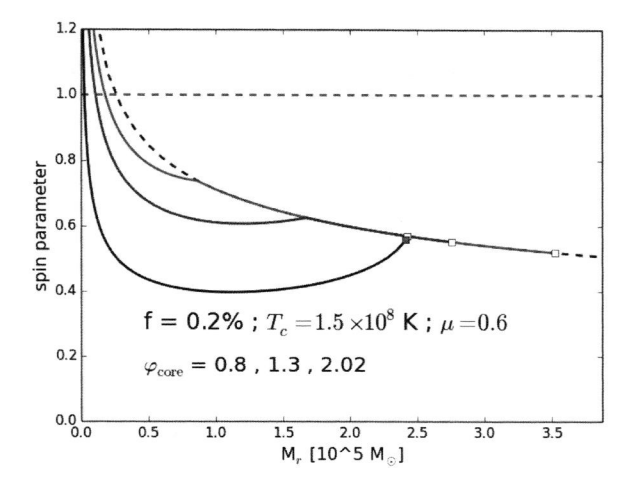

Fig. 8. Profiles of the spin parameter cJ_r/GM_r^2 at the onset of GR instability, for typical conditions of atomically cooled halos. The profiles (solid lines) are shown for three hylotropes with different **core mass-fraction $M_{\rm core}/M$: the black profile corresponds to a fully convective star $M_{\rm core} = M$ (polytrope), the dark blue profile corresponds to $M_{\rm core}/M = 60\%$ and the light blue profile to $M_{\rm core}/M = 25\%$.** The white squares indicate the surface **(i.e. the total mass) of the three models (the polytrope has the lowest mass, $M_{\rm core}/M = 25\%$ the highest).** Only for the fully convective model a comparison with ISCO angular momentum suggests that a tiny fraction of the **outer** mass ($\sim 1\%M$) remains in orbit outside the horizon at black hole formation, which is indicated by the red square. The black dashed line shows the angular momentum accretion law. The red dashed line indicates the maximum value of the spin parameter consistent with Kerr black holes. (Figure from.[34])

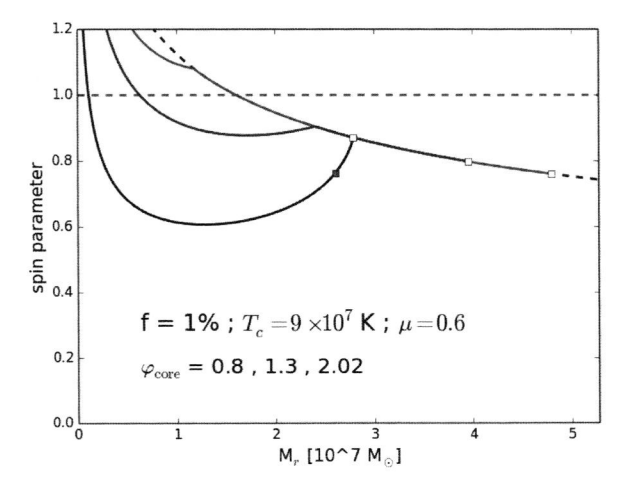

Fig. 9. Same as figure 8 for typical conditions of merger-driven direct collapse. Here, the **outer** mass fraction of the fully convective model that remains in orbit at black hole formation represents $\sim 10\%$ of the stellar mass (red square). (Figure from.[34])

angular momentum to be sufficiently decentralised. Overall, these models suggest that gravitational wave emission and ultra-long gamma-ray bursts at black hole formation are consistent with the conditions of galaxy mergers, but not with those of atomically cooled halos. In both scenarios, the centrifugal barrier is inefficient to prevent the direct formation of a massive black hole seed at the collapse of the supermassive stellar progenitor.

6. Summary and conclusions

SMSs represent promising candidates for the progenitors of the SMBHs that power the most massive quasars detected at redshifts 6 – 7, since direct collapse appears as the most efficient scenario to form SMBHs in short timescales. This scenario faces several bottlenecks, however, but solutions have been proposed to all of them. The angular momentum problem represents certainly one of the strongest, as discussed in section 3.

In spite of the low spins imposed by the $\Omega\Gamma$-limit (section 2, figure 3), rotation impacts critically the life and death of SMSs. As an outstanding effect, it allows rapidly accreting SMSs to increase their final masses by several orders of magnitude compared to the non-rotating case, before they reach the GR instability and collapse into a SMBH (section 4, figures 6-7). According to hylotropic models, the masses of the black hole seeds belong to distinct ranges depending on the direct collapse channel:

- 10^5 $M_\odot \lesssim M \lesssim 10^6$ $M_\odot$ for atomically cooled halos;
- 10^6 $M_\odot \lesssim M \lesssim 10^9$ $M_\odot$ for merger-driven direct collapse.

Moreover, the conditions of merger-driven direct collapse are expected to be more favourable than those of atomically cooled halos for gravitational wave emission and ultra-long gamma-ray bursts at the collapse of the SMS (section 5, figures 8-9).

Many uncertainties remain, however, in these scenarios, most of them relying on the lack of consistency of the models for the formation of the black hole seed itself. Due to their hypothetical nature, SMSs have been much less studied than other classes of stars, and the picture given here deserves to be refined by additional models accounting for full stellar evolution up to the largest masses and accretion rates, including a self-consistent treatment rotation, multiplicity and radiative feedback. In particular, reliable theoretical predictions for the observational signatures of SMBH formation by direct collapse require precise determination of the properties of the stellar progenitor. In that respect, the future generation of space-based telescopes and gravitational wave observatories could unveil the most massive stars ever formed in Universe's history. Interestingly, according to the models described here, the maximum mass of these stars is set by **the interplay between general relativity and** rotation.

References

1. F. Hoyle, W. A. Fowler, 1963a, Nature, 197, 533.
2. F. Hoyle, W. A. Fowler, 1963b, MNRAS, 125, 169.
3. D. Lynden-Bell, 1969, Nature, 223, 690.
4. M. J. Rees, 1984, ARA&A, 22, 471.
5. M. Volonteri, M. C. Begelman, 2010, MNRAS, 409, 1022.
6. F. Wang, J. Yang, X. Fan, et al. 2021, ApJ, 907, L1.
7. T. E. Woods, B. Agarwal, V. Bromm, et al., 2019, PASA, 36, e027.
8. L. Haemmerlé, L. Mayer, R. S. Klessen, et al., 2020, SSR, 216, 48.
9. R. Klessen, 2019, Formation of the first stars, ed. M. Latif & D. Schleicher, 67–97.
10. A. Lupi, M. Colpi, B. Devecchi, G. Galanti, M. Volonteri, 2014, MNRAS, 442, 3616.
11. K. Omukai, 2001, ApJ, 546, 635.
12. M. A. Latif, D. R. G. Schleicher, W. Schmidt, J. C. Niemeyer, 2013, MNRAS, 436, 2989.
13. S. Chon, T. Hosokawa, N. Yoshida, 2018, MNRAS, 475, 4104.
14. J. A. Regan, E. Visbal, J. H. Wise, et al., 2017, Nature Astronomy, 1, 0075.
15. L. Mayer, S. Bonoli, 2019, Reports on Progress in Physics, 82, 016901.
16. P. J. Montero, H.-T. Janka, E. Müller, 2012, ApJ, 749, 37.
17. P. Bodenheimer, 1995, ARA&A, 33, 199.
18. H. Lee, S.-C. Yoon, 2016, ApJ, 820, 135.
19. L. Haemmerlé, P. Eggenberger, G. Meynet, et al., 2017, A&A, 602, A17.
20. S. Z. Takahashi, K. Omukai, 2017, MNRAS, 472, 532.
21. M. C. Begelman, M. Volonteri, M. J. Rees, 2006, MNRAS, 370, 289.
22. L. Haemmerlé, T. E. Woods, R. S. Klessen, A. Heger, D. J. Whalen, 2018a, ApJ, 853, L3.
23. M. C. Begelman, 2010, MNRAS, 402, 673.
24. T. Hosokawa, H. W. Yorke, K. Inayoshi, K. Omukai, N. Yoshida, 2013, ApJ, 778, 178.
25. L. Haemmerlé, T. E. Woods, R. S. Klessen, A. Heger, D. J. Whalen, 2018, MNRAS, 474, 2757.
26. L. Haemmerlé, G. Meynet, L. Mayer, et al., 2019, A&A, 632, L2.
27. L. Haemmerlé, 2020, A&A, 644, A154.
28. A. Maeder, G. Meynet, 2000, A&A, 361, 159.
29. L. Haemmerlé, G. Meynet, 2019, A&A, 623, L7.
30. J. H. Grunhut, G. A. Wade, C. Neiner, et al., 2017, MNRAS, 465, 2432.
31. T. Hosokawa, S. Hirano, R. Kuiper, et al., 2016, ApJ, 824, 119.
32. J. H. Wise, M. J. Turk, T. Abel, 2008, ApJ, 682, 745.
33. S. Chandrasekhar, 1964, ApJ, 140, 417.
34. L. Haemmerlé, 2021, A&A, 650, A204.
35. L. Sun, V. Paschalidis, M. Ruiz, M., S. L. Shapiro, 2017, Phys. Rev. D, 96, 043006.
36. L. Sun, M. Ruiz, M., S. L. Shapiro, 2018, Phys. Rev. D, 98, 103008.
37. W. A. Fowler, 1966, ApJ, 144, 180.
38. T. W. Baumgarte, S. L. Shapiro, 1999, ApJ, 526, 937.

Cosmology with high-redshift FRBs

A. Fialkov

Institute of Astronomy, University of Cambridge, Madingley Road, Cambridge, CB3 0HA, UK
Kavli Institute for Cosmology, Madingley Road, Cambridge, CB3 0HA, UK
E-mail: afialkov@ast.cam.ac.uk

The quest for high redshift Fast Radio Bursts (FRBs) is ongoing with telescopes such as the Five-hundred-meter Aperture Telescope (FAST) and the Green Bank Telescope (GBT) looking for highly dispersed events. If FRB-producing systems exist at early times, such sources would provide new unique ways to probe cosmic dawn and Reionization. On one hand, FRB dispersion would allow us to probe the history and topology of Reionization. On the other hand, number counts of high redshift FRBs would indirectly probe galaxy formation at high-redshifts. Here we consider prospects of advancing our understanding of the first billion years of cosmic history with high-redshift FRBs.

Keywords: High redshift Universe, Fast Radio Bursts

1. Introduction

The field of cosmology experienced breathtaking growth in the past several decades. Owing to the measurements of the Cosmic Microwave Background (CMB) by telescopes such as WMAP,[1] Planck[2] and others, which reveal a snapshot of the Universe shortly after the Big Bang, we now know that the Universe is well-described by a rather simple six-parameter model (ΛCDM) in which the total energy balance is share between dark energy (Λ), dark matter (that is usually assumed to be cold), baryons and radiative degrees of freedom.

The CMB is also sensitive to the process of reionization. The Epoch of Reionization (EoR) is often referred to as the last phase transition in the history of the evolution of the Universe.[3,4] During the EoR the ultraviolet light produced by young stars in early populations of galaxies ionized the previously neutral intergalactic medium (IGM) turning it into hot plasma. The EoR imprints faint traces in the CMB via the scattering of CMB photon off the ionized gas. Therefore, although the effect is very weak, the CMB observations can be used to constrain this epoch. The redshift of reionization, as inferred from the CMB data, is $\approx 7.5 \pm 0.82$.[2]

The CMB observations have greatly advanced our understanding of cosmology. Given the richness of information extracted from the CMB and the amount of scientific discoveries stemming from these data, it is surprising to realize that the CMB probes only a thin (nearly 2-dimensional) volume of the Universe located at $z \sim 1100$ when the Universe was only 0.4 million years old (for comparison it is 13.8 billion years old today). However, the CMB observations are only weakly sensitive to the processes at later times. Located between the CMB last scattering surface and us are multiple layers of cosmic history harbouring events such as the formation of first dark matter halos massive enough to accret and cool gas, formation of the first stars and galaxies, and other processes, which cannot be probed by the CMB.

By probing the late-time Universe, large scale structure and galaxy surveys provide complimentary information to what is found in the CMB. These measurements are of the evolved cosmic web and mature populations of galaxies (for example, the Dark Energy Survey measured ~ 300 million galaxies[5]). Much like the CMB these data helped to advance our understanding of the Universe. We now know that the expansion of the Universe is accelerated, low-redshift observations provide ample opportunities to test General Relativity across a wide range of regimes, and we can test galaxy formation theories with data.

However, despite this impressive effort, we do not have the whole picture of how the Universe transitioned from the pristine primordial state observed in the CMB to the evolved state in which it is found today. Even the state-of-the-art observations are limited and can only probe a small part of cosmic history. Large surveys mostly cover our cosmic neighbourhood (out to $z \sim 3$) with only the brightest objects observed at higher redshifts (although using clusters of galaxies as gravitational lenses can help to grasp a more representative picture of the high-redshift Universe[6]). In addition, some of the low redshift observations are inconsistent with the CMB data (e.g. the H_0 discrepancy[7]), and so the true state of the Universe remains ambiguous. Moreover, the elegant and simple ΛCDM theory itself suffers from several shortcomings. To name a few: the nature of dark matter and dark energy, which together compose $\sim 95\%$ of the total energy density in the Universe, is undetermined; not all baryons that are measured from the CMB are accounted for at lower redshifts (*the missing baryon problem*); we have already mentioned the infamous H_0 tension; galaxy formation is not fully understood as well as the structure and composition of the IGM. Finally, the first billion years of cosmic history remain poorly explored.

FRBs, transient radio signals of yet unestablished nature, might result to be unique probes of the EoR, thus advancing our understanding of the first billion years of cosmic history. High-redshift FRBs, if exist, would probe the EoR in a unique way compared to the established tracers such as the high-redshift quasars, galaxies and the CMB. Thus, if a sample of high-redshift FRBs is collected, they will offer new ways to probe cosmology.

FRBs are significantly dispersed by the ionized medium distributed along the path between the sources and the observer. For most of the detected FRBs, the observed dispersion of FRB pulses, quantified in terms of dispersion measure (DM) is much larger than the contribution of our local environment. Therefore, it is now known that the overwhelming majority of FRBs are of extra-Galactic origin. For a typical FRB the largest contribution to the dispersion is from the ionized intergalactic medium, $DM^{\rm IGM}$, which depends on the number density of free electrons along the line of sight. For FRBs coming from redshift z, the mean IGM contribution is given by

$$\overline{DM}^{\rm IGM}(z) = \int_0^z \frac{n_e(z')}{1+z'} dl = \int_0^z \frac{cn_e(z')}{H(z')(1+z')^2} dz', \qquad (1)$$

where the first integral is along the line of sight with dl being the line element. $n_e(z')$ is the mean number density of free electrons at redshift z', c the speed of light and $H(z')$ is the Hubble expansion rate. The electron density directly depends on the ionized fraction of hydrogen $x_i(z)$, which at high redashifts traces the EoR. We will refer to the redshift dependence of the ionized fraction, $x_i(z)$, as the *EoR history*. Dependence of $DM^{\rm IGM}$ on redshift is illustrated in Figure 1 (image credit: A. Tocher).

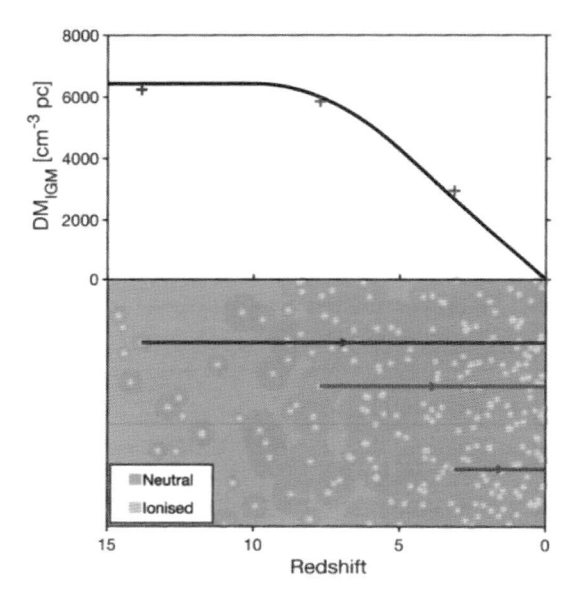

Fig. 1. Dependence of $DM^{\rm IGM}$ on redshift (top) and cartoon of the corresponding EoR history (bottom). Blue regions are the neutral patches, red regions are ionized, yellow markers represent star forming regions. Coloured crosses (top) correspond to three randomly generated FRBs and coloured lines (bottom) are the corresponding lines of sight through the EoR. Illustration credit: A. Tocher.

At low redshifts FRBs have already proven to be valuable cosmological probes. Dependence of $DM^{\rm IGM}$ on the cosmological redshift, z, of the FRB hosts (e.g., see Figure 1) could pin down properties of the IGM[9,11,12] and probe cosmological parameters.[10,11,13,15–21] To give an example, with a sample of localized low-redshift FRBs (host redshifts of $z \lesssim 0.66$), Macquart et al. (2020)[11] showed that the dispersion measure of these transients depends on the baryonic content of the Universe (along the line of sight) and, thus, can help identifying the missing baryons in the IGM by counting the total number of baryons along the line of sight. For higher redshift FRBs, theoretical predictions show that a population of FRBs at $z \sim 3-4$ could be used to constrain helium reionization occurring around redshift $z \sim 3.5$,[22–26] while signals from $z > 5$ would primarily trace the evolution of the hydrogen ionization state, and, thus, probe the EoR.[10]

Constraining the high-redshift Universe with FRBs might be observationally plausible as the existing telescopes such as the Five-hundred-meter Aperture Telescope (FAST) and the Green Bank Telescope (GBT) can in principle detect bright signals out to $z \sim 10$, i.e. deep into the EoR.[8,14] The future Square Kilometre Array (SKA) will be capable to map the FRB sky detecting thousands of sources from early times.[10,33]

2. Tracing reionization with FRBs

If found, high redshifts FRBs could be used as probes of the EoR owing to the dependence of $DM^{\rm IGM}$ on $n_e(z')$ and, through it, on the EoR history, $x_i(z)$.

Existing constraints on the EoR are very weak. The CMB optical depth, defined as

$$\tau = \int \sigma n_e dl, \quad (2)$$

where σ is the scattering cross-section, is measured from the CMB data (e.g. state-of-the-art constraints from *Planck*[2]) with the relative error being at the level of $6 - 10\%$. This large uncertainty in τ degrades precision with which other cosmological parameters are measured (e.g. see the discussion by Liu et al. (2015)[27]). For example, the effect of the EoR on the CMB is degenerate with the amplitude of primordial fluctuations from inflation A_s. Additional constraints on the EoR come from quasar observations. For instance, using the dark fraction of Lyman α and β forest observations in tandem with Planck measurements Greig & Mesinger (2017)[28] constrain the redshift of the midpoint of reionization to $\sim 12\%$ (at 68% confidence level). Observations of the hydrogen 21-cm line are predicted to eventually provide precise measurement of τ as well as map the entire history of reionization. However, currently, the EoR constraints derived from the first upper limits on the 21-cm signal are very weak and only rule out the most extreme scenarios.[29,30]

Prospects of mapping the EoR with high-redshift FRBs has been discussed in literature.[10,31–34] Both $DM^{\rm IGM}$ and τ depend on the same physical quantity, namely the mean number density of free electrons weighted differently with redshift (compare between Eqs. 1 and 2). Therefore, it should be plausible to extract reionization history from the dispersion measure of high-redshift FRBs if a large enough sample with host localizations is obtained. Existing works on this topic (apart from the recent publication by Heimersheim et al. (2021)[35] which we highlight here), make assumptions about the reionization history that either lead to biases in the results or limit the constraining power of the data. In an earlier work we[10] were the first to realize that FRBs could be used as tracers of the reionization history EoR, and might allow us to significantly tighten the constraints on τ. We performed a simplified estimation of the relative error in τ showing that the expected accuracy is much better than the current state-of-the-art, e.g. from *Planck*. This work stimulated further studies (a similar analysis was later carried out by Beniamini et al. (2020)[31]). Other examples of EoR constraints include the works by Beniamini et al. (2020)[31] and Hashimoto et al. (2021)[33] who proposed probing the EoR history by grouping FRBs into redshift bins and considering the difference between mean $DM^{\rm IGM}$ in adjacent bins. Due to the binning procedure, information on each individual FRB is lost and with it the possibility to smoothly trace the reionization history. In addition, in the absence of a defined $x_i(z)$ relation, this approach does not allow us making use of dependences (such as the monotonic growth of $x_i(z)$ with time) across cosmic time.

Details of reionization history $x_i(z)$ affect the dependence of FRB dispersion measure on redshift,[10] i.e. the functional form of $DM^{\rm IGM}$ (example shown in Figure 1). This dependence can, therefore, be used to extract the EoR history if a sample of high redshift FRBs (from before the end of the EoR at $z \sim 5$) is observed and localized. When extracting the EoR history from a sample of high-redshift FRBs it is important to keep a model-independent approach and stay agnostic about the true history of reionization. In Heimersheim et al. (2021)[35] we showed that assuming specific shape of $x_i(z)$ leads to biases in the derived EoR parameters. For example, we find that fixing the reionization history to the symmetric tanh function, parameterized by the duration and midpoint of the EoR, underestimates the value of τ by $\sim 10\%$.

2.1. *Bias-free constraints on Reionization*

Inspired by the model-independent approach adopted in the CMB community, in Heimersheim et al. (2021)[35] we have investigated the possibility of deriving the EoR history from the mock data without assuming a-priori knowledge of its redshift dependence. We constructed a mock catalogue of $DM^{\rm IGM}$, host redshifts and associated uncertainties (see details in Heimersheim et al. (2021)[35]). An illustration of our mock FRB catalogue is shown in Figure 2 (illustration credit: S. Heimersheim).

In the base of our analysis pipeline is the free-form "FlexKnot" method[36] where the entire EoR history is defined by a series of free-moving knots (rather than by a specific functional form). For each such FlexKnot parameterization we model the expected dispersion measure relation, $DM^{\rm IGM}$, and calculate its likelihood given the mock data (e.g. Figure 2). Finally, we employ Bayesian inference to derive constraints on the parameter space (including input cosmological parameters as well as the reionization history specified in terms of the positions and number of knots). This method allows us to extract the reionization history as well as cosmological parameters from the mock data. Importantly, the FexKnot parametrization allows

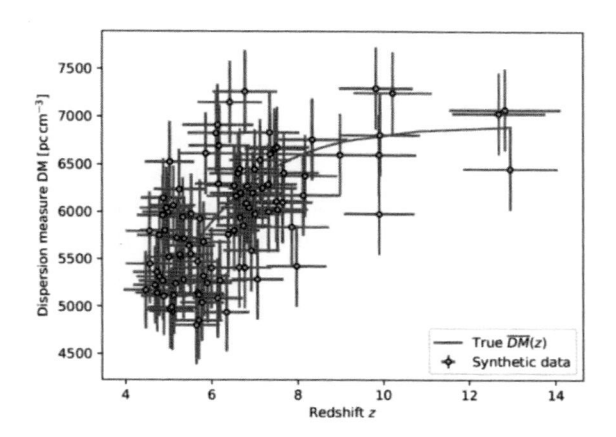

Fig. 2. Illustration of our mock FRB catalogue. Illustration credit: S. Heimersheim.

us to go over the entire space of plausible $x_i(z)$s without making assumptions about their functional shapes. Thus our results are bias-free.

In Heimersheim et al. (2021),[35] we apply the described method to our synthetic FRB catalogue and find that strong constraints on reionization history can be obtained. Figure 3 (Fig. 1 of Heimersheim et al. (2021)) shows the constraints on the reionization history marginalized over individual knot locations and cosmological parameters (only the parameters that have effect on DM^{IGM} were varied). In addition, we include the CMB polarization constraint on the high-redshift portion of the total optical depth τ from $z = 15 - 30$ (based on Planck measurements[37]).

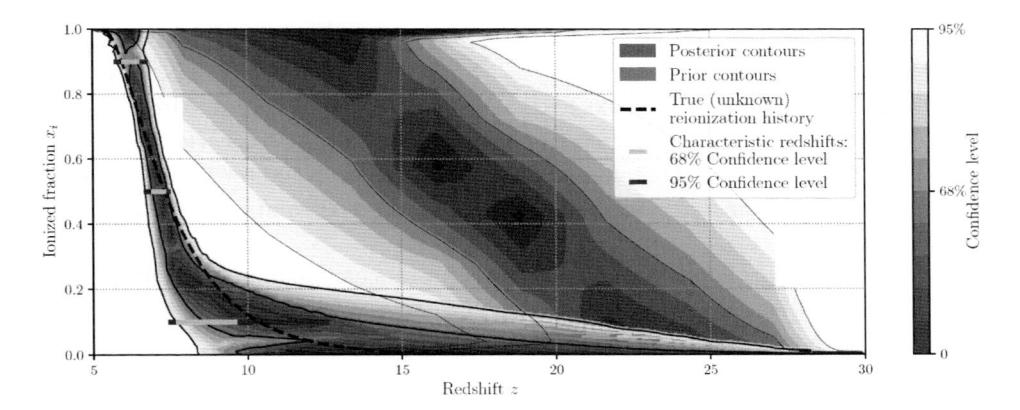

Fig. 3. Illustration of the prior (purple) and extracted (orange) reionization histories. Blue error bars show the constraints on the milestones of the EoR history, namely the start ($x_i = 0.1$), midpoint ($x_i = 0.5$) and end ($x_i = 0.9$) of reionization. Illustration credit: S. Heimersheim. Based on Figure 1 from Heimersheim et al., (2021).

In Figure 3 we demonstrate how the method works by showing the posterior and prior distributions of $x_i(z)$ (indicated by the orange and purple contours respectively, with 68% and 95% confidence intervals marked by the solid lines). We see that the posterior provides tight constraint on the reionization history, and encompasses the true reionization history used to generate the mock data (dashed cyan). Note that the analysis pipeline was not informed about this input history.

We find that, owing to the model assumption that FRB number counts trace star formation rate, the FRB data can constrain the reionization history especially well at low redshift ($z < 10$) where the vast majority (97%) of the FRB sources in our synthetic catalogue are located. Because there is only a small number of FRBs at higher redshifts, the EoR constraints at $z = 10 - 30$ are much weaker.

Owing to the flexibility of the FlexKnot method and because we have the full information on the EoR history for every parameter sample, we can directly constrain key points of the EoR history. To demonstrate this capability, we calculate posterior probabilities of the start ($x_i = 0.1$), midpoint ($x_i = 0.5$) and end ($x_i = 0.9$) of reionization. The error bars are shown in Figure 3 indicating 68% and 95% confidence limits in start, midpoint and end of the EoR, and the numerical results can be found in Table 1 of Heimersheim et al. (2021). We find that with 100 FRBs we constrain the end, midpoint and start of reionization to an accuracy of 7%, 6% and 13% respectively at 68% confidence level, achieving a better accuracy of 5%, 3% and 12% respectively for the sample with 1000 FRBs. The FRB constraints on the midpoint of the EoR would be much stronger than the limits from quasars.[28]

Marginalizing over all other parameters, including all the possible parametrizations of reionization histories, in Heimersheim et al. (2021)[35] we also derive posterior probability distributions for τ from the mock samples of 100 and 1000 FRBs (see Figure 2 in Heimersheim et al. (2021)) and quote the detailed 68% and 95% limits in Table 1 of Heimersheim et al. (2021). In summary, we find that 100 and 1000 FRBs can constrain the optical depth to 11% and 9% accuracy respectively (68% confidence). Our results for 100 FRBs are competitive with the *Planck*[2] measurement, while the accuracy for 1000 FRBs surpasses that of *Planck*. Moreover, the FRB constraint on τ is antisymmetric, owing to the sample of FRBs skewed towards the lower redshifts. Therefore, FRBs provide a much tighter lower limit on τ compared to that from the CMB. We also show the constraints on the amplitude of the primordial power spectrum.

Further details of the method and scientific results can be found in Heimersheim et al. (2021).[35]

Finally, we note that, in addition to serving as cosmological probes, high-redshift FRBs could result to be very useful probes of high-redshift stellar populations (Population III and Population II). The ambiguity regarding the sources of FRBs and the nature of their hosts remains with magnetars being one of the most popular candidates.[38,39] It is also possible that either magnetars or FRBs themselves, are produced as a result of stellar mergers (see discussion in Heimersheim et al. 2021).

In this case, the anticipated number of FRBs would strongly depend on the unknown initial mass function of the early populations of stars. Therefore, mapping the population of FRBs from the first billion years of cosmic history could shed light on the properties of high-redshift stars.

3. Summary

With this work we would like to encourage observational search for FRBs from the first billion years of cosmic history. Observational capability is nearly there with existing telescopes such as FAST and GBT sensitive enough to detect bright FRBs out to redshift of ~ 10, ASKAP excelling in localizing the FRBs and CHIME detecting large numbers of FRBs (although still at relatively low redshifts). If a sample of $100 - 1000$ FRBs from the first billion years of cosmic history can be measured and localized, these events will advance our understanding of the evolution of the Universe in this poorly constrained regime. As we showed in Heimersheim et al. (2021), high redshift FRBs could offer precision constraints on the EoR history and optical depth as well as tightening constraints on the primordial power spectrum and the sum of neutrino masses. In addition, they could serve as probes of high-redshift astrophysics, Population III and Population II stars and binaries. FRBs would probe the high-redshift Universe in new way independent from all the other known probes (high-redshift quasars, the CMB, and the 21-cm signal of hydrogen) thus providing an unparalleled view of this era.

Acknowledgments

This work was supported by the Royal Society University Research Fellowship of Fialkov.

References

1. Lewis, A. Cosmological parameters from WMAP 5- year temperature maps. Phys. Rev. D 78, 023002. arXiv: 0804.3865 [astro-ph] (July 2008).
2. Planck Collaboration et al. Planck 2018 results. VI. Cosmological parameters. arXiv e-prints, arXiv:1807.06209. arXiv: 1807.06209 [astro-ph.CO] (July 2018).
3. Barkana R., 2018, The Encyclopedia of Cosmology. Volume 1: Galaxy Formation and Evolution Rennan Barkana Tel Aviv University, doi:10.1142/9496-vol1.
4. Mesinger A., 2019, The Cosmic 21-cm Revolution; Charting the first billion years of our universe, doi:10.1088/2514- 3433/ab4a73
5. Sevilla-Noarbe I., et al. Dark Energy Survey Year 3 Results: Photometric Data Set for Cosmology. ApJS, 254, 24 (2021).
6. Atek, H. The extreme faint end of the UV luminosity function at $z \sim 6$ through gravitational telescopes: A comprehensive assessment of strong lensing uncertainties. MNRAS, 479, 5184 (2018).
7. Freedman, W. L. Measurements of the Hubble Constant: Tensions in Perspective. ApJ, 919, 16 (2021).

8. Agarwal, D. et al. Initial results from a real-time FRB search with the GBT. MNRAS 497, 352–360. arXiv: 2003.14272 [astro-ph.IM] (Sept. 2020).
9. Deng W. & Zhang B. Cosmological Implications of Fast Radio Burst/Gamma-Ray Burst Associations. ApJ 783, L35. arXiv: 1401.0059 [astro-ph.HE] (Mar. 2014).
10. Fialkov, A. & Loeb, A. Constraining the CMB optical depth through the dispersion measure of cosmological radio transients. JCAP 2016, 004. arXiv: 1602.08130 [astro-ph.CO] (May 2016).
11. Macquart, J. P. et al. A census of baryons in the Universe from localized fast radio bursts. Nature 581, 391–395. arXiv: 2005.13161 [astro-ph.CO] (May 2020).
12. McQuinn, M. Locating the "Missing" Baryons with Extragalactic Dispersion Measure Estimates. ApJ 780, L33. arXiv: 1309.4451 [astro-ph.CO] (Jan. 2014).
13. Yang Y.-P. & Zhang B. Extracting Host Galaxy Dispersion Measure and Constraining Cosmological Parameters using Fast Radio Burst Data. ApJ 830, L31. arXiv: 1608.08154 [astro-ph.HE] (Oct. 2016).
14. Zhang B. Fast Radio Burst Energetics and Detectability from High Redshifts. ApJ 867, L21. arXiv: 1808.05277 [astro-ph.HE] (Nov. 2018).
15. Zhou, B., Li, X.,Wang, T., Fan, Y.-Z. & Wei, D.-M. Fast radio bursts as a cosmic probe? Phys. Rev. D 89, 107303. arXiv: 1401.2927 [astro-ph.CO] (May 2014).
16. Gao, H., Li, Z. & Zhang, B. Fast Radio Burst/Gamma-Ray Burst Cosmography. ApJ 788, 189. arXiv: 1402.2498 [astro-ph.CO] (June 2014).
17. Walters, A., Weltman, A., Gaensler, B. M., Ma, Y.-Z. & Witzemann, A. Future Cosmological Constraints From Fast Radio Bursts. ApJ 856, 65. arXiv: 1711.11277 [astro-ph.CO] (Mar. 2018).
18. Jaroszynski, M. Fast radio bursts and cosmological tests. MNRAS 484, 1637–1644. arXiv: 1812.11936 [astro-ph.CO] (Apr. 2019).
19. Madhavacheril, M. S., Battaglia, N., Smith, K. M. & Sievers, J. L. Cosmology with kSZ: breaking the optical depth degeneracy with Fast Radio Bursts. arXiv e-prints, arXiv:1901.02418. arXiv: 1901.02418 [astro-ph.CO] (Jan. 2019).
20. Wu, Q., Yu, H. & Wang, F. Y. A New Method to Measure Hubble Parameter H(z) Using Fast Radio Bursts. ApJ 895, 33. arXiv: 2004.12649 [astro-ph.CO] (May 2020).
21. Hagstotz, S., Reischke, R. & Lilow, R. A new measurement of the Hubble constant using Fast Radio Bursts. arXiv e-prints, arXiv:2104.04538. arXiv: 2104.04538 [astro-ph.CO] (Apr. 2021).
22. Zheng, Z., Ofek, E. O., Kulkarni, S. R., Neill, J. D. & Juric, M. Probing the Intergalactic Medium with Fast Radio Bursts. ApJ 797, 71. arXiv: 1409.3244 [astro-ph.HE] (Dec. 2014).
23. Caleb, M., Flynn, C. & Stappers, B. W. Constraining the era of helium reionization using fast radio bursts. MNRAS 485, 2281–2286. arXiv: 1902.06981 [astro-ph.HE] (May 2019).
24. Linder, E. V. Detecting helium reionization with fast radio bursts. Phys. Rev. D 101, 103019. arXiv: 2001.11517 [astro-ph.CO] (May 2020).
25. Lau, A. W. K., Mitra, A., Shafiee, M. & Smoot, G. Constraining HeII reionization detection uncertainties via fast radio bursts. New Astron. 89, 101627 (Nov. 2021).
26. Bhattacharya, M., Kumar, P. & Linder, E. V. Fast radio burst dispersion measure distribution as a probe of helium reionization. Phys. Rev. D 103, 103526. arXiv:2010.14530 [astro-ph.CO] (May 2021).
27. Liu, A., Pritchard, J. R., Mortonson, M., Parsons, A. & HERA Collaboration. Improving Cosmic Microwave Background Constraints with 21cm Cosmology in American Astronomical Society Meeting Abstracts 225 (Jan. 2015), 318.01.

28. Greig, B. & Mesinger, A. The global history of reionization. MNRAS 465, 4838–4852. arXiv: 1605.05374 [astro-ph.CO] (Mar. 2017).
29. Mondal, R. et al. Tight constraints on the excess radio background at z = 9.1 from LOFAR. MNRAS, 498, 4178 (2020).
30. The HERA Collaboration. HERA Phase I Limits on the Cosmic 21-cm Signal: Constraints on Astrophysics and Cosmology During the Epoch of Reionization. arXiv:2108.07282 (2021).
31. Beniamini P., Kumar P., Ma X. & Quataert E. Exploring the epoch of hydrogen reionization using FRBs. MNRAS 502, 5134–5146. arXiv: 2011.11643 [astro-ph.CO] (Apr. 2021).
32. Zhang, Z. J., Yan, K., Li, C. M., Zhang, G. Q. & Wang, F. Y. Intergalactic Medium Dispersion Measures of Fast Radio Bursts Estimated from IllustrisTNG Simulation and Their Cosmological Applications. ApJ 906, arXiv: 2011.14494 [astro-ph.CO] (Jan. 2021).
33. Hashimoto, T. et al. Revealing the cosmic reionization history with fast radio bursts in the era of Square Kilometre Array. MNRAS502, 2346–2355. arXiv: 2101.08798 [astro-ph.CO] (Apr. 2021).
34. Pagano, M. & Fronenberg, H. Constraining the epoch of reionization with highly dispersed fast radio bursts. MNRAS 505, 2195–2206. arXiv: 2103.03252 [astro-ph.CO] (Aug. 2021).
35. Heimersheim S., et al. What it takes to measure reionization with fast radio bursts. arXiv:2107.14242 (2021).
36. Millea M. & Bouchet F. Cosmic microwave background constraints in light of priors over reionization histories. A&A 617, A96. arXiv: 1804.08476 [astro-ph.CO] (Sept. 2018).
37. Heinrich C. & Hu W. Reionization effective likelihood from Planck 2018 data. Phys. Rev. D 104, 063505. arXiv: 2104.13998 [astro-ph.CO] (Sept. 2021).
38. Petroff, E. et al. FRBCAT: The Fast Radio Burst Catalogue. Publ. Astron. Soc. Aust. 33, e045. arXiv: 1601.03547 [astro-ph.HE] (Sept. 2016).
39. The CHIME/FRB Collaboration et al. A bright millisecond-duration radio burst from a Galactic magnetar. Nature 587, 54–58 (Nov. 2020).

Closing the cosmological loop with the redshift drift

C. J. A. P. Martins

*Centro de Astrofísica da Universidade do Porto, and
Instituto de Astrofísica e Ciências do Espaço, Universidade do Porto,
Rua das Estrelas, 4150-762 Porto, Portugal
E-mail: Carlos.Martins@astro.up.pt*

C. S. Alves

*Department of Physics and Astronomy, University College London,
Gower Street, London WC1E 6BT, United Kingdom, and
Centro de Astrofísica da Universidade do Porto,
Rua das Estrelas, 4150-762 Porto, Portugal*

J. Esteves

*Université de Montpellier,
163 rue Auguste Broussonnet, 34090 Montpellier, and
Centro de Astrofísica da Universidade do Porto,
Rua das Estrelas, 4150-762 Porto, Portugal*

A. Lapel

*Institut d'Astrophysique de Paris,
98bis Bd Arago, 75014 Paris, France and
Centro de Astrofísica da Universidade do Porto,
Rua das Estrelas, 4150-762 Porto, Portugal*

B. G. Pereira

*Faculdade de Ciências, Universidade do Porto,
Rua do Campo Alegre, 4150-007 Porto, Portugal, and
Centro de Astrofísica da Universidade do Porto,
Rua das Estrelas, 4150-762 Porto, Portugal*

The redshift drift (also known as the Sandage Test) is a model-independent probe of fundamental cosmology, enabling us to watch the universe expand in real time, and thereby to confirm (or not) the recent acceleration of the universe without any model-dependent assumptions. On the other hand, by choosing a fiducial model one can also use it to constrain the model parameters, thereby providing a consistency test for results obtained with other probes. The drift can be measured by the Extremely Large Telescope and also by the full SKA. Recently two alternative measurement methods have been proposed: the cosmic accelerometer, and the differential redshift drift. Here we summarize a comparative analysis of the various methods and their possible outcomes, using both Fisher Matrix and MCMC techniques. We find that no single method is uniformly better than the others. Instead, their comparative performance depends both on experimental parameters (including the experiment time and redshift at which the measurement is made) and also on the scientific goal (e.g., detecting the drift signal with high statistical

significance, constraining the matter density, or constraining the dark energy properties).
In other words, the experiment should be optimized for the preferred scientific goal.

Keywords: Observational cosmology; Redshift drift; Extremely Large Telescope.

1. Introduction

The observational evidence for the acceleration of the universe shows that our canonical theories of cosmology and particle physics are at least incomplete, and possibly incorrect. New physics is out there, waiting to be discovered; we must search for, identify and characterize this new physics. But so far, the interpretation of all our extant cosmological observations is model-dependent, in the sense that it requires a number of assumptions on an underlying cosmological model. Ideally, one would like some fully model-independent observables, enabling consistency tests of these underling assumptions. And indeed there is one conceptually simple, but operationally very challenging, such observable: the redshift drift of objects following the cosmological expansion.

The CosmoESPRESSO team uses the universe as a laboratory to address, with precision spectroscopy and other observational, computational and theoretical tools, grand-challenge questions including the universality of physical laws, the characterization of the large-scale behaviour of gravity (and specifically of the source of the recent acceleration of the universe) and the study of fossil relics or early stages of the universe's evolution, together with contributions to ESO and ESA next-generation facilities and to education and public understanding of science. In what follows we highlight recent contributions of the CosmoESPRESSO team to this fundamental quest, pertaining to the cosmological impact of forthcoming redshift drift measurements. Further details can be found in Ref. 1 and Ref. 2.

2. The redshift drift and its sensitivity

The idea that the redshift of objects following the cosmological expansion changes with time—known as the redshift drift— is many decades old.[3,4] Conceptually, a measurement of the redshift drift is fundamentally different from our other astrophysical observables. In our observations at cosmological distances done so far, we are mapping our present-day past light cone. Instead, the redshift drift allows us to compare different past light cones. More crudely, this corresponds to watching the Universe expand in real time. Other than being a different probe of the universe, its conceptual importance is that it is a model-independent probe of the expansion of the universe, making no assumption on geometry, clustering or the behaviour of gravity, and therefore of crucial importance for fundamental cosmology.

The practical difficulty is that cosmologically relevant timescales are orders of magnitude larger than human ones: a measurement of the redshift drift therefore requires exquisite sensitivity, several orders of magnitude better than currently available: the best currently available bound,[5] is about three orders of magnitude larger than the signal expected for the standard ΛCDM cosmology with reasonable choices of its model parameters, and contains systematic errors comparable to or larger than the statistical ones. Nevertheless, measuring this drift is a key science and design driver for the development of the Extremely Large Telescope (ELT), and specifically for its high-resolution spectrograph currently known as ELT-HIRES.[6]

A detailed feasibility study of high-redshift measurements by the ELT, on a decade timescale, was done in Ref. 7, who also discussed possible targets. It is important to note that although ELT redshift drift measurements, on their own, lead to cosmological parameter constraints that are not tighter than those available by more classical probes (such as supernovae or the CMB) they do probe regions of parameter space that are different from (and sometimes actually orthogonal to) those of other probes, enabling the breaking of degeneracies and therefore leading to more stringent combined constraints;[1] we will provide an explicit demonstration later in this contribution. More recently, it has also been pointed out that measurements at low redshifts can in principle be made by the full Square Kilometre Array (SKA),[8] while measurements at intermediate redshifts can be done by intensity mapping measurements such as CHIME[9] and HIRAX.[10] Measurements of all three of these will require appropriate hardware configurations.

Redshift drift measurements are a key part of what is commonly called real-time cosmology.[11] Usually they rely on the first derivative of the redshift. Recently the role of second derivatives of the redshift, which should also be within the reach of the full SKA, has been studied by Ref.[12] Fisher Matrix techniques[13,14] are well suited for a comparative study of the cosmological impact of redshift drift measurements by these facilities; such a study is described in detail in Ref. 1.

The redshift drift of an astrophysical object following the cosmological expansion, for an observer looking at it over a time span Δt, is

$$\frac{\Delta z}{\Delta t} = H_0 \left[1 + z - E(z) \right], \qquad (1)$$

where for convenience we have defined the dimensionless Hubble parameter $E(z) = H(z)/H_0$, although the actual astrophysical observable is usually a spectroscopically measured velocity

$$\Delta v = \frac{c \Delta z}{1+z} = (cH_0 \Delta t) \left[1 - \frac{E(z)}{1+z} \right]. \qquad (2)$$

The dependence on the Hubble parameter naturally leads to a model-dependent redshift dependence of the drift. Broadly speaking, in a universe that is currently accelerating but was deccelerating in the past the drift will be positive at low redshifts and negative for higher redshifts, while in a universe that always deccelerates the redshift drift would always be negative. To give a specific example, for a flat ΛCDM model, apart from trivially vanishing at $z = 0$, the signal will also vanish at

$$z_{zero} = \frac{1 - 3\Omega_m + \sqrt{1 + 2\Omega_m - 3\Omega_m^2}}{2\Omega_m}, \qquad (3)$$

while the redshift of maximum spectroscopic velocity is

$$z_{v,max} = \left[\frac{2(1-\Omega_m)}{\Omega_m}\right]^{1/3} - 1 \qquad (4)$$

and the maximum of the drift itself is obtained by solving the quartic equation

$$9\Omega_m^2(1+z)^4 = 4\Omega_m(1+z)^3 + 4(1-\Omega_m). \qquad (5)$$

More specifically, if we choose $\Omega_m = 0.3$ (in agreement with contemporary cosmological data) we obtain $z_{zero} =\sim 2.09$, $z_{v,max} \sim 0.67$ and $z_{z,max} \sim 0.95$. It is interesting to note that for flat ΛCDM with $\Omega_m = 0.3$, the acceleration phase does start at redshift $z_{v,max}$, while the cosmological constant only starts dominating the Friedmann equation at

$$z_\Lambda = \left[\frac{(1-\Omega_m)}{\Omega_m}\right]^{1/3} - 1, \qquad (6)$$

which for Ω_m leads to $z_\Lambda \sim 0.33$.

We can analytically explore the sensitivity of the redshift drift to the cosmological parameters, for a fiducial flat CPL model.[15,16] In this case we can write the Friedmann equation as

$$E^2(z) = \Omega_m(1+z)^3 + \Omega_\phi(1+z)^{3(1+w_0+w_a)} \exp\left[-\frac{3w_a z}{1+z}\right]. \qquad (7)$$

It is also convenient to define a dimensionless redshift drift

$$S_z = \frac{1}{H_{100}}\frac{\Delta z}{\Delta t} = h\left[1 + z - E(z)\right], \qquad (8)$$

where we have defined $H_0 = hH_{100}$ with $H_{100} = 100$ km/s/Mpc; the corresponding observable spectroscopic velocity will be denoted

$$S_v = \Delta v = kh\left[1 - \frac{E(z)}{1+z}\right]. \qquad (9)$$

In these we have introduced $k = cH_{100}\Delta t$, which is a constant parameter for a given observation time, with units of cm/s: for $\Delta t = 1$ year, $k = 3.064$ cm/s. This provides a rough estimate of the magnitude of the signal in the relevant time span, and therefore also an estimate of the required sensitivity of the spectroscopic measurements. Then for each cosmological parameter p_i the sensitivities of S_z and S_v are related via

$$\frac{\partial S_v/\partial p_i}{\partial S_z/\partial p_i} = \frac{k}{1+z}. \qquad (10)$$

For our fiducial model we can then find the following sensitivities

$$\frac{\partial S_z}{\partial h} = 1 + z - E(z) \qquad (11)$$

$$\frac{\partial S_z}{\partial \Omega_m} = -\frac{h(1+z)^3}{2E(z)}\left[1 - (1+z)^{3(w_0+w_a)}\exp\left[\frac{-3w_a z}{1+z}\right]\right] \qquad (12)$$

$$\frac{\partial S_z}{\partial w_0} = -\frac{3h(1-\Omega_m)}{2E(z)}(1+z)^{3(1+w_0+w_a)}\ln(1+z)\exp\left[\frac{-3w_a z}{1+z}\right] \quad (13)$$

$$\frac{\partial S_z}{\partial w_a} = -\frac{3h(1-\Omega_m)}{2E(z)}(1+z)^{3(1+w_0+w_a)}\left[\ln(1+z) - \frac{z}{1+z}\right]\exp\left[\frac{-3w_a z}{1+z}\right]. \quad (14)$$

Note that the sign of the $\partial S_z/\partial h$ term will depend on redshift, while those of the other derivatives are always negative for observationally reasonable values of the model parameters.

Some sensitivity ratios are also illuminating. Consider that of the two dark energy equation of state parameters

$$\frac{\partial S_z/\partial w_a}{\partial S_z/\partial w_0} = 1 - \frac{z}{(1+z)\ln(1+z)}; \quad (15)$$

as one would expect this approaches zero as $z \to 0$ and unity as $z \to \infty$. On the other hand, comparing the sensitivities to the matter density and the present-day dark energy equation of state one finds

$$\frac{\partial S_z/\partial \Omega_m}{\partial S_z/\partial w_0} = \frac{1 - (1+z)^{3(w_0+w_a)}\exp\left[\frac{-3w_a z}{1+z}\right]}{3(1-\Omega_m)\ln(1+z)(1+z)^{3(w_0+w_a)}\exp\left[\frac{-3w_a z}{1+z}\right]}, \quad (16)$$

which tends to $(-w_0)/(1-\Omega_m)$ as $z \to 0$ and to infinity as $z \to \infty$ (though note that in this we are neglecting the radiation density). Considering the specific case of a fiducial ΛCDM model with $\Omega_m = 0.3$, at $z = 1$, the ratios are respectively

$$\frac{\partial S_z/\partial w_a}{\partial S_z/\partial w_0} = 1 - \frac{1}{2\ln 2} \sim 0.28 \quad (17)$$

$$\frac{\partial S_z/\partial \Omega_m}{\partial S_z/\partial w_0} \sim \frac{7}{2.1\ln 2} \sim 4.8. \quad (18)$$

Finally, it is also illuminating to consider the low-redshift limits of the various derivative terms. To obtain them, one uses the fact that as $z \to 0$ we have

$$E(z) = 1 + \frac{3}{2}\left[1 + (1-\Omega_m)w_0\right]z + \mathcal{O}(z^2). \quad (19)$$

For the derivatives with respect to h, Ω_m and w_0 we then find, respectively

$$\frac{\partial S_z}{\partial h} \longrightarrow -\frac{1}{2}\left[1 + 3(1-\Omega_m)w_0\right]z \quad (20)$$

$$\frac{\partial S_z}{\partial \Omega_m} \longrightarrow \frac{3}{2}hw_0 z \quad (21)$$

$$\frac{\partial S_z}{\partial w_0} \longrightarrow -\frac{3}{2}h(1-\Omega_m)z \quad (22)$$

while that with respect to w_a (whose value, interestingly, does not affect any of the other three) is of higher order.

Figure 1 depicts the redshift dependence of the two observational sensitivities, $\partial S_v/\partial p_i$ and $\partial S_z/\partial p_i$, for a flat ΛCDM fiducial model with $\Omega_m = 0.3$ and $h = 0.7$.

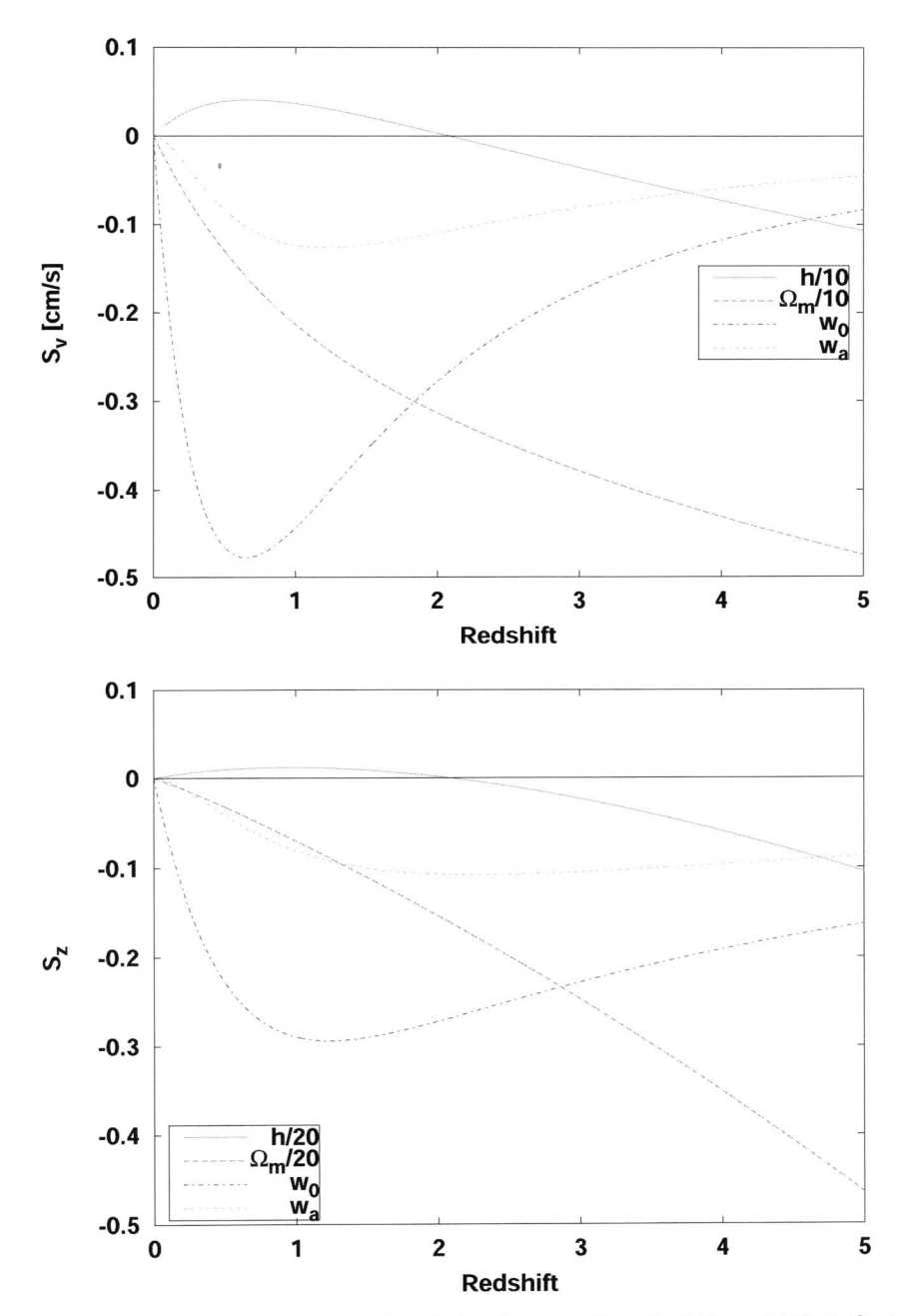

Fig. 1. Sensitivities of the spectroscopic velocity (top panel) and of the redshift drift signal (bottom panel) to the cosmological parameters in the CPL parametrization, for a flat ΛCDM fiducial. For plotting convenience the sensitivities to h and Ω_m have been divided by a factor of 10 in the top panel and by a factor of 20 in the bottom panel. The zero sensitivity line is shown in black. Similar plots can be found in Figure 4 of Ref. 1.

Note that the two are slightly different, being related by a redshift-dependent factor. Also note the different units in the vertical axes of the two panels: $\partial S_z/\partial p_i$ is dimensionless, while $\partial S_v/\partial p_i$ has units of cm/s.

As expected the sensitivity on the dimensionless Hubble constant h (which is proportional to the redshift drift signal itself) is the only one that changes sign; this and the sensitivity on Ω_m are also larger than those on the dark energy equation of state parameters w_0 and w_a. Nevertheless, the most noteworthy point is that the various sensitivity curves have different redshift dependencies. While the matter density sensitivity increases monotonically (in absolute value) with redshift, those of w_0 and w_a are maximal at around the onset of acceleration (just below $z = 1$, with the value being slightly different for S_v and S_z), and the former has a stronger redshift dependence than the latter. This is important because it implies that as long as one is able to do these measurements at sufficiently broad redshift ranges there should not be strong covariances between the parameters.[1]

3. Three experimental strategies

As previously mentioned, redshift drift measurements are unique in comparing different past light cones in a fully model-independent way, rather than mapping our present-day past light cone. Nevertheless, these measurements can complement traditional probes in constraining specific cosmological models. Indeed they have an important role to play here, since they do probe different regions of parameter space, enabling the breaking of key degeneracies upon combination. One may therefore ask how an experimental strategy aimed at maximizing the cosmological constraining power of the redhift drift (on its own or in combination with traditional probes) compares with a strategy aimed at maximizing the statistical significance of the detection of the drift signal itself.

This is a particularly pressing question since two other approaches to detecting the redshift drift have been recently proposed. The Cosmic Accelerometer[17] aims to lower the cost of the experiment, while the Acceleration Programme[18] proposes to measure the differential redshift drift between two non-zero redshifts, rather than measuring the drift with respect to today. In Ref. 2 we again used Fisher Matrix techniques in a comparative study of the cosmological impact of the three approaches. The fiducial model choices were also those described above, to maintain consistency with Ref. 1. Herewith we introduce these alternative strategies and summarize the results of this analysis.

The case study for redshift measurements by the ELT has been done in Ref. 7. The measurement relies on absorption features in the Lyman-α forest, complemented by metal absorption lines redwards of it. The main practical result of this study is that the spectroscopic velocity uncertainty is well described by

$$\sigma_v = \sigma_e \left(\frac{2370}{S/N}\right) \sqrt{\frac{30}{N_{QSO}}} \left(\frac{1 + z_{QSO}}{5}\right)^{-\lambda} cm/s, \qquad (23)$$

where the last exponent is $\lambda = 1.7$ up to $z = 4$ and $\lambda = 0.9$ for higher redshifts. Consistently with this and also with the latest top-level requirements for the ELT-HIRES spectrograph,[6] we assume that each measurement has a signal to noise ratio $S/N = 3000$ and uses data from $N_{QSO} = 6$ quasars; as baseline values we take $\sigma_e = 1.35$ and an experiment time $\Delta t = 20$ years, but we also explore different choices for these two parameters. The ELT can measure the redshift drift in the approximate redshift range $2.0 \leq z \leq 4.5$. The main bottleneck, in addition to the spectrograph stability which is thought not to be a bottleneck,[19] is the availability of bright quasars providing the required signal to noise in reasonable amounts of telescope time. The discovery of additional bright quasars will improve the experiment feasibility,[20] so our previously reported ELT analysis[2] might be conservative.

The first alternative, dubbed the Cosmic Accelerometer[17] (henceforth CAC) can be crudely thought of as a low-cost version of the ELT experiment, relying on commercial off the shelf equipment. The proposal is part of the Astro2020 decadal survey, and to our knowledge no detailed feasibility study has been carried out so far. We therefore take at face value the spectroscopic velocity uncertainty given in the proposal white paper

$$\sigma_v = \sigma_c \sqrt{\frac{6}{t_{exp}}} \; cm/s \,, \qquad (24)$$

with the baseline value of $\sigma_c = 1.5$ and that of the experiment time $t_{exp} = 6$ years; the authors of the decadal survey proposal state that a further advantage of this approach would be a detection of the redshift drift on a shorter time scale than that of the ELT. In any case, we will again explore the impact of different values of these parameters. The redshift ranges probed are, in principle, similar to those for the ELT.

The second alternative is the Acceleration Programme[18] (henceforth APR), which uses the ELT as described above but proposes to measure the drift between sources at two different non-zero redshifts along the same line of sight. This is to be compared to the standard approach, where one of these redshifts is always $z = 0$. The measured quantity in this case will be a spectroscopic velocity difference, which making use of previously introduced definitions we can write as

$$\Delta v_{ir} = (cH_0 \Delta t) \left[\frac{E(z_r)}{1+z_r} - \frac{E(z_i)}{1+z_i} \right] \,, \qquad (25)$$

where z_r and z_i are the redshifts of the reference and intervening sources, implying that $z_i < z_r$. The rationale for this proposal is that for some choices of redshifts the absolute value of the detected drift signal (or, more precisely, that of the corresponding spectroscopic velocity) can be significantly larger than in the standard approach. Since the absolute value of the spectroscopic velocity uncertainty of the measurement, σ_v, is determined by the spectrograph's technical specifications, maximizing the value of the signal to be detected leads to an increased statistical significance of the detection.

4. Cosmological constraints based experimental trade-offs

Our main comparison diagnostic is the derived uncertainty in the cosmological parameters being considered, specifically the matter density fraction and the CPL dark energy equation of state parameters. Our fiducial model for the comparison is flat ΛCDM, with $\Omega_m = 0.3$, $H_0 = 70$ km/s/Mpc, $w_0 = -1$ and $w_a = 0$.

To compare the ELT and CAC it is convenient to assume a single measurement of the redshift drift. Clearly, even for a flat ΛCDM fiducial model a single redshift drift measurement can't simultaneously constrain the Hubble constant and the matter density, so one adopts ample uniform priors for both of these. We can then explore the impact of choices of normalization of the spectroscopic velocity uncertainties (σ_e and σ_c), of the experiment time, and of the redshift at which the measurement is made. Our specific metric in this case be the posterior matter density constraint, σ_m.

The crucial point for this analysis, already discussed and illustrated in Fig. 1 is that the cosmological parameter sensitivities of the redshift drift are redshift-dependent.[1] This sensitivity must therefore be convolved with the spectroscopic velocity uncertainty of each experiment, bearing in mind that the ELT one is redshift dependent (cf. Eq. 23) while the CAC one is not (cf. Eq. 24), at least if one takes the CAC proposal at face value.

In a nutshell, the main result of this comparison is that for identical experiment times the CAC does better, though the difference decreases for larger redshifts. A possible advantage of the CAC (in addition to cost) would be a lower experiment time. The top panel of Figure 2 compares the constraints on σ_m for a 6 year CAC and a 20 year ELT experiment, and one finds that in these circumstances the ELT does clearly better at the redhsifts of interest—up to 62% better. The reason for this is clear. While absolute uncertainties σ_v may be smaller for the CAC, the relative ones will be larger due to smaller experiment times, since a key feature of the redshift drift is that the signal grows linearly in time. The bottom panel of the same figure compares both experiments at 20 years; in this case the CAC is more constraining—by up to a factor of six for measurements around redshift $z \sim 2$.

We therefore see that an experiment optimized to detect the redshift drift signal is not necessarily optimized to constrain particular cosmological models, or indeed specific model parameters. In the example of Figure 2 the constraints on the matter density can be substantially different, but those on the Hubble constant never differ by more than a few percent.[2]

Analogous results ensue when comparing the parameter uncertainties in the canonical redshift drift and the differential redshift drift, for the CPL parameterization. To remain consistent with the work on the canonical redshift drift,[1] in Ref. 2 we used a set of five redshift drift measurements at reference redshifts

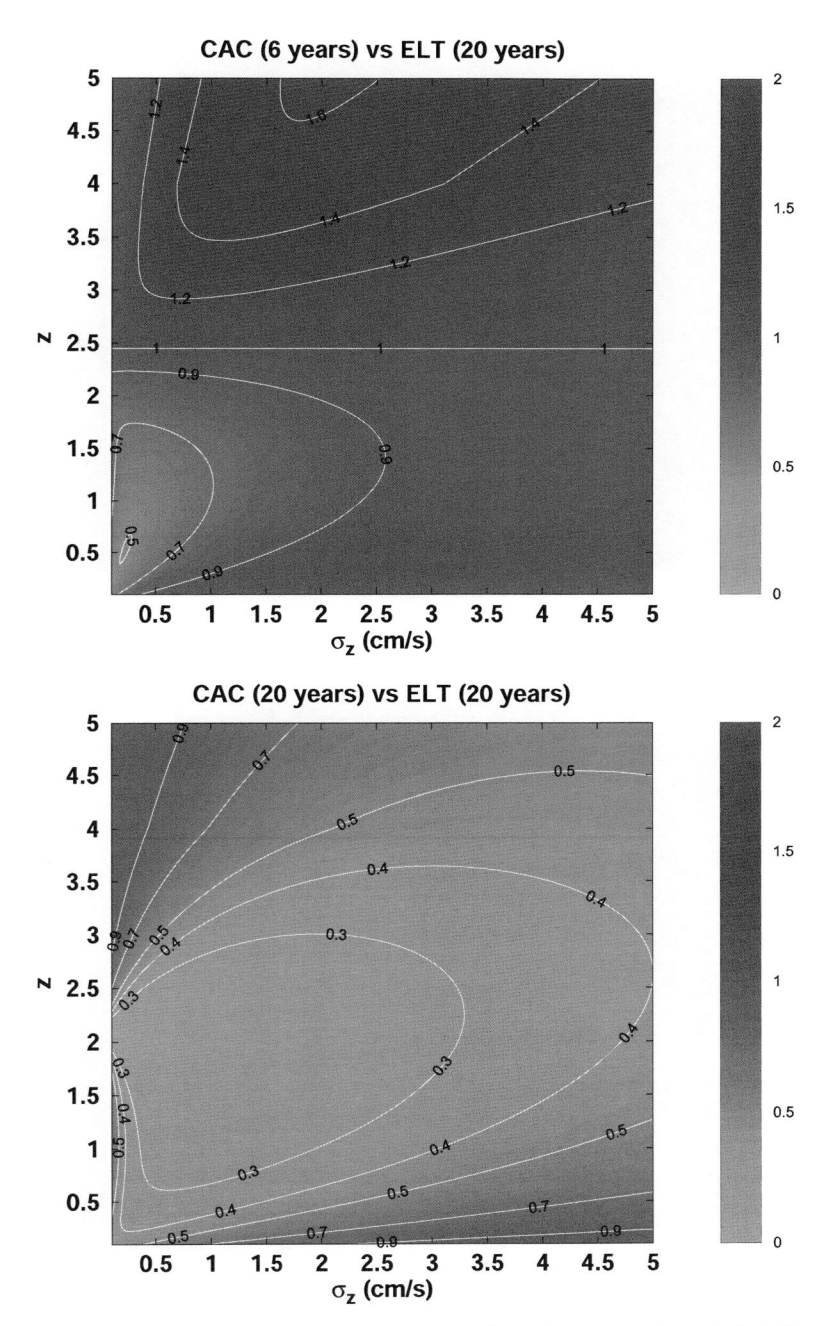

Fig. 2. Ratio of the constraints on the matter density (σ_m) from a single redshift drift measurement by the CAC and ELT, as a function of the redshift of the measurement (z) and the velocity uncertainty (σ_z), with a CAC experiment time of 6 or 20 years (top and bottom panels), and 20 years for ELT in both cases. A ratio larger than unity implies that the ELT measurement is more constraining. An alternative depiction of this comparison can be found in Figure 2 of Ref. 2.

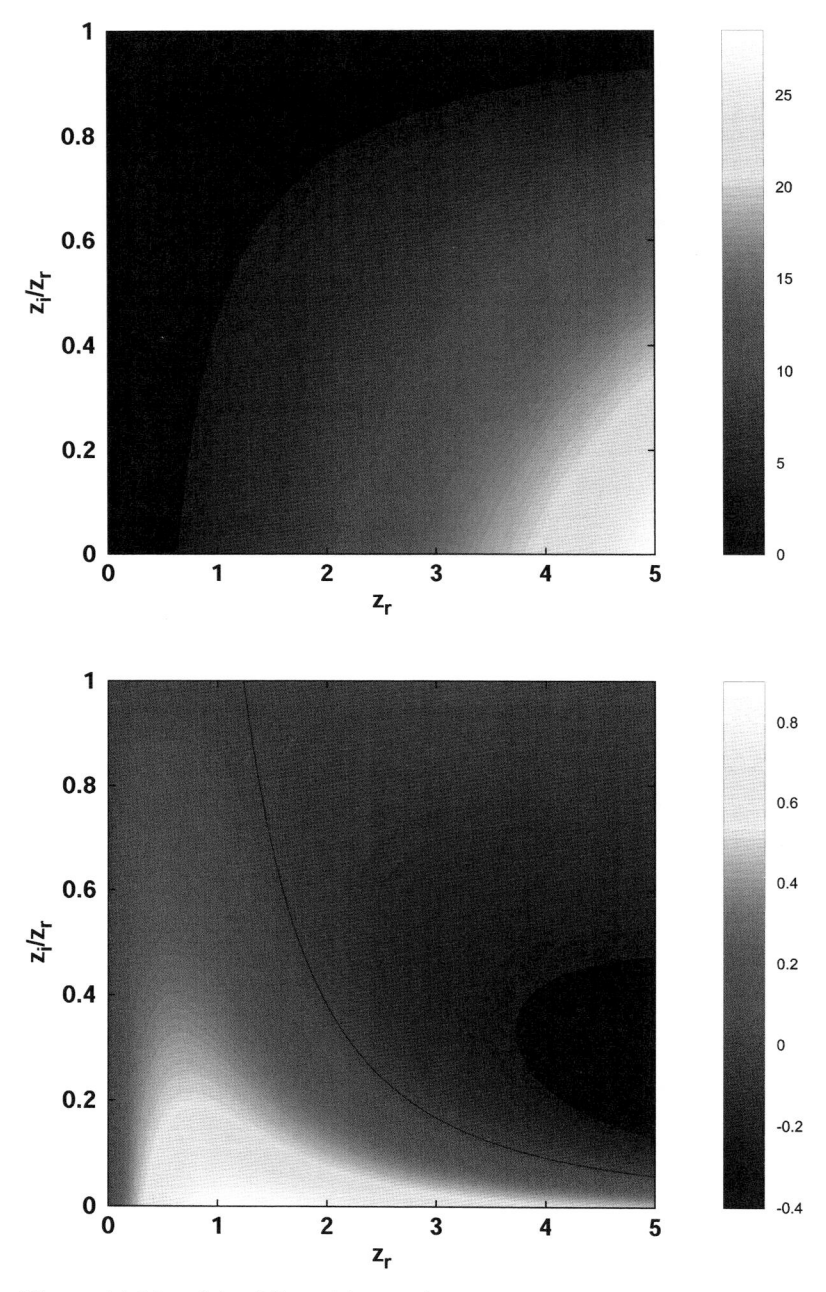

Fig. 3. The sensitivities of the differential redshift drift to the cosmological parameters Ω_m (top) and w_0 (bottom), as a function of the reference redshift z_r and the ratio of intervening and reference redshifts z_i/z_r. The colormaps show the sensitivity in cm/s per year of observation, and the black curves show the locus of zero sensitivity (for Ω_m there is no such non-trivial locus). An alternative depiction of these sensitivities, also for h and w_a, can be found in Figure 3 of Ref. 2.

$z_r = \{2.0, 2.5, 3.0, 3.5, 4.5\}$, and a 20 years experiment. As for the choice of intervening redshifts one may consider two representative choices one with all $z_1 = 0.67$ (this being the redshift with maximum positive spectroscopic velocity for our choice of fiducial model) and another numerically determined with the goal of maximizing the Figure of Merit for the dark energy equation of state parameters, w_0 and w_a, defined as the inverse of the area of the one-sigma confidence contour in the two-dimensional parameter space.

The results, further detailed in Ref. 2, confirm that amplifying the signal for the redshift drift does not necessarily improve the uncertainties of any parameters. However, the numerically determined set of redshifts shows that in ideal circumstances the uncertainties for w_0 and w_a can be improved by one to two orders of magnitude with respect to the canonical redshift drift, while the uncertainties for h and Ω_m were also improved. Nevertheless this advantage is diluted when priors are added, due to relatively high non-diagonal terms in the Fisher matrices. (In particular, we see that constraints on the dark energy equation of state parameters are dominated by the priors, making the ratios of the corresponding uncertainties become unity.) It will be important to validate these results though a MCMC analysis.

These results can be understood by calculating the sensitivity coefficients of the differential redshift drift to our four cosmological parameters, $\partial(\Delta v_{ir})/\partial p$, where p is one of (h, Ω_m, w_0, w_a), These are analogous to the ones shown in Fig. 1 for the standard redshift drift, except that they now depend on both the reference and intervening redshifts. As expected, one finds that the sensitivity to Ω_m is much larger than the others. Crucially, the sensitivity to Ω_m is maximized for $z_i = 0$ and maximal z_r: in other words, if the goal is to constrain Ω_m, the canonical redshift drift measurement is always the optimal strategy. On the other hand, for the other model parameters the differential redshift drift can provide tighter constraints.

5. Synergy with classical cosmological probes

Throughout this analysis, it has become clear that optimal constraints on the background quantities dynamically involved in the redshift-drift require wide redshift intervals to take advantage of the individual parameter sensitivities over the expansion history. This justifies, inter alia, the complementarity of redshift drift experiments, whose main candidates are embodied by the phase-2 SKA for low-redshift spiral galaxies and the ELT for distant quasars. Indeed, as previously pointed out, not only do these experiments complement each other, but there are also hints that they present promising synergies with traditional cosmological probes, potentially allowing to achieve more stringent joint constraints over cosmological parameters of the concordance model and its extensions.[1] Specifically, the fundamentally different nature of the redshift-drift experiment with respect to CMB, SNe, galaxy clustering, or weak lensing experiments, allows for novel correlations within the relevant parameter space, witnessed by degeneracy breaking. As a consistency check and to gain further insights on the degeneracies of the dark energy parameters, it is of great interest to complement current Fisher forecasts with a more thorough MCMC analysis for accurate sampling of the distributions.

Similarly to the previous section, we account for a possible dynamical behavior of dark energy with two degrees of freedom, w_0 and w_a, through the CPL parametrization. The mock dataset for the ELT is generated according to the prescriptions of the third section for 30 QSOs populating 5 redshift bins between $z = 2$ and $z = 4.5$. As for the total uncertainty over the simulated data, Eq. (23) is used with a somewhat more optimistic value of unity for σ_e, reflecting the fact that redshifts are measured only at two distinct times (the underlying motivation is to compare the full potential of the redshift-drift against tight CMB and SNe constraints). Moreover, random noise is generated from a Gaussian distribution around the theoretical redshift-drift value, with a standard deviation of σ_v to mimic genuine measurements from Lyman-α forests. As for the phase-2 SKA galaxy sample, 5 bins are generated between redshifts 0.2 and 1.0 with redshift-dependent relative uncertainties of 10% following recommendations of previous estimations,[12] to which is added the same artificial Gaussian noise over the theoretical signal.

We implemented the theoretical redshift-drift signal to the dynamical landscape at the background level within the Boltzmann solver CLASS.[21] The theoretical drift is constrained to follow Planck 2018's cosmology[22] not to bias the relative distributions and to ease the comparison. The true posterior is then sampled with the Bayesian sampler MontePython[23] in which we integrated the simulated datasets and the scripts to generate the associated Gaussian likelihoods. The priors over all relevant cosmological parameters are consistent with the ones used in the Planck analysis.

The most noteworthy results from the forecast illustrated in Fig. 4 are first that there is no significant deviation from Gaussianity within the distribution, which further legitimates previous Fisher analyses. More importantly, one can note the remarkable degeneracy breaking of the redshift drift probability density function on most of the parameters with respect to the other probes. In particular, the clear degeneracy within the w_0–w_a space tends to suggest that the joint analysis of classical probes with future redshift drift datasets could further improve the constraints on the first-order term of the CPL parametrization and therefore work toward a better characterization of the possible dynamical behavior of dark energy. Here, the contribution of the low redshift SKA2 sample is important to this endeavor as it probes the dark energy-dominated era and allows to reveal a positive correlation between the two parameters whereas w_0 and w_a are anticorrelated for the other current cosmological observables. Nevertheless, one should keep in mind that such a combination of datasets requires particular attention to the possible correlations between probes and individual systematics.

That being said, in the light of these results, we should expect a consistent gain in the constraints on Ω_m, w_0, and w_a with this type of configuration for SKA and ELT from the joint analysis of the redshift drift measurements with current

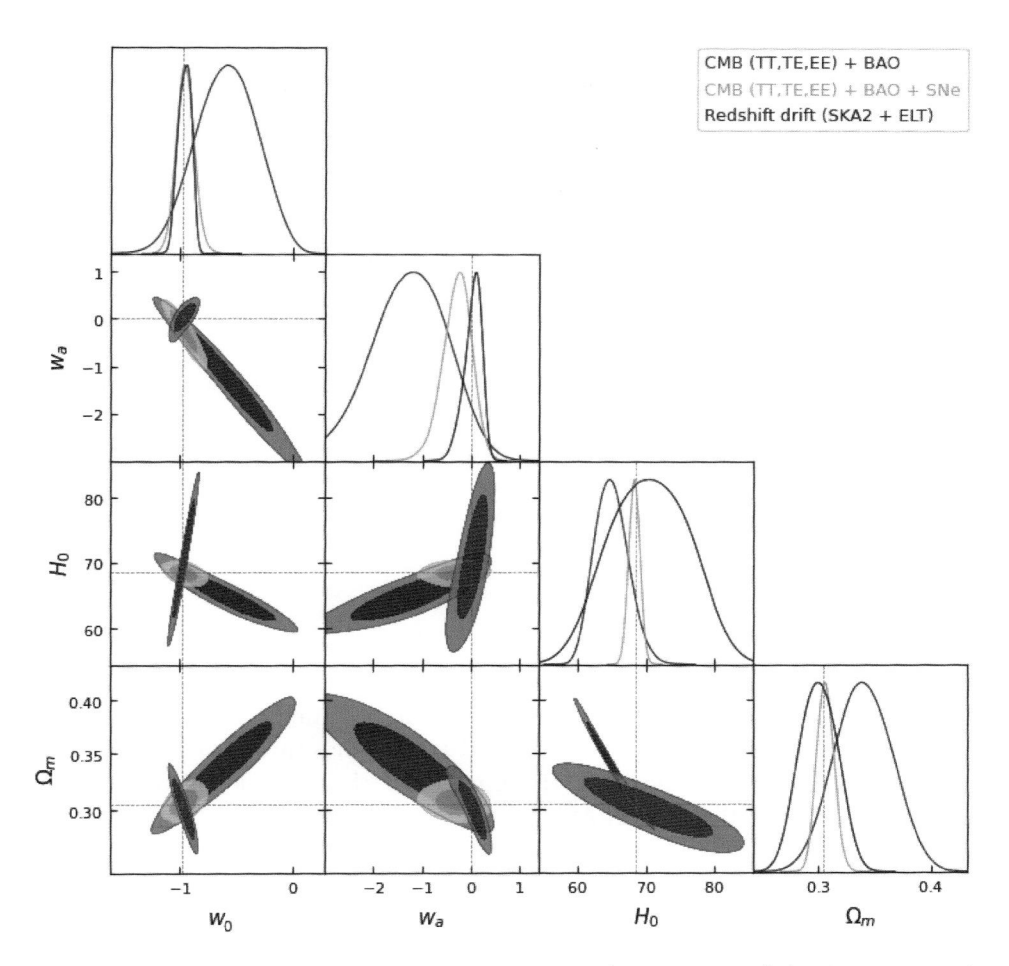

Fig. 4. Marginalized posterior distributions in the space $\{\Omega_m, H_0, w_0, w_a\}$ for the joint contribution of redshift drift experiments (red), CMB experiment with BAO measurement (teal) and CMB + BAO + supernovae (yellow). The data considered for the redshift drift experiments are the mock SKA2 and ELT samples whereas classical probes (CMB, BAO, SNe) are respectively taken from Planck, BOSS DR12, and the Pantheon supernovae samples.

cosmological probes. In the near future, a better instrumental characterization of these facilities is likely to refine the present conservative forecasts, and the CAC program, as well as intensity mapping experiments, will provide more data samples and homogenize the covered redshift range. Furthermore, by the time of the first observations of the redshift drift, next-generation galaxy surveys (Euclid, DESI), supernovae surveys (Vera C. Rubin Observatory) but also CMB experiments (Simons observatory, CMB-S4) will improve individual constraints, although in absence of new observable to present different correlations, these experiments will still highly benefit from the redshift drift degeneracy breaking.

6. Conclusions and outlook

The era of redshift drift measurements (rather than upper limits) is coming. These experiments need to be optimized for a specific purpose, which might be the detection of the drift signal itself, or constraining specific model parameters, such as the matter density or the energy equation of state, or providing a definitive consistency test for the model-dependent analysis of traditional cosmological datasets. Our analysis shows that optimized observational strategies for each of these are significantly different.

We note that an assumption of our analysis is that the measurement redshifts are free parameters, thus ignoring instrumental and observational limitations. In practice one can only do the measurements with the known bright quasars and their absorption systems. The number of astrophysical targets for these measurements remains relatively small despite recent progress.[7,20] The Phase B of construction of the ELT-HIRES spectrograph, which will likely do the first redshift drift measurements, is about to start, and it will include a detailed feasibility study that will further explore the issues raised herein.

Acknowledgments

This work was financed by FEDER—Fundo Europeu de Desenvolvimento Regional funds through the COMPETE 2020—Operational Programme for Competitiveness and Internationalisation (POCI), and by Portuguese funds through FCT - Fundação para a Ciência e a Tecnologia in the framework of the project POCI-01-0145-FEDER-028987 and PTDC/FIS-AST/28987/2017. This work was partially enabled by funding from the UCL Cosmoparticle Initiative.

References

1. C. S. Alves, A. C. O. Leite, C. J. A. P. Martins, J. G. B. Matos and T. A. Silva, Forecasts of redshift drift constraints on cosmological parameters, *Mon. Not. Roy. Astron. Soc.* **488**, 3607 (2019).
2. J. Esteves, C. J. A. P. Martins, B. G. Pereira and C. S. Alves, Cosmological impact of redshift drift measurements, *Monthly Notices of the Royal Astronomical Society: Letters* **508**, L53 (08 2021).
3. A. Sandage, The Change of Redshift and Apparent Luminosity of Galaxies due to the Deceleration of Selected Expanding Universes., *Ap. J.* **136**, p. 319 (1962).
4. G. C. McVittie, Appendix to The Change of Redshift and Apparent Luminosity of Galaxies due to the Deceleration of Selected Expanding Universes., *Ap. J.* **136**, p. 334 (1962).
5. J. Darling, Toward a Direct Measurement of the Cosmic Acceleration, *Astrophys. J.* **761**, p. L26 (2012).
6. J. Liske *et al.*, *Top Level Requirements For ELT-HIRES*, tech. rep., Document ESO 204697 Version 1 (2014).
7. J. Liske *et al.*, Cosmic dynamics in the era of Extremely Large Telescopes, *Mon. Not. Roy. Astron. Soc.* **386**, 1192 (2008).

8. H.-R. Klockner, D. Obreschkow, C. Martins, A. Raccanelli, D. Champion, A. L. Roy, A. Lobanov, J. Wagner and R. Keller, Real time cosmology - A direct measure of the expansion rate of the Universe with the SKA, *PoS* **AASKA14**, p. 027 (2015).
9. H.-R. Yu, T.-J. Zhang and U.-L. Pen, Method for Direct Measurement of Cosmic Acceleration by 21-cm Absorption Systems, *Phys. Rev. Lett.* **113**, p. 041303 (2014).
10. L. B. Newburgh *et al.*, HIRAX: A Probe of Dark Energy and Radio Transients, *Proc. SPIE Int. Soc. Opt. Eng.* **9906**, p. 99065X (2016).
11. C. Quercellini, L. Amendola, A. Balbi, P. Cabella and M. Quartin, Real-time Cosmology, *Phys. Rept.* **521**, 95 (2012).
12. C. J. A. P. Martins, M. Martinelli, E. Calabrese and M. P. L. P. Ramos, Real-time cosmography with redshift derivatives, *Phys. Rev.* **D94**, p. 043001 (2016).
13. A. Albrecht *et al.*, Report of the Dark Energy Task Force, arXiv: astro-ph/0609591, (2006).
14. A. Albrecht *et al.*, Findings of the Joint Dark Energy Mission Figure of Merit Science Working Group, arXiv: astro-ph/0901.0721, (2009).
15. M. Chevallier and D. Polarski, Accelerating universes with scaling dark matter, *Int. J. Mod. Phys.* **D10**, 213 (2001).
16. E. V. Linder, Exploring the expansion history of the universe, *Phys. Rev. Lett.* **90**, p. 091301 (2003).
17. S. S. Eikenberry *et al.*, Astro2020 Project White Paper: The Cosmic Accelerometer (7, 2019).
18. R. Cooke, The ACCELERATION programme: I. Cosmology with the redshift drift, *Mon. Not. Roy. Astron. Soc.* **492**, 2044 (2020).
19. D. Milaković, L. Pasquini, J. K. Webb and G. Lo Curto, Precision and consistency of astrocombs, *Mon. Not. Roy. Astron. Soc.* **493**, 3997 (2020).
20. K. Boutsia, A. Grazian, G. Calderone, S. Cristiani, G. Cupani, F. Guarneri, F. Fontanot, R. Amorin, V. D'Odorico, E. Giallongo and et al., The spectroscopic follow-up of the qubrics bright quasar survey, *The Astrophysical Journal Supplement Series* **250**, p. 26 (Sep 2020).
21. J. Lesgourgues, The cosmic linear anisotropy solving system (class) i: Overview (2011).
22. N. Aghanim, Y. Akrami, M. Ashdown, J. Aumont, C. Baccigalupi, M. Ballardini, A. J. Banday, R. B. Barreiro, N. Bartolo and et al., Planck 2018 results, *Astronomy & Astrophysics* **641**, p. A6 (Sep 2020).
23. T. Brinckmann and J. Lesgourgues, Montepython 3: boosted mcmc sampler and other features (2018).

Gamma-Ray Bursts as potential cosmological probes

L. Izzo

DARK, Niels Bohr Institute, University of Copenhagen,
Niels Bohr Building, Jagtvej 128, 2200, Copenhagen, Denmark
E-mail: luca.izzo@nbi.ku.dk

Gamma-ray bursts are among the most luminous transients in the Universe, a characteristic that permits us to observe them at very high redshifts. For this reason, many efforts have been made to identify a method to use GRBs as cosmological distance indicators through the use of luminosity correlations between their high-energy observable quantities. Some of the most promising methods proposed so far to standardize GRBs and their possible contribution to cosmology are presented and discussed, with a special emphasis on the Combo relation.

Keywords: Cosmology: distance scale; Gamma-ray bursts: general; Cosmology: cosmological parameters.

1. Introduction

Gamma-ray bursts (GRBs) are quick flashes of high-energy radiation initially observed in gamma-rays, where their temporal emission, also called ther "prompt" radiation is quite diversified.[1,2] The energy distribution of the photons emitted during the prompt emission can be successfully modelled with a phenomenological function, the Band model,[3] which can be described by two power-law functions smoothly connected at a given energy value, namely the peak energy of the prompt emission E_{peak}. GRBs can also be classified in two families, the *short* and *long* events, based on the T_{90} duration of the prompt emission.[4] This classification is also reflected in the hardness of the prompt photon energy spectrum, with short bursts having higher E_{peak} values than long events.[5] This classification is not only phenomenological, but it can be related to the physical progenitors of these powerful explosions: short bursts originate in the merger of two compact neutron stars,[6,7] an evidence confirmed by the recent discovery of a double neutron stars merger detected by gravitational wave detectors associated with a short GRB,[8] while long GRBs emitted during the collapse of highly-rotating massive stars.[9,10] The detection of an accompanying supernova few days after nearby long GRBs has given support in the last years to this model.[11,12]

As the time goes on, the bulk of the radiation emitted by GRBs moves to lower energies, such as in the X-rays,[13–15] at optical[16] and radio frequencies.[17] The emission observed in this so-called "afterglow" component looks at this stage more homogeneous, in particular at X-rays where it can be categorized in few subclasses.[18] The associated afterglow optical emission, detected in a good fraction majority of GRBs, has also permitted to identify the cosmological nature of these explosions, through the identification of the redshift, and then to quantify with good accuracy their energetics and luminosities.[19–21]

2. GRBs luminosity correlations

GRBs are very energetic and luminous events. This property permits to observe them at very far distances: the most distant GRB was observed at a redshift of $z = 9.4$,[22] few hundred millions after the Big Bang and well inside the reionization epoch, when the first galaxies begun to form.[23] Then, it was almost natural to search a method to render GRBs a possible standardizable distance indicator to scrutiny the far Universe, and to search for possible exotic behavior of the dark energy component. The most used method consists in using some correlations between high-energy GRB observables, where at least one of the parameters involved is dependent on the background cosmology while the remaining ones do not. Gamma-ray photons ($\nu > 5 keV$) can travel in the empty space without being affected by inter-stellar and inter-galactic absorbers, such as dust extinction, which however affects the use of optical distance indicators such as type-Ia SNe,[24] and this represents one important advantage for using GRBs as distance tools.

One of the most promising and very tested GRB correlation is the E_{peak}-E_{iso} relation, also known as the Amati relation.[25] Here, the intrinsic peak energy of the GRB prompt emission estimated within the T_{90} was found to be related with the isotropic energy emitted in the same time interval. This correlation is satisfied by all long GRBs within a large interval for the energy (almost six orders of magnitude). To illustrate the concept of GRBs as standardizable candles, the E_{peak} is the quantity that represents our cosmology-independent observable while E_{iso} is our "candle": the latter quantity is indeed related to the underlying cosmology through the luminosity distance d_l, and quantified by the bolometric fluence, which is given by the integrated GRB prompt flux in a specific energy range.[26, 27] Once we derive the distance for a large sample of GRBs, we can start to build an Hubble diagram and then test the cosmological model.[28] The use of the Amati relation has provided for the first time an interesting estimate of the cosmological parameters with GRBs,[29, 30] if compared with other non-standard probes.

Observing these events for more than 20 years with space-based satellites such as *Swift*[31] and *Fermi*,[32] has permitted to build large dataset of GRBs. Moreover, other correlations between GRB observed quantities started to appear frequently in literature.[33] The majority of these correlations have also been used to test cosmological models with some interesting applications. A very promising method that has provided some very interesting results is based on the use of a correlation that connects prompt and afterglow quantities, namely the Combo relation.[34] This relation originates from two existing proposed correlations, the previously-cited Amati relation and its extension to X-rays.[18, 35] The core of the Combo relation is represented by a light-curve fitting procedure to model the entire X-ray afterglow emission: the use of a code able to model the X-ray light curve and that permits to get rid of over-imposed flares by using a very efficient iterative method[35] allows to measure the "candle". From this procedure, the X-ray afterglow observables, namely the luminosity of the afterglow L_0, the time when the late time decay starts t_a and the power-law index of the late light curve decay α are computed and have been found in a tight relation with the GRB prompt peak energy E_{peak}.

The final result is a correlation that is satisfied by all long GRBs, e.g. no outliers,[36] for which there exist a known value for E_{peak} and with a complete observed X-ray afterglow by the X-ray Telescope (XRT) instrument on-board *Swift*. About a physical interpretation of the correlation, the connection between prompt and afterglow properties has been investigated only in recent times[37] but its use to constrain the cosmological models and some exotic variant has provided very interesting results (see also Fig. 1). In recent times, Muccino et al.[36] have found a possible indication of an evolution of the dark energy equation of state parameter w with redshift. However, the standard ΛCDM model with the constant solution $w = -1$ is still consistent with the statistical uncertainties derived by their analysis, which suggests the possibility that unaccounted systematics have a great influence on GRB luminosity correlations.

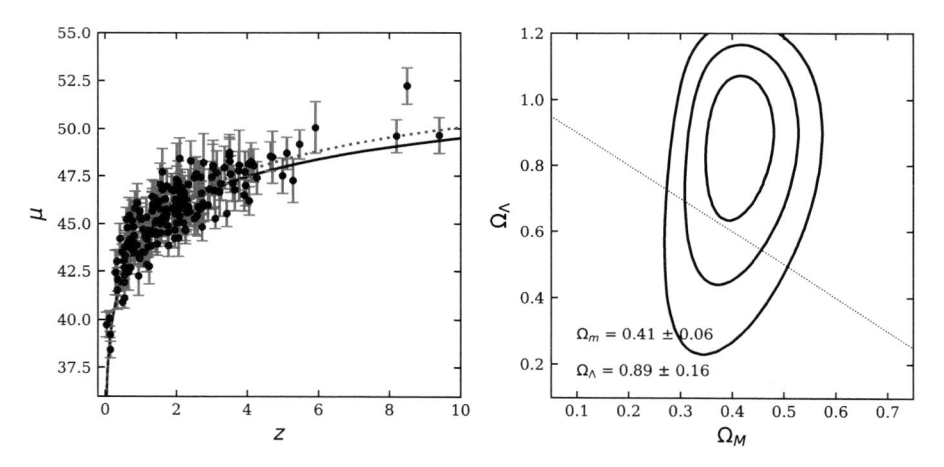

Fig. 1. *(Left panel)* The Hubble diagram built with 174 GRBs satisfying the Combo relation. The black curve corresponds to the best fit model in the context of a non-flat ΛCDM cosmological scenario, while the dotted curve represents a fiducial ΛCDM model with $H_0 = 70$ km/s/Mpc, $\Omega_m = 0.3$ and $\Omega_\Lambda = 0.7$. *Right panel* The best-fit confidence regions obtained by fitting the Combo GRB sample of 174 events within the context of a non-flat ΛCDM cosmological scenario. Here H_0 was fixed to 70 km/s/Mpc. Extra scatter uncertainties and systematics have not been included in the analysis.

3. Drawbacks

So far so good! However, it is mandatory to discuss the main sources of uncertainties that affect the use of GRBs as standardized candles. First, the lack of a considerable number of GRBs at low redshifts ($z < 0.02$) prevents us to use accurate primary distance indicators to calibrate GRB luminosity correlations. The only GRB event observed at very close distances, GRB 980425,[11] does not have a great coverage in X-rays, given the lack of rapidly-slewing detectors such as *Swift* at the epoch of its discovery. Moreover, its very faint emission and luminosity do not assure that GRB 980425 is really a "cosmological" GRB but it can be originated in other energetic events such as the break-out of the shock wave following the collapse of a massive star.[38]

This problem led several authors to use alternative approaches to calibrate GRB relations, such as 1) the use of an underlying cosmology as explained in the review by Schaefer,[27] a method that includes an intrinsic circularity; 2) the use of alternative techniques that approximate the behavior of the luminosity distance evolution with the use of series expansion for the Hubble-Lemaitre law,[39–41] which however lead to serious problems at high-redshifts, or 3) the use of secondary distance indicators such as type-Ia SNe.[40,42] The latter method is very promising, given the high level of accuracy that type-Ia SN cosmology has reached in the last years.[43] However, in this approach the procedure of calibrating GRB luminosity relation is actually a seven-step method (type-Ia SNe are indeed calibrated using other primary distance indicators and so on). Moreover, given that the most used sample of type-Ia SNe, such as the Pantheon[44] spans a large distance range, any cosmological inference obtained using GRBs calibrated with type-Ia SNe will be strongly biased by the cosmology traced by these SNe, being their luminosity correlations characterised by a great accuracy. In this light, GRBs can only be considered as a mere extension of type-Ia SN Hubble Diagram and not an independent probe.

Selection effects and systematics errors also represent a big source of uncertainty when computing the accuracy (e.g. the scatter) of luminosity relations, but they have been rarely taken into account. In literature, it is common to find GRB samples that have been built using data coming from different detectors, mostly at high-energies (hard X-rays), which are characterised by different energy sensitivities, and then sensitive to specific GRB events. Finally, Malmquist bias also has a strong impact on the detection of the brightest events, and then on the final construction of the sample considered. This also affects the GRB redshift identification, which then becomes possible only for the brightest events. Correcting for the Malmquist bias is not easy, given that the distribution of GRB properties (luminosity function, physical characteristics of their progenitors, etc.) can vary with redshift, and then the use of incomplete GRB samples can lead to ambiguous results.[45]

4. Perspectives

Apart from getting more GRBs at high redshifts, a mission that will be the goal of future space missions, attempting to solve the above issues represents a mandatory step to render more reliable the use of GRBs as distance indicators. The scatter of all GRB luminosity correlations is also not competitive if compared with type-Ia

SNe. However, incoming surveys are currently discovering SNe at redshift comparable to the low end of the GRB distance distribution, and with the Rubin Legacy Survey of Space and Time (LSST) project, starting in few years, we can easily arrive to discover several type-Ia SNe at redshift $z \sim 2$. This will permit to compare GRBs and SNe correlations in a wide redshift range, allowing us to refine the calibration of GRB correlations. An important support on this line comes from the use of machine learning algorithms to reconstruct the distance luminosity function with the redshift, independently on the underlying cosmology. Similar approaches have been already developed, e.g.,[46,47] with very promising results. However, also this approach includes some hidden uncertainties that depend on the model used to train the calibrating sample and the sample itself: uncertainties affecting the training sample[48] will propagate on the calibration of GRB correlations, leading to a completely wrong posterior distributions when using GRBs as cosmological tools. Finally, without a correct treatment of the systematics affecting all GRB correlations, all the results should be treated with large caution.

5. Conclusions

GRB luminosity correlations represent a powerful tool to investigate the high redshift Universe, but their use is still affected by several issues that their application as accurate distance indicators is still far to come. The lack of a complete treatment of uncertainties, in particular of the systematics affecting their observables, and of an unbiased calibration technique represents the main barrier to overcome in order to take advantage of the information that these powerful explosions can give us on the early Universe.

Acknowledgments

Li is extremely grateful to Marco Muccino, Elena Zaninoni and Giovanni Battista Pisani for their support and collaboration. LI was supported by grants from VILLUM FONDEN (project num-ber 16599 and 25501).

References

1. B. Zhang, *The Physics of Gamma-Ray Bursts* 2018.
2. A. Levan, *Gamma-Ray Bursts* 2018.
3. D. Band, J. Matteson, L. Ford, B. Schaefer, D. Palmer, B. Teegarden, T. Cline, M. Briggs, W. Paciesas, G. Pendleton, G. Fishman, C. Kouveliotou, C. Meegan, R. Wilson and P. Lestrade, BATSE Observations of Gamma-Ray Burst Spectra. I. Spectral Diversity, *ApJ* **413**, p. 281 (August 1993).
4. C. Kouveliotou, C. A. Meegan, G. J. Fishman, N. P. Bhat, M. S. Briggs, T. M. Koshut, W. S. Paciesas and G. N. Pendleton, Identification of Two Classes of Gamma-Ray Bursts, *ApJ* **413**, p. L101 (August 1993).

5. J. Hjorth, D. Watson, J. P. U. Fynbo, P. A. Price, B. L. Jensen, U. G. Jørgensen, D. Kubas, J. Gorosabel, P. Jakobsson, J. Sollerman, K. Pedersen and C. Kouveliotou, The optical afterglow of the short γ-ray burst GRB 050709, *Nature* **437**, 859 (October 2005).
6. D. Eichler, M. Livio, T. Piran and D. N. Schramm, Nucleosynthesis, neutrino bursts and γ-rays from coalescing neutron stars, *Nature* **340**, 126 (July 1989).
7. R. Perna and K. Belczynski, Short Gamma-Ray Bursts and Mergers of Compact Objects: Observational Constraints, *ApJ* **570**, 252 (May 2002).
8. A. Goldstein, P. Veres, E. Burns, M. S. Briggs, R. Hamburg, D. Kocevski, C. A. Wilson-Hodge, R. D. Preece, S. Poolakkil, O. J. Roberts, C. M. Hui, V. Connaughton, J. Racusin, A. von Kienlin, T. Dal Canton, N. Christensen, T. Littenberg, K. Siellez, L. Blackburn, J. Broida, E. Bissaldi, W. H. Cleveland, M. H. Gibby, M. M. Giles, R. M. Kippen, S. McBreen, J. McEnery, C. A. Meegan, W. S. Paciesas and M. Stanbro, An Ordinary Short Gamma-Ray Burst with Extraordinary Implications: Fermi-GBM Detection of GRB 170817A, *ApJ* **848**, p. L14 (October 2017).
9. S. E. Woosley, Gamma-Ray Bursts from Stellar Mass Accretion Disks around Black Holes, *ApJ* **405**, p. 273 (March 1993).
10. A. I. MacFadyen and S. E. Woosley, Collapsars: Gamma-Ray Bursts and Explosions in "Failed Supernovae", *ApJ* **524**, 262 (October 1999).
11. T. J. Galama, P. M. Vreeswijk, J. van Paradijs, C. Kouveliotou, T. Augusteijn, H. Böhnhardt, J. P. Brewer, V. Doublier, J. F. Gonzalez, B. Leibundgut, C. Lidman, O. R. Hainaut, F. Patat, J. Heise, J. in't Zand, K. Hurley, P. J. Groot, R. G. Strom, P. A. Mazzali, K. Iwamoto, K. Nomoto, H. Umeda, T. Nakamura, T. R. Young, T. Suzuki, T. Shigeyama, T. Koshut, M. Kippen, C. Robinson, P. de Wildt, R. A. M. J. Wijers, N. Tanvir, J. Greiner, E. Pian, E. Palazzi, F. Frontera, N. Masetti, L. Nicastro, M. Feroci, E. Costa, L. Piro, B. A. Peterson, C. Tinney, B. Boyle, R. Cannon, R. Stathakis, E. Sadler, M. C. Begam and P. Ianna, An unusual supernova in the error box of the γ-ray burst of 25 April 1998, *Nature* **395**, 670 (October 1998).
12. J. Hjorth, J. Sollerman, P. Møller, J. P. U. Fynbo, S. E. Woosley, C. Kouveliotou, N. R. Tanvir, J. Greiner, M. I. Andersen, A. J. Castro-Tirado, J. M. Castro Cerón, A. S. Fruchter, J. Gorosabel, P. Jakobsson, L. Kaper, S. Klose, N. Masetti, H. Pedersen, K. Pedersen, E. Pian, E. Palazzi, J. E. Rhoads, E. Rol, E. P. J. van den Heuvel, P. M. Vreeswijk, D. Watson and R. A. M. J. Wijers, A very energetic supernova associated with the γ-ray burst of 29 March 2003, *Nature* **423**, 847 (June 2003).
13. B. Zhang, Y. Z. Fan, J. Dyks, S. Kobayashi, P. Mészáros, D. N. Burrows, J. A. Nousek and N. Gehrels, Physical Processes Shaping Gamma-Ray Burst X-Ray Afterglow Light Curves: Theoretical Implications from the Swift X-Ray Telescope Observations, *ApJ* **642**, 354 (May 2006).
14. J. A. Nousek, C. Kouveliotou, D. Grupe, K. L. Page, J. Granot, E. Ramirez-Ruiz, S. K. Patel, D. N. Burrows, V. Mangano, S. Barthelmy, A. P. Beardmore, S. Campana, M. Capalbi, G. Chincarini, G. Cusumano, A. D. Falcone, N. Gehrels, P. Giommi, M. R. Goad, O. Godet, C. P. Hurkett, J. A. Kennea, A. Moretti, P. T. O'Brien, J. P. Osborne, P. Romano, G. Tagliaferri and A. A. Wells, Evidence for a Canonical Gamma-Ray Burst Afterglow Light Curve in the Swift XRT Data, *ApJ* **642**, 389 (May 2006).
15. R. Willingale, P. T. O'Brien, J. P. Osborne, O. Godet, K. L. Page, M. R. Goad, D. N. Burrows, B. Zhang, E. Rol, N. Gehrels and G. Chincarini, Testing the Standard Fireball Model of Gamma-Ray Bursts Using Late X-Ray Afterglows Measured by Swift, *ApJ* **662**, 1093 (June 2007).

16. D. A. Kann, S. Klose, B. Zhang, D. Malesani, E. Nakar, A. Pozanenko, A. C. Wilson, N. R. Butler, P. Jakobsson, S. Schulze, M. Andreev, L. A. Antonelli, I. F. Bikmaev, V. Biryukov, M. Böttcher, R. A. Burenin, J. M. Castro Cerón, A. J. Castro-Tirado, G. Chincarini, B. E. Cobb, S. Covino, P. D'Avanzo, V. D'Elia, M. Della Valle, A. de Ugarte Postigo, Y. Efimov, P. Ferrero, D. Fugazza, J. P. U. Fynbo, M. Gålfalk, F. Grundahl, J. Gorosabel, S. Gupta, S. Guziy, B. Hafizov, J. Hjorth, K. Holhjem, M. Ibrahimov, M. Im, G. L. Israel, M. Jelínek, B. L. Jensen, R. Karimov, I. M. Khamitov, Ü. Kiziloğlu, E. Klunko, P. Kubánek, A. S. Kutyrev, P. Laursen, A. J. Levan, F. Mannucci, C. M. Martin, A. Mescheryakov, N. Mirabal, J. P. Norris, J. E. Ovaldsen, D. Paraficz, E. Pavlenko, S. Piranomonte, A. Rossi, V. Rumyantsev, R. Salinas, A. Sergeev, D. Sharapov, J. Sollerman, B. Stecklum, L. Stella, G. Tagliaferri, N. R. Tanvir, J. Telting, V. Testa, A. C. Updike, A. Volnova, D. Watson, K. Wiersema and D. Xu, The Afterglows of Swift-era Gamma-ray Bursts. I. Comparing pre-Swift and Swift-era Long/Soft (Type II) GRB Optical Afterglows, *ApJ* **720**, 1513 (September 2010).
17. D. A. Frail, S. R. Kulkarni, R. Sari, G. B. Taylor, D. S. Shepherd, J. S. Bloom, C. H. Young, L. Nicastro and N. Masetti, The Radio Afterglow from GRB 980519: A Test of the Jet and Circumstellar Models, *ApJ* **534**, 559 (May 2000).
18. M. G. Bernardini, R. Margutti, E. Zaninoni and G. Chincarini, A universal scaling for short and long gamma-ray bursts: $E_{X,iso}$ - $E_{\gamma,iso}$ - E_{pk}, *MNRAS* **425**, 1199 (September 2012).
19. N. Kawai, G. Kosugi, K. Aoki, T. Yamada, T. Totani, K. Ohta, M. Iye, T. Hattori, W. Aoki, H. Furusawa, K. Hurley, K. S. Kawabata, N. Kobayashi, Y. Komiyama, Y. Mizumoto, K. Nomoto, J. Noumaru, R. Ogasawara, R. Sato, K. Sekiguchi, Y. Shirasaki, M. Suzuki, T. Takata, T. Tamagawa, H. Terada, J. Watanabe, Y. Yatsu and A. Yoshida, An optical spectrum of the afterglow of a γ-ray burst at a redshift of z = 6.295, *Nature* **440**, 184 (March 2006).
20. J. Greiner, C. Clemens, T. Krühler, A. von Kienlin, A. Rau, R. Sari, D. B. Fox, N. Kawai, P. Afonso, M. Ajello, E. Berger, S. B. Cenko, A. Cucchiara, R. Filgas, S. Klose, A. Küpcü Yoldaş, G. G. Lichti, S. Löw, S. McBreen, T. Nagayama, A. Rossi, S. Sato, G. Szokoly, A. Yoldaş and X. L. Zhang, The redshift and afterglow of the extremely energetic gamma-ray burst GRB 080916C, *A&A* **498**, 89 (April 2009).
21. N. R. Tanvir, D. B. Fox, A. J. Levan, E. Berger, K. Wiersema, J. P. U. Fynbo, A. Cucchiara, T. Krühler, N. Gehrels, J. S. Bloom, J. Greiner, P. A. Evans, E. Rol, F. Olivares, J. Hjorth, P. Jakobsson, J. Farihi, R. Willingale, R. L. C. Starling, S. B. Cenko, D. Perley, J. R. Maund, J. Duke, R. A. M. J. Wijers, A. J. Adamson, A. Allan, M. N. Bremer, D. N. Burrows, A. J. Castro-Tirado, B. Cavanagh, A. de Ugarte Postigo, M. A. Dopita, T. A. Fatkhullin, A. S. Fruchter, R. J. Foley, J. Gorosabel, J. Kennea, T. Kerr, S. Klose, H. A. Krimm, V. N. Komarova, S. R. Kulkarni, A. S. Moskvitin, C. G. Mundell, T. Naylor, K. Page, B. E. Penprase, M. Perri, P. Podsiadlowski, K. Roth, R. E. Rutledge, T. Sakamoto, P. Schady, B. P. Schmidt, A. M. Soderberg, J. Sollerman, A. W. Stephens, G. Stratta, T. N. Ukwatta, D. Watson, E. Westra, T. Wold and C. Wolf, A γ-ray burst at a redshift of z~8.2, *Nature* **461**, 1254 (October 2009).
22. A. Cucchiara, A. J. Levan, D. B. Fox, N. R. Tanvir, T. N. Ukwatta, E. Berger, T. Krühler, A. Küpcü Yoldaş, X. F. Wu, K. Toma, J. Greiner, F. E. Olivares, A. Rowlinson, L. Amati, T. Sakamoto, K. Roth, A. Stephens, A. Fritz, J. P. U. Fynbo, J. Hjorth, D. Malesani, P. Jakobsson, K. Wiersema, P. T. O'Brien, A. M. Soderberg, R. J. Foley, A. S. Fruchter, J. Rhoads, R. E. Rutledge, B. P. Schmidt, M. A. Dopita, P. Podsiadlowski, R. Willingale, C. Wolf, S. R. Kulkarni and P. D'Avanzo, A Photometric Redshift of z ~9.4 for GRB 090429B, *ApJ* **736**, p. 7 (July 2011).

23. N. R. Tanvir, A. J. Levan, A. S. Fruchter, J. P. U. Fynbo, J. Hjorth, K. Wiersema, M. N. Bremer, J. Rhoads, P. Jakobsson, P. T. O'Brien, E. R. Stanway, D. Bersier, P. Natarajan, J. Greiner, D. Watson, A. J. Castro-Tirado, R. A. M. J. Wijers, R. L. C. Starling, K. Misra, J. F. Graham and C. Kouveliotou, Star Formation in the Early Universe: Beyond the Tip of the Iceberg, *ApJ* **754**, p. 46 (July 2012).
24. K. S. Mandel, G. Narayan and R. P. Kirshner, Type Ia Supernova Light Curve Inference: Hierarchical Models in the Optical and Near-infrared, *ApJ* **731**, p. 120 (April 2011).
25. L. Amati, F. Frontera, M. Tavani, J. J. M. in't Zand, A. Antonelli, E. Costa, M. Feroci, C. Guidorzi, J. Heise, N. Masetti, E. Montanari, L. Nicastro, E. Palazzi, E. Pian, L. Piro and P. Soffitta, Intrinsic spectra and energetics of BeppoSAX Gamma-Ray Bursts with known redshifts, *A&A* **390**, 81 (July 2002).
26. L. Amati, The $E_{p,i}$-E_{iso} correlation in gamma-ray bursts: updated observational status, re-analysis and main implications, *MNRAS* **372**, 233 (October 2006).
27. B. E. Schaefer, The Hubble Diagram to Redshift ∼6 from 69 Gamma-Ray Bursts, *ApJ* **660**, 16 (May 2007).
28. L. Izzo, S. Capozziello, G. Covone and M. Capaccioli, Extending the Hubble diagram by gamma ray bursts, *A&A* **508**, 63 (December 2009).
29. L. Amati, C. Guidorzi, F. Frontera, M. Della Valle, F. Finelli, R. Landi and E. Montanari, Measuring the cosmological parameters with the $E_{p,i}$-E_{iso} correlation of gamma-ray bursts, *MNRAS* **391**, 577 (December 2008).
30. L. Amati and M. Della Valle, Measuring Cosmological Parameters with Gamma Ray Bursts, *International Journal of Modern Physics D* **22**, p. 1330028 (December 2013).
31. N. Gehrels, E. Ramirez-Ruiz and D. B. Fox, Gamma-Ray Bursts in the Swift Era, *ARA&A* **47**, 567 (September 2009).
32. W. S. Paciesas, C. A. Meegan, A. von Kienlin, P. N. Bhat, E. Bissaldi, M. S. Briggs, J. M. Burgess, V. Chaplin, V. Connaughton, R. Diehl, G. J. Fishman, G. Fitzpatrick, S. Foley, M. Gibby, M. Giles, A. Goldstein, J. Greiner, D. Gruber, S. Guiriec, A. J. van der Horst, R. M. Kippen, C. Kouveliotou, G. Lichti, L. Lin, S. McBreen, R. D. Preece, A. Rau, D. Tierney and C. Wilson-Hodge, The Fermi GBM Gamma-Ray Burst Catalog: The First Two Years, *ApJS* **199**, p. 18 (March 2012).
33. M. Dainotti, R. Del Vecchio and M. Tarnopolski, Gamma Ray Burst Prompt correlations, *arXiv e-prints*, p. arXiv:1612.00618 (December 2016).
34. L. Izzo, M. Muccino, E. Zaninoni, L. Amati and M. Della Valle, New measurements of Ω_m from gamma-ray bursts, *A&A* **582**, p. A115 (October 2015).
35. E. Zaninoni, M. G. Bernardini, R. Margutti, S. Oates and G. Chincarini, Gamma-ray burst optical light-curve zoo: Comparison with X-ray observations, *A&A* **557**, p. A12 (September 2013).
36. M. Muccino, L. Izzo, O. Luongo, K. Boshkayev, L. Amati, M. Della Valle, G. B. Pisani and E. Zaninoni, Tracing Dark Energy History with Gamma-Ray Bursts, *ApJ* **908**, p. 181 (February 2021).
37. G. Oganesyan, S. Ascenzi, M. Branchesi, O. S. Salafia, S. Dall'Osso and G. Ghirlanda, Structured Jets and X-Ray Plateaus in Gamma-Ray Burst Phenomena, *ApJ* **893**, p. 88 (April 2020).
38. E. Nakar and R. Sari, Relativistic Shock Breakouts—A Variety of Gamma-Ray Flares: From Low-luminosity Gamma-Ray Bursts to Type Ia Supernovae, *ApJ* **747**, p. 88 (March 2012).
39. M. Visser, Cosmography: Cosmology without the Einstein equations, *General Relativity and Gravitation* **37**, 1541 (September 2005).
40. S. Capozziello and L. Izzo, Cosmography by gamma ray bursts, *A&A* **490**, 31 (October 2008).

41. V. Vitagliano, J.-Q. Xia, S. Liberati and M. Viel, High-redshift cosmography, **2010**, p. 005 (March 2010).
42. M. Demianski, E. Piedipalumbo, D. Sawant and L. Amati, Cosmology with gamma-ray bursts. I. The Hubble diagram through the calibrated $E_{p,I}$-E_{iso} correlation, *A&A* **598**, p. A112 (February 2017).
43. A. G. Riess, S. Casertano, W. Yuan, J. B. Bowers, L. Macri, J. C. Zinn and D. Scolnic, Cosmic Distances Calibrated to 1% Precision with Gaia EDR3 Parallaxes and Hubble Space Telescope Photometry of 75 Milky Way Cepheids Confirm Tension with ΛCDM, *ApJ* **908**, p. L6 (February 2021).
44. D. M. Scolnic, D. O. Jones, A. Rest, Y. C. Pan, R. Chornock, R. J. Foley, M. E. Huber, R. Kessler, G. Narayan, A. G. Riess, S. Rodney, E. Berger, D. J. Brout, P. J. Challis, M. Drout, D. Finkbeiner, R. Lunnan, R. P. Kirshner, N. E. Sanders, E. Schlafly, S. Smartt, C. W. Stubbs, J. Tonry, W. M. Wood-Vasey, M. Foley, J. Hand, E. Johnson, W. S. Burgett, K. C. Chambers, P. W. Draper, K. W. Hodapp, N. Kaiser, R. P. Kudritzki, E. A. Magnier, N. Metcalfe, F. Bresolin, E. Gall, R. Kotak M. McCrum, K. W. Smith, The Complete Light-curve Sample of Spectroscopically Confirmed Type Ia Supernovae from Pan-STARRS1 and Cosmological Constraints from The Combined Pantheon Sample, *ApJ*, **859**, p. 101 (2018).
45. A. Pescalli, G. Ghirlanda, R. Salvaterra, G. Ghisellini, S. D. Vergani, F. Nappo, O. S. Salafia, A. Melandri, S. Covino and D. Götz, The rate and luminosity function of long gamma ray bursts, *A&A* **587**, p. A40 (March 2016).
46. O. Luongo and M. Muccino, Model-independent calibrations of gamma-ray bursts using machine learning, *MNRAS* **503**, 4581 (May 2021).
47. L. Tang, X. Li, H.-N. Lin and L. Liu, Model-independently Calibrating the Luminosity Correlations of Gamma-Ray Bursts Using Deep Learning, *ApJ* **907**, p. 121 (February 2021).
48. A. Ahlstrom Kjerrgren and E. Mortsell, On the use of galaxies as clocks and the universal expansion, *arXiv e-prints*, p. arXiv:2106.11317 (June 2021).

Surface brightness fluctuations: The method and future applications

Michele Cantiello

INAF — Astronomical Observatory of Abruzzo,
Via Maggini, 64100, Teramo, Italy
E-mail: michele.cantiello@inaf.it

The surface brightness fluctuations method is one of the most robust extragalactic distance indicators: with an accuracy comparable to type Ia supernovae Ia and Cepheids ($\sim 5\%$ per galaxy) it is used in a wide range of distances: from very local, up to values relevant for measuring H_0.

In these proceedings, I present an overview of the technique and of the main results it allowed to obtain, further discussing the great potential with future applications based on forthcoming ground and space-based facilities.

Keywords: Cosmological Parameters; Hubble-Lemaitre Constant; Galaxy Distances

1. Introduction

The idea of using stellar counts to study the distance or the star content of a stellar population dates back to the first half of the previous century.[1,2] With the advent of CCDs, Ref. 3 introduced the surface brightness fluctuations (SBF hereafter) method as a modern formalism to obtain distances to stellar systems relying on the discrete nature of star counts. The SBF definition by Ref. 3 uses the Poisson statistics of star counts to measure a quantity that is closely linked to the mean brightness of red giant branch (RGB) stars in the target galaxy or, more in general, in the observed stellar system.

To date, the SBF method is one of the most robust extragalactic distance indicators: with an accuracy comparable to type Ia supernovae (SNe Ia) or Cepheids ($\sim 5\%$ per galaxy) without the limitations of the serendipitousness intrinsic to SNe, or the long observing campaigns needed for Cepheids. Moreover, it is used in a wide range of distances: from the Local Group, up to values relevant for measuring H_0.

Qualitatively, the idea behind the SBF is relatively simple: the stars which appear as resolved sources at relatively small distances, gradually "blend" in a smooth brightness profile when the stellar system moves to larger and larger distances (Figure 1).

Quantitatively, *SBFs are defined as the ratio of the second to the first moment of the stellar luminosity function in a population of stars*. From this basic definition some of the most relevant characteristics of the method follow: how SBF can be measured and what are the inherent complexities, what are the preferred targets, the opportunity of calibrating SBF magnitudes using empirical methods or stellar population synthesis techniques, etc.

In what follows, I will overview the technique, providing a detailed description of the method and on how measurements are carried out, what are the main limitations and sources of uncertainty, and present its great potential with applications based on forthcoming ground and space-based telescopes.

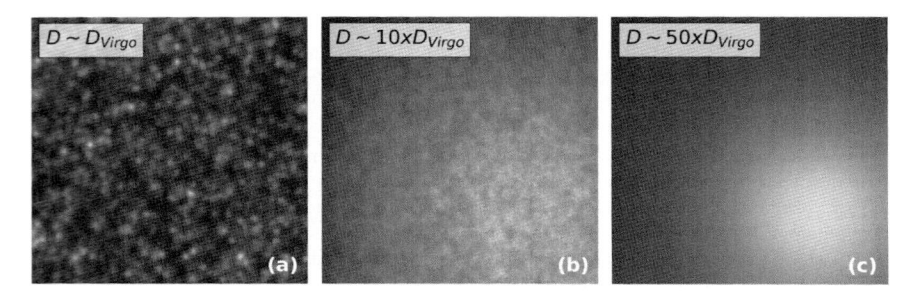

Fig. 1. Qualitative illustration of SBF signal. Panel (a): Simulation of the stellar population in a spheroidal galaxy at the distance of the Virgo cluster ($d \simeq 16.5$ Mpc, Ref. 4) as will be observed with the E-ELT in $\sim$1 hour exposure time (Cantiello et al., 2022, in prep.). (b) Same as in panel (a), but for a galaxy ten times more distant. Panel (c): Same as in panel (a), but for a galaxy fifty times more distant. Stars, which appear marginally resolved in panel (a), blend into a smooth brightness profile at larger distances.

2. From SBF analysis to galaxy distances

The SBF signal is not easy visualize as it might be for various other classical standard rulers (variable stars, parallaxes, SNe Ia etc.) and, consequently, it does not appear trivial how star-counts fluctuations can be translated into a distance estimate. For this reason, below I provide a concise and detailed description on how the SBF magnitudes $\overline{m}$ are measured, what are the preferred targets, how distances are then derived, and what are the dominant sources of errors.

2.1. *Measurements*

2.1.1. *Determining SBF magnitudes*

The SBF signal, in the absence of instrumental blurring and of other sources of fluctuations but the stellar counts, would simply be the Poisson variance between pixels due to the varying number of stars per pixel, normalized to the galaxy local mean flux. The instrumental point spread function (PSF) blurring forces a correlation between adjacent resolution elements, thus the SBF signal results to be convolved with the PSF, and its measure needs to be carried out in the Fourier domain.

A further complication is that there are sources of *spurious* non-stellar fluctuations. The presence of globular clusters (GCs) in the galaxy, of background galaxies in the observed field, of morphological irregularities due to dust contamination, or

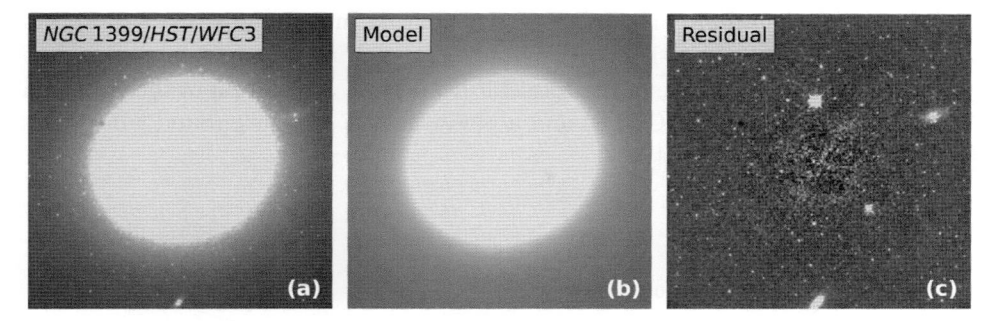

Fig. 2. Illustration of the SBF measurements. (a) Near-infrared image of NGC 1399 from the HST WFC3 camera. (b) Model of NGC 1399's surface brightness distribution derived from the WFC3/IR image. (c) Residual frame, obtained from the galaxy image (a) minus the model (b).

of obvious regions with markedly different stellar populations (e.g. star forming regions, overlapping regions of companion bright galaxies, etc.), affect the Poisson stellar fluctuation counts. Hence, to estimate fluctuation magnitude $\overline{m}$ all these possible sources of contamination need to be taken into account and removed.

The details of the procedures adopted for measuring SBFs are described in details in a number of papers.[5-12] Here, we summarize the main steps of the procedure, which consists of deriving the:

i) average galaxy surface brightness profile: this corresponds to the first moment of the host stellar luminosity function (model frame in Fig. 2 (b));

ii) residual frame: the galaxy subtracted frame. This image basically corresponds to the second moment of the luminosity function (Fig. 2 Panel (c));

iii) mask frame: all sources of non-stellar variance (dust, GCs, background galaxies, etc.) are identified and masked out;

iv) residual, masked frame normalized to the model frame: this image contains the bumpiness from the stellar fluctuations, plus the fluctuations of un-excised sources;

iv) power spectrum of the total fluctuations frame. The fluctuations are convolved with the instrumental PSF, thus in the Fourier domain they are multiplied to the Fourier transform of the PSF. Once derived the PSF and its power spectrum, the SBF amplitude is obtained as the constant term P_0 giving the best match between the power spectrum of the total fluctuations frame, $P(K)$, to the power spectrum of the PSF, $E(k)$, plus a white noise P_1 component: $P(k) = P_0 \times E(k) + P_1$. Figure 3 (left panel) shows a schematic example of the fitting procedure;

v) correction for spurious residual fluctuations. The masking process is effective down to a given magnitude limit: the deeper the magnitude limit the higher the detection limit of contaminating sources. However, the spurious fluctuations arising from GCs and background galaxies fainter than the detection limit need to be evaluated and subtracted out. A fit of the combined luminosity functions (LF hereafter) of GCs and background galaxies above the limiting magnitude is used to obtain by extrapolation the extra-fluctuations term, P_r, due to sources fainter than the detection limit. An example of the total LF fit, derived as the sum of the Gaussian LF for GCs in the galaxy (GCLF) and a power law LF for background galaxies, is shown in Fig. 3 (right panel).

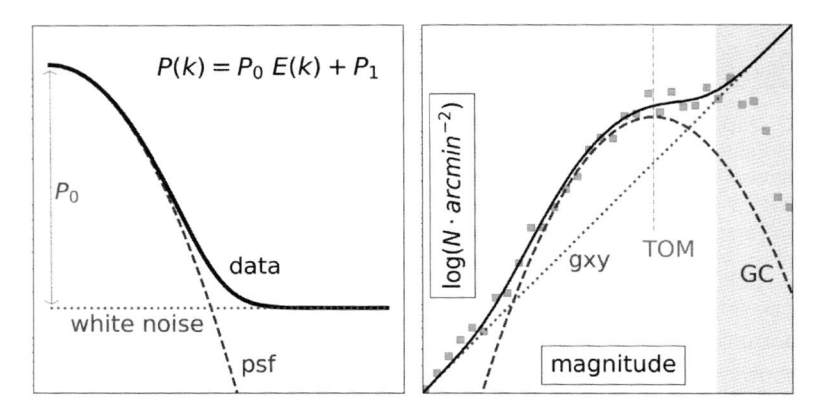

Fig. 3. Left: A schematic illustration of the SBF power spectrum analysis. Right panel: Typical luminosity function analysis for estimating the residual variance P_r due to contaminating sources: green squares show the data, the blue curve and red line show the fits to the GCs and background galaxies LFs, respectively, and the solid black line is the combined model luminosity function (data and fits are from Ref. 13). The vertical grey dashed line indicates the GCLF turnover magnitude, TOM, and the shaded area shows the magnitude interval where the detection is incomplete.

The residual variance is then evaluated from the integral of the second moment of the total luminosity function in the flux interval $[0, f_{lim}]$:

$$\sigma_r^2 = \int_0^{f_{lim}} n_{obj}(f) \times f^2 df \qquad (1)$$

where f_{lim} is the flux corresponding to the limiting magnitude, m_{lim}, and $n_{obj}(f)$ is the GC and background galaxies combined LF (Fig. 3, right panel). The residual variance P_r is then derived from σ_r^2 normalized by the galaxy surface brightness;

vi) *SBF magnitudes*: once measured the total fluctuation amplitude, P_0, and estimated the spurious fluctuations term P_r, the stellar fluctuations follows as $P_f = P_0 - P_r$, and then the SBF magnitude as $\bar{m} = -2.5\log(P_f) + mag_{z.p.}$, where the $mag_{z.p.}$ term is the instrumental zero point magnitude.

Finally, to convert $\bar{m}$ into a distance, the characteristic absolute SBF magnitude of the population, $\bar{M}$, needs to be known. By combining the absolute and apparent SBF magnitudes, the distance modulus μ_0 follows as usual: $\mu_0 = \bar{m} - \bar{M}$ and, then, the distance d is derived by inverting relation $\mu_0 = 5\log(d/Mpc) + 25$.

2.1.2. Calibrating SBF magnitudes

To obtain a calibration of $\bar{M}$, to be used for deriving μ_0, two different approaches are typically adopted: empirical calibrations or population synthesis models.

$\bar{M}$ can be described as a one-parameter family, with the integrated color of the galaxy (or, more in general, of the stellar population) used as main correlation parameter, i.e. $\overline{M} = \alpha + \beta \times color$; at fixed pass-band $\bar{M}$ is a universal function of the color, with residual intrinsic dispersion which can be as ~ 0.05 mag depending on the pass-band.[4,9]

Using theoretical calibrations the SBF method is a primary distance indicator: it does not carry over the systematic uncertainty from the first steps of the calibration. Despite the generally good match between predictions from independent stellar population synthesis models, this is mostly limited to the optical bands. The matching of SBF magnitudes from different models in the blue passbands (more sensitive to stellar population properties), or in the near-IR (where the stellar models are yet not as robust is in the optical bands), is of the order of ~ 0.2 mag. The difference between models is then significantly larger than the estimated SBF cosmic scatter derived empirically.

Finally, although there are obvious advantages from using calibrations based on stellar population models, to date most of the available SBF distances rely on empirical calibrations.[4,11,14,15]

2.1.3. Caveats in measuring SBF

One of the major problems in measuring SBF is the contamination from GCs. As the distance of the galaxy increases, the detection of GCs gets more complicated by the combination of GCs crowding and flux limit, consequently the contamination from GCs increases.

Since the estimate of the contamination from unidentified GCs is made by extrapolating the observed GCLF at magnitude levels fainter than the limiting magnitude (Fig. 3, right panel), the brighter the limiting magnitude is, the greater the uncertainty due to the extrapolation is, and the larger is the P_r correction. The relative error on P_r is typically assumed to be of the order of 20-25%,[5,16] hence a reliable SBF measurement requires $P_f >> P_r$. A P_r correction less than 10% P_f, or lower, is an essential condition for obtaining reasonably robust estimates of SBF and, therefore, reliable distances. In optical bands, this condition is typically satisfied when the limiting magnitude is at least one magnitude fainter than the GCLF peak magnitude (TOM in Fig. 3, right). In near-infrared bands this condition is less stringent, as the contrast between M_{TOM} and $\bar{M}$ is more favourable to SBF than in optical bands. Even a limiting magnitude m_{lim} close to the TOM, or one magnitude brighter then that, can be enough for accurate measurements.

The present distance limit for SBF is then due to GCs crowding confusion and detection limit. The level of such limit improves with space-based data, where the PSF is typically sharper ($\sim 0\farcs1$ for HST observations).

The contamination due to background galaxies is normally a negligible problem compared to GCs. GCs have a spatial distribution strongly concentrated on the galaxy, while the density of background galaxies per angular unit is roughly constant over the observed field, and substantially smaller than GCs in the bright galaxy regions where the SBF signal is measured.

2.2. *Preferred targets and pass-bands*

Currently, the bands considered for SBF analysis range from the $\sim I$ (central wavelength $\sim 7.5 - 8.0 \mu m$) to $\sim K$ (at $\sim 2.2 \mu m$). SBF at shorter wavelengths are not of great interest, due to the non-negligible dependence on the properties of stellar populations in these bands,[7,16] combined with the more dramatic effect of the contamination of GCs and dust.

The small intrinsic scatter of $\overline{m}$, empirically constrained to ~ 0.05 mag, comes from optical studies in the I and z bands for massive ellipticals. To date, the intrinsic dispersion of $\overline{m}$ in the near-IR bands is much less constrained, but it appears to be a factor of two larger than in the optical bands, likely because of the larger scatter arising from bright giant branch stars.[17] Hence, the preference would seem to be for bands like I or z due to the advantages from the smaller irreducible intrinsic scatter, there are undeniable advantages in near-IR bands. At longer wavelengths SBFs are intrinsically brighter, there is a larger and more favourable contrast with respect to GCs –hence the contamination from these sources is less dramatic–, and the presence of residual dust contamination is typically negligible.

In addition to such advantages, it is worth recalling that some of the key facilities of the next decade will have their highest efficiency at near-IR wavelengths (Sect. 3).

Given the peculiarities of SBF, the ideal target for the measurements is any elliptical galaxy free of dust, with a well identifiable GC system and with a relatively homogeneous population of stars: in other words a passively evolving, red and dead galaxy.

Empirical calibrations show that for bright red galaxies, the linear correlations between $\overline{M}$ and colors have a markedly lower scatter then in the fainter blue galaxies regime. In fact, SBF distances for massive galaxies reach very small statistical uncertainty, 5% or lower.[4,9,10,12] The analysis of integrated colors and SBF for intermediate-mass galaxies, shows that they host a more complex stellar population, consequently the intrinsic scatter of the $\overline{M}$-vs-color relations is larger than for red massive galaxies. Finally, bluer dwarf ellipticals can host stars with low metallicities and/or young ages, or a combination of both. This results in an observed scatter $\gtrsim 0.2$ mag, and statistical uncertainties on distances $\gtrsim 10\%$ due to the calibration effects alone.[12]

In conclusion, red massive galaxies are the ideal target for SBF, yet red bulges of spiral galaxies, or low mass dwarf ellipticals, or any other non-ideal SBF target, represent a plausible object for SBF measurements in all cases where there are no reliable methods to estimate distances.

2.3. *Uncertainties*

2.3.1. *Main Statistical Errors*

We can group statistical uncertainties affecting SBF in two main categories: uncertainties from the measurement of the fluctuations and uncertainties related to the calibration.

For the uncertainties directly linked to the SBF measurement, we mention the accuracy of the galaxy model (item *i* in section 2.1.1), the fit of the external sources (item *v*), the fit of the spatial power spectrum (item *iv*), the determination of the correct normalization to the PSF (which is a systematic uncertainty for a given data set), and the presence of undetected dust.

Concerning the calibration, excluding the zero-point, the total uncertainty of $\bar{M}$ stems from the combination of the uncertainty on the integrated color of the galaxy and of the intrinsic dispersion of the calibration equation (irreducible and wavelength dependent) due to the dispersion of the properties of the stellar population in the galaxy.

Although numerous, statistical uncertainties can be individually minimized by means of suitable observing and data analysis strategies. As reported in the various works,[11,18,19] the total statistical uncertainty on $\bar{m}$ can be 0.05 mag or smaller, while that on $\bar{M}$ is limited by cosmic scatter which, in some bands, can reach levels of 0.06 mag.[4]

In summary, statistical uncertainties in well-conceived observations can be kept at levels below 3% on the distance of the single galaxy.

2.3.2. *Systematic Uncertainties*

For data-sets from different instruments, the only systematic source of error on SBF arises from the calibration zero-point.

Most of the empirical calibrations reported in the literature are based on the zero-point from the SBF ground-based survey by Tonry and collaborators,[14] which obtained SBF for bulges of spiral galaxies with known distance estimates from the Cepheids P-L relations.

In Ref. 11 a total systematic uncertainty of 0.10 mag on SBF distance moduli is cited. This includes a contribution of ∼ 0.08 mag from the tie between SBF and Cepheids,[20] and a contribution of ∼ 0.06 mag for the Cepheid zero-point, dominated by uncertainty in the distance of the LMC.[21]

Ref. 22 have recently revised the LMC distance using a sample of 20 detached eclipsing binaries, the new distance is ∼1% lower than the one used Tonry & coll. and, more important than that, the LMC distance is obtained to 1% precision. The increased accuracy of the LMC distance brings the overall Cepheid zero-point error to 0.028 mag.[23] Consequently, besides a minor effect on the absolute calibration of $\bar{M}$, this revision lowers the systematic error on $\bar{M}$ to ∼ 0.085 mag, slightly more than ∼ 4% on the distance.

An alternative to further lower the systematic error derives from the consideration that the ideal target for SBF are elliptical or lenticular galaxies (Sect. 2.2), which have no distance estimates via Cepheid P-L relations. Classical Cepheid stars are high-mass young stars, preferentially found in the dust rich environments of irregular and spiral galaxies, namely the type of target of no interest for SBF. As an alternative to Cepheids, the RGB Tip method (TRGB[24]) is the ideal candidate for measuring distances of early-type galaxies and obtaining an independent calibration of SBF.

A first attempt to calibrate SBF with TRGB, by Ref. 25, used a sample of 16 galaxies within 10 Mpc dominated by relatively blue objects. The authors found negligible changes on distances. However, obtaining a significant sample of SBF and TRGB distances for massive red elliptical galaxies requires reaching the Virgo cluster, and there are few TRGB distances to early-type galaxies at this distance.

Ref. 19 ([B21] hereafter) analyzed the few galaxies for which these measures exist: the massive bright ellipticals M 60 and M 87 in Virgo, and the dusty merger remnant NGC 1316 in Fornax. Excluding the problematic calibrator NGC 1316, the authors find that the mean offset between the SBF and TRGB distances of the two galaxies in Virgo is approximately -0.01 mag. Although preliminary, this result shows no significant difference between Cepheid- and TRGB-based SBF zero-points.

3. Results and future applications

3.1. Recent results

The SBF method has been in use for more than three decades. By counting the survey works with more than ~ 50 targets measured, the ~ 600 distances in the range from Local Group to 130 Mpc[a] have proven to be a valuable resource for numerous studies. The reliability and precision of these surveys is quite heterogeneous, with errors on the derived distances typically of 4-5% from HST observations, and of $\sim 10\%$ or more for ground-based SBF (ignoring systematic zero-point uncertainty).

These studies covered, or allowed to cover, a wide range of scientific topics in which the measurement of the distance plays a key role. Among the others, we cite *i*) the measurement of distances for massive galaxies to obtain robust relationship between the mass of the black hole and the bulk dynamics of the galaxy;[18] *ii*) the distance to the first observed dark-matter deficient ultra-diffuse galaxy;[26] *iii*) the detailed structure of the Virgo cluster and the measure of the relative Fornax to Virgo cluster distance with exquisite and still unpaired precision;[4] *iv*) the most precise distance to the host galaxy of the binary neutron star merger event GW170817, i.e. the only GW event also observed in the EM spectrum.

---

[a]Without checking for duplicates, we included 300 galaxies from Ref. 14, 130 from Ref. 15 and Ref. 18, 140 from Ref. 4 from the ACSFCS and ACSVCS (see also Ref. 9), 80 from Ref. 11 based on the NGVS survey soon to be complemented with 200 more (Cantiello et al., 2022, in prep.).

The study of the Hubble-Lemaitre parameter H_0 deserves a more detailed discussion. Various estimates of this key cosmological parameter have been obtained,[14,27–29] where SBF are either used to calibrate other distance indicators, like SNe Ia, or directly adopted to estimate the local H_0 value. Here, we focus on two recent studies from Ref. 30 and B21.

Ref. 30 presented a re-calibration of the peak magnitude for a sample of 24 local SNe Ia in galaxies based on SBF distances. The authors adopted a rather heterogeneous sample of SBF-based distances, collected from sets of observations spanning over twenty years –combined with a similarly heterogeneous sample of SNeIa. In spite of the difficulties of renormalizing the SBF-distances to a common reference, the heterogeneity of the sample brings with it some advantages, like the possibility to dramatically lower the impact of any instrument- or data-analysis driven systematic effect (e.g. linked to the PSF templates used). Adopting a hierarchical Bayesian approach, the authors extended the calibration to a sample of SNe Ia at redshift $0.02 < z < 0.08$, thus obtaining $H_0 = 71.25 \pm 2.37(\text{stat.}) \pm 3.38(\text{sys.})\text{km s}^{-1} \text{ Mpc}^{-1}$[b]. Such estimate lies in between the value by Ref. 23 based on SNe Ia and Cepheids ($H_0 = 74.03 \pm 1.42$ km s^{-1} Mpc^{-1} including systematics), and the value by Ref. 31 ($H_0 = 67.4 \pm 0.5$ km s^{-1} Mpc^{-1} obtained assuming the standard Λ CDM Cosmology). Hence, the estimate by Ref. 30 lies at $\sim 1\sigma$ from the H_0 estimates which started the debate on the "tension" in the Hubble-Lemaitre constant.[23,31]

B21, using a catalog of SBF distances for 63 early-type galaxies out to 100 Mpc obtained from WFC3/IR HST data,[18] revised the Hubble-Lemaitre parameter to $H_0 = 73.3 \pm 0.7(\text{stat.}) \pm 2.4(\text{sys.})$ km s^{-1} Mpc^{-1}. An estimate that agrees within $\sim 0.5\sigma$ with the value from SNe Ia, and a discrepancy larger than $\sim 5\sigma$ with respect to the estimates from Cosmological models and CMB anisotropy measurements (we ignored the systematic uncertainties on SBF). The H_0 by B21 is from SBF distance estimates for galaxies in the range of 15 and 100 Mpc: a distance where peculiar velocities can have a significant impact on the recessional velocities of the galaxies. Hence a regime where accurate velocities are equally important as accurate distances. In their analysis, B21 included as a test the analysis of four different treatments of the galaxy velocities: group velocities, individual velocities, and two flow-corrected model velocities to verify the robustness of their result within the reported errors. It is also worth noting that, as mentioned in Sect. 2.3, B21 adopts a joint calibration averaging the results for the Cepheid and TRGB which reduced uncertainty on H_0.

The work by B21 demonstrates that, in the next future, using a richer sample of massive galaxies with near-IR SBF within 100 Mpc and with improved constraints on the calibrations and on the cosmic-flow model, it will be possible to obtain SBF-based H_0 estimates at 1% or lower statistical uncertainty. Lowering

---

[b]The final value adopted by Ref. 30, $H_0 = 70.50$km s^{-1} Mpc^{-1} uses the old LMC zero-point; using the revised LMC distance, reported in the references cited in section 2.3, there is a solid 0.023 mag shift toward fainter distance moduli, which leads to an H_0 value of 71.25 km s^{-1} Mpc^{-1}.

the residual 3-4% systematic uncertainty, requires improving zero-point calibration effort as described in section 2.3 and in the next section.

It should be noted that the estimates of Ref. 30 & B21 agree within $\sim 1\sigma$ the respective statistical errors, also due to the relatively large uncertainty of the former estimate because of the heterogeneity of the sample and to the fact that Ref. 30 has an extra calibration step (SNe Ia calibration with SBF) compared to B21.

3.2. *Future applications*

The perspectives of this method can be divided into two three categories: "going wide" with the next generation survey telescopes, "going deep" with the JWST and AO-assisted facilities at 30-40m class telescopes, and "going precise" with programs aimed at lowering systematic errors and with new stellar population models.

3.2.1. *Large and deep sky surveys*

The forthcoming large sky surveys, including the LSST by the Vera Rubin Observatory and the Euclid wide survey, will produce a breakthrough in many fields of Astronomy. The expectations for SBF measurements, hence for mapping the 3D distribution of galaxies in the low-redshift Universe, are rather high.

At the time of writing, the LSST is expected to produce multi-band optical *ugrizy* observations, with typical seeing of 0.7", and 5σ point source depth of $i \sim 26.8$ mag for stationary sources after the 10 years of the main survey. Adopting the i as reference pass-band, we predict LSST will allow reaching bright massive galaxies at ~ 70 Mpc, that is the distance where the TOM+1 mag is reached at $\sim 5\sigma$ point source depth[c].

The Euclid satellite has about one fourth the collecting area of HST, but compared to LSST it has the advantage of the near-IR observations[d] and the sharp PSF (~ 0.2") allowed by space-based observations. Taking as reference the Euclid/NISP H-band, which is predicted reaching 5σ point source depth of $H \sim 24$ mag, and adopting $H_{TOM} \sim -8.3$ mag,[33] the TOM+1 magnitude will be reached for all bright galaxies at a distance of ~ 30 Mpc. However, in the H-band, the TOM+1 depth rule can be relaxed and a depth at 5σ the TOM could be sufficient in this band for reliable SBF measurement (Sect. 2.1.1), corresponding to a distance limit of ~ 70 Mpc.

Tests on the feasibility of SBF measurements with either Euclid instruments and with LSST precursor data are being carried out. If both instruments will be successful for SBF applications, we will have $\sim 18.000\ deg^2$ of the LSST covering the

---

[c]Assuming an $i_{TOM} \sim -8.5$ mag,[32] we obtain a limiting distance modulus of $(m-M)_{limit} \sim 34.3$, or $D \sim 72.5$ Mpc.

[d]The wide passband of the optical instrument, VIS, basically covers the entire optical spectrum, thus we expect that the intrinsic scatter of SBF due to stellar population effects will be too large for precise distances from this instrument.

southern skies and $\sim$ 15.000 deg^2 of Euclid in the North, that will potentially allow obtaining the most accurate and complete 3-D map of massive red galaxies in the sky out to $\sim$ 70 Mpc. Certainly a large number of lower mass, bluer galaxies at lower distances will also be mapped. The combination of these two data sets will provide exquisitely accurate cosmic flow models to be used for peculiar-velocity corrected flows, and an incredibly large sample of galaxies with SBF distances, useful for H_0 and for the needs of any near-field Cosmology study.

A further instrument of great impact will be the Roman telescope: with the same aperture of HST, similar PSF sharpness, $\sim$ 100 times the HST field of view, near-IR coverage, and 5σ point-source depth in 1 hr of 28 mag in J and H band, this telescope will combine survey to depth capabilities, allowing to measure SBF for galaxies in clusters or groups at distances out to 100 Mpc and more.

3.2.2. *JWST and 40m ground-based telescopes*

The JWST and the 30-40m class telescopes –like the E-ELT– will have near-IR imaging capabilities at a resolution like HST or better, combined with substantially larger collecting areas, a field of view of the order of one to a few arcminutes, more modern and efficient detectors: all these characteristics combined make it plausible to predict that these telescopes will allow to overcome the 150 Mpc limit, currently "held" by SBF with the HST.[28,29]

JWST is the natural heir of HST: with a similarly sharp (FWHM$\sim$ 0.1") and stable PSF, it has $\sim$ 7.5× the HST aperture, possibly sufficient to enable us measuring SBF distances for galaxies at 300 Mpc limit or beyond. The limiting factors at such large distances will be, in this case, the contaminating GCs and obtaining reliable estimates for k-corrections.

The perspectives for ground-based 30-40m telescopes are at the same time exciting and challenging. The next-generation adaptive-optic (AO) modules at near-IR imagers will provide PSF reaching the limit of FWHM$\sim$0.01", thus one order of magnitude better than the best resolution presently available (even better than the JWST), combined with a collecting area at least 150 times larger than HST, and increased detector efficiency. Would this mean that the potential of the SBF with AO assisted imaging data is to reach distances even one order of magnitude farther than present limits, breaking the 1 Gpc limit (z$\sim$0.2)? To date, no answer can be given to the question, because of the lack of studies on the measurement of fluctuations from data taken with AO modules. Although some studies have been made of this topic,[34] quantitative demonstrations are lacking, because of the complexity of combining AO observations for extended objects with the issues of deriving reliable SBF amplitudes from AO supported imaging data. Let us take as example the complexities with the PSF: AO observations are characterized by a PSF variable in space and time, the lack of good PSF candidates within the galaxy field of view because of the small field of the present generation of AO systems, and by the unknown effect on SBF from the large spread of the PSF in diffraction-limited conditions. In spite of such non-trivial issues, the forthcoming generation of 30-40m ground-based telescopes can be expected to produce breakthroughs in this field. Currently, cosmological studies based on direct distance indicators mostly rely on SNe Ia, which, although calibrated with high precision, are serendipitous events that present a zoo of peculiarities. Furthermore, SNe Ia distances rely on purely empirical information: we still lack a detailed modeling of the phenomena involved in SNe Ia explosion, useful for numerical calibrations of distances. On the other hand, the SBF measurement requires only data of suitable quality (no surreptitiousness), and relies on a signal whose origin is well known (star counts). In other words, though extremely more challenging than with the ideal JWST or Roman telescopes, SBF with 30-40m ground-based AO-assisted telescopes, could lead to SBF estimates out to redshift $z > 0.1$. At such distances, cosmological effects are predicted producing variations measurable with a distance indicator characterized by an accuracy of $\sim 5\%$. Hence, a dozen of well selected targets could be used to back up the SNe Ia on an independent route to precise cosmological parameters.

3.2.3. Stellar population models and calibrations

Possible refinements on the accuracy and precision of SBF distances will depend on the availability of new stellar population models and on improved $\overline{M}$ calibrations.

At large distances, i.e. $d > 100$ Mpc, magnitudes (both "standard" and SBF magnitudes) and colors require k-corrections, which can only be derived from stellar population models. The most recent estimates for k-corrections on SBF magnitudes, date back to the 2000,[35] and predict a correction of ~ 0.1 mag for the HST/NICMOS $F160W$ filter ($\sim H$ band) at 200 Mpc. The correction changes significantly with wavelength (as an example it is significantly smaller in the J band, ~ 0.012 mag) and needs to be accounted for also in the colors, which are used for estimating $\overline{M}$.

Hence, any detailed study of cosmological parameters from SBF magnitudes for galaxies at distances where the peculiar velocities are negligible with respect to the Hubble-flow, cannot ignore using reliable k-corrections which, to date, are still poorly constrained or completely unavailable for some filters or distances.

Concerning the SBF calibration, there are here too opportunities for improvements. At present, the dominant systematic error comes from the ~ 0.08 mag tie between SBF and Cepheids (Sec. 2.3). The results from Gaia will certainly have a positive impact on that: both because of the direct detection of Cepheids in M 31 (one of the SBF calibrators), and thanks to the more accurate and precise results on P-L relations from the data of thousands Galactic and Local Group Cepheids with measured parallaxes.[36]

A further opportunity could be deriving new SBF measurements for the same six calibrators used by Tonry & coIs. (based on imaging data taken prior to 1997) or from new calibrators.

Finally, as also pointed out in B21, the complete independence the Cepheid and the TRGB-based calibrations could also be used as a further factor to reduce the systematic uncertainty on a joint Cepheid/TRGB calibration, leading to a combined zero-point uncertainty of $\lesssim 2\,\%$ in distance (assuming the uncertainty on the TRGB zero-point TRGB is similar to that of Cepheids).

The upcoming launch of the James Webb Space Telescope (JWST) will allow for more numerous TRGB distances to the Virgo early-type galaxies in only modest observation times. Ultimately, we hope to anchor the SBF method using a much larger sample of giant ellipticals with TRGB distances calibrated using Gaia's parallaxes.

4. Conclusions

The SBF technique, with direct distances on single galaxies reaching an accuracy of $\sim 5\%$, is at present one of the most accurate extragalactic distance indicator in the distance regime between a few Mpc to ~ 150 Mpc.

In this contribution, I have described the basic characteristics of the method, how SBFs are measured, calibrated and used to estimate distances. I also provided a summary of the main scientific results obtained.

The next-generation of ground- and space-based telescopes will provide a variety of data that will generate thrilling results in many fields of Astronomy, not least the study of Cosmology based on direct distances from SBF. The extensive use of near-IR observations with high-resolution cameras –from JWST or E-ELT–, the deep surveys that will cover a large fraction of the sky –from the Vera Rubin Observatory or the Euclid satellite–, the improvements on SBF calibrations –from Gaia and from new stellar population models– will push forward this technique. By combining accuracy with depths and sky coverage, new data will allow using SBF distances for constraining cosmological models using a new path, independent from other direct distance methods, like SNe Ia.

References

1. W. Baade, The Resolution of Messier 32, NGC 205, and the Central Region of the Andromeda Nebula., *The Astroph. Journ.* **100**, p. 137 (September 1944).
2. B. J. Bok, *The Distribution of the Stars in Space* 1937.
3. J. Tonry and D. P. Schneider, A new technique for measuring extragalactic distances, *The Astroph. Journ.* **96**, 807 (September 1988).
4. J. P. Blakeslee, A. Jordán, S. Mei, P. Côté, L. Ferrarese, L. Infante, E. W. Peng, J. L. Tonry and M. J. West, The ACS Fornax Cluster Survey. V. Measurement and Recalibration of SBF and a Precise Value of the Fornax-Virgo Relative Distance, *The Astroph. Journ.* **694**, 556 (March 2009).
5. J. L. Tonry, E. A. Ajhar and G. A. Luppino, Observations of SBF in Virgo, *The Astroph. Journ.* **100**, p. 1416 (November 1990).
6. J. B. Jensen, J. L. Tonry and G. A. Luppino, Measuring Distances Using Infrared SBF, *The Astroph. Journ.* **505**, 111 (September 1998).
7. J. P. Blakeslee, A. Vazdekis and E. A. Ajhar, Stellar populations and SBF: New observations and models, *Mon. Not. Roy. Ast. Soc.* **320**, p. 193 (January 2001).

8. M. Cantiello, J. P. Blakeslee, G. Raimondo, S. Mei, E. Brocato and M. Capaccioli, Detection of Radial SBF and Color Gradients in Elliptical Galaxies with the Advanced Camera for Surveys, *The Astroph. Journ.* **634**, p. 239 (November 2005).
9. J. P. Blakeslee, M. Cantiello, S. Mei, P. Côté, R. Barber DeGraaff, L. Ferrarese, A. Jordán, E. W. Peng, J. L. Tonry and G. Worthey, SBF in the Hubble Space Telescope ACS/WFC F814W Bandpass and an Update on Galaxy Distances, *The Astroph. Journ.* **724**, 657 (November 2010).
10. J. B. Jensen, J. P. Blakeslee, Z. Gibson, H.-c. Lee, M. Cantiello, G. Raimondo, N. Boyer and H. Cho, Measuring Infrared SBF Distances with HST WFC3: Calibration and Advice, *The Astroph. Journ.* **808**, p. 91 (July 2015).
11. M. Cantiello, J. B. Jensen, J. P. Blakeslee, E. Berger, A. J. Levan, N. R. Tanvir, G. Raimondo, E. Brocato, K. D. Alexander, P. K. Blanchard, M. Branchesi, Z. Cano, R. Chornock, S. Covino, P. S. Cowperthwaite, P. D'Avanzo, T. Eftekhari, W. Fong, A. S. Fruchter, A. Grado, J. Hjorth, D. E. Holz, J. D. Lyman, I. Mandel, R. Margutti, M. Nicholl, V. A. Villar and P. K. G. Williams, A Precise Distance to the Host Galaxy of the Binary Neutron Star Merger GW170817 Using SBF, *The Astroph. Journ. Letters* **854**, p. L31 (February 2018).
12. S. G. Carlsten, R. L. Beaton, J. P. Greco and J. E. Greene, Using SBF to Study Nearby Satellite Galaxy Systems: Calibration and Methodology, *The Astroph. Journ.* **879**, p. 13 (July 2019).
13. M. Cantiello, I. Biscardi, E. Brocato and G. Raimondo, VLT optical BVR observations of two bright supernova Ia hosts in the Virgo cluster. SBF analysis, *Astron. & Astroph.* **532**, p. A154 (August 2011).
14. J. L. Tonry, A. Dressler, J. P. Blakeslee, E. A. Ajhar, A. B. Fletcher, G. A. Luppino, M. R. Metzger and C. B. Moore, The SBF Survey of Galaxy Distances. IV. SBF Magnitudes, Colors, and Distances, *The Astroph. Journ.* **546**, p. 681 (January 2001).
15. J. B. Jensen, J. L. Tonry, B. J. Barris, R. I. Thompson, M. C. Liu, M. J. Rieke, E. A. Ajhar and J. P. Blakeslee, Measuring Distances and Probing the Unresolved Stellar Populations of Galaxies Using Infrared SBF, *The Astroph. Journ.* **583**, 712 (February 2003).
16. M. Cantiello, G. Raimondo, E. Brocato and M. Capaccioli, New Optical and Near-Infrared SBF Models: A Primary Distance Indicator Ranging from Globular Clusters to Distant Galaxies?, *The Astroph. Journ.* **125**, p. 2783 (June 2003).
17. G. Raimondo, E. Brocato, M. Cantiello and M. Capaccioli, New Optical and Near-Infrared SBF Models. II. Young and Intermediate-Age Stellar Populations, *The Astronomical Journal* **130**, 2625 (December 2005).
18. J. B. Jensen, J. P. Blakeslee, C.-P. Ma, P. A. Milne, P. J. Brown, M. Cantiello, P. M. Garnavich, J. E. Greene, J. R. Lucey, A. Phan, R. B. Tully and C. M. Wood, Infrared SBF Distances for MASSIVE and Type Ia Supernova Host Galaxies, *arXiv e-prints*, p. arXiv:2105.08299 (May 2021).
19. J. P. Blakeslee, J. B. Jensen, C.-P. Ma, P. A. Milne and J. E. Greene, The hubble constant from infrared sbf distances, *The Astroph. Journ.* **911**, p. 65 (apr 2021).
20. J. L. Tonry, J. P. Blakeslee, E. A. Ajhar and A. Dressler, The SBF Survey of Galaxy Distances. II. Local and Large-Scale Flows, *The Astroph. Journ.* **530**, 625 (February 2000).
21. W. L. Freedman and B. F. Madore, The Hubble Constant, *Ann. Rev. Astron. & Astroph.* **48**, 673 (September 2010).
22. G. Pietrzyński, D. Graczyk, A. Gallenne, W. Gieren, I. B. Thompson, B. Pilecki, P. Karczmarek, M. Górski, K. Suchomska, M. Taormina, B. Zgirski, P. Wielgórski,

Z. Kołaczkowski, P. Konorski, S. Villanova, N. Nardetto, P. Kervella, F. Bresolin, R. P. Kudritzki, J. Storm, R. Smolec and W. Narloch, A distance to the Large Magellanic Cloud that is precise to one per cent, *Nature* **567**, 200 (March 2019).
23. A. G. Riess, S. Casertano, W. Yuan, L. M. Macri and D. Scolnic, Large Magellanic Cloud Cepheid Standards Provide a 1% Foundation for the Determination of the Hubble Constant and Stronger Evidence for Physics beyond ΛCDM, *The Astroph. Journ.* **876**, p. 85 (May 2019).
24. J. Soltis, S. Casertano and A. G. Riess, The Parallax of ω Centauri Measured from Gaia EDR3 and a Direct, Geometric Calibration of the Tip of the Red Giant Branch and the Hubble Constant, *The Astroph. Journ. Letters* **908**, p. L5 (February 2021).
25. J. Mould and S. Sakai, The Extragalactic Distance Scale Without Cepheids. II. SBF, *The Astroph. Journ.* **694**, 1331 (April 2009).
26. P. van Dokkum, S. Danieli, Y. Cohen, A. J. Romanowsky and C. Conroy, The Distance of the Dark Matter Deficient Galaxy NGC 1052-DF2, *The Astroph. Journ. Letters* **864**, p. L18 (September 2018).
27. E. A. Ajhar, J. L. Tonry, J. P. Blakeslee, A. G. Riess and B. P. Schmidt, Reconciliation of the SBF and Type Ia Supernova Distance Scales, *The Astroph. Journ.* **559**, 584 (October 2001).
28. J. B. Jensen, J. L. Tonry, R. I. Thompson, E. A. Ajhar, T. R. Lauer, M. J. Rieke, M. Postman and M. C. Liu, The Infrared SBF Hubble Constant, *The Astroph. Journ.* **550**, 503 (April 2001).
29. I. Biscardi, G. Raimondo, M. Cantiello and E. Brocato, Optical SBF of Shell Galaxies toward 100 Mpc, *The Astroph. Journ.* **678**, 168 (May 2008).
30. N. Khetan, L. Izzo, M. Branchesi, R. Wojtak, M. Cantiello, C. Murugeshan, A. Agnello, E. Cappellaro, M. Della Valle, C. Gall, J. Hjorth, S. Benetti, E. Brocato, J. Burke, D. Hiramatsu, D. A. Howell, L. Tomasella and S. Valenti, A new measurement of the Hubble constant using Type Ia supernovae calibrated with SBF, *Astron. & Astroph.* **647**, p. A72 (March 2021).
31. Planck Collaboration, Planck 2018 results. VI. Cosmological parameters, *Astron. & Astroph.* **641**, p. A6 (September 2020).
32. W. E. Harris, Globular cluster systems, in *Saas-Fee Advanced Course 28: Star Clusters*, 2001.
33. J. B. Nantais, J. P. Huchra, P. Barmby, K. A. G. Olsen and T. H. Jarrett, Nearby Spiral Globular Cluster Systems. I. Luminosity Functions, *The Astronomical Journal* **131**, 1416 (March 2006).
34. D. Gouliermis, W. Brandner, D. Butler and S. Hippler, SBF: A Case for Extremely Large Telescopes, in *Science with Adaptive Optics*, eds. W. Brandner and M. E. KasperJanuary 2005.
35. M. C. Liu, S. Charlot and J. R. Graham, Theoretical Predictions for SBF and Implications for Stellar Populations of Elliptical Galaxies, *The Astroph. Journ.* **543**, 644 (November 2000).
36. G. Clementini, V. Ripepi, R. Molinaro, A. Garofalo, T. Muraveva, L. Rimoldini, L. P. Guy, G. Jevardat de Fombelle, K. Nienartowicz, O. Marchal, M. Audard, B. Holl, S. Leccia, M. Marconi, I. Musella, N. Mowlavi, I. Lecoeur-Taibi, L. Eyer, J. De Ridder, S. Regibo, L. M. Sarro, L. Szabados, D. W. Evans and M. Riello, Gaia Data Release 2. Specific characterisation and validation of all-sky Cepheids and RR Lyrae stars, *Astron. & Astroph.* **622**, p. A60 (February 2019).

Preliminary results of analysis of Ia supernovae redshift distributions on data of the Asiago Supernova and Open Supernova Catalogues

I.V. Arkhangelskaja

Division of Nuclear Physics and Technologies, National Research Nuclear University MEPhI, Kashirskoe shosse, 31, Moscow, 115409, Russia
E-mail: IVArkhangelskaya@mephi.ru
https://home.mephi.ru/en/users/1525/public

The shape of redshift distribution for uniform sources set in our Metagalaxy defined by cosmological parameters and properties of space. The suggestion that type Ia supernovae might be used as standard candles for cosmological measurements allow considered these objects as homogeneous subsample. This mention occurs since the earliest studies of supernovae in 1938. Firstly the parameters of our Metagalaxy Ω and Λ were determine due sample of Ia supernovae from the Supernova Cosmology Project analysis in 1998. It was found due SN1a characteristics analysis that space in our Metagalaxy is Euclidean at small redshifts and de-Sitter at high ones. Now several tens of thousands supernovae' characteristics analyzed in various catalogues.

The preliminary results of the redshift distribution analysis for SNIa from the Asiago Supernova and Open Supernova Catalogues are discussed in this work. Firstly it was shown that several peculiarities are presented in Ia supernovae redshift distribution. The deviation in the band $0.015 < z < 0.13$ accordingly Open Supernova Catalogue (OSC) data contain more faint supernovae. Two peculiarities also were found in the region $0.25 < z < 0.45$ on data of this catalogue. One of it's contain more faint events, other contain more bright supernovae.

Also faint$_m$ and bright$_m$ supernovae areas could be separated by $m_{fb} \sim 20$ in distribution of object amount on apparent magnitude on both catalogues data. Furthermore, the distribution of SNIa on apparent magnitudes and angular distance to host centre on OSC data also reveal two areas (faint$_{dist}$ and bright$_{dist}$ objects) and ratio between these regions populations is different for different subsamples in OSC (Pan-STARRS1 (PS1) Medium Deep Survey, ASASSN and so on).

Moreover, SNIa apparent magnitudes could differ for $\Delta m_{onehost} \sim 2.5$ within one host galaxy (for example, in UGC03432) and this difference bigger that systematic uncertainties of SN1a characteristics observations. Also there are no specific absorption lines in the energy spectra of these SNIa which exclude influence of surrounding media.

The separated peculiarities and areas could not be explained due 2 groups of type Ia SNe explosions scenarios and dimming of flux due interaction of surrounding media. But it could affect at power in dependence of distance modulus μ on redshift, and, correspondingly, the H_0 tension between various subsamples of SN1a data. May be such tension was caused by different ratio of two SNIa classes objects in analysed catalogues and value of H_0 defined from supernovae subsets analysis became lower after correction for results of dependence of apparent magnitude on distance to host centre.

Thus such peculiarities presence could be caused by several unknown aspects of SNIa explosions scenarios or really changing of the parameters of our Metagalaxy. Further conclusions required subsequent OSC database treatment in combination with high redshift datasets, for example, addition of Dark Energy Survey Supernova Program catalogue into data analysis.

Keywords: SNIa redshift distribution

1. Introduction

The homogeneous subsample characteristics understanding is necessary for the investigation of any astrophysical objects redshift distribution, for example, gamma-ray bursts. The shape of redshift distribution for uniform sources set in our Metagalaxy defined by cosmological parameters and properties of spacetime. Type Ia supernovae considered as such standatd candels since 1995.[1] The effect of a cosmological constant leads to dimming of observed brightnesses of highredshift supernovae than would have been the case with $\Omega_\Lambda = 0$ and allowed to estimate cosmological parameters due analysis of Hubble diagram contain dependence of on redshift — see, for example, Ref. 2.

The interest of the scientific community on supernovae (SNe) has increased in the recent years for several reasons. Mostly they are the advances in the understanding of the SN phenomena obtained with the intensive study of nearby SNe, first of all SN 1987A, which have raised new more fundamental questions with regard to progenitor evolution, explosion mechanism and nucleosynthesis — see, for instance, Refs. 3, 4. In addition, the at least two facts have renewed the interest for the using of SNIa as distance indicators up to cosmological distances. The first one was the calibration of the absolute magnitudes of a few SNIa obtained using the Cepheid variables found in their parent galaxies.[5] The second fact was the discovery of empirical relations between the absolute magnitudes at maximum and the shape of the light curves of SN Is.[6] Other exciting advances are expected for the association of some SNe with the other interest objects, for example, GRBs. Another reason is the necessaries of homogeneous subsample characteristics understanding for the investigation of any astrophysical objects redshift distribution, for instance, also GRB — see Ref. 7. Such wide interest has activate new deep SNe searches and creation or revision of catalogues based of its results. Now the amount of SNe listed in various catalogues is about one hundred thousands which mentioned in several tens of catalogues — see, for instance, Refs. 8–11. SN1a are approximately 25% of this subset volume — see, for instance, Refs. 9, 10, 12.

Firstly the parameters of our Metagalaxy Ω and Λ were determine due sample of Ia supernovae from the Supernova Cosmology Project analysis in 1997 — see Refs. 2, 13. Figure 1 represents the results of tis investigation. The combination of Hubble diagrams for 42 high-redshift type Ia supernovae from the Supernova Cosmology Project and and 18 low-redshift ones from the Supernova Calalan/Tololo Survey was approximated by power law fit. It was found that this fit corresponds to following composition of our Metagalaxy: 70% of dark energy, 25% of dark matter and only 5% of ordinary baryonic matter.[2,13] Later it was found that several objects from this sample are not SNIa, but a valid asymptotic estimations still remain.[14]

2. Asiago Supernova Catalogue

The history of the Asiago SN catalogue began in 1984 with the publication of data for 568 objects.[15] This was compiled starting from the Palomar Supernova Master

[Figure: Hubble diagram showing effective m_B vs redshift z, with data from Supernova Cosmology Project and Calan/Tololo.]

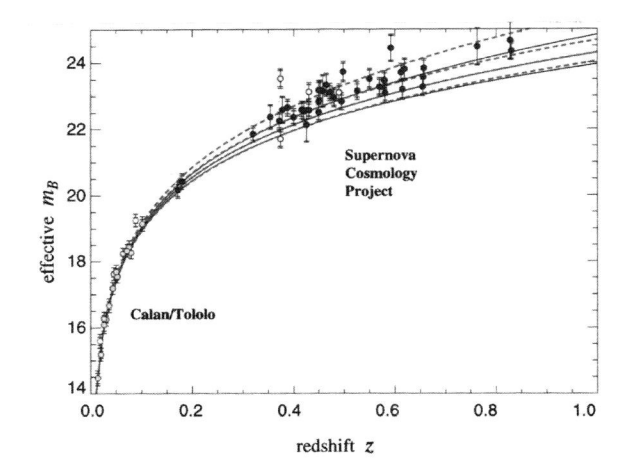

Fig. 1. Hubble diagram for 42 high-redshift type Ia supernovae from the Supernova Cosmology Project and 18 low-redshift type Ia supernovae from the Supernova Calalan/Tololo Survey. Adopted from Ref. 13.

List which since 1958 from time to time appeared in the literature see, for example, Refs. 8, 9, 16. During the same period two other SN listing have been published,[17,18] the Ref. 18 also contains the complete bibliography for each object. The 1984 Asiago SN Catalogue was superseded by a new edition in 1989[19] which listed information for the 661 supernovae discovered up to December 31, 1988.

More recently, van den Bergh at Ref. 20 published a list containing the 203 supernovae discovered between January 1, 1989 and April 3, 1994. Also the Catalogue of extragalactic Supernovae, complete up to 1993, was published in volume V of the General Catalogue of Variable Stars Ref. 21. In the last few years the Asiago Supernova Catalogue was widely used through the literature and available at the Ref. 22. Other supernova listings are available electronically, e.g. the list at the CBAT,[23] and Sternberg Astronomical Institute Supernova Catalogue.[24] The Asiago Supernova Catalogue consists of following datasets contain more than 100 supernovae:

(1) SDSS-II,
(2) LOSS,
(3) LOTOSS,
(4) ESSENCE,
(5) Puckett,
(6) SCP,
(7) HZSST.

Other 27 supernovae datasets included in this catalogue consist of less amount of members. For example, ones BAOSS and CFHT-LSSP contain only 34 and 13 objects correspondingly.

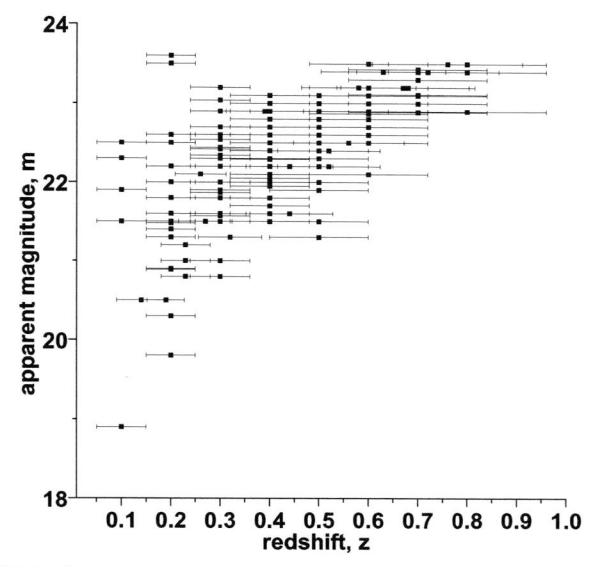

Fig. 2. Plot of SN Ia distribution on apparent magnitude dependence and redshift for ESSENCE experiment data accordingly to Asiago Supernova Catalogue.

Unfortunately the redshift data of several experiments (for example, ESSENCE – see Figure 2) contain big errors. This effect leads to several "lines" looks to areas with z=const occurs in plots of distributions on redshift. Such artefacts makes difficult to process these data and such datasets were excluded from analysis.

The Asiago Supernova Catalogue was last updated on 2 October 2017 and consist of data about 6530 supernovae.[22] The subsample of SN1a contains 3135 objects but redshifts with sufficient for analysis accuracy are known only for 2336 ones.

3. Open Supernova Catalogue

The Open Supernova Catalogue[11,12] is online collection of observations and metadata for presently 92632 supernovae and related candidates. The catalog is freely available on the web.[11] Its main interface having been designed to be a searchable table accessible on desktop and mobile devices due GitHub.[27] It represents an ongoing community driven project to collect and clean supernova metadata and observations spanning X-ray, ultraviolet, optical, infrared, and radio frequencies. At present, ∼14000 events in the catalog include light curves with at least 5 photometric points, and in total the catalogue contains ∼678000 individual photometric detections. Within the catalogue there are ∼4250 supernovae that include spectra, with ∼21000 spectra in total. In addition to the primary catalogue table containing supernova metadata, an individual page is generated for each supernova which displays its available metadata, light curves, and spectra from X-ray to radio frequencies. The information presented in the catalog is automatically rebuilt on a daily basis and is constructed due parsing several sources, including the data presented in the supernova literature and from secondary sources such as other web-based catalogs — see, for example, Refs. 28–30. The objects included in the catalogue are intended to be entirely supernovae, i.e. the complete destruction of a star by an explosive event that may or may not leave behind a compact remnant, and objects that have been definitively identified as other transient types were actively removed. One difference between Open Supernova Catalogue and some other supernova catalogues is that authors augment the known supernovae with known supernova remnants,[31] which are thought to be supernovae but (currently) with no known associated transient. Absolute magnitudes calculated in the Open Supernova Catalogue take into account luminosity distance and redshift decrements. The Open Supernova Catalogue consists of following lists contain more than 1000 supernovae:

(1) The Open Supernova Catalogue,
(2) Sloan Digital Sky Survey,
(3) Latest Supernovae,
(4) JLA supernovae,
(5) SIMBAD astronomical database,
(6) Transient Name Server,
(7) THE SLOAN DIGITAL SKY SURVEY-II SUPERNOVA SURVEY,
(8) Pan-STARRS 3Pi,
(9) Asiago Supernova Catalogue,
(10) A unified supernova catalogue,
(11) NED-D,
(12) WISeREP—An Interactive Supernova Data Repository,
(13) Catalina Sky Survey,
(14) NASA/IPAC Extragalactic Database,
(15) Sternberg Astronomical Institute Supernova Light Curve Catalogue.

Other 828 supernovae lists included in this catalogue consist of 5 – 919 objects. For example, ones UCB Filippenko Group's Supernova Database (SNDB) and DES Bright Transients contain only 134 and 17 objects correspondingly. Also information about characteristics of individual supernova included in this catalogue due more than 130000 circulars, such as CBET, IAUC, ATel, etc. The Open Supernova Catalogue updated up to now[11] and its subsample of SNIa contains 16428 objects but redshifts are known only for 14607 ones.

4. The preliminary results of data analysis

This section presents the preliminary results of analysis of subsets of Ia type supernovae with known redshifts from the Asiago Supernova (ASC) and the Open Supernova (OSC) catalogues.

The distribution of SNIa on redshift and apparent magnitudes on data of these catalogues are shown on Fig. 3. Both distributions are more wide than mentioned on Fig. 1 and contain several peculiarities. Moreover, the sample OSC has deviation in the band $0.015 < z < 0.13$ contain more faint supernovae and two peculiarities in the region $0.25 < z < 0.45$. One of its contain more dim events, other contain more bright supernovae. But both analysable subsets contain data from several catalogues and at first we should exclude selection effects. These characteristic features appears at distribution on absolute magnitude and redshift too — see Fig. 4.

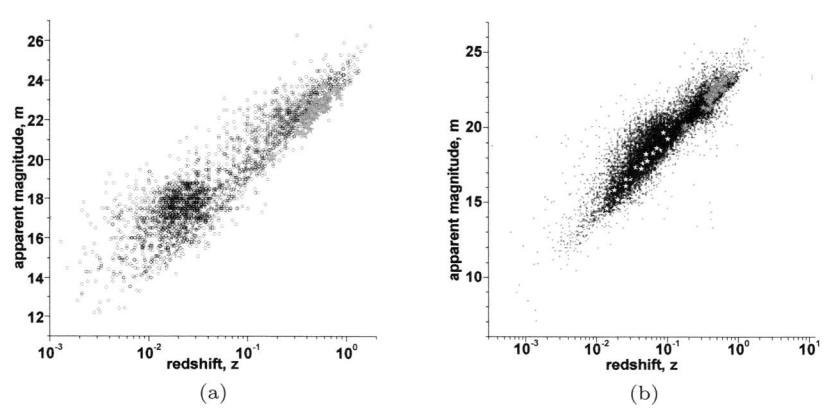

Fig. 3. The distribution of SNIa amount on redshift and apparent magnitudes on data of following catalogues: (a) Asiago Supernova and (b) Open Supernova. Gray stars show Supernova Cosmology Project data, open ones represent subsample from the Supernova Calalan/Tololo Survey mentioned on Fig. 1.

The uncertainties in recent SN Ia cosmology analyses usually excluded due following methods[32]: probing relations between luminosity and properties of the host galaxies of the SNe (see Refs. 33, 34) and analyses of the light-curve parameters of SNe and how these parameters relate to luminosity.[35,36] Many of the associated systematic uncertainties of these effects are on the 1% level, and considering a typical SN distance modulus is measured with roughly 15% precision.[32] Also K-corrections should be used to provide a transformation between an observed-frame magnitude and a rest-frame one and account for the SN redshift (see, for example, Refs. 37–40), but object magnitude was maximally shifted for value less then 1.2 and no systematic effects were found for such corrections. Thus all uncertainties could not influence to shapes of observed distributions.

Several peculiarities in the plots of the distributions of SNIa on redshift and apparent magnitudes for HZSST and SCP experiments within Asiago Supernova Catalogue are are presented on Fig. 5. Also some peculiarities in the plots of the distributions of SNIa on redshift and apparent magnitudes for Sternberg Astronomical

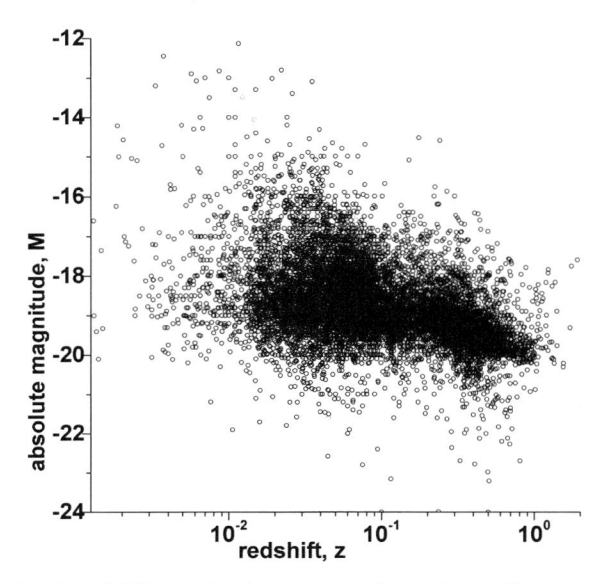

Fig. 4. The distribution of SNIa on absolute magnitudes and redshift on data of Open Supernova catalogue.

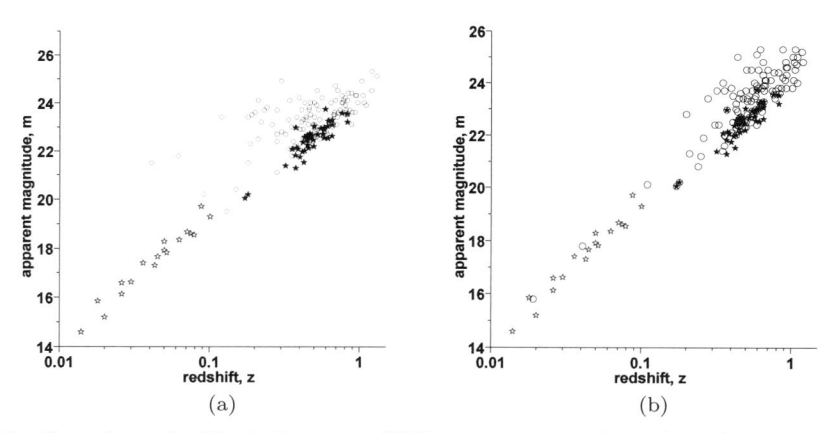

Fig. 5. Several peculiarities in the plots of SNIa apparent magnitude dependence on redshift for HZSST (a) and SCP (b) experiments. Black stars show Supernova Cosmology Project data, open ones represent subsample from the Supernova Calalan/Tololo Survey. Black stars show Supernova Cosmology Project data, open ones represent subsample from the Supernova Calalan/Tololo Survey mentioned on Fig. 1.

Institute Supernova Light Curve Catalogue[24] and Pan-STARRS1 (PS1) Medium Deep Survey[29,32] within Open Supernova Catalogue are are presented on Fig. 6. The discussed in the previous paragraph uncertainties could not caused such features too.

The distributions of SNIa amount on redshift on data of the Asiago Supernova and the Open Supernova catalogues are shown on Fig. 7. It is seen feature at $z > 0.2$ on Open Supernova dataset possible connected with peculiarities in the region $0.25 < z < 0.45$ on Fig. 3. Than we consider the distributions of these catalogues data on apparent magnitude — see Fig. 8. Preliminary analysis results have shown the presence of two subsets (faint$_m$ and bright$_m$ supernovae) at each distributions separated by $m_{fb} \sim 20$. These dual structure appear in the same distributions of catalogues composing OSC — see, for example, Fig. 9.

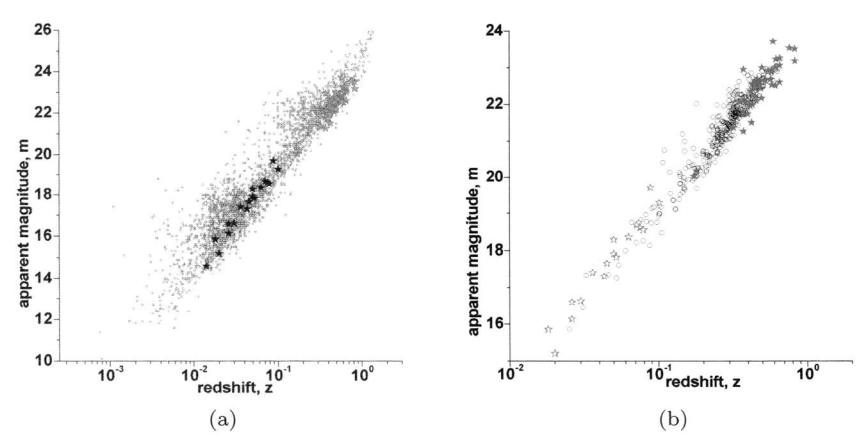

Fig. 6. Several peculiarities in the plots of the distributions of SNIa on redshift and apparent magnitudes for: (a) Sternberg Astronomical Institute Supernova Light Curve Catalogue, (b) Pan-STARRS1 (PS1) Medium Deep Survey within Open Supernova Catalogue. Stars show data, mentioned on Fig. 1. Grey ones show Supernova Cosmology Project data, open and black stars represent subsample from the Supernova Calalan/Tololo Survey at panels (a) and (b) correspondingly.

The distribution of SNIa on apparent magnitudes and angular distance to host centre for OSC objects is presented at Fig. 10. Also two areas (faint$_{dist}$ and bright$_{dist}$ SNIa) separated at this distribution. Preliminary analysis results allow conclude several differences between these regions and peculiarities on distributions of SNIa amount on apparent magnitude and redshift also with one on redshift. Moreover, these area not fully correspond to subsets on the distributions of apparent magnitudes from Fig. 8b and Fig. 9.

Let's consider two SNIa at $z_1 = 0.0039$ and $z_2 = 0.0037$: 1998aq and 2004W. The difference in the apparent magnitudes of these objects is ~ 6: $m1_{max} = 12.5$ (bright SNIa at Fig. 10) and $m2_{max} = 18.5$ (faint SNIa at Fig. 10) correspondingly accordingly Ref. 11. Also the same differences observed at various redshifts — see Table 1. Moreover, some hosts contain several supernovae but its apparent magnitudes could differ for $\Delta m_{onehost} \sim 2.5$. For example, galaxy UGC03432 with

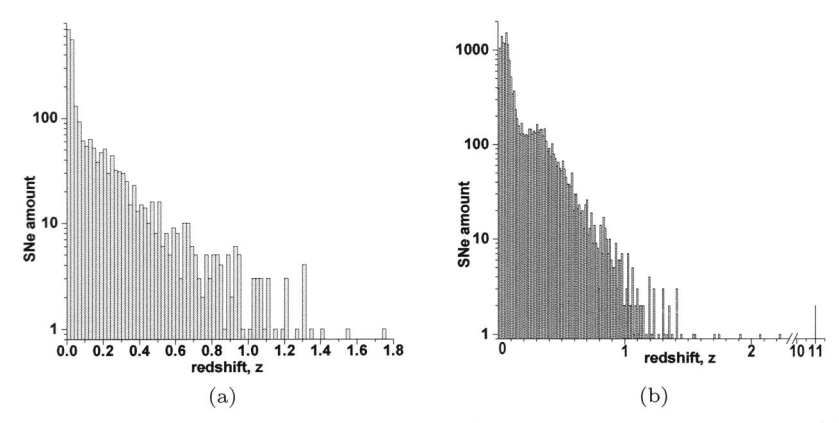

Fig. 7. The distribution of SNIa amount on redshift on data of following catalogues: (a) Asiago Supernova and (b) Open Supernova.

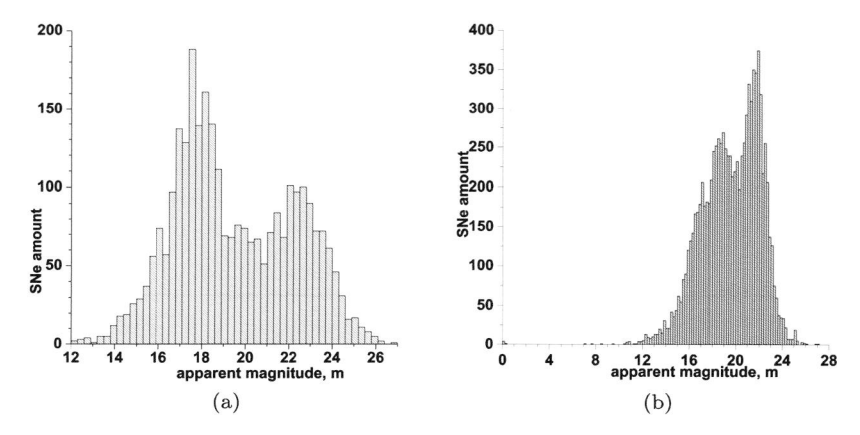

Fig. 8. The distribution of SNIa amount on apparent magnitudes on data of following catalogues: (a) Asiago Supernova and (b) Open Supernova.

$m_{gal} = 15.51$ at z=0.016667 contain two SNIa 1996bv has $m_1 = 15.5$ and 2003kb has $m_2 = 18$. But usually supernovae has the same characteristics within one host. For instance, two SNIa 2004br and 1994M had m=16.3 within galaxy NGC4493 with $m_{gal} = 14.951$ at z=0.02315.

Up to now there are no evidence for an astrophysical origin of the apparent faintness of SNe Ia has been found (see Refs. 41, 42). Early only SFR (star-formation rate) of the parent galaxies was considered as influence factor for diminution of SN apparent magnitudes. Thus, dependence of distant SN Ia light-curve shapes on star-formation in the host galaxy was studied in Ref. 34, and it was found that passive galaxies without star-formation, preferentially host dimmer SNe Ia with faster-declining light-curves, while brighter events with slower-declining ones only

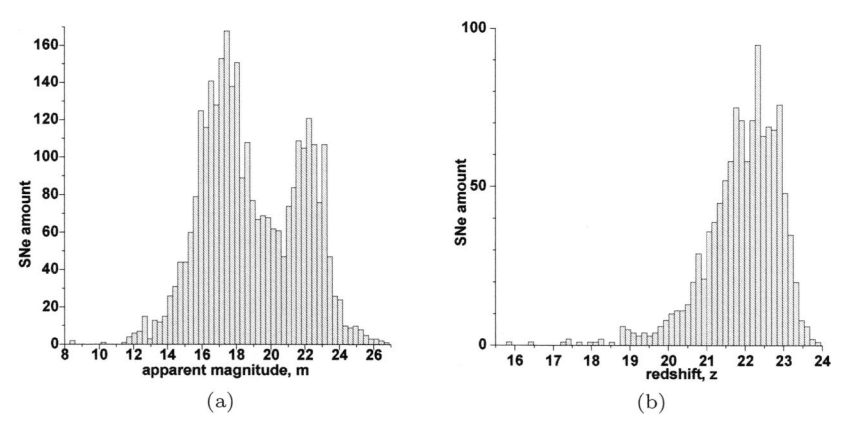

Fig. 9. The distribution of SNIa amount on apparent magnitudes on data of: (a) Sternberg Astronomical Institute Supernova Light Curve Catalogue, (b)Pan-STARRS1 (PS1) Medium Deep Survey within Open Supernova Catalogue.

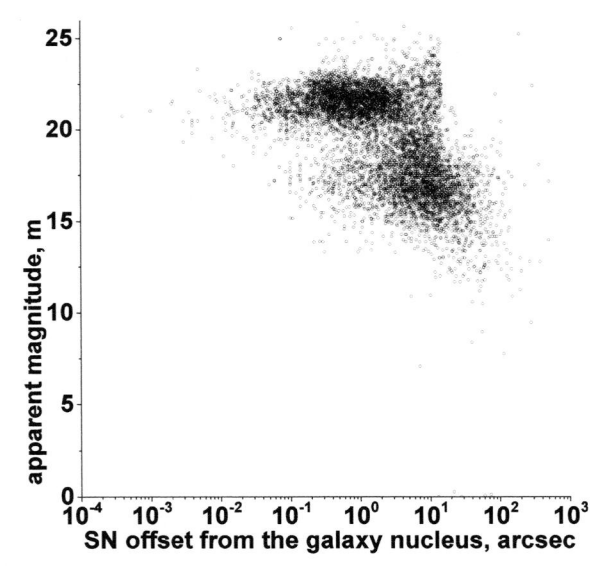

Fig. 10. The distribution of SNIa on apparent magnitudes and SN offset from the galaxy nucleus on data of Open Supernova catalogue.

originated from systems with ongoing star-formation. The mean stretch smaller for 0.08 against the typical precision on the stretch measure is ±0.01 − 0.02 at 95% confidence, which change distance modulus μ less than for 1% and could not explain the observed difference in the apparent magnitudes of SNIa $\Delta m_{onehost}$. All mentioned objects were observed by LEDA and there are no any evidences to suppose additional matter presence between observer and SN##1–4 because additional absorption lines are absent in the spectra of these supernovae — see, for example, Refs. 25, 26.

Table 1. The examples of difference in the apparent magnitudes of SNIa at various redshifts.

#	SN	redshift z	m_{max}	Δm_{max}	m_{host}
1	2004W	0.0037	18.5	~ 6	9.8
2	1993c	0.012	18.0	~ 4.4	13.3
3	2007if	0.04	20.5	~ 4.4	16.3
4	1999G	0.10	21.4	~ 3.5	18.4
5	1998aq	0.0039	12.5	~ 6	10.9
6	1999cw	0.013	14.3	~ 4.4	14.2
7	2009do	0.04	16.1	~ 4.4	16.1
8	2012X	0.10	17.9	~ 3.5	17.7

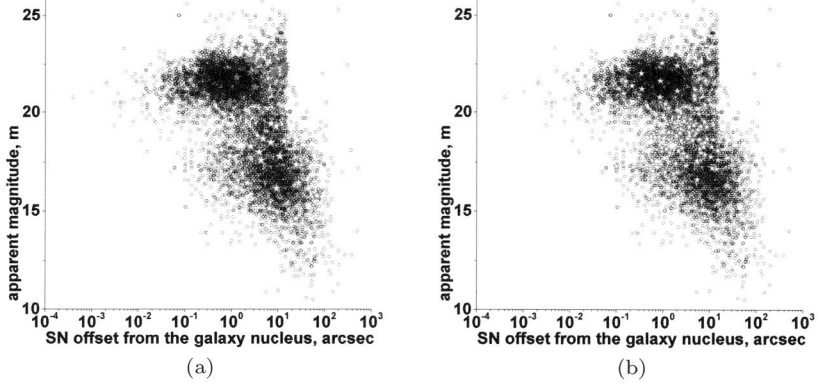

Fig. 11. The illustration of different ratio of two classes of SNIa on the distribution of SNIa on apparent magnitudes and offset from the galaxy nucleus on data of Open Supernova catalogues (open circles) in: (a) subsamples of Supernova Cosmology Project (grey stars) and Supernova Calalan/Tololo Survey (open stars) mentioned on Fig. 1 and (b) Pan-STARRS1 (PS1) Medium Deep Survey data (open stars).

Thus we have found several areas on distributions of SNIa from OSC on apparent magnitude and apparent magnitude vs offset from the galaxy nucleus. However the type Ia supernovae models not explain such subtypes. These models can be divided into two broad categories (Single Degenerate and Double Degenerate scenarios of Type Ia SNe explosions), but the authors of these scenarios concluded that both scenarios are able to correctly predict the bulk properties of Type Ia observations.[43–45] One type of progenitors are a $1.4 M_\odot$ white dwarves that are likely created in an accretion process and self-ignite due to high central pressure/density. Other ones are white dwarves too but of considerably lesser mass ($1 M_\odot$) can be ignited in shell detonations or in the merging process that formed them. Both scenarios are able to correctly predict the bulk properties of Type Ia observations and widely discussed difficulties in recognition of models of concrete SNIa.

Such areas presence in various ratio in subsamples contain OSC — see Fig. 11 and could affect at power in dependence of distance modulus μ on redshift, and, correspondingly, the H_0 tension in various subsamples of SN1a data. The H_0 tension[46–48] occurs due comparison of estimation of the current expansion rate of the Netagalaxy H_0 due CMB data[50] and results of observations of astrophysical objects such as SNIa and so on — see, for example, Ref. 51. Now this tension is more than 5σ: accordingly to CMB measurements[50] a value for $H_0 = 67.36 \pm 0.54$ km s^{-1} Mpc^{-1}, but the best-fits of the SNIa data[51,52] gave the values of $H_0 = 73.2 \pm 1.3$ km s^{-1} Mpc^{-1} and $H_0 = 75.4 \pm 1.7$ km s^{-1} Mpc^{-1} correspondingly. May be such discrepancy were caused by different ratio of two SNIa classes objects in analysed catalogues and value of H_0 defined from supernovae subsets analysis became lower.

5. Conclusions

The preliminary results of the redshift distribution analysis for SNIa from the Asiago Supernova and Open Supernova Catalogues are discussed in this work. The Asiago Supernova Catalogue (ASC) was last updated on 2 October 2017 and consist of data about 6530 supernovae.[22] The subsample of SN1a contains 3135 objects but redshifts with sufficient for analysis accuracy are known only for 2336 ones. The Open Supernova Catalogue (OSC) updated up to now[11] and its subsample of SNIa contains 16428 objects but redshifts are known only for 14607 ones. It was concluded that not all experiments from the catalogue could analysed (small statistics or big errors in the determination of z caused difficulties in data representation and analysis), for example, ESSENCE experiment data within Asiago Supernova Catalogue.[22]

The shape of redshift distribution for uniform sources set in our Metagalaxy defined by cosmological parameters and properties of space. The suggestion that type Ia supernovae might be used as standard candles[1] for cosmological measurements allow considered these objects as homogeneous subsample. Firstly the parameters of our Metagalaxy Ω and Λ were determine due sample of Ia supernovae from the Supernova Cosmology Project analysis in 1998.[2] It was found due SN1a characteristics analysis that space in our Metagalaxy is Euclidean at small redshifts and de-Sitter at high ones. Now several tens of thousands supernovae' characteristics analyzed in various catalogues.

The various redshifts distributions of SNIa from ASC and OSC have analysed. Firstly it was shown that several peculiarities are presented in Ia supernovae redshift distribution. The deviation in the band $0.015 < z < 0.13$ accordingly Open Supernova Catalogue (OSC) data contain more faint supernovae. Two peculiarities also were found in the region $0.25 < z < 0.45$ on data of this catalogue. One of it's contain more faint events, other contain more bright supernovae.

Also faint$_m$ and bright$_m$ supernovae areas could be separated by $m_{fb} \sim 20$ in distribution of object amount on apparent magnitude on both catalogues data. Furthermore, the distribution of SNIa on apparent magnitudes and angular distance to host centre on OSC data also reveal two areas (faint$_{dist}$ and bright$_{dist}$ objects) and ratio between these regions populations is different for different subsamples in OSC (Pan-STARRS1 (PS1) Medium Deep Survey, ASASSN and so on).

Moreover, SNIa apparent magnitudes could differ for $\Delta m_{onehost} \sim 2.5$ within one host galaxy (for example, in UGC03432) and this difference bigger that systematic uncertainties of SN1a characteristics observations. Also there are no specific absorption lines in the energy spectra of these SNIa which exclude influence of surrounding media.

The separated peculiarities and areas could not be explained due 2 groups of type Ia SNe explosions scenarios (see, for example, Refs. 43–45) and dimming of flux due interaction of surrounding media. But it could affect at power in dependence of distance modulus μ on redshift, and, correspondingly, the H_0 tension between various subsamples of SN1a data. May be such tension was caused by different ratio of two SNIa classes objects in analysed catalogues and value of H_0 defined from supernovae subsets analysis became lower after correction for results of dependence of apparent magnitude on distance to host centre

Thus such peculiarities presence could be caused by several unknown aspects of SNIa explosions scenarios or really changing of the parameters of our Metagalaxy. Further conclusions required subsequent OSC database treatment in combination with high redshift datasets, for example, addition of Dark Energy Survey Supernova Program catalogue[53] into data analysis.

Acknowledgments

Author thank for the support from National Research Nuclear University MEPhI in the framework of the Russian Academic Excellence Project (contract No. 02.a03.21.0005, 27.08.2013).

References

1. A. Goobar and S. Perlmutter, Feasibility of Measuring of the Cosmological Constant Λ and Mass Density Ω Using Yype Ia Supernovae, *The Astrophisical journal* **450** 14 (1995).
2. S. Perlmutter, G. Aldering, S. Deustua, S. Fabbro1, G. Goldhaber, D. E. Groom, A. G. Kim, M. Y. Kim, R.A. Knop, P. Nugent, C. R. Pennypacker, et al., Cosmology from Type Ia Supernovae, *Bulletin of the American Astronomical Society* **29** 1351 (1997).
3. H. A. Bethe, P. Pizzochero, Mass-Energy Relation for SN 1987A from Observations, *ApJL*, **350**, L33 (1990).
4. N. Soker, Possible post-kick jets in SN 1987A, *New Astronomy*, **84**, article id. 101548 (2021).
5. A. Saha, A. Sandage, G. A. Tammann, L. Labhardt, F. D. Macchetto, N. Panagia, Cepheid Calibration of the Peak Brightness of SNe Ia – IX. SN 1989B in NGC 3627, *The Astrophysical Journal* **522** 802 (1999).

6. M. M. Phillips, A. G. Riess, W. H. Press, R. Kirshner, Improved Distances to Type Ia Supernovae with Multicolor Light-Curve Shapes: MLCS2k2, *The Astrophysical Journal* **473** 88 (1996).
7. I. V. Arkhangelskaja, The sources of long GRBs: Population inhomogeneity or possibility its using as standard candles, *Journal of Physics: Conf. Ser.* **1181** article id. 012050 (2019).
8. C. T. Kowal, W. L. W. Sargent, Supernovae discovered since 1885, *Astronomical Journal* **76** 756 (1971).
9. W. L. W. Sargent, L. Searle, C. T. Kowal, Supernovae and Supernova Remnants, *Cosmovici C.B. D. Reidel Publ. Dordrecht* 33 (1974).
10. Browse Software Development Team, Asiago Supernova Catalog http://heasarc.gsfc.nasa.gov/W3Browse/star-catalog/asiagosn.html#sn_type.
11. J. Guillochon, J. Parrent, The Open Supernova Catalog https://sne.space/.
12. Guillochon, J. Parrent, L. Z. Kelley, R. Margutti, An Open Catalog for Supernova Data, *ApJ*, **835**, article id. 64 (2017).
13. S. Perlmutter, G. Aldering, G. Goldhaber, R. A. Knop, P. Nugent, P. G. Castro, S. Deustua, S. Fabbro, A. Goobar, D. E. Groom, I. M. Hook, A. G. Kim, M. Y. Kim, J. C. Lee, N. J. Nunes, R. Pain, C. R. Pennypacker and R. Quimby et al, Measurements of Ω and Λ from 42 High-Redshift Supernovae, *The Astrophysical Journal* **517** 565 (1999).
14. T. J. Bronder, I. M. Hook, P. Astier, *et al.*, SNLS spectroscopy: Testing for evolution in type la supernovae, *A&A* **477**, 717–734 (2008).
15. R. Barbon, E. Cappellaro, F. Ciatti, M. Turatto, T. Kowal, The supernova 1984A in NGC4419, *Astronomy and Astrophysics* **220** 83 (1989).
16. F. Zwicky, Clusters of Galaxies. in *Handbuch der Physik*, eds. S. Flugge, *Springer,Verlag, Berlin* **51** 390 (1959).
17. M. Karpowicz, K. Rudnicki, Preliminary catalogue of supernovae, discovered till the end of 1967. *Publ. Astron. Obs. Warsaw*, **15** 189 (1968).
18. P. Flin, M. Karpowicz, W. Murawski, K. Rudnicki, Catalogue of supernovae, *Acta Cosmologica* **8**, 5 (1979).
19. R. Barbon, E. Cappellaro, M. Turatto, Photometric and spectroscopic observations of four supernovae, *Astronomy and Astrophysics* 410 (1989).
20. S. van den Bergh, A Catalog of Recent Supernovae, *Astroph. J. Suppl.* **92** 219 (1994).
21. N. N. Samus, General Catalogue of Variable Stars, fourth edition, *Kosmosinform* **5** (Moscow, 1995).
22. https://heasarc.gsfc.nasa.gov/W3Browse/all/asiagosn.html.
23. http://www.cbat.eps.harvard.edu/lists/RecentSupernovae.html.
24. D. Yu. Tsvetkov, N. N. Pavlyuk, O. S. Bartunov, Yu. P. Pskovskii, SAI Supernova Catalog http://stella.sai.msu.ru/~pavlyuk/sncat/pages.php?results_per_page=500&resorder=0&ascdesc=1&resnewwin=0.
25. Moore, M.; Li, W.; Filippenko, A. V.; Chornock, R.; Foley, R. J. Supernovae 2004T, 2004U, and 2004W IAU Circ., No. 8286, #2 (2004).
26. D. Branch, P. Garnavich, T. Matheson, E. Baron, R. C. Thomas, K. Hatano, P. Challis, S. Jha, R. P. Kirshner, Optical Spectra of the Type Ia Supernova 1998aq, *The Astrophysical Journal* **126** 1489 (2003).
27. astrocatalogs/supernovae https://github.com/astrocatalogs/supernovae/issues.
28. P. J. Brown, A. Breeveld, P. W. Roming and M. Siegel, Swift Supernovae, *The Astrophysical Journal*, **152(4)**, article id. 102 (2016).
29. The Pan-STARRS1 data archive home page, https://panstarrs.stsci.edu/.
30. List of Recent Supernovae, http://www.cbat.eps.harvard.edu/lists/RecentSupernovae.html.

31. D. A. Green, A catalogue of 294 Galactic supernova remnants, *BASI*, **42**, 47 (2014).
32. D. M. Scolnic, D. O. Jones, A. Rest, Y. C. Pan, R. Chornock, R. J. Foley, The Complete Light-curve Sample of Spectroscopically Confirmed SNe Ia from Pan- STARRS1 and Cosmological Constraints from the Combined Pantheon Sample, *The Astrophysical Journal* **859** 101 (2018).
33. Kelly, P. L., Hicken, M., Burke, D. L., Mandel, K. S., Kirshner, R. P., Hubble Residuals of Nearby Type Ia Supernovae are Correlated with Host Galaxy Masses, ApJ, 715, 743 (2010).
34. Sullivan, M., Conley, A., Howell, D. A., Neill, J. D.; Astier, P.; Balland, C.; Basa, S.; Carlberg, R. G.; Fouchez, D.; Guy, J.; Hardin, D.; Hook, I. M. search by orcid; Pain, R.; Palanque-Delabrouille, N.; Perrett, K. M.; Pritchet, C. J.; Regnault, N.; Rich, J.; Ruhlmann-Kleider, V.; Baumont, S. Hsiao, E.; Kronborg, T.; Lidman, C.; Perlmutter, S.; Walker, E. S., The dependence of Type Ia Supernovae luminosities on their host galaxies, *MNRAS*, **406** 782 (2010).
35. D. Scolnic and R. Kessler, *The Astrophysical Journal Letters* **822** L35 (2016).
36. K. S. Mandel, D. Scolnic, H. Shari, R. J. Foley, R. P. Kirshner, ArXiv e-prints, arXiv:1609.04470 (2016).
37. J. Guy, M. Sullivan, A. Conley, et al., The Supernova Legacy Survey 3-year sample: Type Ia supernovae photometric distances and cosmological constraints, *Astronomy and Astrophysics* **523** id:A7 (2010).
38. E. F. Schlafly and D. P. Finkbeiner, MEASURING REDDENING WITH SLOAN DIGITAL SKY SURVEY STELLAR SPECTRA AND RECALIBRATING SFD, *The Astrophysical Journal* **737** id:103 (2011).
39. A. Kim, A. Goobar, S. Perlmutter, A Generalized Correction for Type Ia Supernovae: Comparing R-band Photometry Beyond z=0.2 with B, V, and R-band Nearby Photometry, *Publications of the Astronomical Society of the Pacific* **108** 190 (1996).
40. W. D. Kenworthy, D. O. Jones, M. Dai,R. Kessler,D. Scolnic, D. Brout, M. R. Siebert, J. D. R. Pierel,K. G. Dettman, G. Dimitriadis, R. J. Foley, S. W. Jha, Y.-C. Pan, A. Riess, S. Rodney, and C. Rojas-Bravo, SALT3: An Improved Type Ia Supernova Model for Measuring Cosmic Distances, arXiv:2104.07795v1 (2021).
41. A. G. Riess, Kinematics and Dark Energy from Supernovae at $z > 1$, *ASP Conference Series*, **339** 39 (2005).
42. M. Sullivan, R. S. Ellis, G. Aldering, R. Amanullah, P. Astier, G. Blanc, M. S. Burns, A. Conley, S. E. Deustua, M. Doi, S. Fabbro, G. Folatelli, A. S. Fruchter, G. Garavini, R. Gibbons, G. Goldhaber, A. Goobar, D. E. Groom, D. Hardin, I. Hook, D. A. Howell, M. Irwin, A. G. Kim, R. A. Knop, C. Lidman, R. McMahon, J. Mendez, S. Nobili, P. E. Nugent, R. Pain, N. Panagia, C. R. Pennypacker, S. Perlmutter, R. Quimby, J. Raux, N. Regnault, P. Ruiz-Lapuente, B. Schaefer, K. Schahmaneche, A. L. Spadafora, N. A. Walton, L. Wang, W. M. Wood-Vasey and N. Yasuda, The Hubble diagram of type Ia supernovae as a function of host galaxy morphology, *MNRAS*, **340** 1057 (2003).
43. F. Hoyle and W. A. Fowler, Nucleosynthesis in Supernovae., *The Astrophysical Journal* **132** 565 (1960).
44. W. Hillebrandt, M. Kromer, F. K. Röpke and A. J. Ruiter, Towards an understanding of Type Ia supernovae from a synthesis of theory and observations, *Frontiers of Physics* **8** 116 (2013).
45. O. G. Benvenuto, J. A. Panei, K. Nomoto, H. Kitamura, I. Hachisu, Final Evolution and Delayed Explosions of Spinning White Dwarfs in Single Degenerate Models for Type Ia Supernovae, *The Astrophysical Journal Letters* **809** id:L6 (2015).
46. S. Heimersheim, N. Schoneberg, D. C. Hooper, J. Lesgourgues, Cannibalism hinders growth: Cannibal Dark Matter and the S8 tension, *arXiv:2008.08486v2* (7 Sep 2020).

47. L. A. Anchordoqui, E. Di Valentino, S. Pan, W. Yang, Dissecting the H_0 and S_8 tensions with Planck + BAO + supernova type Ia in multi-parameter cosmologies, *Journal of High Energy Astrophysics* **32**, 28 (2021).
48. R. C. Nunes, E. Di Valentino, Dark sector interaction and the supernova absolute magnitude tension, *Physical Review D* **104** id:063529 (2021).
49. G. Fanizza, Precision Cosmology and Hubble tension in the era of LSS surveys, CERN preprint # CERN-TH-2021-173 (2021), arXiv:2110.15272v2.
50. N. Aghanim *et al.*, Planck 2018 results. VI. Cosmological parameters, *Astron. Astrophys.* **641**, p. A6 (2020).
51. A. G. Riess, S. Casertano, W. Yuan, J. B. Bowers, L. Macri, J. C. Zinn and D. Scolnic, Cosmic Distances Calibrated to 1% Precision with Gaia EDR3 Parallaxes and Hubble Space Telescope Photometry of 75 Milky Way Cepheids Confirm Tension with ΛCDM, *Astrophys. J. Lett.* **908**, L6 (2021).
52. D. Camarena and V. Marra, Local determination of the Hubble constant and the deceleration parameter, *Phys. Rev. Res.* **2** id: 013028 (2020).
53. J. Elvin-Poole, M. Crocce, A. J. Ross, T. Giannantonio, Dark Energy Survey Year 1 Results: Galaxy clustering for combined probes *Monthly Notices of the Royal Astronomical Society* **478** 592 (2018) https://des.ncsa.illinois.edu/releases/sn.

Understanding prompt emission: Where do we stand?

Asaf Pe'er

Department of Physics, Bar Ilan University,
Ramat-Gan 52900, Israel
E-mail: asaf.peer@biu.ac.il
asafpeer2.ph.biu.ac.il/

In recent years, there is a renewed debate about the origin of the observed prompt emission signal. Some authors found that synchrotron emission can dominate the spectra of several long bursts, and a recent analysis show that it may be possible to overcome the famous 'line of death' argument by a direct fitting procedure. On the other hand, several recent works showed that non-dissipative photosphere is preferred as the dominant emission model in at least 1/4 of long and 1/3 of short GRB population. Here I critically review the arguments given as well as their physical consequences. I present some recent results that show a connection between the prompt spectra and the early afterglow emission, thereby argue for an independent method of discriminating the physical conditions that result in the different dominant radiative processes.

Keywords: Gamma-ray: bursts; Radiative mechanisms: non-thermal; photosphere; polarization

1. Introduction

After more than three decades of an extensive study, there is a broad consensus about many of the observational properties defining gamma-ray bursts (GRBs), yet there is still a strong debate about the correct way of interpreting the data. One of the key problems is that when interpreting the observed data, one may conclude about the leading radiative process that produces the observed signal. However, the radiative process is the last in a long chain of physical processes, that include gravitational energy extraction, relativistic motion, kinetic energy dissipation, particle acceleration and radiative process that eventually result in the observed signal. It is therefore impossible to disentangle the radiative process from the rest of this chain. Furthermore, the underlying physics of most of these processes is still only partially understood, and is the subject of an intensive research. As a result of this complexity, the leading radiative process is still uncertain.

When looking at the data, common to all GRBs are the following. The spectra has a peak in the sub-MeV range; at lower energies (below this peak) the spectral slopes are steep, $F_\nu \propto \nu^\alpha$, with $\alpha \approx 0$, but with considerable variation between bursts, and sensitive to the fitting procedure; In several bursts a higher energy emission, at the GeV-TeV range is seen; and when making spectral fittings for bursts with strong enough signal, multiple components are identified.[1]

The lightcurve of the prompt emission, which lasts for a few- few tens of seconds generally varies at a sub-second level. The prompt phase itself is distinguished from later emission ("afterglow") by a sharp decay in the flux. In a large fraction - 10's of % of GRBs, an X-ray plateau is detected, lasting for a few thousands seconds following the prompt phase. At later phase, a decaying "afterglow" which is well modeled by a self-similar expansion phase (the "Blandford-McKee" solution) is frequently detected. Furthermore, to many nearby long GRBs, evidence for a coinciding supernovae explosion exist. Finally, the connection between GRB170817 and the gravitational wave (GW) event clearly indicates that this particular event is associated with the merger of binary neutron stars.[2]

Following these plethora of data, already in the early 1990's the basic "fireball" picture had emerged,[3-6] according to which the gravitational energy released during the collapse of a massive star (or merger of binaries) is partially converted to kinetic energy in the form of a relativistic jet. At a second stage, part of this kinetic energy is released by internal dissipation (e.g., shock waves). Part of this energy is used in a accelerating particles, which then emit the observed signal. This model could explain both the high energy ($>$ MeV) emission, which is above the threshold for pair production, as well as the high variability detected in the lightcurve. It further obtained the afterglow as a prediction, to be later confirmed after the launch of the Beppo-SAX satellite.

Despite this success, many of the basic questions remain unanswered in the framework of this model. These include: (i) the nature of the progenitor star, and the event that led to its explosion and death; (ii) the nature of the launching mechanism of the relativistic jet[7,8]; (iii) The composition of the jet, and in particular its magnetization; (iv) The structure (geometry), dynamics (velocity field) and evolution of the propagating jet; (v) The nature of the kinetic energy dissipation mechanism - while initially internal shocks were considered, it became evident that they are not very efficient energy converters,[9] and additional mechanisms were proposed, mainly involving strong magnetic fields[10,11]; This directly related to the question of particle acceleration, which is associated with this dissipation. (vi) The nature of the radiative processes involved in producing the observed signal. (vii) Addressing these questions is important in understanding the connection of GRBs to other objects of interest and field of active research, such as stellar evolution, star formation, pop-III stars, supernovae, binary star evolution, cosmic rays, energetic neutrinos, and more. Finally, complete understanding of the nature of GRBs could be useful for addressing fundamental questions in cosmology (e.g., about the expansion of the universe) and Lorentz violation.

The key problem remains that while many theories exist for each of these open questions, in order to test the theoretical ideas one has to rely on the observed signal, which is the result of the long chain of physical processes. Thus, one has to find clever ways of discriminating between the models based on the final outcome, which is not directly related to the processes themselves, and in many cases is very confusing.

2. The leading radiative processes

Very broadly speaking, there are three competing models that are in wide use in explaining the observed prompt emission signal. These are synchrotron as a leading radiative process, hadronic and photospheric model.

The idea that synchrotron emission (possibly accompanied by inverse-Compton [IC] scattering at higher energies) is the leading radiative process during the prompt phase of GRBs was in wide use in the 1990's,[12,13] and regain interest in recent years.[14–16] Synchrotron emission is indeed very ubiquitous in many different astronomical objects, and in many GRBs it provides very good fitting to the lightcurve and spectra seen during the afterglow phase. Indeed, it is a very efficient way of extracting energy from energetic electrons via radiation. Furthermore, the conditions for this process to occur, namely the existence of energetic electrons and a magnetic field are both believed to exist as part of the dissipation process of the relativistic jet's kinetic energy. This is despite the fact that a complete model for the dissipation process still does not exist.

A second possibility that had been discussed is that of a hadronic origin, namely that the observed signal is due to emission from energetic protons, e.g., via synchrotron emission,[17] or possibly photo-meson (pion production) or Bethe-Heitler (pair production) interaction of the protons with the ambient photon field. In order for this process to take place, existence of energetic protons and a magnetic field are required. While synchrotron emission from protons is considerably less efficient than emission from the electrons due to the smaller cross-section, the advantage is that observations of energetic cosmic rays provide a direct evidence that proton acceleration to high energies necessarily exist in astronomical objects, while evidence for acceleration of electrons exist only indirectly. Thus, as long as the theoretical understanding of particle acceleration is incomplete, we do have certainty that this process does exist, though of course it is not clear whether the conditions that exist during GRB prompt emission are sufficient.

The third radiative process discussed is emission from the photosphere.[18] As opposed to the previous alternatives, this can be considered as a more complete model. As part of the GRB "fireball" model, the flow begins its relativistic expansion while being optically thick. Thus, at a certain radius, it must become optically thin - this is the photospheric radius, where photons escape. Thus, a photospheric component naturally exists in expanding, (initially) optically-thick flows, and in particular as part of the GRB "fireball" model. Furthermore, as no additional kinetic energy dissipation is required, this process can be highly efficient, with 10s of % of energy being released as photons at the photosphere.[19–21] On the other hand, in order to gain high efficiency, one requires to avoid adiabatic losses, namely that the photospheric radius r_{ph} is not much above the coasting radius, which marks the end of the acceleration of the jetted material.

3. Confronting synchrotron emission with the data

Already in the 1990's, synchrotron emission was suggested as a leading radiative model to explain the prompt emission from GRBs. This is based on the fact that for relativistic expansion with $\Gamma \gtrsim 100$ and dissipated kinetic energy that is spread roughly equally between accelerating electrons and generating magnetic fields (i.e., equipartition), the observed peak energy, $\nu_m^{ob.} \sim 500$ KeV is in good agreement with the peak observed energy.

However, a closer look reveals that under such a strong magnetic field, the electrons will rapidly cool (namely, will be in the "fast cooling" regime), in which case the expected low energy spectral slope is much shallower than the observed one. This is the famous "synchrotron line of death" problem,[22] which made this model less appealing for many years.

In recent years, as the quality of data increased, several attempts were made to overcome this problem. For example, Refs.[14,15,23] argue that the low energy spectral slope (below the peak) cannot be considered as a single power low, but rather there is an intermediate break at several tens of keV. This break enables to fit the spectra with a smaller than equipartition value of the magnetic field, thereby relaxing the 'line of death' restriction. Recently, Ref.[16] correctly argued that one should not attempt to fit the synchrotron spectra to the already fitted "Band" function, as is commonly the case, but rather directly to the raw data. When doing so, they managed to provide acceptable fits to the data within the framework of the synchrotron emission model.

Despite this success, a close look reveals that in providing these fits, the magnetic field assumed was extremely weak, ~ 1 G, and the emission radius obtained from the fit was $\sim 10^{17}$ cm. These require a ratio of burst energy to ambient density of $E_{53}/n_0 \sim 10^8$, which is 8 orders of magnitude larger than inferred from afterglow data (here and below, $Q_x = Q/10^x$). Thus, while the shape of the spectra can be fitted with such a model, the values of parameters obtained make it physically unacceptable.

Similarly, the idea of synchrotron emission from protons was investigated by several authors.[17,24] The allowed parameter space in this scenario, $B \sim 10^6$ G and emission radius of $R \sim 10^{13}$ cm, are much in line with the parameter estimate from afterglow data. However, due to the much less efficient radiative energy extraction from the protons (as compared to the electrons), this scenario requires that the total amount of energy given to the accelerated protons, E_p exceeds the jet kinetic energy, namely $E_p > E_k$. Thus, this scenario challenges models of particle acceleration.

4. Confronting photospheric emission with the data

The drawbacks of the synchrotron model mentioned above, led several authors to consider photospheric emission as an alternative.[18,19,25] However, this alternative was less appealing for many years, due to the fact that the observed spectra never appears as a "pure black body" (Planck), but rather is much broader.

This situation changes with the observation of GRB090902B.[26] This was a particularly bright burst, which showed clear evidence for a dominant narrow peak, Planck-like component. Furthermore, its extreme brightness enabled a time-resolved analysis during the onset of the prompt phase. This analysis proved that the spectrum change during the prompt phase: it started as a very narrow peak, close to a black body, and then gradually widened to resemble the common "Band" spectra. This had demonstrated the importance of **time-resolved** analysis, as an essential tool needed to understand the origin of the prompt phase.[27]

Recently, a similar analysis done on a large number of bursts[28] showed that this behavior is in fact common among pulses seen in many bright GRBs: initially, many pulses are narrow (hard spectrum) which become softer in time. This may be interpreted as a change in the leading radiative process with time: an initial thermal (or quasi-thermal) emission decays, and a later synchrotron emission becomes dominate at later times.

Furthermore, theoretical works[29–31] proved that in fact the initial expectation for a "Planck" spectrum was misleading: due to light aberration from the relativistically expanding jet, even a "pure" photospheric emission (so called "non-dissipative photosphere", or NDP) would be detected as a broader spectra, with spectral slope $dN/dE \propto E^{-\alpha}$ and $\alpha \approx 0.4$ below the peak[30] (compare with the Rayleigh-Jeans slope of $\alpha = 1$). Even this, though, is an asymptotic limit: when considering the finite detector's energy range, and the "curvature" of the spectrum near the energy peak, it is found that the expected observed values of the low energy spectral slope are even smaller than this.[32]

After considering these effects, a recent analysis show that in fact more than 1/4 of long GRBs, and 1/3 of short GRBs are consistent with having a pure thermal origin.[33,34] When adding a possible sub-photospheric energy dissipation that can potentially broaden the spectra, these fraction of course becomes much larger.

5. Applications

The realization that a photospheric emission does not appear as a textbook-solution blackbody, but rather is modified, enabled a refined analysis of the GRB properties. For example, Ref.[34] showed that the short GRB population that are consistent with having a pure thermal origin can be divided into two separate populations, clearly divided by their peak energy, E_{pk}, duration (T_{90}) and inferred Lorentz factor. One of these populations forms a continuation of the properties of the long GRB population, while the other one is separated. This result thus suggests that the classical separation of the GRB population to "long" and "short", which is based nearly entirely on the duration (T_{90}) is likely insufficient, and additional criteria are needed. Part of the "short" GRB population is in fact a continuation of the long GRB population.

One of the most puzzling questions is the observed isotropic energy-peak energy ("Amati") or luminosity - peak energy ("Yonetoku") relations reported. One appealing advantage of the photospheric emission model is that it may provide a natural explanation to the observed correlation, as due to viewing angle effect. Observers at different angles see the photons with different Doppler shifts, as $\nu^{ob.} = D\nu'$ (here, $D = [\Gamma(1 - \beta \cos\theta)]^{-1}$ is the Doppler shift, and primed quantities are in the co-moving frame). Using the invariance of L'/ν^2, the observed luminosity is related to the peak energy via $L^{ob.} \propto (\nu^{ob.})^2 \sim E_{pk}^2$, providing a natural explanation to the Yonetoku relation.[35]

While this may provide a very elegant explanation to the observed relation, this analysis relies on the underlying assumption that the comoving luminosity and comoving temperature are related via $L' \propto (T')^2$, while one expect the comoving temperature to decay with radius.[36] Thus, an underlying assumption here is that the photospheric radius is roughly similar in many different GRBs, which is unknown. I further discuss this issue in section 7 below.

6. Broadening of the photospheric emission

Numerical simulations of jets propagating inside and outside the collapsing star[21,37–39] clearly demonstrate that part of the jet kinetic energy is dissipated at various radii, in many cases below the photosphere. Such a dissipation can result from recollimation shock with the collapsing stellar material, magnetic energy dissipation or internal collisions. The resulting spectra was studied by various authors, e.g., Refs.[19,25,40–42] to name a few.

In this scenario, the dissipated energy is used to heat the plasma, which is then characterized by 2 temperatures: an electron temperature T_e which is greater than the photon temperature. Under these conditions, the resulting spectrum above the thermal peak is mainly due to inverse Compton (IC) scattering of the photons inside the plasma. It depends mainly on 2 parameters: the number of scattering (namely, the optical depth at the location of the energy dissipation) and the available energy, namely the ratio between the electron and the photon field energies, u_{el}/u_{ph}.

Below the thermal peak, one may expect an additional modification due to synchrtron emission from the (newly) heated electrons. Above the thermal peak, multiple scattering broadens the peak; if the optical depth is high enough, a new thermal peak would emerge, at higher temperatures. But in the intermediate case, $\tau \lesssim 100$, there is no simple analytical solution, and one has to refer to numerical works,[25,30,43–45] which show the plethora of possible spectra.

Another, independent broadening mechanism to be considered is geometrical broadening, which is the relativistic version of the "limb darkening" effect. Even for a spherical explosion, the photospheric radius is a function of the angle to the line of sight, θ, via $r_{ph}(\theta) \propto \left(\Gamma^{-2} + \theta^2/3\right)$, where Γ is the Lorentz factor of the flow.[29] This implies that photons emerging from angles $\theta > \Gamma^{-1}$ escape the expanding plasma at large radii. Furthermore, the photons have a finite probability of escaping the expanding plasma at different radii, leading to the concept of "vague photosphere".[29,30] This distribution inherently results in broadening of the emerging signal.

The explosion, though is not expected to be spherical, but rather a jet-like, with a finite jet opening angle. The flow properties may best be approximated as $\Gamma(\theta) \propto \Gamma_0/\sqrt{(1+(\theta/\theta_j)^{2p}}$ (see simluation by[38]), where θ_j is the jet opening angle, and p represents the "steepness" of the velocity profile. In this case, the observed signal depends, in addition, on the viewing angle, θ_v.[46] This scenario naturally leads to an enhancement of the limb darkening effect, as the Doppler boost of photons emitted from larger angles and larger radii is considerably smaller than that of photons emitted from the central jet regions. As a result, these photons are observed at much lower energies, and the observed spectrum – purely from the photosphere – is nearly flat for a wide energy range, for different jet parameters and viewing angles.[46]

This scenario naturally results in a polarized signal, for an off-axis observer. The scattered photons are 100% polarized, the photon field is anisotropic near the photosphere, and the rotational symmetry is broken for $\theta_v > 0$ (observer off the jet axis). The resulting polarization can reach 10's of % ($Q/I \lesssim 40\%$ for an off-axis observer, with flux that is still detectable). Another prediction of the theory is $\pi/2$ shift in polarization angle,[47] with spectra that is so smeared it looks very different from a pure "Planck". Indeed, such a polarization angle change was recently detected by the ASTROSAT mission,[48] though its exact origin is still debated.

7. Back scattering photospheric model

An underlying assumption of the discussion above is that the source of photons is the expanding plasma inside the jet: either via acceleration of particles that radiate synchrotron, or that the photons are coupled to the plasma below the photosphere. However, one may envision a different scenario, in which, following an initial expansion of the jet which clears a cavity inside the collapsing star,[39,49] continuous production of pairs via, e.g., neutrino annihilation occurs close to the newly formed black hole. These pairs then annihilate to produce photons. The photons, in turn, propagate inside the empty funnel until being scattered by the expanding stellar "cork" (made of stellar material cleared by the jet and by the surrounding cocoon).

In this scenario, therefore, the photons are back scattered by the relativistically expanding cork ahead of them from behind. Due to the relativistic motion of the cork, in the frame of an observer at infinity these photons are scattered in the forward direction, at some angle to the cork propagation direction. Due to the different Doppler boosts, photons scattered at different angles are seen at different energies. The obtained spectra integrated over different viewing angles, $dN/d\epsilon \propto \epsilon^1$ for energies below the peak, resembles the observed one.[50] For hot cork, multiple scattering inside the cork leads to photon energy gain,and the high energy spectral slope obtained is also similar to the observed.[51]

Perhaps the greatest achievement of this model is its ability to naturally explain the $E_{pk} - E_{iso}$ correlation ("Amati" relation) as a natural outcome of observers located at different angles, without the need to invoke any additional underlying assumptions, as in the "classical" photospheric model discussed above.

8. Summary

Understanding the origin of GRB prompt emission remains one of the big puzzles in the study of gamma-ray bursts. It is of particular importance, due to the fact that understanding it directly enables to probe the key physical ingredients involved in producing the GRB phenomena.

In recent years, there is a healthy debate between different ideas of interpreting the observed signal. As it turned out, different models both seem to produce key parts of the spectra. However, the physical parameters required for the synchrotron radiation to be the dominant mechanism seem at odds with afterglow observations.

Photospheric emission model turned out to be much more complicated than initially thought. Various effects and mechanisms act to modify the observed signal, which does not resemble the textbook "Planck" function. Among them are the finite detector's bandwidth, the jet velocity profile and sub-photospheric energy dissipation. For jet viewed off-axis, as in the vast majority of jets, the observed signal may be highly polarized. Another major advantage is the ability to explain the observed $E_{pk} - E_{iso}$ correlation, which is a natural outcome of a model in which the source of photons is not relativistically moving, but rather the photons are back-scattered from the expanding cork.

Acknowledgments

I wish to thank Damien Begue, Husne Dereli-Begue, Liang Li, Felix Ryde, Vidushi Sharma and Mukesh Vyas for many helpful discussions. This talk is attributed to the memory of Prof. David Eichler, a collaborator and friend, who sadly passed away earlier this year.

References

1. S. Iyyani, F. Ryde, J. M. Burgess, A. Pe'er and D. Bégué, Synchrotron emission in GRBs observed by Fermi: Its limitations and the role of the photosphere, *Mon. Not. R. Astron. Soc.* **456**, 2157 (February 2016).
2. B. P. Abbott, R. Abbott, T. D. Abbott, F. Acernese, K. Ackley, C. Adams, T. Adams, P. Addesso, R. X. Adhikari, V. B. Adya and et al., Multi-messenger Observations of a Binary Neutron Star Merger, *Astrophys. J.* **848**, p. L12 (October 2017).
3. B. Paczynski, Gamma-ray bursters at cosmological distances, *Astrophys. J.* **308**, L43 (September 1986).
4. J. Goodman, Are gamma-ray bursts optically thick?, *Astrophys. J.* **308**, L47 (September 1986).

5. M. J. Rees and P. Meszaros, Relativistic fireballs - Energy conversion and time-scales, *Mon. Not. R. Astron. Soc.* **258**, 41P (September 1992).
6. M. J. Rees and P. Meszaros, Unsteady outflow models for cosmological gamma-ray bursts, *Astrophys. J.* **430**, L93 (August 1994).
7. R. D. Blandford and R. L. Znajek, Electromagnetic extraction of energy from Kerr black holes, *Mon. Not. R. Astron. Soc.* **179**, 433 (May 1977).
8. R. Popham, S. E. Woosley and C. Fryer, Hyperaccreting Black Holes and Gamma-Ray Bursts, *Astrophys. J.* **518**, 356 (June 1999).
9. S. Kobayashi, T. Piran and R. Sari, Can Internal Shocks Produce the Variability in Gamma-Ray Bursts?, *Astrophys. J.* **490**, p. 92 (November 1997).
10. G. Drenkhahn, Acceleration of GRB outflows by Poynting flux dissipation, *Astron. Astrophys.* **387**, 714 (May 2002).
11. G. Drenkhahn and H. C. Spruit, Efficient acceleration and radiation in Poynting flux powered GRB outflows, *Astron. Astrophys.* **391**, 1141 (September 2002).
12. P. Meszaros, P. Laguna and M. J. Rees, Gasdynamics of relativistically expanding gamma-ray burst sources - Kinematics, energetics, magnetic fields, and efficiency, *Astrophys. J.* **415**, 181 (September 1993).
13. M. Tavani, A Shock Emission Model for Gamma-Ray Bursts. II. Spectral Properties, *Astrophys. J.* **466**, p. 768 (August 1996).
14. M. E. Ravasio, G. Oganesyan, G. Ghirlanda, L. Nava, G. Ghisellini, A. Pescalli and A. Celotti, Consistency with synchrotron emission in the bright GRB 160625B observed by Fermi, *Astron. Astrophys.* **613**, p. A16 (May 2018).
15. G. Oganesyan, L. Nava, G. Ghirlanda, A. Melandri and A. Celotti, Prompt optical emission as a signature of synchrotron radiation in gamma-ray bursts, *Astron. Astrophys.* **628**, p. A59 (August 2019).
16. J. M. Burgess, D. Bégué, J. Greiner, D. Giannios, A. Bacelj and F. Berlato, Gamma-ray bursts as cool synchrotron sources, *Nature Astronomy* **4**, 174 (February 2020).
17. N. Gupta and B. Zhang, Prompt emission of high-energy photons from gamma ray bursts, *Mon. Not. R. Astron. Soc.* **380**, 78 (September 2007).
18. M. J. Rees and P. Mészáros, Dissipative Photosphere Models of Gamma-Ray Bursts and X-Ray Flashes, *Astrophys. J.* **628**, 847 (August 2005).
19. A. Pe'er, P. Mészáros and M. J. Rees, Peak Energy Clustering and Efficiency in Compact Objects, *Astrophys. J.* **635**, 476 (December 2005).
20. K. Ioka, K. Toma, R. Yamazaki and T. Nakamura, Efficiency crisis of swift gamma-ray bursts with shallow X-ray afterglows: prior activity or time-dependent microphysics?, *Astron. Astrophys.* **458**, 7 (October 2006).
21. O. Gottlieb, A. Levinson and E. Nakar, High efficiency photospheric emission entailed by formation of a collimation shock in gamma-ray bursts, *Mon. Not. R. Astron. Soc.* **488**, 1416 (September 2019).
22. R. D. Preece, M. S. Briggs, R. S. Mallozzi, G. N. Pendleton, W. S. Paciesas and D. L. Band, The Synchrotron Shock Model Confronts a "Line of Death" in the BATSE Gamma-Ray Burst Data, *Astrophys. J.* **506**, L23 (October 1998).
23. M. E. Ravasio, G. Ghirlanda, L. Nava and G. Ghisellini, Evidence of two spectral breaks in the prompt emission of gamma-ray bursts, *Astron. Astrophys.* **625**, p. A60 (May 2019).
24. G. Ghisellini, G. Ghirlanda, G. Oganesyan, S. Ascenzi, L. Nava, A. Celotti, O. S. Salafia, M. E. Ravasio and M. Ronchi, Proton-synchrotron as the radiation mechanism of the prompt emission of gamma-ray bursts?, *Astron. Astrophys.* **636**, p. A82 (April 2020).

25. A. Pe'er, P. Mészáros and M. J. Rees, The Observable Effects of a Photospheric Component on GRB and XRF Prompt Emission Spectrum, *Astrophys. J.* **642**, 995 (May 2006).
26. A. A. Abdo, M. Ackermann, M. Ajello, K. Asano, W. B. Atwood, M. Axelsson, L. Baldini, J. Ballet, G. Barbiellini, M. G. Baring and et. al., Fermi Observations of GRB 090902B: A Distinct Spectral Component in the Prompt and Delayed Emission, *Astrophys. J.* **706**, L138 (November 2009).
27. F. Ryde, A. Pe'er, T. Nymark, M. Axelsson, E. Moretti, C. Lundman, M. Battelino, E. Bissaldi, J. Chiang, M. S. Jackson, S. Larsson, F. Longo, S. McGlynn and N. Omodei, Observational evidence of dissipative photospheres in gamma-ray bursts, *Mon. Not. R. Astron. Soc.* **415**, 3693 (August 2011).
28. L. Li, F. Ryde, A. Pe'er, H.-F. Yu and Z. Acuner, Bayesian Time-resolved Spectroscopy of Multipulse GRBs: Variations of Emission Properties among Pulses, *Astrophys. J.* **254**, p. 35 (June 2021).
29. A. Pe'er, Temporal Evolution of Thermal Emission from Relativistically Expanding Plasma, *Astrophys. J.* **682**, 463 (July 2008).
30. A. M. Beloborodov, Collisional mechanism for gamma-ray burst emission, *Mon. Not. R. Astron. Soc.* **407**, 1033 (September 2010).
31. A. Pe'er and F. Ryde, A Theory of Multicolor Blackbody Emission from Relativistically Expanding Plasmas, *Astrophys. J.* **732**, 49 (May 2011).
32. Z. Acuner, F. Ryde and H.-F. Yu, Non-dissipative photospheres in GRBs: Spectral appearance in the Fermi/GBM catalogue, *Mon. Not. R. Astron. Soc.* **487**, 5508 (August 2019).
33. Z. Acuner, F. Ryde, A. Pe'er, D. Mortlock and B. Ahlgren, The Fraction of Gamma-Ray Bursts with an Observed Photospheric Emission Episode, *Astrophys. J.* **893**, p. 128 (April 2020).
34. H. Dereli-Bégué, A. Pe'er and F. Ryde, Classification of Photospheric Emission in Short GRBs, *Astrophys. J.* **897**, p. 145 (July 2020).
35. H. Ito, J. Matsumoto, S. Nagataki, D. C. Warren, M. V. Barkov and D. Yonetoku, The photospheric origin of the Yonetoku relation in gamma-ray bursts, *Nature Communications* **10**, p. 1504 (April 2019).
36. A. Pe'er, B.-B. Zhang, F. Ryde, S. McGlynn, B. Zhang, R. D. Preece and C. Kouveliotou, The connection between thermal and non-thermal emission in gamma-ray bursts: General considerations and GRB 090902B as a case study, *Mon. Not. R. Astron. Soc.* **420**, 468 (February 2012).
37. M. A. Aloy, E. Müller, J. M. Ibáñez, J. M. Martí and A. MacFadyen, Relativistic Jets from Collapsars, *Astrophys. J.* **531**, L119 (March 2000).
38. W. Zhang, S. E. Woosley and A. I. MacFadyen, Relativistic Jets in Collapsars, *Astrophys. J.* **586**, 356 (March 2003).
39. D. López-Cámara, B. J. Morsony, M. C. Begelman and D. Lazzati, Three-dimensional Adaptive Mesh Refinement Simulations of Long-duration Gamma-Ray Burst Jets inside Massive Progenitor Stars, *Astrophys. J.* **767**, p. 19 (April 2013).
40. D. Giannios, Prompt emission spectra from the photosphere of a GRB, *Astron. Astrophys.* **457**, 763 (October 2006).
41. I. Vurm, Y. Lyubarsky and T. Piran, On Thermalization in Gamma-Ray Burst Jets and the Peak Energies of Photospheric Spectra, *Astrophys. J.* **764**, p. 143 (February 2013).
42. H. Ito, S. Nagataki, J. Matsumoto, S.-H. Lee, A. Tolstov, J. Mao, M. Dainotti and A. Mizuta, Spectral and Polarization Properties of Photospheric Emission from Stratified Jets, *Astrophys. J.* **789**, p. 159 (July 2014).

43. I. Vurm, A. M. Beloborodov and J. Poutanen, Gamma-Ray Bursts from Magnetized Collisionally Heated Jets, *Astrophys. J.* **738**, 77 (September 2011).
44. D. Lazzati and M. C. Begelman, Non-thermal Emission from the Photospheres of Gamma-ray Burst Outflows. I. High-Frequency Tails, *Astrophys. J.* **725**, 1137 (December 2010).
45. D. Giannios, The peak energy of dissipative gamma-ray burst photospheres, *Mon. Not. R. Astron. Soc.* **422**, 3092 (June 2012).
46. C. Lundman, A. Pe'er and F. Ryde, A theory of photospheric emission from relativistic, collimated outflows, *Mon. Not. R. Astron. Soc.* **428**, 2430 (January 2013).
47. C. Lundman, A. Pe'er and F. Ryde, Polarization properties of photospheric emission from relativistic, collimated outflows, *Mon. Not. R. Astron. Soc.* **440**, 3292 (June 2014).
48. V. Sharma, S. Iyyani, D. Bhattacharya, T. Chattopadhyay, S. V. Vadawale and V. B. Bhalerao, Spectropolarimetric analysis of prompt emission of GRB 160325A: Jet with evolving environment of internal shocks, *Mon. Not. R. Astron. Soc.* **493**, 5218 (April 2020).
49. O. Bromberg, Z. Mikolitzky and A. Levinson, Sub-photospheric Emission from Relativistic Radiation Mediated Shocks in GRBs, *Astrophys. J.* **733**, p. 85 (June 2011).
50. M. K. Vyas, A. Pe'er and D. Eichler, A Backscattering-dominated Prompt Emission Model for the Prompt Phase of Gamma-Ray Bursts, *Astrophys. J.* **908**, p. 9 (February 2021).
51. M. K. Vyas, A. Pe'er and D. Eichler, Predicting Spectral Parameters in the Backscattering-dominated Model for the Prompt Phase of GRBs, *Astrophys. J.* **918**, p. L12 (September 2021).

On explaining prompt emission from GRB central engines with photospheric emission model

M. Bhattacharya[1,*] and P. Kumar[2]

[1]*Department of Physics, Pennsylvania State University, University Park, PA 16802, USA*
E-mail: mmb5946@psu.edu
[2]*Department of Astronomy, University of Texas, Austin, TX 78712, USA*

Although the observed spectra for gamma-ray burst (GRB) prompt emission is well constrained, the underlying radiation mechanism is still not very well understood. We explore photospheric emission in GRB jets by modelling the Comptonization of fast cooled synchrotron photons whilst the electrons and protons are accelerated to highly relativistic energies by repeated energy dissipation events as well as Coulomb collisions. In contrast to the previous simulations, we implement realistic photon-to-particle number ratios of $N_\gamma/N_e \sim 10^5$ or higher, that are consistent with the observed radiation efficiency of relativistic jets. Using our Monte Carlo radiation transfer (MCRaT) code, we can successfully model the prompt emission spectra when the electrons are momentarily accelerated to highly relativistic energies (Lorentz factor $\sim 50-100$) after getting powered by $\sim 30-50$ episodic dissipation events in addition to their Coulomb coupling with the jet protons, and for baryonic outflows that originate from moderate optical depths $\sim 20-30$. We also show that the resultant shape of the photon spectrum is practically independent of the initial photon energy distribution and the jet baryonic energy content, and hence independent of the emission mechanism.

Keywords: Gamma-ray burst: general; methods: numerical; radiation mechanisms: thermal; radiative transfer; scattering.

1. Introduction

The radiation mechanism responsible for the prompt emission of long-duration GRBs has remained elusive ever since their discovery. The observed photon spectrum has a distinctly non-thermal shape and is generally modelled using the Band function,[1] which is a smoothly connected broken power-law with peak energy $E_{\rm peak} \sim 300\,{\rm keV}$ and the low/high energy dependence[2,3] given by $f_\nu \propto \nu^0/f_\nu \propto \nu^{-1.2}$. A robust radiation mechanism should explain the non-thermal features observed in the prompt emission spectrum in a self-consistent manner. The two most widely explored models to this end are the synchrotron and photospheric models.[4–6]

In the synchrotron model, the electrons accelerated by either internal shocks[4] or magnetic reconnection[7] produce the prompt radiation via synchrotron emission process.[8] Although this model accounts for the non-thermal nature of the photon spectrum, it cannot explain the high observed radiation efficiencies up to few tens of percent.[9] Moreover, the observed hard GRB spectra at low energies cannot be explained with synchrotron emission process.[10,11] Owing to these shortcomings of the synchrotron model, many researchers have considered photospheric emission model in more detail.[12,13] Unlike the synchrotron model, photospheric model naturally explains the observed high radiation efficiencies and spectral shape is completely determined by photon-matter interactions irrespective of the dissipation mechanism involved. Although there have been many successful attempts to explain the high-energy non-thermal behaviour using sub-photospheric dissipation,[7,14,15] explaining the low-energy non-thermal tails has turned out to be really challenging.[16]

Here we study the sub-photospheric Comptonisation of synchrotron seed photons[5,17] to find the plausible conditions under which both low/high-energy non-thermal behaviour and observed peak energy can be explained self-consistently. The particles in the jet are accelerated to relativistic energies by repeated dissipation events such as internal shocks[4,18] or magnetic reconnection.[7,19] The photons continue to scatter electrons while the outflow is optically thick and gain energy until either the average photon energy matches that of the electrons or the outflow becomes optically thin so that the photons escape the photosphere. We determine a correlation between the number of reheating events and initial optical depth, and perform an exhaustive parametric space search to obtain a Band-like photon spectrum. We also perform analytical calculations to examine the evolution of photon energy spectrum with multiple scatterings and validate the numerical results.

2. Energy requirement for photons and particles

We first estimate the average energy $E_{\gamma,\text{avg}}$ that the jet photons need to have to generate a Band-like output spectrum. As most of this energy is transferred by hot electrons through Comptonisation, this also places a threshold energy requirement $\gamma_{e,\text{crit}}$ on the electrons. As the electrons are maintained at $\gamma_e \sim \gamma_{e,crit}$ by energy gained from either Coulomb collisions or repeated dissipation events and subsequent cooling due to IC, we further constrain the injected energy and the number of episodic dissipation events required.

2.1. *Analytical estimate for* $E_{\gamma,\text{avg}}$ *and* $\gamma_{e,\text{crit}}$

The observed photon spectrum has a Band-like shape with a low/high-energy dependence, $f_\nu \propto \nu^0/\nu^{-1.2}$ in the energy range $\sim 10 \text{ keV} - 300 \text{ keV}/\sim 300 \text{ keV} - 10 \text{ MeV}$, where f_ν denotes the photon flux per unit frequency. The average observed energy of each photon in the lab frame is then $E'_{\gamma,\text{avg}} \sim 300 \text{ eV}$, assuming a jet bulk Lorentz factor $\Gamma = 300$. Equating the total energy content of the photons with the maximum energy that the electrons can deposit via Comptonisation gives

$$N_\gamma E'_{\gamma,\text{avg}} = N_e(\gamma_{e,\text{crit}} - 1)m_e c^2 \left(\tau_{\text{in}} t'_{\text{dyn}}/t'_{\text{IC}}\right), \qquad (1)$$

where τ_{in} is the initial optical depth, $t'_{\text{dyn/IC}}$ is the dynamical/inverse-Compton (IC) timescale and $\tau_{\text{in}} t'_{\text{dyn}}/t'_{\text{IC}} \sim$ number of times the electrons interact with photons during jet expansion. The characteristic dynamical timescale is $t'_{\text{dyn}} = R_{\text{in}}/\Gamma c$ while the IC timescale is $t'_{\text{IC}} = 3(\gamma_e - 1)m_e c/4 U'_\gamma \sigma_T \gamma_e^2 \beta_e^2$. Here, R_{in} is the photon injection radius, σ_T is the Thomson cross section, γ_e is the electron energy and U'_γ is the radiation energy density. Substituting typical GRB parameters gives $\gamma_{e,crit} = 1.352$.

We now estimate the electron super-Coulomb efficiency parameter η which leads to $\gamma_e = 1.352$. For electrons to remain in equilibrium as a result of Coulomb heating and IC cooling over the jet expansion timescale,

$$\frac{(\gamma_e - 1)m_e c^2}{5 \times 10^{-19} n'_e} \cdot \frac{(8.3 \times 10^{-15} T'^{3/2}_e + \beta_p^3)}{\beta_p^2} \cdot \frac{1}{\eta} = \frac{3}{4} \frac{(\gamma_e - 1)m_e c}{U'_\gamma \sigma_T \gamma_e^2 \beta_e^2}, \quad (2)$$

where electron density $n'_e = L/(4\pi R^2 m_p c^3 \Gamma^2) = 4.17 \times 10^{15}$ cm^{-3}, radiation energy density $U'_\gamma = L_\gamma/(4\pi R^2 \Gamma^2 c) = 2 \times 10^{11}$ erg/cm^3 and $T'_e = \frac{1}{k_B}(\gamma_{e,ad} - 1)(\gamma_e - 1)m_e c^2 = 1.98 \times 10^9 (\gamma_e - 1/\gamma_e)$ is the electron temperature for a Maxwellian distribution. Here, $\gamma_{e,ad} = (4\gamma_e + 1)/(3\gamma_e)$ is the adiabatic index of the electrons and β_p is the speed of protons divided by the speed of light. Substituting $\gamma_p \sim 1.123$ for $\tau_{in} = 8$ and $\gamma_e = \gamma_{e,crit} = 1.352$, we obtain $\eta = 4.5$.[15]

The electrons cannot be continuously heated by Coulomb collisions if the protons cool down to energies comparable to that of electrons within the dynamical timescale. While the protons cool down due to Coulomb collisions and adiabatic expansion, the electrons gain energy through Coulomb and get cooled due to adiabatic cooling and IC. The electrons cannot be heated any further when

$$N_p(\gamma_p - 1)m_p c^2 - N_p \int_0^{t'} \frac{5 \times 10^{-19} n'_e \beta_p^2}{[0.73(\gamma_e - 1/\gamma_e)^{3/2} + \beta_p^3]} \eta dt' - N_p \int_0^{t'} \frac{(\gamma_p - 1)m_p c^2}{R/\Gamma c} dt'$$

$$= N_e(\gamma_e - 1)m_e c^2 + N_e \int_0^{t'} \frac{5 \times 10^{-19} n'_e \beta_p^2}{[0.73(\gamma_e - 1/\gamma_e)^{3/2} + \beta_p^3]} \eta dt'$$

$$- N_e \int_0^{t'} \frac{(\gamma_e - 1)m_e c^2}{R/\Gamma c} dt' - N_e \int_0^{t'} (4/3) U'_\gamma \sigma_T (\gamma_e^2 - 1) c dt'. \quad (3)$$

which simplifies for a neutral jet to, $1.5 \times 10^{-3}(1 - \ln\lambda) + 3.21 \times 10^{-5}(1 - 1/\lambda) = 1.15 \times 10^{-4} \eta(1 - 1/\lambda)\tau_{in}$. For $\lambda \sim 2$ i.e. for protons to cool down to electron energies in $t' = 2t'_{dyn}$, $\eta\tau_{in} \sim 8.28$. This means that for $\tau_{in} \gtrsim 10$, the protons cool down too fast and super-Coulomb interaction cannot keep the electrons hot beyond $t' = 2t'_{dyn}$. This necessitates the heating of electrons by some alternate sub-photospheric dissipation mechanism. Even though the electrons tend to cool down rapidly due to Comptonization, their energy can still be maintained at $\gamma_e \gtrsim \gamma_{e,crit}$ provided the episodic heating events are frequent enough.

2.2. *Electron heating by repeated dissipation events*

As the total energy gained by the photons is the total energy that is transferred by the electrons through Comptonisation

$$N_\gamma \tau_{in}^{2/3} \left(E'_{\gamma,avg,obs} - E'_{\gamma,avg,i} \right) = N_e \int_0^{\tau_{in} t'_{dyn}} (4/3) U'_\gamma \tau_{in}^{-2/3} \sigma_T \gamma_e^2 \beta_e^2 c \, dt'.$$

which simplifies to

$$10^5 \tau_{in}^{2/3} E'_{\gamma,avg,obs} = 8.72 \times 10^6 L_{\gamma,50} \tau_{in}^{-2/3} \int_{R_{in}}^{\tau_{in} R_{in}} (\gamma_e^2 - 1) \frac{dR}{R^2}$$

$$\sim \frac{8.72 \times 10^6 L_{\gamma,50} \tau_{in}^{-2/3} (\gamma_e^2 - 1)}{R_{in}}.$$

Substituting $R_{in} \sim 2.17 \times 10^{11} \tau_{in}^{-1}$ cm, yields $\gamma_{e,crit} \sim \sqrt{1 + 1.2\, L_{\gamma,50}^{-1} \tau_{in}^{1/3}}$. The critical electron energy obtained here is similar to $\gamma_{e,crit} \sim 1.352$ obtained earlier, especially for small initial optical depths $\tau_{in} \sim 1$.

We consider repeated sub-photospheric dissipation events that can re-accelerate the electrons as well as protons to their initial energies.

Using the fact that the electrons remain in equilibrium with energy $\gamma_{e,\mathrm{crit}} \sim \sqrt{1 + 1.2\, L_{\gamma,50}^{-1} \tau_{\mathrm{in}}^{1/3}}$, we constrain the energy injected per electron $E_{inj} = N_{rh}(\gamma_{e,in} - 1) m_e c^2$. In particular,

$$N_e \tau_{in}^{4/3} (\gamma_e - 1) m_e c^2 = N_e \int_0^{\tau_{in} t'_{dyn}} \frac{5 \times 10^{-19} n'_e \beta_p^2 \tau_{in}^{-4/3}}{[0.73(\gamma_e - 1/\gamma_e)^{3/2} + \beta_p^3]} dt'$$

$$+ N_e N_{rh} (\gamma_{e,in} - 1) m_e c^2 - N_e \int_0^{\tau_{in} t'_{dyn}} (4/3) U'_\gamma \tau_{in}^{-2/3} \sigma_T \gamma_e^2 \beta_e^2 c\, dt', \quad (4)$$

where $\gamma_e \approx \gamma_{e,crit}$ and $\tau_{in}^{-4/3}/\tau_{in}^{-2/3}$ is the adiabatic cooling factor for relativistic electrons/photons. We consider the episodic dissipation events to be equally spaced over the jet expansion timescale $\tau_{in} t'_{dyn}$ and to supply fixed energy (equal to initial energy, $\gamma_{e,in}/\gamma_{p,in}$) to the electrons/protons at each instance. Substituting $R_{\mathrm{in}} = 2.17 \times 10^{11}\, \tau_{\mathrm{in}}^{-1}$ cm and simplifying yields

$$\tau_{in}^{4/3} (\gamma_e - 1) m_e c^2 = \frac{10^{-4} \tau_{in}^{-4/3}}{[0.73(\gamma_e - 1/\gamma_e)^{3/2} + (2/\tau_{in})^{3/2}]} + E_{\mathrm{inj,cr}} - 3.21 \times 10^{-5} \tau_{in}^{-2/3}, \quad (5)$$

which constrains the critical injected energy $E_{inj,cr}(\tau_{in}) = N_{rh}(\gamma_{e,in} - 1) m_e c^2$ per electron in terms of τ_{in}. Equation (5) is only a necessary and not sufficient condition to obtain Band-like photon spectrum as it determines the average photon energy but does not impose any constraints on the general shape of the photon spectrum. For large E_{inj}, photon peak energy $E_{\gamma,peak} \gg E_{\gamma,obs} \sim 300$ keV while $E_{\gamma,peak} \ll E_{\gamma,obs}$ for large τ_{in}, due to significant energy loss from adiabatic cooling.

3. MCRaT code description

We discuss here the implementation of our MCRaT code and give an overview of the basic physics included. We first list the jet parameters and describe the initial distributions of the particles and the photons. We then discuss how the jet particles and photons are affected by the physical processes. Lastly, we describe the algorithm of our photospheric MCRaT code.

3.1. Relativistic jet parameters

The jet parameters provided as input for the code are:

- *Isotropic equivalent luminosity, L*: The bulk of the jet luminosity is contributed by the protons. We consider $L = 10^{51}, 10^{52}$ erg/s.[20]
- *Jet bulk Lorentz factor, Γ*: The bulk Lorentz factor is related to L and $E_{\gamma,peak}$. We consider $\Gamma = 30, 100, 300$ in this work.[21]
- *Initial optical depth, τ_{in}*: The optical depth is measured relative to $R = L\sigma_T/(8\pi m_p c^3 \beta \Gamma^3 \tau)$ which is the photon radial distance from central engine in the observer frame. τ_{in} corresponds to the radial distance from central engine where all particles and photons are injected. We consider $\tau_{in} = 10, 20, 40$.

3.2. Initial distributions

We describe here the initial energy and velocity distributions of the jet electrons, protons and photons.

- *Electrons and protons:* We consider a charge-neutral jet with particle number $N_e = N_p = 2 \times 10^2$. The initial particle velocities are distributed randomly in the jet-comoving frame. All particles are uniformly distributed in the jet-comoving frame at initial time. The initial energy of the electrons are determined from the Maxwellian distribution with temperature $k_B T'_{e,in} = (\gamma_{e,ad,in} - 1)(\gamma_{e,in} - 1)m_e c^2$ while the protons are mono-energetic with $\gamma_p = \gamma_{p,in}$. We consider $\gamma_{e,in} = 2, 10, 30, 100$ and $\gamma_{p,in} = 1.01, 1.1$ for our simulations.
- *Photons:* In order to maintain $N_\gamma/N_e = 10^5$, we consider $N_\gamma = 2 \times 10^7$ for our simulations.[15] The initial photon velocities are randomly distributed in the jet-comoving frame and photon positions are uniformly distributed within a cone of solid angle $1/\Gamma$ pointing towards the observer. The initial photon energy distribution is given by the synchrotron distribution for fast cooling electrons[5]

$$f_\nu = \begin{cases} \left(\frac{\nu_{ac}}{\nu_{sa}}\right)^{11/8} \left(\frac{\nu}{\nu_{ac}}\right)^2, & \nu_{min} < \nu < \nu_{ac} \\ \left(\frac{\nu}{\nu_{sa}}\right)^{11/8}, & \nu_{ac} < \nu < \nu_{sa} \\ \left(\frac{\nu}{\nu_{sa}}\right)^{-1/2}, & \nu_{sa} < \nu < \nu_m \\ \left(\frac{\nu_m}{\nu_{sa}}\right)^{-1/2} \left(\frac{\nu}{\nu_m}\right)^{-p/2}, & \nu_m < \nu < \nu_{max} \end{cases} \quad (6)$$

where f_ν is the peak normalised photon flux per unit frequency and $p = 2.5$ is the spectral index at high energies.[6]

3.3. Physical processes in the jet

Here we discuss the physical interactions between the electrons, protons and photons that can further affect the output photon spectrum.

- *Adiabatic cooling:* As the relativistic jet expands outward, the photon and particle energies drop considerably as

$$(\gamma_{e,f} - 1)/(\gamma_{e,i} - 1) = \left(R_{\rm in} + \beta c \Gamma t'_f / R_{\rm in} + \beta c \Gamma t'_i\right)^{-2(\gamma_{\rm ad,e}-1)},$$
$$(\gamma_{p,f} - 1)/(\gamma_{p,i} - 1) = \left(R_{\rm in} + \beta c \Gamma t'_f / R_{\rm in} + \beta c \Gamma t'_i\right)^{-2(\gamma_{\rm ad,p}-1)},$$
$$E_{\gamma,f}/E_{\gamma,i} = \left(R_{\rm in} + \beta c \Gamma t'_f / R_{\rm in} + \beta c \Gamma t'_i\right)^{-2/3}, \tag{7}$$

where the subscript i/f denotes the initial/final value of the physical quantity and $\gamma_{ad,e/p} = (4\gamma_{e/p} + 1)/(3\gamma_{e/p})$ is the electron/proton adiabatic index.

- *Coulomb collisions:* While the electrons are continuously heated by the protons in the jet, they also interact with each other to quickly attain thermal equilibrium. The corresponding timescales are given by[22]

$$\dot{E}_{e-p} = \frac{5 \times 10^{-19} n'_e \beta^2_{\rm p,avg}}{8.3 \times 10^{-15} T'^{3/2}_{\rm e,avg} + \beta^3_{\rm p,avg}},$$
$$\dot{E}_{e-e} = \frac{5 \times 10^{-19} n'_e \beta^2_{\rm e,avg}}{8.3 \times 10^{-15} T'^{3/2}_{\rm e,avg} + \beta^3_{\rm e,avg}}, \tag{8}$$

where $\beta_{p,avg}$, $\beta_{e,avg}$ and $T'_{e,avg}$ are number-averaged quantities. The electron distribution is re-initialized to Maxwellian distribution on a timescale $t'_{e-e} = (\gamma_{e,avg} - 1)m_e c^2 / \dot{E}_{e-e} \ll t'_{e-p}$.

- *IC scattering:* The distance s' that a photon travels before scattering an electron is given by probability density $p(s') \propto \exp(-s'/l'_{\rm mfp})$, where $l'_{\rm mfp} = 1/(n'_e \sigma_T)$ is the photon mean free path. The scattering probability of a particular electron with a photon is[15]

$$P_{sc}(\beta_e, \theta'_e) = \frac{1}{4\pi \beta^2_e}(1 - \beta_e \cos \theta'_e), \tag{9}$$

where β_e is the electron speed divided by speed of light and θ'_e is the angle between electron and photon velocities before scattering. Average number of scatterings that a photon experiences before escaping is $\sim 2\tau_{in}$.[23]

- *Pair production/annihilation:* Due to the episodic jet dissipation events, the electrons are often accelerated to highly relativistic energies $\gamma_e = \gamma_{e,in} \sim 100$ and can scatter energetic photons with $E'_\gamma \gtrsim 10\ E'_{\gamma,peak}$ to energies $\gtrsim 4E'_{\gamma,avg}\gamma^2_e \sim m_e c^2 \sim 5 \times 10^5$ eV, before cooling down rapidly to non-relativistic energies. For synchrotron photons that we consider (see equation 6), a considerable fraction $\sim 30\%$ have sufficient energy to generate electron-positron pairs which can affect the shape of the output photon spectrum, especially for large $\tau_{in} \gtrsim 10$.

3.4. Code implementation

The travel distances are first drawn for all photons depending on their mean free path and the photons are propagated. The new photon positions are evaluated to check if any photon escapes the photosphere, in which case the energy is calculated and stored. Other photons are stored in a priority queue where they are ordered based on travel distances. Next, the photon at the top of the queue is propagated, a proton is randomly selected and an electron is selected using the scattering probability, P_{sc}. The particle and photon energies are then updated due to adiabatic cooling and Coulomb collisions. The outgoing velocities and energies of the photon and electron are calculated if IC scattering occurs. Subsequently, the next photon in the queue is drawn and electron-positron pair production cross section is evaluated. If the cross section is large, a new electron and positron are generated and photons are not placed back in the queue. If positron number is non-zero, a positron is drawn randomly and the pair annihilation cross section with the electron is calculated. Two new photons are created and added to the queue, if the cross section is significant. The method described above is repeated until a third of the total photons in the jet escape and a time-averaged output photon spectrum is obtained.

4. Photospheric simulation results

Here we present the results of our photospheric MCRaT simulations. The photon energy spectrum and the electron kinetic energy spectrum are shown in the lab frame at the end of each simulation in all the figures. The photon and electron energy spectrum are Doppler boosted from the jet-comoving frame to the lab frame in all the figures. The electron kinetic energy spectra are peaked at significantly larger energies compared to the photon spectra for all the simulations as shown in the figures. In the rest of this paper, we denote the low/high energy photon spectral index by α/β and the observed photon peak energy by $E_{\gamma,obs}$.

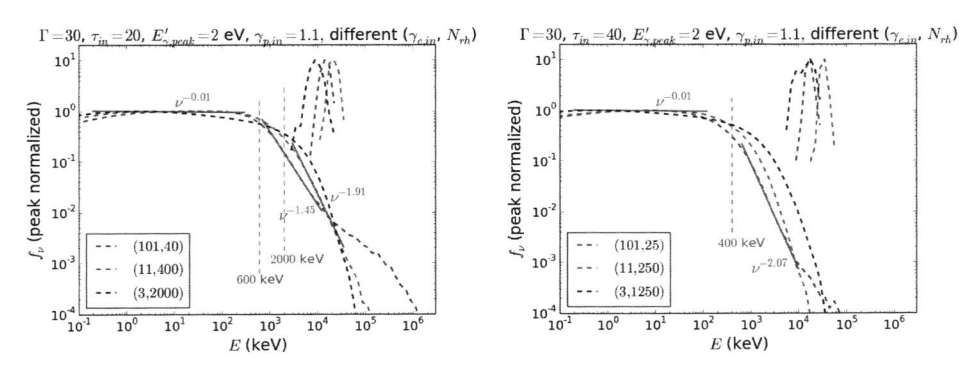

Fig. 1. **Effect of $\gamma_{e,\mathrm{in}}$ at constant $E_{\mathrm{inj}} = E_{\mathrm{inj,cr}}(\tau_{\mathrm{in}})$ and for different τ_{in}.** The input parameters used are $E'_{\gamma,\mathrm{peak}} = 2$ eV, $\gamma_{p,\mathrm{in}} = 1.1$, $L = 10^{52}$ erg/s and $\Gamma = 30$. Left panel: $\tau_{\mathrm{in}} = 20$, $E_{\mathrm{inj}} = 4000\ m_e c^2$ and $(N_{\mathrm{rh}}, \gamma_{e,\mathrm{in}}) = (40, 101)/(400, 11)/(2000, 3)$. Right panel: $\tau_{\mathrm{in}} = 40$, $E_{\mathrm{inj}} = 2500\ m_e c^2$ and $(N_{\mathrm{rh}}, \gamma_{e,\mathrm{in}}) = (25, 101)/(250, 11)/(1250, 3)$.

In Figure 1, we present the simulation results for fixed injected energy $E_{\mathrm{inj,cr}} = N_{\mathrm{rh,cr}}(\gamma_{e,\mathrm{in}} - 1)\ m_e c^2 = 4000/2500\ \mathrm{m}_e c^2$ at $\tau_{\mathrm{in}} = 20/40$ and different $\gamma_{e,\mathrm{in}} = 3, 11, 101$. The photons/protons are initialized with $E'_{\gamma,\mathrm{peak}} = 2$ eV$/\gamma_{p,\mathrm{in}} = 1.1$

with jet parameters, $L = 10^{52}$ erg/s and $\Gamma = 30$. We find that $\alpha \sim 0$ is practically unaffected by decrease in electron energy $\gamma_{e,in}$ (irrespective of τ_{in}) and is solely determined by the critical injected energy $E_{inj,cr}$. As $\gamma_{e,in}$ increases for a given $E_{inj,cr}$, the photons tend to have lower peak energy $E_{\gamma,peak}$ and there are fewer/more photons with $E_\gamma \sim 1-10$ MeV/$\gtrsim 100$ MeV. This is expected as the electrons with $\gamma_{e,in} = 101$ are accelerated much less frequently compared to those with $\gamma_{e,in} \sim 3-11$ and then subsequently cool down very rapidly to non-relativistic γ_e after being considerably hotter for a shorter duration $\sim 10^{-3}\, t_{dyn}$ when they accelerate many photons to $E_\gamma \gtrsim 100$ MeV. The high energy bump in f_ν and deviation from power-law behaviour for large $\gamma_{e,in}$ is seen only at moderate $\tau_{in} \lesssim 20$ and is not appreciable for larger $\tau_{in} \gtrsim 40$ as the high energy photons cool down rapidly from adiabatic losses.

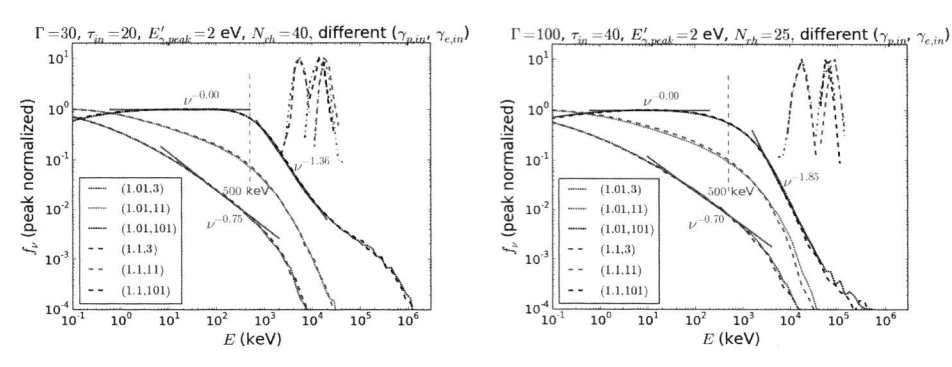

Fig. 2. **Effect of $\gamma_{p,in}$ and $\gamma_{e,in}$ for $N_{rh} = 40$ ($\tau_{in} = 20, \Gamma = 30$) and $N_{rh} = 25$ ($\tau_{in} = 40, \Gamma = 100$).** The input parameters used are $E'_{\gamma,peak} = 2$ eV and $L = 10^{51}$ erg/s. Left panel: $\Gamma = 30$, $\tau_{in} = 20$, $N_{rh} = 40$: $\gamma_{p,in} = (1.01, 1.1)$ and $\gamma_{e,in} = (3, 11, 101)$. Right panel: $\Gamma = 100$, $\tau_{in} = 40$, $N_{rh} = 25$: $\gamma_{p,in} = (1.01, 1.1)$ and $\gamma_{e,in} = (3, 11, 101)$.

We find an increase in $|\beta|$ with decrease in $\gamma_{e,in}$ for a fixed $E_{inj,cr}(\tau_{in})$ as well as with increase in τ_{in}. Moreover, $\beta \sim \beta_{obs}$ for $\gamma_{e,in} \sim$ few 10s -100 and $\tau_{in} \lesssim 20$ while the high-energy spectrum is much steeper, $f_\nu \propto \nu^{-2}$ for $\tau_{in} \gtrsim 40$, almost independent of N_{rh}. While relatively continuous energy injection (small $\gamma_{e,in} \sim$ few and large $N_{rh,cr} \sim$ few 1000s) results in steeper high energy spectra $|\beta| > |\beta_{obs}|$ along with $E_{\gamma,peak}/E_{\gamma,obs} \gtrsim 10$, episodic energy injection (large $\gamma_{e,in} \sim 100$ and small $N_{rh,cr} \sim$ few 10s) gives a high energy power-law spectrum consistent with observations for moderate optical depths $\tau_{in} \lesssim 20$. In order to have both $E_{\gamma,peak} \sim 500$ keV and $|\beta| \sim 1.2-1.5$, the particles and photons have to be initialized at $\tau_{in} \sim 20-40$ and $E_{inj,cr}(\tau_{in}) \sim 2500-4000\, m_e c^2$ energy needs to be injected into electrons with $\gamma_{e,in} \sim$ few 10s.

In Figure 2, we present the simulation results for fixed $N_{rh,cr}(\tau_{in}) = 40/25$ at $\tau_{in} = 20\ (\Gamma = 30)/40\ (\Gamma = 100)$ with different combinations of $\gamma_{e,in} = 3, 11, 101$ and $\gamma_{p,in} = 1.01, 1.1$. The seed photons have energy $E'_{\gamma,peak} = 2$ eV with jet luminosity

$L = 10^{51}$ erg/s. We see that $\gamma_{p,\text{in}}$ does not affect the photon output spectra irrespective of the optical depth, which is expected as the Coulomb collisions timescale $t'_{e-p} = (\gamma_{e,\text{avg}} - 1)m_e c^2/\dot{E}_{e-p}$ is considerably longer than the Comptonization timescale t'_{IC}. A minimum electron energy $\gamma_e \gtrsim 11$ is needed in order to have photons with $E_\gamma \gtrsim 10$ MeV and peak energy $E_{\gamma,\text{peak}} \sim 1$ MeV for both τ_{in} considered. The output photon spectrum does not show a power-law dependence at both low and high energies when the electron initial energy is small $\gamma_{e,\text{in}} \lesssim 11$. While the output photon spectrum shows $\alpha \sim \alpha_{obs}$ and $E_{\gamma,\text{peak}} \sim E_{\gamma,obs}$ at both optical depths for electrons with $\gamma_{e,\text{in}} = 101$ only, the high energy power-law spectral index $|\beta| \gg |\beta_{obs}|$ for $\tau_{in} = 40$ and $\sim |\beta_{obs}|$ for $\tau_{in} = 20$.

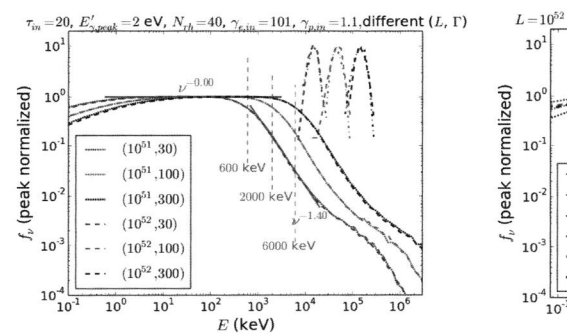

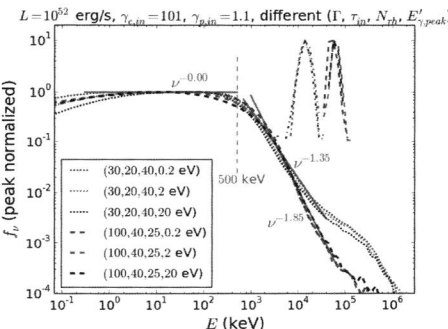

Fig. 3. *Left panel:* MCRaT simulations showing the effect of $L = (10^{51}, 10^{52})$ erg/s and $\Gamma = 30, 100, 300$ for constant $N_{rh} = 40$, $\gamma_{e,\text{in}} = 101$ and $\tau_{in} = 20$. For these simulations, we consider input parameters $E'_{\gamma,\text{peak}} = 2$ eV and $\gamma_{p,\text{in}} = 1.1$. *Right panel:* MCRaT simulations showing the effect of $E'_{\gamma,\text{peak}} = 0.2, 2, 20$ eV for $N_{rh} = 40$ ($\tau_{in} = 20, \Gamma = 30$) and $N_{rh} = 25$ ($\tau_{in} = 40, \Gamma = 100$). For these simulations, we consider input parameters $\gamma_{e,\text{in}} = 101$, $\gamma_{p,\text{in}} = 1.1$ and $L = 10^{52}$ erg/s.

In the left panel of Figure 3, we show the simulation results for fixed $E_{\text{inj,cr}} = 4000\ m_e c^2$ at $\tau_{in} = 20$ and for different combinations of $L = 10^{51}, 10^{52}$ erg/s and $\Gamma = 30, 100, 300$. The photons/electrons/protons are initialized with energies $E'_{\gamma,\text{peak}} = 2$ eV/$\gamma_{e,\text{in}} = 101$/$\gamma_{p,\text{in}} = 1.1$ at optical depth $\tau_{in} = 20$. While the jet luminosity L has no noticeable effect on the output photon spectrum, increase in bulk Lorentz factor Γ shifts the photon peak energy to higher values. We find that even though Γ does not affect α and β, it rescales photon peak energy as $E_{\gamma,\text{peak}} \propto \Gamma$. The output photon spectrum shows $E_{\gamma,\text{peak}} \sim E_{\gamma,obs}$ only for smaller $\Gamma \sim 30$ values. While larger $\Gamma \sim 100$ can also reproduce $E_{\gamma,\text{peak}} \sim 500$ keV and $\alpha \sim 0$ at $\tau_{in} \gtrsim 40$ in agreement with the observations, it cannot explain the observed high energy spectral index (see right panel of Figure 2).

In the right panel of Figure 3, we show the simulation results for fixed $N_{rh,cr}(\tau_{in}) = 40/25$ at $\tau_{in} = 20$ ($\Gamma = 30$)/40 ($\Gamma = 100$) and different seed photon energies $E'_{\gamma,\text{peak}} = 0.2, 2, 20$ eV. The electrons/protons are initialized with energies $\gamma_{e,\text{in}} = 101$/$\gamma_{p,\text{in}} = 1.1$ with jet luminosity $L = 10^{52}$ erg/s. We find that for both $E_{inj,cr}(\tau_{in}) = 2500\ m_e c^2$ and $4000\ m_e c^2$, the low/high energy spectral index α/β and the output photon peak energy $E_{\gamma,peak}$ are practically unaffected by the choice of $E'_{\gamma,peak}$. The specific photon flux f_ν falls off considerably at energies less than $\Gamma E'_{\gamma,peak}$ as most of the photons gain energy and do not populate the low energy tail after getting scattered by the electrons. For larger τ_{in}, the photons get scattered multiple times thereby increasing the probability of differential number of scatterings before escaping the photosphere and subsequent broadening of the spectrum. As a result, more photons populate the low energy tail and the spectra with different initial energies $\Gamma E'_{\gamma,peak}$ become indistinguishable for $\tau_{in} \gtrsim 40$.

5. Photon spectra for repeated scatterings

Assuming that Comptonization is the dominant process influencing the output photon spectrum, we will first evaluate the energy spectrum of synchrotron photons after they experience single scattering with the electrons. Then we extend our formalism to find the photon energy spectrum for the realistic case when they undergo repeated scatterings with the electrons in the jet before exiting the photosphere. The energy distribution of the scattered photons depends mainly on the incident photon spectrum and the electron energy distribution.

5.1. *Photon distribution after one scattering*

For our calculation, we consider electrons and incident photons with isotropic distributions in the jet-comoving frame. In this case, the scattered photons are also distributed isotropically in the jet-comoving frame. For simplicity, we only consider Thomson scattering in the rest frame of the electron and assume that all scattering events are elastic in nature. For incident photons with energy ϵ scattering off electrons with energy $\gamma m_e c^2$, the total scattered power per energy per volume is[24]

$$\frac{dE}{dV\,dt\,d\epsilon_1} = \frac{3}{4} c\sigma_T \int_{\epsilon_1/4\gamma^2}^{\infty} d\epsilon \frac{\epsilon_1}{\epsilon^2} f(\epsilon) \int_1^{\infty} \frac{d\gamma}{\gamma^2} n_e(\gamma) g_{iso}\left(\frac{\epsilon_1}{4\gamma^2 \epsilon}\right), \quad (10)$$

where, ϵ_1 is the scattered photon energy, $f(\epsilon)$ is the photon distribution function, $n_e(\gamma)$ is the electron distribution function and $g_{iso}(x) = \frac{2}{3}(1-x)$ for isotropic photon distribution in the jet-comoving frame. We consider the simple case in which the incident photons have a synchrotron/piecewise power-law energy distribution,

$$f_{in}(\epsilon) = f_0 \begin{cases} (\epsilon/\epsilon_0)^a, & \epsilon < \epsilon_0 \\ (\epsilon/\epsilon_0)^{-b}, & \epsilon > \epsilon_0 \end{cases} \quad (11)$$

and the electrons are mono-energetic with $n_e(\gamma) = n_0 \delta(\gamma - \gamma_0)$. Substituting $x = 4\gamma_0^2 \epsilon/\epsilon_1$ for relativistic electrons yields

$$\frac{dE}{dV\,dt\,d\epsilon_1} = 2c\sigma_T n_0 \int_1^{\infty} \frac{dx}{x^2}\left(1 - \frac{1}{x}\right) f\left(\frac{\epsilon_1 x}{4\gamma_0^2}\right). \quad (12)$$

For photons below peak energy $\epsilon_1 < 4\gamma_0^2\epsilon_0$, we can further define $\epsilon_1/4\gamma_0^2 = \eta\epsilon_0$ with $\eta < 1$. For low energy photons with $\eta \ll 1$, if the incident photons have a hard spectrum with $0 < a < 1$, the scattered photon distribution $f_{sc}(\epsilon_1) \propto dE/(dV\,dt\,d\epsilon_1) \propto \eta^a \propto \epsilon_1^a/(\gamma_0^{2a}\epsilon_0^a)$ is the same as that of the incident photons. However, for a softer low energy incident photon spectrum with $a \geq 1$ and $\eta \ll 1$, we obtain $f_{sc}(\epsilon_1) \propto dE/(dV\,dt\,d\epsilon_1) \propto \epsilon_1$. Therefore, after single scattering of synchrotron photons with broken power-law energy distribution, the low energy spectrum is unaffected for hard spectra with $a < 1$ whereas $f_{sc}(\epsilon) \propto \epsilon$ for softer spectra. For photons above peak energy $\epsilon_1 > 4\gamma_0^2\epsilon_0$ and $\eta \gtrsim 1$. This gives $dE/(dV\,dt\,d\epsilon_1) \propto \epsilon_1^{-b}/(\gamma_0^{-2b}\epsilon_0^{-b})$, same as the incident photon spectrum. For fast cooled synchrotron photon spectrum, we have $a = 2$ and $b = -1$, and the scattered photon distribution after single scattering is

$$f_1(\epsilon) = f_{sc}(\epsilon) \propto f_0 \begin{cases} (\epsilon/\epsilon_0)^1, & \epsilon < \epsilon_0 \\ (\epsilon/\epsilon_0)^{-1}, & \epsilon > \epsilon_0. \end{cases} \quad (13)$$

In reality, however, each photon experiences $\sim 2\tau_{in}$ scatterings on an average before escaping the photosphere.

5.2. Photon distribution after repeated scatterings

With $f_1(\epsilon)$ as the incident photon distribution, we can now extend the same formalism to calculate the photon spectrum after subsequent scattering events assuming that the electron and photon distributions remain isotropic in the jet-comoving frame. The low and the high energy spectrum after each photon in the jet has undergone exactly two scatterings is

$$f_{2,l}(\epsilon_1) = 2c\sigma_T n_0 f_0 \left(-\eta\ln\eta + \frac{2}{3}\eta^2 - \frac{1}{2}\eta\right) \propto \frac{\epsilon_1}{4\gamma_0^2\epsilon_0}\ln\left(\frac{\epsilon_1}{4\gamma_0^2\epsilon_0}\right),$$

$$f_{2,u}(\epsilon_1) = 2c\sigma_T n_0 f_0 \int_1^\infty dx \frac{1}{x^2}\left(1 - \frac{1}{x}\right)\eta^{-1}x^{-1} \propto \gamma_0^2\epsilon_0/\epsilon_1.$$

The scattered photon spectrum is then

$$f_2(\epsilon) \propto f_0 \begin{cases} (\epsilon/\epsilon_0)\ln(\epsilon/\epsilon_0), & \epsilon < \epsilon_0 \\ (\epsilon/\epsilon_0)^{-1}, & \epsilon > \epsilon_0. \end{cases} \quad (14)$$

After each photon has undergone exactly three scatterings, the low and high energy spectra are given as

$$f_{3,l}(\epsilon_1) \propto \frac{\epsilon_1}{4\gamma_0^2\epsilon_0}\left[\ln\left(\frac{\epsilon_1}{4\gamma_0^2\epsilon_0}\right)\right]^2,$$

$$f_{3,u}(\epsilon_1) = 2c\sigma_T n_0 f_0 \int_1^\infty dx \frac{1}{x^2}\left(1 - \frac{1}{x}\right)\eta^{-1}x^{-1} \propto \gamma_0^2\epsilon_0/\epsilon_1,$$

and the scattered photon spectrum is

$$f_3(\epsilon) \propto f_0 \begin{cases} (\epsilon/\epsilon_0)\left[\ln(\epsilon/\epsilon_0)\right]^2, & \epsilon < \epsilon_0 \\ (\epsilon/\epsilon_0)^{-1}, & \epsilon > \epsilon_0 \end{cases} \quad (15)$$

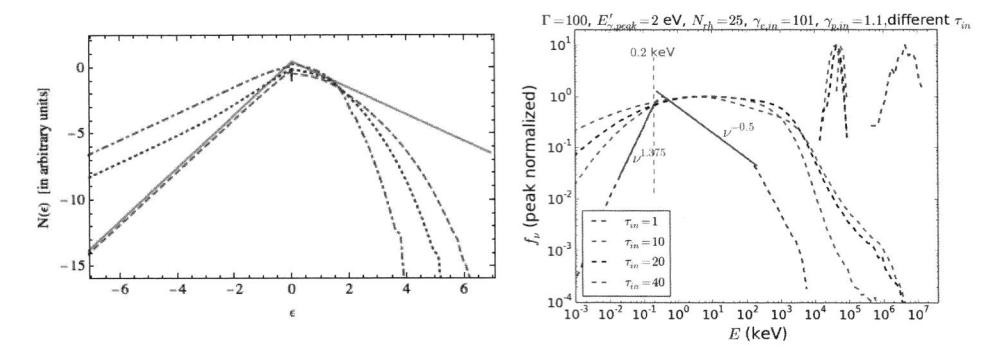

Fig. 4. **Effect of geometrical broadening on the photon spectrum for increasing optical depth.** *Left panel:* IC spectrum for synchrotrom photons with energy $\epsilon_0 = 1$ and Maxwellian electrons with peak energy $\gamma_{e,0} = 1.1$. The solid green line, brown dashed line, blue dotted line and red dot-dashed lines are the scattered photon spectra after $N = 0, 1, 2$ and 5 scatterings, respectively. *Right panel:* MCRaT simulations showing the effect of geometrical broadening on the photon spectrum at $\tau_{in} = 1, 10, 20, 40$ for $(N_{rh}, \gamma_{e,in}) = (25, 101)$ and $\gamma_{p,in} = 1.1$. For these simulations, we consider input parameters $L = 10^{52}$ erg/s, $E'_{\gamma,peak} = 2$ eV and $\Gamma = 100$.

We can generalize the above results further for $N \sim 2\tau_{in}$ scatterings per photon

$$f_N(\epsilon) \propto f_0 \begin{cases} (\epsilon/4\gamma_0^2\epsilon_0)\left[\ln(\epsilon/4\gamma_0^2\epsilon_0)\right]^{N-1}, & \epsilon < \epsilon_0 \\ (\epsilon/4\gamma_0^2\epsilon_0)^{-1}, & \epsilon > \epsilon_0 \end{cases} \quad (16)$$

In Figure 4, we show how the photon spectrum is affected by Comptonization with electrons as τ_{in} and number of scatterings increase. In the left panel, the IC scattered photon spectrum for fast cooled synchrotron seed photons (Equation 11, with $a = 2$ and $b = -1$) with energy $\epsilon_0 = m_e c^2$ and Maxwellian electrons with peak energy $\gamma_{e,0} = 1.1$ is shown for scattering orders $N = 0, 1, 2, 5$. As predicted by equation (16), the photon spectrum becomes gradually softer below peak energy as the scattering order increases. The photons scattering off Maxwellian electrons with fixed energy get thermalized at equilibrium to attain a high-energy exponential tail for large optical depths/scatterings. Furthermore, there is gradual flattening of the low-energy spectrum with increase in scattering order N.

In the right panel of Figure 4, we present the MCRaT simulation results for $E_{\text{inj,cr}} = 2500 \ m_e c^2$ and different optical depths $\tau_{in} = 1, 10, 20, 40$. The number of repeated dissipation events in the jet are $N_{rh} = 25$ with initial photon/electron/proton energy $E'_{\gamma,peak} = 2$ eV$/\gamma_{e,in} = 101/\gamma_{p,in} = 1.1$ and jet parameters $L = 10^{52}$ erg/s and $\Gamma = 100$. With increase in scattering order ($\propto \tau_{in}$), the high energy photon spectrum becomes steeper with a simultaneous decrease in $E_{\gamma,peak}$. These photons then populate the low energy spectrum and extend the nonthermal tail to energies much lower than $E_{\gamma,peak} \sim 0.2$ keV. The photon spectra from simulations are also considerably broader compared to the analytical results for similar values of N.

6. Summary and conclusions

We have utilized our MCRaT photospheric code to explain the distinct non-thermal behaviour of GRB prompt emission spectrum, $f_\nu \propto \nu^0 / f_\nu \propto \nu^{-1.2}$ at low/high photon energies along with observed peak energy at $E_{\gamma,peak} \sim 300$ MeV. For our simulations, we considered Comptonization of fast cooled synchrotron photons with Maxwellian electrons and for photon to particle number ratio $N_\gamma/N_e \sim 10^5$. The jet electrons are accelerated by two different mechanisms: 1. continuous energy transfer via Coulomb collisions with mono-energetic protons, 2. repeated episodic energy dissipation events that are equally spaced over time and accelerate particles back to their initial energies.

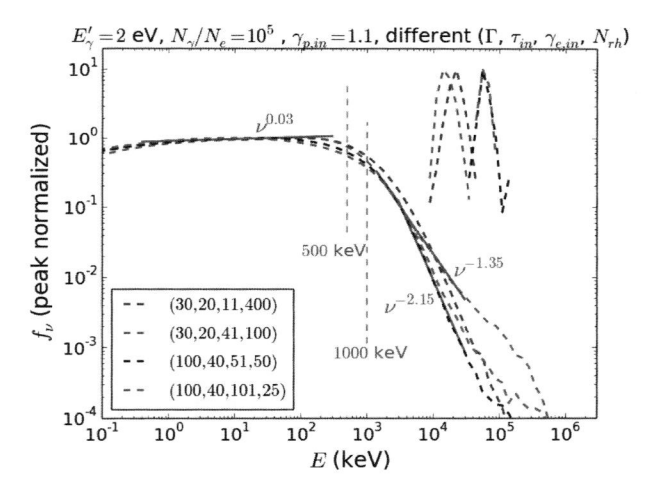

Fig. 5. **MCRaT simulation results with the best set of parameters for a jet with** $N_\gamma/N_e = 10^5$. The relativistic jet with $L = 10^{52}$ erg/s has photons with $E'_{\gamma,\text{peak}} = 2$ eV and protons with $\gamma_{p,\text{in}} = 1.1$. The energy injection necessary in order to produce an output photon spectrum with the observed Band-like spectral properties depends on τ_{in} and Γ. Here we consider $E_{\text{inj}} = 4000/2500 \ m_e c^2$ for $\Gamma = 30/100$ and $\tau_{\text{in}} = 20/40$, for two distinct electron energies $\gamma_{e,\text{in}} = (11,41)/(51,101)$.

The parameters that significantly affect the spectral properties for a given N_γ/N_e are $E_{\text{inj}}(\gamma_{e,\text{in}}, N_{\text{rh}})$, Γ and τ_{in}. Figure 5 shows the most probable parameter set that gives output photon spectrum with $(\alpha, \beta, E_{\gamma,\text{peak}})$ very similar to the observed GRB prompt spectrum. The photons/protons in these simulations are initialized with energies $E'_{\gamma,\text{peak}} = 2$ eV/$\gamma_{p,\text{in}} = 1.1$ for jet parameters $L = 10^{52}$ erg/s, $N_\gamma/N_e = 10^5$ and $\Gamma \sim 30 - 100$. The particles are injected with energy $E_{\text{inj,cr}} \sim 2500 - 4000 \ m_e c^2$ per electron for a range of $\tau_{\text{in}} \sim 20 - 40$. For smaller $\tau_{\text{in}} \sim 20$ and $\Gamma \sim 30$, $(\alpha, \beta, E_{\gamma,peak}) \sim (0, -1.4, 1 \text{ MeV})$ is obtained with $E_{\text{inj,cr}} \sim 4000 \ m_e c^2$ and $\gamma_{e,\text{in}} \gtrsim 40$. Although $\alpha \sim 0$ and $E_{\gamma,peak} \sim 500$ keV for $E_{\text{inj,cr}} \sim 2500 \ m_e c^2$ at larger $\tau_{\text{in}} \sim 40$ and $\Gamma \sim 100$, the high energy spectrum is significantly steeper than the observed prompt spectrum with $\beta \sim -2.1$, especially for $\gamma_{e,in} \lesssim 50$.

The main results of this work can be summarised as:

(1) The electrons cool down rapidly to non-relativistic energies in the absence of jet dissipation events. This entails energy injection into the jet particles via either (continuous) Coulomb collisions or (episodic) sub-photospheric dissipation events. However, for Coulomb heating, the protons lose a considerable fraction of their energy within $\sim t_{dyn}$, for $\tau_{in} \gtrsim 10$, to attain non-relativistic energies. Therefore, continuous energy injection by protons is not sufficient to maintain electrons at $\gamma_e \sim \gamma_{e,crit}$.

(2) Energy injection can be achieved with episodic sub-photospheric dissipation events which can keep the electrons at energies $\gamma_e \gtrsim \gamma_{e,crit}$ provided that they are sufficiently energetic and frequent. For large E_{inj}, the photon peak energy $E_{\gamma,\text{peak}} \gg E_{\gamma,\text{obs}} \sim 300$ keV, while for large τ_{in}, $E_{\gamma,\text{peak}} \ll E_{\gamma,\text{obs}}$ due to significant adiabatic loss. From MCRaT simulations, we quantify the $E_{inj} - \tau_{\text{in}}$ correlation: injected energy $E_{inj,cr} = 4000/2500\ m_e c^2$ per electron for initial optical depth $\tau_{in} = 20/40$.

(3) In the output photon spectrum, α critically depends on E_{inj} whereas β and $E_{\gamma,\text{peak}}$ are almost entirely determined by τ_{in}. With an increase in τ_{in}, $E_{\gamma,\text{peak}}$ decreases and the high-energy photon spectrum becomes steeper. Additionally, $|\beta|$ also increases with decrease in initial electron energy $\gamma_{e,in}$ for fixed $E_{\text{inj,cr}} = N_{rh,cr}(\gamma_{e,in} - 1)\ m_e c^2$. We find that $E_{\gamma,\text{peak}} \sim E_{\gamma,\text{obs}}$ only for smaller $\Gamma \sim 30$ - while larger $\Gamma \sim 100$ gives $E_{\gamma,peak} \sim 500$ keV at $\tau_{in} \sim 40$, the high energy photon spectrum is considerably steeper than observed.

(4) For isotropic electrons scattering isotropic photons, the scattered photon energy distribution can be analytically evaluated for lower order scatterings, given the electron and photon energy distributions. For Comptonization of synchrotron photons with Maxwellian electrons, $\alpha \sim 0$ behaviour is retained at low energies whereas $f_\nu \propto e^{-\nu}$ at high energies. Qualitatively, the low-energy non-thermal dependence is obtained from multiple scatterings and subsequent geometrical broadening of the spectrum whereas the high-energy power-law dependence is attributed to repeated episodic and continuous energy injection events.

References

1. D. Band, et al., *ApJ* **413**, 281 (1993).
2. R. D. Preece, M. S. Briggs, R. S. Mallozzi, G. N. Pendleton, W. S. Paciesas, D. L. Band, *ApJS* **126**, 19 (2000).
3. Y. Kaneko, R. D. Preece, M. S. Briggs, W. S. Paciesas, C. A. Meegan, D. L. Band, *ApJS* **166**, 298 (2006).
4. M. J. Rees, P. Meszaros, *ApJ* **430**, L93 (1994).
5. T. Piran, *Reviews of Modern Physics* **76**, 1143 (2004).
6. P. Kumar, B. Zhang, *Phys. Rep.* **561**, 1 (2015).
7. D. Giannios, *A&A* **457**, 763 (2006).
8. T. Piran, *Phys. Rep.* **314**, 575 (1999).
9. B. Zhang, et al., *ApJ* **655**, 989 (2007).

10. R. D. Preece, M. S. Briggs, R. S. Mallozzi, G. N. Pendleton, W. S. Paciesas, D. L. Band, *ApJ* **506**, L23 (1998).
11. G. Ghirlanda, A. Celotti, G. Ghisellini, *A&A* **406**, 879 (2003).
12. M. J. Rees, P. Meszaros, *ApJ* **628**, 847 (2005).
13. M. Bhattacharya, P. Kumar, *MNRAS* **491**, 4656 (2019).
14. D. Lazzati, M. C. Begelman, *ApJ* **725**, 1137 (2010).
15. M. Bhattacharya, W. Lu, P. Kumar, R. Santana, *ApJ* **852**, 1 (2018).
16. A. Chhotray, D. Lazzati, *ApJ* **802**, 132 (2015).
17. J. Granot, T. Piran, R. Sari, *ApJ* **534**, L163 (2000).
18. K. Toma, X. F. Wu, P. Meszaros, *MNRAS* **415**, 1663 (2011).
19. C. Thompson, *MNRAS* **270**, 480 (1994).
20. E. Liang, B. Zhang, F. Virgili, Z. G. Dai, *ApJ* **662**, 1111 (2007).
21. R. R. Xue, Y. Z. Fan, D. M. Wei, *A&A* **498**, 671 (2009).
22. R. Schlickeiser, Cosmic Ray Astrophysics. Springer, New York (2002).
23. D. Begue, I. A. Siutsou, G. V. Vereshchagin, *ApJ* **767**, 139 (2013).
24. G. B. Rybicki, A. P. Lightman, Radiative Processes in Astrophysics. A Wiley-Interscience publication, Wiley (1979).

Monte Carlo simulations of photospheric emission in Gamma Ray Bursts

T. M. Parsotan* and D. Lazzati

Department of Physics, Oregon State University,
Corvallis, OR 97331, USA
*E-mail: parsotat@umbc.edu

The study of Gamma Ray Bursts (GRBs) has the potential to improve our understanding of high energy astrophysical phenomena. In order to reliably use GRBs to this end, we first need to have a well-developed grasp of the mechanism that produces the radiation within GRB jets and how that relates to their structure. One model for the emission mechanism of GRBs invokes radiation produced deep in the jet which eventually escapes the jet at its photosphere. While this model has been able to explain a number of observed GRB characteristics, it is currently lacking in predictive power and in ability to fully reproduce GRB spectra. In order to address these shortcomings of the model, we have expanded the capabilities of the MCRaT code, a state of the art radiative transfer code that can now simulate optical to gamma ray radiation propagating in a hydrodynamically simulated GRB jet. Using the MCRaT code, we have constructed mock observed light curves, spectra, and polarization from optical to gamma ray energies for the simulated GRBs. Using these mock observables, we have compared our simulations of photospheric emission to observations and found much agreement between the two. Furthermore, the MCRaT calculations combined with the hydrodynamical simulations allow us to connect the mock observables to the structure of the simulated GRB jet in a way that was not previously possible. While there are a number of improvements that can be made to the analyses, the steps taken here begin to pave the way for us to fully understand the connection between the structure of a given GRB jet and the radiation that would be expected from it.

Keywords: Gamma-rays: Bursts; relativistic outflows; radiation transfer.

1. Introduction

Gamma Ray Bursts (GRBs) typically produce high energy X-ray and gamma-ray radiation that is detected within the first few tens of seconds of the event. The origin of this so called prompt emission is still not well understood even after decades of investigation. The two most common models that are used to describe the prompt emission of GRBs either employ synchrotron emission from jets with magnetic fields[1–4] or emission from the photospheres of GRB jets.[5–15]

Each model has its own advantanges and disadvantages allowing them to describe GRB observations at gamma-ray and X-ray energies in varying capacities. Models that rely on synchrotron emission are able to account for the non-thermal characteristics of GRB spectra[4,16] but are unable to fully account for various GRB observational relationships such as the Amati[17] and Yonetoku[18] relations.[1] The photospheric model on the other hand is able to reproduce the Amati and

Yonetoku relations[10,12,13,15,19,20] but has issues with reproducing typical GRB spectral parameters.[12,13] In order to fully distinguish between these models additional data at different wavelengths is needed.

There have been a number of optical prompt emission detections that can be used for the purpose of model comparison (see[21] and references therein). Additionally, there has been one detection of optical prompt polarization[22] that can also be used in comparison with optical polarization predictions obtained from synchrotron and the photospheric model calculations. The synchrotron model has traditionally been favored by these optical prompt detections[23-27] however the photospheric model has not been fully explored in its ability to reproduce these optical prompt detections.

The ability to simulate radiation signatures produced under the photospheric model has recently been improved.[11-15,21,28,29] These analyses have combined the realistic treatment of radiation with hydrodynamically simulated time-dependent GRB jets. As a result, studies of how the GRB jet structure affects the detected radiation signatures are now possible. With the ability of these state-of-the-art radiative transfer calculations to also calculate the effects of cyclo-synchrotron emission and absorption,[21,29] these types of analyses are also now possible from optical to gamma-ray energies. In this proceeding, we highlight the results of conducting radiative transfer calculations of hydrodynamically simulated GRB jets and the construction of mock observations from these calculations. We show how the mock observables can be related to the structure of the simulated GRB jets and how these analysis can help us interpret GRB observations under the photospheric model. Finally, we conclude with a summary and highlight ways that these types of global radiative transfer calculations can push the field forward.

2. Methods

2.1. *The MCRaT Code*

We have used the open-source **M**onte **C**arlo **Ra**diation **T**ransfer (MCRaT) code[30] to analyze the evolution of radiation trapped within hydrodynamical simulations of GRB jets. The MCRaT code considers photons in the astrophysical outflow that interact via Compton scattering including the effects of the full Klein-Nishina cross section with polarization. The code also considers photons that have been absorbed and emitted in the outflow due to cyclo-synchrotron (CS) emission and absorption. We summarize the algorithm here, however detailed descriptions of the code are outlined in[21] and.[29] As is outlined in Figure 1, the code loads a SRHD simulation frame and injects photons into the simulated GRB jet where the optical depth $\tau > 100$. The code will calculate the mean free paths of each photon in the simulation in order to determine which will scatter. After this calculation, MCRaT advances the simulation time to correspond to when the scattering will occur and propagates each photon by a distance corresponding to the amount of time passing in the simulation. The code then conducts the scattering considering the full Klein-Nishina

OUTLINE OF THE MCRAT ALGORITHM

[Flowchart with the following boxes and connections:]

LOAD HYDRO SIMULATION FRAME → INJECT PHOTONS $\propto T_i, \Gamma_i, \theta_i$ → EMIT POOL OF THERMAL CYCLO-SYNCHROTRON (CS) PHOTONS WITH $\nu_{c,i}$ → CALCULATE MFP'S BASED ON LOCAL PROPERTIES → SELECT PHOTON TO SCATTER BASED ON SMALLEST MFP → SIMULATION TIME AND PHOTON POSITIONS ADVANCED TO TIME OF SCATTERING → BOOST SCATTERED PHOTON TO FLUID FRAME → GENERATE ELECTRON FROM FLUID PROPERTIES → CONDUCT COMPTON SCATTERING → BOOST PHOTON TO LAB FRAME → ABSORB PHOTONS WITH $\nu \leq \nu_{c,i}$ → (back to LOAD HYDRO SIMULATION FRAME)

If the scattered photon was a CS photon: REPLENISH SCATTERED CS PHOTON

If the time is less than the time corresponding to the next hydro frame

If the photon did not scatter

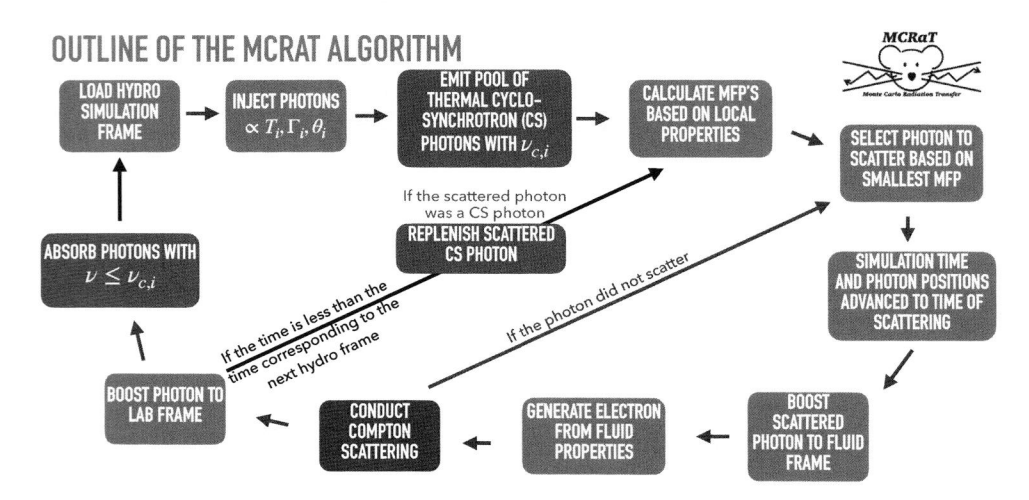

Fig. 1. The outline of the MCRaT code, see text for in depth explanation.

cross section with polarization, which means that the photons have some probability of not scattering in the electron rest frame. If the chosen photon ends up not being scattered, MCRaT chooses the next photon that would have scattered and advances the simulation time and the location of each photon. If the photon is scattered, then the new four momentum and polarization of the photon is calculated. The code continues to scatter photons until the time in MCRaT corresponds to the time in the next SRHD simulation frame. If CS emission and absorption is also taken into account in the simulation then the steps in the red boxes are taken which numerically simulate CS emission and absorption processes in MCRaT.

2.2. Mock Observations

With a given MCRaT simulation completed, we use the open-source ProcessMCRaT code[31] to produce mock observed light curves, spectra, and polarization measurements that can be compared to actual GRB observations on a more equal basis. This code allows photons from an MCRaT simulation to be binned in time and energy in order to produce the mock observables, similar to how actual photons measured in a given GRB event are binned. Detailed descriptions of how we construct the mock observable quantities for observers at various viewing angles with respect the jet axis, θ_v, can be found in.[12-14,21] We use the same gamma-ray and optical energy ranges as in.[29] The gamma-ray mock observables are calculated from photons with energies between 20-800 keV which corresponds to the polarimetry energy range of POLAR-2.[32] The optical mock observables are calculated from photons with energies between 1597-7820 Å ($\sim 1.5 - 7.7$ eV), which aligns with the Swift UVOT White bandpass.[33,34]

The way that we connect the mock observables to the structure of the simulated GRB jets is through equal arrival time surfaces (EATS)[7,35,36] of the photons in the GRB jet. For a given time bin, in the mock observed light curve, we can calculate surfaces that would be emitting photons towards a given observer's line of sight. These surfaces are calculated following the method of,[14] who describe the procedure for constructing these EATS.

2.3. *The Simulation Set*

The MCRaT code was used to analyze a set of two special relativistic hydrodynamical simulations (SRHD) of GRB jets. These SRHD simulations were conducted using the FLASH hydrodynamics code[37] and their properties are outlined in.[14,21,29] These two SRHD simulations are referred to as the *16TI* and *40sp_down* simulations and they represent GRB jets that have a time-constant and time-variable injection of energy, respectively.

3. Results

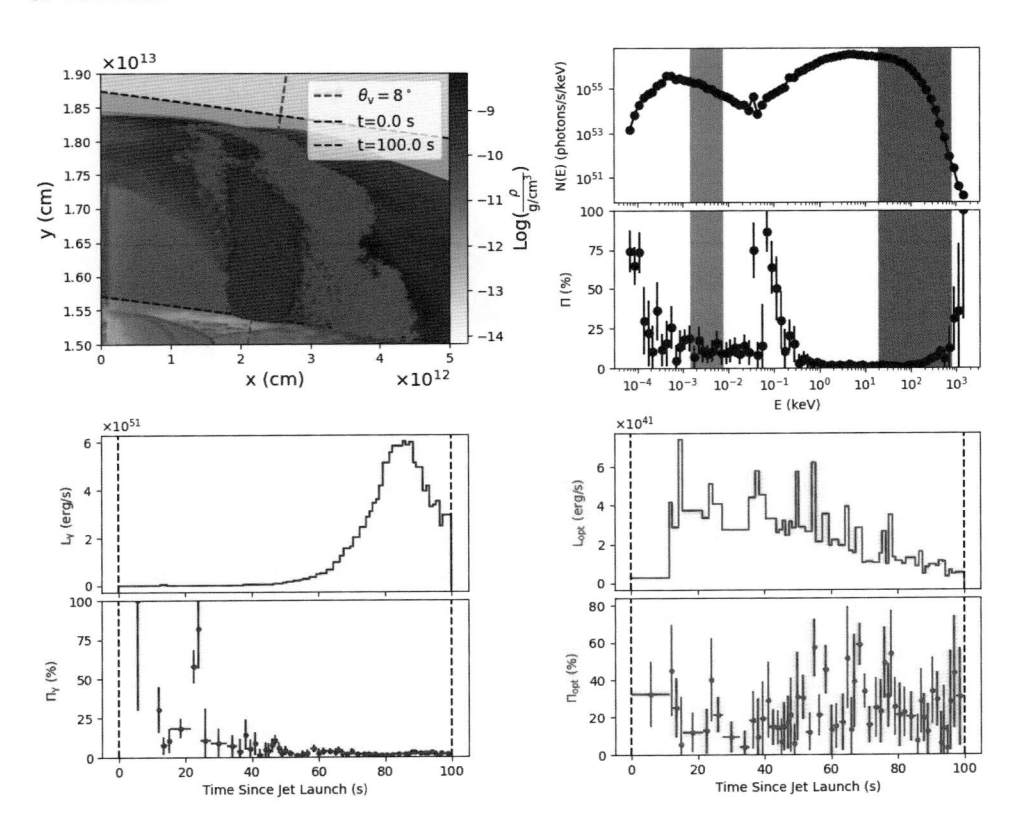

Fig. 2. The relation between the mock observed quantities and the jet structure of the *16TI* simulation for $\theta_v = 8°$. See text for full description.

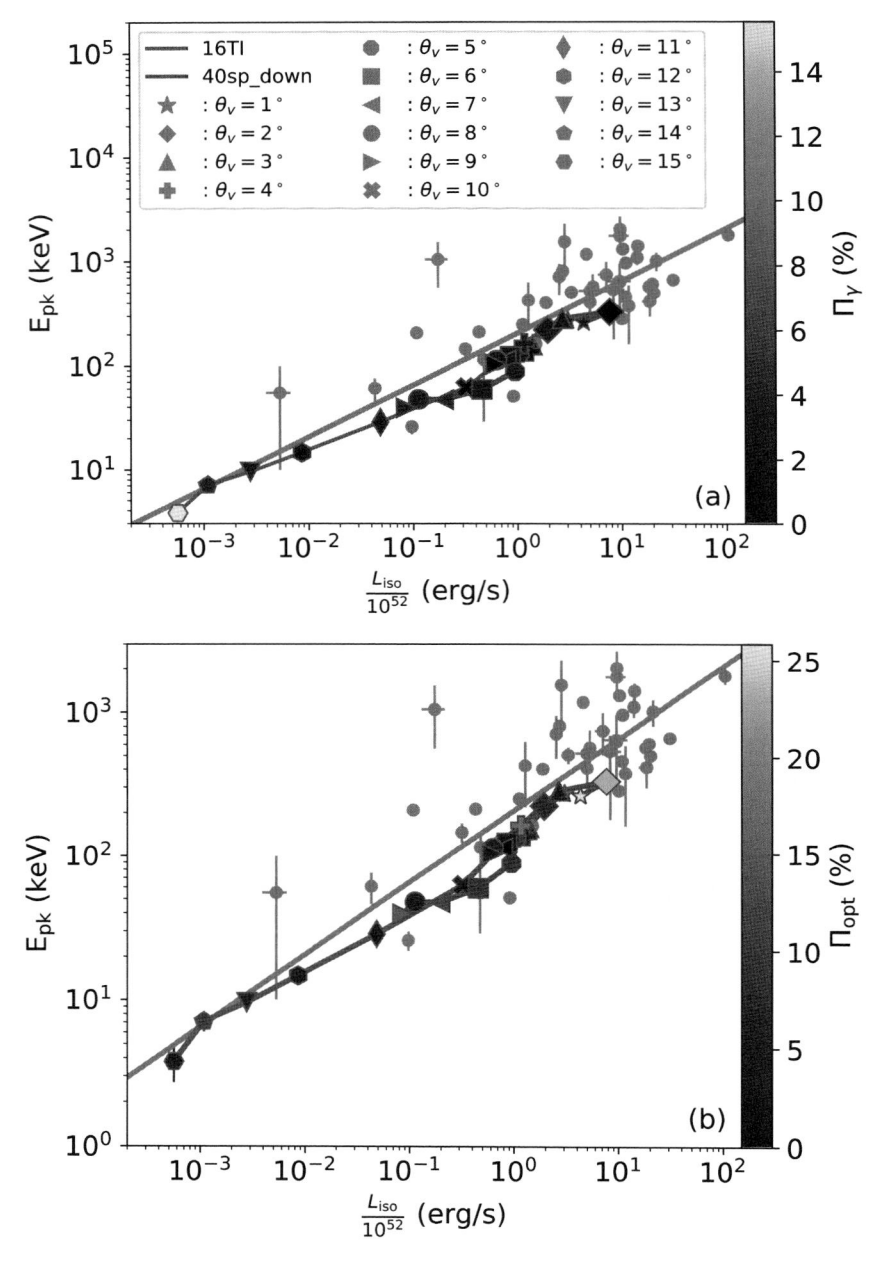

Fig. 3. The *16TI* and *40sp_down* simulations plotted alongside the Yonetoku relationship[18] in red and green lines and marker outlines, respectively. In Figure (a), the fill color of the marker denotes the mock observed time-integrated Π_γ while in Figure (b) the fill color shows the time-integrated MCRaT Π_{opt}. The different marker shapes for the MCRaT simulations show the placement of the simulations on the Yonetoku relationship as determined by observers at various θ_v. In each panel the observational relationship is shown as the grey solid line and observed data from[38] are plotted as grey markers. Figure adapted from.[29]

Our MCRaT simulations have shown that optical and gamma ray photons probe different regions of GRB outflows under the photospheric model, as is shown in Figure 2. Here, we show all the photons that have been detected by an observer located at $\theta_v = 8°$ in optical and gamma-ray energies. The top left panel shows the location of each photon in relation to the density structure of the SRHD simulated GRB jet. The density of the jet is shown as a pseudocolor plot where darker colors show denser regions and the dashed red line denoted the line of sight of the observer at $\theta_v = 8°$. The optical photons are shown in red while gamma-ray photons are depicted in blue. Furthermore, the photon markers are translucent allowing us to identify regions of the jet where the photons are densely located (due to the concentration of blue or red). Additionally, the markers are different sizes in order to show the weight of each photon in the calculation of the various mock observable quantities. The top right panel shows the time integrated spectrum of these photons with highlighted red and blue regions that highlight the energy ranges which were used to calculate the optical and gamma-ray light curves (L_γ and $L_{\rm opt}$) and polarizations (Π_γ and $\Pi_{\rm opt}$). These time-resolved mock observables are shown in the bottom 4 panels. These analysis allow us to connect the mock observables of light curves, spectra, and polarizations with the locations of where the photons are within the jet and what the jet structure is at those locations. As is shown in Figure 2, the optical photons are distrubuted widely about the observer's line of sight with their locations being focused at the dense jet-cocoon interface (JCI;[39]). The gamma-ray photons instead are mostly concentrated along the observer's line of sight with the exception of some gamma-ray photons being located near the core of the jet. Thus, optical prompt emission probes the dense JCI while the gamma-ray emission probes the portion of the jet that is directly along the observer's line of sight.

The results of our MCRaT simulations can also be used to assess how well the simulations reproduce various observational relationships, such as the Yonetoku relation,[18] and make additional predictions that can be tested against data. Figure 3 shows the comparison between the *16TI* and *40sp_down* simulations, in red and green marker edge colors and lines respectively, and the Yonetoku relation. Various observed GRBs from[38] are also shown as grey circles. We also show the time-integrated Π_γ and $\Pi_{\rm opt}$ in Figure 3(a) and (b) respectively, through the fill-color of each marker. In each panel, we see that both the *40sp_down* and *16TI* simulations are able to recover the normalization and slope of the Yonetoku relation for a variety of θ_v. With this success of the photospheric model, we can also now use the simulated polarization mock observations to make predictions. We find that the time-integrated Π_γ should increase as θ_v increases which has been found in other studies.[40,41] Thus, bursts that are bright and energetic (in the top right of the Yonetoku relation) should have low time-integrated Π_γ. On the other hand, the time-integrated $\Pi_{\rm opt}$ should be larger for θ_v that are close to the jet axis. As a result, we would expect that bursts located in the top right of the Yonetoku relation would have large time-integrated $\Pi_{\rm opt}$.

4. Conclusion

Using the MCRaT radiative transfer code, we have conducted post-processing analysis of the radiation expected from time-dependent special relativistic hydrodynamic simulations of GRB jets. These global radiative transfer simulations allow for the connection between observed radiation signatures and the structure of the GRB jet, which was not possible prior to these types of analysis. These analyses are commonplace in other areas of astrophysics such as galaxy formation and have proved fruitful in connecting radiation processes to the structure of galaxies and in testing observational data analysis techniques (see e.g.[42] and[43]). While these types of analysis are beginning to emerge in the study of GRBs (see references within), we need widespread adoption of these simulations within the community for any SRHD simulations that have been conducted of GRB jets. This would allow the community to build a library of GRB jet simulations and their associated radiation signatures that can be used in comparison to GRB observations, greatly enhancing our knowledge of GRB jets and the prompt emission.

References

1. B. Zhang and H. Yan, The Internal-Collision-Induced Magnetic Reconnection and Turbulence (ICMART) model of gamma-ray bursts, *The Astrophysical Journal* **726**, p. 90 (dec 2011).
2. M. J. Rees and P. Mészáros, Unsteady outflow models for cosmological gamma-ray bursts, *ApJL* **430**, L93 (August 1994).
3. F. Daigne and R. Mochkovitch, Gamma-ray bursts from internal shocks in a relativistic wind: temporal and spectral properties, *Monthly Notices of the Royal Astronomical Society* **296**, 275 (1998).
4. F. Daigne, Ž. Bošnjak and G. Dubus, Reconciling observed gamma-ray burst prompt spectra with synchrotron radiation?, *Astronomy & Astrophysics* **526**, p. A110 (2011).
5. M. J. Rees and P. Mészáros, Dissipative photosphere models of gamma-ray bursts and x-ray flashes, *The Astrophysical Journal* **628**, p. 847 (2005).
6. A. Pe'er, Temporal evolution of thermal emission from relativistically expanding plasma, *The Astrophysical Journal* **682**, p. 463 (2008).
7. A. Pe'er and F. Ryde, A theory of multicolor blackbody emission from relativistically expanding plasmas, *The Astrophysical Journal* **732**, p. 49 (2011).
8. A. Pe'er, P. Mészáros and M. J. Rees, The observable effects of a photospheric component on grb and xrf prompt emission spectrum, *The Astrophysical Journal* **642**, p. 995 (2006).
9. A. M. Beloborodov, Collisional mechanism for gamma-ray burst emission, *Monthly Notices of the Royal Astronomical Society* **407**, p. 1033 (2010).
10. D. Lazzati, B. J. Morsony, R. Margutti and M. C. Begelman, Photospheric emission as the dominant radiation mechanism in long-duration gamma-ray bursts, *The Astrophysical Journal* **765**, p. 103 (2013).
11. D. Lazzati, Monte carlo radiation transfer simulations of photospheric emission in long-duration gamma-ray bursts, *The Astrophysical Journal* **829**, p. 76 (2016).

12. T. Parsotan and D. Lazzati, A monte carlo radiation transfer study of photospheric emission in gamma-ray bursts, *The Astrophysical Journal* **853**, p. 8 (2018).
13. T. Parsotan, D. López-Cámara and D. Lazzati, Photospheric emission from variable engine gamma-ray burst simulations, *The Astrophysical Journal* **869**, p. 103 (2018).
14. T. Parsotan, D. López-Cámara and D. Lazzati, Photospheric polarization signatures from long gamma-ray burst simulations, *The Astrophysical Journal* **896**, p. 139 (2020).
15. H. Ito, J. Matsumoto, S. Nagataki, D. C. Warren, M. V. Barkov and D. Yonetoku, The photospheric origin of the yonetoku relation in gamma-ray bursts, *Nature communications* **10**, 1 (2019).
16. G. Oganesyan, L. Nava, G. Ghirlanda, A. Melandri and A. Celotti, Prompt optical emission as a signature of synchrotron radiation in gamma-ray bursts, *Astronomy & Astrophysics* **628**, p. A59 (aug 2019).
17. Amati, L., Frontera, F., Tavani, M., in 't Zand, J. J. M., Antonelli, A., ta, E. Co, Feroci, M., Guidorzi, C., e, J. Hei, etti, N. Ma, Montanari, E., tro, L. Nica, Palazzi, E., Pian, E., Piro, L. and Soffitta, P., Intrinsic spectra and energetics of bepposax gamma ray bursts with known redshifts, *A&A* **390**, 81 (2002).
18. D. Yonetoku, T. Murakami, T. Nakamura, R. Yamazaki, A. K. Inoue and K. Ioka, Gamma-ray burst formation rate inferred from the spectral peak energy-peak luminosity relation, *The Astrophysical Journal* **609**, p. 935 (2004).
19. D. Lazzati, B. J. Morsony and M. C. Begelman, Very high efficiency photospheric emission in long-duration γ-ray bursts, *The Astrophysical Journal Letters* **700**, p. L47 (2009).
20. D. López-Cámara, B. J. Morsony and D. Lazzati, Photospheric emission from long-duration gamma-ray bursts powered by variable engines, *Monthly Notices of the Royal Astronomical Society* **442**, p. 2202 (2014).
21. T. Parsotan and D. Lazzati, Photospheric prompt emission from long gamma ray burst simulations–i. optical emission, *arXiv preprint arXiv:2105.06505* (2021).
22. E. Troja, V. Lipunov, C. Mundell, N. Butler, A. Watson, S. Kobayashi, S. Cenko, F. Marshall, R. Ricci, A. Fruchter *et al.*, Significant and variable linear polarization during the prompt optical flash of grb 160625b, *Nature* **547**, 425 (2017).
23. J. L. Racusin, S. V. Karpov, M. Sokolowski, J. Granot, X. F. Wu, V. Pal'shin, S. Covino, A. J. van der Horst, S. R. Oates, P. Schady, R. J. Smith, J. Cummings, R. L. C. Starling, L. W. Piotrowski, B. Zhang, P. A. Evans, S. T. Holland, K. Malek, M. T. Page, L. Vetere, R. Margutti, C. Guidorzi, A. P. Kamble, P. A. Curran, A. Beardmore, C. Kouveliotou, L. Mankiewicz, A. Melandri, P. T. O'Brien, K. L. Page, T. Piran, N. R. Tanvir, G. Wrochna, R. L. Aptekar, S. Barthelmy, C. Bartolini, G. M. Beskin, S. Bondar, M. Bremer, S. Campana, A. Castro-Tirado, A. Cucchiara, M. Cwiok, P. D'Avanzo, V. D'Elia, M. D. Valle, A. de Ugarte Postigo, W. Dominik, A. Falcone, F. Fiore, D. B. Fox, D. D. Frederiks, A. S. Fruchter, D. Fugazza, M. A. Garrett, N. Gehrels, S. Golenetskii, A. Gomboc, J. Gorosabel, G. Greco, A. Guarnieri, S. Immler, M. Jelinek, G. Kasprowicz, V. L. Parola, A. J. Levan, V. Mangano, E. P. Mazets, E. Molinari, A. Moretti, K. Nawrocki, P. P. Oleynik, J. P. Osborne, C. Pagani, S. B. Pandey, Z. Paragi, M. Perri, A. Piccioni, E. Ramirez-Ruiz, P. W. A. Roming, I. A. Steele, R. G. Strom, V. Testa, G. Tosti, M. V. Ulanov, K. Wiersema, R. A. M. J. Wijers, J. M. Winters, A. F. Zarnecki, F. Zerbi, P. Mészáros, G. Chincarini and D. N. Burrows, Broadband observations of the naked-eye γ-ray burst grb 080319b, *Nature* **455**, 183 (sep 2008).

24. R.-F. Shen and B. Zhang, Prompt optical emission and synchrotron self-absorption constraints on emission site of GRBs, *Monthly Notices of the Royal Astronomical Society* **398**, 1936 (09 2009).
25. S. M. Tang and S. N. Zhang, Time lag between prompt optical emission and γ-rays in GRBs, *Astronomy & Astrophysics* **456**, 141 (aug 2006).
26. Y.-Z. Fan, B. Zhang and D.-M. Wei, Naked-eye optical flash from gamma-ray burst 080319b: Tracing the decaying neutrons in the outflow, *Physical Review D* **79** (jan 2009).
27. Y.-C. Zou, T. Piran and R. Sari, CLUES from the prompt emission of GRB 080319b, *The Astrophysical Journal* **692**, L92 (jan 2009).
28. H. Ito, J. Matsumoto, S. Nagataki, D. C. Warren and M. V. Barkov, Photospheric emission from collapsar jets in 3d relativistic hydrodynamics, *The Astrophysical Journal Letters* **814**, p. L29 (2015).
29. T. Parsotan and D. Lazzati, Photospheric Prompt Emission From Long Gamma Ray Burst Simulations – II. Spectropolarimetry, *arXiv e-prints* , p. arXiv:2108.11412 (August 2021).
30. T. Parsotan, lazzati-astro/MCRaT: MCRaT with Cyclo-synchrotron Emission/Absorption (June 2021).
31. T. Parsotan, parsotat/processmcrat: Cyclo-synchrotron release (June 2021).
32. J. Hulsman, Polar-2: a large scale gamma-ray polarimeter for grbs, in *Space Telescopes and Instrumentation 2020: Ultraviolet to Gamma Ray*, 2020.
33. T. Poole, A. Breeveld, M. Page, W. Landsman, S. Holland, P. Roming, N. Kuin, P. Brown, C. Gronwall, S. Hunsberger *et al.*, Photometric calibration of the swift ultraviolet/optical telescope, *Monthly Notices of the Royal Astronomical Society* **383**, 627 (2008).
34. C. Rodrigo and E. Solano, The svo filter profile service, in *Contributions to the XIV.0 Scientific Meeting (virtual) of the Spanish Astronomical Society*, 2020.
35. W. Deng and B. Zhang, Low energy spectral index and ep evolution of quasi-thermal photosphere emission of gamma-ray bursts, *The Astrophysical Journal* **785**, p. 112 (2014).
36. A. M. Beloborodov, Radiative transfer in ultrarelativistic outflows, *The Astrophysical Journal* **737**, p. 68 (2011).
37. B. Fryxell, K. Olson, P. Ricker, F. Timmes, M. Zingale, D. Lamb, P. MacNeice, R. Rosner, J. Truran and H. Tufo, Flash: An adaptive mesh hydrodynamics code for modeling astrophysical thermonuclear flashes, *The Astrophysical Journal Supplement Series* **131**, p. 273 (2000).
38. L. Nava, R. Salvaterra, G. Ghirlanda, G. Ghisellini, S. Campana, S. Covino, G. Cusumano, P. D'Avanzo, V. D'Elia, D. Fugazza, A. Melandri, B. Sbarufatti, S. D. Vergani and G. Tagliaferri, A complete sample of bright swift long gamma-ray bursts: testing the spectral-energy correlations, *Monthly Notices of the Royal Astronomical Society* **421**, p. 1256 (2012).
39. O. Gottlieb, E. Nakar and O. Bromberg, The structure of hydrodynamic γ-ray burst jets, *Monthly Notices of the Royal Astronomical Society* **500**, 3511 (2021).
40. H. Ito, S. Nagataki, J. Matsumoto, S.-H. Lee, A. Tolstov, J. Mao, M. Dainotti and A. Mizuta, Spectral and polarization properties of photospheric emission from stratified jets, *The Astrophysical Journal* **789**, p. 159 (2014).
41. C. Lundman, A. Pe'er and F. Ryde, Polarization properties of photospheric emission from relativistic, collimated outflows, *Monthly Notices of the Royal Astronomical Society* **440**, 3292 (2014).

42. T. Parsotan, R. Cochrane, C. Hayward, D. Angles-Alcazar, R. Feldmann, C.-A. Faucher-Giguere, S. Wellons and P. Hopkins, Realistic mock observations of the sizes and stellar mass surface densities of massive galaxies in fire-2 zoom-in simulations, *Monthly Notices of the Royal Astronomical Society* **501**, 1591 (2021).
43. R. Cochrane, C. Hayward, D. Anglés-Alcázar, J. Lotz, T. Parsotan, X. Ma, D. Kereš, R. Feldmann, C. Faucher-Giguere and P. Hopkins, Predictions for the spatial distribution of the dust continuum emission in star-forming galaxies, *Monthly Notices of the Royal Astronomical Society* **488**, 1779 (2019).

The photosphere emission spectrum of hybrid relativistic outflow for Gamma-Ray Bursts

Yan-Zhi Meng,[1,2,3] Jin-Jun Geng[1] and Xue-Feng Wu[1]

[1]*Purple Mountain Observatory, Chinese Academy of Sciences, Nanjing 210023, China*
[2]*School of Astronomy and Space Science, Nanjing University, Nanjing 210023, China*
[3]*Key Laboratory of Modern Astronomy and Astrophysics (Nanjing University), Ministry of Education, China*
E-mail: yzmeng@nju.edu.cn (YZM), jjgeng@pmo.ac.cn (JJG) and xfwu@pmo.ac.cn (XFW)

The photospheric emission in the prompt phase is the natural prediction of the original fireball model for gamma-ray burst (GRB) due to the large optical depth ($\tau > 1$) at the base of the outflow, which is supported by the quasi-thermal components detected in several *Fermi* GRBs. However, which radiation mechanism (photosphere or synchrotron) dominates in most GRB spectra is still under hot debate. The shape of the observed photosphere spectrum from a pure hot fireball or a pure Poynting-flux-dominated outflow has been investigated before. In this work, we further study the photosphere spectrum from a hybrid outflow containing both a thermal component and a magnetic component with moderate magnetization ($\sigma_0 = L_P/L_{\rm Th} \sim 1-10$), by invoking the probability photosphere model. The high-energy spectrum from such a hybrid outflow is a power law rather than an exponential cutoff, which is compatible with the observed Band function in large amounts of GRBs. Also, the distribution of the low-energy indices (corresponding to the peak-flux spectra) is found to be quite consistent with the statistical result for the peak-flux spectra of GRBs best-fitted by the Band function, with similar angular profiles of structured jet in our previous works. Finally, the observed distribution of the high-energy indices can be well understood after considering the different magnetic acceleration (due to magnetic reconnection and kink instability) and the angular profiles of dimensionless entropy with the narrower core.

Keywords: Gamma-ray burst: general – radiation mechanisms: thermal – radiative transfer – scattering

1. Introduction

After decades of researches, the radiation mechanism of GRB prompt emission is still unclear.[30–33] The photospheric emission model seems to be a promising scenario.[12,19–21,24,27] The photospheric emission model naturally interprets the clustering of the peak energies[14] and the high radiation efficiency[16] observed.

Indeed, a quasi-thermal component has been found in great amounts of BATSE GRBs[25] and several *Fermi* GRBs (GRB 090902B[1]). To account for the broad spectra of other GRBs, the quasi-thermal spectrum need to be broadened. Two different mechanisms of broadening have been proposed theoretically, i.e., the subphotospheric dissipation[7,24] and the geometric broadening.[4,17,19,20,22] This geometric broadening, namely the probability photosphere model, is the result of the fact that photons can be last scattered at any place (r, Ω) inside the outflow if only the electron exists there.[3,22,23] Then, the observed photosphere spectrum is the superposition of a series of blackbodies with different temperature, thus broadened.

In studies on the probability photosphere model till now,[4,17,20] the jet is accelerated solely by the radiative pressure of the thermal photons. However, the magnetically driven acceleration[5,7] may also play an important role in the real situation, which has not been properly considered in the framework of the probability photosphere model. In this work we study the photospheric emission spectrum within the framework of the probability photosphere model for a hybrid relativistic outflow, which contains a thermal component and a magnetic component, including both the thermally and magnetically driven acceleration.

The paper is organized as follows. In Section 2, we describe the calculations of the photospheric emission spectrum for a hybrid outflow within the probability photosphere model, including the energy injections of impulsive injection and more reasonable continuous wind. The calculated spectral results and parameter dependencies are shown in Section 3. The conclusions are summarized in Section 4.

2. Probability photosphere emission from a hybrid jet

2.1. *Hybrid jet and its dynamics*

A hybrid jet is composed of a thermal component and a magnetic component, which could be described by the dimensionless entropy η and the initial magnetization parameter σ_0. The dynamics for a hybrid jet may be approximated as

$$\Gamma(r) = \begin{cases} \frac{r}{r_0}, & r_0 < r < R_{\rm ra}; \\ \Gamma_{\rm ra} \left(\frac{r}{R_{\rm ra}}\right)^\delta, & R_{\rm ra} < r < R_c; \\ \Gamma_c, & r > R_c, \end{cases} \qquad (1)$$

where r_0 is the radius at the jet base, $\Gamma_{\rm ra} = \max(\eta, [\eta(1+\sigma_0)]^{1/3})$ is the Lorentz factor at $R_{\rm ra}$, $\Gamma_c \simeq \eta(1+\sigma_0)$ is the coasting Lorentz factor, $R_{\rm ra}$ is the rapid acceleration radius and R_c is the coasting radius.

2.2. *Time-resolved spectra from probability photosphere emission*

2.2.1. *Impulsive injection*

For the probability photosphere model, the observed spectrum is a superposition of a series of blackbodies emitted from any place in the outflow with a certain probability, which is calculated by

$$F_\nu(\nu,t) = \frac{N_0}{4\pi d_L^2} \iint P_1(r,\mu) P_2(\nu,T) h\nu \times \delta\left(t - \frac{ru}{\beta c}\right) d\mu dr, \qquad (2)$$

where $u = 1 - \beta\cos\theta$, and $N_0 = L_w/2.7k_{\rm B}T_0$ is the number of photons injected impulsively at the base of the outflow, $P_1(r,\mu)$ represents the probability density function for the final scattering to occur at the coordinates (r,θ), $\mu = \cos\theta$, $P_2(\nu,T)$ represents the probability for a photon of the observed frequency ν last-scattered at (r,θ) with the observer frame temperature of T.

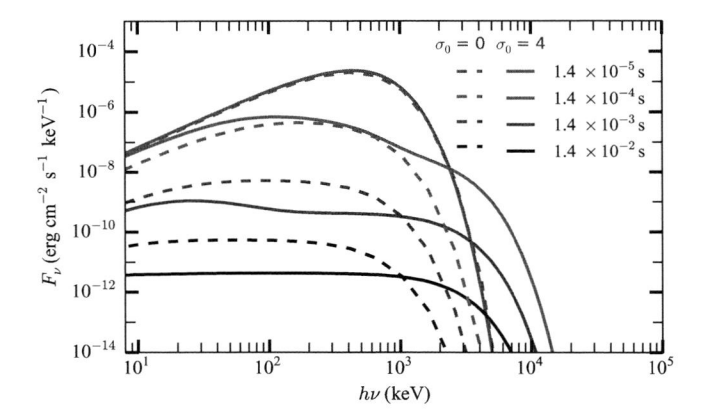

Fig. 1. The time-resolved spectra of impulsive injection for the jet with and without magnetization. The solid lines show the calculated time-resolved spectra for the hybrid jet with a hot fireball component ($\eta = 400$) and a cold Poynting-flux component ($\sigma_0 = 4$). Also, a total outflow luminosity of $L_w = 10^{53}$ erg s^{-1} is assumed, base outflow radius $R_0 = 3 \times 10^8$ cm, and luminosity distance $d_L = 4.85 \times 10^{28}$ cm ($z = 2$). Different colors represent different observational times. For comparison, the dashed lines illustrate the time-resolved spectra calculated for the jet without magnetization.[4] Obviously, at later times the time-resolved spectra extend to much higher energy and a power-law component emerges in the low-energy end.

2.2.2. *Continuous wind*

It is more realistic to consider the continuous wind from the central engine since the GRBs have relatively long duration (> 1 s). For a layer ejected from $\hat{t}$ to $\hat{t} + d\hat{t}$, the observed spectrum at the observer time t is

$$\hat{F}_\nu(\nu, t, \hat{t}) = \frac{N_0}{4\pi d_L^2} \iint P_1(r,\mu) P_2(\nu, T) h\nu \times \delta(t - \hat{t} - \frac{ru}{\beta c}) d\mu dr. \qquad (3)$$

Then, integrating over all the layers, we obtain the observed time-resolved spectrum to be

$$F_\nu(\nu, t) = \int_0^t \hat{F}_\nu(\nu, t, \hat{t}) d\hat{t}. \qquad (4)$$

3. Calculated results

3.1. *Impulsive injection*

The calculated time-resolved spectra are shown in Figure 1 (the solid lines). It is found that at the later times (the high-latitude emission dominates) the time-resolved spectra firstly show a power-law shape extending to a much higher energy than the early-time blackbody. Then, the power-law component vanishes gradually towards the low-energy end and the peak energy on the high-energy end remains constant.

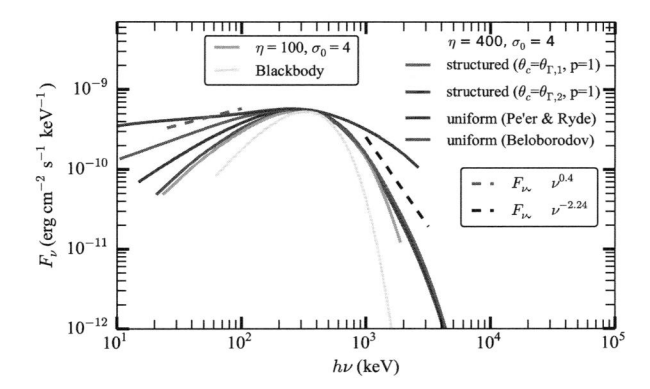

Fig. 2. The time-resolved spectra at later times ($t \geq 1$ s) of a continuous wind for the hybrid jet with magnetization $\sigma_0 = 4$ and various values or angular profiles of dimensionless entropy η. Here, $\theta_{\Gamma,1} = 1/400$ and $\theta_{\Gamma,2} = 1/4000$. All the time-resolved spectra have been normalized to the same peak energy and peak flux as the case of $\eta = 400$ and $\sigma_0 = 4$ (green line) to compare clearly the low-energy and high-energy indices. For comparison, the yellow line shows the spectrum of blackbody. Also, the red and black dashed lines represent respectively the average low-energy index (-0.6) and high-energy index (-3.24) fitted with the Band function for the time-resolved spectra of a large sample of single pulses.[29]

3.2. *Continuous wind*

For the continuous wind with constant wind luminosity, the spectrum at a later time ($t \geq 1$ s) which corresponds to the observed peak-flux spectrum is calculated by Equation (4). This calculated time-resolved spectrum, with the same parameters as Figure 1 ($\eta = 400$, $\sigma_0 = 4$) is illustrated by the green lines (with the probability density function introduced in[3]) in Figure 2. Apparently, the spectrum on the high-energy end is a power law rather than an exponential cutoff, which is the natural result of the power-law component extending to much higher energy in Figure 2.

Furthermore, we calculate the spectrum (with the probability density function described in[23]) for the case of the dimensionless entropy η of a lateral structure, with which the observed typical low-energy spectral index $\alpha \approx -1$ can be obtained for the unmagnetized jet under the framework of the probability photosphere model.[17,20] The considered angular profile consists of an inner constant core with width θ_c and the outer power-law decreased component with power-law index p. Note that an angle-independent luminosity is considered, because the spectrum expected to be observed is formed by the photons making their last scattering at approximately $\lesssim 5/\Gamma_0$ (as shown in[17]) and the isotropic angular width for Lorentz factor $\theta_{c,\Gamma}$ is likely to be much smaller than the isotropic angular width for luminosity $\theta_{c,L}$.[6,13,15,26,34] The red line in Figure 2 represents the calculated spectrum for a hybrid jet with $\theta_c = \theta_{\Gamma,1} = 1/400$ and $p = 1$, corresponding to the typical value $\alpha \sim -1$ for an unmagnetized jet. While the blue line is the spectrum for hybrid jet with $\theta_c = \theta_{\Gamma,2} = 1/4000$ and $p = 1$, corresponding to the minimum value $\alpha \sim -2$ for unmagnetized jet (see Figure 7d in[20]). To compare clearly the low-energy and high-energy indices, in Figure 2 the calculated actual time-resolved spectra have been normalized to the same peak energy and peak flux as the case of $\eta = 400$ and $\sigma_0 = 4$.

We then find that the spectrum of the hybrid jet possesses the much harder low-energy spectral index than that of the unmagnetized jet with the same angular profile, $\alpha \sim -0.6$ for $\theta_c = \theta_{\Gamma,1}$, $p = 1$ and $\alpha \sim -1$ for $\theta_c = \theta_{\Gamma,2}$, $p = 1$. The high-energy power-law index β is the same as the uniform case for $\theta_c = \theta_{\Gamma,1}$, $p = 1$ ($\beta \sim -4$, see Figure 3 and the discussion in Section 3.3), and much larger ($\beta \sim -1.6$) for $\theta_c = \theta_{\Gamma,2}$, $p = 1$. In a word, the spectrum of the hybrid jet is analogue to the empirical Band function[2] spectrum, whereas the spectrum of the unmagnetized jet corresponds to the spectrum of the empirical cutoff power-law model,[20] within the framework of the probability photosphere model.

Interestingly, in all the statistical works of a large sample of GRBs,[9–11,14,28] the average low-energy spectral index for the GRBs best-fitted by the Band function is harder ($0.1 \sim 0.3$) than that for the GRBs best-fitted by the cutoff power-law model, for both the time-integrated and the peak-flux spectra. This hardness is quite consistent with our results for the probability photosphere model discussed in the previous paragraph. Also, for the distributions of the low-energy and high-energy indices, our results (corresponding to the peak-flux spectra) are quite similar to the statistical results of the peak-flux spectra for the GRBs best-fitted by the Band function. For the low-energy spectral index, the typical value is $\alpha \sim -0.6$ and the minimum value $\alpha \sim -1$. While for the high-energy spectral index, the maximum value $\beta \sim -1.6$ in our model is close to the statistical result. The typical value $\beta \sim -4$ in our model seems to be much softer than the well-known $\beta \sim -2.5$, which we consider to arise from the assumption of the single pulse, namely without the overlap of the pulses. This consideration is proposed recently,[29] where the time-resolved spectral analysis of a large sample of single pulses has been performed and the average high-energy spectral index ($\beta \sim -3.24$) indeed is found to be much softer. Noteworthily, the average high-energy spectral index $\beta \sim -3.24$ in that work can be well reproduced with our hybrid jet model, by considering the parameter dependence on the power-law index of magnetic acceleration δ (see Figure 3 and the discussion in Section 3.3). In Figure 2, the red and black dashed lines represent the average low-energy index (-0.6) and high-energy index (-3.24) in that work, respectively.

3.3. *Parameter dependence*

In the above discussion, for the magnetically driven acceleration, we only consider the case of magnetic reconnection for the non-axisymmetric rotator.[5] Whereas, for an initially axisymmetric flow, the acceleration can happen through the kink instability.[8,18] Besides, the magnetic acceleration driven by the kink instability seems to be more rapid than the magnetic reconnection case, with a larger power-law index δ of $\sim 2/5$ or even $\sim 1/2$ (see Figure 5 in[8]). Thus, in Figure 3 we compare the

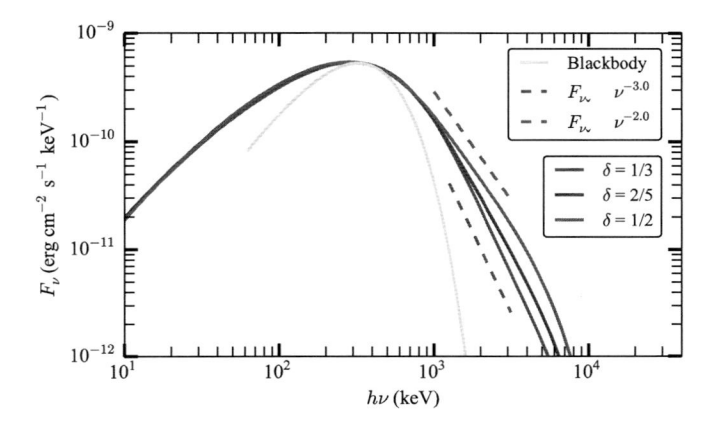

Fig. 3. The calculated time-resolved spectra at later times ($t \geq 1$ s) of continuous wind with different power-law index of magnetic acceleration δ. The green, blue and red lines are for $\delta = 1/3$, $\delta = 2/5$ and $\delta = 1/2$ respectively, along with magnetization $\sigma_0 = 9$. While the green and red dashed lines represent the high-energy spectral index $\beta = -4$ and $\beta = -3$, respectively. The yellow line is the spectrum of blackbody.

calculated spectra of our model for $\delta = 1/3$, $\delta = 2/5$ and $\delta = 1/2$, and find that their high-energy power-law indices are quite different while the low-energy indices remain the same. For $\delta = 1/3$, we have $\beta = -4$; for $\delta = 1/2$, we obtain $\beta = -3$; and β lies between -4 and -3 for $\delta = 2/5$. Surprisingly, this rough distribution of β (-4 to -3) is well consistent with the β distribution of the softer cluster for a large sample of single pulses,[29] where the β distribution seems to show the bimodal distribution with a harder typical cluster (peaks at -2.5) and a softer cluster (peaks at -3.5; see Figure 1 therein).

4. Conclusions

In this paper, by invoking the probability photosphere model we investigate the shape of the photospheric emission spectrum for the hybrid outflow, which contains a thermal component and a magnetic component with moderate magnetization ($\sigma_0 = L_P/L_{\rm Th} \sim 1-10$). The following conclusions are drawn.

(1) The photosphere spectrum on the high-energy end is a power law rather than an exponential cutoff.

(2) With the similar angular profiles of the dimensionless entropy η as the unmagnetized jet, considered in previous works,[17,20] the distribution of the low-energy indices (corresponding to the peak-flux spectra) for our photosphere model is quite consistent with the statistical result of the peak-flux spectra for the GRBs best-fitted by the Band function.

(3) The high-energy power-law index β for our photosphere model solely depends on the power-law index of magnetic acceleration δ. Also, the observed β distribution could be well interpreted with the photosphere model in this work.

Acknowledgements

This work is supported by the National Natural Science Foundation of China (Grant Nos. 11725314, 12041306, 11903019, 11833003), the Major Science and Technology Project of Qinghai Province (2019-ZJ-A10). Y.Z.M. is supported by the National Postdoctoral Program for Innovative Talents (grant No. BX20200164).

References

1. Abdo, A. A., Ackermann, M., Ajello, M., et al. 2009, *Astrophys. J.*, 706, L138
2. Band, D., Matteson, J., Ford, L., et al. 1993, *Astrophys. J.*, 413, 281
3. Beloborodov, A. M. 2011, *Astrophys. J.*, 737, 68
4. Deng, W., & Zhang, B. 2014, *Astrophys. J.*, 785, 112
5. Drenkhahn, G. 2002, *Astron. Astrophys.*, 387, 714
6. Geng, J.-J., Zhang, B., Kölligan, A., Kuiper, R., & Huang, Y.-F. 2019, *Astrophys. J.*, 877, L40
7. Giannios, D. 2006, *Astron. Astrophys.*, 457, 763
8. Giannios, D., & Spruit, H. C. 2006, *Astron. Astrophys.*, 450, 887
9. Goldstein, A., Burgess, J. M., Preece, R. D., et al. 2012, *Astrophys. J.*, 199, 19
10. Goldstein, A., Preece, R. D., Mallozzi, R. S., et al. 2013, *Astrophys. J.*, 208, 21
11. Gruber, D., Goldstein, A., Weller von Ahlefeld, V., et al. 2014, *Astrophys. J.*, 211, 12
12. Hou, S.-J., Zhang, B.-B., Meng, Y.-Z., et al. 2018, *Astrophys. J.*, 866, 13
13. Ito, H., Just, O., Takei, Y., et al. 2021, arXiv:2105.09323
14. Kaneko, Y., Preece, R. D., Briggs, M. S., et al. 2006, *Astrophys. J.*, 166, 298
15. Lazzati, D., Morsony, B. J., & Begelman, M. C. 2007, Philosophical Transactions of the Royal Society of London Series A, 365, 1141
16. Lloyd-Ronning, N. M., & Zhang, B. 2004, *Astrophys. J.*, 613, 477
17. Lundman, C., Pe'er, A., & Ryde, F. 2013, *Mon. Not. R. Astron. Soc.*, 428, 2430
18. Lyutikov, M., & Blandford, R. 2003, arXiv:astro-ph/0312347
19. Meng, Y.-Z., Geng, J.-J., Zhang, B.-B., et al. 2018, *Astrophys. J.*, 860, 72
20. Meng, Y.-Z., Liu, L.-D., Wei, J.-J., Wu, X.-F., & Zhang, B.-B. 2019, *Astrophys. J.*, 882, 26
21. Mészáros, P., & Rees, M. J. 2000, *Astrophys. J.*, 530, 292
22. Pe'er, A. 2008, *Astrophys. J.*, 682, 463
23. Pe'er, A., & Ryde, F. 2011, *Astrophys. J.*, 732, 49
24. Rees, M. J., & Mészáros, P. 2005, *Astrophys. J.*, 628, 847
25. Ryde, F., & Pe'er, A. 2009, *Astrophys. J.*, 702, 1211
26. Tchekhovskoy, A., McKinney, J. C., & Narayan, R. 2008, *Mon. Not. R. Astron. Soc.*, 388, 551
27. Thompson, C. 1994, *Mon. Not. R. Astron. Soc.*, 270, 480
28. Yu, H.-F., Preece, R. D., Greiner, J., et al. 2016, *Astron. Astrophys.*, 588, A135
29. Yu, H.-F., Dereli-Bégué, H., & Ryde, F. 2019, *Astrophys. J.*, 886, 20
30. Zhang, B., & Yan, H. 2011, *Astrophys. J.*, 726, 90
31. Zhang, B. 2020, Nature Astronomy, 4, 210
32. Zhang, B.-B., Zhang, B., Liang, E.-W., et al. 2011, *Astrophys. J.*, 730, 141
33. Zhang, B.-B., Zhang, B., Castro-Tirado, A. J., et al. 2018a, Nature Astronomy, 2, 69
34. Zhang, W., Woosley, S. E., & MacFadyen, A. I. 2003, *Astrophys. J.*, 586, 356.

On diffusive photospheres in Gamma-Ray Bursts

G. V. Vereshchagin

ICRANet, 65122, p.le della Repubblica, 10, Pescara, Italy
ICRA and Dipartimento di Fisica, Sapienza Università di Roma, P.le Aldo Moro 5, 00185
Rome, Italy
ICRANet-Minsk, National Academy of Sciences of Belarus, Nezavisimosti ave. 68, 220072
Minsk, Belarus
INAF, Viale del Parco Mellini 84, 00136 Rome, Italy
E-mail: veresh@icra.it

Photospheric emission from relativistic outflows may originate in two different regimes: photon decoupling within the outflow or radiative diffusion. I show that observed thermal component in the early afterglows of gamma-ray bursts can originate from such diffusive photospheres.

Keywords: Thermal radiation, gamma-ray bursts

1. Introduction

Gamma-ray bursts (GRBs) are strong and short irregular flashes of hard "prompt" radiation, followed by the long lasting fading out smooth "afterglow" emission spanning from sub-TeV energies to radio. Since their discovery a number of dedicated space observatories and ground based telescopes are constantly monitoring the sky daily reporting new bursts and measuring distance to their host galaxies. GRBs come in two kinds[1]: short and long, with their possible progenitors being binary neutron star mergers and collapsing massive stars reaching the endpoint of their evolution, respectively. Extremely large energies released in γ-rays ($\leq 10^{54}$ erg) as well as a short variability time (≤ 10 ms) point to ultrarelativistic outflows giving rise to the observed emission.[2]

The spectrum of the prompt emission is non-thermal, its origin can be traced to the synchrotron mechanism in relativistic shock waves, generated by the relativistic material breaking in the interstellar medium.[3] Photospheric models with possible dissipation of kinetic energy of the outflow are attractive alternative to the synchrotron models since observation of thermal radiation allows for the determination of basic hydrodynamic characteristics of the outflow from which these bursts originate.[4–6] The photons in these models are trapped and advected with the opaque outflow, until it becomes transparent. In many GRBs, a subdominant thermal component was detected during their prompt emission, while in several, such as GRB 090902B observed spectrum is almost thermal.[7,8]

Thermal components are also detected in time resolved spectra during the early afterglow in a number of GRBs.[9–14] So far several mechanisms to generate such emission are proposed. They include a shock breakout from a progenitor star or a stellar wind[15] and a hot cocoon formed when the relativistic jet emerges from the stellar surface.[16,17] Some authors argue that shock breakouts are not energetic enough and do not last long enough to explain the observed thermal emission,[13] leaving cocoons as a favourite model. In addition, there is an alternative proposal of a cloud or a clump with small mass, accelerated by the GRB outflow.[18]

Most studies dealing with the photospheric emission, e.g.,[19–25] for a review see,[5] adopt the hydrodynamic model of a steady and infinite wind. However, finite duration of GRBs implies finite width of the wind. Winds of *finite duration* are classified as photon thin and photon thick.[4,26,27] Decoupling of photons from plasma in the latter case occurs simultaneously in the entire outflow, while in the former case photons are transported to the boundaries of the outflow by radiative diffusion, just like in nonrelativistic outflows, e.g. in supernova ejecta. Emission in this case originates not at the photospheric radius, but at smaller radii. The photon thick case, corresponding to the steady wind, appears to be justified for typical GRB parameters. Photon thin regime is overlooked in the literature, as it is assumed that at large radii the outflow is spreading[28,29] due to strong velocity gradients initially generated in the outflow, see e.g.[28,29] Such spreading outflows indeed correspond to the photon thick case.[30] However, the origin of these gradients is not clear. Even if initially present, such gradients may be erased in initial phases of expansion, e.g. by oblique shocks or other mechanisms. Hence the outflow can be photon thin. In such a case decoupling of photons from expanding plasma occurs in the diffusive regime.[27]

Radiative diffusion is known to be relevant for expanding ejecta in supernovae explosions.[31] Recently the theory of photospheric emission[27] was further extended.[32] In particular, physical parameters of such outflows were determined using the observational data.

The paper is organized as follows. The definition of relativistic photosphere is recalled in Section 2. Observational properties of diffusive photospheres are discussed in Section 3. The method for determination of physical parameters of the outflow is presented in Section 4. Physical parameters of GRB cocoons are discussed in Section 5. Case studies of GRBs with thermal emission in the early afterglow are reported in Section 6. Discussion and conclusion follow.

2. Relativistic photosphere

Consider a relativistic outflow launched at a radius R_0. The outflow is characterized by its activity time Δt, the luminosity L and mass injection rate $\dot{M}$. The associated thickness of the outflow is $l = c\Delta t$. The entropy in the region where the energy is released is parametrized by a dimensionless parameter $\eta = L/\dot{M}c^2$. Spherical symmetry is assumed, but generalization for anisotropic case with $\eta(\theta)$, where θ is the polar angle is straightforward. When $\eta \gg 1$ the bulk Lorentz factor changes with the radial distance as

$$\Gamma \simeq \begin{cases} \dfrac{r}{R_0}, & R_0 < r < \eta R_0, \\ \eta \simeq \text{const}, & r > \eta R_0, \end{cases} \quad (1)$$

During both acceleration and coasting phases the continuity equation for the laboratory number density reduces to

$$n = \begin{cases} n_0 \left(\dfrac{R_0}{r}\right)^2, & R(t) < r < R(t) + l, \\ 0, & \text{otherwise}, \end{cases} \quad (2)$$

where $R(t)$ is the radial position of the inner boundary of the outflow.

The optical depth for a spherically symmetric outflow is[27,33]

$$\tau = \int_R^{R+\Delta R} \sigma n \left(1 - \beta \cos\theta\right) \dfrac{dr}{\cos\theta}, \quad (3)$$

where $R + \Delta R$ is the radial coordinate at which the photon leaves the outflow, and θ is the angle between the velocity vector of the outflow and the direction of propagation of the photon, n is the laboratory number density of electrons and positrons, which may be present due to pair production. The dominant interaction of photons in our case is Compton scattering in the non-relativistic regime, so σ is the Thomson cross section.

Electron-positron-photon plasma with baryon loading reaches thermal equilibrium before its expansion starts.[34,35] With decreasing entropy η opacity due to electrons associated with baryons increases and eventually dominates over pair opacity. For the laboratory density profile (2) one has in the radial direction

$$\tau = \begin{cases} \dfrac{1}{6}\tau_0 \left(\dfrac{R_0}{R}\right)^3, & R_0 \ll R \ll \eta R_0, \\ \dfrac{1}{2\eta^2}\tau_0 \left(\dfrac{R_0}{R}\right), & \eta R_0 \ll R \ll \eta^2 R_0, \\ \tau_0 \left(\dfrac{R_0}{R}\right)^2, & R \gg \eta^2 R_0, \end{cases} \quad (4)$$

where

$$\tau_0 = \dfrac{\sigma L}{4\pi m_p c^3 R_0 \eta} = n_0 \sigma R_0. \quad (5)$$

The first two lines correspond to a *photon thick outflow* and the third line corresponds to a *photon thin outflow*.[27]

The photospheric radius R_{ph} is defined by equating (4) to unity

$$R_{ph} = \begin{cases} R_0 \left(\frac{\tau_0}{6}\right)^{1/3}, & \tau_0 \ll \eta^3, \\ R_0 \frac{\tau_0}{2\eta^2}, & \eta^3 \ll \tau_0 \ll 4\eta^4 \frac{l}{R_0}, \\ (\tau_0 R_0 l)^{1/2}, & \tau_0 \gg 4\eta^4 \frac{l}{R_0}. \end{cases} \quad (6)$$

In eqs. (4) and (6) the regions of validity of different approximations are expressed either for radius or for parameters of the outflow. The crucial parameter which determines whether the outflow is photon thick or thin is the ratio

$$\chi = \frac{\tau_0}{4\eta^4} \frac{l}{R_0}. \quad (7)$$

The outflow is photon thin for $\chi \gg 1$ and it is photon thick otherwise.

3. Relativistic diffusive photosphere

The definition of the photosphere implies that at this position in space the outflow as a whole becomes transparent to radiation. However, emission emerges from the outflow when it is optically thick as well. Such emission is due to radiative diffusion, which transfers the energy from deeper parts of the outflow towards its surface. Naively one can think that such an effect is negligible in ultrarelativistic outflows. However, this is not the case.[4] Indeed, the comoving time, which photon takes to cross the outflow with comoving thickness $l_c = \Gamma l$ is $t_c = l_c^2/D_c$, where $D_c = c/3\sigma n_c$ is the diffusion coefficient, $n_c = n/\Gamma$ is the comoving density of the outflow. The radial coordinate of the outflow at this time is $R \simeq \Gamma c t_c$.

This diffusion radius is found in Ref. 27, and it is given by

$$R_D = \left(\tau_0 \eta^2 R_0 l^2\right)^{1/3}, \quad (8)$$

where eq. (5) has been used. It turns out to be always smaller than the photospheric radius of photon thin outflow, $R_D \ll R_{ph}$, so the radiation escapes such an outflow before it becomes transparent, just like in the supernova ejecta. In this sense the characteristic radius of the photospheric emission is not the photospheric radius found from (4), but the radius of diffusion (8). The probability distribution of last scattering of photons in diffusive photospheres is qualitatively different from the usual photospheric emission.[26] Besides, the comoving temperature of escaping radiation is different from the temperature at the photospheric radius. Applicability of the photon thin asymptotics, last line in eq. (6), can be written using eq. (8) as

$$l \ll \frac{R_D}{\sqrt{2}\eta^2}. \quad (9)$$

For larger thickness l photon thin asymptotics disappears, so in the limit $l \to \infty$ the stationary wind with photon thick asymptotics is recovered.

Adiabatic expansion implies[36] that the observed temperature of the outflow does not change while it is accelerating, and it decreases as $T_{obs} \propto R^{-2/3}$ at the coasting phase. Taking into account the finite size of emitter and the cosmological redshift z one has[37]

$$T_{obs} = \frac{\xi}{1+z} T_0 \left(\frac{\eta R_0}{R_D}\right)^{2/3}, \qquad (10)$$

where ξ is a numerical factor of order unity. In estimates below $\xi = 1.48$ is assumed following Ref. 37, which is found from the Monte Carlo simulations in the infinite wind approximation, though the value of ξ in the acceleration phase and in the photon thin case could be slightly different. The temperature at the base of the outflow is

$$T_0 \simeq \left(\frac{L}{4\pi c a R_0^2}\right)^{1/4}, \qquad (11)$$

where $a = 4\sigma_{SB}/c$ is the radiation constant, σ_{SB} is the Stefan-Boltzmann constant. Finally, the duration of photospheric emission for a distant observer is

$$t_a^D = (1+z)\frac{R_D}{2\eta^2 c}. \qquad (12)$$

In the photon thick case the duration of thermal emission is determined by the width of the outflow l, which is unconstrained. In the photon thin case this duration is given by eq. (12) and it is a function of the diffusion radius and the Lorentz factor.

The luminosity of photospheric component scales with radius as

$$L_{ph} = L_0 \left(\frac{\eta R_0}{R}\right)^{8/3}, \qquad (13)$$

and the applicability condition of the photon thin case in eq. (6) and together with the definition of diffusion radius in eq. (8) imply for the luminosity of diffusive photosphere

$$L_{thin} < L_0 \left(\frac{R_0}{\eta l}\right)^{8/3} \ll L_0. \qquad (14)$$

This means that thermal emission is much weaker than the emission of the prompt radiation, if γ-rays are produced with high efficiency there. For $l \sim R_0$ this condition strongly favours small values of η and, consequently, small Lorentz factors of the outflow.

4. Determination of initial radius and bulk Lorentz factor of the outflow

Assuming that the observed thermal component in early afterglows of some GRBs is of photospheric origin, one can estimate initial radius of the outflow directly from observations.[37] Indeed, in the ultrarelativistic regime one has

$$\mathcal{R} \equiv \left(\frac{F_{obs}^{BB}}{\sigma_{SB}T_{obs}^4}\right)^{1/2} = \zeta \frac{(1+z)^2}{d_L} \frac{R}{\Gamma}, \quad (15)$$

where R is the emission radius, d_L is the luminosity distance, ζ is a numerical factor of order unity. Following Ref. 37 $\zeta = 1.06$ is assumed for the estimates below. In Ref. 37 the emission radius R was associated with the photosphere of the *photon thick* outflows. However, this relation is valid for any ultrarelativistic emitter. Therefore, from eqs. (10), (15) and (11) the initial radius is

$$R_0 = \frac{4^{3/2} d_L}{\xi^6 \zeta^4 (1+z)^2} \mathcal{R} \left(\frac{F_{obs}^{BB}}{Y F_{obs}}\right)^{3/2}. \quad (16)$$

In the derivation of this results only two assumptions are made. First, the outflow should be coasting at ultrarelativistic speed, $\Gamma = \eta \gg 1$. Secondly, the relation $L = 4\pi d_L^2 Y F_{obs}$ is used, where Y is the fraction of the total luminosity L and the energy emitted in X and γ-rays *in the prompt phase*.

In addition to the initial radius R_0 an equation for the Lorentz factor can be obtained. Since the emitter radius for the *photon thin* outflows is the diffusion radius $R = R_D$, from eqs. (8) and (15) one obtains, see also Ref. 38

$$\frac{\eta}{l} = \frac{\zeta^{3/2}(1+z)^3}{d_L^{1/2}} \left(\frac{\sigma Y F_{obs}}{m_p c^3 \mathcal{R}^3}\right)^{1/2}. \quad (17)$$

Therefore, the Lorentz factor can be determined if l is known. In the particular case $l = R_0$ from (17) it follows the minimum Lorentz factor for which the photon thin case applies

$$\eta_{thin} = (1+z) \left(d_L \frac{Y F_{obs} \sigma}{m_p c^3 \mathcal{R}}\right)^{1/2} \frac{4^{3/2}}{\zeta^{5/2} \xi^6} \left(\frac{F_{obs}^{BB}}{Y F_{obs}}\right)^{3/2}. \quad (18)$$

The condition (9) determines the applicability limit of the photon thin case, so for $\sqrt{2}\eta^2 l = R_D$ the photon thick case is recovered[37]

$$\eta_{thick} = \left[\zeta(1+z)^2 d_L \frac{\sigma Y F_{obs}}{m_p c^3 \mathcal{R}}\right]^{1/4}. \quad (19)$$

Equations (17) and (18) allow the determination of the bulk Lorentz factor of the *photon thin* outflow, provided the measurement of the total flux F_{obs} and the parameter $\mathcal{R}$. Comparing eqs. (18) and (19) leads to the conclusion that the Lorentz factor inferred from the photon thin asymptotics is typically smaller than the one of the photon thick case; besides, it contains the inverse of the Y parameter, unlike a factor $Y^{1/4}$ in the latter case.

It is important to stress that from the theoretical point of view, given the total luminosity and the initial radius of the outflow one cannot distinguish between photon thick and photon thin cases as both sets of parameters are possible with different η and photospheric radius. These parameters are related by eq. (15), therefore independent observational information is required in order to differentiate between the two cases.

5. GRB cocoons

Consider typical parameters relevant for GRB jets which is penetrating the progenitor.[17] In what follows introduce the notation $A_x = A/10^x$, so the luminosity L_{52} stands for 10^{52} erg/s, which is the isotropic luminosity. While the entropy of the jet can take large values, the mixing between the progenitor and the jet lowers the entropy of the cocoon, so $\eta = 10$ is chosen, as a reference value. It is also likely that the entropy is a decreasing function of the angular distance from the jet. Assume that initial radius of the wind R_0 is given by the radius of the core of the progenitor WR star $R_0 \sim 10^9$ cm, and the thickness of the wind corresponds to the size of the WR star $l_{12} = 10^{12}$ cm.[39] The crucial parameter which determines whether the outflow is photon thick or thin is the ratio

$$\chi \simeq 29 L_{52} l_{12}^{-1} \eta_1^{-5}. \tag{20}$$

For $\chi \gg 1$ the outflow is photon thin, which is the case for our fiducial parameters. Considering the extreme dependence on η, for smaller η the condition is clearly satisfied. Hence the cocoon is in the photon thin regime and therefore the radiation from the cocoons is governed by radiative diffusion. The diffusion radius is

$$R_D \simeq 4.9 \times 10^{14} L_{52}^{1/3} \eta_1^{1/3} l_{12}^{2/3} \text{ cm}, \tag{21}$$

and the arrival time corresponding to this radius is

$$t_a^D = (1+z) \frac{R_D}{2\eta^2 c} \simeq 81.7 (1+z) L_{52}^{1/3} \eta_1^{-5/3} l_{12}^{2/3} \text{ s}, \tag{22}$$

which is the typical duration of thermal emission observed in early afterglows of GRBs.

The observed temperature at the diffusion radius is

$$T_{obs} = 0.12 L_{52}^{1/36} R_9^{1/6} \eta_1^{4/9} l_{12}^{-4/9} \text{keV}, \tag{23}$$

which is also a typical temperature of thermal emission in early afterglows of GRBs.[13]

Such inferred values of temperature and duration call for closer attention to the radiation properties of photon thin outflows.

6. Case studies

All GRBs reported in Ref. 13 with measured redshifts and thermal component detected in their early afterglows were considered, namely GRBs 060218, 090618, 101219B, 111123A, 111225A, 121211A, 131030A, 150727A, 151027A. Observed temperature, thermal flux and total flux were averaged for the entire duration of the thermal emission. The initial radius was found from eq. (16). Two values of the

Lorentz factor in photon thin, eq. (18), and photon thick, eq. (19), cases were determined. Then the minimum value of the Y parameter is found which allows the duration of the photospheric emission (12) to be not less than the observed duration of the thermal component. Only six cases allow both photon thick and photon thin interpretations for the photosphere; for other cases photon thin case does not apply because eq. (19) gives smaller Lorentz factor than eq. (18).

GRB 060218. This is a well studied nearby GRB[15] with record breaking duration of the thermal signal interpreted as the break out of a shock driven by a mildly relativistic shell into the dense wind surrounding the progenitor, see however Refs. 40, 41. The thermal emission in this burst with observed temperature $T_{BB} = 0.15$ keV may be also explained as a photosphere of a cocoon launched from initial radius 3.18×10^{11} cm with a mildly relativistic Lorentz factor $1.2Y^{-1} < \Gamma < 1.6Y^{1/4}$ emitting in the photon thin regime. This estimate of the Lorentz factor is in agreement with radio observation at 2 days, requiring $\Gamma \sim 2$.[42] Given that the condition $\Gamma \gg 1$ is not satisfied, results of the theory of diffusive ultrarelativistic photospheres can be applied to this case with great care. In particular, the estimated duration of the thermal signal is only $13Y$ s.

GRB 090618. This burst may represent a canonical case of photon thin outflow launched from the initial radius 10^9 cm with the Lorentz factor $3Y^{-1} < \Gamma < 40Y^{1/4}$. Assuming instantaneous energy injection with $l = R_0$ one finds $Y = 5.7$. The duration of the thermal emission with observed temperature about 1 keV is about $6Y$ s. Note that thermal emission has also been claimed in the prompt phase, with a higher temperature ranging from 54 to 12 keV.[43] Such thermal emission in the prompt phase may be interpreted as a photosphere of the photon thick outflow. Indeed, if the initially high entropy η decreases with time the outflow should experience a transition from photon thick to photon thin case.

GRB 111225A. This case is similar to GRB 060218, but with smaller initial radius of 8.3×10^9 cm and Lorentz factor in the range $1 < \Gamma < 6.0Y^{1/4}$. The duration of the thermal emission with observed temperature of 0.18 keV is about $126Y$ s, with $Y = 2.0$ for $l = R_0$. The lower bound on the Lorentz factor in unconstrained. It may correspond to a cocoon emitting in the diffusive photon thin regime.

GRB 131030A. This case is a typical long burst, similar to GRB 090618, it allows Lorentz factors in the photon thin case in the following range: $4.3Y^{-1} < \Gamma < 66Y^{1/4}$. The duration of the thermal emission with observed temperature of 1.12 keV is about $2.0Y$ s. The initial radius is 3.74×10^8 cm. For instantaneous energy injection $Y = 19$.

GRB 150727A. This case is similar to GRB 111225A with initial radius 1.1×10^9 cm and Lorentz factors in the range $1 < \Gamma < 11Y^{1/4}$, allowing for a photon thin interpretation. The duration of the thermal emission with observed temperature of 0.47 keV is about $191Y$ s, with $Y = 2.1$.

GRB 151027A. This case is similar to GRBs 090618 and 131030, however with quite large initial radius 1.5×10^{10} cm and Lorentz factors in the narrow range

$23 < \Gamma < 26Y^{1/4}$. The duration of the thermal emission with observed temperature of 0.96 keV is about $0.47Y$ s, with $Y = 64$.

7. Discussion

The difference between the present work and the approach followed in Ref. 16 should be emphasized. The main assumption of that work is the presence of unknown dissipation mechanism, which transforms part of the kinetic energy of the outflow into radiation, postulated in Ref. 44. Such dissipation can boost the luminosity of thermal emission and it might be required to explain subdominant thermal component during the prompt emission or even the prompt emission itself, see Ref. 45. Concerning observations of this component in the early afterglow, dissipation is not required, as it is much weaker than the prompt radiation.

Similarly, there is a difference between the present work and the work in Ref. 17. There two regimes of expansion are considered: Newtonian ($v < c$) and ultrarelativistic $\eta \gg 1$. For the latter, which is of interest here, the emission was assumed to originate at the photospheric radius, given by the last line in eq. (6). As discussed in Sec. 3 above, photons in this case diffuse out much earlier, so that no photons are left in the outflow when it arrives to the photospheric radius. For this reason estimations of the luminosity and observed temperature in that paper cannot be used.

Qualitative difference in dependence of observed flux and temperature on time for photon thin outflows determine their observed properties. In particular, since the flux up to diffusion time (22) is almost constant and its luminosity is much weaker than the prompt radiation luminosity, see eq. (14), the thermal component become visible after the steep decrease of observed luminosity following the end of the prompt phase. This is indeed where such thermal component is identified in many GRBs. Its disappearance is naturally explained by diffusion of the radiation kept in the outflow. Hence it implies that no more photons are generated neither in the outflow nor in the central engine.

We show that in several GRBs, namely GRB 060218, 111225A and 150727A, the thermal component observed in the early afterglow may originate from mildly relativistic cocoons emerging from the progenitors together with the jet, due to relatively small values of inferred Lorentz factors $\Gamma < 10$.

Such emission observed in other GRBs such as 090618, 131030A and 151027A correspond to large Lorentz factors $\Gamma > 10$, indicating a jet origin of the photospheric emission. Besides, these results suggest that the progenitors of some long GRBs, in particular GRB 090618 and 131030A could be rather compact objects, with radius $l \sim 10^9$ cm.

It is important to stress that the relatively low temperature of the thermal component observed in the early afterglow with $T \sim 0.1 - 10$ keV, in contrast with typical temperatures detected during the prompt emission with $T \sim 10 - 100$ keV does not indicate small Lorentz factor of the outflow. Conversely, it may point to photospheric origin of the thermal emission in the photon thin regime. Instead, large Lorentz factors $\Gamma \gg 1$ assumed in the model imply small mass of the emitting plasma, which is consistent with the cocoon interpretation.[17]

Notice that possible presence of thermal components both in the prompts radiation and in the early afterglow, as well as the presence of breaks in temperature dependence on time found in many cases[46–48] may correspond to the transition from photon thick to photon thin asymptotics in hydrodynamic evolution of the outflow powering GRBs.

In this work the theory of diffusive emission from relativistic photospheres is confronted with observational data on a sample of GRBs with thermal component in the early afterglows. The measurement of temperature and flux of the thermal component along with the total flux in the prompt phase are used to determine initial radii of the outflows as well as their Lorentz factors. The results indicate that in several cases (GRBs 060218, 111225A and 150727A) the inferred Lorentz factors are relatively small, $\Gamma < 10$, while in other cases (GRBs 090618, 131030A and 151027A) the inferred Lorentz factors are larger, $\Gamma > 10$. Such differences suggest two possible sources of the thermal component: mildly relativistic cocoons or highly relativistic jets. Results obtained above are valid only for those cases, where inferred Lorentz factor is relatively small, below few tens. For other cases identified in Ref. 13 inferred Lorentz factors are larger, and photon thin interpretation does not apply.

These results are the first indication that radiative diffusion may play an important role not only in nonrelativistic outflows, but also in ultrarelativistic outflows, represented by GRBs.

References

1. C. Kouveliotou, C. A. Meegan, G. J. Fishman, N. P. Bhat, M. S. Briggs, T. M. Koshut, W. S. Paciesas and G. N. Pendleton, Identification of Two Classes of Gamma-Ray Bursts, *ApJ* **413**, p. L101 (August 1993).
2. B. Zhang, *The Physics of Gamma-Ray Bursts* (Cambridge University Press, 2018).
3. P. Meszaros and M. J. Rees, Relativistic Fireballs and Their Impact on External Matter: Models for Cosmological Gamma-Ray Bursts, *ApJ* **405**, p. 278 (March 1993).
4. G. V. Vereshchagin, Physics of Nondissipative Ultrarelativistic Photospheres, *International Journal of Modern Physics D* **23**, 1430003 (Dec 2014).
5. A. Pe'er and F. Ryde, Photospheric emission in gamma-ray bursts, *International Journal of Modern Physics D* **26**, 1730018 (Jan 2017).
6. B. Zhang, Y. Wang and L. Li, Dissecting the Energy Budget of a Gamma-Ray Burst Fireball, *ApJ* **909**, p. L3 (March 2021).
7. F. Ryde, M. Axelsson, B. B. Zhang, S. McGlynn, A. Pe'er, C. Lundman, S. Larsson, M. Battelino, B. Zhang, E. Bissaldi, J. Bregeon, M. S. Briggs, J. Chiang, F. de Palma, S. Guiriec, J. Larsson, F. Longo, S. McBreen, N. Omodei, V. Petrosian, R. Preece and A. J. van der Horst, Identification and Properties of the Photospheric Emission in GRB090902B, *ApJ* **709**, L172 (February 2010).
8. F. Ryde, C. Lundman and Z. Acuner, Emission from accelerating jets in gamma-ray bursts: radiation-dominated flows with increasing mass outflow rates, *MNRAS* **472**, 1897 (December 2017).

9. K. L. Page, R. L. C. Starling, G. Fitzpatrick, S. B. Pandey, J. P. Osborne, P. Schady, S. McBreen, S. Campana, T. N. Ukwatta, C. Pagani, A. P. Beardmore and P. A. Evans, GRB 090618: detection of thermal X-ray emission from a bright gamma-ray burst, *Monthly Notices of the Royal Astronomical Society* **416**, 2078 (September 2011).
10. R. L. C. Starling, K. L. Page, A. Pe'er, A. P. Beardmore and J. P. Osborne, A search for thermal X-ray signatures in gamma-ray bursts - I. Swift bursts with optical supernovae, *Monthly Notices of the Royal Astronomical Society* **427**, 2950 (December 2012).
11. M. Sparre and R. L. C. Starling, A search for thermal X-ray signatures in gamma-ray bursts - II. The Swift sample, *Monthly Notices of the Royal Astronomical Society* **427**, 2965 (December 2012).
12. M. Friis and D. Watson, Thermal Emission in the Early X-Ray Afterglows of Gamma-Ray Bursts: Following the Prompt Phase to Late Times, *The Astrophysical Journal* **771**, p. 15 (July 2013).
13. V. Valan, J. Larsson and B. Ahlgren, Thermal components in the early X-ray afterglows of GRBs: likely cocoon emission and constraints on the progenitors, *MNRAS* **474**, 2401 (February 2018).
14. L. Izzo, A. de Ugarte Postigo, K. Maeda, C. C. Thöne, D. A. Kann, M. Della Valle, A. Sagues Carracedo, M. J. Michałowski, P. Schady, S. Schmidl, J. Selsing, R. L. C. Starling, A. Suzuki, K. Bensch, J. Bolmer, S. Campana, Z. Cano, S. Covino, J. P. U. Fynbo, D. H. Hartmann, K. E. Heintz, J. Hjorth, J. Japelj, K. Kamiński, L. Kaper, C. Kouveliotou, M. Krużyński, T. Kwiatkowski, G. Leloudas, A. J. Levan, D. B. Malesani, T. Michałowski, S. Piranomonte, G. Pugliese, A. Rossi, R. Sánchez-Ramírez, S. Schulze, D. Steeghs, N. R. Tanvir, K. Ulaczyk, S. D. Vergani and K. Wiersema, Signatures of a jet cocoon in early spectra of a supernova associated with a γ-ray burst, *Nature* **565**, 324 (January 2019).
15. S. Campana, V. Mangano, A. J. Blustin, P. Brown, D. N. Burrows, G. Chincarini, J. R. Cummings, G. Cusumano, M. Della Valle, D. Malesani, P. Mészáros, J. A. Nousek, M. Page, T. Sakamoto, E. Waxman, B. Zhang, Z. G. Dai, N. Gehrels, S. Immler, F. E. Marshall, K. O. Mason, A. Moretti, P. T. O'Brien, J. P. Osborne, K. L. Page, P. Romano, P. W. A. Roming, G. Tagliaferri, L. R. Cominsky, P. Giommi, O. Godet, J. A. Kennea, H. Krimm, L. Angelini, S. D. Barthelmy, P. T. Boyd, D. M. Palmer, A. A. Wells and N. E. White, The association of GRB 060218 with a supernova and the evolution of the shock wave, *Nature* **442**, 1008 (August 2006).
16. A. Pe'er, P. Meszaros and M. J. Rees, Radiation from an Expanding Cocoon as an Explanation of the Steep Decay Observed in GRB Early Afterglow Light Curves, *The Astrophysical Journal* **652**, 482 (November 2006).
17. E. Nakar and T. Piran, The Observable Signatures of GRB Cocoons, *ApJ* **834**, p. 28 (January 2017).
18. R. Ruffini, G. V. Vereshchagin and Y. Wang, Thermal emission in the early afterglow of gamma-ray bursts from their interaction with supernova ejecta, *A&A* **600**, p. A131 (April 2017).
19. P. Mészáros and M. J. Rees, Steep Slopes and Preferred Breaks in Gamma-Ray Burst Spectra: The Role of Photospheres and Comptonization, *ApJ* **530**, 292 (February 2000).
20. A. Pe'er, Temporal Evolution of Thermal Emission from Relativistically Expanding Plasma, *ApJ* **682**, 463 (July 2008).
21. A. Pe'er and F. Ryde, A Theory of Multicolor Blackbody Emission from Relativistically Expanding Plasmas, *ApJ* **732**, 49 (May 2011).

22. A. M. Beloborodov, Radiative Transfer in Ultrarelativistic Outflows, *ApJ* **737**, 68 (August 2011).
23. C. Lundman, A. Pe'er and F. Ryde, A theory of photospheric emission from relativistic, collimated outflows, *MNRAS* **428**, 2430 (January 2013).
24. R. Santana, P. Crumley, R. A. Hernández and P. Kumar, Monte Carlo simulations of the photospheric process, *MNRAS* **456**, 1049 (February 2016).
25. M. Bhattacharya, W. Lu, P. Kumar and R. Santana, Monte Carlo Simulations of Photospheric Emission in Relativistic Outflows, *ApJ* **852**, p. 24 (January 2018).
26. D. Bégué, I. A. Siutsou and G. V. Vereshchagin, Monte Carlo Simulations of the Photospheric Emission in Gamma-Ray Bursts, *ApJ* **767**, p. 139 (Apr 2013).
27. R. Ruffini, I. A. Siutsou and G. V. Vereshchagin, A Theory of Photospheric Emission from Relativistic Outflows, *The Astrophysical Journal* **772**, p. 11 (July 2013).
28. T. Piran, A. Shemi and R. Narayan, Hydrodynamics of Relativistic Fireballs, *MNRAS* **263**, 861 (August 1993).
29. P. Mészáros, P. Laguna and M. J. Rees, Gasdynamics of relativistically expanding gamma-ray burst sources - Kinematics, energetics, magnetic fields, and efficiency, *ApJ* **415**, 181 (September 1993).
30. R. Ruffini, I. A. Siutsou and G. V. Vereshchagin, Spreading of ultrarelativistically expanding shell: An application to GRBs, *New Astronomy* **27**, 30 (Feb 2014).
31. D. Arnett, *Supernovae and Nucleosynthesis: An Investigation of the History of Matter from the Big Bang to the Present* (Princeton University Press, 1996).
32. G. V. Vereshchagin and I. A. Siutsou, Diffusive photospheres in gamma-ray bursts, *MNRAS* **494**, 1463 (May 2020).
33. M. A. Abramowicz, I. D. Novikov and B. Paczynski, The appearance of highly relativistic, spherically symmetric stellar winds, *ApJ* **369**, 175 (March 1991).
34. A. G. Aksenov, R. Ruffini and G. V. Vereshchagin, Thermalization of the mildly relativistic plasma, *Phys. Rev. D* **79**, p. 043008 (February 2009).
35. A. G. Aksenov, R. Ruffini and G. V. Vereshchagin, Thermalization of Electron-Positron-Photon Plasmas with an application to GRB, in *American Institute of Physics Conference Series*, American Institute of Physics Conference Series Vol. 966, January 2008.
36. R. Ruffini and G. Vereshchagin, Electron-positron plasma in GRBs and in cosmology, *Il Nuovo Cimento C* **36**, p. 255 (May 2013).
37. A. Pe'er, F. Ryde, R. A. M. J. Wijers, P. Mészáros and M. J. Rees, A New Method of Determining the Initial Size and Lorentz Factor of Gamma-Ray Burst Fireballs Using a Thermal Emission Component, *ApJ* **664**, L1 (Jul 2007).
38. D. Bégué and S. Iyyani, Transparency Parameters from Relativistically Expanding Outflows, *ApJ* **792**, p. 42 (September 2014).
39. P. A. Crowther, Physical Properties of Wolf-Rayet Stars, *ARA&A* **45**, 177 (September 2007).
40. G. Ghisellini, G. Ghirlanda and F. Tavecchio, Did we observe the supernova shock breakout in GRB 060218?, *Monthly Notices of the Royal Astronomical Society: Letters* **382**, L77 (November 2007).
41. S. W. K. Emery, M. J. Page, A. A. Breeveld, P. J. Brown, N. P. M. Kuin, S. R. Oates and M. De Pasquale, The early optical afterglow and non-thermal components of GRB 060218, *MNRAS* **484**, 5484 (April 2019).
42. A. M. Soderberg, S. R. Kulkarni, E. Nakar, E. Berger, P. B. Cameron, D. B. Fox, D. Frail, A. Gal-Yam, R. Sari, S. B. Cenko, M. Kasliwal, R. A. Chevalier, T. Piran, P. A. Price, B. P. Schmidt, G. Pooley, D. S. Moon, B. E. Penprase, E. Ofek, A. Rau,

N. Gehrels, J. A. Nousek, D. N. Burrows, S. E. Persson and P. J. McCarthy, Relativistic ejecta from X-ray flash XRF 060218 and the rate of cosmic explosions, *Nature* **442**, 1014 (August 2006).
43. L. Izzo, R. Ruffini, A. V. Penacchioni, C. L. Bianco, L. Caito, S. K. Chakrabarti, J. A. Rueda, A. Nandi and B. Patricelli, A double component in GRB 090618: a proto-black hole and a genuinely long gamma-ray burst, *A&A* **543**, p. A10 (Jul 2012).
44. M. J. Rees and P. Mészáros, Dissipative Photosphere Models of Gamma-Ray Bursts and X-Ray Flashes, *ApJ* **628**, 847 (August 2005).
45. M. Bhattacharya and P. Kumar, Explaining GRB prompt emission with sub-photospheric dissipation and Comptonization, *MNRAS* **491**, 4656 (February 2020).
46. F. Ryde, The Cooling Behavior of Thermal Pulses in Gamma-Ray Bursts, *ApJ* **614**, 827 (October 2004).
47. F. Ryde, Is Thermal Emission in Gamma-Ray Bursts Ubiquitous?, *ApJ* **625**, L95 (June 2005).
48. F. Ryde and A. Pe'er, Quasi-blackbody Component and Radiative Efficiency of the Prompt Emission of Gamma-ray Bursts, *ApJ* **702**, 1211 (September 2009).

Summary of the parallel session GB3

G. V. Vereshchagin

ICRANet, p. della Repubblica, 10, 65100 Pescara, Italy
E-mail: veresh@icra.it

D. Bégué

Bar-Ilan University Ramat-Gan 5290002, Israel
E-mail: begueda@biu.ac.il

In this proceedings, we give a brief general overview of the parallel session on photospheric emission in gamma-ray bursts (GRBs), which took place during the online 16th Marcel Grossmann Meeting. The session covered theoretical and observational aspects of photospheric emission. In particular, spectral, temporal and polarization properties were discussed.

Keywords: Gamma-ray bursts, Photospheric emission, Thermal emission, Non-thermal emission, Jet simulations.

1. State of the art

Photospheric emission models are seen as prime contenders to explain the prompt phase of gamma-ray bursts, see *e.g.*[1] for a review. This emission is produced when the expanding jet becomes optically thin to Compton scattering,[2] which is the dominant interaction mode for photon of comoving energy $\sim$ 1keV. Photospheric emission is a naturally expected process in the widely discussed fireball model.[3–6] It can be highly efficient if the transparency takes place at small radius, that is to say close to the transition radius between accelerating and coasting phase,[3,7–9] and it naturally predicts a clustering of the spectral peak energy around 500 keV.[10]

It has long been known that photospheric models in their simplest flavors fail to explain the shallow low energy spectral slope seen in most GRBs.[11–15] This picture changed in the past 15 years when it was realized that the spectra produced at the photosphere can be highly non-thermal due to 1- energy dissipation below the photosphere either via shocks,[16–18] magnetic reconnection[19–22] or neutron decay,[23] and 2- geometrical effects due to the structure of the jets[24,25] and the photon last scattering position.[11,14,23]

The aforementioned effects are difficult to study analytically, as any analysis depends on ad hoc assumptions on the geometry of the jet, dissipation mechanisms and their localization. In recent years, 3D (GR) MHD simulations coupled to Monte-Carlo radiative transfer calculations were designed to study photospheric emission in the context of GRBs solve those opens issues.[26–33] One of the most interesting finding is that the luminosity drop for off-axis observers is limited by the structure of the jet.

Moreover, the simulations were successful in reproducing correlations between observer position, luminosity, peak energy, and observed polarization. In particular, several important successes were obtained in explaining the Amati correlation[34] (between the isotropic total energy E_{iso} and the peak energy E_p), the Yonetoku correlation[35] (between the isotropic luminosity L_{iso} and E_p) and the Goletneskii relation[36] (between the luminosity and E_p) by considering a distribution of off-axis observers.

Finally, the simulations permitted to obtain detailed polarization predictions. In particular, it was found from numerical simulations of photon propagation inside a jet that a high degree of time-resolved polarization requires off-axis observers, while the polarization for on-axis observers is lower.[37–39] Using a semi-analytical jet model, it was found that the polarization degree correlates to a substantial drop in luminosity.[37,40] Instead, recent hydrodynamical simulations[38,39] showed that the drop in luminosity for observer angles might be smaller than expected thanks to emission from the jet cocoon. Extending the analysis to lower frequencies it was shown that the polarization degree is larger at low energies, either thanks to the effect of synchrotron emission[41] or due to higher scattering angle towards the observer.[39]

Despite these many successes, the correlation analysis is limited to a few initial setups because of the large resources needed for each independent simulations and their post-processing analysis. In the forthcoming years, the reliability of the already obtained correlation results will be tested and refined against many more runs with different initial conditions and methods. In addition, the simulations are not yet mature enough to produce detailed spectral predictions, which could be confronted to observed data.

Concerning the spectral analysis in the context of photospheric emission, two different paths were explored in the past few years. First, detailed time-resolved spectral analysis of GBM data from many bursts were performed.[42–44] Specifically, the spectra were fitted with a cut-off power-law and the obtained low energy slope distribution were carefully investigated. It was realized that many bursts have one to several time bins with spectra harder than the limits from the synchrotron line of death. These studies concluded that photospheric emission should be the mechanism at work in those bursts, textbfsee however[45].

Second, simplified photospheric models, such as the DREAM model,[46,47] were directly fitted to observed GBM spectra[48] finding 1- good agreement for the bursts with the hardest low energy slope when considering the photospheric emission taking place at the transition between accelerating and coasting phase, and 2- good overall agreement with other bright bursts, when considering localized energy dissipation. It is expected that those studies will be extended to larger sample and refined models in the near future.

2. Talks at the session

The session was run in two blocks of three hours.

Asaf Pe'er delivered a review talk "Understanding prompt emission: where do we stand?" where he summarized basic observational information about the prompt emission and problems originating from misconceptions which are related to usage of models (including the progenitor, jet launching, dynamics and dissipation), the nature and dynamics of the outflow (e.g. baryonic vs. magnetic) and the radiation mechanisms (e.g. photospheric vs. synchrotron). He also discussed the spectral and polarization properties of non-dissipative photospheric emission, and its ability to explain observed correlation. Finally, he mentioned a new model of the prompt emission based on backscattering of the seed photons on a cold relativistic cork which appears natualy in front of the jet in many progenitor models.

Ore Gottlieb presented a talk "Probing the jet launching mechanism from prompt emission of GRBs" where he described the ways to infer the information on the jet launching mechanism and its dynamics from the comparison of observations with numerical simulations of jet propagation and its the photospheric emission, focusing specifically on the role of magnetization of the jet. In particular, based on numerical hydrodynamic simulations, including self-consistent simulations within the collapsar model, he discussed and ability to produce jet tilt, intermittency, position of the magnetic dissipation region, and the role of different progenitors in jet launching and cocoon formation.

Gregory Vereshchagin reported a study "Diffusive photospheres in gamma-ray bursts" describing the results of the application of the theory of photospheric emission to the thermal radiation, detected in the early afterglows of some gamma-ray bursts. The inferred Lorentz factors of the outflow are clustered in two groups: few hundreds, indicating classical photospheric emission from ultrarelativistic outflow, and few tens, indicating diffusive regime of the photospheric emission, possibly from jet cocoons.

Tyler Parsotan delivered a talk "Monte Carlo Simulations of Photospheric Emission in Gamma Ray Bursts" in which he described the MCRaT code and its coupling to relativistic hydrodynamical simulations in order to obtain mock observations. He discussed how his code allows him to obtain predictions of the photospheric model, in particular prediction about optical prompt percursors of gamma-ray bursts.

Hirotaka Ito presented results on "Numerical simulations of photospheric emission in GRBs" focusing on the jet structure and its consequences for spectral shapes, polarization signal and correlations between observed quantities, based on hydrodynamical simulations and post processing with the radiative transport.

Yan-Zhi Meng reported the talk "Photosphere emission spectrum of hybrid relativistic outflow for gamma-ray bursts", considering both impulsive injection and continuous wind cases.

J. Michael Burgess in his talk "Spectroscopy of GRBs: Where are we now?" discussed how fitting physical models, instead of phenomenological ones, is important in order to infer physical information from observations. He mentioned several "myths" about the synchrotron emission model such as the line-of-death and width problem and showed how proper folding through the response function of the instruments demonstrates viability of this model.

Hüsne Dereli-Bégué presented a talk "Classification of Photospheric Emission in sGRBs" where she discussed the fit of a large sample of short GRBs with a phenomenological model based on a non-dissipative photosphere model. The main conclusions are that nearly one third of the spectra are consistent with purely thermal emission, and that a large fraction of bursts may come from subphotospheric dissipation.

Björn Ahlgren discussed "Subphotospheric dissipation evaluated using joint Fermi-Swift observations" and pointed out the importance of using XRT data in addition to the BAT data from the SWIFT satellite, in order to distinguish between photospheric and synchrotron mechanisms of emission in the context of fitting of dissipative photospheric model to the data, focusing specifically on the DREAM model.

Liang Li reported on "Bayesian Time-resolved Spectroscopy of Multipulse GRBs: Variations of Emission Properties among Pulses" where he discussed construction of the catalogue of multipulse bursts, the fitting procedure and the outcomes. In particular, he discussed different trends and correlations between observed quantities such as $F - \alpha$ and $F - E_p$.

The outcome of the discussion with participation of Gregory Vereshchagin, Pe'er Asaf, J. Michael Burgess and Damien Begue is that generally speaking about gamma-ray bursts, despite strong progress both in theory and in observations there are still many unresolved issues such as the origin of the jet, the mechanism of energy dissipation, and the nature of observed variability.

The field is observationally driven, with new recent observational results such as the "anomalous" X-ray behavior of GRB 170817A and the detection of very high energy emission from several sources such as GRB 190114C. However, there are some key observational results, which still need explanation from the theory, in particular the strong spectral evolution within each pulse, the power-law decay of the peak energy, the time evolution of the temperature and so on. From the observational viewpoint, one of the most promising direction is the study of polarization of gamma-ray bursts.

3. Conclusions

To conclude, many critical progresses were made and problem addressed in the past few years. In particular, theoretical and numerical predictions start to be mature enough to allow direct comparison to observations, either via direct spectral fitting or via comparison to the global population parameters. It is expected that this trend will continue, allowing for a refinement of the photospheric emission theories, a better understanding of the data and of gamma-ray bursts.

References

1. A. Pe'er, Physics of Gamma-Ray Bursts Prompt Emission, *Advances in Astronomy* **2015**, p. 907321 (2015).
2. M. A. Abramowicz, I. D. Novikov and B. Paczynski, The appearance of highly relativistic, spherically symmetric stellar winds, *Astrophys. J.* **369**, 175 (March 1991).
3. J. Goodman, Are gamma-ray bursts optically thick?, *Astrophys. J.* **308**, L47 (September 1986).
4. B. Paczynski, Gamma-ray bursters at cosmological distances, *Astrophys. J.* **308**, L43 (September 1986).
5. M. J. Rees and P. Meszaros, Relativistic fireballs - Energy conversion and time-scales, *Mon. Not. R. Astron. Soc.* **258**, 41P (September 1992).
6. M. J. Rees and P. Meszaros, Unsteady outflow models for cosmological gamma-ray bursts, *Astrophys. J.* **430**, L93 (August 1994).
7. F. Ryde and A. Pe'er, Quasi-blackbody Component and Radiative Efficiency of the Prompt Emission of Gamma-ray Bursts, *Astrophys. J.* **702**, 1211 (September 2009).
8. D. Bégué and S. Iyyani, Transparency Parameters from Relativistically Expanding Outflows, *Astrophys. J.* **792**, p. 42 (September 2014).
9. F. Ryde, C. Lundman and Z. Acuner, Emission from accelerating jets in gamma-ray bursts: radiation-dominated flows with increasing mass outflow rates, *Mon. Not. R. Astron. Soc.* **472**, 1897 (December 2017).
10. A. Pe'er, P. Mészáros and M. J. Rees, Peak Energy Clustering and Efficiency in Compact Objects, *Astrophys. J.* **635**, 476 (December 2005).
11. A. Pe'er, Temporal Evolution of Thermal Emission from Relativistically Expanding Plasma, *Astrophys. J.* **682**, 463 (Jul 2008).
12. A. M. Beloborodov, Radiative Transfer in Ultrarelativistic Outflows, *Astrophys. J.* **737**, p. 68 (August 2011).
13. R. Ruffini, I. A. Siutsou and G. V. Vereshchagin, A Theory of Photospheric Emission from Relativistic Outflows, *Astrophys. J.* **772**, p. 11 (July 2013).
14. D. Bégué, I. A. Siutsou and G. V. Vereshchagin, Monte Carlo Simulations of the Photospheric Emission in Gamma-Ray Bursts, *Astrophys. J.* **767**, p. 139 (April 2013).
15. W. Deng and B. Zhang, Low Energy Spectral Index and E_p Evolution of Quasi-thermal Photosphere Emission of Gamma-Ray Bursts, *Astrophys. J.* **785**, p. 112 (April 2014).
16. A. Pe'er and E. Waxman, Prompt Gamma-Ray Burst Spectra: Detailed Calculations and the Effect of Pair Production, *Astrophys. J.* **613**, 448 (September 2004).
17. C. Lundman, A. Beloborodov and I. Vurm, Radiation mediated shocks in gamma-ray bursts: Pair creation, *ArXiv e-prints* (August 2017).
18. H. Ito, A. Levinson, B. E. Stern and S. Nagataki, Monte Carlo simulations of relativistic radiation-mediated shocks - I. Photon-rich regime, *Mon. Not. R. Astron. Soc.* **474**, 2828 (February 2018).
19. G. Drenkhahn and H. C. Spruit, Efficient acceleration and radiation in Poynting flux powered GRB outflows, *Astron. Astrophys.* **391**, 1141 (September 2002).
20. D. Giannios, Prompt emission spectra from the photosphere of a GRB, *Astron. Astrophys.* **457**, 763 (October 2006).
21. D. Giannios and D. A. Uzdensky, GRB and blazar jets shining through their stripes, *Mon. Not. R. Astron. Soc.* **484**, 1378 (March 2019).
22. Y.-Z. Meng, J.-J. Geng and X.-F. Wu, The Photosphere Emission Spectrum of Hybrid Relativistic Outflow for Gamma-ray Bursts, *arXiv e-prints*, p. arXiv:2107.04532 (July 2021).
23. A. M. Beloborodov, Collisional mechanism for gamma-ray burst emission, *Mon. Not. R. Astron. Soc.* **407**, 1033 (September 2010).

24. C. Lundman, A. Pe'er and F. Ryde, A theory of photospheric emission from relativistic, collimated outflows, *Mon. Not. R. Astron. Soc.* **428**, 2430 (January 2013).
25. Y.-Z. Meng, L.-D. Liu, J.-J. Wei, X.-F. Wu and B.-B. Zhang, The Time-resolved Spectra of Photospheric Emission from a Structured Jet for Gamma-Ray Bursts, *Astrophys. J.* **882**, p. 26 (September 2019).
26. D. Lazzati, Monte Carlo Radiation Transfer Simulations of Photospheric Emission in Long-duration Gamma-ray Bursts, *Astrophys. J.* **829**, p. 76 (October 2016).
27. A. Chhotray and D. Lazzati, Dynamic Monte Carlo Simulations of Radiatively Accelerated GRB Fireballs, *ArXiv e-prints* (May 2017).
28. T. Parsotan and D. Lazzati, A Monte Carlo Radiation Transfer Study of Photospheric Emission in Gamma-Ray Bursts, *Astrophys. J.* **853**, p. 8 (January 2018).
29. T. Parsotan, D. López-Cámara and D. Lazzati, Photospheric Emission from Variable Engine Gamma-Ray Burst Simulations, *Astrophys. J.* **869**, p. 103 (December 2018).
30. O. Gottlieb, A. Levinson and E. Nakar, Intermittent hydrodynamic jets in collapsars do not produce GRBs, *arXiv e-prints* , p. arXiv:2002.12384 (February 2020).
31. H. Ito, O. Just, Y. Takei and S. Nagataki, A Global Numerical Model of the Prompt Emission in Short Gamma-ray Bursts, *Astrophys. J.* **918**, p. 59 (September 2021).
32. O. Gottlieb, O. Bromberg, A. Levinson and E. Nakar, Intermittent mildly magnetized jets as the source of GRBs, *Mon. Not. R. Astron. Soc.* **504**, 3947 (July 2021).
33. O. Gottlieb, A. Lalakos, O. Bromberg, M. Liska and A. Tchekhovskoy, Black hole to breakout: 3D GRMHD simulations of collapsar jets reveal a wide range of transients, *arXiv e-prints* , p. arXiv:2109.14619 (September 2021).
34. L. Amati, F. Frontera, M. Tavani, J. J. M. in't Zand, A. Antonelli, E. Costa, M. Feroci, C. Guidorzi, J. Heise, N. Masetti, E. Montanari, L. Nicastro, E. Palazzi, E. Pian, L. Piro and P. Soffitta, Intrinsic spectra and energetics of BeppoSAX Gamma-Ray Bursts with known redshifts, *Astron. Astrophys.* **390**, 81 (July 2002).
35. D. Yonetoku, T. Murakami, T. Nakamura, R. Yamazaki, A. K. Inoue and K. Ioka, Gamma-Ray Burst Formation Rate Inferred from the Spectral Peak Energy-Peak Luminosity Relation, *Astrophys. J.* **609**, 935 (July 2004).
36. S. V. Golenetskii, E. P. Mazets, R. L. Aptekar and V. N. Ilinskii, Correlation between luminosity and temperature in γ-ray burst sources, *Nature* **306**, 451 (December 1983).
37. C. Lundman, A. Pe'er and F. Ryde, Polarization properties of photospheric emission from relativistic, collimated outflows, *Mon. Not. R. Astron. Soc.* **440**, 3292 (June 2014).
38. T. Parsotan, D. López-Cámara and D. Lazzati, Photospheric Polarization Signatures from Long Gamma-Ray Burst Simulations, *Astrophys. J.* **896**, p. 139 (June 2020).
39. T. Parsotan and D. Lazzati, Photospheric Prompt Emission From Long Gamma Ray Burst Simulations – II. Spectropolarimetry, *arXiv e-prints* , p. arXiv:2108.11412 (August 2021).
40. R. Gill, J. Granot and P. Kumar, Linear polarization in gamma-ray burst prompt emission, *Mon. Not. R. Astron. Soc.* **491**, 3343 (January 2020).
41. C. Lundman, I. Vurm and A. M. Beloborodov, Polarization of Gamma-Ray Bursts in the Dissipative Photosphere Model, *Astrophys. J.* **856**, p. 145 (April 2018).
42. H.-F. Yu, H. Dereli-Bégué and F. Ryde, Bayesian Time-resolved Spectroscopy of GRB Pulses, *Astrophys. J.* **886**, p. 20 (November 2019).
43. H. Dereli-Bégué, A. Pe'er and F. Ryde, Classification of Photospheric Emission in Short GRBs, *Astrophys. J.* **897**, p. 145 (July 2020).
44. Z. Acuner, F. Ryde, A. Pe'er, D. Mortlock and B. Ahlgren, The Fraction of Gamma-Ray Bursts with an Observed Photospheric Emission Episode, *Astrophys. J.* **893**, p. 128 (April 2020).

45. J. M. Burgess, D. Bégué, J. Greiner, D. Giannios, A. Bacelj and F. Berlato, Gamma-ray bursts as cool synchrotron sources, *Nature Astronomy* **4**, 174 (February 2020).
46. B. Ahlgren, J. Larsson, T. Nymark, F. Ryde and A. Pe'er, Confronting GRB prompt emission with a model for subphotospheric dissipation, *Mon. Not. R. Astron. Soc.* **454**, L31 (November 2015).
47. B. Ahlgren, J. Larsson, E. Ahlberg, C. Lundman, F. Ryde and A. Pe'er, Testing a model for subphotospheric dissipation in GRBs: fits to Fermi data constrain the dissipation scenario, *Mon. Not. R. Astron. Soc.* **485**, 474 (May 2019).
48. G. Vianello, R. Gill, J. Granot, N. Omodei, J. Cohen-Tanugi and F. Longo, The Bright and the Slow—GRBs 100724B and 160509A with High-energy Cutoffs at $\lesssim$100 MeV, *Astrophys. J.* **864**, p. 163 (September 2018).

Synchrotron and synchrotron self-Compton emission components in GRBs detected at very high energies

Jagdish C. Joshi* and Vikas Chand[†]

School of Astronomy and Space Science, Nanjing University, Nanjing 210093, China
Key laboratory of Modern Astronomy and Astrophysics (Nanjing University),
Ministry of Education, Nanjing 210093, China
* E-mail: jagdishcjoshi86@gmail.com
[†] E-mail: vikasK2@nju.edu.cn

Soebur Razzaque

Centre for Astro-Particle Physics (CAPP) and Department of Physics, University of Johannesburg, PO Box 524, Auckland Park 2006, South Africa
E-mail: srazzaque@uj.ac.za

Gamma-Ray Bursts (GRBs) are energetic transients originating in a violent explosion of a massive star or merger of two compact objects in a binary system. These explosions create a relativistic blastwave which inevitably collides with the circumburst medium and results in external shocks. The emission produced thereby is the afterglow observed in GRBs after the initial prompt phase. The properties of the emitting region, i.e., non-thermal particle spectrum, magnetic amplification, and micro-physical parameters, etc., can be probed by monitoring and modelling the afterglow radiation. The recent detection of very high energy (VHE, > 100 GeV) gamma rays from GRBs has opened a possibility to test theoretical models such as the synchrotron self-Compton (SSC) in GRBs till late times in the afterglow phase. We find that the SSC model explains the afterglow observations of MAGIC-detected GRB 190114C and H.E.S.S.-detected GRB 180720B.

Keywords: GRBs: VHE Components, Afterglow Emission.

1. Introduction

GRBs, one of the brightest electromagnetic events in the universe, are produced in cataclysmic astrophysical events like the collapse of a massive star or mergers of compact binary stars (a neutron star – neutron star or a neutron star and a black hole system).[1,2] The initial prompt burst of the energy is primarily in gamma-rays, and its origin though still debated is linked to the energy released from the central source which is dissipated at the internal shocks or emitted at the photosphere.[3–6] Afterglow emission follows once the prompt emission phase ends in GRBs. The afterglow of GRBs is important to understand the circumburst environment, jet parameters, geometry of the jet and the central engine. Recently, a VHE component is discovered by the ground-based MAGIC telescopes[7–9] and H.E.S.S. telescopes.[10,11] This was anticipated based on the standard afterglow models and its origin was postulated via the inverse Compton scattering of the synchrotron radiation (synchrotron self-Compton).[12–22] Comparatively, other radiation channels like proton synchrotron require acceleration of protons up to 10^{21} eV and currently are considered less favorable.[23] However, for a combination of afterglow parameters, proton synchrotron can dominate compared to electron synchrotron emission as discussed in the literature.[20,24]

Synchrotron radiation from a decelerating blastwave can explain the multiwavelength afterglow emission from radio to gamma-rays observed in GRBs. The maximum energy detected in GRB 190114C by the MAGIC telescopes and in GRB 180720B by the H.E.S.S. telescopes is higher than the maximum energy that can be produced by synchrotron mechanism, and therefore, self-Compton of these synchrotron photons in the GRB blastwave is invoked to explain these energetic photons.[21]

In this work, we discuss GRB afterglow model and provide multiwavelength modeling of the observations of GRB 180720B and GRB 190114C (Section 2). We summarize our results in Section 3.

2. GRB blast-wave expansion and afterglow radiation

We consider the synchrotron radiation from the electrons accelerated to relativistic energies in the forward shock. Further, these synchrotron photons are upscattered by the same population of relativistic electrons. We revisit the synchrotron self-Compton model by[21] and the details of the expressions used here are taken from the SSC formalism for GRBs.[25]

Table 1. Afterglow model parameters used for the interpretation of multiwavelength observation of GRB 180720B and GRB 190114C. The VHE component detection time information $t_{\rm VHE,obs}$ is taken from[10] for GRB 180720B and from[7,8] for GRB 190114C respectively.

Parameters	GRB 180720B	GRB 190114C
$t_{\rm VHE,obs}$(s)	$> 3.6 \times 10^4$	> 55
$E_{k,\rm iso}$(erg)	4.5×10^{54}	$4 \times 10^{54} (1 \times 10^{53})$
Γ	400	300(36)
$t_{\rm dec}$(s)	69	$52.6 (2.3 \times 10^4)$
$t_{0,\rm SSC}$(s)	6×10^{-6}	8.5(61)
$A_\star$		0.02(0.02)
n_0(cm^{-3})	0.035	
p	2.4	2.18(2.5)
ϵ_e	0.05	0.03(0.08)
ϵ_B	1.2×10^{-5}	0.01(0.07)
ϕ	1	1 (1)

2.1. GRB 190114C multiwavelength emission

GRB 190114C was located at a redshift $z = 0.4245 \pm 0.005$[27] and its prompt gamma-ray emission releases isotropic energy $\sim 3 \times 10^{53}$ erg.[26] The very high energy gamma-ray detection from GRB 190114C was reported by MAGIC telescope.[26,28]

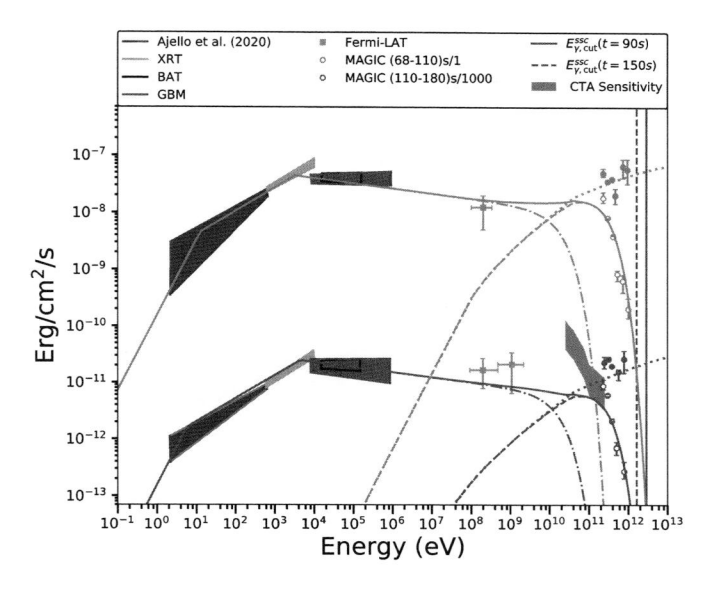

Fig. 1. SED for GRB 190114C reproduced from our earlier work,[25] with slightly different values of input model parameters. The data is extracted from.[26]

This source was observed in multiwavelengths (radio to gamma rays) by 6 satellites and 15 ground based telescopes.[26] We modelled GRB 190114C SEDs and light curves simultaneously and found that in late time the optical emission appears to be harder, which cannot be accounted for by the contribution from the host galaxy. Refreshed shocks are slow shells that will catch up with the afterglow shock region at late times.[29, 30] This will enhance the energy of the forward shock medium and can be useful to explain the optical hardness seen in case of GRB 190114C. The flux below the cooling frequency due to refershed shock emission is $((1 + f^{(3+p)/4}))F_{Sy}$, where F_{Sy} is the synchrotron flux due to the forward moving shell and $f = 5$ is the amount of higher flux compared to the optical emission of forward moving shell. The flux above the cooling frequency due to refershed shock emission is $((1 + f^{(2+p)/4}))F_{Sy}$.

In our Fig. 2 we have included the contribution due to a refreshed shock which can explain the late time optical flux and at the same time won't exceed the flux in X-rays. The late time onset of the afterglow constrains the initial Lorentz factor value of the slow moving shell to be ~ 36. The SSC emission is considered in the Thomson scattering regime (for details, see[25]). The Compton parameter is approximately constant and $Y \sim t_2^{-0.1}$, also shown in Figure 5.

2.2. GRB 180720B multiwavelength emission

GRB 180720B was located at a redshift $z = 0.653$[31] and its prompt gamma ray emission releases isotropic energy $\sim 6 \times 10^{53}$ erg.[10] In case of GRB 180720B, VHE

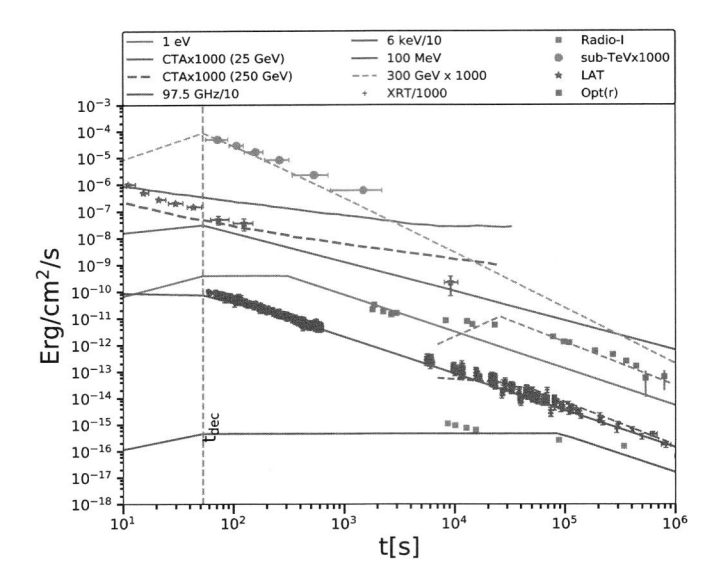

Fig. 2. Light Curves for GRB 190114C where the late time optical emission is explained via refreshed shock scenario. The data used here is extracted from[26] and Swift XRT database, https://www.swift.ac.uk/analysis/xrt/.

gamma-rays were detected by the H.E.S.S. telescopes after 10 hours.[32] Due to this late time detection we find that the emission of sub-TeV photons falls in the Klein Nishina (KN) regime, the medium is thin to pair production of VHE gamma rays, and we utilize the KN feedback effects on the cooling of electrons based on the formalism discussed by.[33] A comparison of Compton parameter is shown in Figure 5 for Thomson and KN cases. The afterglow model explains the data well as shown in Figures 3 and 4, where the SED and light curves are plotted for same set of input parameters. The model predicts higher levels of optical emission and we need to consider the absorption effects which lowers the optical flux by a factor of 0.5. The model parameters used in our work are shown in Table 1.

3. Summary and Conclusion

The VHE gamma-ray observations of two GRBs studied here are well explained using the synchrotron and SSC models. The late time optical afterglow for these two objects are in contrast to each other. In GRB 190114C the optical emission is harder and we required a refreshed shock to explain it, however for GRB 180720B the model produces higher level of optical flux by a factor of 0.5. Hence there is absorption of optical flux in the host Galaxy of GRB 180720B. The absorption of VHE photons for pair-production, in the blastwave, is negligible. The extra-galactic background light (EBL) absorption are considered for finding the maximum energy of the photons based on the model by.[34] These cut-off effects are important above

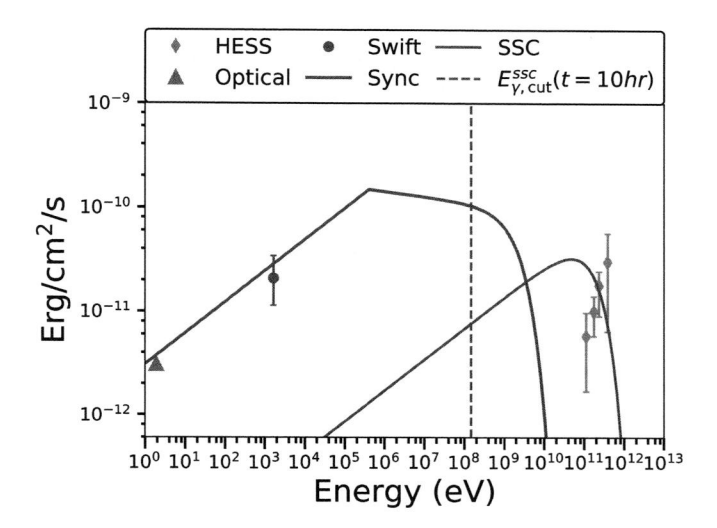

Fig. 3. SED for GRB 180720B using SSC model plotted against the HESS onservations[10] at duration 10 hr.

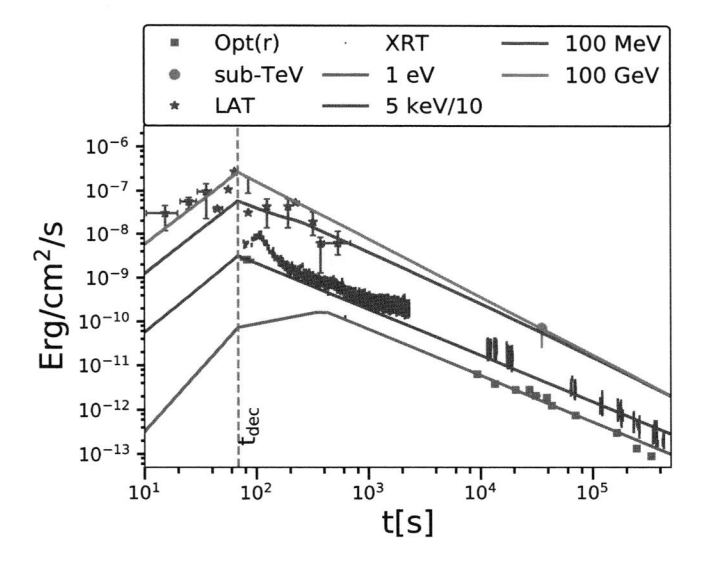

Fig. 4. Light Curves for GRB 180720B, the data used here is extracted from[10] and Swift XRT database, https://www.swift.ac.uk/analysis/xrt/.

200 GeV and 160 GeV for GRB 190114C and GRB 180720B respectively. The t^2 dependence for the blastwave flux before deceleration is used for both the ism and wind media since the flux dominates due to the area of the blastwave expansion. The bulk Lorentz factor Γ and $E_{k,\mathrm{iso}}$ and ϵ_e have approximately similar values for

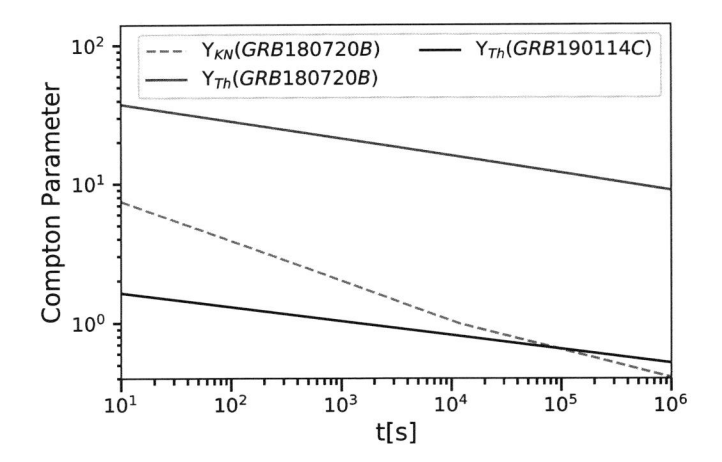

Fig. 5. Compton parameter Y estimated for two GRBs. We have modelled GRB 190114C using Thomson approximation, however for GRB 180720B we required SSC in KN regime.

both GRBs, however the fraction of energy in the magnetic field ϵ_B is very low in GRB 180720 B. This low value of ϵ_B is also reported in the SSC modelling of this source in other works.[35] Also for GRB 180720B we find the ISM medium is more suitable for modelling, which is consistent with the X-ray afterglow observations.[36]

References

1. S. E. Woosley and J. S. Bloom, The Supernova Gamma-Ray Burst Connection, *araa* **44**, 507 (September 2006).
2. D. Eichler, M. Livio, T. Piran and D. N. Schramm, Nucleosynthesis, neutrino bursts and γ-rays from coalescing neutron stars, *nature* **340**, 126 (July 1989).
3. R. Sari and T. Piran, Variability in Gamma-Ray Bursts: A Clue, *apj* **485**, 270 (August 1997).
4. S. Kobayashi, T. Piran and R. Sari, Can Internal Shocks Produce the Variability in Gamma-Ray Bursts?, *apj* **490**, p. 92 (November 1997).
5. F. Daigne and R. Mochkovitch, Gamma-ray bursts from internal shocks in a relativistic wind: temporal and spectral properties, *mnras* **296**, 275 (May 1998).
6. A. M. Beloborodov and P. Mészáros, Photospheric emission of gamma-ray bursts, *Space Science Reviews* **207**, 87 (Jul 2017).
7. MAGIC Collaboration, V. A. Acciari, S. Ansoldi *et al.*, Observation of inverse Compton emission from a long γ-ray burst, *nature* **575**, 459 (November 2019).
8. MAGIC Collaboration, V. A. Acciari, S. Ansoldi *et al.*, Teraelectronvolt emission from the γ-ray burst GRB 190114C, *nature* **575**, 455 (November 2019).
9. V. A. Acciari, S. Ansoldi, L. A. Antonelli *et al.*, MAGIC Observations of the Nearby Short Gamma-Ray Burst GRB 160821B, *apj* **908**, p. 90 (February 2021).
10. H. Abdalla, R. Adam, F. Aharonian *et al.*, A very-high-energy component deep in the γ-ray burst afterglow, *nature* **575**, 464 (November 2019).

11. H. E. S. S. Collaboration, H. Abdalla, F. Aharonian *et al.*, Revealing x-ray and gamma ray temporal and spectral similarities in the GRB 190829A afterglow, *Science* **372**, 1081 (June 2021).
12. B. Paczynski and J. E. Rhoads, Radio Transients from Gamma-Ray Bursters, *apjl* **418**, p. L5 (November 1993).
13. P. Meszaros, M. J. Rees and H. Papathanassiou, Spectral Properties of Blast-Wave Models of Gamma-Ray Burst Sources, *apj* **432**, p. 181 (September 1994).
14. P. Mészáros and M. J. Rees, Optical and Long-Wavelength Afterglow from Gamma-Ray Bursts, *apj* **476**, 232 (February 1997).
15. M. Vietri, The Soft X-Ray Afterglow of Gamma-Ray Bursts, A Stringent Test for the Fireball Model, *apjl* **478**, L9 (March 1997).
16. A. Panaitescu and P. Mészáros, Dynamical Evolution, Light Curves, and Spectra of Spherical and Collimated Gamma-Ray Burst Remnants, *apj* **526**, 707 (December 1999).
17. R. Sari, T. Piran and R. Narayan, Spectra and Light Curves of Gamma-Ray Burst Afterglows, *apjl* **497**, L17 (April 1998).
18. J. Chiang and C. D. Dermer, Synchrotron and Synchrotron Self-Compton Emission and the Blast-Wave Model of Gamma-Ray Bursts, *apj* **512**, 699 (February 1999).
19. R. A. Chevalier and Z.-Y. Li, Wind Interaction Models for Gamma-Ray Burst Afterglows: The Case for Two Types of Progenitors, *apj* **536**, 195 (Jun 2000).
20. B. Zhang and P. Mészáros, High-Energy Spectral Components in Gamma-Ray Burst Afterglows, *apj* **559**, 110 (September 2001).
21. R. Sari and A. A. Esin, On the Synchrotron Self-Compton Emission from Relativistic Shocks and Its Implications for Gamma-Ray Burst Afterglows, *apj* **548**, 787 (February 2001).
22. J. Granot and R. Sari, The Shape of Spectral Breaks in Gamma-Ray Burst Afterglows, *apj* **568**, 820 (April 2002).
23. M. Vietri, GeV Photons from Ultrahigh Energy Cosmic Rays Accelerated in Gamma Ray Bursts, *prl* **78**, 4328 (June 1997).
24. S. Razzaque, A Leptonic-Hadronic Model for the Afterglow of Gamma-ray Burst 090510, *apjl* **724**, L109 (November 2010).
25. J. C. Joshi and S. Razzaque, Modelling synchrotron and synchrotron self-Compton emission of gamma-ray burst afterglows from radio to very-high energies, *mnras* **505**, 1718 (August 2021).
26. MAGIC Collaboration, V. A. Acciari, S. Ansoldi *et al.*, Observation of inverse Compton emission from a long γ-ray burst, *nature* **575**, 459 (November 2019).
27. A. J. Castro-Tirado, Y. Hu, E. Fernandez-Garcia *et al.*, GRB 190114C: refined redshift by the 10.4m GTC., *GRB Coordinates Network* **23708**, p. 1 (January 2019).
28. MAGIC Collaboration, V. A. Acciari, S. Ansoldi *et al.*, Teraelectronvolt emission from the γ-ray burst GRB 190114C, *nature* **575**, 455 (November 2019).
29. R. Sari and P. Mészáros, Impulsive and Varying Injection in Gamma-Ray Burst Afterglows, *apjl* **535**, L33 (May 2000).
30. J. Granot, E. Nakar and T. Piran, Astrophysics: refreshed shocks from a γ-ray burst, *nature* **426**, 138 (November 2003).
31. P. M. Vreeswijk, D. A. Kann, K. E. Heintz *et al.*, GRB 180720B: VLT/X-shooter redshift., *GRB Coordinates Network* **22996**, p. 1 (January 2018).
32. H. Abdalla, R. Adam, F. Aharonian *et al.*, A very-high-energy component deep in the γ-ray burst afterglow, *nature* **575**, 464 (November 2019).
33. E. Nakar, S. Ando and R. Sari, Klein-Nishina Effects on Optically Thin Synchrotron and Synchrotron Self-Compton Spectrum, *apj* **703**, 675 (September 2009).

34. J. D. Finke, S. Razzaque and C. D. Dermer, Modeling the Extragalactic Background Light from Stars and Dust, *apj* **712**, 238 (March 2010).
35. X.-Y. Wang, R.-Y. Liu, H.-M. Zhang *et al.*, Synchrotron Self-Compton Emission from External Shocks as the Origin of the Sub-TeV Emission in GRB 180720B and GRB 190114C, *apj* **884**, p. 117 (October 2019).
36. N. Fraija, S. Dichiara, A. C. C. d. E. S. Pedreira *et al.*, Modeling the Observations of GRB 180720B: from Radio to Sub-TeV Gamma-Rays, *apj* **885**, p. 29 (November 2019).

The VERITAS gamma-ray burst follow-up program

D. Ribeiro* for the VERITAS Collaboration[†]

Physics Department, Columbia University,
New York, NY 10027, USA
*E-mail: dr2792@columbia.edu

Recent detections of gamma-ray bursts (GRBs) at energies above 100 GeV demonstrate that imaging atmospheric Cherenkov telescopes (IACTs) operating in the very-high-energy range (VHE; E > 100 GeV) can provide insights into the physics of GRBs. By searching for the highest-energy photons emitted by GRBs, these telescopes can help answer questions about the particle acceleration and emission processes that occur during both the prompt and afterglow phases of GRBs. VERITAS is a very-high-energy IACT array located at the Whipple Observatory in southern Arizona, which has maintained an active GRB observing program since mid-2006. In this presentation, we will share some of the recent achievements of the VERITAS GRB follow-up program. We will discuss the development of analysis methods tailored to transient signals, and how the upper limits on the VHE emission obtained from observations of prominent bursts by VERITAS allowed us to constrain radiation mechanisms in the afterglow (e.g., for GRB 130427A) and constrain properties of the environment in which the burst took place (e.g., for GRB 150323A). Compact binary mergers that trigger short GRBs may also result in gravitational wave emission, so we will review both our follow-up program from LIGO/Virgo triggers, and also the use of archival VERITAS data to search for short GRBs based on sub-threshold events for LIGO/Virgo. Lastly, based on the properties of the VHE-detected GRBs, we will discuss recent changes to our follow-up strategy to account for the *Swift*/XRT properties for optimal VERITAS observing sensitivity.

Keywords: Gamma-ray bursts, GRBs, gravitational waves

1. Introduction

Gamma-ray bursts (GRBs) are a class of astrophysical explosions that are some of the brightest events in the universe. Emitting total energies greater than 10^{53} erg/s, these events are detected in the optical, X-ray and high-energy (HE) to very-high-energy (VHE) gamma-rays. The physical mechanisms to explain the source of the high-energy emission range from synchrotron to synchrotron-self-Compton (SSC) processes based on the environment of the GRB emission regions. Particularly important are the highest energy photons in the VHE range that can constrain the properties of the GRB emission. Ground-based gamma-ray telescopes are well suited to these observations, and the recent detections of photons above 100 GeV by H.E.S.S. and MAGIC provide insights into the physics of GRBs[1–5]

In this paper, the VERITAS GRB follow-up program is discussed. Section 2, describes the VERITAS instrument and observation capabilities. In Section 3, the

---

[†]https://veritas.sao.arizona.edu

GRB observations by VERITAS are summarized. In Section 4, the techniques used to improve future observations and optimize data analyses are described. Section 5 describes how the VERITAS GRB follow-up program is enhanced by the new gravitational wave trigger with the start of operation of the LIGO/Virgo gravitational wave (GW) observatory.

2. VERITAS

The Very Energetic Radiation Imaging Telescope Array System (VERITAS) is a ground-based imaging atmospheric Cherenkov telescope (IACT) array located in southern Arizona, USA. VERITAS consists of four 12-m IACTs, each equipped with a 499 photo-multiplier tube (PMT) camera and 350 hexagonal mirror facets arranged in a Davies-Cotton optical design.[6] This system enables the detection of air showers formed in the atmosphere by the cascade of particles created from the interaction of the original gamma-ray photon and molecules in the atmosphere.

VERITAS is sensitive to gamma rays of energy 100 GeV to 30 TeV. The mechanical structure of each IACT is capable of a maximum slew speed of 1 degree per second. Each camera has a field of view of 3.5 degrees. VERITAS has a 68% containment radius less than 0.1 degree at 1 TeV.[7] The recorded data is analyzed by two independent pipelines (to enable cross-checking) to reliably select gamma-ray and cosmic-ray events from the camera images, determine energy, angular direction and arrival time of the original photon, and reconstruct a skymap of the observed region.[8,9]

In the scale of short timescale events such as GRBs and other astrophysical transients, the sensitivity is statistics dependent: by one widely required standard, the detection criterion is achieved when observing a minimum number of signal counts ($N_s = 10$), the signal above the background is at least five times the systematic uncertainty in the background estimation, assumed to be 1%, and the Li & Ma statistical significance is 5σ or more.[10] These requirements weaken the achievable flux sensitivity at very short observation times ≤ 100 seconds, particularly for higher energy photons under the assumed power law spectral model, compared to longer term observation campaigns of steady sources.[11] In Figure 1, the relative short timescale sensitivities are shown for *Fermi*-LAT, VERITAS, MAGIC, H.E.S.S. and the future CTA observatories. For a Crab Nebula-like point source detection, VERITAS is capable of a 5σ detection in about 2 minutes.

3. Summary of Observations

VERITAS has followed up on more than 200 GRBs since the beginning of its GRB follow-up program in 2006. The Gamma-ray Coordinates Network (GCN) provides real-time coordinates (via *Notices*) and follow-up reports (via *Circulars*). VERITAS is subscribed to this system and has integrated an automated tracking response for incoming GCN notices. Alerts are quickly parsed and reviewed by on-site observers,

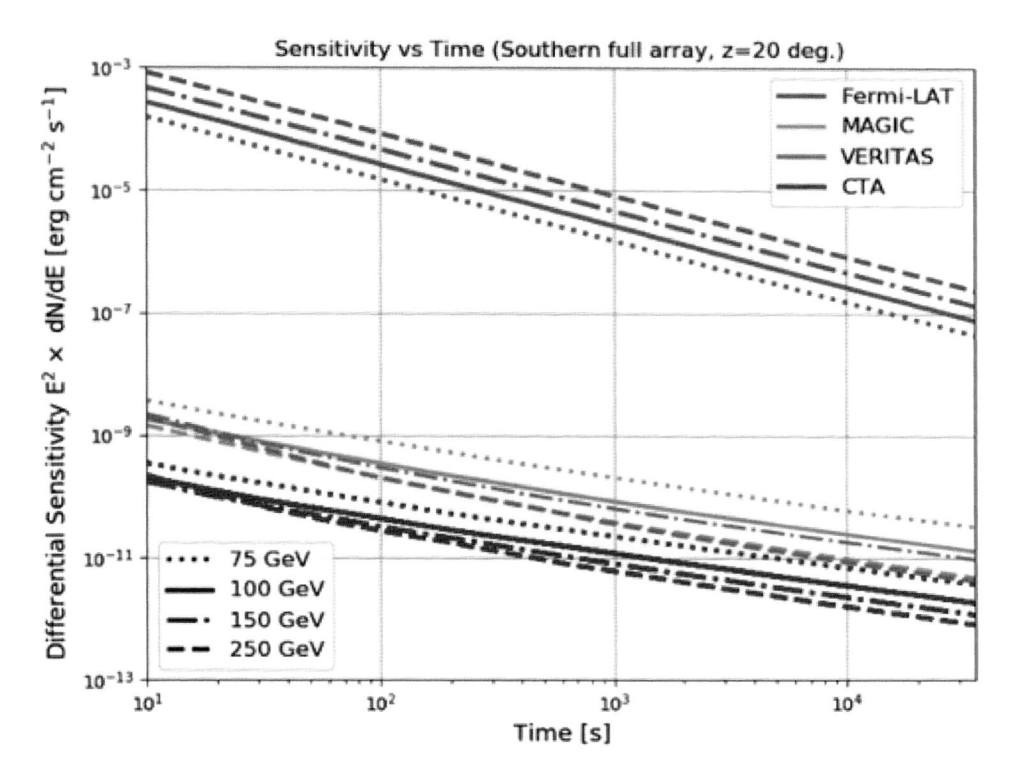

Fig. 1. The short timescale differential sensitivity of various gamma-ray observatories to Crab-like point sources (from[11]). The assumed spectral model is a power law with spectral index of -2.5. Four differential energy bins between 75 and 250 GeV are selected due to the relative overlap between the each observatory's operational energy ranges.

who assess visibility (i.e. checking for observable conditions such as pointing direction, slew time, and weather) and decide whether to follow up with a user-friendly pop-up GUI.

The distribution of the sources of GRB triggers observed is shown in Figure 2. *Swift* and *Fermi*-GBM dominate the alerts with their surveying-mode monitoring systems. Figure 3 shows the frequency of *Swift* (3a) and *Fermi*-LAT (3b) observed bursts since the beginning of the VERITAS GRB program. While *Swift* bursts are significantly more common, *Fermi*-LAT events are prioritized due to their high energy components and a few *Fermi*-LAT bursts are observed every season.

The standard protocol for observing is as follows: if the alert came from *Swift*-BAT, *Swift*-XRT or *Fermi*-LAT, observe up to trigger time plus 3 hours (for a maximum of 3 hours); if the alert came from *Fermi*-GBM only and the burst position is determined to $\leq 5°$, observe up to the trigger time plus 1 hour (for a maximum of 1 hour). This protocol prioritizes well-localized and high-probability candidate GRBs. In some extreme cases, exceptions have been made from this protocol, such as GRB 130427A discussed in section 3.1. Figure 4 shows the distribution of delay

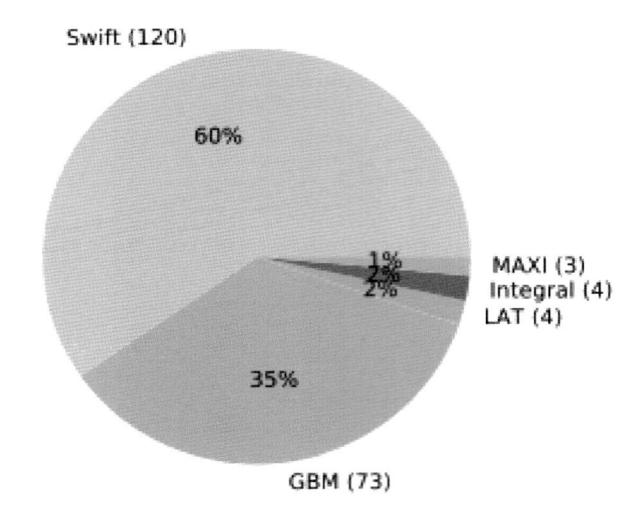

Fig. 2. Distribution of the source of trigger alerts for VERITAS followed-up GRBs.

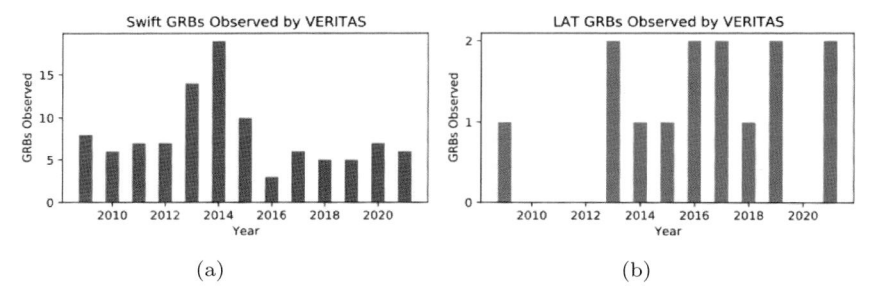

Fig. 3. Distribution of *Swift* (a) and *Fermi*-LAT (b) observed GRBs since 2009.

times: most have been observations beginning between 10^2 and 10^4 seconds after the burst detections, while a handful of exceptions were made for bright bursts with observations starting $\geq 2 \times 10^4$ seconds.

In the subsections below, three exceptional GRBs followed by VERITAS are discussed, GRB 130427A, GRB 150323A and GRB 190114C.

3.1. *GRB 130427A*

GRB 130427A was a *Fermi*-LAT-detected GRB that was bright enough for VERITAS to follow up almost 20 hours after the burst, yielding meaningful upper limits for the VHE acceleration mechanism.[12] Originally detected by *Fermi*-GBM and *Swift*-BAT, the burst was later associated with a Type Ic supernova (SN2013cq) at redshift of z=0.34.[13] The *Fermi*-LAT spectrum is consistent with a powerlaw spectral model with index of -2.2 up to 20 ks, while the later VERITAS upper

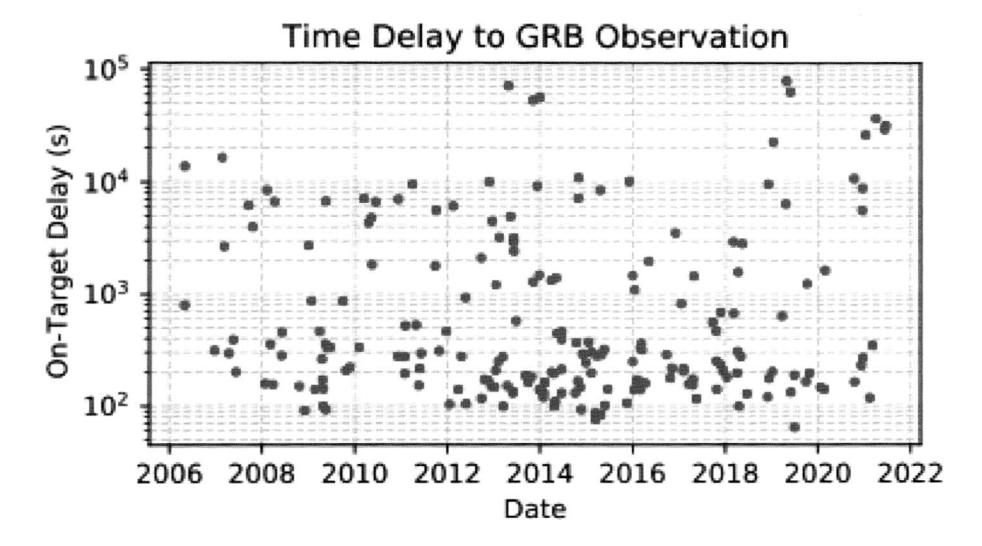

Fig. 4. Delay between the GRB trigger time and the beginning of observations by VERITAS. Most observations were followed up within 3 hours of the alert, while a few exceptionally-bright events were followed up by as much as 20 hours later. The fastest follow-up was ≈ 1 minute after the alert.

limit was calculated assuming a power law model with index -2 (see table 1). The *Fermi*-LAT light curve evolved with a temporal power-law with index of -1.4 ($dN/dt \propto t^{-1.35 \pm 0.08}$). GRB 130427A is one of the brightest bursts ever followed up by VERITAS.

Table 1. The VERITAS observation of GRB 130427A from (from[14]).

Day	N_{on}	N_{off}	α[a]	σ[b]	UL erg cm^{-2} s^{-1}
1	165	1164	0.125	1.3	9.4×10^{-12}
2	322	2120	0.143	1.1	6.6×10^{-12}
3	402	2820	0.147	-0.5	2.7×10^{-12}
Total	889	6104	0.141	0.9	3.3×10^{-12}

Note: [a] Relative ratio of exposures of On and Off observing regions.
[b] Li & Ma (1983) test statistic.[10]

Both synchrotron and SSC models proposed to explain high-energy and very-high-energy emission are constrained by the VERITAS VHE upper limit. In the synchrotron model, the VERITAS upper limit can constrain the magnetic field of an assumed interstellar medium (ISM), $B_{ISM} \leq 5\mu G \; E_{53}^{1/8} \varepsilon_{B,-4}^{1/2} n_0^{3/8} (t/t_V)^{-3/8}$ where the terms are explained in[14] (see[14,15]). In the SSC model, the VERITAS upper limit constrains the synchrotron emission of the electron population within the emission region, limiting the Klein-Nishina energy to $E_{\text{KN}} < 120$ GeV as determined by *Fermi*-LAT temporal data. However, for lower E_{KN}, the VERITAS upper limit does not constrain the SSC model, and combined with the single zone interpretation from the early afterglow data, the synchrotron model is preferred.

3.2. GRB 150323A

GRB 150423A was a *Swift*-BAT-detected GRB that was observed with the standard follow-up protocol within 270 seconds of the prompt emission peak and at a relatively low redshift of $z = 0.6$. Although not necessarily noteworthy by other observatories, this burst was selected because it had one of the highest observation flux weights compared to other bursts observed by VERITAS.[16]

The derived observational weight combines the extragalactic background light (EBL) absorption factor for each burst with the time delay between burst explosion T_0 and VERITAS observation start time. The EBL absorption is defined by the burst redshift and photon energy ($e^{-\tau(z,E)}$), where the energy is chosen to be the telescope energy threshold, which is a strong function of the telescope elevation angle. The weight can be interpreted as being proportional to the approximate flux of the burst at the time of the observation, where the burst is assumed to have a temporal dependence of $1/t$.

VERITAS began the observation about 2 min after the BAT emission peak. The observation significance is 0.36σ, and with the limited EBL attenuation (only 50% at 100-200 GeV), the upper limit is $< 1\%$ of the prompt fluence. The differential upper limit (99% C.L.) at 140 GeV is 3.7×10^{-10} TeV^{-1} cm^{-2} s^{-1}, while the integral upper limit from 140 GeV to 30 TeV is 1.6×10^{-11} cm^{-2} s^{-1}. The strong upper limit on VHE emission favors an explosion into the stellar wind of a dense progenitor (Wolf-Rayet star), or a weak blast wave in a tenuous ISM.[17]

3.3. GRB 190114c

VERITAS also followed up the first IACT-detected GRB 190114C, observed by the MAGIC telescope[a].[1,2,18] VERITAS received the alert during daytime (UT 20:57:04) and waited for the object to rise before beginning observations several hours later. Due to moonlight, the VERITAS cameras were operating with reduced high voltage, which decreases the sensitivity to low-energy gamma-ray events. The low elevation of the burst location ($\leq 32°$) during the observation further impacts the energy threshold. Additionally, clouds occluded the field of view leading to lost data through the observation. Due to these unique observation conditions, VERITAS is currently working toward a calibrated analysis pipeline custom to the challenges of this burst.

---

[a]https://www.astronomerstelegram.org/?read=12390

4. Optimizations

The observation of the prompt and afterglow emission of GRBs is a primary goal of the VERITAS follow-up program. However, due to the combination of observation conditions such as weather, moonlight, and pointing direction, with the variation of GRB flux and redshift, a significant GRB detection by VERITAS in the VHE range has remained elusive. In light of the probabilistic challenges associated with observing a bright, nearby GRB shortly after a trigger is announced, the following optimization strategies are employed: section 4.1 describes a strategy to monitor and follow-up certain bright *Swift*-XRT GRB candidates, and section 4.2 describes an offline analysis method to incorporate the time dependence of the GRB light curve into the calculation of the significance of excess photon counts.

4.1. Swift *Monitored Triggers*

Some GRBs have bright, extended afterglows in the X-ray band. These bursts may also be bright in the VHE band. Table 2 shows several VHE-detected GRBs and their inferred *Swift*-XRT X-ray flux at the time of detection (along with the corresponding delay between T_0 and the start of the observation). Using these H.E.S.S. and MAGIC detected afterglows, it is prudent to use the *Swift*-XRT inferred flux as a guide for following up on bursts that are more likely to be seen in the VHE band.

VERITAS might be missing some of the bright afterglows for GRBs that become observable at $T > T_0 + 3$ hrs, and therefore we have modified the standard GRB follow-up protocol to include the *Swift*-XRT flux (if available) to adjust the amount of time allocated for each burst. If a *Swift*-XRT flux is available, the spectrum is extrapolated to the VHE range and the light curve is extrapolated for the remainder of the observing window. GRBs with inferred fluxes $> 10^{-11}$ erg cm^{-2} s^{-1} in the X-ray band are observed for as long as they are still above that threshold. Bursts that might have been missed after passing the $T > T_0 + 3$ cutoff can now remain candidates if the X-ray band is still bright. The remaining alerts without a *Swift*-XRT counterpart follow the standard protocol. This selection threshold prioritizes bright events, increasing our probability of detecting VHE events.

4.2. *Time Dependence*

In the conventional analysis of sources observed by IACTs, background and signal regions are determined a priori so that an excess count can be calculated that characterizes the source count rate during an observation period. Following the criteria established, the statistical significance is calculated using Eq. 17 of Li & Ma.[10] However, in this formulation, both the source and background rates are assumed to be time independent. In the case of GRBs and other strongly time-dependent sources, the excess counts may be dominant in certain time bins within the observation and negligible in others, such that the excess counts summed over all time bins are not significant.

Table 2. VHE detected GRBs, as well as the bright GRB130427A, and their inferred XRT flux at the time of observation. The sustained XRT flux in these VHE detections suggests an X-ray threshold for guidance to trigger VHE follow-up observations.

GRB	Afterglow Detected	Follow-up Delay	Inferred XRT Flux after Delay [erg cm-2 s-1]
130427A	Detected (Fermi-LAT)	~20 Hrs (VERITAS)	4.1×10^{-11}
180720B	Detected (H.E.S.S)	~10 Hrs (H.E.S.S)	7.7×10^{-11}
190114C	Detected (MAGIC)	~6 Hrs (VERITAS)	6.5×10^{-11}
190829A	Detected (H.E.S.S)	~4.5 Hrs (H.E.S.S)	9.9×10^{-11}

To solve this problem, the time dependence of the source count rate is assumed in a parameterized form $s(t)$ and the test statistic is re-derived following the strategy outlined by Li & Ma (1983).[19] The maximum likelihood estimate is used to optimize the signal and background count rates, collected within the *On* and *Off* observation regions defined as $\langle N_{on} \rangle = (\bar{b} + \bar{s}(t))T_{on}$ and $\langle N_{off} \rangle = \bar{b}T_{off}$ for observation times T_{on} and T_{off}, respectively. Assuming a Poisson distribution of counts, the general form of the test statistic is a ratio of the likelihoods for the null and alternate hypotheses $\mathcal{L}_0$ and $\mathcal{L}$:

$$\frac{\mathcal{L}_0}{\mathcal{L}} = \frac{\bar{b}_0^{N_{on}+N_{off}}}{(\bar{b}+\bar{s})^{N_{on}} \bar{b}^{N_{off}}}, \qquad (1)$$

where $\bar{b}$ and $\bar{s}$ are the time average background and signal count rates, and $\bar{b}_0$ is the time averaged rate when all counts observed are background.

To apply the time dependence, the T_{on} observation time is split into N bins of Δt, where the probability of the number of counts for each bin is independent and $N\Delta t = T_{on}$. For a parameterized $s(t)$, at the limit of $N \to \infty$, $\Delta t \to 0$, the likelihood ratio reduces to:

$$\frac{\mathcal{L}_0}{\mathcal{L}} = \frac{b_0^{N_{on}+N_{off}}}{\left(\Pi_{t_i \in \{t_{on}\}}(b+s(t_i))\right) b^{N_{off}}} \qquad (2)$$

where $s(t) \equiv \theta \times t^{-1}$. The time dependence of the signal was assumed to be $1/t$ since it is most similar to many GRBs light curves,[20] where θ is a normalization constant for the time-dependent count rate.

This modified likelihood ratio was validated with a Monte Carlo simulation. Using a toy-model MC of a GRB, with 5×10^5 observations starting 2 min after burst trigger, the time-dependent signal $s(t) = \theta \times t^{-1}$, and the typical IACT background rate (1 γ /min), the following simulation results provided evidence for some additional conclusions (see also Figure 2 of[19]). For a 35-min observation, the mean significance over all the simulated observations increased from 4σ to 5σ once time dependence is included, a 25% increase in sensitivity. For a 100-min observation: the simulated observations reveal that the overall significance improves from 3.4σ to 5.2σ with time weighting for that observation time. Comparing 35-min and 100-min simulations, the time-independent method has a reduced sensitivity from 4σ to 3.4σ as expected with the increase in background counts, while the time-dependent model increases from 5σ to 5.2σ, indicating that the time dependence allows for an improved estimate of the background and signal rates for longer observation times.

The simulation showed that the significance is dependent on the length of the observation. The standard significance[10] peaks and then declines over time as the background rate accumulates counts toward the *On* region and dilutes the signal counts. However, the time-dependent likelihood ratio grows monotonically if events are weighted to account for the GRB's time dependence, up to as much as 10-25% increase from the time-independent significance (see Fig. 3 of.[19]) Some common analysis software packages within the gamma-ray astrophysics field (e.g. CTOOLs) include a temporal model in the maximum likelihood fitting in addition to the spatial and spectral models.[21]

5. Gravitational Wave Follow-Up

Compact binary coalescences (CBCs) may trigger short GRBs (sGRBs). The detection of the binary neutron star (BNS) merger GW170817 was associated with GRB 170817A, a sGRB observed by *Fermi*-GBM triggered by a kilonova.[22,23] The multi-messenger detection of this event encourages a VHE follow-up program for future GW BNS trigger candidates. Both real-time VHE follow-ups (5.1) and archival searches by VERITAS are discussed (5.2).

5.1. *Real Time VHE Follow-Up*

The LIGO BNS sensitivity indicates a horizon between 111 Mpc and 134 Mpc from the third observation run (O3) for LIGO Livingston Observatory (LLO) and LIGO Hanford Observatory (LHO), respectively.[24,25] At this distance range, VHE photons are relatively unaffected by the extragalactic background light, which could generate a favorable selection of candidate GRB triggers for VERITAS follow-up. The joint detection of both GWs and VHE emission from GRBs may be possible through the real time follow-up of GW triggers by VERITAS.

The VERITAS follow-up strategy during O3 involved calculating the visibility of the GW localization region to select an observable portion. The visibility is the amount of time available for each sky coordinate for the next 24 hours. If the moon is above the horizon, the angular distance is limited to the range between $60°$ and $120°$ while the moon illumination is low enough. Using a Greedy Traveling Salesman heuristic, the pointings that tile the observable portion are defined and sorted such that the probability covered is maximized and the slewing time is minimized. The exposure per pointing is currently set at 5 min, for a maximum of three hours total.

Pointings were limited to those visible at $> 50°$ elevation from VERITAS during the night.

The validation and summary of the VERITAS GW follow-up strategy was presented in.[26] The VERITAS follow-up of GW170104 and later observations were validated with a dedicated observation of the Crab Nebula under the same conditions described above, with six 5-min pointings tiled around the Crab Nebula position (Figure 2 in[26]). Table 1 in[26] lists a selection of O3 triggers followed up by VERITAS, including the BNS event GW190425.[27]

5.2. Archival Search

In addition to real-time GW follow-ups, VERITAS also developed an archival search for VHE gamma-ray emission in coincident observations of sub-threshold LIGO/VIRGO GW candidates.[28] In this search, there were 7 sub-threshold candidates found in serendipitous coincidence with VERITAS archival observations (11 pointings, ≤ 10 hr). The candidates were selected from a published collection of sub-threshold triggers from O1.[29]

An important consideration for other observatories while evaluating this algorithm is that there was no extra cost to the IACT or a dedicated observation campaign. Although VERITAS has a small field of view (FoV) (3.5° diameter), this is large enough for coincident observations. However, the sensitivity decreases for greater distance away from the camera center. Cross-checking the list of published sub-threshold triggers for coincident VERITAS observations was completed offline. In the search, observations were considered coincident if they passed good weather selection criteria, were contained within the 90% probability region of the original LIGO/Virgo candidate map, and overlapped with the time window $-10 \leq t_0 \leq 10^4$ seconds of the coalescence time t_0.

The archival search of VERITAS observations yielded upper limits across the field of view for each observation run. For each observation, the flux upper limit was calculated at each pixel of that observation and the geometric mean was reported to characterize the observed field for comparison with the LIGO sub-threshold candidate probability region. Each of the candidate observation upper limits was then compared to a fluence model based on sGRB 090510, for a 75 Mpc distance over the [0.24 TeV, 30 TeV] energy band. This distance was chosen to match the LIGO sensitivity range for O1, while the energy range was chosen to match the VERITAS energy range.

The comparison of the GRB model to the VERITAS observations shows an estimated sensitivity to $\approx 10^{-3}$ times the fluence of the GRB. The probability that at least one truly astrophysical merger was observed by VERITAS within the observation was estimated to be 0.04%. These results indicate that archival searches of coincident VHE observations with GW candidates may constrain the fluence of the progenitor burst and provide meaningful upper limits to the broadband spectral and light curve models that characterize these events. The weak constraints shown here indicate that stronger conclusions may be possible provided that there are enough coincident observations with sub-threshold GW candidates or more opportune events.

6. Summary and Outlook

In summary, VERITAS has an active and exciting GRB follow-up program. Since 2006, over 200 bursts have been followed-up. While no detections were made in the VHE range, meaningful upper limits were derived for a small selection of bursts. Both GRB 130427A and 150323A yielded constraints on the environment of the bursts and VHE production mechanism.

Optimizations were made to improve the likelihood of new detections. The addition of a *Swift*-XRT-guided observation strategy to optimize for bright bursts increased the amount of time dedicated to X-ray bright candidate bursts, increasing the likelihood of VHE detection. A time-dependent significance calculation improved the sensitivity to weak bursts, weighing the most likely time bins more heavily in the calculation.

The gravitational wave prompt follow-up program provides another source of triggers for sGRBs, increasing the number of GRB targets and the likelihood of detection. The GW sub-threshold archival search is a promising new method for seeking signals in archival data and setting constraints on the fluence of potential sGRB counterparts.

Acknowledgments

This research is supported by grants from the U.S. Department of Energy Office of Science, the U.S. National Science Foundation and the Smithsonian Institution, by NSERC in Canada, and by the Helmholtz Association in Germany. This research used resources provided by the Open Science Grid, which is supported by the National Science Foundation and the U.S. Department of Energy's Office of Science, and resources of the National Energy Research Scientific Computing Center (NERSC), a U.S. Department of Energy Office of Science User Facility operated under Contract No. DE-AC02-05CH11231. DR is supported by NSF award 2013109. We acknowledge the excellent work of the technical support staff at the Fred Lawrence Whipple Observatory and at the collaborating institutions in the construction and operation of the instrument.

References

1. Acciari, V.A. et al, Teraelectronvolt Emission from the Gamma-Ray Burst GRB 190114c, *Nature* **575**, 455 (November 2019).
2. Derishev, E. and Piran, T., GRB afterglow parameters in the era of TeV observations: The case of GRB 190114C (June 2021).

3. Wang, X.Y., Liu, R.Y., Zhang, H.M., Xi, S.Q. and Zhang, B., Synchrotron Self-Compton Emission from External Shocks as the Origin of the Sub-TeV Emission in GRB 180720B and GRB 190114C, *The Astrophysical Journal* **884**, p. 117 (October 2019).
4. Abdalla, H. et al, A Very-High-Energy Component Deep in the Gamma-Ray Burst Afterglow, *Nature* **575**, 464 (November 2019).
5. H.E.S.S. Collaboration et al, Revealing X-Ray and Gamma Ray Temporal and Spectral Similarities in the GRB 190829a Afterglow, *Science* **372**, 1081 (June 2021).
6. Holder, J. et al, The First VERITAS Telescope, *Astroparticle Physics* **25**, 391 (July 2006).
7. Park, N., Performance of the VERITAS experiment, *Proceedings of Science* **30-July-20** (August 2015).
8. Christiansen, J., Characterization of a Maximum Likelihood Gamma-Ray Reconstruction Algorithm for VERITAS, in *Proceedings of Science*, (Sissa Medialab, Trieste, Italy, August 2017).
9. Maier, G. and Holder, J., Eventdisplay: An Analysis and Reconstruction Package for Ground-based Gamma-ray Astronomy, in *Proceedings of Science*, (Sissa Medialab Srl, August 2017).
10. Li, T.P. and Ma, Y.Q., Analysis methods for results in gamma-ray astronomy, *The Astrophysical Journal* **272**, p. 317 (September 1983).
11. Fioretti, V. et al, The Cherenkov Telescope Array Sensitivity to the Transient Sky, in *Proceedings of Science*, (Sissa Medialab, Trieste, Italy, July 2019).
12. Tam, P.H.T., Tang, Q.W., Hou, S.J., Liu, R.Y. and Wang, X.Y., Discovery of an Extra Hard Spectral Component in the High-Energy Afterglow Emission of Grb 130427a, *Astrophysical Journal Letters* **771**, p. L13 (July 2013).
13. Xu, D. et al, Discovery of the Broad-Lined Type Ic Sn 2013cq Associated with the Very Energetic Grb 130427a, *The Astrophysical Journal* **776**, p. 98 (October 2013).
14. Aliu, E. et al, Constraints on very high energy emission from GRB130427A, *Astrophysical Journal Letters* **795**, p. L3 (October 2014).
15. Kouveliotou, C. et al, Nustar Observations of GRB 130427a Establish a Single Component Synchrotron Afterglow Origin for the Late Optical to Multi-Gev Emission, *The Astrophysical Journal* **779**, p. L1 (November 2013).
16. Weiner, O.M., A New Time-Dependent Likelihood Technique for Detection of Gamma-Ray Bursts with IACT Arrays, *Proceedings of Science* **30-July-20** (September 2015).
17. Abeysekara, A.U. et al, A Strong Limit on the Very-high-energy Emission from GRB 150323A, *The Astrophysical Journal* **857**, p. 33 (April 2018).
18. Acciari, V.A. et al, Observation of Inverse Compton Emission from a Long Gamma-Ray Burst, *Nature* **575**, 459 (November 2019).
19. Weiner, O.M., Humensky, T.B., Mukherjee, R. and Santander, M., Estimating significance in observations of variable and transient gamma-ray sources, *Astroparticle Physics* **93**, 1 (July 2017).
20. Ackermann, M. et al, The First *fermi*-Lat Gamma-Ray Burst Catalog, *The Astrophysical Journal Supplement Series* **209**, p. 11 (October 2013).
21. Knödlseder, J. et al, Ctools: Cherenkov Telescope Science Analysis Software (2016).
22. Abbott, B.P. et al, Gravitational Waves and Gamma-Rays from a Binary Neutron Star Merger: GW170817 and GRB 170817A, *The Astrophysical Journal* **848**, p. L13 (October 2017).
23. Abbott, B.P. et al, Multi-messenger Observations of a Binary Neutron Star Merger, *The Astrophysical Journal* **848**, p. L12 (October 2017).

24. Abbott, R. et al, Population Properties of Compact Objects from the Second LIGO–Virgo Gravitational-Wave Transient Catalog, *The Astrophysical Journal Letters* **913**, p. L7 (May 2021).
25. Buikema, A. et al, Sensitivity and performance of the Advanced LIGO detectors in the third observing run, *Physical Review D* **102**, p. 062003 (September 2020).
26. Santander, M., Recent results from the VERITAS multimessenger program, in *36th International Cosmic Ray Conference (ICRC2019)*, September 2019.
27. Abbott, B.P. et al, GW190425: Observation of a Compact Binary Coalescence with Total Mass $\sim 3.4\ M_\odot$, *The Astrophysical Journal* **892**, p. L3 (March 2020).
28. Adams, C.B. et al, An Archival Search for Neutron-star Mergers in Gravitational Waves and Very-high-energy Gamma Rays, *The Astrophysical Journal* **918**, p. 66 (September 2021).
29. Magee, R. et al, Sub-threshold Binary Neutron Star Search in Advanced LIGO's First Observing Run, *The Astrophysical Journal* **878**, p. L17 (June 2019).

MAGIC view of Gamma-Ray Bursts at very high energies

A. Berti* on behalf of the MAGIC collaboration

Max-Planck-Institut für Physik,
Munich, 80805, Germany
*E-mail: aberti@mpp.mpg.de

The detection of gamma-ray bursts (GRBs) is one of the main scientific targets pursued by the MAGIC collaboration since almost 20 years. The MAGIC telescopes were specifically designed for this purpose: the main figures of merit are the fast slewing speed (7deg/s), the low energy threshold (50 GeV at zenith) and the high sensitivity in the low energy regime. These features make MAGIC one of the most suitable instrument for the follow-up and detection of GRBs. After more than 15 years of dedicated searches, finally the first detection at teraelectronvolt energies of a GRB, namely GRB 190114C, was achieved by the MAGIC collaboration, revealing a new emission component in the afterglow phase. This discovery opened up a new era in field of GRB studies, which is now witnessing other detections, as demonstrated with the case of GRB 201216C. Furthermore, a hint of detection by MAGIC from the short and nearby GRB 160821B gives precious hints on the possible very high energy emission from this class of bursts, also in relation to searches of gravitation wave counterparts. Therefore, MAGIC is giving a crucial contribution to GRB physics, leading to a better understanding of the mechanisms underlying these peculiar objects. In this contribution I will introduce the MAGIC follow-up program, focusing on the aspects which led to the successful detection of GRBs and highlighting some key results. Finally, I will present the future challenges in these observations, discussing how MAGIC can contribute even more to the field.

Keywords: Gamma-ray bursts; MAGIC; very-high-energy

1. Introduction

The search for very high energy (VHE, $E \gtrsim 100\,\mathrm{GeV}$) emission from gamma-ray bursts (GRBs) is one of the key projects of the imaging atmospheric Cherenkov telescopes (IACTs) currently in operation:

- MAGIC (*Major Atmospheric Gamma-ray Imaging Cherenkov*), located in the Canary island of La Palma, Spain;
- H.E.S.S. (*High Energy Stereoscopic System*), operative in Namibia;
- VERITAS (*Very Energetic Radiation Imaging Telescope Array System*), located in Arizona.

In these proceedings we focus on MAGIC, a system of two Cherenkov telescopes located at about 2200 meters above sea level in the Observatorio del Roque de Los Muchachos (ORM) in La Palma, Canary Islands, Spain. MAGIC started operations in late 2003 as a single telescope (MAGIC-I) and in 2009 a second one (MAGIC-II) was added to perform stereoscopic observations. In 2012 the camera of MAGIC-I was upgraded in order to be a copy of the one installed in MAGIC-II. Both telescopes have a reflector of 17 meter diameter, corresponding to a reflective surface of $\sim 236\,\mathrm{m}^2$. This allows MAGIC to reach an energy threshold as low as 50 GeV at trigger level when pointing close to zenith. This is an important figure of merit for the observation of GRBs, since they are sources typically located at high redshift and the VHE gamma rays are heavily absorbed due to the interaction with the low energy photons of the extragalactic background light (EBL). Other features making MAGIC a suitable IACT to perform GRB observations are the following (see e.g. ref. 1):

- the high sensitivity even at the lowest energies. MAGIC has a sensitivity of 0.7% of the Crab Nebula flux above 220 GeV in 50 h of observation;
- the large effective area, of the order of $10^5\,\mathrm{m}^2$ which allows to collect many gamma rays to perform detailed temporal and spectral studies;
- the high duty cycle, which is the result of the possibility to observe even during moon time or when pointing to high zenith angles;
- the relatively low weight thanks to the carbon fiber structure, $\sim 70\,\mathrm{t}$ per telescope, allowing fast rotation at $\sim 7\,°\,\mathrm{s}^{-1}$ in the so-called "fast mode";
- the automatized reaction to GRB (and other transients) alerts, reducing the possible delay introduced by a human in the loop.

Indeed, MAGIC was designed with the detection of GRBs in the VHE range as one of its primary scientific goals, therefore many hardware and software developments aimed at improving the performance of the telescopes at the lowest energies. An important step in this direction was the development of the novel Sum-Trigger system, which was used in the past to detect pulsed emission from the Crab pulsar[2] down to 25 GeV and more recently adopted to detect the Geminga pulsar in the 15-75 GeV energy range.[3]

In these proceedings we will describe the GRB follow-up program within MAGIC and the results that could be achieved in the recent years. Finally we will discuss future prospects of GRB observations with MAGIC, highlighting the scientific and technical challenges lying ahead.

2. The MAGIC GRB follow-up program

Even before the beginning of current generation IACTs operation and the launch of the *Fermi* satellite, many theoretical studies predicted that GRBs should have been emitters of high energy and very high energy gamma rays. Such studies considered different mechanisms involving both leptonic and hadronic processes. While high energy emission was detected both in the prompt and afterglow phases of GRBs with *Fermi*-LAT, IACTs could not achieve significant detection in the VHE range for many years despite a considerable amount of hours devoted to GRB observations. The search for VHE emission from GRBs is crucial to answer some important questions, such as the following (not an exhaustive list):

- do GRBs emit at VHE?
- is VHE emission relevant e.g. from the energetic point of view?

- what is the emission process (or processes)? is it a continuation of the low energy spectrum or is it a new emission process?
- can the process producing VHE gamma rays contribute also at lower energies?
- is there VHE emission both in the prompt and the afterglow phases?
- is VHE emission present in both short and long GRBs?

In order to achieve the detection of GRBs, a specific program focuses on their follow-up, including both technical and strategy aspects.

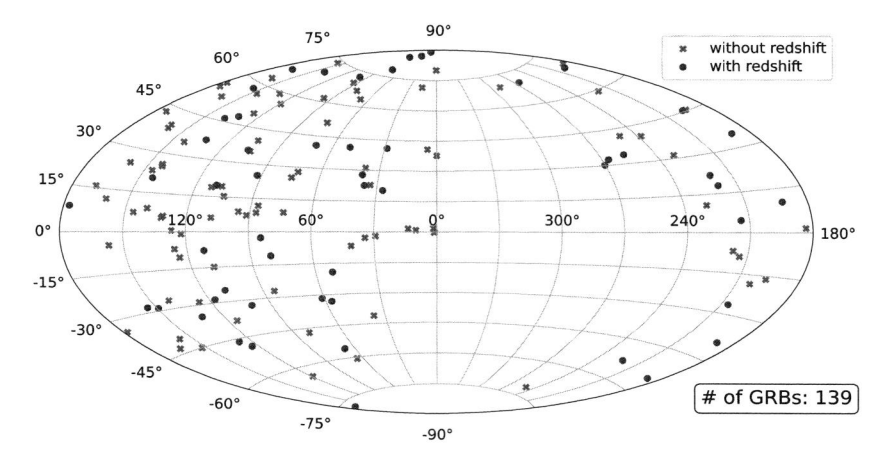

Fig. 1. Aitoff projection skymap showing the sky locations of the GRBs observed by MAGIC up to June 2021. GRBs with redshift estimation are denoted with blue filled circles, while those without redshift with red crosses.

From the technical point of view, given the small field of view of the telescopes (3.5°) and the serendipity of GRBs in both time and sky region, MAGIC relies on external alerts from other instruments. In particular, an automatic alert system (AAS) is in place since 2003 and it is used to receive GRB and other transients (high energy astrophysical neutrinos, gravitational waves, flaring *Fermi* sources, soft gamma-ray repeaters etc.) alerts, mainly from the GCN (*gamma-ray coordinates network*). After receiving a GRB alert, the AAS validates it and checks for the visibility from the MAGIC site according to some predefined criteria. If the GRB sky coordinates are immediately observable, the ongoing observation is stopped and an automatic procedure prepares the telescopes for the GRB observation. In more detail, the telescopes slew towards the GRB position in the so-called "fast mode". During the movement, other subsystems are prepared for data taking e.g. the DAQ is restarted, proper discriminator thresholds are loaded depending on the GRB position with respect to the galactic plane and to the night sky background and mirrors are focused according to the local zenith/azimuth of the GRB. This automatic procedure was upgraded in 2013 to make it more reliable and reduce failures to a minimum. In particular, in the upgraded automatic procedure the DAQ system is not stopped but just reconfigured, and the observation is started in wobble mode, the standard pointing for MAGIC data taking.

During the years, the AAS was updated by adding new alert types and by changing the implemented follow-up strategy. For example, the AAS allows to observe GRBs even at late time with respect to the trigger time, given that *Fermi*-LAT could detect high energy emission several hours in the afterglow phase of some GRBs. A major update in the AAS was deployed in early 2021, namely the standardization to the VOEvent format.[4] Currently the AAS receives alerts from the GCN broker, but other brokers can be easily added depending on the science cases (e.g. supernovae, tidal disruption events etc.). All in all, the AAS is becoming more and more a multimessenger system, with features being added related to different follow-up strategies.

Within the GRB follow-up program, MAGIC observed 139 GRBs from 2004 up to June 2021. A skymap showing the sky positions of the observed GRBs is shown in Figure 1. Of the 139 GRBs, 53 of them have a reported redshift, of which 13 have a redshift less than 1. Most of the GRBs observed by MAGIC are long GRBs and triggered by Swift-BAT, with a minority of alerts followed-up after alerts from Fermi-GBM, Fermi-LAT and INTEGRAL (or HETE in the first years of MAGIC operation).

As far as the delay of the observation is concerned, Figure 2 shows the time delay (computed as the difference between the beginning of the observation and the trigger time of the burst) against the zenith angle at the beginning of the observation. 37 GRBs have a delay less than 100 s, 25 were followed-up within one minute from the onset. 12 GRBs were observed with a delay less than T_{90}, so that the prompt or early afterglow phases could be observed. The fastest follow-up to date was performed in the case of GRB 160821B, where the telescopes started data taking 24 s after the burst onset. Interestingly, all the GRBs detected by MAGIC or with a hint of signal were observed with a delay smaller than 100 s.

3. MAGIC results on GRB observations

3.1. *Status at MG15 meeting*

In 2018 a similar topic was presented at the 15th edition of the Marcel Grossmann meeting. At the time, MAGIC and other IACTs did not detect any GRB in the VHE range, even if a large effort was put to organize efficient GRB follow-up programs. Some interesting observations were reported by the three collaborations, namely GRB 060602B occurring in the field of view for H.E.S.S., GRB 130427A (also known as the "monster burst") by VERITAS and the short GRB 160821B by MAGIC. However no significant detection could be achieved.

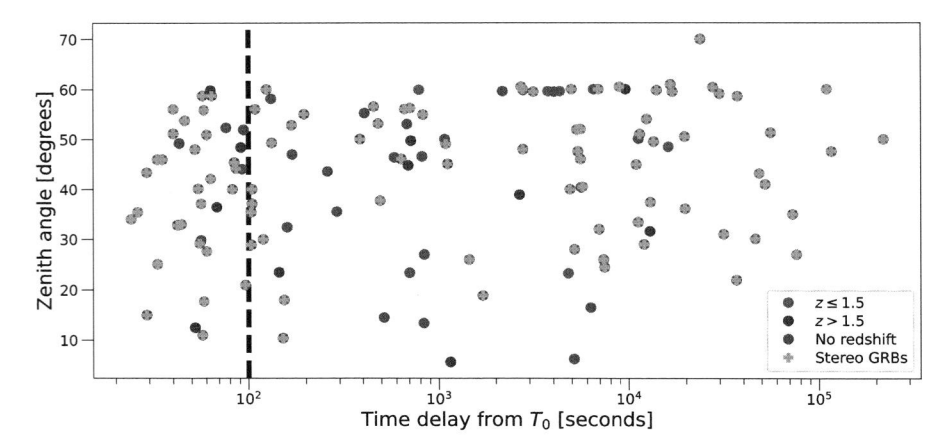

Fig. 2. Plot showing the delay of the start of the observation for GRBs observed by MAGIC up to June 2021. On the vertical axis, the zenith angle at the beginning of the observation is shown. Points with crosses denote GRBs observed in stereoscopic mode, those without were observed in mono mode.

The situation dramatically changed in 2019, which can be considered a golden year for GRB studies. Indeed, in January 2019 the MAGIC collaboration reported the historical detection of the long bright GRB 190114C in the VHE range, followed by the announcement by H.E.S.S. in May 2019 at the Cherenkov Telescope Array (CTA) Symposium in Bologna about the detection of GRB 180720B. Later in the year, at the end of August, the H.E.S.S. collaboration reported the detection of the long and very close GRB 190829A. In 2020 MAGIC reported a strong hint of signal from GRB 201015A and a detection from GRB 201216C. Therefore, the last years saw the long awaited birth of the VHE era for GRBs, finally allowing to explore the physics of these objects at such energies.

In the following section we describe the latest results by MAGIC on the search for VHE emission by MAGIC, focusing on the breakthrough detection of GRB 190114C and on the other detection of 2020.

3.2. *Recent MAGIC GRB results at MG16*

3.2.1. *GRB 190114C*

As mentioned in section 3.1, 2019 was the year starting a new era in GRB studies, which can be called the VHE era. On January 14th 2019 MAGIC detected a very significant (at the 50σ level) emission between 300 GeV and 1 TeV from the long and bright GRB 190114C,[5] initially detected by *Swift*-BAT and *Fermi*-GBM. The results on this GRB were presented in two papers, Refs. 6 and 7, one describing the MAGIC observation and detection, the second focusing on the multi-wavelength picture and on the physical interpretation of the VHE emission. In these proceedings we will focus on the main findings from GRB 190114C observations, for more details the reader can refer to the aforementioned publications or to the contribution by D. Miceli from these proceedings series.

GRB 190114C was a bright ($E_{iso} \sim 3 \times 10^{53}$ erg in the 1 to 10^4 keV energy range), long ($T_{90} = 362$ s as measured by *Swift*-BAT) and quite nearby ($z = 0.4245$) GRB. As shown in Figure 3, MAGIC received the alert from *Swift*-BAT 22 seconds after the onset of the GRB and started observations about 1 minute after the GRB trigger under moderate moon conditions at a relatively high zenith of 58°. From the real-time analysis the GRB was detected with a significance of 20σ in the first 20 minutes of observations above an approximate threshold of 300 GeV, later confirmed as 50σ in offline analyses, see Figure 4. The detection was reported as quickly as possible to the astrophysical community to strongly encourage the follow-up of this event at other wavelengths.

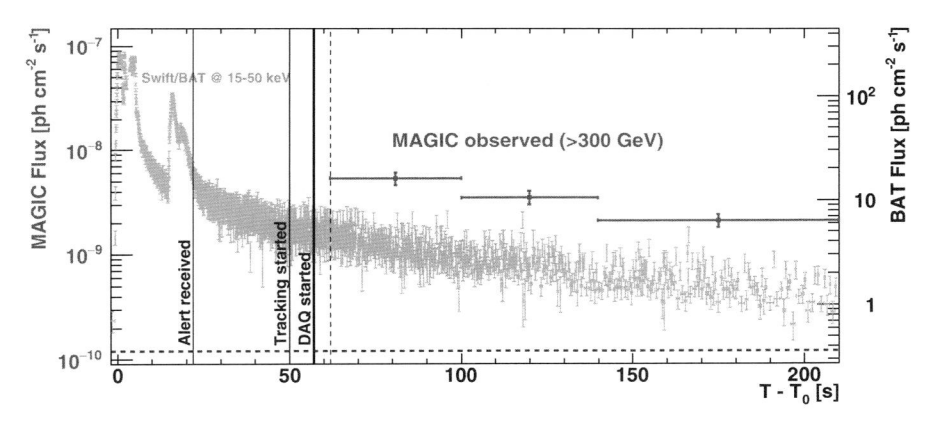

Fig. 3. Light curves for MAGIC and Swift-BAT. Vertical solid lines show the times of events related to the MAGIC automatic procedure. Extracted from Ref. 6.

One of the first questions to be answered was if the emission detected by MAGIC was related to the prompt or afterglow phase of the GRB. While the value of T_{90} may indicate that such emission could belong to the prompt, detailed spectral and temporal studies of the keV-MeV data show that at $\sim T_0 + 25$ s the properties of such low energy emission is typical of the afterglow phase. This is additionally confirmed by the similar temporal decay index between the X-ray (from *Swift*-XRT between 0.1 and 1 keV) and the VHE (between 300 GeV and 1 TeV) energy light curves.

The intrinsic spectrum of the GRB is compatible with a power law with spectral index of $\alpha_{int} = -2$ between 0.2 and 1 TeV, with no indication of any break or cutoff beyond those energies at the 95% confidence level. Such flat spectrum indicated that the energy output in the VHE range is relevant, indeed turning out to be

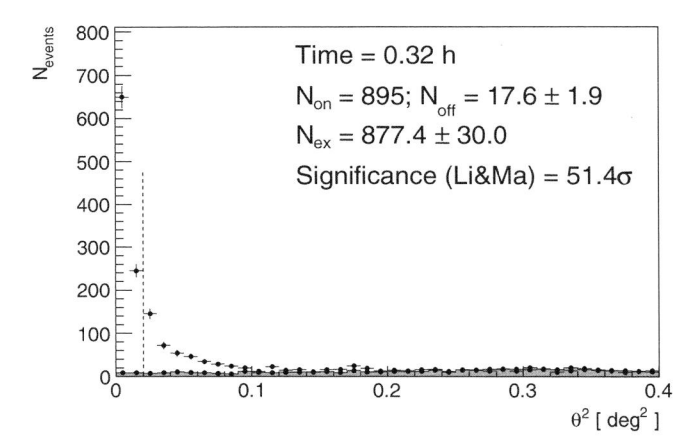

Fig. 4. Plot showing the significance of the gamma-ray signal detected by MAGIC from GRB 190114C. Extracted from Ref. 6.

comparable to the one at low energies. Given the high absorption of the VHE flux by the EBL at the redshift of the GRB, the spectrum observed by MAGIC is rather steep and best described by a power law with index $\alpha_{obs} = -5.43 \pm 0.22$. This was tested against different EBL models, resulting in similar spectral indexes compatible within the statistical uncertainties.

The most important question was related to the origin of the emission detected by MAGIC. The similarity of the temporal decay in X-ray and VHE energy light curves suggests that the emission processes should be linked. While the simplest hypothesis is that the processes producing the X-ray and VHE photons are the same, namely synchrotron emission from relativistic electrons accelerated at the external shock in the afterglow of the GRB, this explanation is ruled out if one takes into account that synchrotron photons reach a maximum energy. This is the so-called burnoff limit and in the external shock of GRBs can be described by the equation $E_{\text{syn,max}}(t) \approx 100(\Gamma_b(t)/1000)\,\text{GeV}$ ($\Gamma_b(t)$ is the Lorentz factor of the GRB blastwave as a function of time). Even assuming a Lorentz factor of ~ 1000, which is not typical for GRBs and in any case it decreases with time, the maximum energy of the photons produced by synchrotron is at most around $100\,\text{GeV}$, even considering different density profiles of the interstellar medium density. This value is much lower than the lowest energy of the photons detected by MAGIC, therefore it is reasonable to assume that the VHE emission is due to another process. In addition, prolonging the low energy synchrotron spectrum (from GBM, XRT and LAT data) would underestimate the MAGIC flux by one order of magnitude, strengthening the conclusion that the VHE photons are indeed produced by a different mechanism. However we note that the burnoff limit interpretation assumes one emission region, while having more emission regions may allow synchrotron photons to reach higher energies.

In the assumption that the VHE emission is not due to synchrotron, the most simple alternative is the so called synchrotron-self Compton (SSC), where the synchrotron photons are upscattered by their parents electrons, thus increasing their energy. The SSC process is not new in VHE astrophysics, indeed it is commonly detected in sources like active galactic nuclei, where the spectral energy distribution shows two peaks, one at low energies due to synchrotron emission and a second one at higher energies, often at in the VHE energy range, due to the SSC process. In GRB 190114C the modeling of the GRB 190114C multi-wavelength data with a synchrotron plus SSC emission model within the external shock scenario in the afterglow shows exactly this two peaks features, therefore confirming the presence of a new emission component never observed before. Another remarkable result is the fact that the parameters describing the broadband emission of GRB 190114C have values similar to the ones found in previous studies of GRB afterglows when data only up to GeV energies were considered. This may hint to the possibility that VHE emission from SSC may be present in all GRBs and that it could be detected by IACTs if favorable conditions apply i.e. a low enough redshift and good observing conditions. This hypothesis can be confirmed only with more GRBs detected in the VHE range, as the current number of GRBs is not enough to draw firm conclusions.

3.2.2. *GRB 201015A and GRB 201216C*

The detection of GRB 190114C gave additional momentum to the searches of GRBs with MAGIC. This led to other two important observations in 2020.

The first observation concerns GRB 201015A, a burst detected by *Swift*. While the GRB showed some features resembling short GRBs, the detection of a supernova signature five days after the onset make this a long GRB.[8] Despite being at a redshift very similar to the one of GRB 190114C ($z = 0.426$), GRB 201015A has a relatively low luminosity of $E_{\mathrm{iso}} \sim 10^{50}$ erg, i.e. three order of magnitude lower. MAGIC started the observations after ~ 1 min after the onset of the GRBs and it reported a hint of detection at the level of more than in 3σ from offline analyses.[9] This strong hint is very interesting if compared to the detection of the low luminosity GRB 190829A by the H.E.S.S. collaboration, located at a much lower redshift $z = 0.08$. For more details, the readers may refer to Suda et al. 2021.

In a second observation in December 2020, MAGIC detected another burst, GRB 201216C.[10] Again, this was a long GRB ($T_{90} = 48\,\mathrm{s}$) with similar energetics to GRB 190114C ($E_{\mathrm{iso}} \sim 5 \times 10^{53}$ erg), but much more distant, having a redshift of $z = 1.1$. A clear detection was achieved, and first preliminary results were presented in ICRC 2021. The most remarkable feature for this GRB is the very high redshift, enlarging the spectrum of GRB properties characterized in VHE observations.

3.2.3. *GRB 160821B*

While all GRBs currently detected at VHE belong to the long class, some progress was done also for short GRBs. Being intrinsically less energetic than long GRBs but at relatively lower redshifts, their detection may be feasible with current IACTs. A good indication for such hypothesis is the observation of GRB 160821B by MAGIC, a short GRB detected by *Swift* located at $z = 0.16$. Additionally, short GRBs are linked with binary neutron star systems, which were proven to be gravitational waves emitters with the GW170817 event. GRB 160821B is one of the few short GRBs with a confirmed kilonova emission, pointing to a possible binary neutron star system as progenitor. As mentioned in section 2, MAGIC started data taking 24 s after the onset of GRB 160821B. The weather conditions were not favorable: moonlight was present and increasing during the observation, the zenith of the target was rather high (between $34°$ and $55°$) and the first part of the data was affected by clouds, resulting in a reduced atmospheric transmission. Despite the unfavorable observing conditions, an evidence of a gamma-ray signal was found at a significance of $\sim 3\sigma$ above ~ 0.5 TeV.[11]

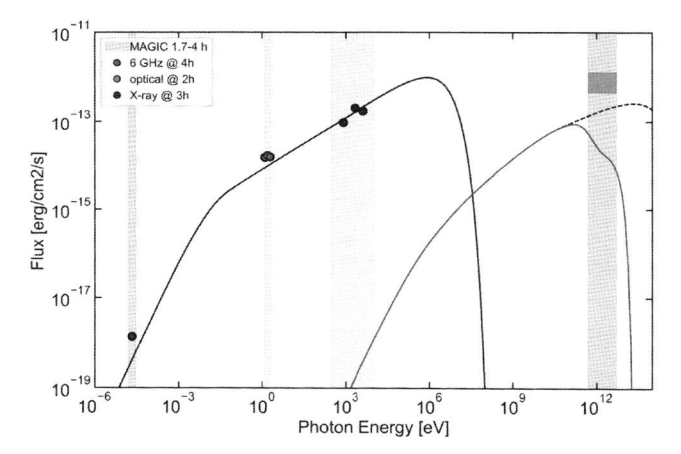

Fig. 5. Spectral energy distribution of GRB 160821B and modeling curves. The solid black line models the synchrotron radiation, while the dashed black line is the intrinsic SSC emission. The red line takes into account the absorption by the EBL. The red box only indicated the putative flux level from MAGIC. Extracted from Ref. 11.

If we assume that the gamma-ray excess is genuine emission from GRB 160821B, the flux predicted by the SSC process in the external forward shock scenario is in tension with the observed TeV flux, see Figure 5. Other scenarios were considered in order to explain the MAGIC data, from proton synchrotron emission, photohadronic cascade emission, external compton, multiple zone emission or SSC from the reverse shock. While hadronic processes are disfavored due to their inefficiency and large energy requirements, the other possibilities are not ruled out. This points to still poorly understood properties of short GRBs, which needs more observations at GeV-TeV energies in the future to fill in the picture, also in relation to gravitational wave searches.

4. Future perspectives for GRBs detection with MAGIC and conclusions

The recent detection of GRBs in the VHE regime opened a new era in this field. Such discoveries were long awaited and they are the result of a continued effort with improvements from the technical and strategy point of view. For the next years, there are other challenges that need to be faced in the search for VHE emission with MAGIC.

First of all, the number of detected GRBs is still low and they were bursts with quite different properties (e.g. distance, brightness). Therefore it is difficult to infer what could be the main factors within a GRB that favor the production of VHE gamma-rays. Despite this, a property seems to be shared among all the GRBs, namely the similar time decay between the X-ray and the VHE flux. In a recent study by Campana and collaborators instead, they discuss the possibility of a relation between a high X-ray column density and the presence of TeV emission, which seems to find confirmation considering the detected GRBs.

A second challenge for MAGIC is the detection of VHE emission in the prompt phase of a GRB. This would constitute another major breakthrough in the field, finally shedding light on which process is responsible for the initial flash of GRBs. MAGIC proved already to be able to begin GRB follow-ups very close to the onset, therefore observing during the late prompt-early afterglow phase of a dozen of GRBs. Therefore, we might expect to have a detection of VHE gamma-rays during the prompt phase to happen soon.

The third challenge was mentioned in section 3.2.3, that is the detection of short GRBs in the VHE regime. The hint of detection reported by MAGIC gives a strong indication that this goal can be achieved. In this case the number of events is quite reduced, given that the majority of GRB alerts received by MAGIC are long GRBs. However, the opportunities may increase with the beginning of the new observational run by LIGO, Virgo and Kagra expected to start in late 2022, O4. As exemplified by the GW170817/GRB170817A event, we may search for short GRBs in spatial and temporal coincidence with gravitational wave signals from the coalescence of binary neutron star or neutron star-black hole systems. As the localization of the GW events is expected to be improved, and thanks to more and more refined follow-up strategies involving both satellite-borne or ground-base telescopes, this might give MAGIC and other IACTs additional chances in detecting short GRBs.

To summarize, the recent detection of GRBs in the last years had clearly a major impact in GRB physics, and gave additional boost to searches in the VHE regime and beyond (e.g. with current and future extensive air shower arrays). The primary goal for MAGIC is to detect more GRBs, profiting of every opportunity and trying to clear the challenges mentioned above. One basic question is if SSC can model the TeV emission from GRBs in a generic way, or if other processes may instead explain it. A possible way to test such hypothesis would be to have simultaneous observation by MAGIC and Fermi-LAT partially overlapping in energy. Assuming the two experiments give similar results in the overlapping energy region (at a few tens of GeV), a break in the MAGIC spectrum at few tens of GeV after which it rises would give a clear indication of an inverse Compton component. Such possibility is realistic given the recent result by MAGIC on the Geminga pulsar, where the SumTrigger system was used to achieve an energy threshold as low as 15 GeV so that part of the spectrum observed by MAGIC overlaps with the one by Fermi-LAT.

From the discussion in these proceedings, it is clear that the field is still young and the possibility of important discoveries is high. MAGIC proved to be up to the expectations and surely it will play a major role in the coming years as well, contributing even more to unveiling many mysteries related to GRBs.

References

1. J. Aleksić et al., The major upgrade of the MAGIC telescopes, Part II: A performance study using observations of the Crab Nebula, *Astroparticle Physics* **72**, 76 (January 2016).
2. E. Aliu et al., Observation of Pulsed γ-Rays Above 25 GeV from the Crab Pulsar with MAGIC, *Science* **322**, p. 1221 (November 2008).
3. MAGIC Collaboration, Detection of the Geminga pulsar with MAGIC hints at a power-law tail emission beyond 15 GeV, *Astronomy & Astrophysics* **643**, p. L14 (November 2020).
4. R. Seaman et al., Sky Event Reporting Metadata Version 2.0 IVOA Recommendation 11 July 2011 (July, 2011).
5. R. Mirzoyan et al., MAGIC detects the GRB 190114C in the TeV energy domain., *GRB Coordinates Network* **23701**, p. 1 (January 2019).
6. MAGIC Collaboration et al., Teraelectronvolt emission from the γ-ray burst GRB 190114C, *Nature* **575**, 455 (November 2019).
7. MAGIC Collaboration et al., Observation of inverse Compton emission from a long γ-ray burst, *Nature* **575**, 459 (November 2019).
8. A. Rossi et al., GRB 201015A: evidence of supernova in LBT spectra, *GRB Coordinates Network* **29306**, p. 1 (January 2021).
9. O. Blanch et al., MAGIC observations of GRB 201015A: hint of very high energy gamma-ray signal, *GRB Coordinates Network* **28659**, p. 1 (October 2020).
10. O. Blanch et al., GRB 201216C: MAGIC detection in very high energy gamma rays, *GRB Coordinates Network* **29075**, p. 1 (December 2020).
11. V. A. Acciari et al., MAGIC Observations of the Nearby Short Gamma-Ray Burst GRB 160821B, *The Astrophysical Journal* **908**, p. 90 (February 2021).

Prospects for VHE monitoring of gamma-ray bursts with SWGO

G. La Mura,[1,*] U. Barres de Almeida,[2] R. Conceição,[1,3] A. de Angelis,[4,5,6] F. Longo,[7,8,9]
M. Pimenta,[1,3] E. Prandini,[6,10] E. Ruiz-Velasco,[11] B. Tomé[1,3]
for the SWGO Collaboration

[1] *Laboratório de Instrumentação e Física Experimental de Partículas (LIP),*
Av. Prof. Gama Pinto 2, Lisboa 1649-003, Portugal
* E-mail: glamura@lip.pt
[2] *Brazilian Center for Physics Research (CBPF), Rua Dr. Xavier Sigaud 150,*
22290-180 Rio de Janeiro, Brazil
[3] *Instituto Superior Técnico (IST), Av. Rovisco Pais 1, 1049-001 Lisboa, Portugal*
[4] *Dipartimento di Fisica e Astronomia - Università di Padova, Via Marzolo 8,*
35131 Padova, Italy
[5] *Dipartimento di scienze matematiche,*
informatiche e fisiche - Università degli Studi di Udine,
Via Palladio 8, 33100 Udine, Italy
[6] *Istituto Nazionale di Fisica Nucleare sez. Padova (INFN), Via Marzolo 8,*
35131 Padova, Italy
[7] *IFPU - Institute for Fundamental Physics of the Universe, Via Beirut 2,*
34014 Trieste, Italy
[8] *INFN, Sezione di Trieste, via A. Valerio 2, 34100 Trieste, Italy*
[9] *Dipartimento di Fisica, Università degli Studi di Trieste, via A. Valerio 2,*
34100 Trieste, Italy
[10] *INAF - Osservatorio Astronomico di Padova, Vicolo dell'Osservatorio 3,*
I-35122 Padova, Italy
[11] *Max-Planck-Institut für Kernphysik, P.O. Box 103980, 69029 Heidelberg, Germany*

It has been established that Gamma-Ray Bursts (GRB) can produce Very High Energy radiation (VHE, $E > 100\,\text{GeV}$), opening a new window for investigating particle acceleration and radiation properties in the most energetic domain. We expect that next-generation instruments in this energy regime, such as the Cherenkov Telescope Array (CTA), will mark a huge improvement in their observation. However, constraints on the target visibility and the limited duty cycle of Imaging Atmospheric Cherenkov Telescopes (IACT), affect their ability to react promptly to transient events. Here we use a grid of instrument performance estimates, based on the Extensive Air Shower (EAS) array concept proposed by the Southern Wide Field-of-view Gamma-ray Observatory (SWGO) collaboration, to evaluate SWGO's potential to detect and track VHE emission from GRBs. Observations by the *Fermi* Large Area Telescope (*Fermi*–LAT) at high energy ($E > 10\,\text{GeV}$), identified some events with a distinct spectral component, which can represent a substantial fraction of the emitted energy and possibly occur very early in the process. Using models based on these properties, we estimate the possibilities that a wide field of view and large effective area ground-based monitoring facility has to probe VHE emission from GRBs. We show that the ability to monitor VHE transients with a nearly continuous scanning of the sky grants us the opportunity to simultaneously observe electromagnetic counterparts to gravitational waves and relativistic particles sources up to cosmological scales, in a way that is not accessible to IACTs.

Keywords: Instrumentation: detectors; gamma rays: general; gamma ray burst: general.

1. Introduction

The study of Gamma-Ray Bursts (GRB) represents one of the most challenging and fascinating frontiers of High Energy Astrophysics. Although they were discovered in the first years of space explorations with high energy detectors,[1] several aspects of their origin, their power, and their radiation mechanisms are still unclear. We know that GRBs are originated by ultra-relativistic jets of plasma, which are produced during the extremely fast accretion process that follows the collapse of a very massive star ($M \geq 20\,\mathrm{M_\odot}$) or the merger of a binary neutron star (NS), to form a *magnetar* or a black hole.[2] The process produces a flash of energetic photons, named *prompt emission*, followed by a smoothly decaying signal, called *afterglow*. Looking at the duration of the prompt phase, GRBs appear to show a bimodal distribution, where we distinguish a class of short events, with a prompt stage lasting less than 2 s, and another of long ones, whose prompt emission takes place for much longer times.[3,4] The two classes of events are consistent with two distinguished possible source types. Long GRBs have been associated with supernova explosions,[5,6] while the short ones fit better in the compact binary merger scenario,[7] as eventually demonstrated by the GRB 170817A–GW 170817 multi-messenger association that was also detected as a *kilonova*.[8–10]

In the past few years, observations performed with ground based Imaging Atmospheric Cherenkov Telescopes (IACT), such as MAGIC[11] and H.E.S.S.,[12] found evidence for Very High Energy γ-ray emission (VHE, $E \geq 100\,\mathrm{GeV}$) in the afterglow of some GRBs.[13,14] In addition, analysis of the data collected by the *Fermi* Large Area Telescope (*Fermi*-LAT)[15] demonstrated the existence of a high energy component in the spectra of some bright GRBs that extends above the 10 GeV energy range and can be detected also in association with the prompt emission.[16–18] Understanding the origin and the distribution of VHE radiation from GRBs is a key issue for their correct interpretation. It is expected that next generation γ-ray instruments, such as, for instance, the Cherenkov Telescope Array (CTA),[19] will provide exceptional new data in this field. Unfortunately, the unpredictable nature of GRBs and their fast spectral evolution makes it extremely difficult, for instruments with narrow field of view (FoV), of the order of few square degrees, to re-point and track GRB emission within very short times (below 10 s). A possible solution to this problem is using Extensive Air Shower detector arrays (EAS) to monitor large areas of the sky, with an instantaneous FoV of more than 1 sr and a nearly continuous duty cycle. Here we discuss the observational opportunities that a new instrument, based on a next-generation EAS array concept investigated by the Southern Wide-field-of-view Gamma-ray Observatory (SWGO),[20] will open in the study of GRBs.

This contribution is structured as follows: in §2 we describe the known and the expected VHE properties of GRBs; in §3 we present the potential monitoring capabilities of SWGO; finally, in §4 we discuss our results and we draw our conclusions.

2. VHE emission from GRBs

Several arguments suggest that GRBs should be able to produce prompt VHE radiation. The most likely interpretation of GRBs invokes relativistic shocks occurring either within the magnetized jet plasma (*internal shocks*, generally associated with the prompt stage), or between the jet and the surrounding environment (*external shocks*, more often considered as the source of the afterglow emission). In both cases, the energies associated with particles and magnetic fields are high enough to produce efficient leptonic radiation mechanisms and possibly to activate hadronic processes.[21–23] The combination of temporal and spectral properties of the emitted radiation provides fundamental indications on the characteristics of the source.

In general, a large fraction of the energy that a GRB releases in the prompt phase is found in the spectral range falling between few hundreds keV to some MeV.[24] The spectrum comes in the form of a combination of power-law components, known as the *Band function*.[25] The presence of relativistic charged particles in an intense magnetic field leads to the natural expectation that powerful synchrotron and inverse Compton radiation should be emitted.[26] While the prompt emission is characterized by fast pulse-like variability, with time-scales down to few milliseconds,[27] implying extremely compact emission regions, the observation of photons up to the MeV and even the GeV energy range requires very large bulk Lorentz factors ($\Gamma >> 100$), in order to suppress pair production opacity. In these conditions, the inverse Compton scattering of synchrotron radiation may lead to the production of photons up to the TeV domain.[28] The occurrence of ultra-relativistic shocks in high density environments, on the other hand, is theoretically able to activate photo-pion interactions that can extend the spectra beyond 300 GeV[23] and lead to potential associations with neutrino events.[29]

So far, the direct detection of VHE radiation has only been possible in the afterglow of a limited number of GRBs, thanks to ground-based follow up observations.[13,30–32] However, the monitoring campaign carried out by the *Fermi*-LAT space observatory led to the identification of a high energy spectral component, coming in the form of power-law emission, that appears to be a common feature of bright GRBs and may even arise very early in the event.[33] Due to the limited collecting area and the typical short duration of GRBs, the LAT observations are not able to place strong constraints on the VHE component of GRBs, as it is suggested by the fact that *Fermi* did not detect photons above $\sim$ 30 GeV from GRB 190114C, while the same event was firmly detected up to almost 1 TeV. As a consequence, the results of *Fermi*-LAT observations can be used as a starting point to estimate the possible extension of the GRB properties to the VHE domain and thereby evaluate their detection opportunities for other instruments.

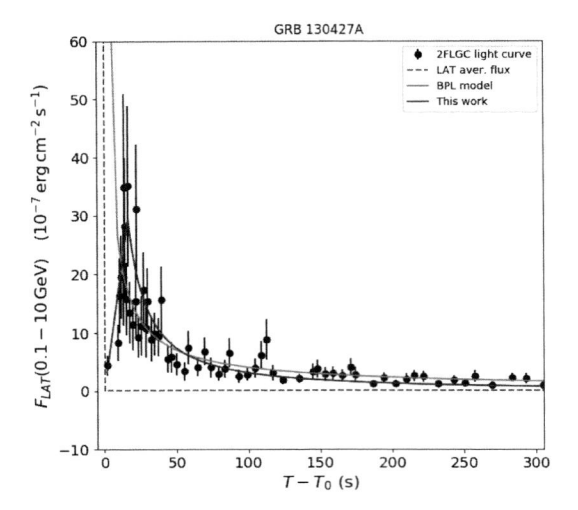

Fig. 1. Comparison between the *Fermi*-LAT light curve of GRB 130427A and the model based on Eq. (1) and Eq. (2). The vertical blue dashed line marks the start of the LAT signal temporal window, the red horizontal line is the average energy flux collected during the entire time of emission, the green continuous line is the 2FLGC power-law fit to the data, while the blue continuous line is a model using the light curve of Eq. (2).

Usually, we can express the high energy spectrum of a GRB as a function of energy in the form of:[a]

$$\frac{\mathrm{d}N(t)}{\mathrm{d}E} = N_0(t)\left(\frac{E}{E_0}\right)^{-\alpha} \exp[-\tau(E,z)] \quad [\mathrm{ph\,cm^{-2}\,s^{-1}\,GeV^{-1}}], \qquad (1)$$

where $N_0(t)$ is the flux of photons per unit energy observed at time t, E_0 is the pivot energy, α is the spectral index, which is often within the range $1.5 \leq \alpha \leq 3$, with an average value close to 2, and $\tau(E,z)$ is the opacity due to pair production on Extragalactic Background Light photons (EBL), given as a function of energy and redshift. The temporal evolution of the flux is typically well represented by a power-law, or a broken power-law, that can be written as:

$$N_0(t) = \begin{cases} N_{peak}\left(\dfrac{t-T_0}{T_{peak}-T_0}\right) & \text{for } T_0 \leq t \leq T_{peak} \\ N_{peak}\left(\dfrac{t}{T_{peak}-T_0}\right)^{-\gamma} & \text{for } t > T_{peak}, \end{cases} \qquad (2)$$

where we denoted with T_0 the trigger time, with T_{peak} the time taken to achieve peak emission, with N_{peak} the maximum flux, and with γ the temporal evolution index, which is often found to be $1 \leq \gamma \leq 2$.

---

[a]We assume for simplicity that the temporal evolution of the spectrum is only limited to a scaling factor, without relevant spectral changes.

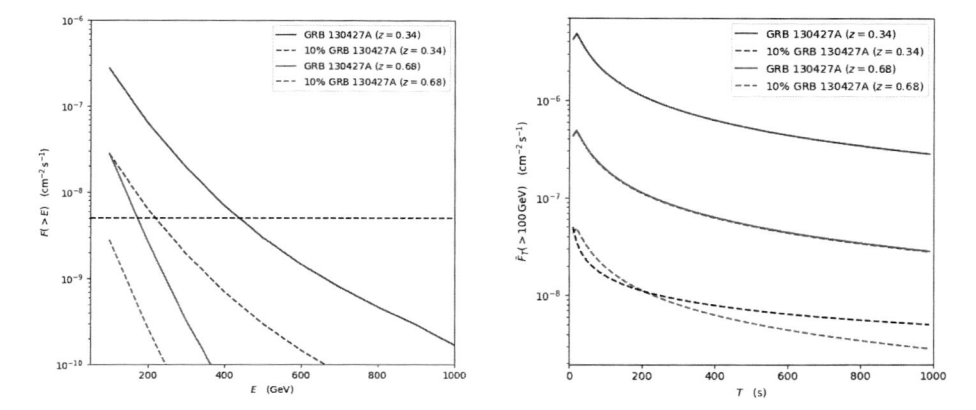

Fig. 2. **Left panel:** average photon flux expected above any given energy in 1000 s for a burst with the spectral and temporal characteristics of GRB 130427A (blue continuous line), an identical burst with 10% its strength (blue dashed line) and the same previous cases computed for twice the measured redshift (red continuous and dashed lines). The horizontal black dashed line represents a reference flux limit of $5 \cdot 10^{-9}$ ph cm^{-2} s^{-1}. **Right panel:** instantaneous integral photon fluxes, expected above 100 GeV as afunction of time, compared with the detection threshold, in the assumption that the limiting flux scales as the square root of the observation time.

Using the second catalog of *Fermi*-LAT detected GRBs (2FLGC),[33] which provides measurements of the observed photon fluxes, in the energy range between 0.1 GeV and 10 GeV, together with information on the spectral index and on the light curve shape, for a sample of GRBs observed during 10 years of regular monitoring operations, we are able to apply Eq. (1), with the inclusion of Eq. (2), to estimate the expected high energy fluxes as a function of time, as it is illustrated for instance in Fig. 1. In principle, we can extend this type of spectra to the VHE domain and, thus, obtain an estimate of the expected fluxes. In practice, this operation is not directly possible, due to the lack of a redshift measurement for the majority of the LAT detected GRBs, which implies an unknown EBL opacity in Eq. (1). Although the effects EBL are generally negligible for the observed LAT band, they become quickly very important at higher energies, with a typical γ-ray horizon set by $\tau = 1$, which, for $z \approx 1$, already occurs at $E = 100$ GeV.[34] For this reason, we combined the spectral and temporal fits, which we obtained from the LAT data, with a set of simulations, aiming at estimating the effects of EBL opacity on the VHE extension of the GRBs that resulted in the brightest LAT observed fluxes.[35]

3. GRB monitoring with SWGO

A direct consequence of Eq. (1) is that the observation of VHE radiation, particularly from fast transient sources, requires the use of large instrumented areas. This characteristic can only be offered by ground-based facilities, such as IACTs or EAS

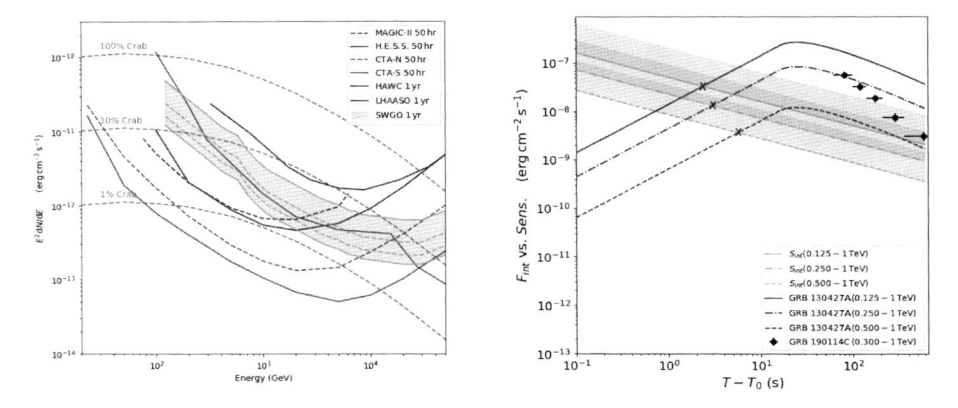

Fig. 3. **Left panel:** Spectral coverage and differential sensitivity of some currently operating and next-generation VHE observatories. The sensitivities are computed for a point-like source at a zenith distance of 20°. Different fractions of the Crab Nebula flux are shown for comparison. The shaded area is the sensitivity range expected for various configurations of SWGO.[36] **Right panel:** The expected integrated flux for a GRB 130427A-like event above 125 GeV, 250 GeV and 500 GeV, compared with the corresponding SWGO expected sensitivities. Crosses mark the estimated detection times. The VHE light curve of GRB 190114C above 300 GeV is also shown.[13]

detector arrays. The main advantage of IACT observatories is that they have excellent angular resolution and background rejection power, achieving the best possible sensitivity. On the other hand, these instruments can only operate during dark time and in clear sky conditions, implying a duty cycle of only $\sim 20\%$. In addition, the small FoV and the consequent need to respond to an external alert with target position information and subsequent re-pointing delay does not allow IACT instruments to cover the early GRB emission regime, where many critical observational constraints are expected by different theoretical models.

Thanks to their larger FoV and to the possibility to operate almost continuously, EAS detector arrays have better chances to cover a GRB and to act as an alert system themselves. The main problems of this solution are that EAS arrays need to be located at high altitudes (> 4500 m a.s.l.), in order to be reached by the particle showers initiated by γ-ray primaries with $E \leq 1$ TeV, and that they need to deal with a strong background of cosmic-ray induced air showers. The sensitivity needed to detect the expected VHE signal of GRBs can be estimated by integrating Eq. (1) in time and in energy, with the observed properties of bright LAT bursts, using known or simulated redshifts. Figure 2 shows an example of such calculation. As it is clearly illustrated by the left panel of Fig. 2, the expected signal is a function of the characteristic burst properties, such has flux, duration, spectral index and redshift, and of the energy band that is covered by the observation. In particular, the amount of flux above 100 GeV is critically affected by redshift, meaning that only bright and relatively nearby events can be detected at larger energies. Taking as reference a limiting flux of $5 \cdot 10^{-9}$ ph cm^{-2} s^{-1}, integrated above 100 GeV for an observing time of 1000 s, which is a reasonable estimate for an instrument concept based on the SWGO reference design,[36] it is possible to reach the VHE signal expected from GRBs down to 10% the power of the brightest LAT detected event up to $z \approx 0.7$.

The SWGO Collaboration is currently investigating the configuration of a next-generation EAS array, based on Water Cherenkov Detectors (WCD), to be installed at a high altitude site in the Southern Hemisphere. By adopting a detector concept able to trigger on low energy shower particles (~ 20 MeV), with high temporal resolution (~ 2 ns), it can be shown that an array of 80 000 m^2 can improve background suppression and achieve very good monitoring sensitivities, below the TeV energy domain.[36] Figure 3 presents an illustration of this concept, compared with other currently operating and planned facilities, together with an example of its expected performance, with respect to the temporal evolution of two GRBs with a detected high energy component. If we define the integrated flux expected in the VHE domain within an observation time T as:

$$F_{int}(T) = \frac{1}{T - T_0} \int_{T_0}^{T} dt \int_{E_{low}}^{1\,\text{TeV}} E \frac{dN(t)}{dE} dE, \qquad (3)$$

where the spectrum is defined through Eq. (1) and Eq. (2), we can easily verify that the times required to detect the incoming fluxes are significantly below 10 s, meaning that such configurations would be particularly effective to react to the early phases of the transient. Given the promising detection chances in case of GRBs with well measured energetic components, SWGO represents an attractive solution to investigate the properties of VHE emission in the early stages of GRBs and, thus, help solving the question of whether an energetic component associated with the burst onset is a common feature of GRBs or a distinguishing property of a specific event class.

4. Conclusions

The systematic investigation of GRBs in the VHE range will cover a fundamental role in the quickly evolving field of Multi-Wavelength and Multi-Messenger Astrophysics. After the first detection of Gravitational Waves (GW), which marked a corner stone in scientific research,[37] the execution of regular monitoring campaigns increased the chances of obtaining multiple detections of fast transients. The associated observation of GW 170817 and of the short GRB 170817A, in particular, represented the first direct evidence of the compact binary merger as a viable explanation to short GRBs and it opened the way to a wealth of cosmological and high energy physics tests.[8,9] A fundamental question related to the nature of GRBs and to their distinction in classes is whether the formation of the jet and its subsequent evolution involve substantial hadronic processes, a matter that could be unambiguously solved by the association of GRBs with neutrino events or with early VHE emission.[38]

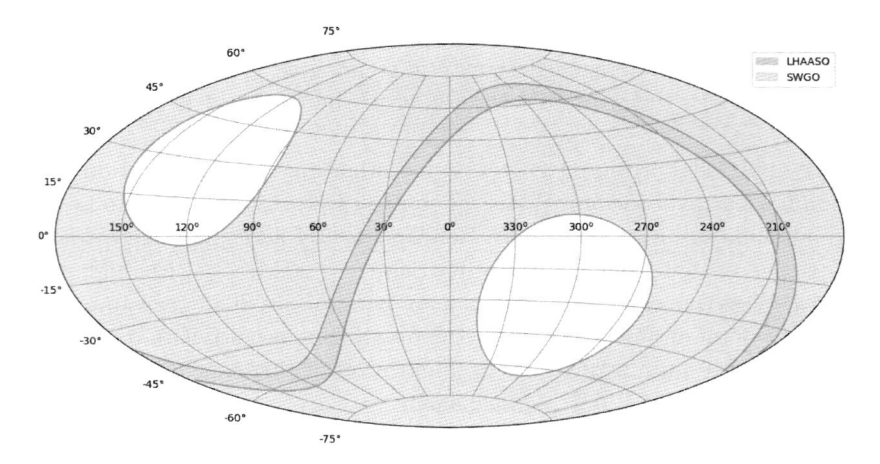

Fig. 4. Representation of the visible sky, within 30° from zenith, showing the sky regions covered by LHAASO (cyan shaded area) and by SWGO, assuming an observatory latitude close to 23° S (orange shaded area). The map is plotted in Galactic coordinates.

Evidence based on existing observations has firmly demonstrated that GRBs can produce energetic radiation and also that this spectral component may be associated with the elusive prompt emission.[17] The observation of early high energy photons, together with hints of the VHE detection of short GRBs, like in the case of GRB 160821B, challenges the external shock model predictions and suggests that additional mechanisms may be at work. Covering the VHE window, particularly in the early emission phase, will be a crucial requirement for the development of more advanced models. The ability to characterise the earliest properties of VHE emission will be fundamental both to improve the time-domain investigation of Multi-Messenger triggers, as well as to offer high quality alerts for follow-up observations that, as demonstrated by H.E.S.S. and further boosted by the upcoming investigations with CTA, can track the VHE evolution up to several hours in the afterglow.[30]

The large FoV and the nearly continuous operating time of EAS arrays make this type of instruments an ideal facility to survey the sky looking for fast transient sources. Their ability to cover large sky areas will help constraining the VHE properties of early GRB emission, with new implications on the involved radiation mechanisms. However, in order to observe events located at cosmological distances, they need to work effectively in the sub-TeV energy domain and, therefore, to be located in high altitude sites. The Large High Altitutde Air Shower Observatory (LHAASO),[39] in the Northern hemisphere, and SWGO, from the Southern hemisphere, have the potential to carry out a VHE monitoring program that will cover a large fraction of the visible sky, as illustrated in Fig. 4. If extended in the sub-TeV domain, this nearly constant scanning of the sky will help clarifying the VHE properties of GRBs by assessing the existence of spectral components that, though predicted in well justified models, are hard to detect with instruments that need to be triggered and subsequently pointed to the target. In addition, fostering a VHE monitoring ability will offer a new window to identify sources of energetic transients, like gravitational waves and high energy neutrinos. Clearly, the identification of possible counterparts to alerts issued by continuously operating experiments, such as *IceCube* and *LIGO/VIRGO*, will undoubtedly benefit from the existence of a network of VHE monitoring programs, able to detect energetic transients and, thus, to further refine the identification of their sources and their energy production mechanisms.

Acknowledgments

The SWGO Collaboration acknowledges the support from the agencies and organizations listed here: https://www.swgo.org/SWGOWiki/doku.php?id=acknowledgements. This research was funded by Fundação para a Ciência e Tecnologia, under project PTDC/FIS-PAR/4300/2020 and grant DL57/2016/cP1330/cT0002. Additional funding by CNPq Productivity Research, Grant no. 311997/2019-8, by Serrapilheira Institute Grant number Serra - 1812-26906, and by FAPERJ Young Scientist Fellowship no. E-26/202.818/2019 is also acknowledged.

References

1. R. W. Klebesadel, I. B. Strong and R. A. Olson, Observations of Gamma-Ray Bursts of Cosmic Origin, *The Astrophysical Journal Letters* **182**, p. L85 (June 1973).
2. S. E. Woosley, Gamma-Ray Bursts from Stellar Mass Accretion Disks around Black Holes, *The Astrophysical Journal* **405**, p. 273 (March 1993).
3. E. P. Mazets, S. V. Golenetskii, V. N. Ilinskii, V. N. Panov, R. L. Aptekar, I. A. Gurian, M. P. Proskura, I. A. Sokolov, Z. I. Sokolova and T. V. Kharitonova, Catalog of cosmic gamma-ray bursts from the KONUS experiment data, *Astrophysics and Space Science* **80**, 3 (November 1981).
4. J. P. Norris, T. L. Cline, U. D. Desai and B. J. Teegarden, Frequency of fast, narrow γ-ray bursts, *Nature* **308**, 434 (March 1984).
5. T. J. Galama *et al.*, An unusual supernova in the error box of the γ-ray burst of 25 April 1998, *Nature* **395**, 670 (October 1998).
6. J. S. Bloom *et al.*, The unusual afterglow of the γ-ray burst of 26 March 1998 as evidence for a supernova connection, *Nature* **401**, 453 (September 1999).
7. D. Eichler, M. Livio, T. Piran and D. N. Schramm, Nucleosynthesis, neutrino bursts and γ-rays from coalescing neutron stars, *Nature* **340**, 126 (July 1989).
8. B. P. Abbott *et al.*, Multi-messenger Observations of a Binary Neutron Star Merger, *The Astrophysical Journal Letters* **848**, p. L12 (October 2017).
9. B. P. Abbott *et al.*, Gravitational Waves and Gamma-Rays from a Binary Neutron Star Merger: GW170817 and GRB 170817A, *The Astrophysical Journal Letters* **848**, p. L13 (October 2017).
10. P. K. Blanchard *et al.*, The Electromagnetic Counterpart of the Binary Neutron Star Merger LIGO/Virgo GW170817. VII. Properties of the Host Galaxy and Constraints on the Merger Timescale, *The Astrophysical Journal Letters* **848**, p. L22 (October 2017).

11. J. Aleksić et al., The major upgrade of the MAGIC telescopes, Part I: The hardware improvements and the commissioning of the system, *Astroparticle Physics* **72**, 61 (January 2016).
12. F. Aharonian et al., Observations of the Crab nebula with HESS, *Astronomy & Astrophysics* **457**, 899 (October 2006).
13. MAGIC Collaboration, Teraelectronvolt emission from the γ-ray burst GRB 190114C, *Nature* **575**, 455 (November 2019).
14. H. Abdalla et al., A very-high-energy component deep in the γ-ray burst afterglow, *Nature* **575**, 464 (November 2019).
15. W. B. Atwood et al., The Large Area Telescope on the Fermi Gamma-Ray Space Telescope Mission, *The Astrophysical Journal* **697**, 1071 (June 2009).
16. A. A. Abdo et al., Fermi Observations of High-Energy Gamma-Ray Emission from GRB 080916C, *Science* **323**, p. 1688 (March 2009).
17. K. Asano, S. Guiriec and P. Mészáros, Hadronic Models for the Extra Spectral Component in the Short GRB 090510, *The Astrophysical Journal Letters* **705**, L191 (November 2009).
18. M. Ackermann et al., Fermi Observations of GRB 090510: A Short-Hard Gamma-ray Burst with an Additional, Hard Power-law Component from 10 keV to GeV Energies, *The Astrophysical Journal* **716**, 1178 (June 2010).
19. CTA Consortium, *Science with the Cherenkov Telescope Array* (World Scientific Publishing Company, 2019).
20. U. Barres de Almeida, G. Giacinti and F. Longo, Benchmarking the Science for the Southern Wide-Field Gamma-ray Observatory (SWGO), *Proceedings of Science* **395**, p. 10 (July 2021).
21. J. I. Katz, Delayed Hard Photons from Gamma-Ray Bursts, *The Astrophysical Journal Letters* **432**, p. L27 (September 1994).
22. M. J. Rees and P. Meszaros, Unsteady Outflow Models for Cosmological Gamma-Ray Bursts, *The Astrophysical Journal Letters* **430**, p. L93 (August 1994).
23. M. Vietri, GeV Photons from Ultrahigh Energy Cosmic Rays Accelerated in Gamma Ray Bursts, *Physical Review Letters* **78**, 4328 (June 1997).
24. D. Gruber et al., The Fermi GBM Gamma-Ray Burst Spectral Catalog: Four Years of Data, *The Astrophysical Journal Supplement Series* **211**, p. 12 (March 2014).
25. D. Band et al., BATSE Observations of Gamma-Ray Burst Spectra. I. Spectral Diversity, *The Astrophysical Journal* **413**, p. 281 (August 1993).
26. H. Papathanassiou and P. Meszaros, Spectra of Unsteady Wind Models of Gamma-Ray Bursts, *The Astrophysical Journal Letters* **471**, p. L91 (November 1996).
27. E. Nakar and T. Piran, Temporal properties of short gamma-ray bursts, *Monthly Notices of the Royal Astronomical Society* **330**, 920 (March 2002).
28. T. Piran, The physics of gamma-ray bursts, *Reviews of Modern Physics* **76**, 1143 (October 2004).
29. M. G. Aartsen et al., An All-sky Search for Three Flavors of Neutrinos from Gamma-ray Bursts with the IceCube Neutrino Observatory, *The Astrophysical Journal* **824**, p. 115 (June 2016).
30. H. Abdalla et al., A very-high-energy component deep in the γ-ray burst afterglow, *Nature* **575**, 464 (November 2019).
31. O. Blanch, GRB 201216C: MAGIC detection in very high energy gamma rays, *The Astronomer's Telegram* **14275**, p. 1 (December 2020).
32. H. E. S. S. Collaboration, Revealing x-ray and gamma ray temporal and spectral similarities in the GRB 190829A afterglow, *Science* **372**, 1081 (June 2021).

33. M. Ajello et al., A Decade of Gamma-Ray Bursts Observed by Fermi-LAT: The Second GRB Catalog, *The Astrophysical Journal* **878**, p. 52 (June 2019).
34. A. Saldana-Lopez, A. Domínguez, P. G. Pérez-González, J. Finke, M. Ajello, J. R. Primack, V. S. Paliya and A. Desai, An observational determination of the evolving extragalactic background light from the multiwavelength HST/CANDELS survey in the Fermi and CTA era, *Monthly Notices of the Royal Astronomical Society* **507**, 5144 (November 2021).
35. G. La Mura, U. Barres de Almeida, R. Conceição, A. De Angelis, F. Longo, M. Pimenta, E. Prandini, E. Ruiz-Velasco and B. Tomé, Gamma-ray burst detection prospects for next generation ground-based VHE facilities, *Monthly Notices of the Royal Astronomical Society* **508**, 671 (November 2021).
36. H. Schoorlemmer, R. Conceição and A. J. Smith, Simulating the performance of the Southern Wide-view Gamma-ray Observatory, *Proceedings of Science* **395**, p. 9 (July 2021).
37. B. P. Abbott et al., Properties of the Binary Black Hole Merger GW150914, *Physical Review Letters* **116**, p. 241102 (June 2016).
38. M. Bustamante, J. Heinze, K. Murase and W. Winter, Multi-messenger Light Curves from Gamma-Ray Bursts in the Internal Shock Model, *The Astrophysical Journal* **837**, p. 33 (March 2017).
39. Z. Cao et al., Introduction to Large High Altitude Air Shower Observatory (LHAASO), *Chinese Astronomy and Astrophysics* **43**, 457 (October 2019).

Theoretical implications on the very high energy emission from GRB 190114C

D. Miceli[1,2,*], A. Berti[3], Z. Bosnjak[4], S. Covino[5], S. Fukami[6], S. Inoue[7], F. Longo[2,8,9], R. Mirzoyan[3], E. Moretti[10], L. Nava[2,5,9], K. Noda[6], D. Paneque[3], A. Stamerra[11], Y. Suda[12], I. Vovk[6] on behalf of the MAGIC Collaboration

[1] *Laboratoire d'Annecy de Physique des Particules (LAPP),*
CNRS-IN2P3, 9 Chemin de Bellevue - BP 110, Annecy Cedex, France
* E-mail: davide.miceli@lapp.in2p3.fr
[2] *INFN, Sezione di Trieste, via Valerio 2, Trieste, Italy*
[3] *Max Planck Institute for Physics, Föhringer Ring 6, Munich, Germany*
[4] *Faculty of Electrical Engineering and Computing, University of Zagreb, Zagreb, Croatia*
[5] *INAF, Osservatorio Astronomico di Brera, Merate, Italy*
[6] *Institute for Cosmic Ray Research, The University of Tokyo,*
Kashiwanoha 5-1-5, Kashiwa, Japan
[7] *RIKEN, Hirosawa 2-1, Wako, Japan*
[8] *University of Trieste, Department of Physics, via Valerio 2, Trieste, Italy*
[9] *Institute for Fundamental Physics of the Universe (IFPU), via Beirut 12, Trieste, Italy*
[10] *Institut de Física d'Altes Energies (IFAE), Edifici Cn, Bellaterra (Barcelona), Spain*
[11] *National Institute for Astrophysics (INAF), I-00136 Rome, Italy*
[12] *Physics Program, Graduate School of Advanced Science and Engineering,*
Hiroshima University, 739-8526 Hiroshima, Japan

Since their discovery in the late 1960s Gamma-Ray Burst (GRB) emission has been deeply investigated with the help of the huge amount of data collected covering the entire electromagnetic spectrum. This large and broadband dataset was essential to constitute a general picture describing the GRB physics, revealing the most credible underlying physical processes and environmental conditions ongoing at the GRB site. A key leap in the comprehension of the GRB physics have been achieved recently, thanks to the detection of the newly energetic component in the Very High Energy (VHE, E > 100 GeV) domain. The possible presence of a TeV spectral window in GRBs was predicted and theorized for several decades, but the first observational proofs of its existence were reached only in 2019 thanks to the discoveries claimed by the MAGIC and H.E.S.S. telescopes. GRB190114C was successfully detected in the TeV band by the MAGIC telescopes starting from around one minute after its trigger time and lasting for nearly 40 minutes. A successful follow-up campaign was performed and the multi-wavelength afterglow emission of the event was collected from 1 to about 2×10^{17} GHz. Such very broad dataset allows to perform unique studies on the radiation mechanisms and on the physical properties of such event. In this contribution I will describe the main results and the theoretical interpretations that have been derived from the multi-wavelength dataset of GRB190114C. In particular, the description of the TeV component detected by the MAGIC telescopes as produced via the Synchrotron Self-Compton (SSC) mechanism and its connection with the emission at lower energy bands will be presented. Such studies are a fundamental starting point for the interpretation of the current and upcoming events that will be observed in the VHE domain.

Keywords: Gamma-ray bursts; very high energy; synchrotron-self compton

1. Introduction

Gamma-Ray Bursts (GRBs) are transient phenomena produced during cataclysmic events such as the death of massive stars or the merging of binary compact objects like neutron stars and black holes.

The GRB electromagnetic radiation is characterized by initial rapid and irregular flashes bright in the keV-MeV band, the so-called *prompt* emission phase followed by a long-lasting broadband fainter emission, named *afterglow*. The duration of the prompt emission spans from milliseconds to thousands of seconds and is used to classify GRBs as *short* and *long* with a separation value of 2 s. The afterglow phase, which follows or partially overlaps with the prompt emission, is usually detectable within timescale of days, weeks or in some cases even months.

Because of its multi-wavelength nature, intense campaigns are performed to search for and follow this broadband emission from radio up to γ-rays, both with ground-based telescopes and space-born satellites. While the prompt emission mechanism is still unclear, the afterglow radiation from radio up to GeV is well described as synchrotron emission produced in the external forward shock scenario due to the interaction between the jet and the surrounding interstellar medium or stellar wind (depending on the progenitor). The possible extension of the GRB emission in the high energy (0.5 MeV < E < 100 GeV, HE) and to the very high energy domain (VHE, E > 100 GeV) has always been one of the most debated open questions in GRB physics. The HE observations have revealed the presence of an emission component with peculiar temporal and spectral properties. The highest energy photons observed by Fermi-LAT are hardly to reconcile with the standard synchrotron afterglow scenario and hint the possibility that a new VHE emission component in GRBs is present.

A firm conclusion could be reached thanks to the observations performed by ground-based imaging Cherenkov telescopes. In particular, the MAGIC and the H.E.S.S. telescopes revealed unequivocally the presence of a VHE emission component in GRB afterglows up to TeV energies.[1] Such detections gave birth to unique studies covering several open topics of the GRB physics. In this contribution we report the analysis results and the theoretical implications derived from the TeV detection of GRB 190114C performed by the MAGIC telescopes. The interpretation of the full GRB 190114C multi-wavelength dataset with the synchrotron and Synchrotron-Self Compton (SSC) scenario and the intimate connection between the TeV emission component and the lower energy ones is presented.[2,3]

2. TeV detection and interpretation of GRB 190114C

GRB 190114C is a long GRB triggered by Swift-BAT and Fermi-GBM space instruments on 14 January 2019, 20:57:03 UT (hereafter T_0). The event was detected also by several other space instruments, namely Fermi-LAT, Swift-XRT, Swift-UVOT, AGILE, INTEGRAL/SPI-ACS, Insight/HXMT, and Konus-Wind. Triggered by space satellite alerts, the event was then followed-up and detected by

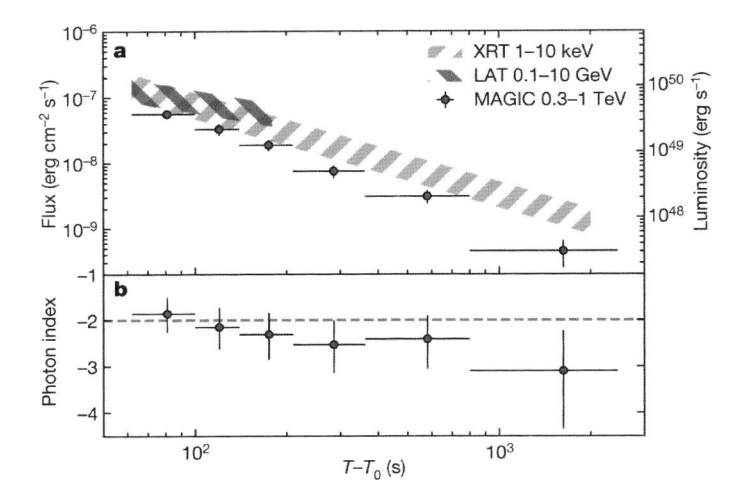

Fig. 1. **a**: MAGIC (red circles), XRT (green band) and LAT (red band) light curves. **b**: temporal evolution of the intrinsic spectral photon index.[2]

the MAGIC telescopes in the VHE band and several optical-NearInfraRed (NIR) and radio ground based telescopes. The Nordic Optical Telescope and the Gran Telescopio Canarias gave a redshift estimation of $z = 0.4245 \pm 0.0005$.

The timeline of the MAGIC observation can be described as follows:

- the Swift-BAT alert was received by the MAGIC automatic alert system at $T_0 + 22$ s. The alert was validated, the event tagged as observable and the automatic fast repositioning procedure started;
- the telescopes reached the target and started tracking at $T_0 + 50$ s;
- the data acquisition started receiving the first events at $T_0 + 57$ s and operated stably from $T_0 + 62$ s;
- observation lasted until $T_0 + 15912$ s when a zenith angle of $81.14°$ was reached.

The observation was performed in good weather conditions and in presence of the Moon, resulting in a night sky background approximately 6 times higher than the standard dark night conditions.

The analysis of the MAGIC dataset was performed with unprecedented accuracy performing many checks and tests to investigate the behaviour of the subsystems during the repointing and data taking. Moreover, several dedicated MC sets were produced in order to match the GRB observational conditions in the most precise way. The result of the offline analysis shows a clear detection above the 50 sigma level in the first 20 minutes of observation.

The light curve for the intrinsic flux corrected for the Extragalactic Background Light (EBL) absorption in the 0.3–1 TeV range was derived. A comparison of this light curve with the simultaneous X-ray and HE emission is shown in Figure 1.

From the evolution of the light curve and the comparison with the lower energy band emission it is possible to derive clues on the origin and the amount of power radiated in the TeV component. The TeV light curve is well described with a simple power-law temporal decay with index $\beta = 1.60 \pm 0.07$. A similar behaviour can also be seen in the X-ray and HE band. These properties, together with the absence of breaks, cutoffs or irregular variability, support the conclusion that the observed VHE emission component belong to the afterglow phase. Nevertheless, the presence of a subdominant prompt component cannot be excluded.

The comparison of the simultaneous light curves shows also that the radiated power in the TeV band is mostly comparable, within a factor of about 2, with the X-ray and HE bands. This means that a non-negligible fraction of energy is radiated in the TeV band. A rough estimate, calculated assuming that the onset of the afterglow is at $T_0 + 6$ s[4] and following the time evolution estimated by the MAGIC light curve is of around $\sim 10\%$ of the isotropic-equivalent energy of the prompt emission E_{iso}.

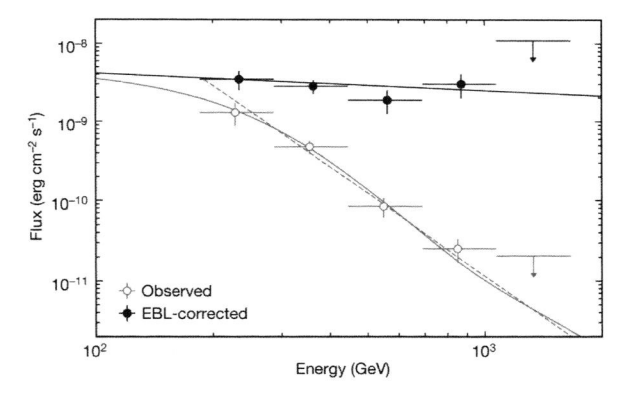

Fig. 2. GRB 190114C Observed (grey open circles) and intrinsic (black filled circles) spectral energy distribution in the time interval $T_0 + 62$ s and $T_0 + 2454$ s. The best fit power-law functions (black solid line and dashed grey line) and the EBL attenuated curve (solid grey line) are also shown.[2]

In Figure 1 also the temporal evolution of the intrinsic spectral photon index α_{int} of the TeV differential photon spectrum is shown. A constant value of $\alpha_{int} \approx -2$ is consistent with the data, considering the statistical and systematic errors. As a result, throughout the MAGIC observation, no spectral variability can be claimed. This value indicates that the radiated power is equally distributed in the 0.3-1 TeV energy range.

The observed and EBL-corrected spectral energy distributions in the 0.2-1 TeV energy range and ($T_0 + 62$ s - $T_0 + 2454$ s) time interval were also derived. Both the spectra are fitted with a simple power-law with indices $\alpha_{obs} = -5.34 \pm 0.22$ and $\alpha_{int} = -2.22^{+0.23}_{-0.25}$ respectively for the observed and EBL-corrected spectrum.

This result states that the VHE component observed by MAGIC is extended up to TeV energies. Moreover, the steep observed spectrum obtained certificates the strong effect of the EBL absorption (a factor of ~ 300 at 1 TeV) in shaping the GRB spectra in the VHE domain.

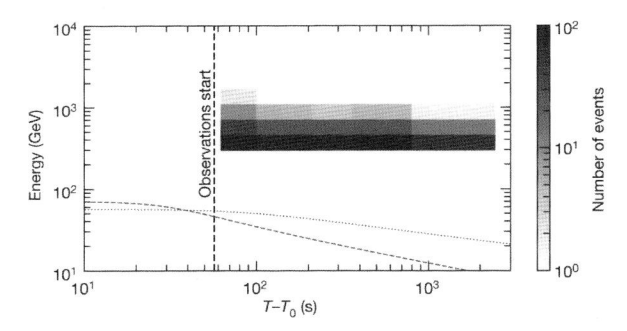

Fig. 3. Distribution of the number of GRB 190114C γ-ray events observed by MAGIC binned in time and energy and colour-coded. The synchrotron burnoff limiting curves are also displayed with two different assumptions for the external medium surrounding the GRB site: constant-density interstellar medium (dotted curve) and wind-like scenario (dashed curve).[2]

The similarities observed between the X-ray and the TeV light curves point towards the possibility that the same radiation mechanism is responsible for both components. Nevertheless, we proved that the TeV component cannot be interpreted as a simple extension in energy of the electron synchrotron emission mechanism. Indeed, in this scenario the energy of the accelerated electrons and hence of the synchrotron photons emitted is limited to a maximum value. This value can be estimated by equating the acceleration timescale and the synchrotron losses timescale, which dominates the electron energy losses. As a result, the maximum synchrotron photon energy, also called *synchrotron burnoff limit* is estimated as $E_{\rm syn,max} \sim 0.1 \Gamma_{\rm b}(t)/(1+z)$ GeV where $\Gamma_{\rm b}(t)$ is the Lorentz bulk factor of the GRB jet and z is the redshift. In Figure 3 we compared the energy of the observed photons by MAGIC binned in time and energy with $E_{\rm syn,max}$ assuming two possible scenarios for the dynamical evolution of the GRB blast wave. It can be clearly seen that events detected by MAGIC are well more energetic than $E_{\rm syn,max}$ in both scenarios. This gives a strong proof that a different radiation mechanism than electron synchrotron radiation must be claimed to explain such VHE emission component in GRB 190114C.

3. Multi-wavelength afterglow modeling

A multi-wavelength interpretation is fundamental for an in-depth study of the properties of the TeV emission and its connection with the lower energy band radiation. GRB 190114C emission was detected across 17 orders of magnitude in energy and

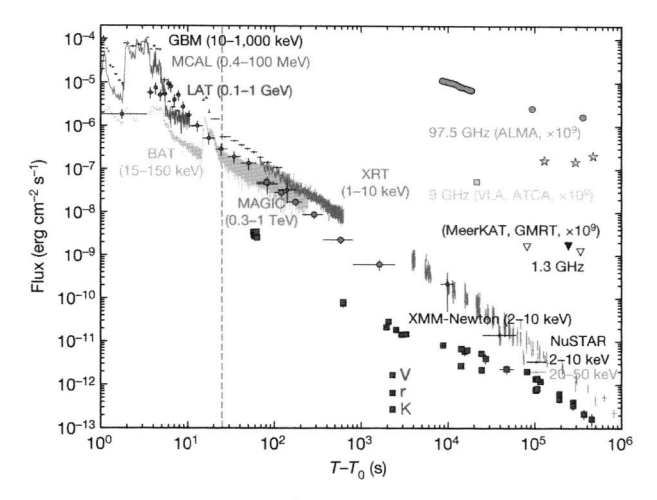

Fig. 4. Broadband light curves of GRB 190114C. Data from radio up to γ-rays are included. The vertical dashed line marks approximately the end of the prompt phase, identified as the end of the last flaring episode.[3]

by more than 20 instruments both from ground and in space (see Figure 4). In particular, the simultaneous data collected in a few time intervals in the X-ray (XRT, BAT, GBM), HE (LAT) and VHE (MAGIC) domain allow to build multi-wavelength time-binned spectra (see Figure 5). In the first time interval (68-110 s) the usual synchrotron peak flux is located in the X-ray band. Subsequently, in the HE band a decreasing flux behaviour is observed. Then, the VHE data implies the presence of a second peak in the flux and a spectral hardening for energies $E > 0.2$ TeV. This behaviour can be explained only if we assume that the TeV emission is not an extention of the X-ray synchrotron emission component but it is produced by a different radiation mechanism.

The most credible scenario able to describe consistently the multi-wavelength data is the *synchrotron and SSC external shock scenario*. In this picture, the SSC radiation mechanism produces the TeV photons while the synchrotron emission can explain the lower energy band radiation. The distribution of accelerated electrons emitting the synchrotron radiation are also responsible for the up-scattering of the same synchrotron photons through inverse Compton mechanism. As a result, a second spectral component peaking in the VHE band is generated. The afterglow emission is usually well described through external shocks. SSC radiation at TeV level can be also produced in internal shock synchrotron models for the prompt emission. However, for GRB 190114C it was estimate that it can only partially contribute ($\lesssim 20\%$) for the flux emitted at early times ($\lesssim 100$ s). As a result, the SSC radiation in the afterglow scenario is the most viable process.

The validity of this scenario was tested thanks to a numerical modeling. The full multi-wavelength dataset was modelled with a numerical code reproducing the

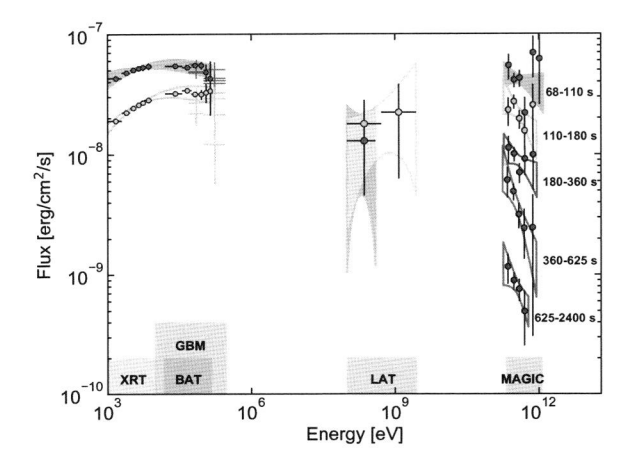

Fig. 5. Multi-band SEDs in five different time intervals. MAGIC data analysis results are corrected for the EBL attenuation. MAGIC and LAT contour regions are drawn from the 1σ error of their best-fit power-law functions. For Swift data, the regions show the 90% confidence contours for the joint fit for XRT and BAT, obtained by fitting a smoothly broken power law to the data.[3]

synchrotron plus SSC radiation emitted in the external forward shock afterglow scenario. In Figure 6 the modeling for two time intervals and for the X-ray, HE and VHE bands is shown. The numerical code solves the time-evolving electron distribution and calculates the corresponding photon emission covering the entire electromagnetic spectrum. The following radiation processes are considered: electron synchrotron emission and self-absorption, SSC emission, adiabatic losses, γ-γ absorption and emission from pairs. A set of inputs parameters containing some assumptions due to unknown properties of the acceleration process, of the shock microphysics, of the external medium and of the GRB jet and the initial conditions of the system are given in the code. The soft spectrum derived from the MAGIC dataset constrain the peak of the SSC component to be below 200 GeV. Such condition is obtained assuming that the SSC process is in Klein-Nishina regime and the γ-γ internal absorption has a non-negligible contribution in shaping the higher energy tail of the VHE spectrum.

Acceptable modeling of the multi-wavelength afterglow spectra have been found with an initial isotropic-equivalent kinetic energy of the blastwave $E_k \gtrsim 3 \times 10^{53}$ erg. The electron and magnetic field equipartition parameters are respectively $\varepsilon_e \approx 0.05 - 0.15$ and $\varepsilon_b \approx 0.05 - 1 \times 10^{-3}$, the density of the external medium is $n \approx 0.5 - 5$ cm^{-3} and the distribution of the accelerated electrons is described with a power-law of index $p \approx 2.4 - 2.6$. This set of values for the GRB afterglow parameters is similar to the one used for past GRB afterglow studies at lower frequencies. This is an indication that the SSC component can be a relatively common process for GRB afterglows.

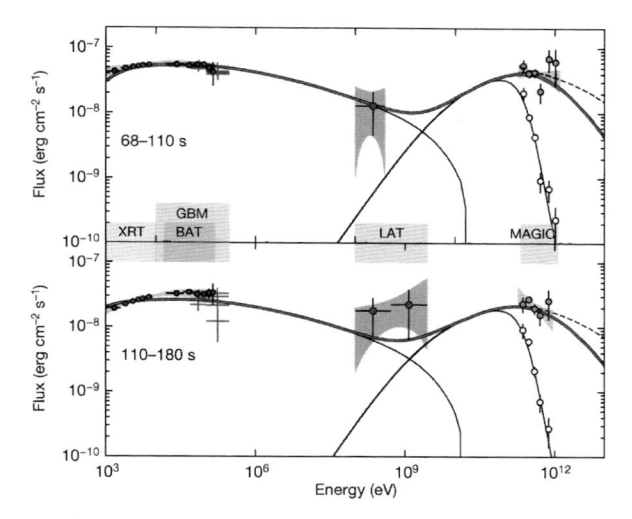

Fig. 6. Modeling of GRB 190114C spectral energy distributions in two different time intervals. Observed (thin solid line) and deabsorbed (thick blue line) spectrum are displayed. The dashed line is the SSC component neglecting the effects of internal γ-γ opacity.[3]

4. Conclusions

Observation and detection of GRB 190114C is a key milestone for the study and the interpretation of GRB physics. After decades of searches, the unambiguous discovery of a TeV component in GRBs made it possible to address for the first time ever several open questions. The newly open TeV spectral window also gives rise to new challenges for the observation and interpretation of GRBs.

A complete multiwavelength modeling of the GRB 190114C data covering the entire electromagnetic spectrum from radio up to TeV was presented. The full evolution of the afterglow emission was interpreted with the synchrotron plus SSC external forward shock scenario. The afterglow parameters used in the modeling of the X-ray, HE and VHE data have relatively common values, similar to those used in previous studies on GRBs where VHE emission was not detected. When evolving this solution to later times (see Figure 7) the optical and radio emission is overpredicted with respect to the observations. This inconsistency between the data and the modeling can be interpreted as an indication that some of the fixed parameters of the afterglow theory (e.g. the electron and magnetic field equipartition parameters) may evolve in time.

The intrinsic properties of GRB 190114C are not so exceptional when compared with the sample of the observed long GRBs. Despite being an energetic event (the isotropic-equivalent energy from the prompt is $\approx 3 \times 10^{53}$), it lies in the highest 30% distribution in energy for long GRBs.[5] This suggests that a larger sample of GRBs can have a detectable TeV component. On the other hand, favourable observational conditions and redshift play a crucial role in order to make TeV detections possible.

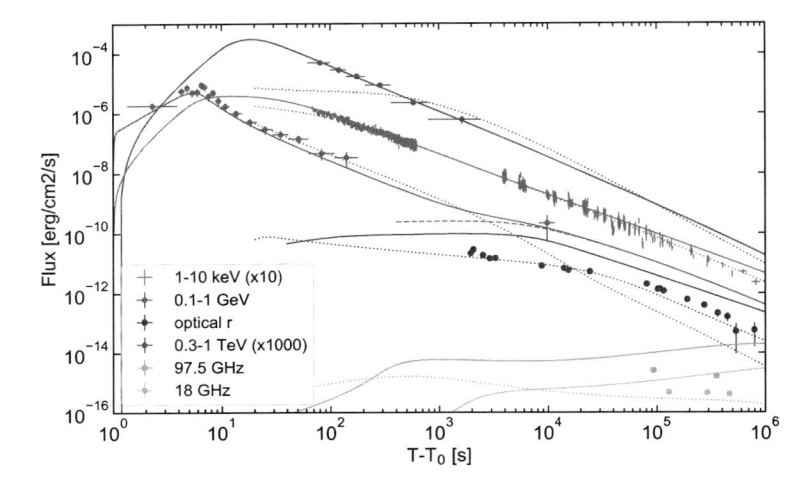

Fig. 7. Modeling of GRB 190114C afterglow light curves from radio up to TeV. Two different sets of parameters, respectively displayed in solid and dotted lines are compared to the observations. The former one is optimized for the X-ray, GeV and TeV data while the latter one well reproduces the late time optical modeling but do not explain the early time TeV emission. The dashed red line indicate the SSC contribution in the 0.1-1 GeV band.[3]

This was proved by the TeV detections of other three long GRBs: GRB 180720B,[6] GRB 190829A[7] and GRB 201216C.[8] These discoveries showed that TeV detections can be possible even at late times (hours on even a day after the trigger like in the case of GRB 180720B and GRB 190829A), or in low-luminosity events ($E_{iso} \approx 3 \times 10^{50}$ in GRB 190829A), or at higher redshift ($z = 1.1$ for GRB 201216C). The first population studies of GRBs at VHE will provide the possibility to investigate the conditions which favour a TeV detection.

The TeV photons detected from GRB 190114C were also used to give insights on some fundamental physics questions. An example is given by the study and the bounds derived on the Lorentz invariance violation effect.[9]

Furthermore, the ongoing observations of GRBs in the VHE domain will be fundamental to state the presence of a TeV emission component in short GRBs (a hint of detection, but still not conclusive, was claimed for GRB 160821B[10]) or during the prompt emission phase. Short GRBs are known to be linked with gravitational wave events. Therefore, the detection of a TeV emission component could give information on the structure of GRB jets as well as on the geometry of the merger event. The detection of TeV emission in the prompt emission phase shall provide essential information on the radiation mechanisms involved which are still unknown.

Further detections of GRBs in the VHE domain will be also useful to test the current most credible scenario for the TeV afterglow emission, namely the SSC external forward shock scenario. At the current stage, the results published for GRB 190114C,[3] GRB 180720B[6] and GRB 190829A[11] can be satisfactorily interpreted with the SSC scenario. Nevertheless, several open questions and assumptions on the acceleration process, shock microphysics and environmental condition are still unclear.

In this evolving context the robust results obtained from the analysis and the interpretation of GRB 190114C will be a reference point for future studies of the properties of the VHE emission component in GRBs.

References

1. Zhang, B. (2019). Extreme emission seen from γ-ray bursts. Nature, 575(7783), 448-449.
2. MAGIC Collaboration, Nature, 575, 455-458 (2019)
3. MAGIC Collaboration et al., Nature, 575, 459-453 (2019)
4. Ravasio, M. E. et al., Astronomy & Astrophysics, 626, A12 (2019)
5. Nava, L. et al., Mon. Not. R. Astron. Soc. 421, 1256–1264 (2012).
6. H.E.S.S. Collaboration et al., Nature, 575, 464–467 (2019)
7. H.E.S.S. Collaboration et al., Science, 372, 1081-1085 (2021)
8. S. Fukami et al., ICRC2021 proceedings, (2021)
9. MAGIC Collaboration et al., Physical Review Letters, 125, 021301 (2020)
10. V. A. Acciari et al., Astrophysical Journal, 908, 90 (2021)
11. Salafia, O. et al, ArXiv e-prints, 2106.07169, (2021)

AGILE and GRBs: 13 years of observations

A. Ursi*, on behalf of the AGILE Team

INAF/IAPS, via del Fosso del Cavaliere 100, I-00133 Roma (RM), Italy
* E-mail: alessandro.ursi@inaf.it

Over a time frame of 13 years, from November 2007 to November 2020, the AGILE MiniCALorimeter (MCAL; 0.4-100 MeV), detected 503 Gamma-Ray Bursts (GRBs). This sample is constituted by 44% short GRBs and 56% long GRBs, as retrieved from the study of the associated T_{50} and T_{90} burst duration distribution. For 258 GRBs, it was possible to perform a spectral analysis by adopting a single power law model; for 43 of them, also a spectral fit with a Band model with peak energy E_p above 400 keV was possible. More than 90% of these bursts were also detected by the AGILE Scientific RateMeters (RMs), providing comprehensive simultaneous observations from few tens keV to 100 MeV. The MCAL GRBs mostly consists of short-duration, spectrally hard events, due to the energy range of the detector and the adopted onboard trigger configurations, representing a burst sample which can be used to provide further insights on the high-energy component of hard-spectrum bursts.

Keywords: GRBs, high-energy, catalog, AGILE

1. Introduction

Discovered in the late 1960s,[1] Gamma-Ray Bursts (GRBs) still represent an intriguing and not completely understood phenomenon. These events consist of transients bursts of hard X- and gamma-rays, emitted by ultra-relativistic particles which have been accelerated in extragalactic central engines, releasing isotropic energies of about $E_{iso} \gtrsim 10^{51} - 10^{52}$ erg.[2] On the basis of their spectral hardness and time duration, GRBs are usually divided in short GRBs, lasting less than ~ 2 s and exhibiting a hard spectrum up to MeV energies, and long GRBs, lasting more than ~ 2 s and exhibiting a softer spectrum. The first ones are produced by the merger of binary neutron stars (BNS),[3–7] whereas the second ones are associated with Type Ic core-collapse supernovae.[8,9]

2. The AGILE satellite

The Astrorivelatore Gamma ad Immagini LEggero (AGILE) is an Italian space mission for high-energy astrophysics.[10] Its payload consists of a tungsten-silicon imaging tracker, sensitive in the 30 MeV - 50 GeV energy range, a non-imaging CsI(Tl) scintillation MiniCALorimeter (MCAL), sensitive in the 0.4-100 MeV energy range, a coded mask X-ray imager SuperAGILE (SA), sensitive in the 18-60 keV energy range, and an Anti-Coincidence (AC) system, sensitive in the 50-200 keV energy range. The suite of silicon tracker and MCAL detectors constitute the Gamma-Ray Imaging Detector (GRID).

Starting 2009, the satellite underwent a failure of the reaction wheel, losing the possibility to point sources in the sky and starting to spin around the sun-pointing axis, with an angular velocity of 1 rotation / 7 min. Spinning does not represent an issue for the MCAL detector, due to its ideal 4π sr FoV; moreover, it does not affect GRB detection, given the isotropic nature of these events. However, spinning could have an effect for what concerns spectral analysis of long GRBs, as such long-lasting events would be detected under different angles, throughout their whole duration, requiring the retrieval of several response matrices, and making the spectral fit more complex.

2.1. *MCAL and scientific ratemeters*

The AGILE Mini-CALorimeter (MCAL)[11,12] is a non-imaging scintillation detector, sensitive between 400 keV and 100 MeV, composed of 30 CsI(Tl) scintillator bars. MCAL is a self-triggered detector, issuing a data acquisition with 2 μs time resolution whenever a count rate exceeding a given threshold is encountered. The trigger system acts on different trigger logic timescales: in particular, the so-called "hardware" logic works on short-duration timescales (0.293 ms, 1 ms, 16 ms) and adopts a static trigger with a fixed threshold count rate required to issue a data acquisition, whereas the so-called "software" logic works on longer-duration timescales (64 ms, 256 ms, 1024 ms, and 8192 ms) and adopts an adaptive trigger with a threshold count rate dependent on the background rate.

For what concerns the detection of GRBs, differently from the silicon tracker and SuperAGILE, MCAL does not require these events to lay within a given FoV, allowing a continuous monitoring of an ideal $\sim 4\pi$ sky. Moreover, MCAL focuses on the poorly investigated tens of MeV energy range, allowing to provide insights on the high-energy component of hard-spectrum bursts.

A first MCAL GRB Catalog with 84 events detected in the first two years of the AGILE mission, in the so-called "pointing mode" (2007-2009), was released in 2013[13] and a second MCAL GRB Catalog with 503 events, covering also the successive 11 years in the so-called "spinning mode" (2007-2020) was recently submitted to ApJ.[14] MCAL is part of the 3rd Inter-Planetary Network (IPN), providing GRB detections which can be used for triangulation and localization of the bursts. Starting 2017, a new real time pipeline system has been established, for the automatic offline analysis of MCAL data and the prompt delivery of GCN Notices and Circular to the scientific community, in case of a transient detection ([a]). In recent years, the onboard trigger configuration was modified to increase the MCAL detection efficiency to short-duration transients, in order to improve the detector sensitivity to possible electromagnetic counterparts of gravitational wave events, during the LIGO-Virgo observational runs O2 and O3, and in order to save onboard mass memory, to deal with severe telemetry restrictions undergone in recent years.

---

[a]https://gcn.gsfc.nasa.gov/agile_mcal.html

The MCAL, SA, and AC data are continuously recorded in telemetry as scientific RateMeter (RM) data, with a 0.5 s (for SA) and 1.0 s (for MCAL, and AC) time resolution, to provide a monitoring of the X- and gamma-ray background modulation throughout the satellite orbital phases. Nevertheless, the AGILE RMs allow to independently detect a large number of high-energy transients, as GRBs, Soft Gamma-ray Repeaters (SGRs), or solar flares. Despite the coarse time resolution, RM data might serve as back-up of data acquired by the onboard detectors, as well as to provide cross-check and validation of GRBs detected by MCAL.

3. Methods

A cross-search between $\sim 10^6$ AGILE MCAL triggers, issued onboard from November 2007 to November 2020, and ~ 4500 IPN[15] bursts (IPN webpage:[b]), reported by the network in the same time interval, lead to the identification of 476 GRBs in the MCAL data. Due to the better efficiency of MCAL to detect short-duration transients, 109 long GRBs were only partially acquired onboard by the detector. Despite being incomplete, these events may serve as further detections which can be used to improve sky localizations via triangulation.

A parallel blind search in the MCAL data, using the offline burst search algorithm,[16] led to the detection of other 27 candidate short GRBs, not reported by other space missions. The total MCAL GRB sample is therefore constituted by 503 bursts, as reported in the second AGILE MCAL GRB Catalog,[14] recently submitted to ApJ and available on line on the ASI Space Science Data Center (SSDC) web portal at[c]. About 90% of these events have been also detected by one or more scientific RMs. A simultaneous detection of all scientific RMs would provide a broad band characterization of these events, from few tens keV to tens of MeV. In particular, the RMs detection is very suitable when dealing with partially acquired long GRBs, in order to reconstruct the whole light curve of the event and provide insights in different wavelengths.

3.1. Time analysis

For the 394 fully detected GRBs, it was possible to reconstruct the complete light curves of the events and to study their temporal properties. The T_{50} and T_{90} time distributions[17] of these bursts ended up with 173 short GRBs and 221 long GRBs, as shown in Fig. 1. The sample shows a large fraction (44%) of short GRBs, with respect to that retrieved by other space missions, as INTEGRAL,[18] Fermi GBM,[19] and Konus-Wind.[20] This can be ascribed to different reasons: first of all, the onboard trigger configuration optimized for the detection of short-duration transients, as already exposed in Section 2.1; the second reason is related to the relatively high-energy (> 400 keV) range of MCAL, which makes the detector more sensitive

---

[b]http://www.ssl.berkeley.edu/ipn3/
[c]https://www.ssdc.asi.it/mcal2grbcat/

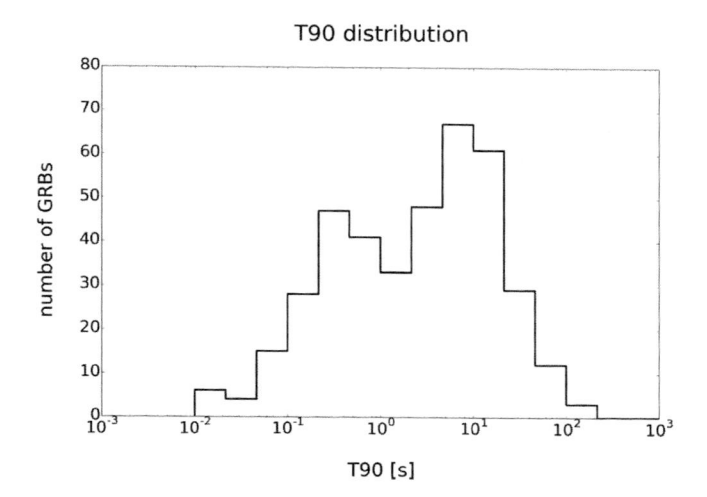

Fig. 1. T_{50} and T_{90} distributions of 394 GRBs fully detected onboard by MCAL. The typical bimodal distribution consists in 44% short GRBs and 56% long GRBs.

to hard-spectrum bursts, typically short GRBs. Moreover, the 0.4-100 MeV energy range allows to investigate only a limited spectral component of the detected bursts: a GRB will typically last longer if considering the whole spectrum including also the keV - tens of keV energy range. An example of this is shown in Fig. 2, where the same burst, GRB 200829A, is detected by the SA and the MCAL RMs, and the event clearly exhibit a longer time duration in the softer SA regime (15.3 ± 0.5 s), with respect to that observed in the harder MCAL regime (8.1 ± 0.5 s). The SA light curves have been rescaled in order to have similar background rates and to better highlight the time duration difference in the two energy ranges.

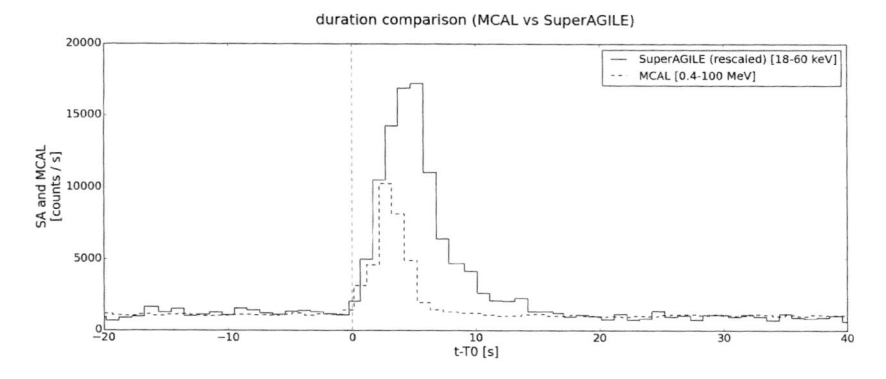

Fig. 2. GRB 200829A as detected by SuperAGILE, in the 18-60 keV energy range, and by MCAL, in the 0.4-100 MeV energy range. The event clearly lasts longer (15.3 ± 0.5 s) in the softer energy range, with respect to the MCAL high-energy range (8.1 ± 0.5 s). Data are rescaled in order to have similar background rates and highlight the time duration difference.

3.2. *Spectral analysis*

MCAL GRB sky distribution

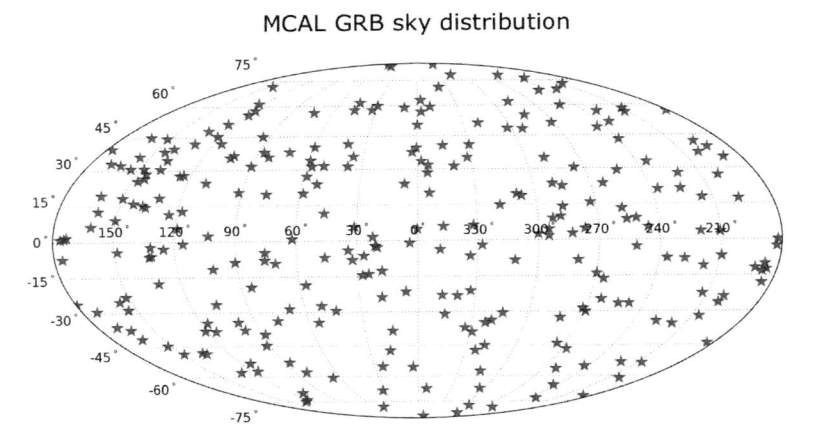

Fig. 3. Sky distribution of 276 MCAL GRBs, for which it was possible to retrieve an external localization from other space missions, or from IPN triangulations. Among them, 258 events could be fitted with a single power law model, and 43 events could be fitted also with a Band model.

In order to perform spectral analysis of the MCAL GRBs, it is necessary to retrieve the corresponding sky localizations, in order to reconstruct the appropriate response matrix of the instrument at the time of the detection. As MCAL is a non-imaging detector, localizations were retrieved from other space missions with imaging capabilities, or from IPN triangulations. In particular, it was possible to retrieve the sky localization of 276 GRBs of the MCAL sample, from detections by Fermi GBM, Fermi LAT, Swift BAT, Swift XRT, INTEGRAL ISGRI, or IPN triangulations. The spatial distibution of these events is shown in Fig. 3. Exploiting these localizations, on the basis of the available count statistics, it was possible to carry out a spectral fit for 258 GRBs. Spectral analysis was carried out using the XSpec package (version 12.9.0[21]), and adopting different fitting statistics depending on the count and background rates. Spectral fit was carried out in the fixed energy range from 400 keV to 50 MeV.

For 258 GRBs, a spectral fit with a single power law model was possible. The average photon index obtained from this sample is equal to $\langle \beta \rangle \sim -2.3$, highlighting the hardness of these bursts. The distribution of the power law photon index is shown in Fig. 4. The MCAL GRB fluxes, obtained from the spectal fitting with a power law model and estimated with a 90% confidence level, range between $3.9 \cdot 10^{-7}$ erg cm^{-2} s^{-1} and $1.0 \cdot 10^{-2}$ erg cm^{-2} s^{-1}, whereas the corresponding fluences, integrated over the related T_{90} time durations, range from $5.5 \cdot 10^{-8}$ erg cm^{-2} and $1.3 \cdot 10^{-2}$ erg cm^{-2}. The distribution of GRB fluxes is reported in Fig. 5. Moreover, for 43 particularly hard GRBs, it was possible to obtain a good spectral fit also by adopting a Band model[22] with peak energy $E_p > 400$ keV. In particular, these events

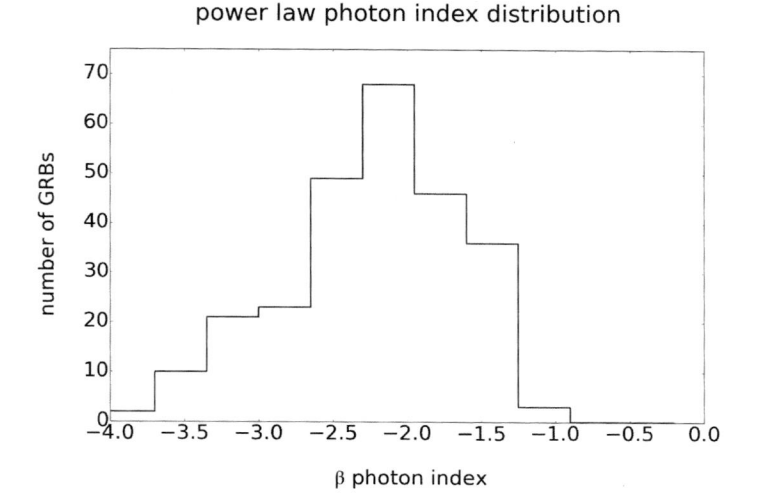

Fig. 4. Distribution of the photon index β of the single power law adopted to fit 258 MCAL GRBs. The average photon index results equal to $\langle \beta \rangle \sim -2.3$.

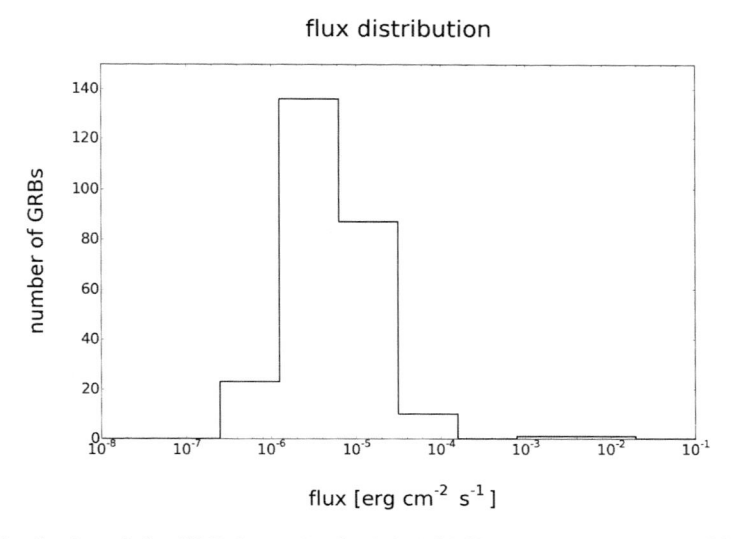

Fig. 5. Distribution of the GRB fluxes, in the 0.4-50 MeV energy range, obtained by fitting 258 burst with a single power law model.

exhibit a mean low-energy photon index $\langle \alpha \rangle \sim -0.6$, a mean high-energy photon index $\langle \beta \rangle \sim -2.5$, and a mean peak energy $\langle E_p \rangle \sim 640$ keV. The distribution of the high-energy photon index β resulting from the fit with a Band model is shown in Fig. 6.

It is interesting to notice that 92 GRBs can be fitted with power laws with photon indices $\beta > -2$, which correspond to hard-spectrum events with spectral

high-energy photon index distribution

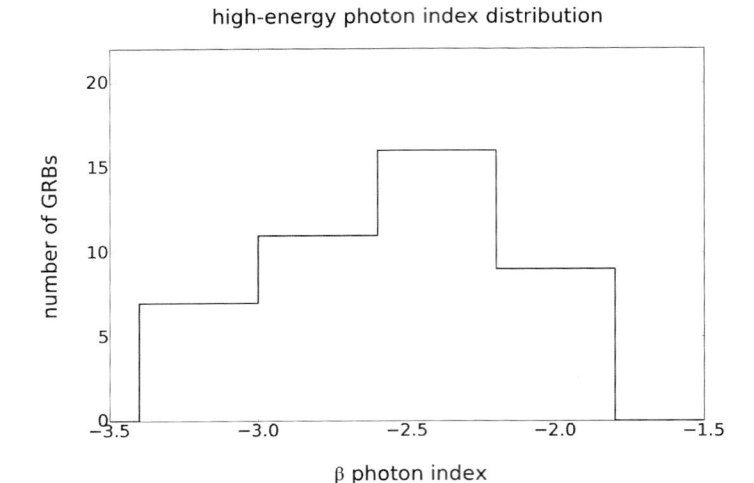

Fig. 6. Distribution of the high-energy photon index β of the Band model adopted to fit 43 MCAL GRBs. The average photon index results equal to $\langle\beta\rangle \sim -2.5$.

energy densities νF_ν with positive slopes, extending the emission up to the highest energies. These events and the 43 bursts fitted with Band models with $E_p > 400$ keV represent the hardest spectrum GRB subsample detected by the AGILE MCAL. Among them, 20 events have a simultaneous Fermi LAT detection.

3.3. GRB population decline and Amati relation

Adopting fluxes retrieved by spectral fits with power law model, an MCAL GRB $logN - logF$ brightness distribution can be reconstructed, as shown in Fig. 7. Such distribution provides information on the intrinsic spatial properties of GRBs and on the GRBs population decline at large distances. As MCAL is an all-sky monitor, the $logN - logF$ is not affected by on-axis area variations. Issues which can limit the monitoring of the sky, such as passages into the South Atlantic Anomaly, where the detector is switched off, or Earth occultations, which constantly hide about 35% of the available sky, can be neglected over a time frame of 13 years. The deviation at faint fluxes from a -3/2 slope, retrieved at large fluxes and typical of a Euclidean universe, makes the spatial distribution of GRBs unconsistent with a homogeneous universe.

For 8 events out of the 43 MCAL GRBs fitted with a Band model with $E_p > 400$ keV it was possible to retrieve the corresponding redshift, provided by X-ray or optical observations of their afterglow. Using a standard cosmological model with $H_0 = 67.3$ km s^{-1} Mpc^{-1}, $\Omega_M = 0.315$, and $\Omega_\Lambda = 0.685$, it was possible to evaluate the GRB related rest-frame parameters, such as the intrinsic peak energy $E_{p,i} = (1+z)E_p$ of the time integrated spectrum and the isotropic equivalent

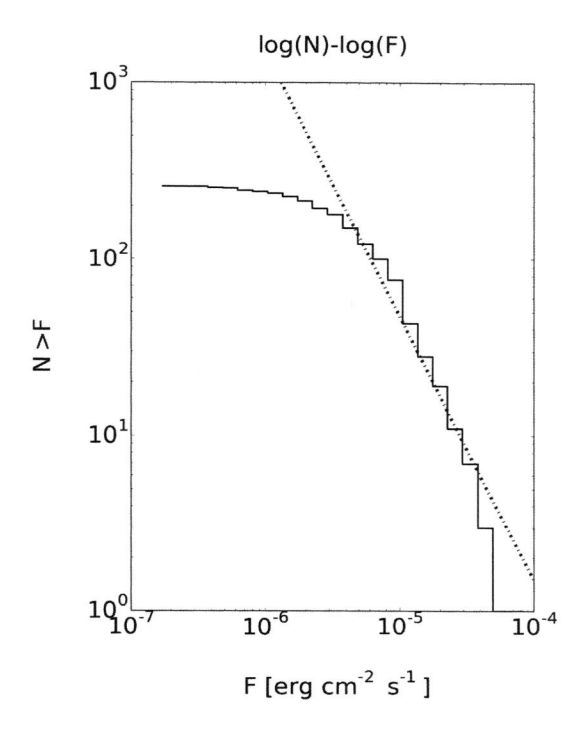

Fig. 7. GRB population decline obtained from the $logN - logF$ distribution of 258 MCAL bursts, fitted with a power law model. For faint fluxes, the brightness distribution departs from a $-3/2$ slope (dash-dotted line), typical of a Euclidean three-dimensional space, making the GRB spatial distribution not consistent with a homogenoeus universe.

energy E_{iso} in the 1-10000 keV energy range. The Amati relation[23,24] obtained from this sample results in a best-fit of the $E_{pi} = K(E_{iso}/10^{52})^m$ curve with a slope $m = 0.130 \pm 0.067$, as shown in Fig. 8. The coefficient obtained for MCAL GRBs is slightly more gentle with respect to the typical value of $m \sim 0.45$ reported by other space missions, due to the due to the non-uniform spectral hardness of the analyzed sample.

4. Conclusions

In more than 10 years activity, the AGILE MCAL detected 503 GRBs in the 0.4-100 MeV energy range. About 90% of these events were also simultaneously detected by the AGILE scientific RMs, covering a wide energy range, from 20 keV to 100 MeV. For 394 events, it was possible to reconstruct the T_{50} and T_{90} durations, ending up with 44% short GRBs and 56% long GRBs, resulting in a large fraction of short-duration bursts. 476 of these events are confirmed by simultaneous detections by other space missions, as reported by the IPN network, whereas 27 of these events are GRB candidates, so far only reported by MCAL. Using localizations provided

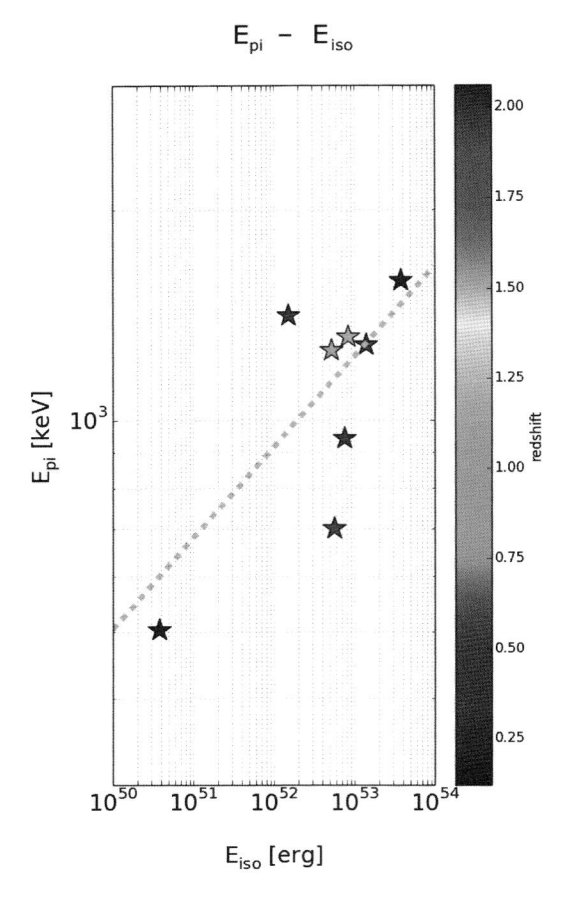

Fig. 8. Rest-frame $E_{iso} - E_{p,i}$ plane with 8 MCAL GRBs with known redshifts (colorbar), fitted with a Band model with $E_p > 400$ keV, in the 1-10000 keV energy range. The dashed line corresponds to the best-fit Amati relation, with slope $m = 0.130 \pm 0.067$.

by other missions, or by IPN triangulations, it was possible to carry out a spectral analysis of the time integrated spectrum for 258 GRBs. In particular, these events are well fitted by a single power law model, with a mean photon index $\langle \beta \rangle \sim -2.3$. For 43 events, also a Band model with peak energy $E_p > 400$ keV provided a good fit. The large fraction of bursts with durations $T_{90} < 2$ s and fittable either with power laws with photon index $\beta > -2$ or with a Band model indicates that MCAL GRBs mainly consists in short-duration, hard-spectrum bursts, which constitute an interesting and suitable sample that can be used to better investigate events with high-energy spectral components in the tens of MeV energy range.

References

1. R. W. Klebesadel, I. B. Strong and R. A. Olson, Observations of Gamma-Ray Bursts of Cosmic Origin, *Astrophys. J.l* **182**, p. L85 (June 1973).

2. N. Gehrels and P. Mészáros, Gamma-Ray Bursts, *Science* **337**, p. 932 (August 2012).
3. B. P. Abbott, R. Abbott, T. D. Abbott, F. Acernese, K. Ackley, C. Adams, T. Adams, P. Addesso, R. X. Adhikari, V. B. Adya and et al., GW170104: Observation of a 50-Solar-Mass Binary Black Hole Coalescence at Redshift 0.2, *Physical Review Letters* **118**, p. 221101 (June 2017).
4. B. P. Abbott, R. Abbott, T. D. Abbott, F. Acernese, K. Ackley, C. Adams, T. Adams, P. Addesso, R. X. Adhikari, V. B. Adya and et al., GW170608: Observation of a 19 Solar-mass Binary Black Hole Coalescence, *Astrophysical Journal Letters* **851**, p. L35 (December 2017).
5. B. P. Abbott, R. Abbott, T. D. Abbott, F. Acernese, K. Ackley, C. Adams, T. Adams, P. Addesso, R. X. Adhikari, V. B. Adya and et al., GW170814: A Three-Detector Observation of Gravitational Waves from a Binary Black Hole Coalescence, *Physical Review Letters* **119**, p. 141101 (October 2017).
6. V. Connaughton, A. Goldstein and Fermi GBM - LIGO Group, Multi-Messenger Time-Domain Astronomy with the Fermi Gamma-ray Burst Monitor, in *American Astronomical Society Meeting Abstracts #229*, American Astronomical Society Meeting Abstracts Vol. 229, January 2017.
7. A. Goldstein, P. Veres, E. Burns, M. S. Briggs, R. Hamburg, D. Kocevski, C. A. Wilson-Hodge, R. D. Preece, S. Poolakkil, O. J. Roberts, C. M. Hui, V. Connaughton, J. Racusin, A. von Kienlin, T. Dal Canton, N. Christensen, T. Littenberg, K. Siellez, L. Blackburn, J. Broida, E. Bissaldi, W. H. Cleveland, M. H. Gibby, M. M. Giles, R. M. Kippen, S. McBreen, J. McEnery, C. A. Meegan, W. S. Paciesas and M. Stanbro, An Ordinary Short Gamma-Ray Burst with Extraordinary Implications: Fermi-GBM Detection of GRB 170817A, *Astrophysical Journal Letters* **848**, p. L14 (October 2017).
8. T. J. Galama, P. M. Vreeswijk, J. van Paradijs, C. Kouveliotou, T. Augusteijn, H. Böhnhardt, J. P. Brewer, V. Doublier, J.-F. Gonzalez, B. Leibundgut, C. Lidman, O. R. Hainaut, F. Patat, J. Heise, J. in't Zand, K. Hurley, P. J. Groot, R. G. Strom, P. A. Mazzali, K. Iwamoto, K. Nomoto, H. Umeda, T. Nakamura, T. R. Young, T. Suzuki, T. Shigeyama, T. Koshut, M. Kippen, C. Robinson, P. de Wildt, R. A. M. J. Wijers, N. Tanvir, J. Greiner, E. Pian, E. Palazzi, F. Frontera, N. Masetti, L. Nicastro, M. Feroci, E. Costa, L. Piro, B. A. Peterson, C. Tinney, B. Boyle, R. Cannon, R. Stathakis, E. Sadler, M. C. Begam and P. Ianna, An unusual supernova in the error box of the γ-ray burst of 25 April 1998, *Nature* **395**, 670 (October 1998).
9. K. Z. Stanek, T. Matheson, P. M. Garnavich, P. Martini, P. Berlind, N. Caldwell, P. Challis, W. R. Brown, R. Schild, K. Krisciunas, M. L. Calkins, J. C. Lee, N. Hathi, R. A. Jansen, R. Windhorst, L. Echevarria, D. J. Eisenstein, B. Pindor, E. W. Olszewski, P. Harding, S. T. Holland and D. Bersier, Spectroscopic Discovery of the Supernova 2003dh Associated with GRB 030329, *Astrophysical Journal Letters* **591**, L17 (July 2003).
10. M. Tavani, G. Barbiellini, A. Argan, F. Boffelli, A. Bulgarelli, P. Caraveo, P. W. Cattaneo, A. W. Chen, V. Cocco, E. Costa, F. D'Ammando, E. Del Monte, G. de Paris, G. Di Cocco, G. di Persio, I. Donnarumma, Y. Evangelista, M. Feroci, A. Ferrari, M. Fiorini, F. Fornari, F. Fuschino, T. Froysland, M. Frutti, M. Galli, F. Gianotti, A. Giuliani, C. Labanti, I. Lapshov, F. Lazzarotto, F. Liello, P. Lipari, F. Longo, E. Mattaini, M. Marisaldi, M. Mastropietro, A. Mauri, F. Mauri, S. Mereghetti, E. Morelli, A. Morselli, L. Pacciani, A. Pellizzoni, F. Perotti, G. Piano, P. Picozza, C. Pontoni, G. Porrovecchio, M. Prest, G. Pucella, M. Rapisarda, A. Rappoldi, E. Rossi, A. Rubini, P. Soffitta, A. Traci, M. Trifoglio, A. Trois, E. Vallazza, S. Vercellone, V. Vittorini, A. Zambra, D. Zanello, C. Pittori, B. Preger, P. Santolamazza, F. Verrecchia, P. Giommi, S. Colafrancesco, A. Antonelli, S. Cutini, D. Gasparrini, S. Stellato, G. Fanari, R. Primavera, F. Tamburelli, F. Viola, G. Guarrera, L. Salotti, F. D'Amico,

E. Marchetti, M. Crisconio, P. Sabatini, G. Annoni, S. Alia, A. Longoni, R. Sanquerin, M. Battilana, P. Concari, E. Dessimone, R. Grossi, A. Parise, F. Monzani, E. Artina, R. Pavesi, G. Marseguerra, L. Nicolini, L. Scandelli, L. Soli, V. Vettorello, E. Zardetto, A. Bonati, L. Maltecca, E. D'Alba, M. Patané, G. Babini, F. Onorati, L. Acquaroli, M. Angelucci, B. Morelli, C. Agostara, M. Cerone, A. Michetti, P. Tempesta, S. D'Eramo, F. Rocca, F. Giannini, G. Borghi, B. Garavelli, M. Conte, M. Balasini, I. Ferrario, M. Vanotti, E. Collavo and M. Giacomazzo, The AGILE Mission, *Astron. Astrophys.* **502**, 995 (August 2009).
11. C. Labanti *et al.*, The Mini-Calorimeter of the AGILE satellite, *proceedings of SPIE* **6266**, p. 62663Q (2006).
12. C. Labanti, M. Marisaldi, F. Fuschino, M. Galli, A. Argan, A. Bulgarelli, G. di Cocco, F. Gianotti, M. Tavani and M. Trifoglio, Design and construction of the Mini-Calorimeter of the AGILE satellite, *Nuclear Instruments and Methods in Physics Research A* **598**, 470 (January 2009).
13. M. Galli, M. Marisaldi, F. Fuschino, C. Labanti, A. Argan, G. Barbiellini, A. Bulgarelli, P. W. Cattaneo, S. Colafrancesco, E. Del Monte, M. Feroci, F. Gianotti, A. Giuliani, F. Longo, S. Mereghetti, A. Morselli, L. Pacciani, A. Pellizzoni, C. Pittori, M. Rapisarda, A. Rappoldi, M. Tavani, M. Trifoglio, A. Trois, S. Vercellone and F. Verrecchia, AGILE mini-calorimeter gamma-ray burst catalog, *Astron. Astrophys.* **553**, p. A33 (May 2013).
14. A. Ursi, M. Romani, F. Verrecchia, C. Pittori, M. Tavani, M. Marisaldi, M. Galli, C. Labanti, N. Parmiggiani, A. Bulgarelli, A. Addis, L. Baroncelli, M. Cardillo, C. Casentini, P. W. Cattaneo, A. Chen, A. Di Piano, F. Fuschino, F. Longo, F. Lucarelli, A. Morselli, G. Piano and S. Vercellone, The Second AGILE MCAL GRB Catalog: 13 Years of Observations, *Astrophysical Journal* , p. xx (2021).
15. K. Hurley, V. D. Pal'shin, R. L. Aptekar, S. V. Golenetskii, D. D. Frederiks, E. P. Mazets, D. S. Svinkin, M. S. Briggs, V. Connaughton, C. Meegan, J. Goldsten, W. Boynton, C. Fellows, K. Harshman, I. G. Mitrofanov, D. V. Golovin, A. S. Kozyrev, M. L. Litvak, A. B. Sanin, A. Rau, A. von Kienlin, X. Zhang, K. Yamaoka, Y. Fukazawa, Y. Hanabata, M. Ohno, T. Takahashi, M. Tashiro, Y. Terada, T. Murakami, K. Makishima, S. Barthelmy, T. Cline, N. Gehrels, J. Cummings, H. A. Krimm, D. M. Smith, E. D. Monte, M. Feroci and M. Marisaldi, The Interplanetary Network Supplement to the Fermi GBM Catalog of Cosmic Gamma-ray Bursts, *The Astrophysical Journal Supplement Series* **207**, p. 39 (aug 2013).
16. A. Ursi, M. Tavani, F. Verrecchia, M. Marisaldi, A. Argan, A. Trois and P. Tempesta, A New AGILE MCAL Configuration to Detect Gamma-Ray Bursts and Sub-threshold Events in the Multimessenger Era, *Astrophysical Journal* **871**, p. 27 (January 2019).
17. T. M. Koshut, W. S. Paciesas, C. Kouveliotou, J. van Paradijs, G. N. Pendleton, G. J. Fishman and C. A. Meegan, Systematic Effects on Duration Measurements of Gamma-Ray Bursts, *Astrophysical Journal* **463**, p. 570 (June 1996).
18. v. Bošnjak, D. Götz, L. Bouchet, S. Schanne and B. Cordier, The spectral catalogue of INTEGRAL gamma-ray bursts: results of the joint IBIS/SPI spectral analysis, *Astron. Astrophys.* **561**, p. A25 (2014).
19. P. N. Bhat, C. A. Meegan, A. von Kienlin, W. S. Paciesas, M. S. Briggs, J. M. Burgess, E. Burns, V. Chaplin, W. H. Cleveland, A. C. Collazzi, V. Connaughton, A. M. Diekmann, G. Fitzpatrick, M. H. Gibby, M. M. Giles, A. M. Goldstein, J. Greiner, P. A. Jenke, R. M. Kippen, C. Kouveliotou, B. Mailyan, S. McBreen, V. Pelassa, R. D. Preece, O. J. Roberts, L. S. Sparke, M. Stanbro, P. Veres, C. A. Wilson-Hodge,

S. Xiong, G. Younes, H.-F. Yu and B. Zhang, The Third Fermi GBM Gamma-ray Burst Catalog: The First Six Years, *The Astrophysical Journal Supplement Series* **223**, p. 28 (apr 2016).

20. D. S. Svinkin, D. D. Frederiks, R. L. Aptekar, S. V. Golenetskii, V. D. Pal'shin, P. P. Oleynik, A. E. Tsvetkova, M. V. Ulanov, T. L. Cline and K. Hurley, The Second Konus-Wind Catalog of Short Gamma-ray Bursts, *The Astrophysical Journal Supplement Series* **224**, p. 10 (may 2016).

21. K. A. Arnaud, XSPEC: The First Ten Years, in *Astronomical Data Analysis Software and Systems V*, eds. G. H. Jacoby and J. Barnes, Astronomical Society of the Pacific Conference Series, Vol. 101, January 1996.

22. D. Band, J. Matteson, L. Ford, B. Schaefer, D. Palmer, B. Teegarden, T. Cline, M. Briggs, W. Paciesas, G. Pendleton, G. Fishman, C. Kouveliotou, C. Meegan, R. Wilson and P. Lestrade, BATSE observations of gamma-ray burst spectra. I - Spectral diversity, *Astrophys. J.* **413**, 281 (aug 1993).

23. L. Amati *et al.*, Intrinsic spectra and energetics of BeppoSAX gamma-ray bursts with known redshifts, *Astron. Astrophys.* **390**, p. 81 (2002).

24. W. J. Azzam and M. J. Alothman, Redshift Independence of the Amati and Yonetoku Relations for Gamma-Ray Bursts, *International Journal of Astronomy and Astrophysics* **3**, 372 (January 2013).

Searching for Gamma-Ray Bursts with the High-Altitude Water Cherenkov (HAWC) observatory

K.L. Engel* for the HAWC Collaboration

Department of Physics, University of Maryland, College Park; 4150 Campus Dr, College Park, MD, USA 20742
* E-mail: klengel@umd.edu

Satellites and imaging atmospheric Cherenkov telescopes (IACTs) have shown that gamma-ray bursts (GRBs) are capable of producing very-high-energy photons— most notably GRB 190114C, observed up to 1 TeV by the MAGIC telescopes approximately one minute after triggering the Fermi GBM and Swift BAT satellites. Particularly suited to such searches and follow-up studies is the High-Altitude Water Cherenkov (HAWC) Observatory, which monitors 1/6th of the sky at any one time, complementing the pointed observations of TeV telescopes. It covers 2/3rds of the sky every day, with near continuous uptime. The HAWC GRB program comprises two dedicated analyses: a self-triggered all-sky search and a rapid response follow-up of GRBs reported by satellites. Both methods are performed in real time at the HAWC site and additionally repeated on archival data with improved calibration and reconstruction algorithms. Recent upgrades have HAWC poised for detection of the highest-energy gamma rays associated with GRBs, which are key to developing GRB emission models as well as constraining possible beyond-the-Standard-Model physics.

Keywords: Instrumentation: detectors; gamma rays: general; gamma ray burst: general

1. Introduction

Gamma-ray bursts (GRBs) remain one of the most enigmatic astrophysical sources, with the potential to shed light on topics at the forefront of the field, including physics beyond the Standard Model. Measurements of the highest-energy gamma rays associated with GRBs are key to developing models of the relativistic jets powering emission.[1] This is because observations of a spectral cutoff at the highest photon energies can be interpreted as estimation of the bulk Lorentz factor, Γ, in the region where gamma rays are produced,[2] providing insight into the internal GRB environment as well as the expected neutrino flux from GRBs, which is sensitive to Γ (see Ref. 3). In addition, the GRB spectrum above 10 GeV, such as that searched for with the High-Altitude Water Cherenkov (HAWC) Observatory's GRB program, can be used to constrain possible Beyond-the-Standard-Model physics that contains Lorentz invariance violations.[4] Alternatively, interpreting a spectral cutoff as attenuation of GRB photons from pair-production on extragalactic background light (EBL) provides constraints on EBL density over cosmological distances.[5]

There are at least two known classes of GRBs: short GRBs have durations of less than two seconds and a peak νF_ν at Earth of ~ 1 MeV,[4] whereas long GRBs last more than two seconds and the peak of νF_ν at Earth is $\sim$ 150–200 keV.[6] Short GRBs, with their harder spectrum, are believed to be the result of the merger of two compact objects, such as two neutron stars or a neutron star and a solar mass black hole.[7–9] Core-collapse supernova type Ic are believed to be the progenitors of long GRBs, supported by observed coincidences of the two phenomena.[10] However, because the occurrences of either class of GRB cannot be predicted, ground-based observations of such sources are limited by slewing times— especially detrimental for short GRBs.

2. The Highest-Energy Emission from GRBs

For both short and long GRBs, emission is believed to happen in highly relativistic narrow jets that point in the direction of Earth. Prompt GRB emission (that is, emission from the first seconds of the GRB) is detected in the keV–MeV band by space-borne instruments such as the *Fermi*-GBM[11] and Swift-BAT.[12] Satellites with instruments sensitive to hard gamma rays, such as the *Fermi*-LAT and imaging atmospheric Cherenkov telescopes (IACTs) such as the MAGIC telescopes and the HESS array, have shown that GRBs are capable of producing very-high-energy (VHE) photons. Prominent examples include GRB 130427A,[13] observed up to 126 GeV by the *Fermi*-LAT; GRB 180720B,[14] detected using the H.E.S.S. Array at 100 GeV $< E_\gamma <$ 1 TeV; and GRB 190114C,[15,16] observed up to 1 TeV by the MAGIC telescopes approximately one minute after triggering the *Fermi*-GBM and Swift-BAT. However, due to the limited field-of-view of IACTs, it is difficult for observations above the energy threshold for the *Fermi*-LAT to occur in the first few seconds of the GRB. By contrast, the HAWC Observatory observes 1/6th of the sky at once and has near-continuous uptime to search for GRBs, making both short GRBs and long GRBs ideal observational topics. This uninterrupted analysis of air showers would be ideal for capturing a high-energy component of the prompt emission, should one be present.

3. The High-Altitude Water Cherenkov (HAWC) Observatory

The HAWC Observatory, a successor to the Milagro Observatory,[17] is a very-high-energy ground-based air shower array located on the side of the Sierra Negra volcano in Mexico at an altitude of 4,100 m above sea level. It has a wide field-of-view of $\sim$ 2 sr at any one time (observing 2/3rds of the sky each day) and covers an energy range from $\sim$300 GeV to above 100 TeV. HAWC consists of 300 cylindrical water tanks in the main array covering a total area of 22,000 m^2. Each tank in the main array is 7.3 m in diameter and 4.5 m deep and is equipped with four (three 8″- and one 10″-diameter) upward-facing photomultiplier tubes (PMTs) anchored to the bottom of the tank.

HAWC has completed installing and integrating an additional "outrigger" array[18] composed of 345 cylindrical tanks 1.55 m in diameter and 1.65 m deep, each containing a single 8″ PMT. The outriggers are arranged in a concentric, circular, symmetric pattern around the main array, covering an additional instrumented area of ~ 4.5 times that of the main array. The outriggers provide enhanced sensitivity above 10 TeV by allowing the accurate determination of core position for showers off the main tank array and increase the effective area above 10 TeV by a factor of 3–4.

In both the main array and the outriggers, the PMTs detect Cherenkov light from secondary particles created in extensive air showers induced by very-high-energy gamma rays and cosmic rays incident on Earth's atmosphere. The main data acquisition system measures the arrival time of secondary particles at ground level and the amplitude of the PMT signals. This information, processed in near real time (only ~ 4 seconds delay), is used to reconstruct the arrival direction and energy of the primary particle all day, every day. The angular resolution of HAWC ranges from $\sim 0.2°$ (at its highest energies) to $1.0°$ (at its lowest energies).[19] With these features and a duty cycle greater than 95%, HAWC is ideally suited to continuously monitor the Northern Hemisphere sky for high-energy emission from gamma-ray transients such as GRBs to find new sources as well as search archival data.

3.1. *The Gamma-Ray Detector Landscape*

HAWC's wide field-of-view and continuous operations are advantageous for detecting burst transients with emission durations shorter than the slewing times of Imaging Atmospheric Cherenkov Telescopes (IACTs), such as the prompt emission from GRBs. IACTs are also additionally limited by the need for small localization errors on triggered sources and their requirements for good weather and nighttime-only observations. While satellites are obviously very effective tools for the observation of both short and long GRBs, their limited size means satellites are not expected to provide useful statistics above tens of TeV— HAWC's effective area is > 100 times the size of *Fermi* at energies > 100 GeV. Additionally, HAWC's ability to observe GRBs before, during, and after the prompt emission phase measured by satellites is essential for determining the start time and duration of prompt emission at ~ 300 GeV— relatively unknown given the paucity of photons detected by satellites at these energies.

While HAWC is more sensitive to long GRBs, it occupies a unique position in terms of observing short GRBs due to the lack of slewing time and high energy range. This detector is therefore poised as a double-threat ad both classes of GRBs should be prime observational and analytical targets for us. The half-decade sensitivity calculations project a higher quasi-differential sensitivity than the *Fermi*-LAT[20] to both short and long bursts in the energy regime of interest herein, as shown in Figure 1.

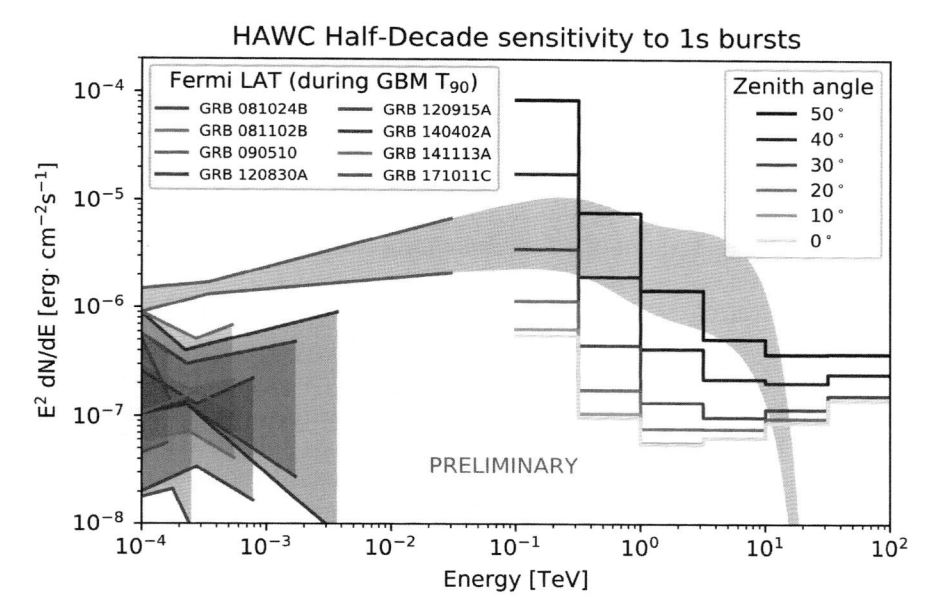

(a) HAWC quasi-differential sensitivity to 1s bursts

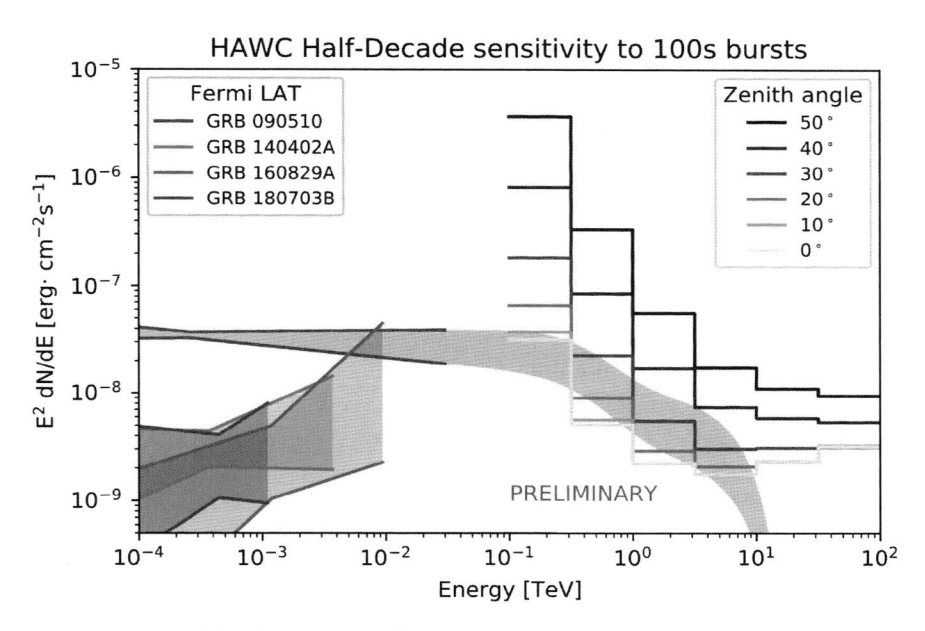

(b) HAWC quasi-differential sensitivity to 100s bursts

Fig. 1. HAWC quasi-differential sensitivity to both short (a) and long (b) bursts as a function of zenith angle, defined as the mean flux in a given half-decade that would result in at least a 5σ detection half of the time. For reference we include spectra measured by the Fermi-LAT detector for short GRBs (on the order of 1s) and long GRBs (duration > 70 s), respectively. Figures by Israel Martinez-Castellanos.

4. The HAWC GRB Program

The HAWC GRB program consists of two dedicated analyses: a self-triggered, all-sky search, and rapid response follow-ups of GRBs reported by satellites. Both methods are performed in real time using the quick-look air shower reconstruction produced at the HAWC site with a latency of ∼five seconds. Additionally, each search is repeated on archival data with improved calibration and reconstruction algorithms.[1] This archival data is especially important for following up on reported emission from IACTs.

From the sensitivity of the HAWC Observatory, ∼ 0.5 GRB detections per year are expected from following satellite-reported GRBs alone, assuming most GRBs do not contain an intrinsic cutoff below 200 Gev.[4] The all-sky search method yields similar expectation as the trials penalty taken when searching the full sky is roughly compensated by the ability to search data without satellite coverage.[21] Thus far, there have been no significant detections of GRB transients since the inauguration of the full HAWC detector on March 20, 2015.

4.1. *Self-Triggered, All-Sky Search*

The self-triggered all-sky method continuously searches for transient signals from GRBs above an energy threshold of 300 GeV using sliding time windows. The four time windows used are of lengths 0.2, 1, 10, and 100 seconds, typical of peak structures within GRB light curves. The all-sky search shifts each window forward in time by 10% of its width, binning air shower events during that window using a grid of $2.1° \times 2.1°$ square spatial bins covering all points within $50°$ of detector zenith,[21] as shown in Figure 2. The number of showers in each spatial bin is then compared to the expectation from well-modeled, charged cosmic-ray backgrounds, producing a p-value. Locations with an air-shower excess corresponding to a post-trials false alarm rate of one event per day are considered candidates for GRB transients and reported internally within HAWC.

This style of analysis is not limited to having to continuously search the entirety of the sky for a transient signal, but also possesses the ability to be passed an external trigger in order to perform a limited sliding time window search near the trigger time and location of known GRBs beyond just that of the satellite follow-ups described below. The analysis chain is the same whether continuous or externally triggered. This allows for the fine-tuning of the start time of very-high-energy emission when performing follow-ups. Though this analysis is performed in real-time, especially for external triggers, performing this analysis on archival data allows inspection *before* the trigger time, an ability unique to wide-field-of-view survey instruments such as HAWC, which are not limited to only looking forward in the way that IACTs are.

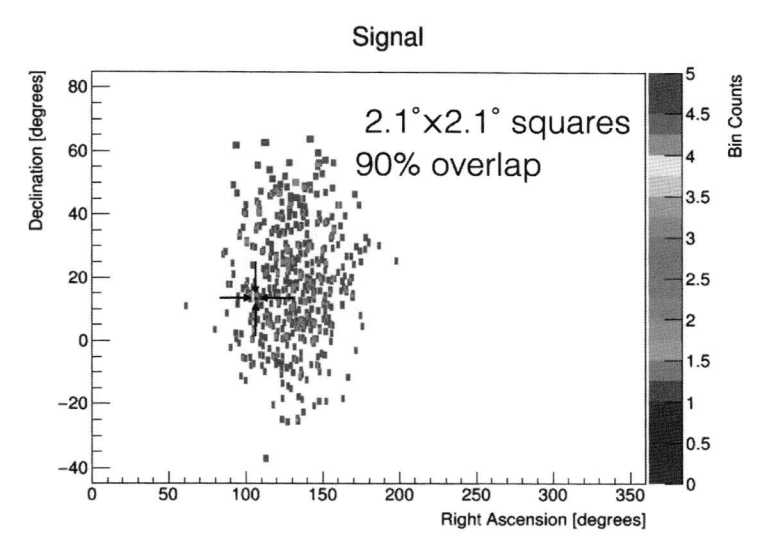

Fig. 2. The 90% overlap in spatial bins created by shifting each window by 10% of its width guarantees that the signal will be ideally oversampled such that there is a bin in which the signal is centered. Figure by Joshua Wood.

4.2. *Rapid Response Follow-Up*

The method for rapid response follow-up of reported GRBs is simpler in that it fixes the search window start time to match the external trigger time provided by a satellite (*e.g.*, the *Fermi*-GBM[11]); follow-ups of GCN Notices for triggered searches occur with ~ 30 minutes latency. Additionally, the spatial portion of the search is restricted to the reported error on the GRB location. The analytical framework is the same as with the all-sky search, with air-shower events during the search window binned into spatial bins and compared against the expectation from well-modeled, charged cosmic-ray backgrounds.[22] Events can be separated based on quality and background, among other improvements. In cases when T_{90} is available with the external trigger, we search for emission occurring within T_{90} as well as $3 \times T_{90}$ and $10 \times T_{90}$ for long GRBs, and 6 and 20 seconds for short GRBs— the longer windows covering possible extended emission. Otherwise, the follow-up is performed with timescales of 1 and 20 seconds to cover typical T_{90} values as well as a 300-second window to look for extended emission. These timescales grant the ability to test for delayed-onset very-high-energy emission when performing follow-ups of these satellite-detected GRBs. The combined power of observations (or non-observations) from both satellites and ground-based observatories such as HAWC is critical for unlocking the secrets of GRBs, as shown through the agreement of the HAWC limits for both short and long GRBs with GBM observations in Figure 3.

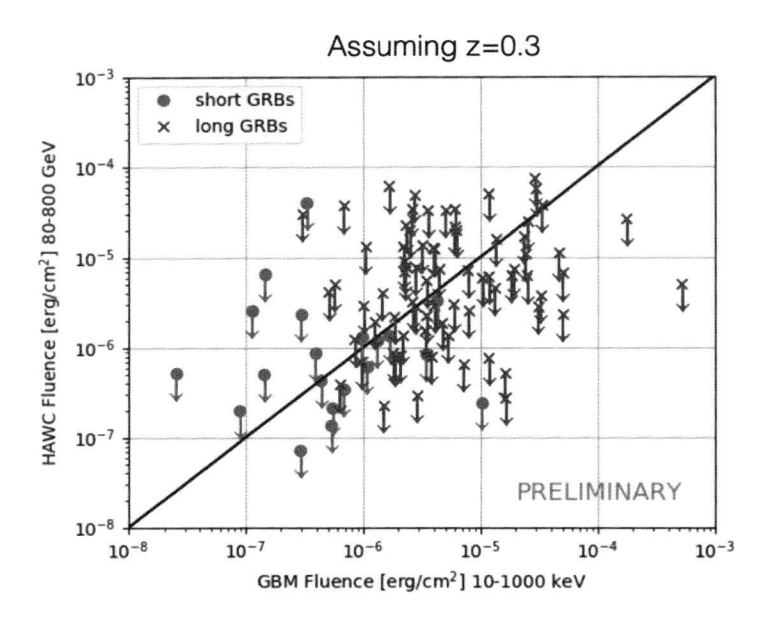

Fig. 3. Even for a non-detection, upper limits for nearby GRBs with known redshift, in combination with information from the triggering satellite(s), can place strong constraints on models.

4.3. *HAWC and the GRB Community*

Despite how ideal the HAWC Observatory is for the observation of very-high-energy emission from GRBs, a significant observation has not yet occurred. Those GRBs that have been detected to-date with a very-high-energy component—GRB 190114C,[15,16] GRB 180720B,[14] and GRB 190829A[23]—were not in the HAWC field of view. However, as shown in Figure 4, HAWC would likely have detected GRB 190114C if it had happened in its field of view.

If HAWC were to trigger on a GRB, structures are in place to alert the community and coordinate alerts between different experiments. The most prompt notification would be the use of GCNs and ATels for confirmed significant observations. HAWC has sent out 47 such circulars in the last year. Additionally, though somewhat delayed, HAWC is already using the Astrophysical Multimessenger Observatory Network (AMON)[24] for sub-threshold triggers. AMON reports "hotspot" parameters for events above the estimated cosmic-ray background level, $> 2.75\sigma$. AMON sends alerts to the GCN if an even passes the false-alarm-rate threshold of one per year, calculated using two years of scrambled datasets from both HAWC and IceCube.

5. Future Outlook

While HAWC has yet to observe a significant signal from a GRB, either self-triggered or as a follow-up, the HAWC Collaboration is very optimistic that recent

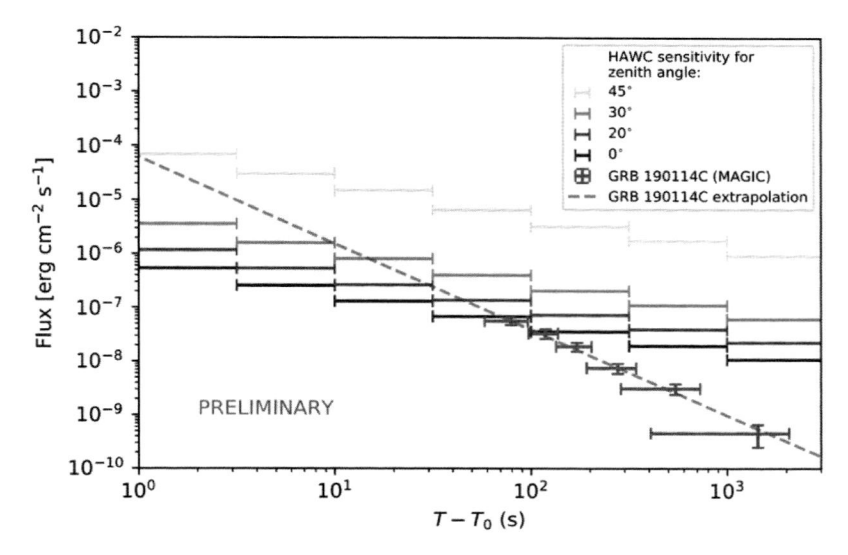

Fig. 4. HAWC's sensitivity at different zenith angles overlaid on an extrapolation of the flux detected by MAGIC from GRB 190114C. Adapted from Ref. 15.

improvements will greatly improve sensitivity to GRBs. This includes better reconstruction for low-energy events (noise reduction), increased statistics from multi-shower fits, and improved angular resolution for multiple showers on the array. Especially critical to the detection of very-high-energy emission from GRBs will be multi-bin, maximum likelihood analyses for short timescales and data reconstructed around known GRBs. The full dataset with these improvements will be ready in the coming months, with planned analyses to utilize these upgrades including both a targeted revisiting of known GRBs in reconstructed archival data, as well as updates to the self-triggered, "blind" search. With such advances at HAWC's fingertips, the HAWC Collaboration is eager for HAWC to broaden the GRB horizons and unlock their secrets through its unique position as a ground-based, wide-field-of-view observatory.

References

1. J. Wood, Results from the first one and a half years of the HAWC GRB program, *PoS* **ICRC2017**, p. 619 (2018).
2. T. Piran, Gamma-ray bursts and the fireball model, *Physics Reports* **314**, p. 575–667 (Jun 1999).
3. E. Waxman and J. Bahcall, High energy neutrinos from cosmological gamma-ray burst fireballs, *Physical Review Letters* **78**, p. 2292–2295 (Mar 1997).
4. I. Taboada and R. C. Gilmore, Prospects for the detection of grbs with hawc, *Nuclear Instruments and Methods in Physics Research Section A: Accelerators, Spectrometers, Detectors and Associated Equipment* **742**, p. 276–277 (Apr 2014).

5. R. C. Gilmore, P. Madau, J. R. Primack, R. S. Somerville and F. Haardt, Gev gamma-ray attenuation and the high-redshift uv background, *Monthly Notices of the Royal Astronomical Society* **399**, p. 1694–1708 (Nov 2009).
6. S. Poolakkil *et al.*, The Fermi-GBM Gamma-Ray Burst Spectral Catalog: 10 yr of Data, *Astrophys. J.* **913**, p. 60 (2021).
7. M. Ruffert and H. Janka, Gamma-ray bursts from accreting black holes in neutron star mergers, *Astron. Astrophys.* **344**, 573 (1999).
8. S. Rosswog, E. Ramirez-Ruiz and M. B. Davies, High-resolution calculations of merging neutron stars - iii. gamma-ray bursts, *Monthly Notices of the Royal Astronomical Society* **345**, p. 1077–1090 (Nov 2003).
9. G. P. Lamb and S. Kobayashi, GRB 170817A as a jet counterpart to gravitational wave trigger GW 170817, *Mon. Not. Roy. Astron. Soc.* **478**, 733 (2018).
10. K. Z. Stanek, T. Matheson, P. M. Garnavich, P. Martini, P. Berlind, N. Caldwell, P. Challis, W. R. Brown, R. Schild, K. Krisciunas and et al., Spectroscopic discovery of the supernova 2003dh associated with grb 030329, *The Astrophysical Journal* **591**, p. L17–L20 (Jun 2003).
11. C. Meegan, G. Lichti, P. N. Bhat, E. Bissaldi, M. S. Briggs, V. Connaughton, R. Diehl, G. Fishman, J. Greiner, A. S. Hoover and et al., The fermi gamma-ray burst monitor, *The Astrophysical Journal* **702**, p. 791–804 (Aug 2009).
12. N. Gehrels, G. Chincarini, P. Giommi, K. O. Mason, J. A. Nousek, A. A. Wells, N. E. White, S. D. Barthelmy, D. N. Burrows, L. R. Cominsky, K. C. Hurley, F. E. Marshall, P. Meszaros, P. W. A. Roming, L. Angelini, L. M. Barbier, T. Belloni, P. T. Boyd, S. Campana, P. A. Caraveo, M. M. Chester, O. Citterio, T. L. Cline, M. S. Cropper, J. R. Cummings, A. J. Dean, E. D. Feigelson, E. E. Fenimore, D. A. Frail, A. S. Fruchter, G. P. Garmire, K. Gendreau, G. Ghisellini, J. Greiner, J. E. Hill, S. D. Hunsberger, H. A. Krimm, S. R. Kulkarni, P. Kumar, F. Lebrun, N. M. Lloyd-Ronning, C. B. Markwardt, B. J. Mattson, R. F. Mushotzky, J. P. Norris, B. Paczynski, D. M. Palmer, H.-S. Park, A. M. Parsons, J. Paul, M. J. Rees, C. S. Reynolds, J. E. Rhoads, T. P. Sasseen, B. E. Schaefer, A. T. Short, A. P. Smale, I. A. Smith, L. Stella, M. Still, G. Tagliaferri, T. Takahashi, M. Tashiro, L. K. Townsley, J. Tueller, M. J. L. Turner, M. Vietri, W. Voges, M. J. Ward, R. Willingale, F. M. Zerbi and W. W. Zhang, Erratum: "The Swift Gamma-ray burst mission" (ApJ, 611, 1005 [2004]), *The Astrophysical Journal* **621**, 558 (mar 2005).
13. P.-H. T. Tam, Q.-W. Tang, S.-J. Hou, R.-Y. Liu and X.-Y. Wang, Discovery of an extra hard spectral component in the high-energy afterglow emission of grb 130427a, *The Astrophysical Journal* **771**, p. L13 (Jun 2013).
14. H. Abdalla, R. Adam, F. Aharonian, F. Benkhali, E. Angüner, M. Arakawa, C. Arcaro, C. Armand, H. Ashkar, M. Backes, V. Barbosa Martins, M. Barnard, Y. Becherini, D. Berge, K. Bernlöhr, E. Bissaldi, R. Blackwell, M. Böttcher and C. Boisson, A very-high-energy component deep in the γ-ray burst afterglow, *Nature* **575**, 464 (11 2019).
15. Teraelectronvolt emission from the γ-ray burst grb 190114c, *Nature* **575**, p. 455–458 (Nov 2019).
16. P. Veres, P. N. Bhat, M. S. Briggs, W. H. Cleveland, R. Hamburg, C. M. Hui, B. Mailyan, R. D. Preece, O. J. Roberts and et al., Observation of inverse compton emission from a long γ-ray burst, *Nature* **575**, p. 459–463 (Nov 2019).
17. The Milagro Collaborations: R. Atkins et al., Milagrito, a TeV air-shower array, *NIM-A* **449**, 478 (2000).

18. V. Joshi and H. Schoorlemmer, Air shower reconstruction using HAWC and the Outrigger array, in *36th International Cosmic Ray Conference (ICRC 2019) Madison, Wisconsin, USA, July 24-August 1, 2019*, 2019.
19. A. U. Abeysekara *et al.*, Observation of the Crab Nebula with the HAWC Gamma-Ray Observatory, *Astrophys. J.* **843**, p. 39 (2017).
20. W. B. Atwood, A. A. Abdo, M. Ackermann, W. Althouse, B. Anderson, M. Axelsson, L. Baldini, J. Ballet, D. L. Band, G. Barbiellini and et al., The large area telescope on the fermi gamma-ray space telescope mission, *The Astrophysical Journal* **697**, p. 1071–1102 (May 2009).
21. J. R. Wood, An All-Sky Search for Bursts of Very High Energy Gamma Rays with HAWC, PhD thesis, University of Maryland, College Park2016.
22. R. Alfaro, C. Alvarez, J. D. Álvarez, R. Arceo, J. C. Arteaga-Velázquez, D. A. Rojas, H. A. A. Solares, A. S. Barber, N. Bautista-Elivar, A. Becerril and et al., Search for very-high-energy emission from gamma-ray bursts using the first 18 months of data from the hawc gamma-ray observatory, *The Astrophysical Journal* **843**, p. 88 (Jul 2017).
23. V. Chand *et al.*, Peculiar Prompt Emission and Afterglow in the H.E.S.S.-detected GRB 190829A, *Astrophys. J.* **898**, p. 42 (2020).
24. H. Ayala Solares, AMON: TeV Gamma and Neutrino Coincidence Alerts from HAWC and IceCube subthreshold data, *PoS* **ICRC2019**, p. 841 (2019).

CALET search for gamma-ray counterparts of gravitational wave events

Masaki Mori

Department of Physical Sciences, Ritsumeikan University,
Kusatu, Shiga 525-8577, Japan
E-mail: morim@fc.ritsumei.ac.jp

for the CALET Collaboration[*]

The CALorimetric Electron Telescope (CALET) cosmic ray detector on the International Space Station (ISS) has been in operation since its launch in 2015. The main instrument, the CALET calorimeter, is monitoring the gamma ray sky from 1 GeV up to 10 TeV with a field-of-view of about 2 sr for more than five years. In this paper, we describe the analysis of gamma ray candidate events observed by the calorimeter and report on a search for gamma-ray emission from gravitational-wave event candidates announced by the LIGO/Virgo third observation run from 2019 April to 2020 March.

Keywords: Gamma rays: general – gravitational waves – methods: observational

1. Introduction

The CALorimetric Electron Telescope (CALET),[1] which was successfully launched and installed on the Japanese Experiment Module (JEM) 'Kibo'-Exposed Facility of the International Space Station (ISS) in August 2015, is a mission of the Japanese Aerospace Exploration Agency (JAXA) in collaboration with the Italian Space Agency (ASI) and NASA. The instrument has been taking science data continuously with no major interruptions since 2015 October. The main target of the CALET calorimeter is observation of high-energy cosmic rays,[2] especially electrons,[3] in the energy range from ~ 1 GeV to tens of TeV, and nuclei,[4] from ~ 10 GeV/n to ~ 100 TeV/n, but its fine detector structure allows us to observe high-energy gamma-rays[5] from ~ 1 GeV to ~ 10 TeV.

In this paper, we describe the analysis of gamma-ray candidate events observed by the CALET calorimeter and report on a search for gamma-ray emission from gravitational-wave event candidates announced by the LIGO/Virgo third observing run in the period April 2019 – March 2020. (See Ref. 6 for results during the first and second runs.) Search for low-energy emission using the CALET Gamma-ray Burst Monitor (CGBM) is reported elsewhere.[7]

2. The CALET detector

The CALET payload (Fig. 1) includes scientific and auxiliary equipment for a total mass of 613 kg, dimensions of $1.9 \times 0.8 \times 1.0$ m^3, nominal power consumption

---

[*]See the last page for the full authors list.

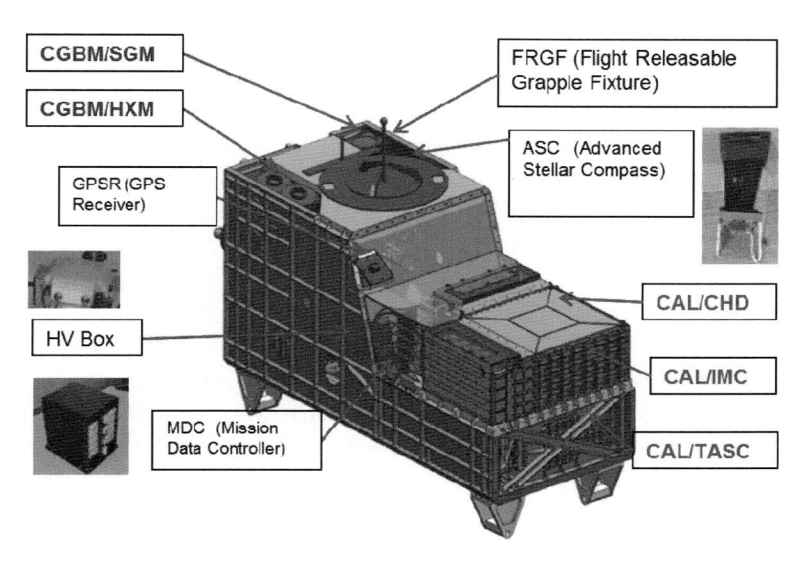

Fig. 1. The CALET payload installed at port No. 9 of the 'Kibo'-Exposed Facility of Japanese Experiment module on the ISS. The CALET calorimeter (CAL) consists of Charge Detector (CHD), Imaging Calorimeter (IMC) and Total Absorption Calorimeter (TASC). The CALET Gamma-ray Burst Monitor (CGBM) consists of two hard X-ray monitor (HXM) units and one soft gamma-ray monitor (SGM) unit.

of 507 W. The main scientific instruments are the electromagnetic calorimeter[1] and the gamma-ray burst monitor (CGBM).[8]

The CALET calorimeter is an all-calorimetric instrument designed to achieve a large proton rejection capability ($>10^5$) with a fine-grained imaging calorimeter (IMC) followed by a total absorption calorimeter (TASC). The overall thickness of CALET at normal incidence is 30 X_0 (radiation length) and ~ 1.3 proton interaction length. The charge identification of individual nuclear species is performed by a two-layered hodoscope of plastic scintillators (CHD) at the top of the apparatus, providing a measurement of the charge Z of the incident particle over a wide dynamic range ($Z = 1$ to ~ 40) with sufficient charge resolution to resolve individual elements ($\Delta Z \sim 0.1$ for light nuclei up to B, 0.3 in the Fe region) and complemented by a redundant charge determination via multiple dE/dx measurements in the IMC.

The IMC is a sampling calorimeter longitudinally segmented into 16 layers of scintillating fibers (SciFi, with 1 mm^2 squared cross-section) interspaced with thin tungsten absorbers. Alternate planes of fibers are arranged along orthogonal directions. Its surface area is 45×45 cm^2 and it can image the early shower profile in the first $3X_0$ and reconstruct the incident direction of cosmic rays with good angular resolution.

The TASC is a $27X_0$ thick homogeneous calorimeter with 12 alternate X-Y layers made of 192 lead-tungstate (PWO) logs. It measures the total energy of the incident particle and discriminates electrons from hadrons with the help of the information from the CHD and IMC. Each log in the top layer is read by a PMT for use in the trigger system, together with CHD and IMC signals. A dual photodiode / avalanche photodiode system (APD/PD, Hamamatsu Photonics S8664-1010/S1227-33BR) is used for the read-out of the other layers. Such a readout system provides a dynamic range covering 6 orders of magnitudes and enables to measure large energy deposit expected from a proton-induced 1000 TeV shower. The TASC measures the energy of the incident particle with excellent resolution: 2% (3%) for electrons (gamma-rays) with energy $E > 10$ GeV, better than 35% for nuclei up to ~ 100 TeV energy.

Charged particles and gamma rays with energy larger than 10 GeV will be triggered above a 15 MIP (minimum ionizing particle) threshold from the sum of the signals from the last two IMC SciFi belts and a 55 MIP threshold from the signal of the top layer in the TASC ("High-energy shower trigger", HE). Electrons and gamma rays in the energy range between 1 GeV and 10 GeV will be observed only for a limited exposure by reducing the IMC trigger threshold ("Low-energy shower trigger", LE, and "Low-energy gamma-ray trigger, LE-γ, respectively).

The data are transferred via two telemetry channels: one is the Ethernet channel which is operated at a medium rate of 600 kbps, and the other is a MIL-STD-1553B channel which provides low rate data at 50 kbps. In the medium rate mode, an event observed by CALET on the ISS will be transferred to the Tsukuba Space Center (TKSC) of JAXA. The low rate mode is used as a redundant channel for telemetering the CALET house keeping data plus a sample of the cosmic-ray events. The CALET data will be transmitted to TKSC via MSFC in the United State, and are sent to the Waseda CALET Operations Center (WCOC) in real time for monitoring data quality and checking for transient events.[9] The off-line data analysis is performed by the international CALET team based on the data delivered from the WCOC.

3. Analysis for gamma rays

We use two trigger modes of CAL for gamma-ray analysis: a low-energy gamma-ray (LE-γ) mode with an energy threshold ~ 1 GeV used at low geomagnetic latitudes and following a CGBM burst trigger, and a high-energy (HE) mode with a threshold ~ 10 GeV used in normal operation for all particles irrespective of geomagnetic latitude.[9]

The selection process of gamma-ray events used for the HE mode is essentially the same as that described in Ref. 10. For the LE-γ mode the selection and analysis are fully described in Refs. 5, 11. Here we briefly summarize the procedures.[6]

Offline trigger – In order to mitigate the inherent variability of hardware condition of flight data sample, energy deposit thresholds higher than those nominally applied by the hardware trigger are imposed both for LE-γ and HE modes.

Tracking – Event tracks are reconstructed for the HE mode using the EM track algorithm[12] developed for the electron analysis which is a powerful method for reconstructing electromagnetic showers. For the LE-γ mode we use the CC track algorithm[5] optimized for photons with energies below 10 GeV. It begins by finding clusters of hit fibers in the three bottom layers of IMC separately for the X- and Y-projections and extending the candidate tracks to upper layers of IMC. The trajectory with the highest total energy deposit is selected. The subsequent analysis applies only to contained events passing through CHD and having track lengths in TASC more than 26.4 cm for the HE mode, and well contained events whose tracks satisfy more sophisticated geometrical conditions for the LE-γ mode.[5]

Shower shape/hadronic rejection – Low energy gamma-ray events can be mimicked by albedo (i.e. upward moving) secondary charged pions from hadronic interactions in the calorimeter or the support structure. These events are vetoed by requiring to deposit more energy in the bottom layer of IMC than in the layer of pair conversion. Further rejection of events with showers not consistent with a pure electromagnetic cascade is provided by a cut on the IMC concentration, which use the lateral spread of the energy deposit distribution in the lower layers of IMC.

In order to reject hadronic events we utilize the K parameter defined as

$$K = \log_{10} F_E + R_E/2\,\mathrm{cm}$$

where F_E is the fractional energy deposit in the bottom TASC layer with respect to the total energy deposit sum in the TASC and R_E is the second moment of the lateral energy deposit distribution in the top layer of TASC. This method is developed for the derivation of the electron flux and is designed to exploit the larger spread and slower development of proton showers due to penetrating secondary pions.[13]

Charge zero – In order to select events consistent with zero primary charge, cuts are made on the energy deposits in CHD and upper IMC layers. These requirements are designed to veto charged particle events effectively. We require one of three filters utilizing CHD and upper IMC layers (see Ref. 5 for detail).

Since CALET is attached to the exposed facility of the JEM on the ISS, gamma-ray observation with CALET/CAL suffers from secondary gamma rays produced in interactions of high-energy cosmic rays with various structures of the ISS surrounding the detector. Some structures, such as the ISS truss and the JEM, are fixed to the ISS, and we can easily cut those secondary gamma rays by limiting our field-of-view (see Fig. 2 (*Left*)). However, moving structures, such as solar panels and robotic arms, produce time-varying backgrounds for gamma ray observation. In our preceding analysis, we simply rejected events coming from the field-of-view affected by moving structures.[5] We have developed moving filter algorithms to reject time-varying portions of our field-of-view by taking account of moving structures, whose operational data are supplied by JAXA, operating the 'Kibo' module, in order to maximize our exposure for cosmic gamma rays.[14]

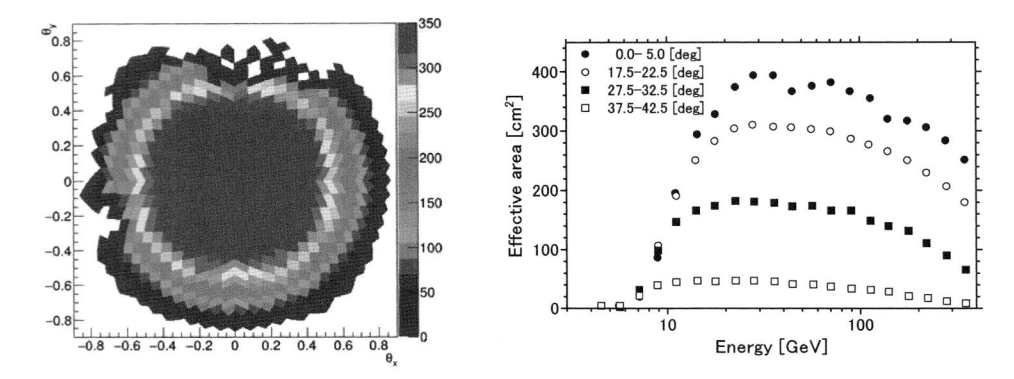

Fig. 2. (*Left*) Field-of-view of CALET/CAL, expressed in effective area (in cm^2) as a function of projected incident angles onto x- and y-plane (θ_x, θ_y). Some inefficient regions seen at edges are caused by cuts to remove secondary gamma rays from ISS structures. (*Right*) Effective area as a function of gamma-ray energy for various incidence-angle ranges.[5]

According to the detailed simulation study, we estimate the effective area and performance. The effective areas for various incident angles are shown in Fig. 2 as a function of energy.[5] The field-of-view is about 2 steradian. The angular resolution[5] and energy resolution[15] are shown in Fig. 3.

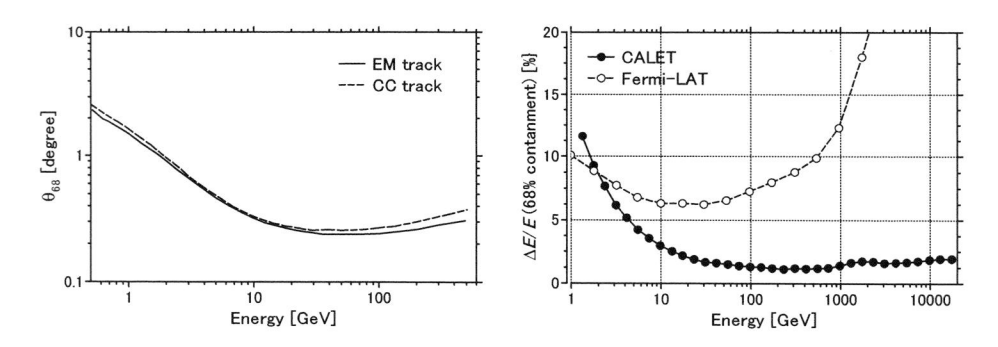

Fig. 3. (*Left*) Angular resolution of CALET for gamma rays as a function of energy, averaged over various shower starting points in IMC.[5] θ_{68} is the half angle of the cone in which 68% of gamma rays are contained. 'EM Track' is an algorithm developed for electron analysis and optimized for HE triggers, and 'CC Track' is another one developed specifically for low-energy (1–10 GeV) gamma-rays. (*Right*) Energy resolution of CALET as a function of energy,[15] compared with that of Fermi-LAT (P8R3SOURCE_V2, Total).[16]

Figure 4 shows a skymap of gamma-ray candidates (LE-γ trigger) for the data during the period 2015 November – 2018 May shown in the Galactic coordinates. Some individual sources are evident. White contours show relative exposures which are not uniform due to the inclined (51.6°) orbit of ISS.

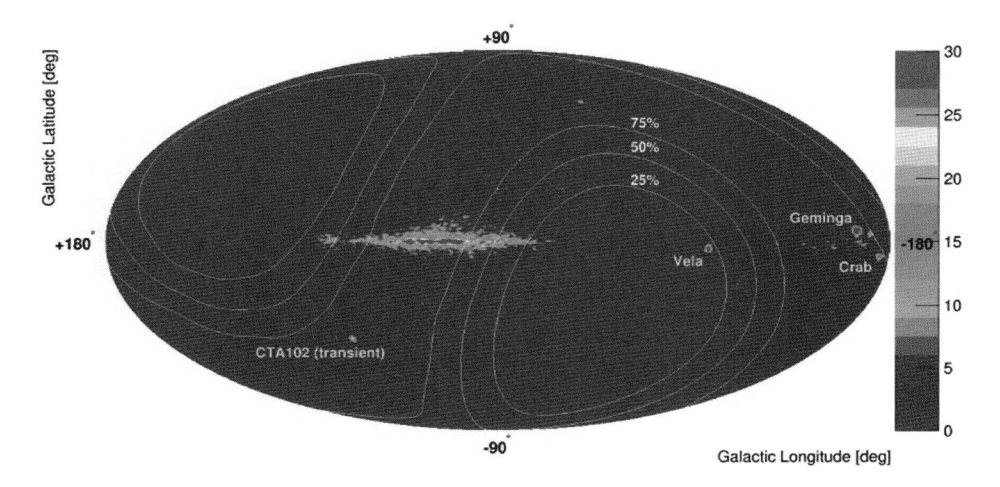

Fig. 4. Skymap of gamma-ray candidates (LE-γ trigger) shown in the Galactic coordinates for the data during the period 2015 November – 2018 May. White contours show relative exposures. Some individual sources are marked.

4. Limits on electromagnetic emission from gravitational events

We have already reported the results on the search for gamma ray emission from gravitational-wave events detected during the first and second observation run of LIGO/Virgo.[6] Also the intermediate result during the third run has been reported.[14] Here we extend the analysis for the whole third run.

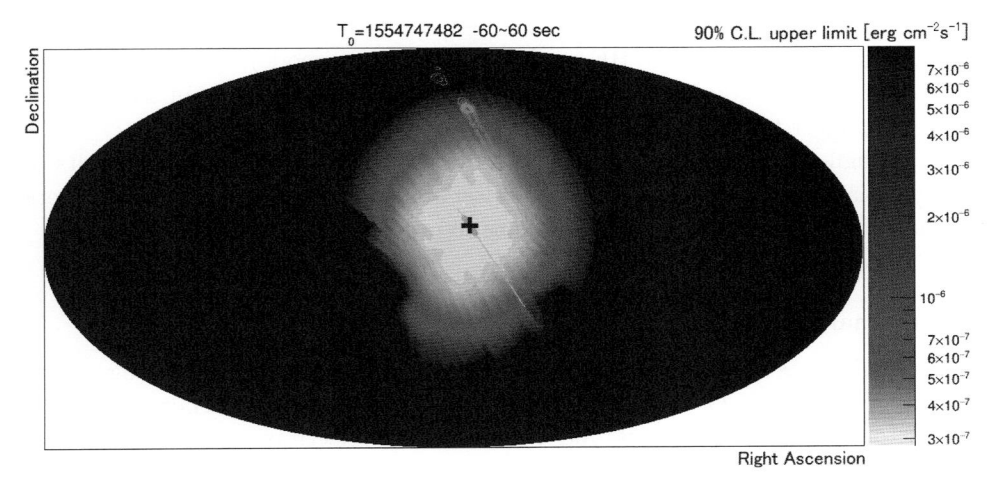

Fig. 5. 90% C.L. upper limit on S190408an energy flux in the energy region 1–10 GeV and time window $[T_0 - 60s, T_0 + 60 s]$ shown in the equatorial coordinates. The thick cyan line shows the locus of the FOV center of CAL, and the plus symbol is that at T_0. Also shown by green contours is the localization significance map of S190408an reported by LIGO/Virgo.

Since the beginning of the third run of LIGO/Virgo, we are monitoring possible gamma-ray emission based on the triggers on gravitational-event candidates supplied by the LIGO/Virgo team, in compliance with the memorandum of understanding between CALET and LIGO and Virgo. In Table 1 we summarize the CALET/CAL observations reported in GCN circulars[17] for the third run of LIGO/Virgo, from 2019 April 1 to 2020 March 27. No gamma-ray candidates have been observed in association with these triggers. Upper limits (U.L.) on the gamma-ray energy fluxes are given in unit of $\mathrm{erg\,cm^{-2}\,s^{-1}}$ for the energy range 10–100 GeV except for those marked with † which are for 1–10 GeV, which corresponds to the HE and the LE-γ mode of the trigger condition of CAL around T_0. 'Coverage' is the fraction of the overlapping region of the LIGO/Virgo localization map covered by the CAL field-of-view at T_0 ('No' means there is no overlap). Also shown are the celestial coordinates of the center of CAL field-of-view at T_0. Event type in 'Comments' comes from GraceDB.[18]

An example of the energy flux limit skymaps is shown in Fig. 5 for the LIGO/Virgo trigger S190408an.[14] In this case 80% of the localization significance map of LIGO/Virgo was covered within ±60 seconds the trigger time (T_0), but there was no gamma-ray candidate. We obtained an upper limit on gamma-ray flux of 2.3×10^{-6} $\mathrm{cm^{-2}\,s^{-1}}$ (90% C.L.) in the energy range 1–10 GeV since the CALET was in the LE-γ mode at that time..

Figure 6 shows the monthly variation of the number of LVC alerts and CALET GCN circulars. About 70% of alerts were followed and reported by CALET. Considering that the field-of-view of CAL extends to $\sim 45°$ from the zenith, the chance to have overlap with the LIGO/Virgo probable region is not small. In summary, CALET/CAL was online for 54 triggers, and for 25 triggers there were some overlapping sky area between the CALET field-of-view and the summed LIGO/Virgo probability maps. (19 in the HE mode, 6 in the LE-γ mode), but there were no gamma-ray events associated with triggers in the time window within ±60 seconds from the trigger time (T_0) .

Although no gamma-ray event has been found for 25 triggers, upper limits on the gamma-ray flux obtained by CALET set some constraints on electromagnetic emission from gravitational-wave events as discussed in Ref. 6.

5. Summary

The CALET cosmic ray detector onboard the ISS has been monitoring cosmic gamma-rays above 1 GeV since 2015 October. In this paper we reported our procedure of gamma-ray analysis and our search for electromagnetic counterparts of gravitational-wave events upon triggers supplied by LIGO/Virgo interferometers during their third observation period, and gave upper limits on gamma-ray emission. Now, since extended operations of CALET have been approved by JAXA/NASA/ASI in March 2021 through the end of 2024, we continue observation

Table 1. Summary of CALET/CAL gamma-ray observations on gravitational-wave event candidates in the LIGO/Virgo third observing run reported in GCN circulars.[17]

GCN No.	LIGO/Virgo trigger	Trigger time T_0 (2019)	Events $T_0 \pm 60$ s	90% C.L. U.L.	Coverage	CAL α (°)	CAL δ (°)	Comments
24088	S190408an	04-08 18:18:02.288 UTC	0	2.3×10^{-6}†	80%	352.9	8.3	BBH (>99%)
24218	S190425z	04-25 08:18:05.017 UTC	0	1.0×10^{-4}	5%	131.3	-43.6	BNS (>99%)
24276	S190426c	04-26 15:21:55.337 UTC	0	2.5×10^{-5}	10%	183	-50.9	BNS (49%)
24403	S190503bf	05-03 18:54:04.294 UTC	0	4.2×10^{-5}	10%	169	-45.5	BBH (96%)
24495	S190510g	05-10 02:59:39.292 UT	0	–	No	295.7	50.8	Terrestrial (58%)
24531	S190512at	05-12 18:07:14.422 UT	0	1.9×10^{-5}	10%	214.9	37.7	BBH (99%)
24548	S190513bm	05-13 20:54:28.747 UT	0	6.0×10^{-5}†	5%	348	4.4	BBH (94%)
24593	S190517h	05-17 05:51:01.831 UT	0	–	No	126.2	-31.9	BBH (98%)
24617	S190519bj	05-19 15:35:44.398 UT	0	–	No	243.1	51.1	BBH (96%)
24648	S190521g	05-21 03:02:29.447 UT	0	6.0×10^{-6}	30%	205.7	49.2	BBH (97%)
24649	S190521r	05-21 07:43:59.463 UT	0	–	No	225.3	51.4	BBH (>99%)
24735	S190602aq	06-02 17:59:27.089 UT	0	2.9×10^{-4}	5%	127.5	45.1	BBH (99%)
24960	S190630ag	06-30 18:52:05.180 UT	0	1.2×10^{-5}	25%	84.0	31.5	BBH (94%)
24970	S190701ah	07-01 20:33:06.578 UT	0	–†	No	286.8	−1.6	BBH (93%)
25027	S190706ai	07-06 22:26:41.345 UT	0	–	No	210.4	−45.4	BBH (99%)
25033	S190707q	07-07 09:33:26.181 UT	0	2.1×10^{-6}†	20%	262.4	2.2	BBH (>99%)
25099	S190718y	07-18 14:35:12.068 UT	0	1.7×10^{-6}†	5%	195.8	−11.1	Terrestrial (98%)
25134	S190720a	07-20 00:08:36.704 UT	0	3.0×10^{-5}	25%	49.7	−32.1	BBH (99%)
25184	S190727h	07-27 06:03:33.986 UT	0	–	No	201.1	38.2	BBH (92%)
25214	S190728q	07-28 06:45:10.529 UT	0	–†	No	184.8	30.3	BBH (95%)
25390	S190814bv	08-14 21:10:39.013 UT	0	–	No	181.3	49.5	NSBH (>99%)
25536	S190828j	08-28 06:34:05.756 UT	0	–	No	13.9	12.6	BBH (>99%)
25537	S190828l	08-28 06:55:09.887 UT	0	–	No	106.9	51.0	BBH (>99%)
25647	S190901ap	09-01 23:31:01.838 UT	0	6.3×10^{-5}†	5%	353.8	16.6	BNS (86%)
25734	S190910d	09-10 01:26:19.243 UT	0	–†	No	100.8	22.9	NSBH (98%)
25735	S190910h	09-10 08:29:58.544 UT	0	9.4×10^{-6}†	10%	294.8	-5.5	BNS (61%)
25770	S190915ak	09-15 23:57:02.691 UT	0	–	No	99.7	-11.1	BBH (99%)
25830	S190923y	09-23 12:55:59.646 UT	0	1.2×10^{-5}	10%	55.3	-2.5	NSBH (68%)
25844	S190924h	09-24 02:18:46.847 UT	0	–	No	273.4	40.2	MassGap (>99%)
25891	S190930s	09-30 13:35:41.247 UT	0	3.5×10^{-5}	5%	20.7	-3.3	MassGap (95%)
25892	S190930t	09-30 14:34:07.685 UT	0	1.7×10^{-5}	5%	235.5	36.3	NSBH (74%)
26195	S191105e	11-05 14:35:21.933 UT	0	–	No	223.0	-27.4	BBH (95%)
26236	S191109d	11-09 01:07:17.221 UT	0	–	No	349.6	-16.6	BBH (>99%)
26321	S191129u	11-29 13:40:29.197 UT	0	–	No	356.9	50.7	BBH (>99%)
26358	S191204r	12-04 17:15:26.092 UT	0	–	No	269.2	34.3	BBH (>99%)
26377	S191205ah	12-05 21:52:08.569 UT	0	–	No	80.2	-32.8	NSBH (93%)
26419	S191213g	12-13 04:34:08.142 UT	0	–	No	20.4	-9.3	BNS (77%)
26465	S191215w	12-15 22:30:52.333 UT	0	–	No	222.3	40.3	BBH (>99%)
26481	S191216ap	12-16 21:33:38.473 UT	0	–†	No	186.8	13.9	BBH (99%)
26602	S191222n	12-22 03:35:37.119 UT	0	–†	No	330.3	-2.1	BBH (>99%)
26664	S200105ae	01-05 16:24:26.057 UT	0	6.5×10^{-6}	60%	50.6	-30.6	Terrestrial (97%)
26740	S200112r	01-12 15:58:38.094 UT	0	1.1×10^{-6}	5%	84.7	40.0	BBH (>99%)
26761	S200114f	01-14 02:08:18.239 UT	0	4.7×10^{-6}	80%	111.2	50.7	–
26797	S200115j	01-15 04:23:09.742 UT	0	1.7×10^{-6}	20%	84.4	45.9	MassGap (>99%)
26941	S200128d	01-28 02:20:11.903 UT	0	4.6×10^{-6}	10%	126.1	23.4	BBH (97%)
26924	S200129m	01-29 06:54:58.435 UT	0	5.7×10^{-5}	5%	288.7	-34.3	BBH (>99%)
27030	S200208q	02-08 13:01:17.991 UT	0	–	No	224.1	-41.8	BBH (>99%)
27084	S200213t	02-13 04:10:40.328 UT	0	–	No	101.4	-36.1	BBH (63%)
27149	S200219ac	02-19 09:44:15.195 UT	0	–	No	298.5	51.6	BBH (96%)
27231	S200224ca	02-24 22:22:34.406 UT	0	5.0×10^{-7}	95%	167.5	-24.8	BBH (>99%)
27232	S200225q	02-25 06:04:21.397 UT	0	–	No	157.8	-32.7	BBH (96%)
27299	S200302c	03-02 01:58:11.519 UT	0	–	No	245.4	51.6	BBH (89%)
27372	S200311bg	03-11 11:58:53.398 UT	0	–	No	191.3	51.5	BBH (>99%)
27405	S200316bj	03-16 21:57:56.157 UT	0	2.8×10^{-6}	35%	144.7	47.5	MassGap (>99%)

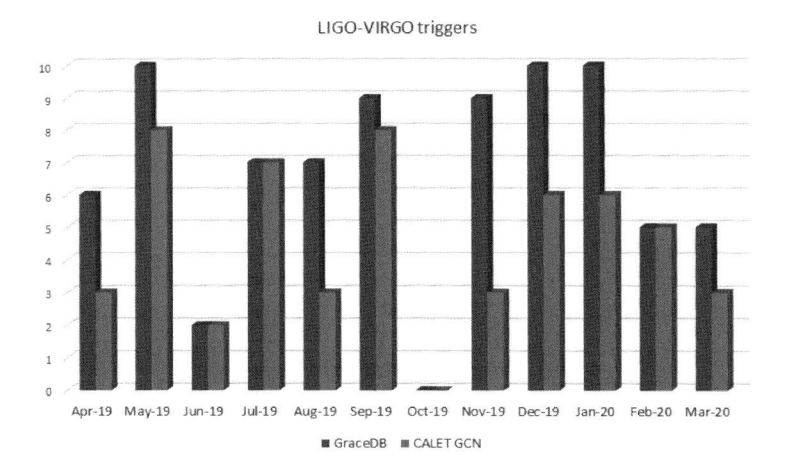

Fig. 6. Monthly variation of LVC O3 alerts and CALET GCNs.

so that we can cover the coming fourth observation run of LIGO/Virgo/KAGRA planned to start no earlier than August 2022.

Acknowledgments

We gratefully acknowledge JAXA's contributions to the development of CALET and to the operations aboard the JEM-EF on the International Space Station. We also wish to express our sincere gratitude to Agenzia Spaziale Italiana (ASI) and NASA for their support of the CALET project. This work was supported in part by JSPS Grant-in-Aid for Scientific Research (S) Number 26220708 and 19H05608, JSPS Grant-in-Aid for Scientific Research (C) Number 16K05382, and by the MEXT-Supported Program for the Strategic Research Foundation at Private Universities (2011-2015) (No. S1101021) at Waseda University. The CALET effort in Italy is supported by ASI under agreement 2013-018-R.0 and its amendments. The CALET effort in the United States is supported by NASA through Grants No. NNX16AB99G, No. NNX16AC02G, and No. NNH14ZDA001N-APRA-0075.

References

1. S. Torii for the CALET Collaboration, "The CALorimetric Electron Telescope (CALET) on the ISS: Preliminary Results from On-orbit Observations since October, 2015", *Proc. 35th ICRC* (Busan, Korea, 2017), PoS (ICRC2017) 1092; Y. Asaoka for the CALET Collaboration, "The CALorimetric Electron Telescope (CALET) on the International Space Station", *Proc. 36th ICRC* (Madison, USA, 2019), PoS (ICRC2019) 001; P. Marrocchesi for the CALET Collaboration, "New Results from the first 5 years of CALET observations on the International Space Station", *Proc. 37th ICRC* (Berlin, Germany/Online, 2021), PoS (ICRC2021) 010.

2. Pier Simone Marrocchesi for the CALET Collaboration, "CALET on the ISS: The first 5 years", in these proceedings (2021).
3. O. Adriani et al., "Extended measurement of cosmic-ray electron and positron spectrum from 11 GeV to 4.8 TeV with the calorimetric electron telescope on the International Space Station", *Phys. Rev. Lett.* **120**, 261102 (2018).
4. O. Adriani et al., "Direct Measurement of the Cosmic-Ray Proton Spectrum from 50 GeV to 10 TeV with the Calorimetric Electron Telescope on the International Space Station", *Phys. Rev. Lett.* **12**, 181102 (2019); O. Adriani et al., "Direct Measurement of the Cosmic-Ray Carbon and Oxygen Spectra from 10 GeV/n to 2.2 TeV/n with the Calorimetric Electron Telescope on the International Space Station", *Phys. Rev. Lett.*, **125**, 251102 (2020); O. Adriani et al., "Measurement of the iron spectrum in cosmic rays from 10 GeV/n to 2.0 TeV/n with the Calorimetric Electron Telescope on the International Space Station", *Phys. Rev. Lett.*, **126**, 241101 (2021).
5. N. Cannady et al., "Characteristics and Performance of the CALorimetric Electron Telescope (CALET) Calorimeter for Gamma-Ray Observations", *Astrophys. J. Suppl.* **238**, 5 (2018).
6. O. Adriani et al., "Search for GeV Gamma-Ray Counterparts of Gravitational Wave Events by CALET", *Astrophys. J.* **863**, 160 (2018).
7. Y. Kawakubo for the CALET Collaboration, "Gamma-ray burst observation & gravitational wave event follow-up with CALET on the International Space Station", Proc. 37th ICRC (Berlin, Germany/Online, 2021), PoS (ICRC2021) 957.
8. K. Yamaoka for the CALET Collaboration, "CALET Gamma-ray Burst Monitor (CGBM)", *Proc. 33rd ICRC* (Rio de Janeiro, Brazil, 2013), Volume 4, 2948.
9. Y. Asaoka et al., "On-orbit Operations and Offline Data Processing of CALET onboard the ISS", *Astropart. Phys.* **100**, 29 (2018).
10. M. Mori for the CALET Collaboration, "Expected Performance of CALET as a High Energy Gamma Ray Observatory", Proc. ICRC (Rio de Janeiro, Brazil, 2013), 0248, 1185.
11. N. Cannady for the CALET Collaboration, "High-Energy Gamma-ray Observations Using the CALorimetric Electron Telescope", *Proc. 35th ICRC* (Busan, Korea, 2017), PoS (ICRC2017) 720.
12. Y. Akaike for the CALET Collaboration, "CALET observational performance expected by CERN beam test", Proc. ICRC (Rio de Janeiro, Brazil, 2013), 0726, 2162.
13. O. Adriani, et al., "Energy Spectrum of Cosmic-Ray Electron and Positron from 10 GeV to 3 TeV Observed with the Calorimetric Electron Telescope on the International Space Station", *Phys. Rev. Lett.* **119**, 181101 (2017).
14. M. Mori for the CALET Collaboration, "High-Energy Gamma-ray Observations Using the CALorimetric Electron Telescope (CALET) on the ISS", *Proc. 36th ICRC* (Madison, USA, 2019), PoS (ICRC2019) 586.
15. Y. Asaoka et al., "Energy Calibration of CALET onboard the Internatinal Space Station", *Astropart. Phys.* **91**, 1 (2017).
16. "Fermi LAT Performance", `https:www.slac.stanford.edu/exp/glast/groups/canda/lat_Performance.htm`.
17. The Gamma-ray Coordinates Network (GCN), `https://gcn.gsfc.nasa.gov/`.
18. The Gravitational-Wave Candidate Event Database (GraceDB), `https://gracedb.ligo.org/`.

Full Authors List: The CALET Collaboration

O. Adriani[1,2], Y. Akaike[3,4], K. Asano[5], Y. Asaoka[5], E. Berti[1,2], G. Bigongiari[6,7], W. R. Binns[8], M. Bongi[1,2], P. Brogi[6,7], A. Bruno[9,10], J. H. Buckley[8], N. Cannady[11,12,13], G. Castellini[14], C. Checchia[6], M. L. Cherry[15], G. Collazuol[16,17], K. Ebisawa[18], A. W. Ficklin[15], H. Fuke[18], S. Gonzi[1,2], T. G. Guzik[15], T. Hams[11], K. Hibino[19], M. Ichimura[20], K. Ioka[21], W. Ishizaki[5], M. H. Israel[8], K. Kasahara[22], J. Kataoka[23], R. Kataoka[24], Y. Katayose[25], C. Kato[26], N. Kawanaka[27,28], Y. Kawakubo[15], K. Kobayashi[3,4], K. Kohri[29], H. S. Krawczynski[8], J. F. Krizmanic[11,12,13], P. Maestro[6,7], P. S. Marrocchesi[6,7], A. M. Messineo[30,7], J.W. Mitchell[12], S. Miyake[32], A. A. Moiseev[33,12,13], M. Mori[34], N. Mori[2], H. M. Motz[35], K. Munakata[26], S. Nakahira[18], J. Nishimura[18], G. A. de Nolfo[9], S. Okuno[19], J. F. Ormes[36], N. Ospina[16,17], S. Ozawa[37], L. Pacini[1,14,2], P. Papini[2], B. F. Rauch[8], S. B. Ricciarini[14,2], K. Sakai[11,12,13], T. Sakamoto[38], M. Sasaki[33,12,13], Y. Shimizu[19], A. Shiomi[39], P. Spillantini[1], F. Stolzi[6,7], S. Sugita[38], A. Sulaj[6,7], M. Takita[5], T. Tamura[19], T. Terasawa[40], S. Torii[3], Y. Tsunesada[41], Y. Uchihori[42], E. Vannuccini[2], J. P. Wefel[15], K. Yamaoka[43], S. Yanagita[44], A. Yoshida[38], K. Yoshida[22], and W. V. Zober[8]

[1]Department of Physics, University of Florence, Via Sansone, 1, 50019 Sesto, Fiorentino, Italy, [2]INFN Sezione di Florence, Via Sansone, 1, 50019 Sesto, Fiorentino, Italy, [3]Waseda Research Institute for Science and Engineering, Waseda University, 17 Kikuicho, Shinjuku, Tokyo 162-0044, Japan, [4]JEM Utilization Center, Human Spaceflight Technology Directorate, Japan Aerospace Exploration Agency, 2-1-1 Sengen, Tsukuba, Ibaraki 305-8505, Japan, [5]Institute for Cosmic Ray Research, The University of Tokyo, 5-1-5 Kashiwa-no-Ha, Kashiwa, Chiba 277-8582, Japan, [6]Department of Physical Sciences, Earth and Environment, University of Siena, via Roma 56, 53100 Siena, Italy, [7]INFN Sezione di Pisa, Polo Fibonacci, Largo B. Pontecorvo, 3, 56127 Pisa, Italy, [8]Department of Physics and McDonnell Center for the Space Sciences, Washington University, One Brookings Drive, St. Louis, Missouri 63130-4899, USA, [9]Heliospheric Physics Laboratory, NASA/GSFC, Greenbelt, Maryland 20771, USA, [10]Department of Physics, Catholic University of America, Washington, DC 20064, USA, [11]Center for Space Sciences and Technology, University of Maryland, Baltimore County, 1000 Hilltop Circle, Baltimore, Maryland 21250, USA, [12]Astroparticle Physics Laboratory, NASA/GSFC, Greenbelt, Maryland 20771, USA, [13]Center for Research and Exploration in Space Sciences and Technology, NASA/GSFC, Greenbelt, Maryland 20771, USA, [14]Institute of Applied Physics (IFAC), National Research Council (CNR), Via Madonna del Piano, 10, 50019 Sesto, Fiorentino, Italy, [15]Department of Physics and Astronomy, Louisiana State University, 202 Nicholson Hall, Baton Rouge, Louisiana 70803, USA, [16]Department of Physics and Astronomy, University of Padova, Via Marzolo, 8, 35131 Padova, Italy, [17]INFN Sezione di Padova, Via Marzolo, 8, 35131 Padova, Italy, [18]Institute of Space and Astronautical Science, Japan Aerospace Exploration Agency, 3-1-1 Yoshinodai, Chuo, Sagamihara, Kanagawa 252-5210, Japan, [19]Kanagawa University, 3-27-1 Rokkakubashi, Kanagawa, Yokohama, Kanagawa 221-8686, Japan, [20]Faculty of Science and Technology, Graduate School of Science and Technology, Hirosaki University, 3, Bunkyo, Hirosaki, Aomori 036-8561, Japan, [21]Yukawa Institute for Theoretical Physics, Kyoto University, Kitashirakawa Oiwake-cho, Sakyo, Kyoto 606-8502, Japan, [22]Department of Electronic Information Systems, Shibaura Institute of Technology, 307 Fukasaku, Minuma, Saitama 337-8570, Japan, [23]School of Advanced Science and Engineering, Waseda University, 3-4-1 Okubo, Shinjuku, Tokyo 169-8555, Japan, [24]National Institute of Polar Research, 10-3, Midori-cho, Tachikawa, Tokyo 190-8518, Japan, [25]Faculty of Engineering, Division of Intelligent Systems Engineering, Yokohama National University, 79-5 Tokiwadai, Hodogaya, Yokohama 240-8501, Japan, [26]Faculty of Science, Shinshu University, 3-1-1 Asahi, Matsumoto, Nagano 390-8621, Japan, [27]Hakubi Center, Kyoto University, Yoshida Honmachi, Sakyo-ku, Kyoto 606-8501, Japan, [28]Department of Astronomy, Graduate School of Science, Kyoto University, Kitashirakawa Oiwake-cho, Sakyo-ku, Kyoto 606-8502, Japan, [29]Institute of Particle and Nuclear Studies, High Energy Accelerator Research Organization, 1-1 Oho, Tsukuba, Ibaraki 305-0801, Japan, [30]University of Pisa, Polo Fibonacci, Largo B. Pontecorvo, 3, 56127 Pisa, Italy, [31]Astroparticle Physics Laboratory, NASA/GSFC, Greenbelt, Maryland 20771, USA, [32]Department of Electrical and Electronic Systems Engineering, National Institute of Technology, Ibaraki College, 866 Nakane, Hitachinaka, Ibaraki 312-8508, Japan, [33]Department of Astronomy, University of Maryland, College Park, Maryland 20742, USA, [34]Department of Physical Sciences, College of Science and Engineering, Ritsumeikan University, Shiga 525-8577, Japan, [35]Faculty of Science and Engineering, Global Center for Science and Engineering, Waseda University, 3-4-1 Okubo, Shinjuku, Tokyo 169-8555, Japan, [36]Department of Physics and Astronomy, University of Denver, Physics Building, Room 211, 2112 East Wesley Avenue, Denver, Colorado 80208-6900, USA, [37]Quantum ICT Advanced Development Center, National Institute of Information and Communications Technology, 4-2-1 Nukui-Kitamachi, Koganei, Tokyo 184-8795, Japan, [38]College of Science and Engineering, Department of Physics and Mathematics, Aoyama Gakuin University, 5-10-1 Fuchinobe, Chuo, Sagamihara, Kanagawa 252-5258, Japan, [39]College of Industrial Technology, Nihon University, 1-2-1 Izumi, Narashino, Chiba 275-8575, Japan [40]RIKEN, 2-1 Hirosawa, Wako, Saitama 351-0198, Japan, [41]Division of Mathematics and Physics, Graduate School of Science, Osaka City University, 3-3-138 Sugimoto, Sumiyoshi, Osaka 558-8585, Japan, [42]National Institutes for Quantum and Radiation Science and Technology, 4-9-1 Anagawa, Inage, Chiba 263-8555, Japan, [43]Nagoya University, Furo, Chikusa, Nagoya 464-8601, Japan, [44]College of Science, Ibaraki University, 2-1-1 Bunkyo, Mito, Ibaraki 310-8512 Japan

Off-axis jet scenario for early afterglow emission of low-luminosity Gamma-Ray Burst GRB 190829A

Yuri Sato[1,*], Kaori Obayashi[1], Ryo Yamazaki[1,2], Kohta Murase[3,4,5,6] and Yutaka Ohira[7]

[1] *Department of Physics and Mathematics, Aoyama Gakuin University, 5-10-1 Fuchinobe, Sagamihara 252-5258, Japan*
[2] *Institute of Laser Engineering, Osaka University, 2-6 Yamadaoka, Suita, Osaka 565-0871, Japan*
[3] *Department of Physics, Pennsylvania State University, University Park, Pennsylvania 16802, USA*
[4] *Department of Astronomy & Astrophysics, Pennsylvania State University, University Park, Pennsylvania 16802, USA*
[5] *Center for Multimessenger Astrophysics, Pennsylvania State University, University Park, Pennsylvania 16802, USA*
[6] *Center for Gravitational Physics, Yukawa Institute for Theoretical Physics, Kyoto University, Kyoto, Kyoto 606-8502, Japan*
[7] *Department of Earth and Planetary Science, The University of Tokyo, 7-3-1 Hongo, Bunkyo-ku, Tokyo 113-0033, Japan*
[*] E-mail: yuris@phys.aoyama.ac.jp

Low-luminosity gamma-ray bursts (GRBs) have small isotropic equivalent gamma-ray energy and luminosity, compared with normal long GRBs. GRB 190829A is a member of this class. Furthermore, very-high-energy gamma-rays were detected by H.E.S.S. with $\sim 20\sigma$ significance. This event had more unusual features. First, it had much smaller isotropic equivalent gamma-ray energy than typical long gamma-ray bursts and is classified as low-luminosity GRB. Second, early X-ray and optical afterglow emission showed a rising part and simultaneously peaked at about 1400 s. We propose an off-axis jet scenario that explains these observational results. In this model, the relativistic beaming effect is responsible for the apparently small isotropic gamma-ray energy and spectral peak energy. Using a jetted afterglow model, we find that the narrow jet, which has the initial Lorentz factor of 350 and the initial jet opening half-angle of 0.015 rad, viewed off-axis can describe the observed achromatic behavior in the X-ray and optical afterglow. Another wide, baryon-loaded jet is necessary for the later-epoch X-ray and radio emissions. Derived parameters explains the very-high-energy gamma-ray flux at 20,000 s.

Keywords: Gamma-ray bursts: individual: GRB 190829A

1. Introduction

Low-luminosity gamma-ray bursts (GRBs) have small isotropic equivalent gamma-ray energy $E_{\rm iso,\gamma}$ and luminosity $L_{\rm iso,\gamma}$, compared with normal long GRBs. For most of them, supernovae are often associated. Currently, the origin is unknown. Possible scenarios are a shock breakout,[18] a low-power relativistic jet,[26] an off-axis jet,[30] and so on.

GRB 190829A is classified as a low-luminosity GRB.[4] The prompt gamma-ray emission (from ~ 10 keV to MeV band) consists of two temporally separated components.[4] The burst started with less energetic emission (hereafter Episode 1 following Chand et al.[4]) with $E_{\text{iso},\gamma} = 3.2 \times 10^{49}$ erg and a peak energy (that is, the photon energy at which the νF_ν-spectrum takes a maximum) $E_p = 120$ keV. After quiescent time interval lasting about 40 s, the second brighter emission (Episode 2) with $E_{\text{iso},\gamma} = 1.9 \times 10^{50}$ erg and $E_p = 11$ keV, appeared. The observed values of $E_{\text{iso},\gamma}$ and E_p of Episode 2 are consistent with Amati relation,[1,21] while those of Episode 1 are in the region of low-luminosity GRBs. Both Episode 1 and 2 have smaller $E_{\text{iso},\gamma}$ and E_p than typical long GRBs.[14] Indeed, GRB 190829A occurred so nearby with a redshift of $z = 0.0785$ that such weak prompt emissions could be observed.

Well-sampled afterglow light curves of GRB 190829A were obtained in X-ray, optical/infrared (IR),[4] radio bands[20] and very-high-enrgy (VHE) gamma-rays.[12] VHE gamma-ray emission was detected by H.E.S.S. about 2×10^4 s after the burst trigger and its significance is $\sim 20~\sigma$.[12] It is remarkable that early X-ray and optical/IR afterglow emission showed a rising part and simultaneously peaked at about 1.4×10^3 s. Such an "achromatic" behavior is difficult to be explained in standard afterglow model, in which the synchrotron emission has the maximum when the typical frequency ν_m crosses the observation bands.[23] In contrast, the other VHE events, GRB 190114C and 180720B, showed monotonically decaying X-ray afterglow emission.[8,29] Possible interpretations of the achromatic bump are the X-ray flare with optical counterpart,[4,32,34] the afterglow onset of baryon loaded outflow,[9] e^+e^- dust shell,[17] and the reverse shock emission.[22] Another interesting point is that late time ($t > 10^{4-5}$ s) optical/IR emissions are dominated by supernova component.[13]

In this proceeding, we consider off-axis jet scenario to explain those unusual observed properties of GRB 190829A. If the jet is viewed off-axis ($\theta_v < \theta_j$), the relativistic beaming effects cause the prompt emission to be dimmer and softer than on-axis ($\theta_v \sim 0$) viewing case.[16,27,28,30] The bulk Lorentz factor of the jet is initially so high that the afterglow emission is very dim because of the relativistic effect. As the jet decelerates, the beaming effect becomes weak, resulting in the emergence of a rising part in afterglow light curves. After the peak of the emission, the jet has smaller Lorentz factors so that the light curve only weakly depends on the viewing angle. For more details, see our paper (Sato et al.[25]).

2. Model

Following Huang et al.,[15] the dynamics of the shock is numerically computed (see Sato et al.[25] for details). The jet with isotropic-equivalent kinetic energy $E_{\text{iso},K}$, initial Lorentz factor Γ_0, and initial jet opening half-angle θ_0 decelerates via interactions with ISM and forms a thin shell. In calculating synchrotron radiation, we assume that microphysics parameters ϵ_e and ϵ_B, the energy fractions of internal energy going into radiating electrons and magnetic field, are constant. The electron energy distribution in the emitting thin shell has a power-law form with index p. In the slow cooling regime, the electron spectrum has a break at the electron cooling

Lorentz factor γ_c, where we take into account the SSC cooling in the Thomson limit as well as synchrotron energy losses.[5,24,31] Then, it has a form $N(\gamma_e) \propto \gamma_e^{-p}$ when $\gamma_m < \gamma_e < \gamma_c$ and $N(\gamma_e) \propto \gamma_e^{-p-1}$ when $\gamma_c < \gamma_e$. The flux density F_ν of the afterglow emission that arrives at the observer time T is obtained by integrating the emissivity over the equal arrival time surface (e.g., Granot, Piran, & Sari[10]). Parameters of the present model are isotropic-equivalent kinetic energy $E_{\text{iso,K}}$, initial Lorentz factor Γ_0, initial jet opening half-angle θ_0, ISM density n_0, microphysics parameters ϵ_e and ϵ_B, electron power-law index p, and the viewing angle θ_v.

3. Results

In this section, we show our numerical results of synchrotron afterglow emission in the X-ray (10^{18} Hz), optical (V-band), and radio (1.3 and 15.5 GHz) bands, and compare them with observation data of GRB 190829A. The X-ray data are extracted from the *Swift* team website[a].[6,7] The optical V-band data (before the absorption correction) are obtained from Chand et al.[4] In our numerical calculation, we take the V-band extinction $A_V = 1.5$ mag.[4] The radio data are taken from Rhodes et al.[20]

First, a single jet viewed off-axis is considered in order to discuss the observed X-ray and optical bumps around $T \sim 1.4 \times 10^2$ s. We adopt $\theta_v = 0.031$ rad, $\theta_0 = 0.015$ rad, $E_{\text{iso,K}} = 4.0 \times 10^{53}$ erg, $\Gamma_0 = 350$, $n_0 = 0.01$ cm^{-3}, $\epsilon_e = 0.2$, $\epsilon_B = 5.0 \times 10^{-5}$ and $p = 2.44$. The initial opening half-angle is small, so that we refer to "narrow jet" in the following. However, the jet is still "fat" in the sense $\theta_0 > \Gamma_0^{-1}$, so that the jet dynamics is able to be discussed as in a standard manner. Our off-axis afterglow model well explains the observational results of early X-ray and optical afterglow from about 8×10^2 to 2×10^4 s. An achromatic behavior in the X-ray and optical bands is evident. The off-axis afterglow starts with a rising part because of the relativistic beaming effect.[11] As the jet decelerates, the observed flux increases. When the jet Lorentz factor becomes $\Gamma \sim (\theta_v - \theta_0)^{-1} = 65$, the afterglow light curve takes a maximum. If the adiabatic evolution ($\Gamma \propto t^{-3/8}$) is assumed, the observer time of the flux maximum is analytically given by

$$T_{pk} \sim (1+z) \left(\frac{3E_{\text{iso,K}}}{4\pi n_0 m_p c^5}\right)^{\frac{1}{3}} (\theta_v - \theta_0)^{\frac{8}{3}} . \tag{1}$$

For our model parameters, we get $T_{pk} \sim 2 \times 10^3$ s, which is consistent with our numerical results within a factor of two. Parameter dependence has been throughly investigated in Sato et al.[25]

Next, a two-component jet model is considered, in which another "wide jet" is introduced in addition to the narrow jet. The observed flux is simply the superposition of each jet emission components. For the wide jet, we adopt $\theta_0 = 0.1$ rad,

---

[a]https://www.swift.ac.uk/xrt_curves/00922968/

$E_{\rm iso,K} = 2.0 \times 10^{53}$ erg, $\Gamma_0 = 20$, $\epsilon_e = 0.4$, $\epsilon_B = 1.0 \times 10^{-5}$, and $p = 2.2$. The values of θ_v and n_0 are common for both jets. We assume that the central axes of the two jets are identical ($\theta = 0$) and that the two jets depart from the central engine ($r = 0$) at the same time. One can find in Fig. 1 that early achromatic peaks in the X-ray and optical bands are explained by the off-axis narrow jet emission (dashed lines in the right panel), and that the late X-ray and radio afterglow is interpreted with the wide jet emission (dotted lines).

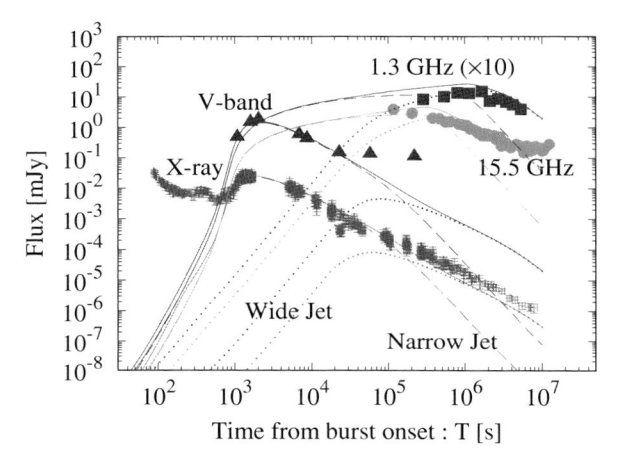

Fig. 1. Afterglow light curves calculated by our two-component jet model — solid lines are the sum of the narrow (dashed lines) and wide (dotted lines) jets in the X-ray (10^{18} Hz: red), optical (V-band: blue) and radio bands (1.3 GHz: orange, 15.5 GHz: green), which is compared with the observed data of GRB 190829A (X-ray: red points, V-band: blue triangles, 1.3 GHz: orange filled-circles, 15.5 GHz: green squares). Note that late-time ($t > 5 \times 10^4$ s) optical band is dominated by supernova component.[13]

4. Discussion

We have investigated an off-axis jet scenario in which we have invoked a two-component jet model to explain the observational results of GRB 190829A. The best-fitted model in this paper is shown by solid lines in Fig. 1. According to our model, the early X-ray and optical afterglow was off-axis emission from the narrow jet, and the late X-ray and radio afterglow came from the wide jet.

There are still some observed components that are brighter than the prediction of our jet model. They may be other components. For example, very early ($T \leq 7 \times 10^2$ s) X-ray emission should be the contribution from late prompt emission like flares. Or if the jet is structured, the early X-ray afterglow shows a plateau phase or an additional peak.[2,3,19] The observed optical flux later than $\sim 5 \times 10^4$ s is a supernova component.[13] At the late epoch ($T \sim 10^7$ s), the 15.5 GHz radio flux also exceeds our numerical result, which could be other components such as counter-jet emission. As seen in Fig. 1, our theoretical radio fluxes in both 1.3 and 15.5 GHz with our parameters sometimes overshot the observed ones. However, the excess is only within a factor of two, and this difference may come from the uncertainty of our simple model.

The prompt emission of GRB 190829A had smaller values of the peak energy $E_{\rm p}$ and the isotropic-equivalent gamma-ray energy $E_{\rm iso,\gamma}$ than typical long GRBs. Here, it is discussed whether $E_{\rm p}$ and $E_{\rm iso,\gamma}$ from our narrow jet were typical or not if it would have been viewed on-axis ($\theta_v \approx 0$). We consider a simple emission model[16,27,28] assuming an instantaneous emission of an infinitesimally thin shell moving with the Lorentz factor Γ_0. If the narrow jet emitted Episode 1 of observed prompt emission (see § 1), that is, $E_p(\theta_v = 0.031) = 120$ keV and $E_{\rm iso,\gamma}(\theta_v = 0.031) = 3.2 \times 10^{49}$ erg,[4] then on-axis quantities, $E_p(0)$ and $E_{\rm iso,\gamma}(0)$, are obtained as $E_p(0) = E_p(\theta_v)/R_1 = 3.7$ MeV and $E_{\rm iso,\gamma}(0) = E_{\rm iso,\gamma}(\theta_v)/R_2 = 2.7 \times 10^{53}$ erg (For details, see Sato et al.[25]). These values are within the range for bursts detected so far (e.g., Zhao et al.[33]). The isotropic equivalent kinetic energy of the narrow jet just after the prompt emission is $E_{\rm iso,K} = 4.0 \times 10^{53}$ erg (see § 3), so that the efficiency of the prompt emission is calculated as $\eta_\gamma = E_{\rm iso,\gamma}(0)/(E_{\rm iso,\gamma}(0)+E_{\rm iso,K}) \approx 0.4$. On the other hand, if the narrow jet is responsible for Episode 2 (that is, $E_p(\theta_v = 0.031) = 11$ keV and $E_{\rm iso,\gamma}(\theta_v = 0.031) = 1.9 \times 10^{50}$ erg), we obtain $E_p(0) = 340$ keV and $E_{\rm iso,\gamma}(0) = 1.6 \times 10^{54}$ erg, which are again similar to typical long GRBs. In this case, the efficiency is $\eta_\gamma \approx 0.8$. If the narrow jet causes Episode 1, then the estimated prompt emission efficiency η_γ is almost typical, however on-axis $E_{\rm p}(0)$ is located at the highest end of the distribution for long GRBs. On the other hand, if the narrow jet produced Episode 2, then on-axis $E_p(0)$ is smaller though η_γ is somewhat higher (but it is still comparable, and one can say that the value is reasonable considering very simple approximation of our prompt emission model). Episode 1 and 2 may be emitted from narrow and wide jets, respectively. Note that if the wide jet emits Episode 2, its efficiency is small, $\eta_\gamma \approx 5 \times 10^{-3}$, so that it might be natural that the narrow jet causes both Episode 1 and 2.

The VHE gamma-ray flux at 2×10^4 s is estimated, where we assume the synchrotron self-Compton emission in the Thomson limit.[24] Our narrow jet parameters determined by X-ray, optical and radio afterglows may roughly explain observed VHE gamma-ray flux at 2×10^4 s.[25] On the other hand, the VHE gamma-ray flux from wide jet has brighten until at 5×10^4 s. After this time, the flux decays.

Acknowledgments

We thank the organizers of the successful MG16 meeting. This research was partially supported by JSPS KAKENHI Grant Nos. 18H01232 (RY), 20H01901 (KM), 20H05852 (KM) and JP19H01893 (YO). R.Y. deeply appreciates Aoyama Gakuin University Research Institute for helping our research by the fund. The work of K.M. is supported by NSF Grant No. AST-1908689. Y.O. is supported by Leading Initiative for Excellent Young Researchers, MEXT, Japan.

References

1. Amati L., et al., *A&A* **390**, 81 (2002).
2. Beniamini P., Duque R., Daigne F., Mochkovitch R., *Mon. Not. R. Astron. Soc.* **492**, 2847 (2020).
3. Beniamini P., Granot J., Gill R., *Mon. Not. R. Astron. Soc.* **493**, 3521 (2020).
4. Chand V., et al., *Astrophys.* **898**, 42 (2020).
5. Dermer C. D., Chiang J., Mitman K. E., *Astrophys.* **537**, 785 (2020).
6. Evans P. A., et al., *A&A* **469**, 379 (2007).
7. Evans P. A., et al., *Mon. Not. R. Astron. Soc.* **397**, 1177 (2009).
8. Fraija N., et al., *Astrophys.* **885**, 29 (2019).
9. Fraija N., eal., 2020, arXiv, arXiv:2003.11252
10. Granot J., Piran T., Sari R., *Astrophys.* **513**, 679 (1999).
11. Granot J., Panaitescu A., Kumar P., Woosley S. E., *Astrophys. Lett.* **570**, L61 (2002).
12. H. E. S. S. Collaboration, *Science* **372**, 1081 (2021).
13. Hu Y.-D., et al., *A&A* **646**, A50 (2021).
14. Huang X.-L., Liang E.-W., Liu R.-Y., Cheng J.-G., Wang X.-Y., *Astrophys. Lett.* **903**, L26 (2021).
15. Huang Y. F., Gou L. J., Dai Z. G., Lu T., *Astrophys.* **543**, 90 (2000).
16. Ioka K., Nakamura T., *Astrophys. Lett.* **554**, L163 (2001).
17. Lu-Lu Z., et al., arXiv:2106.03466.
18. Nakar E., Sari R., *Astrophys.* **747**, 88 (2012).
19. Oganesyan G., Ascenzi S., Branchesi M., Salafia O. S., Dall'Osso S., Ghirlanda G., *Astrophys.* **893**, 88 (2020).
20. Rhodes L., et al., *Mon. Not. R. Astron. Soc.* **496**, 3326 (2020).
21. Sakamoto T., et al., *Astrophys.* **679**, 570 (2008).
22. Salafia O. S., et al., arXiv:2106.07169.
23. Sari R., Piran T., Narayan R., *Astrophys. Lett.* **497**, L17 (1998).
24. Sari R., Esin A. A., *Astrophys.* **548**, 787 (2001).
25. Sato Y., et al., *Mon. Not. R. Astron. Soc.* **504**, 5467 (2021).
26. Toma K., Ioka K., Sakamoto T., Nakamura T., *Astrophys.* **659**, 1420 (2007).
27. Yamazaki R., Ioka K., Nakamura T., *Astrophys. Lett.* **571**, L31 (2002).
28. Yamazaki R., Ioka K., Nakamura T., *Astrophys.* **593**, 941 (2003).
29. Yamazaki R., Sato Y., Sakamoto T., Serino M., *Mon. Not. R. Astron. Soc.* **494**, 5259 (2021).
30. Yamazaki R., Yonetoku D., Nakamura T., *Astrophys. Lett.* **594**, L79 (2003).
31. Zhang B., Mészáros P., *Astrophys.* **559**, 110 (2001).
32. Zhang B. T.. Murase, K., et al., 2020a, arXiv:2012.07796
33. Zhao W., et al., *Astrophys.* **900**, 112 (2020).
34. Zhao L., et al., arXiv:2012.12036.

GRB prompt phase spectra under backscattering dominated model

Mukesh Kumar Vyas* and Asaf Pe'er

*Department of Physics, Bar Ilan University,,
Ramat Gan, 5290002, Israel
* E-mail: mukeshkvys@gmail.com
asaf.peer@biu.ac.il
www.biu.ac.il*

David Eichler

*Ben-Gurion University,
Be'er Sheva, 84105, Israel*

We propose a backscattering dominated prompt emission model for gamma ray bursts (GRB) prompt phase in which the photons generated through pair annihilation at the centre of the burst are backscattered through Compton scattering by an outflowing stellar cork. We show that the obtained spectra are capable of explaining the low and high energy slopes as well as the distribution of spectral peak energies in their observed prompt spectra.

Keywords: High energy astrophysics; Gamma-ray bursts; Relativistic jets; Theoretical models

1. Introduction

In the picture of gamma ray bursts (GRBs), collapse of a massive star gives rise to a long GRB, while a merger of two compact objects leads to a short GRB. In both the cases, strong bipolar jets are produced.[1,2] Radiation from these jets is observed if the observer is near the jet axis. The initial phase of the burst is known as prompt phase. In a typical understanding of this phase, the jet propagates inside the stellar interior and forms an envelope (stellar cork). Finally, the jet breaks out of the cork to be observed.[3,4]

An alternate view of this stage was proposed,[5–9] in which the core of the star produces electron-positron pair plasma through neutrino annihilation. This pair plasma emits radiation in form of a jet through pair annihilation and pushes the stellar material to form the stellar cork. This cork is further pushed to relativistic speeds by radiation pressure. The radiation is not able to pierce the cork and is backscattered. As the cork is moving with relativistic speeds, this radiation is beamed along the direction of the jet and is seen by the observer.

In this work, we carry out Monte Carlo simulations of the interaction of the seed photons with the cork where the backscattered photons lead to the observed spectrum. We show that the spectrum observed is capable of explaining a large range of observed spectral properties like the photon indices at low and high energies along with the spectral peak energies.

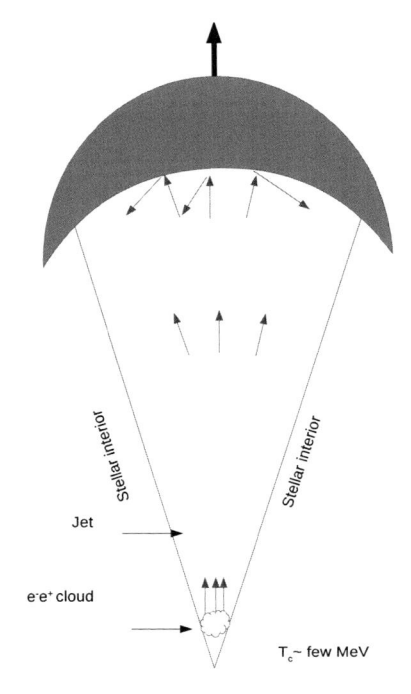

Fig. 1. Geometric representation of the system. The seed photons are generated near the centre of the bursts through pair annihilation and comptonized with the plasma present there. These photons propogate in empty jet funnel and interact with a radially outflowing stellar cork.

2. Physical picture of the system and source of the seed photons

At the time of stellar collapse, neutrinos are produced and get annihilated near the centre of the star. This annihilation produces an electron-positron pair dominated plasma. This pair plasma produces annihilation spectrum along with bremmstrahlung and is further Comptonized by the local plasma. Using Monte Carlo simulations, the resultant spectra were studied by.[10] The spectra were found to be flat with exponential decay at high energies. We obtained numerical fits to his results. For plasma density $n = 2 \times 10^{18}$ cm^{-3} the fitted spectrum is

$$F_\varepsilon = C_0 \exp\left(-\frac{C_1 \varepsilon^2}{\Theta_r^2}\right) \quad \text{KeV/s/KeV}^{-1} \qquad (1)$$

Here ε photon energy normalized to electron's rest mass energy. $\Theta_r = k_B T_r / m_e c^2$ is dimensionless representation of pair temperature T_r with k_B, m_e and c are Boltzmann's constant, rest mass of the electron and light speed, respectively. $C_1 = 0.045$ and $C_0 (= 2 \times 10^{40}$ KeV s^{-1}/KeV). This fit gives reliable spectra for temperatures $\Theta_r > 0.3$. The photons with this spectral shape propagate within the jet funnel and push the stellar matter that forms a stellar cork ahead of it. The cork moves with relativistic speeds and escapes the stellar surface. The seed photons enter the hot cork with temperature T_c (or $\Theta_c = k_B T_c/m_e c^2$). After going through Compton scattering with the electrons inside the cork, the photons gain or loose energy and get backscattered from the rear end. The geometry of this figure is explained in Figure 1. Because of the relativistic motion of the cork with Lorentz factor γ, these photons are then observed by an observer situated at angle θ_{obs} from the jet axis. The cork has curved inner surface and the photons scattered at different locations are observed at different times as well as with different energies producing a light curve as well as spectrum.

3. Solution procedure

Through a Monte Carlo code, we inject approximately 26 million seed photons with the spectral distribution according to Equation 1. These photons are launched at an adiabatically expanding and outflowing cork with temperature T_c and Lorentz factor γ with an opening angle $\theta_j = 0.1$ rad. The photons enter the cork from its rear end (Figure 1) and scattered backwards. Before escaping, the photons go though multiple scattering with energetic electrons inside the cork and thus their energies evolve. More details of the calculation procedure of the Monte Carlo code is described before.[8,11] These photons are then observed in specific angular patch $d\theta_{obs} = 0.005$ rad about the observer's location θ_{obs}. The resultant spectrum is shown in the rest frame of the GRBs with an assumption that the total energy released from the centre is equivalent to 10^{50} erg.

4. Results

In Figure 2, we plot a typical photon spectrum (photons $cm^{-2} KeV^{-1}$) obtained by scattering of seed photons with $\Theta_r = 3$ and cork temperature $\Theta_c = 1.4$. The cork has a bulk Lorentz factor $\gamma = 100$ and initial location at $r_i = 3 \times 10^{12}$ cm from the centre of the star. The opening angle of the cork is taken to be $\theta_j = 0.1$ rad. The spectrum obtained has a low energy photon index $\alpha = -1.1$ while high energy index is $\beta = -2.75$. In Figure 3 we show the variation of spectral emissivity KeV cm^{-2}. The Spectral peak is obtained to be at $\varepsilon_{peak} = 30$ MeV. This typical spectrum obtained resembles the well known GRB prompt phase spectral shape with two power laws separated by a spectral peak.[12]

Keeping the same parameters as above, we plot the variation of ε_{peak} with observer's position θ_{obs} in Figure 4 and find that it varies from few 10 MeV to few KeV as the observing angle changes from 0 to 0.35 rad. The evolution of peak energies are followed due to relativistic kinematics. The photons are blueshifted for an on axis observer while a far off axis observer sees the photons to be having relatively less energies. This shifts the spectra to lower energies and subsequently low peak energies are observed. The obtained range of peak energies explains the typically observed range of the spectral peaks in GRB prompt phase spectra.[13]

Finally, in Figure 5 we show that the photon indices α and β are sensitive to the cork temperature Θ_c. In the range $\Theta_c = 1 - 10$, the magnitude of both indices decreases making the spectra harder. It is understandable as the spectrum becomes harder due to high energy electrons in cork at high temperatures.

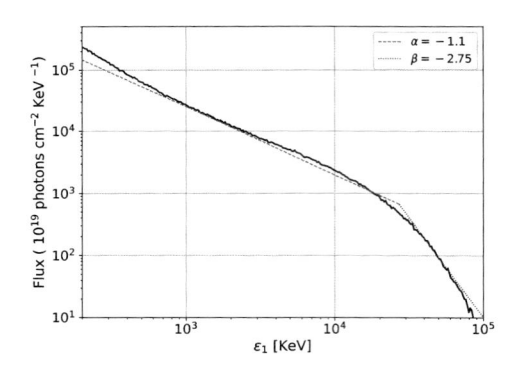

Fig. 2. Photon spectrum obtained for $\Theta_c = 1.4$, and $\theta_j = 0.1$ rad. The observer is situated at $\theta_{obs} = 0.05$ rad. Here $\Theta_r = 3.0$ and $\gamma = 100$

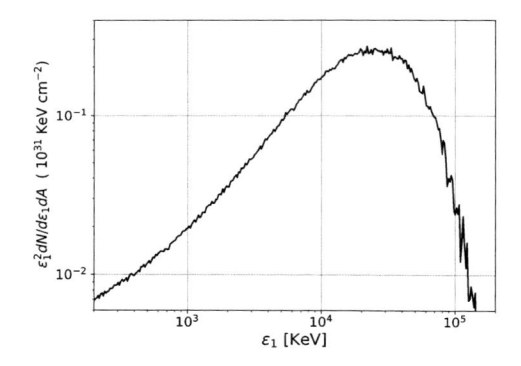

Fig. 3. Emissivity KeV cm^{-2} for the same parameters as in Figure 2

5. Conclusions

In this proceedings, we have shown that the typical spectrum of a gamma ray prompt phase is consistent with the theoretical prediction of backscattering dominated picture. We show that the spectrum has negative α and steeper β. The ranges obtained for both the indices is $\alpha \sim -1.9$ to -1.1 and $\beta \sim -3$ to -2.4. The spectral peak energies decrease as the observer is located farther from the axis or θ_{obs} is greater. In such as case, the peak energies are obtained to be in the range $\varepsilon_{peak} =$ few 10 KeV to few 10 MeV. All the obtained ranges of these parameters, α, β and ε_{peak} are within the observed ranges of GRB prompt phase observations.[12–14]

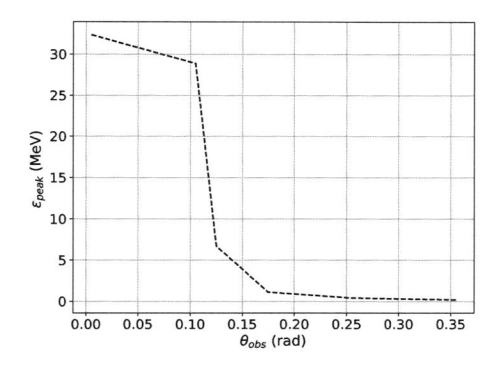

Fig. 4. Variation of the spectral peak energy ε_{peak} with observer's angle θ_{obs} for the parameters as in Figure 2.

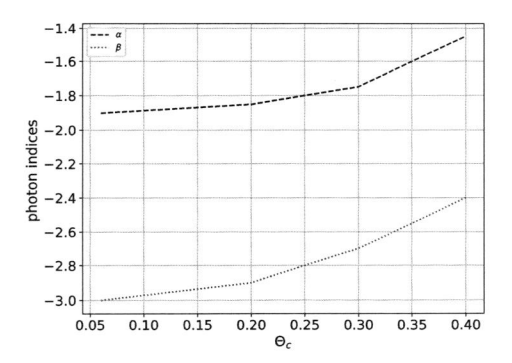

Fig. 5. Variation of photon indices α and β with the cork temperature Θ_c for $\Theta_r = 3$ and $\theta_{obs} = 0.105$ rad.

Acknowledgments

After recent demise of our collaborator late David Eichler, the completion of this work is a tribute to him.

References

1. A. Levinson and D. Eichler, Baryon purity in cosmological gamma-ray bursts as a manifestation of event horizons, *The Astrophysical Journal* **418**, p. 386 (1993).
2. A. MacFadyen and S. Woosley, Collapsars: Gamma-ray bursts and explosions in "failed supernovae", *The Astrophysical Journal* **524**, p. 262 (1999).
3. E. Ramirez-Ruiz, A. I. MacFadyen and D. Lazzati, Precursors and e± pair loading from erupting fireballs, *Monthly Notices of the Royal Astronomical Society* **331**, 197 (2002).
4. W. Zhang, S. Woosley and A. MacFadyen, Relativistic jets in collapsars, *The Astrophysical Journal* **586**, p. 356 (2003).

5. D. Eichler and H. Manis, Spectral lags explained as scattering from accelerated scatterers, *The Astrophysical Journal Letters* **689**, p. L85 (2008).
6. D. Eichler, Cloaked gamma-ray bursts, *The Astrophysical Journal Letters* **787**, p. L32 (2014).
7. D. Eichler, Short gamma-ray bursts viewed from far off-axis, *The Astrophysical Journal Letters* **869**, p. L4 (2018).
8. M. K. Vyas, A. Pe'er and D. Eichler, A backscattering-dominated prompt emission model for the prompt phase of gamma-ray bursts, *The Astrophysical Journal* **908**, p. 9 (2021).
9. M. K. Vyas, A. Pe'er and D. Eichler, Predicting spectral parameters in the backscattering dominated model for the prompt phase of GRBs, *The Astrophysical Journal Letters* **918**, p. L12 (2021).
10. A. Zdziarski, Effect of compton scattering on the pair annihilation and bremsstrahlung spectra, *Physica Scripta* **1984**, p. 124 (1984).
11. A. Pe'er, Temporal evolution of thermal emission from relativistically expanding plasma, *The Astrophysical Journal* **682**, p. 463 (2008).
12. R. D. Preece, M. S. Briggs, R. S. Mallozzi, G. N. Pendleton, W. Paciesas and D. L. Band, The batse gamma-ray burst spectral catalog. i. high time resolution spectroscopy of bright bursts using high energy resolution data, *The Astrophysical Journal Supplement Series* **126**, p. 19 (2000).
13. G. Ghirlanda, G. Ghisellini and L. Nava, Short and long gamma-ray bursts: Same emission mechanism?, *Monthly Notices of the Royal Astronomical Society: Letters* **418**, L109 (2011).
14. A. Pe'er, Physics of gamma-ray bursts prompt emission, *Advances in Astronomy* **2015** (2015).

Applying models of pulsar wind nebulae to explain X-ray plateaux following short Gamma-Ray Bursts

L. C. Strang* and A. Melatos

School of Physics, University of Melbourne,
Parkville, VIC 3010, Australia
**E-mail: lstrang@student.unimelb.edu.au*

Australian Research Council Centre of Excellence in Gravitational-wave Discovery (OzGrav),
School of Physics, University of Melbourne,
Parkville, VIC 3010, Australia
**E-mail: lstrang@student.unimelb.edu.au*

Many short Gamma-Ray Bursts (sGRBs) have a prolonged plateau in the X-ray afterglow lasting up to tens of thousands of seconds. A central engine injecting energy into the remnant may fuel the plateau. A simple analytic model describing the interaction of the magnetized relativistic wind from a rapidly-rotating magnetar with the surrounding environment can reproduce X-ray plateaux and instantaneous spectra. The model is analogous to classic, well-established models of young supernova remnants and applies the underlying physics to sGRB remnants. The light curve and spectra produced by the model are compared to observations of GRB 130603B. The spectra are also used to estimate parameters of the magnetar including its poloidal field strength and angular frequency. If combined with a gravitational wave signal, this model could provide insight into multimessenger astronomy and neutron star physics.

Keywords: Gamma-ray bursts; afterglow; supernova remnants

1. Introduction

Many short gamma-ray bursts (sGRBs) display long-lived emission in the X-ray band. A subset of the X-ray afterglows are "canonical" afterglows with three components: an initial decay, a flat plateau lasting from 10 s – 10^5 s, and a final decay (typically $\sim t^{-2}$).[1,2] The luminosity and duration of the plateau are correlated, with brighter plateaux ending sooner.[3] A similar phenomenon is observed in long gamma-ray bursts (LGRBs), but the two populations are statistically distinct and likely have different progenitors for the afterglow as well as the prompt emission.[4–6]

Binary neutron star coalescence has been confirmed as a progenitor of sGRBs,[7,8] suggesting the evolution of the post-merger remnant dictates the evolution of the afterglow. X-ray plateaux have inspired several models including fireballs (with[9,10] and without[11] energy injection), fall-back accretion onto a black hole,[12] and ongoing energy injection via a central engine,[13] commonly assumed to be a millisecond magnetar.[14] In the latter scenario, the rotational energy of the magnetar is converted to X-rays via an unknown dissipative process, perhaps involving a relativistic wind.[13–19] Previous models have considered the evolution of a magnetar surrounded by a shroud of optically-thick ejecta material[20–22] or the production of X-rays via radiative losses from interactions with the surrounding environment.[23,24]

In this work, we present results from Ref. 25 and Ref. 26 exploring a millisecond magnetar central engine through the lens of classic models of pulsar wind nebulae (PWNe), also known as plerions. The term plerion is used throughout Ref. 25 and Ref. 26. Here, we use the term PWNe throughout to emphasize the analogy to supernova remnant models such as Ref. 27 (although technically, we are discussing a magnetar wind nebula and not a pulsar wind nebula). In the PWNe model, the X-ray plateau is caused by a magnetized bubble of electrons fuelled by the relativistic wind of the magnetar. We summarize the model presented in Ref. 25 in Sec. 2 and explore associated synchrotron light curves in Sec. 3. In Sec. 4, we quote results from Ref. 26 inferring parameters of the central engine using instantaneous spectra. We conclude in Sec. 5. This paper borrows substantially from the form and content of Ref. 25 and Ref. 26; among other things, it includes Fig. 3 from Ref. 26 unchanged.

2. Pulsar Wind Model

If a neutron star survives the sGRB, it evolves under the same physics that dictates the early evolution of PWNe. Classic one-zone models for PWNe provide an analytic estimate of the synchrotron luminosity of the remnant without specifying its detailed geometry.[27,28] In Ref. 25, an analogous model is developed and applied to X-ray plateaux. In this scenario, the sGRB heralds the birth of a rapidly-rotating neutron star with a dipole, magnetar-strength external magnetic field with angular frequency $\Omega(t)$, initial angular frequency Ω_0, and polar surface magnetic field strength B_0. Simultaneously, an isotropic, relativistic blast wave (described by the Blandford-McKee self-similar solution[29]) detonates and sweeps up the surrounding interstellar medium into a spherical shell expanding at v_s.

The neutron star spins down under pure magnetic-dipole braking and radiates energy at a rate

$$L_{\rm sd}(t) = L_0 \left(1 + \frac{t}{\tau}\right)^{-2} \quad (1)$$

where $L_0 \propto B_0^2 \Omega_0^4$ is the initial spin-down luminosity and $\tau \propto B_0^{-2} \Omega_0^{-2}$ is the characteristic spin-down timescale. Through analogy with classic models of PWNe, we assume the energy is extracted as a magnetized, relativistic electron-positron wind with velocity $v_{\rm w} \gg v_{\rm s}$. The ratio of the Poynting flux to kinetic-energy flux in the wind, σ, is expected to be $\gtrsim 1$ (i.e. the wind is Poynting-flux dominated) near the star and $\ll 1$ (i.e. kinetic-energy flux dominated) at distances far beyond the co-rotation radius $c/\Omega(t)$ ($\sigma \approx 10^{-3}$ for the Crab[30–32]).

As in PWNe, a reverse shock forms at radius $r_{\rm rs}$ where the ram pressure of the wind $P_{\rm ram}(r)$ balances the external static pressure $P_{\rm stat}(r)$.[28] As the shock propagates into the wind, the electrons are shocked into a power-law energy distribution $\propto E^{-a}$. Reference 25 models the electron population with a spherical, homogeneous bubble characterized by its properties at r_{rs} (i.e. at $r = \dot{r}_{rs}t$ for constant $\dot{r}_{rs}$). Under this assumption, the fresh electrons in the energy range $[E_{-0}, E_{+0}]$ are injected into the bubble at a rate

$$\dot{N}_{\text{inj}} = \frac{L_{\text{sd}}(t) E^{-a}(a-2)}{(1+\sigma)\left(E_{-0}^{2-a} - E_{+0}^{2-a}\right)}. \tag{2}$$

The bubble expands at a rate $\dot{r}_{rs}$, so electrons cool according to adiabatic expansion at a rate

$$-\left.\frac{dE}{dt}\right|_{\text{adiabatic}} = \frac{E}{t}. \tag{3}$$

Given a magnetic field in the bubble $B(t)$, the electrons also cool via synchrotron radiation at a rate

$$-\left.\frac{dE}{dt}\right|_{\text{synch}} = c_s E^2 B(t)^2 \tag{4}$$

where $c_s = \mu_0 e^4 / 9\pi c^3 m_e^4$. Two magnetic field configurations are presented in Ref. 25. In the first case, henceforth model A, $B(t)$ is taken to be the far-field extension of the stellar dipole field at radial distance $\dot{r}_{rs}t$ (see Eq. (9) in Ref. 25). In the second case, henceforth model B, $B(t)$ is taken to be an arbitrary, constant B. Model B serves two purposes. One, it allows the PWNe model (including magnetar spin down, electron injection, and cooling mechanisms) to be assessed in general terms, even if the specific magnetic field structure in model A is a poor approximation to reality. Two, model B decouples $B(t)$ and the central engine parameters B_0 and Ω_0 (which also govern $\dot{N}_{\text{inj}}$), allowing for the possibility that $B(t)$ may be affected by components of the post-merger environment other than the central engine.

The number density of electrons per unit energy $N(E, t)$ can be found via the time-dependent, inhomogeneous partial-differential equation

$$\frac{\partial N(E,t)}{\partial t} = \frac{\partial}{\partial E}\left[\left.\frac{dE}{dt}\right|_{\text{adiabatic}} + \left.\frac{dE}{dt}\right|_{\text{synch}}\right] + \dot{N}_{\text{inj}} \tag{5}$$

where adiabatic cooling is defined as in Eq. (3), synchrotron cooling is defined in Eq. (4), and electron injection $\dot{N}_{\text{inj}}$ is defined in Eq. (2). Two analytic Green's function solutions (corresponding to models A and B) are found in Ref. 25 and integrated to obtain $N(E, t)$.

3. Light Curves

In this section, we highlight results from Ref. 25 comparing the X-ray synchrotron light curves predicted by the model in Sec. 2 to those observed by the Neil Gehrels *Swift* telescope.[33–35]

The synchrotron spectrum of an electron with energy E_c may be approximated as a Dirac-delta function centred at the characteristic synchrotron frequency

$\nu_c \propto E_c^2 B(t)$. The source frame synchrotron luminosity in the range $[\nu_{\min}, \nu_{\max}]$ is

$$L_{\nu_{\min}-\nu_{\max}} = \int_{\nu_{\min}}^{\nu_{\max}} d\nu c_s B(t)^2 E_c^2 N(E_c, t). \qquad (6)$$

We define L_X as the source-frame luminosity in the band corresponding to the 0.3 keV – 10 keV band in the lab frame, i.e. the luminosity observable by *Swift*.

We use GRB 130603B as a representative example of X-ray plateaux following sGRBs because it has a known redshift[36] and has been inferred to spin down under magnetic-dipole braking.[19] We display the observed light curve in Fig. 1 and overplot with a projected light curve from the PWNe model. Black crosses are observations of GRB 130603B by *Swift* and corrected to the source frame. The blue curve is the X-ray light curve predicted by the PWNe model with $B = 10\,\mathrm{G}$, $B_0 = 4 \times 10^{15}\,\mathrm{G}$, $\Omega_0/2\pi = 140\,\mathrm{Hz}$, and $a = 2.8$. The parameters are chosen by hand, guided by results from Ref. 26. The observed and predicted light curve are in broad agreement.

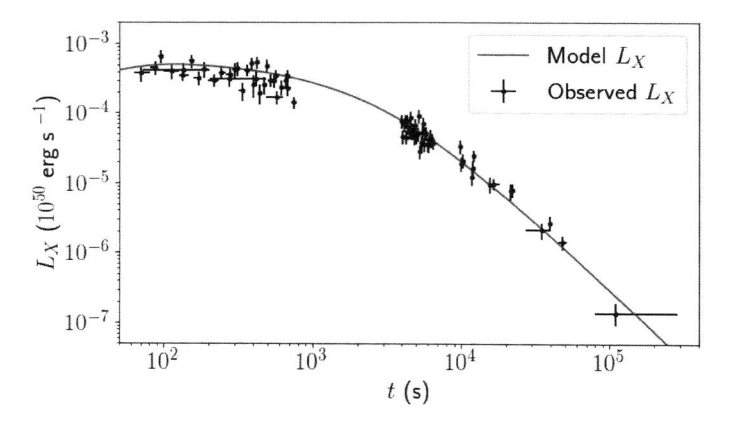

Fig. 1. X-ray luminosity in the source frame L_X ($10^{50}\,\mathrm{erg\,s^{-1}}$) versus time t (s). Here "X-ray" refers to the 0.3 keV – 10 keV band observable by *Swift* corrected to the source frame. Black crosses are observations of GRB 130603B by *Swift* and corrected to the source frame. The blue curve is the X-ray light curve predicted by the PWNe model with $B = 10\,\mathrm{G}$, $B_0 = 4 \times 10^{15}\,\mathrm{G}$, $\Omega_0/2\pi = 140\,\mathrm{Hz}$, and $a = 2.8$. Parameters chosen by hand, guided by results from Ref. 26.

In some cases, such as GRB 090515, the plateau ends abruptly. In the context of the central engine model, this has been interpreted as the neutron star collapsing to a black hole and terminating energy injection[18] (we note, however, recent population-based arguments against this hypothesis[37]). In the PWNe model, the collapse of the neutron star halts injection only but does not remove the existing population of electrons, so the afterglow persists for some time, given approximately by the synchrotron lifetime $t_{\mathrm{synch}} \sim 2 \times 10^{-9}\,[B/(1\,\mathrm{G})]^{-3/2}\,[\nu_c/(1\,\mathrm{keV})]^{-1/2}$ s. In the X-ray band, and for the parameters in Figure 1, t_{synch} amounts to nanoseconds.

3.1. Luminosity-time correlation

The Dainotti correlation connects the plateau luminosity L_p and plateau duration t_p in GRB plateaux which states that brighter plateaux have shorter durations than dimmer plateaux.[3,38,39] This correlation has been studied extensively for LGRBs under a variety of assumptions[40,41] (see Ref. 42 for a thorough review on the correlation and its uses).

The PWNe model presented in Ref. 25 naturally reproduces the observed correlation for reasonable definitions of L_p and t_p. One reasonable choice is to define the X-ray plateau duration as $t_\mathrm{p} = \tau$ and the corresponding luminosity as $L_\mathrm{p} = L_\mathrm{X}(t = \tau)$. The light blue region in Fig. 2 indicates the full range of $(L_\mathrm{p}, t_\mathrm{p})$ pairs generated by the PWNe model for $B = 5.0 \times 10^{-1}\,\mathrm{G}$, $E_{-0} = 2.5 \times 10^{-2}\,\mathrm{erg}$, $10^{12} \leq B_0/(1\,\mathrm{G}) \leq 10^{16}$, and $\Omega_0/2\pi \leq 10^3\,\mathrm{Hz}$. The black line and grey-shaded region corresponds to the best-fit correlation from Ref. 18 based on a sample of 159 sGRBs and LGRBs. The observed correlation falls entirely within the range permitted by the PWNe model.

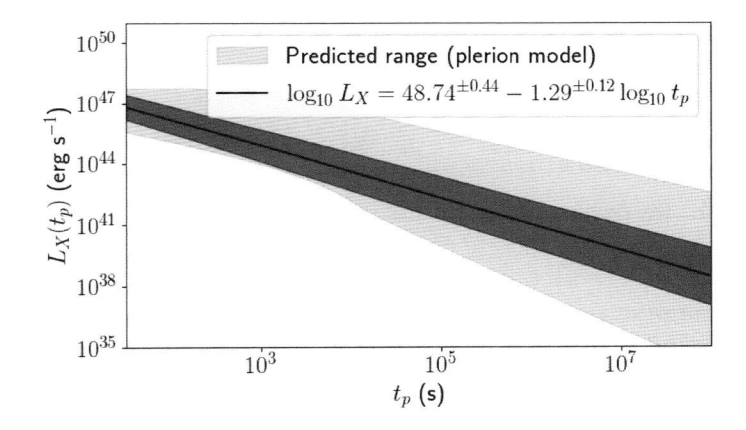

Fig. 2. X-ray plateau luminosity in the source frame $L_\mathrm{p} = L_\mathrm{X}(t_\mathrm{p})\,(\mathrm{erg\,s^{-1}})$ versus X-ray plateau duration $t_\mathrm{p}\,(\mathrm{s})$. The black line and grey-shaded region correspond to the best-fit correlation from Ref. 18 from a sample of 159 GRBs. The light blue shaded region corresponds to the range of $(L_\mathrm{p}, t_\mathrm{p})$ pairs generated by the PWNe model for $B = 5.0 \times 10^{-1}\,\mathrm{G}$, $10^{12} \leq B_0/(1\,\mathrm{G}) \leq 10^{16}$, and $\Omega_0/2\pi \leq 10^3\,\mathrm{Hz}$. Model parameters were chosen based on results presented in Ref. 26.

4. Inferring Parameters of the Central Engine

In this section, we review results presented in Ref. 26 inferring B_0, Ω_0, $E_{\pm 0}$, a, and (for model B) B using the X-ray afterglow for six sGRBs of known redshift with an X-ray plateau. We reproduce here the necessary physics to interpret the results and leave the details of the analysis to Ref. 26.

The source-frame synchrotron spectrum at time t is

$$F_\nu(t,\nu) = N(E,t) \left.\frac{\mathrm{d}E}{\mathrm{d}t}\right|_{\text{synch}} \frac{\mathrm{d}E}{\mathrm{d}\nu}. \qquad (7)$$

The synchrotron cooling rate and the characteristic synchrotron frequency depend on the magnetic field in the bubble, which is determined by B_0 and Ω_0 in model A and by B in model B. The dependence on $N(E,t)$ indicates F_ν is dependent on B, B_0, Ω_0, $E_{\pm 0}$, and a, so a single point-in-time spectrum is sufficient to infer posteriors on each parameter. For a full discussion of the results and method, see Sec. 4 in Ref. 26. For both models, one has a neutron star with an approximately millisecond spin period ($\Omega_0/2\pi \lesssim 10^3$ Hz) and a magnetar-strength poloidal magnetic field ($B_0 \sim 10^{15}$ G) i.e. a millisecond magnetar. The correlations between B_0 and Ω_0 reflect their relation to the spin-down luminosity $L_0 \propto B_0^2 \Omega_0^4$ and $\tau \propto B_0^{-2} \Omega_0^{-2}$. For model B, the posteriors on B cover the range $10^{-1} \lesssim B/(1\,\text{G}) \lesssim 1$. This is much stronger than the magnetic field in the interstellar medium ($\sim 10^{-6}$ G) but smaller than the expected field advected outwards from the central object by the relativistic outflow (i.e. the magnetic field in model A). For both models, $E_{-0} \sim 10^{-3}$ erg, which is consistent with a population of electrons accelerated in the magnetar's magnetosphere and injected into the magnetar wind with a radiation-reaction-limited Lorentz factor.

4.1. *Spectral evolution*

In this section, we review briefly results presented in Ref. 26 using the spectrum of GRB 130603B at four separate epochs to infer B_0, Ω_0, $E_{\pm 0}$, a, and B for each epoch. We label each epoch t_i with corresponding magnetic field B_i for $i \in [1,4]$ and use log uniform priors such that $10^{-6} < B_i/(1\,\text{G}) < 10^6$. For each epoch with flux data F_{ν_i}, flux uncertainty σ_i, and model flux $F_\nu(t_i,\nu)$ given by Eq. (7), we define a Gaussian likelihood $P_i \propto \exp\left\{[F_{\nu_i} - F_\nu(t_i,\nu)]^2/(2\sigma_i^2)\right\}$ such that the priors on B_0, Ω_0, $E_{\pm 0}$ and a are the same at each epoch. The analysis is performed on the joint likelihood $\Pi_i P_i$.

The median values of the posterior describe a millisecond magnetar with $B_0 \approx 2 \times 10^{15}$ G and $\Omega_0/2\pi \approx 600$ Hz, supplying the remnant with relativistic electrons with $a \approx 1.9$, $E_{-0} \approx 3.2 \times 10^{-5}$ erg, and $E_{+0} \approx 1$ erg. The median magnetic fields B_i suggest the field drops at an average rate of $0.04\,\text{G\,s}^{-1}$ from $B_1 = 2 \times 10^2$ G at $t_1 = 643$ s to $B_4 = 5 \times 10^{-1}$ G at $t_4 = 5735$ s. This is both slower and weaker than what is expected for the field in the termination shock of the wind in model A, which scales roughly as $B(t) \propto B_0 t^{-2}$ for $t \gtrsim \tau$, if the wind expands at a constant, relativistic speed (as in Ref. 25). The scale and temporal evolution of the B_i indicate the time-dependent magnetic field in the bubble requires revision. Several mechanisms for this are discussed in Ref. 26, including varying the expansion rate of the bubble or choosing an entirely separate magnetic field configuration.

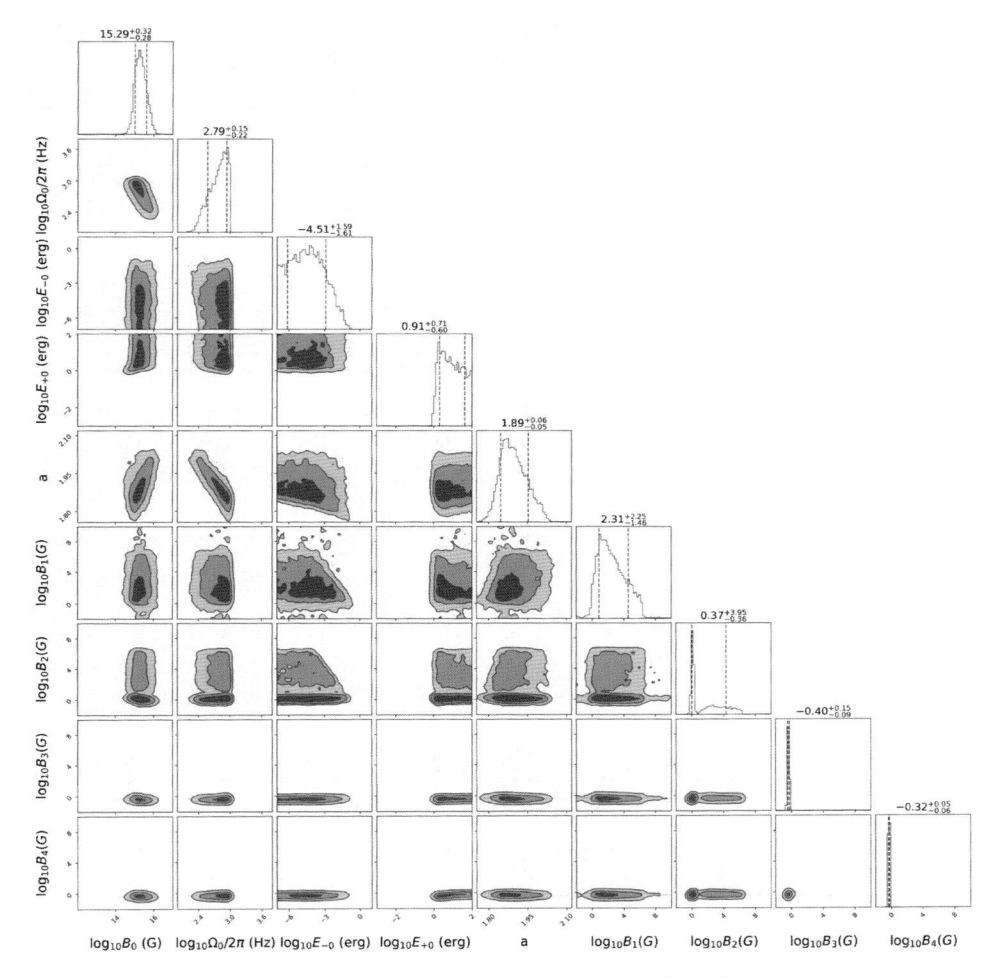

Fig. 3. Corner plot showing the posterior distribution obtained for four instantaneous spectra for GRB130603B for the parameters $\log_{10} B_0$ (G), $\log_{10} \Omega_0/2\pi$ (Hz), $\log_{10} E_{\pm 0}$ (erg), a, and $\log_{10} B_i$ ($1 \leq i \leq 4$) (G). Figure reproduced from Ref. 26

5. Conclusion

A millisecond magnetar engine based on classic models of PWNe can explain some of the observed features of canonical sGRB afterglows. Plateau light curves are broadly consistent with the synchrotron output of an electron population $N(E,t)$ evolving under ongoing, power-law injection and adiabatic and synchrotron cooling. Such a model may be referred to as a plerion model (as in Ref. 25 and Ref. 26) or, as a synonym, a PWNe model (as we do in this work). The model is able to reproduce both the shape of the afterglow and correlations L_p–t_p. Furthermore, the instantaneous spectra can be used to infer B, B_0, Ω_0, $E_{\pm 0}$, and a within the context of the model. However, the model summarized here (originally in Ref. 25) is highly idealized and does not include the important effects of merger ejecta on the evolution of the remnant (considered in e.g. Refs. 20–22). Also, as presented in Ref. 26, the temporal evolution of the spectrum implies a magnetic field that is inconsistent with both a dipole field (model A) and a constant field (model B). Future modeling improving on the work in Ref. 25 and integrating it into existing models for sGRB remnants should ultimately be compared to a broad sample of sGRBs.

Acknowledgments

This work makes use of data supplied by the UK Swift Science Data Centre at the University of Leicester. Parts of this research were conducted by the Australian Research Council Centre of Excellence for Gravitational Wave Discovery (OzGrav), through Project Number CE170100004. The work is also supported by an Australian Research Council Discovery Project grant (DP170103625).

References

1. B. Zhang, Y. Z. Fan, J. Dyks, S. Kobayashi, P. Mészáros, D. N. Burrows, J. A. Nousek and N. Gehrels, Physical Processes Shaping Gamma-Ray Burst X-Ray Afterglow Light Curves: Theoretical Implications from the Swift X-Ray Telescope Observations, *ApJ* **642**, 354 (May 2006).
2. J. A. Nousek, C. Kouveliotou, D. Grupe, K. L. Page, J. Granot, E. Ramirez-Ruiz, S. K. Patel, D. N. Burrows, V. Mangano, S. Barthelmy, A. P. Beardmore, S. Campana, M. Capalbi, G. Chincarini, G. Cusumano, A. D. Falcone, N. Gehrels, P. Giommi, M. R. Goad, O. Godet, C. P. Hurkett, J. A. Kennea, A. Moretti, P. T. O'Brien, J. P. Osborne, P. Romano, G. Tagliaferri and A. A. Wells, Evidence for a Canonical Gamma-Ray Burst Afterglow Light Curve in the Swift XRT Data, *ApJ* **642**, 389 (May 2006).
3. M. G. Dainotti, V. F. Cardone and S. Capozziello, A time-luminosity correlation for γ-ray bursts in the X-rays, *Monthly Notices of the Royal Astronomical Society* **391**, L79 (November 2008).
4. M. G. Dainotti, R. Willingale, S. Capozziello, V. Fabrizio Cardone and M. Ostrowski, Discovery of a Tight Correlation for Gamma-ray Burst Afterglows with "Canonical" Light Curves, *ApJL* **722**, L215 (October 2010).
5. A. Rowlinson, B. P. Gompertz, M. Dainotti, P. T. O'Brien, R. A. M. J. Wijers and A. J. van der Horst, Constraining properties of GRB magnetar central engines using the observed plateau luminosity and duration correlation, *Monthly Notices of the Royal Astronomical Society* **443**, 1779 (September 2014).
6. N. Rea, M. Gullón, J. A. Pons, R. Perna, M. G. Dainotti, J. A. Miralles and D. F. Torres, Constraining the grb-magnetar model by means of the galactic pulsar population, *The Astrophysical Journal* **813**, p. 92 (2015).
7. B. P. Abbott *et al.*, GW170817: Observation of Gravitational Waves from a Binary Neutron Star Inspiral, *Physical Review Letters* **119**, p. 161101 (2017).
8. B. P. Abbott *et al.*, Gravitational Waves and Gamma-Rays from a Binary Neutron Star Merger: GW170817 and GRB 170817A, *The Astrophysical Journal Letters* **848** (2017).

9. M. J. Rees and P. Mészáros, Refreshed Shocks and Afterglow Longevity in Gamma-Ray Bursts, *ApJL* **496**, L1 (March 1998).
10. M. G. Dainotti, A. L. Lenart, N. Fraija, S. Nagataki, D. C. Warren, B. De Simone, G. Srinivasaragavan and A. Mata, Closure relations during the plateau emission of Swift GRBs and the fundamental plane, *Publications of the Astronomical Society of Japan* **73**, 970 (August 2021).
11. T. Piran, Gamma-ray bursts and the fireball model, *Physics Reports* **314**, 575 (June 1999).
12. P. Kumar, R. Narayan and J. L. Johnson, Properties of Gamma-Ray Burst Progenitor Stars, *Science* **321**, p. 376 (July 2008).
13. Z. G. Dai and T. Lu, Gamma-ray burst afterglows and evolution of postburst fireballs with energy injection from strongly magnetic millisecond pulsars, *Astronomy and Astrophysics* **333**, L87 (May 1998).
14. B. Zhang and P. Mészáros, Gamma-Ray Burst Afterglow with Continuous Energy Injection: Signature of a Highly Magnetized Millisecond Pulsar, *The Astrophysical Journal* **552**, L35 (May 2001).
15. B. Zhang and P. Mészáros, Gamma-Ray Burst Afterglow with Continuous Energy Injection: Signature of a Highly Magnetized Millisecond Pulsar, *ApJ Letters* **552**, L35 (May 2001).
16. Y. Fan and D. Wei, Late internal-shock model for bright x-ray flares in gamma-ray burst afterglows and grb 011121, *Monthly Notices of the Royal Astronomical Society: Letters* **364**, L42 (2005).
17. B. P. Gompertz, P. T. O'Brien, G. A. Wynn and A. Rowlinson, Can magnetar spin-down power extended emission in some short GRBs?, *Monthly Notices of the Royal Astronomical Society* **431**, 1745 (May 2013).
18. A. Rowlinson, P. T. O'Brien, B. D. Metzger, N. R. Tanvir and A. J. Levan, Signatures of magnetar central engines in short GRB light curves, *Monthly Notices of the Royal Astronomical Society* **430**, 1061 (April 2013).
19. P. D. Lasky, C. Leris, A. Rowlinson and K. Glampedakis, The braking index of millisecond magnetars, *The Astrophysical Journal Letters* **843**, p. L1 (2017).
20. B. D. Metzger and A. L. Piro, Optical and X-ray emission from stable millisecond magnetars formed from the merger of binary neutron stars, *Montly Notices of the Royal Astronomical Society* **439**, 3916 (April 2014).
21. D. M. Siegel and R. Ciolfi, Electromagnetic Emission from Long-lived Binary Neutron Star Merger Remnants. I. Formulation of the Problem, *ApJ* **819**, p. 14 (March 2016).
22. Y.-W. Yu, B. Zhang and H. Gao, Bright "Merger-nova" from the Remnant of a Neutron Star Binary Merger: A Signature of a Newly Born, Massive, Millisecond Magnetar, *ApJL* **776**, p. L40 (October 2013).
23. G. Stratta, M. G. Dainotti, S. Dall'Osso, X. Hernandez and G. De Cesare, On the Magnetar Origin of the GRBs Presenting X-Ray Afterglow Plateaus, *ApJ* **869**, p. 155 (December 2018).
24. N. Sarin, P. D. Lasky and G. Ashton, Interpreting the X-ray afterglows of gamma-ray bursts with radiative losses and millisecond magnetars, *Monthly Notices of the Royal Astronomical Society* **499**, 5986 (December 2020).
25. L. C. Strang and A. Melatos, Plerion model of the X-ray plateau in short gamma-ray bursts, *arXiv e-prints*, p. arXiv:1906.02877 (June 2019).
26. L. C. Strang, A. Melatos, N. Sarin and P. D. Lasky, Inferring properties of neutron stars born in short gamma-ray bursts with a plerion-like X-ray plateau, *Monthly Notices of the Royal Astronomical Society* **507**, 2843 (October 2021).

27. F. Pacini and M. Salvati, On the Evolution of Supernova Remnants. Evolution of the Magnetic Field, Particles, Content, and Luminosity, *The Astrophysical Journal* **186**, 249 (November 1973).
28. M. J. Rees and J. E. Gunn, The origin of the magnetic field and relativistic particles in the Crab Nebula, *Monthly Notices of the Royal Astronomical Society* **167**, 1 (April 1974).
29. R. D. Blandford and C. F. McKee, Fluid dynamics of relativistic blast waves, *Physics of Fluids* **19**, 1130 (August 1976).
30. C. F. Kennel and F. V. Coroniti, Confinement of the Crab pulsar's wind by its supernova remnant, *The Astrophysical Journal* **283**, 694 (August 1984).
31. A. Melatos and D. B. Melrose, Energy transport in a rotation-modulated pulsar wind, *Monthly Notices of the Royal Astronomical Society* **279**, 1168 (April 1996).
32. S. V. Bogovalov, D. V. Khangulyan, A. V. Koldoba, G. V. Ustyugova and F. A. Aharonian, Modelling interaction of relativistic and non-relativistic winds in binary system PSR B1259-63/SS2883 - I. Hydrodynamical limit, *Monthly Notices of the Royal Astronomical Society* **387**, 63 (June 2008).
33. N. Gehrels, G. Chincarini, P. Giommi, K. O. Mason, J. A. Nousek, A. A. Wells, N. E. White, S. D. Barthelmy, D. N. Burrows, L. R. Cominsky, K. C. Hurley, F. E. Marshall, P. Mészáros, P. W. A. Roming, L. Angelini, L. M. Barbier, T. Belloni, S. Campana, P. A. Caraveo, M. M. Chester, O. Citterio, T. L. Cline, M. S. Cropper, J. R. Cummings, A. J. Dean, E. D. Feigelson, E. E. Fenimore, D. A. Frail, A. S. Fruchter, G. P. Garmire, K. Gendreau, G. Ghisellini, J. Greiner, J. E. Hill, S. D. Hunsberger, H. A. Krimm, S. R. Kulkarni, P. Kumar, F. Lebrun, N. M. Lloyd-Ronning, C. B. Markwardt, B. J. Mattson, R. F. Mushotzky, J. P. Norris, J. Osborne, B. Paczynski, D. M. Palmer, H. S. Park, A. M. Parsons, J. Paul, M. J. Rees, C. S. Reynolds, J. E. Rhoads, T. P. Sasseen, B. E. Schaefer, A. T. Short, A. P. Smale, I. A. Smith, L. Stella, G. Tagliaferri, T. Takahashi, M. Tashiro, L. K. Townsley, J. Tueller, M. J. L. Turner, M. Vietri, W. Voges, M. J. Ward, R. Willingale, F. M. Zerbi and W. W. Zhang, The Swift Gamma-Ray Burst Mission, *The Astrophysical Journal* **611**, 1005 (August 2004).
34. P. A. Evans, A. P. Beardmore, K. L. Page, L. G. Tyler, J. P. Osborne, M. R. Goad, P. T. O'Brien, L. Vetere, J. Racusin, D. Morris, D. N. Burrows, M. Capalbi, M. Perri, N. Gehrels and P. Romano, An online repository of Swift/XRT light curves of γ-ray bursts, *Astronomy and Astrophysics* **469**, 379 (July 2007).
35. P. A. Evans, A. P. Beardmore, K. L. Page, J. P. Osborne, P. T. O'Brien, R. Willingale, R. L. C. Starling, D. N. Burrows, O. Godet, L. Vetere, J. Racusin, M. R. Goad, K. Wiersema, L. Angelini, M. Capalbi, G. Chincarini, N. Gehrels, J. A. Kennea, R. Margutti, D. C. Morris, C. J. Mountford, C. Pagani, M. Perri, P. Romano and N. Tanvir, Methods and results of an automatic analysis of a complete sample of Swift-XRT observations of GRBs, *Monthly Notices of the Royal Astronomical Society* **397**, 1177 (August 2009).
36. A. Melandri, M. de Pasquale, S. D. Barthelmy, D. N. Burrows, M. H. Siegel and N. Gehrels, Swift Observation of GRB130603B, *GCN Report* **442** (2013).
37. P. Beniamini and W. Lu, Survival times of supramassive neutron stars resulting from binary neutron star mergers, *arXiv e-prints*, p. arXiv:2104.01181 (April 2021).
38. M. G. Dainotti, R. Willingale, S. Capozziello, V. Fabrizio Cardone and M. Ostrowski, Discovery of a Tight Correlation for Gamma-ray Burst Afterglows with "Canonical" Light Curves, *The Astrophysical Journal* **722**, L215 (October 2010).
39. J. Sultana, D. Kazanas and K. Fukumura, Luminosity Correlations for Gamma-Ray Bursts and Implications for Their Prompt and Afterglow Emission Mechanisms, *The Astrophysical Journal* **758**, p. 32 (October 2012).

40. M. G. Dainotti, S. Postnikov, X. Hernandez and M. Ostrowski, A Fundamental Plane for Long Gamma-Ray Bursts with X-Ray Plateaus, *The Astrophysical Journal* **825**, p. L20 (July 2016).
41. M. G. Dainotti, A. D. Boria and J. F. Arratia, Gamma-ray bursts with afterglow plateau phases associated with supernovae, in *Fourteenth Marcel Grossmann Meeting - MG14*, eds. M. Bianchi, R. T. Jansen and R. Ruffini, January 2018.
42. M. Dainotti, *Gamma-ray Burst Correlations; Current status and open questions* 2019.

Searching for strange quark planets

Xu Wang[1,*], Yong-Feng Huang[1,2,†] and Bing Li[3,4]

[1] *School of Astronomy and Space Science, Nanjing University, Nanjing 210023, People's Republic of China*
[2] *Key Laboratory of Modern Astronomy and Astrophysics (Nanjing University), Ministry of Education, People's Republic of China*
[3] *Key Laboratory of Particle Astrophysics, Institute of High Energy Physics, Chinese Academy of Sciences, Beijing 100049, People's Republic of China*
[4] *Particle Astrophysics Division, Institute of High Energy Physics, Chinese Academy of Sciences, Beijing 100049, People's Republic of China*
* E-mail: wx_tba@163.com
† E-mail: hyf@nju.edu.cn

Strange quark matter (SQM) may be the true ground state of matter. According to this SQM hypothesis, the observed neutron stars actually should all be strange quark stars. But distinguishing between neutron stars and strange quark stars by means of observations is extremely difficult. It is interesting to note that under the SQM hypothesis, less massive objects such as strange quark planets and strange dwarfs can also stably exist. The extremely high density and small radius of strange quark planets give us some new perspectives to identify SQM objects and to test the SQM hypothesis. First, the tidal disruption radius of strange quark planets is much smaller than normal planets, so, very close-in exoplanets can be safely identified as candidates of SQM objects. Second, gravitational waves (GW) from mergers of strange quark star-strange quark planet systems are strong enough to be detected by ground-based GW detectors. As a result, GW observation will be a powerful tool to probe SQM stars. At the same time, the tidal deformability of SQM planets can be measured to further strengthen the result.

Keywords: Strange quark stars, Exoplanets, Gravitational waves, Neutron stars

1. Introduction

The central engine of gamma-ray bursts may be compact objects such as neutron stars. However, our knowledge about matter under extreme densities is still quite poor so that the internal composition and structure of neutron stars are largely uncertain to us.[1] It has been argued that the energy per baryon of strange quark matter (SQM), which is composed of three favors of quarks (up, down and strange quarks), could be less than normal hadronic matter. As a result, SQM may be the true ground state of matter.[2,3] If this hypothesis is true, then it is even possible that all the so called "neutron stars" observed in the Universe should actually be strange quark stars.[4,5]

However, it is difficult to distinguish between strange quark stars and neutron stars through current astronomical observations. For a long time, people have tried to find the difference between neutron stars and strange quark stars in terms of mass-radius relationship, cooling rate, the minimum spin period and gravitational wave (GW) features. But for a typical 1.4 M$_\odot$ compact object, the radius difference between a neutron star and a quark star is too small to be detected through current observational technology. Recently, Geng et al pointed out that fast radio busts may originate from the collapses of the crust of strange quark stars.[6,7] It provides an novel visual angle on these interesting objects.

It is interesting to note that, under the SQM hypothesis, quark matter is bounded by strong interaction but not gravity.[5] So, SQM can even exist stably in the form of small chunks in the universe. It implies that planets composed of strange quark matter can also exist stably.[8,9] Strange quark planets are very different from normal planets. They have a much higher mean density and a much smaller radius, which provide us with some effective new methods to test the SQM hypothesis. In our previous studies, we have suggested some new methods to identify strange quark planet.[10–15] In this article, we will summarize the results.

2. Searching for strange quark planets among close-in exoplanets

Planets cannot be too close to their host stars, otherwise they will be tidally broken up by the strong tidal force of their hosts. We can use the tidal disruption radius r_{td} to describe the shortest possible separation between a planet and its host, which can be analytically expressed as[16]

$$r_{td} \approx \left(\frac{6M}{\pi \bar{\rho}}\right)^{\frac{1}{3}}, \tag{1}$$

where M is the mass of the host star and $\bar{\rho}$ is the mean density of the planet. For the convenience of calculation, this equation can be further written as,

$$r_{td} \approx 2.37 \times 10^6 \left(\frac{M}{1.4 M_\odot}\right)^{\frac{1}{3}} \times \left(\frac{\bar{\rho}}{4 \times 10^{14} \mathrm{g cm^{-3}}}\right)^{-\frac{1}{3}} \mathrm{cm}. \tag{2}$$

Suppose a planet orbits around a host star which has a typical mass of 1.4 M$_\odot$. For a strange quark planet, its mean density can be as high as 4×10^{14} g cm^{-3}. With such a high density, the r_{td} of the strange quark planet will be less than 2.37×10^6 cm, which is only about twice the radius of a pulsar.[10,11] But for normal matter planets, the density is on the order of ~ 8 g cm^{-3}, and the corresponding r_{td} is generally larger than 8.7×10^{10} cm. Even if we take the mean density as 30 g cm^{-3}, which is already a very high value for normal matter, the derived r_{td} will still be larger than 5.6×10^{10} cm.[10,11] From these simple calculations, we argued that if the orbital radius of a planet is found to be less than 5.6×10^{10} cm, then the planet should be a strange quark planet.

An extremely close-in strange quark planet cannot be observed directly by imaging method. On the contrary, it can be relatively easily detected via pulsar timing observations. According to Kepler's law, the relationship between the orbital radius and the period can be expressed as

$$\frac{a^3}{P_{\mathrm{orb}}^2} \approx \frac{GM}{4\pi^2}, \tag{3}$$

where G is the gravity constant, a is the orbital radius and $P_{\rm orb}$ is the planet's orbital period. For planets with a smaller than $\sim 5.6 \times 10^{10}$ cm, the orbital period will be less than ~ 6100 s. Therefore, it is argued a planet with the orbital period less than 6100 s should be a strange quark planet.[10,11]

Using the above criterion, Kuerban et al. have tried to search for strange quark planets among exoplanets, especially among pulsar planets.[15] According to their results, the short period pulsar planets of PSR J0636 b, PSR J1807-2459A b and PSR 1719-14 b are good candidates of strange quark planets.

3. Searching for strange quark planets through GW observations

Since 2015, gravitational wave observations have opened a new window for astronomy[17] and are also expected to be a new tool for searching for quark stars.[18] Note that it is still quite difficult to distinguish between binary neutron star mergers and binary quark star mergers by gravitational wave observations, because these two kinds of compact stars have marginal difference in radius at the typical mass of 1.4 $M_\odot$.[19,20] However, gravitational waves may bring new opportunities in searching for strange quark planets.

A normal matter planet can not be too close to its host, otherwise it will be tidally disrupted. Consequently, the gravitational wave emissions from normal planetary systems are usually too weak to be detected. But due to the extremely high density and the very close-in orbit of strange quark planets, a strange star-strange planet system can produce very strong gravitational wave emissions, especially at the final stage of the merging process. If such a merger event occurs in the local universe, it would be detectable for the gravitational wave detectors such as Advanced LIGO and the Einstein Telescope.[12]

GW observations can also help diagnose the internal composition and internal structure of compact stars by means of tidal deformability measurements. The first tidal deformability measurement has been obtained for the binary neutron star merger event of GW170817, which gives a new constraint on the equation of state of dense matter.[21,22]

Tidal deformability is a quantity that describes the deformation of a star in a tidal field, which is defined as

$$\lambda = -\frac{Q_{ij}}{E_{ij}}, \qquad (4)$$

where Q_{ij} is the induced quadrapole moment of the star and E_{ij} is the tidal field that it resides in (i.e., the gravity field produced by its companion). For convenience, this quality is often written in a dimensionless form, i.e.,

$$\Lambda = \frac{\lambda c^{10}}{G^4 m^5}. \qquad (5)$$

Here, c is the speed of light in vacuum and m is the mass of the star.

Generally speaking, a larger tidal deformability means that the star will be relatively easier to be deformed in a tidal field.[22] So, tidal deformability will affect the evolution of the gravitational wave phase, which could be perceived in GW observations.[13] Comparing the observed tidal deformability with that calculated by solving the Tolman-Oppenheimer-Volkoff equation adopting a particular equation of state (EoS), we can get useful information on the internal structure of compact stars.[23,24]

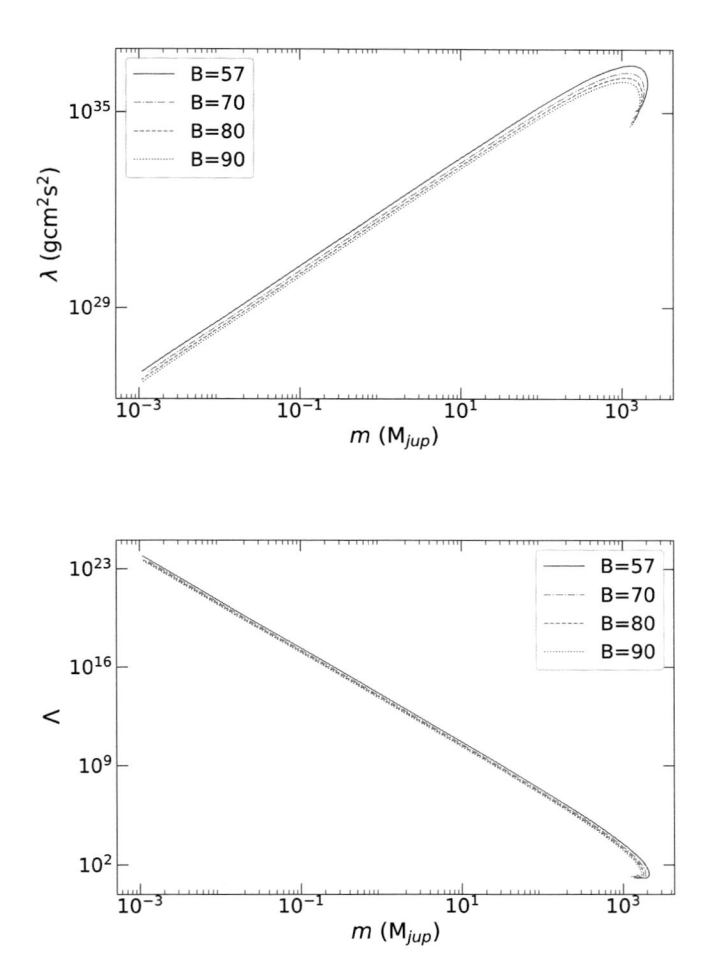

Fig. 1. Tidal deformability (the upper panel) and dimensionless tidal deformability (the lower panel) versus mass for strange quark stars and strange quark planets.[13] Different line styles represent different bag constant, which is marked in the figure in units of MeV/fm^3.

Following the method of Hinderer et al.,[23,24] we have calculated the tidal deformability of strange quark stars, paying special attention on strange dwarfs and strange planets. We engage the bag model for strange quark matter.[4] Our results are shown in Figure 1. We see that as the mass decreases, the value of the deformability also decreases, while the value of the dimensionless tidal deformability keeps increasing. For a planet with a mass of $10^{-3} M_{\rm jup}$, its tidal deformability is up to $\sim 10^{27}$ g cm^2 s^2 and its dimensionless tidal deformability is up to $\sim 10^{23}$, which are much higher than those of normal matter planets. Therefore, the tidal deformability is a useful parameter for identifying strange quark planets.[13]

4. Summary

Discriminating between neutron stars and strange quark stars is a challenging task. In this article, we try to solve the problem from a novel point of view. We mainly concentrate on strange quark planets. It is suggested that there are basically two methods to search for strange quark planets. First, we can try to find close-in pulsar planets with the orbital period less than 6100 s. Encouragingly, at least three possible strange quark planet candidates have been found. Second, we can identify strange quark planets through gravitational wave observations. It is found that the mergers of strange star-strange planet systems can produce strong gravitational wave bursts, which can potentially be detected by the advanced LIGO and the future Einstein Telescope. The tidal deformability of strange quark dwarfs and strange quark planets is specially calculated. In short, we stress that strange quark planets could be a powerful tool for clarifying the nature of the so called "neutron stars".

Acknowledgements

This work is supported by National SKA Program of China No. 2020SKA0120300, by the National Natural Science Foundation of China (Grant Nos. 11873030, 12041306, U1938201), and by the science research grants from the China Manned Space Project with NO.CMS-CSST-2021-B11.

References

1. J. M. Lattimer and M. Prakash, The Physics of Neutron Stars, *Science* **304**, 536 (April 2004).
2. N. Itoh, Hydrostatic Equilibrium of Hypothetical Quark Stars, *Progress of Theoretical Physics* **44**, 291 (July 1970).
3. G. Baym, C. Pethick and P. Sutherland, The Ground State of Matter at High Densities: Equation of State and Stellar Models, *ApJ* **170**, p. 299 (December 1971).
4. E. Farhi and R. L. Jaffe, Strange matter, *PhRvD* **30**, 2379 (December 1984).
5. E. Witten, Cosmic separation of phases, *PhRvD* **30**, 272 (July 1984).
6. J. Geng, B. Li and Y. Huang, Repeating fast radio bursts from collapses of the crust of a strange star, *The Innovation* **2**, p. 100152 (March 2021).
7. Y. Zhang, J.-J. Geng and Y.-F. Huang, Fast Radio Bursts from the Collapse of Strange Star Crusts, *ApJ* **858**, p. 88 (May 2018).
8. N. K. Glendenning, C. Kettner and F. Weber, Possible New Class of Dense White Dwarfs, *PhRvL* **74**, 3519 (May 1995).
9. N. K. Glendenning, C. Kettner and F. Weber, From Strange Stars to Strange Dwarfs, *ApJ* **450**, p. 253 (September 1995).
10. Y. F. Huang and Y. B. Yu, Searching for Strange Quark Matter Objects in Exoplanets, *ApJ* **848**, p. 115 (October 2017).

11. A. Kuerban, J.-J. Geng, Y.-F. Huang, H.-S. Zong and H. Gong, Close-in Exoplanets as Candidates for Strange Quark Matter Objects, *ApJ* **890**, p. 41 (February 2020).
12. J. J. Geng, Y. F. Huang and T. Lu, Coalescence of Strange-quark Planets with Strange Stars: A New Kind of Source for Gravitational Wave Bursts, *ApJ* **804**, p. 21 (May 2015).
13. X. Wang, A. Kuerban, J.-J. Geng, F. Xu, X.-L. Zhang, B.-J. Zuo, W.-L. Yuan and Y.-F. Huang, Tidal Deformability of Strange Quark Planets and Strange Dwarfs, *arXiv e-prints*, p. arXiv:2105.13899 (May 2021).
14. A. Kuerban, J.-J. Geng and Y.-F. Huang, GW emission from merging strange quark star-strange quark planet systems, in *Xiamen-CUSTIPEN Workshop on the Equation of State of Dense Neutron-Rich Matter in the Era of Gravitational Wave Astronomy*, American Institute of Physics Conference Series Vol. 2127July 2019.
15. A. Kuerban, Y.-F. Huang, J.-J. Geng and H.-S. Zong, Searching for Strange Quark Matter Objects Among White Dwarfs, *arXiv e-prints*, p. arXiv:2012.05748 (December 2020).
16. J. G. Hills, Possible power source of Seyfert galaxies and QSOs, *Natur* **254**, 295 (March 1975).
17. B. P. Abbott, R. Abbott, T. D. Abbott, M. R. Abernathy, F. Acernese, K. Ackley, C. Adams, T. Adams, P. Addesso, R. X. Adhikari and et al., Tests of General Relativity with GW150914, *PhRvL* **116**, p. 221101 (June 2016).
18. S. Postnikov, M. Prakash and J. M. Lattimer, Tidal Love numbers of neutron and self-bound quark stars, *PhRvD* **82**, p. 024016 (July 2010).
19. A. Bauswein, R. Oechslin and H. T. Janka, Discriminating strange star mergers from neutron star mergers by gravitational-wave measurements, *PhRvD* **81**, p. 024012 (January 2010).
20. P. H. R. S. Moraes and O. D. Miranda, Probing strange stars with advanced gravitational wave detectors, *MNRAS* **445**, L11 (November 2014).
21. B. P. Abbott, R. Abbott, T. D. Abbott, F. Acernese, K. Ackley, C. Adams, T. Adams, P. Addesso, R. X. Adhikari, V. B. Adya and et al., GW170817: Observation of Gravitational Waves from a Binary Neutron Star Inspiral, *PhRvL* **119**, p. 161101 (October 2017).
22. A. Guerra Chaves and T. Hinderer, Probing the equation of state of neutron star matter with gravitational waves from binary inspirals in light of GW170817: A brief review, *Journal of Physics G Nuclear Physics* **46**, p. 123002 (December 2019).
23. T. Hinderer, Tidal Love Numbers of Neutron Stars, *ApJ* **677**, 1216 (April 2008).
24. T. Hinderer, B. D. Lackey, R. N. Lang and J. S. Read, Tidal deformability of neutron stars with realistic equations of state and their gravitational wave signatures in binary inspiral, *PhRvD* **81**, p. 123016 (June 2010).

Probe the universe by using Gamma-Ray Bursts with X-ray plateaus

Fan Xu[1,*] and Yong-Feng Huang[1,2,†]

[1]*School of Astronomy and Space Science, Nanjing University, Nanjing 210023, People's Republic of China*
[2]*Key Laboratory of Modern Astronomy and Astrophysics (Nanjing University), Ministry of Education, People's Republic of China*
*E-mail: *carpedieminreality@163.com; †hyf@nju.edu.cn*

Gamma-ray Bursts (GRBs) are promising tools to probe the Universe. Especially, we can get constraints on cosmological parameters with the help of GRB luminosity relations. Recently, a tight L-T-E relation has been found. This relation involves a special subclass of GRBs, i.e., GRBs have X-ray plateaus in their X-ray afterglows. The isotropic γ-ray energy of the prompt GRB ($E_{\gamma,\mathrm{iso}}$) are linked with the duration of the plateau phase (T_a) and the X-ray luminosity at the end of the plateau phase (L_X) through this relation. Beside this relation, we find that L_X and T_a also relate to the spectral peak energy (E_p) and we call this relation the L-T-E_p relation. When using these relations to constrain the cosmological parameters, we find the L-T-E relation is insensitive to the cosmological parameters and both of these relations suffer from redshift evolution. We manage to correct the redshift evolution and use the de-evolved L-T-E_p relation to constrain the cosmological parameters. We get the best-fit result as $\Omega_m = 0.389^{+0.202}_{-0.141}$ (1σ) for the flat ΛCDM model. Our result is consistent with that from other probes within 1σ confidence level. Joint constraint on cosmological parameters is presented.

Keywords: Cosmology: dark energy – gamma-ray burst: general – stars: neutron

1. Introduction

Gamma-ray Bursts (GRBs) are extremely high-energy events. The multiband observation of the GRB afterglows has helped us to better understand the true nature of GRBs. Also, the observation of the early afterglow has showed that some GRBs have a plateau phase in their X-ray afterglow. The plateau phase is often thought to be connected with extra energy injection, possibly by a millisecond magnetar as the central engine.[1–3] It is interesting to note that these compact magnetars might actually be strange quark stars.[4]

Since GRBs have a cosmological origin, we can use them as a cosmological probe. The most important application is to constrain the cosmological parameters. The method is very similar to using Supernovae Ia (SNe Ia).[5–7] We need solid luminosity relations to help us convert GRBs to standard candles.[8,9] Compared with using SNe Ia, the gamma photon from GRBs does not suffer from the extinction while they travel through the space.[10]

Several interesting relations are found for GRBs with X-ray plateau. Dainotti et al. (2008) first found a nearly anti-relation between the X-ray luminosity at the end time of the plateau (L_X) and the duration of the plateau phase at the rest frame (T_a).[11,12] This relation is also known as the Dainotti relation. The L-T-E relation found by Xu & Huang links L_X and T_a together with the isotropic γ-ray energy of the prompt GRB ($E_{\gamma,\mathrm{iso}}$).[2] Recently, Tang et al. (2019) have revisited this relation with a sample of 174 GRBs and found $L_X \propto T_a^{-1.01} E_{\gamma,\mathrm{iso}}^{0.84}$.[13] Meanwhile, a fundamental plane relation was established by Dainotti et al. (2016) which connect L_X, T_a, and L_{peak}.[14] Using class-specific GRB samples, these three parameters were very closely connected with each other.[15] Also, a four parameter Combo-relation was recently established which involves α, L_X, T_a, and E_p, where α is the power-law timing index of the afterglow in its normal decay phase and E_p is the spectral peak energy.[16,17] Meanwhile, we have found a new relation between L_X, T_a, and E_p, which we call the L-T-E_p relation.[18] These relations are extensions of the Dainotti relation and reveal the connection between the property of the X-ray plateau with the early prompt emission.

In this paper, we first check the possibility of using the L-T-E relation to constrain the cosmological parameters. We then present the new L-T-E_p relation and constraints on the cosmological parameters.

2. Difficulty of using the L-T-E relation to probe the Universe

The L-T-E relation can be written as

$$\log \frac{L_X}{10^{47}\mathrm{erg/s}} = a + b \log \frac{T_a}{10^3 \mathrm{s}} + c \log \frac{E_{\gamma,\mathrm{iso}}}{10^{53}\mathrm{erg}}. \tag{1}$$

We use the Markov chain Monte Carlo (MCMC) algorithm to get the best-fit with the same sample provided by Tang et al. (2019)[13] and obtain $a = 1.60 \pm 0.06$, $b = -1.01 \pm 0.05$, $c = 0.85 \pm 0.04$ and $\sigma_{\mathrm{ext}} = 0.40 \pm 0.03$, i.e., $L_X \propto T_a^{-1.01 \pm 0.05} E_{\gamma,\mathrm{iso}}^{0.85 \pm 0.04}$. σ_{ext} is the the extrinsic scatter parameter arouse from some hidden variables.

When using GRBs to constrain the cosmological parameters, a solid luminosity relation that works at all redshift is needed. Hence, we divide the full sample into four redshift bins and check the evolution of the coefficients. We find that the coefficients of this relation vary a lot among different redshift bins, especially in the coefficient "c". So the L-T-E relation suffers from the redshift evolution. More importantly, because both L_X and $E_{\gamma,\mathrm{iso}}$ are related to cosmological parameters through the same dependence on the luminosity distance, so the cosmological effect is canceled out in this relation. In other words, this relation is insensitive to cosmological parameters.

3. Cosmology with the L-T-E_p relation

We have found a new relation connects L_X, T_a, and E_p. We call it the L-T-E_p relation and it follows $L_X \propto T_a^{-1.08 \pm 0.08} E_\mathrm{p}^{0.76 \pm 0.14}$ using our sample of 121 GRBs.[18]

Likewise, we check whether this relation suffers from redshift evolution. In fact, this relation indeed evolves with redshifts. We think of two solutions to remove the evolution from this relation. The first solution is trying to find out the redshift evolution in each parameter (i.e., L_X, T_a, and $E_{\gamma,\text{iso}}$) which will be described in Section 3.1. The second one is simply adding an evolution term to account for the redshift evolution in the whole relation and the details of this solution is presented in Section 3.2.

3.1. *Redshift evolution in each parameter*

Following the Efron & Petrosian method,[19] we get the redshift evolution of L_X, T_a, and E_p separately. A simple power-law function $(1+z)^k$ is used as the evolution form of each parameter.[20] Our best-fit results are $k_{L_X} = 3.38 \pm 0.62$, $k_{T_a} = -1.54 \pm 0.30$, and $k_{E_p} = 0.75 \pm 0.25$.[18]

After correcting for the redshift evolution of each parameter, we can get a new separate de-evolved L-T-E_p relation as

$$\log \frac{L_X/(1+z)^{k_{L_X}}}{10^{47}\text{erg/s}} = a''' + b''' \log \frac{T_a/(1+z)^{k_{T_a}}}{10^3\text{s}} + c''' \log \frac{E_p/(1+z)^{k_{E_p}}}{\text{keV}}. \quad (2)$$

3.2. *Redshift evolution of the whole relation*

To get the redshift evolution of the whole relation, we simply put the possible evolution in a single power-law term of $(1+z)^{d'}$,[21] and the L-T-E_p relation can be re-written as

$$\log \frac{L_X}{10^{47}\text{erg/s}} = a' + b' \log \frac{T_a}{10^3\text{s}} + c' \log \frac{E_p}{\text{keV}} + d' \log(1+z). \quad (3)$$

With the MCMC method, we get the best-fit result of parameter d', which is $d' = 1.78 \pm 0.29$.[18] Then we move the evolution term to the left side of Equation 3 and get a de-evolved L-T-E_p relation

$$\log \frac{L_{X,\text{cal}}}{10^{47}\text{erg/s}} = a'' + b'' \log \frac{T_a}{10^3\text{s}} + c'' \log \frac{E_p}{\text{keV}}, \quad (4)$$

where $L_{X,\text{cal}} = L_X/(1+z)^{d'}$.

3.3. *Constraints on cosmological parameters*

With the two de-evolved relations we get above, we can now safely use them to probe the Universe. We fix $H_0 = 70.0$ km s^{-1} Mpc^{-1} for simplicity. When using GRBs to constrain the cosmological parameters, one may face the so-called "circularity problem".[22] Here we consider two methods to avoid this problem. The first method is the "simultaneously fitting method" which means to fit the relation coefficients together with the cosmological parameters.[23] The second is the "standardize with SNe Ia method" which means to use SNe Ia data set as calibrators to calculate the luminosity distances of GRBs independently from cosmological models.[8]

With the separate de-evolved L-T-E_p relation, we perform the simultaneously fitting method and get $\Omega_m = 0.76^{+0.17}_{-0.26}$ for the flat ΛCDM model.

As for the de-evolved L-T-E_p relation, we first perform the simultaneously fitting method. The best-fit result is $\Omega_m = 0.71^{+0.20}_{-0.28}$ for the flat ΛCDM model. Then we use the standardize with SNe Ia method with the "Pantheon sample" of SNe Ia.[24] We plot a Hubble diagram for GRBs, as shown in Figure 1. The low-redshift sample is calibrated by the "Pantheon sample" and shows little dispersion, while the large dispersion of the high-redshift GRB distance modulus comes from the uncertainty of the GRB relation. With the calibrated distance modulus of the high-redshift GRBs, we get the best-fit result as $\Omega_m = 0.389^{+0.202}_{-0.141}$ for the flat ΛCDM model. Also we get $\Omega_m = 0.333^{+0.188}_{-0.142}$ and $\Omega_\Lambda = 0.346^{+0.356}_{-0.249}$ for the non-flat ΛCDM model and $\Omega_m = 0.369^{+0.217}_{-0.191}$ and $w = -0.966^{+0.513}_{-0.678}$ for the flat wCDM model.

Then, we compare these results with those from other probes (i.e., SNe Ia, CMB, BAO) and find that they are consistent with each other in 1σ confidence level. Also, together with other probes, we even get a more accurate constraint on the cosmological parameters. We get $\Omega_m = 0.289 \pm 0.008$ and $\Omega_\Lambda = 0.710 \pm 0.006$ for the non-flat ΛCDM model with all the four probes. As for the flat Universe, combining the four probes, we obtain $\Omega_m = 0.295 \pm 0.006$ and $w = -1.015 \pm 0.015$ under the wCDM model and $\Omega_m = 0.291 \pm 0.005$ for the ΛCDM model. Figure 2 shows the fitting results with different probes under the flat ΛCDM model.

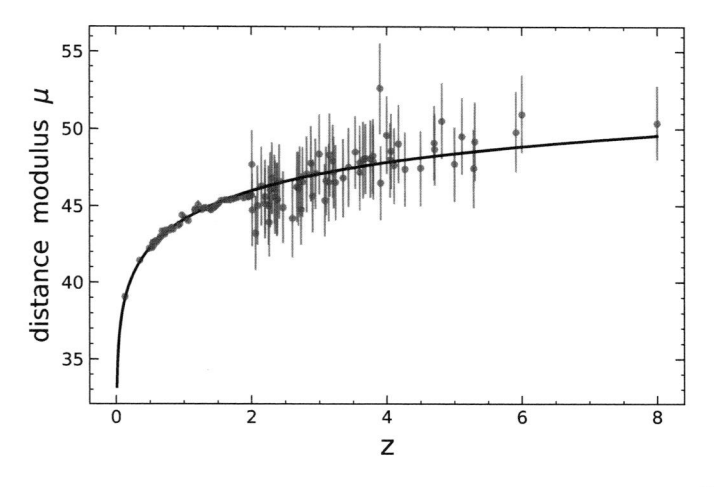

Fig. 1. Calibrated GRB Hubble diagram from the de-evolved L-T-E_p relation.[18] Red points represent our GRB sample and the black line is the theoretical distance modulus calculated with $H_0 = 70.0$ km s^{-1} Mpc^{-1} and $\Omega_m = 0.289$ under the flat ΛCDM model.

4. Summary

In our work we find that the previous L-T-E relation is not a good probe for cosmology and it is possible to use the L-T-E_p relation as a probe. We want to

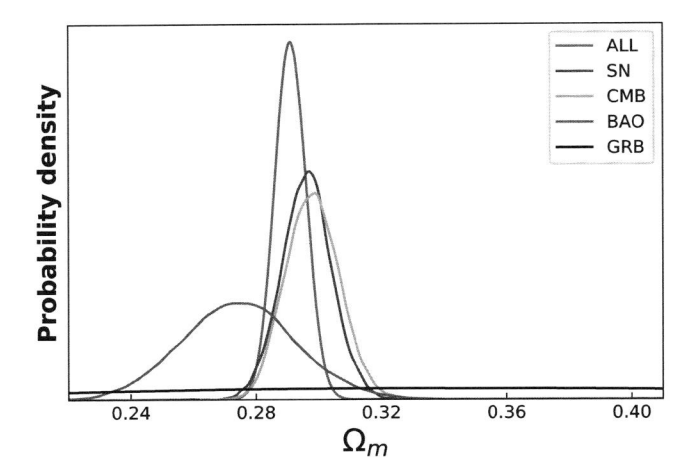

Fig. 2. Under the flat ΛCDM model, we get the probability density on Ω_m with observational data of SNe Ia (blue), CMB (orange), BAO (green), and the de-evolved L-T-E_p relation of GRBs (black). The joint constraint from all the four probes is $\Omega_m = 0.291 \pm 0.005$ (red).

stress that possible redshift evolution in GRB relations need to be removed before they can be used as cosmological probe. From our study, we can see that it is hard to get good constraints with GRBs alone, because of the large dispersion in GRB relations. However, with the improvement of GRB observations, we may tighten these relations in the future.

Acknowledgments

This work was supported by National SKA Program of China No. 2020SKA0120300, by the National Natural Science Foundation of China (Grant Nos. 11873030, 12041306, U1938201), and by the science research grants from the China Manned Space Project with NO. CMS-CSST-2021-B11.

References

1. S. Dall'Osso, G. Stratta, D. Guetta, et al., Gamma-ray bursts afterglows with energy injection from a spinning down neutron star, *A&A* **526**, p. A121 (February 2011).
2. a M. Xu and Y. F. Huang, New three-parameter correlation for gamma-ray bursts with a plateau phase in the afterglow, *A&A* **538**, p. A134 (February 2012).
3. L. Li, X.-F. Wu, W.-H. Lei, et al., Constraining the Type of Central Engine of GRBs with Swift Data, *ApJS* **236**, p. 26 (June 2018).
4. J.-J. Geng, B. Li and Y.-F. Huang, 2021, The Innovation, in press, Repeating Fast Radio Bursts from Collapse of Strange Star Crust, *arXiv e-prints*, p. arXiv:2103.04165 (March 2021).
5. M. M. Phillips, The Absolute Magnitudes of Type IA Supernovae, *ApJL* **413**, p. L105 (August 1993).

6. A. G. Riess, A. V. Filippenko, P. Challis, et al., Observational Evidence from Supernovae for an Accelerating Universe and a Cosmological Constant, *AJ* **116**, 1009 (September 1998).
7. S. Perlmutter, G. Aldering, G. Goldhaber, et al., Measurements of Ω and Λ from 42 High-Redshift Supernovae, *ApJ* **517**, 565 (June 1999).
8. N. Liang, W. K. Xiao, Y. Liu and S. N. Zhang, A Cosmology-Independent Calibration of Gamma-Ray Burst Luminosity Relations and the Hubble Diagram, *ApJ* **685**, 354 (September 2008).
9. L. Amati, R. D'Agostino, O. Luongo, et al., Addressing the circularity problem in the E_p-E_{iso} correlation of gamma-ray bursts, *MNRAS* **486**, L46 (June 2019).
10. F. Y. Wang, Z. G. Dai and E. W. Liang, Gamma-ray burst cosmology, *NewAR* **67**, 1 (August 2015).
11. M. G. Dainotti, V. F. Cardone and S. Capozziello, A time-luminosity correlation for γ-ray bursts in the X-rays, *MNRAS* **391**, L79 (November 2008).
12. M. Dainotti, V. Petrosian, R. Willingale, et al., Luminosity-time and luminosity-luminosity correlations for GRB prompt and afterglow plateau emissions, *MNRAS* **451**, 3898 (August 2015).
13. C.-H. Tang, Y.-F. Huang, J.-J. Geng and Z.-B. Zhang, et al., Statistical Study of Gamma-Ray Bursts with a Plateau Phase in the X-Ray Afterglow, *ApJS* **245**, p. 1 (November 2019).
14. M. G. Dainotti, S. Postnikov, X. Hernandez and M. Ostrowski, A Fundamental Plane for Long Gamma-Ray Bursts with X-Ray Plateaus, *ApJL* **825**, p. L20 (July 2016).
15. M. G. Dainotti, A. Ł. Lenart, G. Sarracino, et al., The X-Ray Fundamental Plane of the Platinum Sample, the Kilonovae, and the SNe Ib/c Associated with GRBs, *ApJ* **904**, p. 97 (December 2020).
16. L. Izzo, M. Muccino, E. Zaninoni, et al., New measurements of Ω_m from gamma-ray bursts, *A&A* **582**, p. A115 (October 2015).
17. M. Muccino, L. Izzo, O. Luongo, et al., Tracing Dark Energy History with Gamma-Ray Bursts, *ApJ* **908**, p. 181 (February 2021).
18. F. Xu, C.-H. Tang, J.-J. Geng, et al., 2021, ApJ, in press, X-ray Plateaus in Gamma-Ray Burst Afterglows and Their Application in Cosmology, *arXiv e-prints*, p. arXiv:2012.05627 (December 2020).
19. B. Efron and V. Petrosian, A Simple Test of Independence for Truncated Data with Applications to Redshift Surveys, *ApJ* **399**, p. 345 (November 1992).
20. M. G. Dainotti, V. Petrosian, J. Singal and M. Ostrowski, Determination of the Intrinsic Luminosity Time Correlation in the X-Ray Afterglows of Gamma-Ray Bursts, *ApJ* **774**, p. 157 (September 2013).
21. M. Demianski, E. Piedipalumbo, D. Sawant and L. Amati, Cosmology with gamma-ray bursts. I. The Hubble diagram through the calibrated $E_{p,I}$-E_{iso} correlation, *A&A* **598**, p. A112 (February 2017).
22. M. G. Dainotti and R. Del Vecchio, Gamma Ray Burst afterglow and prompt-afterglow relations: An overview, *NewAR* **77**, 23 (April 2017).
23. L. Amati, C. Guidorzi, F. Frontera, et al., Measuring the cosmological parameters with the $E_{p,i}$-E_{iso} correlation of gamma-ray bursts, *MNRAS* **391**, 577 (December 2008).
24. D. M. Scolnic, D. O. Jones, A. Rest, et al., The Complete Light-curve Sample of Spectroscopically Confirmed SNe Ia from Pan-STARRS1 and Cosmological Constraints from the Combined Pantheon Sample, *ApJ* **859**, p. 101 (June 2018).

A new perspective on cosmology through Supernovae Ia and Gamma Ray Bursts

B. De Simone

Department of Phyisics "E. R. Caianiello", University of Salerno,
Via Giovanni Paolo II, 132, 84084, Fisciano, Salerno, Italy
E-mail: b.desimone1@studenti.unisa.it
www.df.unisa.it

V. Nielson

SLAC National Accelerator Laboratory, 2575 Sand Hill Road, Menlo Park, CA 94025, USA
Astronomy Department, University of Michigan, Ann Arbor, MI 48109, USA

E. Rinaldi

Physics Department, University of Michigan, Ann Arbor, MI 48109, USA
RIKEN Cluster for Pioneering Research, Theoretical Quantum Physics Laboratory, Wako, Saitama 351-0198, Japan
RIKEN iTHEMS, Wako, Saitama 351-0198, Japan
RIKEN Center for Quantum Computing, Wako, Saitama 351-0198, Japan

M. G. Dainotti*

National Astronomical Observatory of Japan, 2 Chome-21-1 Osawa, Mitaka, Tokyo 181-8588, Japan
The Graduate University for Advanced Studies, SOKENDAI, Shonankokusaimura, Hayama, Miura District, Kanagawa 240-0193, Japan
Space Science Institute, Boulder, CO, USA
E-mail: maria.dainotti@nao.ac.jp
www.guas-astronomy.jp/eng

The actual knowledge of the structure and future evolution of our universe is based on the use of cosmological models, which can be tested through the so-called 'probes', namely astrophysical phenomena, objects or structures with peculiar properties that can help to discriminate among different cosmological models. Among all the existing probes, of particular importance are the Supernovae Ia (SNe Ia) and the Gamma Ray Bursts (GRBs): the former are considered among the best standard candles so far discovered but suffer from the fact that can be observed until redshift $z = 2.26$, while the latter are promising standardizable candles which have been observed up to $z = 9.4$, surpassing even the farthest quasar known to date, which is at $z = 7.64$. The standard candles can be used to test the cosmological models and to give the expected values of cosmological parameters, in particular the Hubble constant value. The Hubble constant is affected by the so-called "Hubble constant tension", a discrepancy in more than $4\,\sigma$ between its value measured with local probes and its value measured through the cosmological probes. The increase in the number of observed SNe Ia, as well as the future standardization of GRBs through their correlations, will surely be of help in alleviating the Hubble constant tension and in explaining the structure of the universe at higher redshifts. A promising class of

---

*Corresponding author

GRBs for future standardization is represented by the GRBs associated with Supernovae Ib/c, since these present features similar to the SNe Ia class and obey a tight correlation between their luminosity at the end of the plateau emission in X-rays and the time at the end of the plateau in the rest-frame.

Keywords: Gamma Ray Bursts, Supernovae Ia, Cosmology, Correlations, Hubble constant, Hubble tension

Introduction

Modern cosmology is based on the so-called ΛCDM model: this is the standard cosmological model based on the Cold Dark Matter (CDM) and containing the cosmological constant Λ that describes the dark energy contribution to the expansion of the cosmos. This model has been widely accepted in the scientific community and can predict the accelerated expansion of the universe, as proved by the outstanding works of Riess et al. (1998)[1] and Perlmutter et al. (1999)[2] where this effect was demonstrated through the use of SNe Ia. Despite being well received, the ΛCDM suffers from some open problems, in particular the Hubble constant (H_0) tension. This is the discrepancy, in more than 4 σ, between the value of H_0 measured with local probes (Cepheids and SNe Ia) and the value obtained through the Cosmic Microwave Background (CMB) radiation data measured by the Planck satellite. To solve this issue, many approaches have been proposed (alternative cosmological models, refined measurements of H_0, etc.), but it is necessary to use reliable probes for testing the cosmological models. From this perspective, the so-called standard candles are very important: these are astrophysical objects or events which have a fixed luminosity or that obey an intrinsic relation between the luminosity and some of the other parameters that do not depend on the luminosity themselves. To date, different objects have been standardized, in particular the SNe Ia which have a nearly uniform peak luminosity, but the problem is that these can cover only a relatively small range of redshifts: the farthest SN Ia so far observed has a redshift of $z = 2.26$.[3] The GRBs may have a key role in the future development of cosmology since they have been observed at higher redshifts than SNe Ia and quasars (currently the farthest quasar being at redshift 7.64[4]) and are able to further extend the Hubble diagram (the distance moduli versus the redshift). A particular class of GRBs, the GRBs with a plateau emission (namely, a relatively flat section of the lightcurve that follows the prompt emission and precedes the afterglow, observed not only in X-rays and optical but also in γ-rays[5]), has proven to be a promising standardizable candle through the application of tight correlations among the GRB lightcurve properties, such as the intrinsic and unbiased correlation between the luminosity at the end of the plateau emission in the X-rays, L_X, with the time at the end of the plateau emission in the rest-frame, T_X^* [6-13] (which was later confirmed also in the optical[14]) and the unbiased one between L_X and the 1s peak prompt luminosity, L_{peak}.[15,16] A combination of these two correlations led to the so-called 3D fundamental plane relation, namely a tight correspondence between L_X, T_X^*, and

L_{peak}.[17–19] For a review of these correlations, see Dainotti & Del Vecchio (2017),[20] Dainotti et al. (2018a,2018b),[21,22] and Dainotti (2019).[23] The GRB correlations are not only useful as cosmological tools, but also as discriminant among theoretical models to explain the GRBs origin, emission mechanism, and the nature of their environment.[24–29] In particular, the plateau emission and the correlations that involve its properties strongly suggest how the typical magnetic fields and spin periods of the magnetars (namely, a fast rotating neutron star) could explain the plateau emission itself (Rowlinson et al. 2014).[25] In a later paper, Rea et al. (2015)[26] show that the magnetar model can be reconciled within the GRB emission in the plateau only if supermagnetar with high magnetic field strengh are allowed. In a successive paper of Stratta et al. (2018)[30] for the first time a non-ideal modelling of spindown magnetar is fitted to the afterglow data with a statistical sample of 40 Long GRBs (LGRBs) with a well-defined plateau and 13 Short GRBs (SGRBs) including the short with extended emission. The conclusion reached in that paper is that SGRBs including the SGRBs with Extended Emission (SEE) and LGRBs can be explained within the magnetar model but with the difference that the LGRBs occupy a lower end in the magnetic field-spin period plane compared to the SGRBs which present a higher spin, P, and a higher magnetic field, B. The correlation between magnetic field and spin period follow the established physics of the spin-up line for accreting neutron star in Galactic binary systems. The B−P relation obtained perfectly matches spin-up line predictions for the magnetar model with mass accretion rates expected in the GRB prompt phase. The latter are ∼ 1114 orders of magnitude higher than those inferred for the Galatic accreting NSs. Thus, correlations are useful to cast more light on the physics of GRBs and this represents an effective support towards the future standardization of these transient phenomena. The current proceeding focuses on two main topics concerning cosmology with SNe Ia and GRBs: (1) the investigation of the H_0 tension through a binning approach on the Pantheon sample of SNe Ia[31] and (2) the use of the GRB fundamental planes in optical and X-ray as cosmological distance indicators and the discussion of their future use as standardizable candles.

1. On the Hubble constant tension in the SNe Ia Pantheon sample

The H_0 tension is the discrepancy in more than 4 σ between the value of H_0 estimated with local probes, such as SNe Ia and Cepheids ($H_0 = 74.03 \pm 1.42$ km $s^{-1} Mpc^{-1}$), and the value of H_0 obtained with the Planck Cosmic Microwave Background (CMB) radiation ($H_0 = 67.4 \pm 0.5$ km $s^{-1} Mpc^{-1}$). It represents one of the most important open problems in modern cosmology. To investigate it, we divided the Pantheon sample (Scolnic et al. 2018[32]), a collection of 1048 spectroscopically confirmed SNe Ia, into 3, 4, 20, and 40 bins ordered in redshift. In our analysis, we considered two cosmological models: the standard ΛCDM model and the $w_0 w_a$CDM model, where the equation of state parameter is expressed according to the Chevallier-Polarski-Linder parametrization ($w(z) = w_0 + w_a * z/(1+z)$).[33,34]

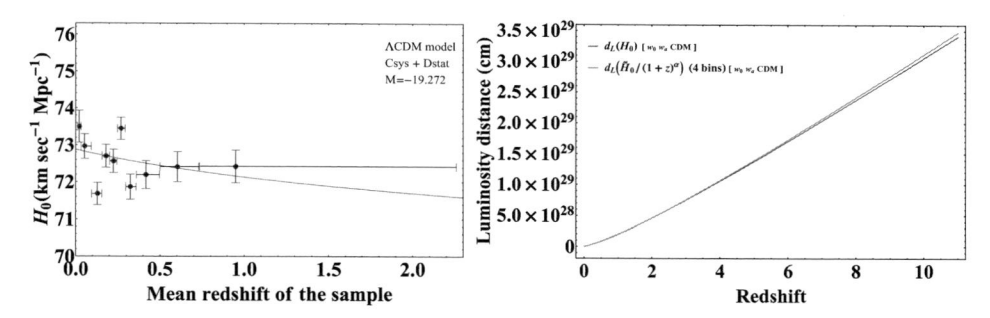

Fig. 1. **Left panel.** The fitting of the H_0 values with redshift in the case of 10 bins of SNe, assuming the ΛCDM model, using the full covariance matrix composed of systematic (C_{sys}) and statistical (D_{stat}) uncertainties,[32] and fixing $M = -19.272$ such that $H_0 = 73.5 km\ s^{-1}\ Mpc^{-1}$ in the first bin. The slow decreasing trend is plain to see. **Right panel.** The comparison between the luminosity distance formula corrected with the $g(z)$ (in green) and the luminosity distance given by the standard $w_0 w_a$CDM model (in red) as functions of the redshift.

Due to the degeneracy between the H_0 and the fiducial absolute magnitude of SNe Ia, M, we set M in such a way that locally the $H_0 = 73.5 km\ s^{-1}\ Mpc^{-1}$. The fiducial values of the total matter density parameters have been assumed as $\Omega_M = 0.298$ (for the ΛCDM model) and $\Omega_M = 0.308$ (for the $w_0 w_a$CDM model). Considering both the cosmological models, for each bin in the 3, 4, 20, and 40 divisions we performed a χ^2 minimization followed by a Monte Carlo Markov Chain simulation to obtain the best-fit H_0 values together with their 1 σ uncertainties. After obtaining these, we fitted them with the following functional form: $g(z) = H'_0/(1+z)^\alpha$, where H'_0 is the value of the Hubble constant at $z = 0$ obtained with the fitting and α is the evolutionary parameter. We found that the H_0 in the Pantheon sample evolves slowly with the redshift, with an α coefficient in the order of 10^{-2} which is compatible with zero from 1.2 σ to 2.0 σ. For example, in the left panel of Figure 1 the case of fitting with 10 bins using the ΛCDM model is shown, while in the right panel a comparison between the standard luminosity distance in the $w_0 w_a$CDM model and the corrected luminosity distance substituting H_0 with $g(z)$ is plotted. Despite the α coefficients being compatible with zero in 3 σ, the highlighted decreasing trend may affect the cosmological results. Indeed, a modification of the luminosity distance formula where H_0 is replaced with the $g(z)$ form shows how the modified luminosity distance curve departs significantly from the ΛCDM canonical one at redshift $z \sim 10$ (see the right panel of Figure 1). To check what would be the behavior of H_0 if the trend was real, we extrapolated its value from the fitting at the redshift of the most distant galaxy so far discovered ($z = 11.09$, Oesch et al. 2016[35]) and at the redshift of the last scattering surface ($z = 1100$). We obtained that the extrapolated value of H_0 at $z = 1100$ is compatible in 1 σ with the one obtained through the Planck CMB measurements. If we consider the discrepancy between the aforementioned values of H_0, namely (74.03 ± 1.42) and (67.4 ± 0.5) $kms^{-1}Mpc^{-1}$ and we compare it with the tension between the fitting values H'_0

(at $z=0$) and $H_0(z=1100)$, we find that our approach leads to alleviate the H_0 tension from 54% to 72% for the ΛCDM and the $w_0 w_a$CDM models, respectively. Thus, we not only found a way to alleviate the Hubble tension, but we provided also a plausible explanation for the observed discrepancy between the values of H_0 coming from probes at different redshifts. The observed decreasing trend may be due to hidden astrophysical biases, selection effects, or even the evolution of SNe Ia lightcurve parameters, as pointed out in Nicolas et al. (2021)[36] where it was shown that the stretch parameter distribution of the Pantheon sample is affected by the drift with the redshift. If this is not the case, and the trend is real instead, the explanation for it may be found in the modified gravity theories. We propose that the $f(R)$ theories in the Jordan frame may explain the observed slow evolution of H_0. However, to prove if this trend is real or not, it is necessary to rely (a) on the future observations of SNe Ia through that will enrich the currently known samples of transient phenomena and (b) on the extension of the Hubble diagram up to redshift ranges that SNe Ia could not cover, thus calling for the use of high-z phenomena such as the GRBs.

2. Optical and X-ray GRB Fundamental Planes as Cosmological Distance Indicators

GRBs, being observed at very high-z (up to $z = 9.4$ so far[37]), have the potential to be employed as standardizable candles, extending the cosmological distance ladder beyond the redshift of SNe Ia. Therefore, we employ them to do so by first standardizing them using the 3D fundamental plane relation. 50 X-ray GRBs cut from a full sample of 222 define the platinum sample, and their corresponding fundamental plane parameter variables are determined by Monte Carlo Markov Chain sampling maintained by Gelman-Rubin statistical constraints. We use both the platinum sample and a well-defined sample of SNe Ia as a combination of probes to accurately constrain the matter content of the modern universe, Ω_M. To do so, the plane parameters are allowed to vary simultaneously with Ω_M within the chain sampling. We find our best results with the addition of a third probe, namely, Baryon Acoustic Oscillations (BAOs), given their reliability as standard rulers. The combination of these three probes allows us to constrain Ω_M to 0.306 ± 0.006, assuming a ΛCDM cosmology. Furthermore, we test, for the first time in this research field, the novel 3D optical correlation as the extension of the 3D fundamental plane in X-ray wavelengths as a cosmological tool and check its applicability compared to that of the confirmed X-ray relation. In doing so, we find that our optical GRB sample is as efficacious in the determination of Ω_M as the platinum X-ray sample. To increase the precision on the estimate of Ω_M, we consider redshift evolutionary effects to overcome common biases such as the Malmquist effect. We employ the reliable Efron & Petrosian (1992)[38] statistical method to ensure that the correlation is intrinsic to the GRB physical mechanics and not due to selection bias. It is by accounting for this that we decrease the intrinsic scatter on the X-ray plane by 44.4%, thus defining

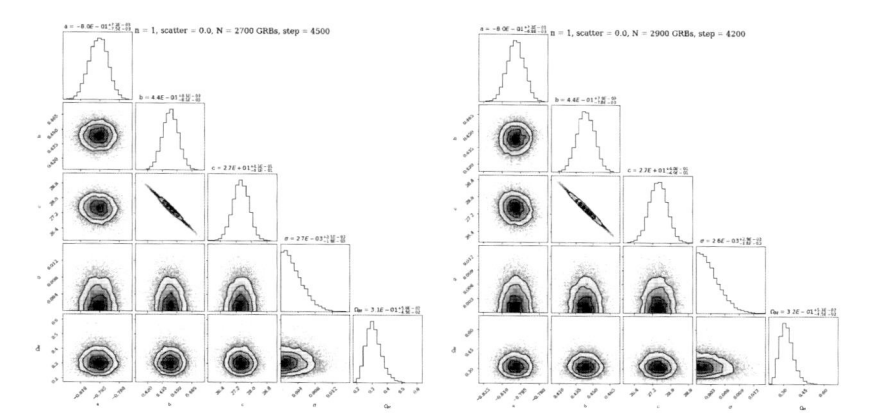

Fig. 2. **Left panel.** Contour plots with the parameters of the fundamental plane relation in X-rays (a, b, c) together with the intrinsic scatter σ and Ω_M, in the case of 2700 simulated GRBs with the evolution correction through the Efron & Petrosian method. **Right panel.** The same of the left panel, considering 2900 simulated GRBs.

the tightest 3D GRB correlation involving plateau features in the literature to date. Using this corrected sample, we confirm a value of 0.306 ± 0.006 defines Ω_M.

To both understand and predict the applicability of GRBs as standalone standard candles, we simulate additional GRBs to see how many are needed to reach uncertainties on Ω_M comparable to that of SNe Ia-derived values; we compare against Conley et al. (2011),[39] Betoule et al. (2014),[40] and Scolnic et al. (2018)[32] symmetrized error and standard deviation limits. In Figure 2, the contours for the parameters of the fundamental plane together with Ω_M after the Efron & Petrosian method application are shown in the case of 2700 (left) and 2900 (right) simulated GRBs. To do so, we first use both the full optical and X-ray GRB samples as independent bases for GRB simulation, conducted again by MCMC techniques. We find that the optical sample yields much smaller uncertainties on each simulation than the X-ray, and consequently a more constrained value of Ω_M. To increase this precision, we explore two methods of trimming our GRB sample leading to tighter planes that are in turn used as the base for simulation; an a posteriori trim using the smallest sample of GRBs for which the intrinsic scatter on the 3D plane which they defined remained near-zero, and an 'a priori' trim for which a number of possible sample sizes were tested and the one that yielded the best results after the fact is chosen. By simulating a large range of GRB sample sizes in both optical and X-ray wavelengths, we find by the construction of probability maps that the same precision as Betoule et al. (2014)[40] is achieved with only 376 simulated optical GRBs for which 47.5% of the fundamental plane variable error bars have been halved by a light curve reconstruction procedure. We find that the Conley et al. (2011)[39] limit is already achievable in most circumstances with current GRB numbers, and that the Scolnic et al. (2018)[32] limit is achieved for 1152 optical GRBs. Considering both the detection power of future deep-space surveys THESEUS[30] and SVOM[41,42] and the nearing capability of machine learning approaches to extract unknown GRB redshifts, we conclude that GRBs will be as efficient standalone probes as SNe Ia by the year 2038. These results are interesting because, as the definition of GRBs as standard candles becomes more reliable with the introduction of the optical and X-ray fundamental planes, the addition of these astrophysical objects to SNe Ia and BAO data will soon give the most precise derivation of Ω_M ever achieved.

3. Summary and Conclusions

In this work, it was highlighted how and to what extent the GRBs may contribute to the cosmological analysis in the future. In the first part (1), the issue of the Hubble constant tension has been investigated with the Pantheon sample of SNe Ia, showing how the H_0 itself is characterized by a slowly decreasing trend with the redshift. This opens the discussion on the reason for this result: together with the possibility that a modified gravity theory could be an explanation, it is also likely that different selection biases persist in the observations of SNe Ia. This strongly suggests that the methods for biases correction, such as the Efron & Petrosian method, are needed in many astrophysical probes to achieve a reliable estimation of the cosmological parameters. Nevertheless, the limited coverage of redshift achieved by SNe Ia leads to the need for probes that can be observed at larger redshift. To this end, in the second part (2) it was shown how the 3D fundamental plane relation in the optical may help the future standardization of GRBs together with its counterpart in the X-rays. In addition, through the simulation of GRBs, it has been shown how this probe is a promising candidate to extend the Hubble diagram up to redshift greater than the ones of SNe Ia. Furthermore, a particular class of objects arouses much interest in the latest years, namely the class of LGRBs associated with Supernovae Ib/c (GRB-SNe): these manifest as supernovae appearing in the afterglow of the LGRBs and are very important since it was highlighted how the associated SNe obey a stretch-luminosity relation similar to the typical one of SNe Ia.[43] The physics behind their emission mechanism has been an object of study on several occasions[44–46] and one of the most interesting features of this class is that within the $L_X - T_X^*$ relation they show a Spearman correlation coefficient higher than the other subclasses of GRBs.[13] Thus, it is possible to use these events as a bridge between the properties of LGRBs and the ones of SNe Ib/c, giving a new perspective on the forthcoming standardization of GRB-SNe Ib/c. It is expected that the next observations of the new transients in the optical through the Subaru Telescope[47] and KISO Telescope[48] will help to investigate for selection biases and correct the current cosmological expectations on the evolution of the universe. Reliable testing of the cosmological models requires always new and more distant standardizable candles, and the GRBs have proven to be a reliable candidate for this purpose.

References

1. Observational evidence from supernovae for an accelerating universe and a cosmological constant, *The Astronomical Journal* **116**, p. 1009–1038 (September 1998).
2. S. Perlmutter, G. Aldering, G. Goldhaber, R. A. Knop, P. Nugent, P. G. Castro, S. Deustua, S. Fabbro, A. Goobar, D. E. Groom, I. M. Hook, A. G. Kim, M. Y. Kim, J. C. Lee, N. J. Nunes, R. Pain, C. R. Pennypacker, R. Quimby, C. Lidman, R. S. Ellis, M. Irwin, R. G. McMahon, P. Ruiz-Lapuente, N. Walton, B. Schaefer, B. J. Boyle, A. V. Filippenko, T. Matheson, A. S. Fruchter, N. Panagia, H. J. M. Newberg, W. J. Couch and T. S. C. Project, Measurements of Ω and Λ from 42 high-redshift supernovae, *The Astrophysical Journal* **517**, 565 (June 1999).
3. S. A. Rodney, A. G. Riess, D. M. Scolnic, D. O. Jones, S. Hemmati, A. Molino, C. McCully, B. Mobasher, L.-G. Strolger, O. Graur and et al., Two Type Ia Supernovae at Redshift $\sim$2 : Improved Classification and Redshift Determination with Mediumband Infrared Imaging, *The Astronomical Journal* **151**, p. 47 (February 2016).
4. F. Wang, J. Yang, X. Fan, J. F. Hennawi, A. J. Barth, E. Banados, F. Bian, K. Boutsia, T. Connor, F. B. Davies, R. Decarli, A.-C. Eilers, E. P. Farina, R. Green, L. Jiang, J.-T. Li, C. Mazzucchelli, R. Nanni, J.-T. Schindler, B. Venemans, F. Walter, X.-B. Wu and M. Yue, A luminous quasar at redshift 7.642, *The Astrophysical Journal Letters* **907**, p. L1 (January 2021).
5. M. G. Dainotti, N. Omodei, G. P. Srinivasaragavan, G. Vianello, R. Willingale, P. O'Brien, S. Nagataki, V. Petrosian, Z. Nuygen, X. Hernandez, M. Axelsson, E. Bissaldi and F. Longo, On the Existence of the Plateau Emission in High-energy Gamma-Ray Burst Light Curves Observed by Fermi-LAT, *The Astrophysical Journal Supplement Series* **255**, p. 13 (July 2021).
6. M. G. Dainotti, V. F. Cardone and S. Capozziello, A time–luminosity correlation for γ-ray bursts in the X-rays, *Monthly Notices of the Royal Astronomical Society: Letters* **391**, L79 (November 2008).
7. M. G. Dainotti, R. Willingale, S. Capozziello, V. F. Cardone and M. Ostrowski, Discovery of a Tight Correlation for Gamma-ray Burst Afterglows with "Canonical" Light Curves, *The Astrophysical Journal* **722**, p. L215–L219 (October 2010).
8. M. G. Dainotti, V. F. Cardone, S. Capozziello, M. Ostrowski and R. Willingale, Study of possible systematics in the L*X - Ta* correlation of Gamma Ray Bursts, *The Astrophysical Journal* **730**, p. 135 (March 2011).
9. M. G. Dainotti, V. Petrosian, J. Singal and M. Ostrowski, Determination of the intrinsic Luminosity Time Correlation in the X-ray Afterglows of GRBs, *The Astrophysical Journal* **774**, p. 157 (August 2013).
10. M. G. Dainotti, V. F. Cardone, E. Piedipalumbo and S. Capozziello, Slope evolution of GRB correlations and cosmology, *Monthly Notices of the Royal Astronomical Society* **436**, 82 (September 2013).
11. M. G. Dainotti, R. D. Vecchio, N. Shigehiro and S. Capozziello, Selection effects in Gamma Ray Bursts correlations: consequences on the ratio between GRB and star formation rates, *The Astrophysical Journal* **800**, p. 31 (February 2015).
12. R. D. Vecchio, M. G. Dainotti and M. Ostrowski, Study of GRB light curve decay indices in the afterglow phase, *The Astrophysical Journal* **828**, p. 36 (August 2016).
13. Dainotti, M. G., Nagataki, S., Maeda, K., Postnikov, S. and Pian, E., A study of gamma ray bursts with afterglow plateau phases associated with supernovae, *A&A* **600**, p. A98 (2017).
14. M. G. Dainotti, S. Livermore, D. A. Kann, L. Li, S. Oates, S. Yi, B. Zhang, B. Gendre, B. Cenko and N. Fraija, The optical luminosity–time correlation for more than 100

gamma-ray burst afterglows, *The Astrophysical Journal Letters* **905**, p. L26 (December 2020).
15. M. G. Dainotti, M. Ostrowski and R. Willingale, Towards a standard gamma-ray burst: tight correlations between the prompt and the afterglow plateau phase emission, *Monthly Notices of the Royal Astronomical Society* **418**, 2202 (December 2011).
16. M. Dainotti, V. Petrosian, R. Willingale, P. O'Brien, M. Ostrowski and S. Nagataki, Luminosity–time and luminosity–luminosity correlations for GRB prompt and afterglow plateau emissions, *Monthly Notices of the Royal Astronomical Society* **451**, 3898 (June 2015).
17. M. G. Dainotti, S. Postnikov, X. Hernandez and M. Ostrowski, A Fundamental Plane for Long Gamma-Ray Bursts with X-Ray Plateaus, *The Astrophysical Journal* **825**, p. L20 (July 2016).
18. M. G. Dainotti, X. Hernandez, S. Postnikov, S. Nagataki, P. O'brien, R. Willingale and S. Striegel, A Study of the Gamma-Ray Burst Fundamental Plane, *The Astrophysical Journal* **848**, p. 88 (October 2017).
19. M. G. Dainotti, A. Ł. Lenart, G. Sarracino, S. Nagataki, S. Capozziello and N. Fraija, The X-Ray Fundamental Plane of the Platinum Sample, the Kilonovae, and the SNe Ib/c Associated with GRBs, *The Astrophysical Journal* **904**, p. 97 (November 2020).
20. M. Dainotti and R. Del Vecchio, Gamma ray burst afterglow and prompt-afterglow relations: An overview, *New Astronomy Reviews* **77**, p. 23–61 (April 2017).
21. M. G. Dainotti, R. Del Vecchio and M. Tarnopolski, Gamma-Ray Burst Prompt Correlations, *Advances in Astronomy* **2018**, p. 1–31 (2018).
22. M. G. Dainotti and L. Amati, Gamma-ray burst prompt correlations: Selection and instrumental effects, *Publications of the Astronomical Society of the Pacific* **130**, p. 051001 (April 2018).
23. M. Dainotti, *Gamma-ray Burst Correlations*2053-2563, 2053-2563 (IOP Publishing, 2019).
24. P. Kumar, R. Narayan and J. L. Johnson, Mass fall-back and accretion in the central engine of gamma-ray bursts, *Monthly Notices of the Royal Astronomical Society* **388**, 1729 (August 2008).
25. A. Rowlinson, B. P. Gompertz, M. Dainotti, P. T. O'Brien, R. A. M. J. Wijers and A. J. van der Horst, Constraining properties of GRB magnetar central engines using the observed plateau luminosity and duration correlation, *Monthly Notices of the Royal Astronomical Society* **443**, 1779 (July 2014).
26. N. Rea, M. Gullón, J. A. Pons, R. Perna, M. G. Dainotti, J. A. Miralles and D. F. Torres, Constraining the GRB-magnetar model by means of the Galactic pulsar population, *The Astrophysical Journal* **813**, p. 92 (November 2015).
27. G. P. Srinivasaragavan, M. G. Dainotti, N. Fraija, X. Hernandez, S. Nagataki, A. Lenart, L. Bowden and R. Wagner, On the Investigation of the Closure Relations for Gamma-Ray Bursts Observed by Swift in the Post-plateau Phase and the GRB Fundamental Plane, *The Astrophysical Journal* **903**, p. 18 (October 2020).
28. M. G. Dainotti, A. . Lenart, N. Fraija, S. Nagataki, D. C. Warren, B. De Simone, G. Srinivasaragavan and A. Mata, Closure relations during the plateau emission of Swift GRBs and the fundamental plane, *Publications of the Astronomical Society of Japan* **73**, p. 970–1000 (June 2021).
29. M. G. Dainotti, V. Petrosian and L. Bowden, Cosmological evolution of the formation rate of short gamma-ray bursts with and without extended emission, *The Astrophysical Journal Letters* **914**, p. L40 (jun 2021).

30. G. Stratta, R. Ciolfi, L. Amati, E. Bozzo, G. Ghirlanda, E. Maiorano, L. Nicastro, A. Rossi, S. Vinciguerra, F. Frontera and et al., THESEUS: A key space mission concept for Multi-Messenger Astrophysics, *Advances in Space Research* **62**, p. 662–682 (August 2018).
31. M. G. Dainotti, B. D. Simone, T. Schiavone, G. Montani, E. Rinaldi and G. Lambiase, On the Hubble Constant Tension in the SNe Ia Pantheon Sample, *The Astrophysical Journal* **912**, p. 150 (May 2021).
32. D. M. Scolnic, D. O. Jones, A. Rest, Y. C. Pan, R. Chornock, R. J. Foley, M. E. Huber, R. Kessler, G. Narayan, A. G. Riess and et al., The Complete Light-curve Sample of Spectroscopically Confirmed SNe Ia from Pan-STARRS1 and Cosmological Constraints from the Combined Pantheon Sample, *The Astrophysical Journal* **859**, p. 101 (May 2018).
33. E. V. Linder, Exploring the expansion history of the universe, *Phys. Rev. Lett.* **90**, p. 091301 (March 2003).
34. M. Chevallier and D. Polarski, Accelerating universes with scaling dark matter, *International Journal of Modern Physics D* **10**, p. 213–223 (April 2001).
35. P. A. Oesch, G. Brammer, P. G. v. Dokkum, G. D. Illingworth, R. J. Bouwens, I. Labbé, M. Franx, I. Momcheva, M. L. N. Ashby, G. G. Fazio and et al., A remarkably luminous galaxy at z=11.1 measured with hubble space telescope grism spectroscopy, *The Astrophysical Journal* **819**, p. 129 (March 2016).
36. N. Nicolas, M. Rigault, Y. Copin, R. Graziani, G. Aldering, M. Briday, Y.-L. Kim, J. Nordin, S. Perlmutter and M. Smith, Redshift evolution of the underlying type ia supernova stretch distribution, *Astronomy & Astrophysics* **649**, p. A74 (May 2021).
37. A. Cucchiara, A. J. Levan, D. B. Fox, N. R. Tanvir, T. N. Ukwatta, E. Berger, T. Krühler, A. K. Yoldaş, X. F. Wu, K. Toma, J. Greiner, F. E. Olivares, A. Rowlinson, L. Amati, T. Sakamoto, K. Roth, A. Stephens, A. Fritz, J. P. U. Fynbo, J. Hjorth, D. Malesani, P. Jakobsson, K. Wiersema, P. T. O'Brien, A. M. Soderberg, R. J. Foley, A. S. Fruchter, J. Rhoads, R. E. Rutledge, B. P. Schmidt, M. A. Dopita, P. Podsiadlowski, R. Willingale, C. Wolf, S. R. Kulkarni and P. D'Avanzo, A photometric redshift of z~ 9.4 for GRB 090429B, *The Astrophysical Journal* **736**, p. 7 (June 2011).
38. B. Efron and V. Petrosian, A simple test of independence for truncated data with applications to redshift surveys, *The Astrophysical Journal* **399** (December 1992).
39. A. Conley, J. Guy, M. Sullivan, N. Regnault, P. Astier, C. Balland, S. Basa, R. G. Carlberg, D. Fouchez, D. Hardin and et al., Supernova Constraints and Systematic Uncertainties from the First 3 Years of the Supernova Legacy Survey, *The Astrophysical Journal Supplement Series* **192**, p. 1 (December 2010).
40. M. Betoule, R. Kessler, J. Guy, J. Mosher, D. Hardin, R. Biswas, P. Astier, P. El-Hage, M. Konig, S. Kuhlmann and et al., Improved cosmological constraints from a joint analysis of the SDSS-II and SNLS supernova samples, *Astronomy & Astrophysics* **568**, p. A22 (August 2014).
41. B. Cordier, J. Wei, J. L. Atteia, S. Basa, A. Claret, F. Daigne, J. Deng, Y. Dong, O. Godet, A. Goldwurm, D. Götz, X. Han, A. Klotz, C. Lachaud, J. Osborne, Y. Qiu, S. Schanne, B. Wu, J. Wang, C. Wu, L. Xin, B. Zhang and S. N. Zhang, The SVOM gamma-ray burst mission (2015).
42. B. Cordier, D. Götz and C. Motch, The SVOM mission, a pathfinder for THESEUS (2018).
43. Z. Cano, Gamma-ray burst supernovae as standardizable candles, *The Astrophysical Journal* **794**, p. 121 (Oct 2014).

44. Dainotti, M. G., Bernardini, M. G., Bianco, C. L., Caito, L., Guida, R. and Ruffini, R., Grb 060218 and grbs associated with supernovae ib/c, *A&A* **471**, L29 (2007).
45. M. Dainotti, The astrophysical trypthic: Grb, sn and urca can be extended to grb060218?, *Journal of The Korean Physical Society - J KOREAN PHYS SOC* **56** (05 2010).
46. Z. Cano, S.-Q. Wang, Z.-G. Dai and X.-F. Wu, The observer's guide to the gamma-ray burst supernova connection, *Advances in Astronomy* **2017**, p. 1–41 (2017).
47. J.-i. Watanabe, D. Kinoshita, Y. Komiyama, F. Tetsuharu, Y. Urata and F. Yoshida, Optical Follow-up of the GRB 010222 Afterglow by Subaru Telescope1, *Publications of the Astronomical Society of Japan* **53**, L27 (08 2001).
48. S. Sako, R. Ohsawa, H. Takahashi, Y. Kojima, M. Doi, N. Kobayashi, T. Aoki, N. Arima, K. Arimatsu, M. Ichiki, S. Ikeda, K. Inooka, Y. Ita, T. Kasuga, M. Kokubo, M. Konishi, H. Maehara, N. Matsunaga, K. Mitsuda, T. Miyata, Y. Mori, M. Morii, T. Morokuma, K. Motohara, Y. Nakada, S.-I. Okumura, Y. Sarugaku, M. Sato, T. Shigeyama, T. Soyano, M. Tanaka, K. Tarusawa, N. Tominaga, T. Totani, S. Urakawa, F. Usui, J. Watanabe, T. Yamashita and M. Yoshikawa, The Tomo-e Gozen wide field CMOS camera for the Kiso Schmidt telescope, in *Ground-based and Airborne Instrumentation for Astronomy VII*, eds. C. J. Evans, L. Simard and H. Takami (SPIE, 2018).

Theory of plateau phase in Gamma-Ray Bursts

Asaf Pe'er

Department of Physics, Bar Ilan University,
Ramat-Gan 52900, Israel
E-mail: asaf.peer@biu.ac.il
asafpeer2.ph.biu.ac.il/

Since its discovery in 2005, the plateau phase seen in the early x-ray afterglow of a significant fraction (10's of %) of GRBs confuse theoreticians. A close look reveals that "plateau" bursts nearly never show evidence for LAT emission, neither a strong thermal component. Using this a hint, I argue that the plateau is due to the coasting of GRB jets in a "wind"-like medius. I provide the theoretical arguments for the evolution of the lightcurve, and show how both the X-ray and optical lightcurves are naturally fitted within the framework of this model. The end of the plateau thus marks the transition between the coasting and the self-similar motion phases.

Keywords: Gamma rays: bursts; Jets: relativistic; X-rays

1. Introduction

Following the launch of the *Swift* satellite in 2004, it became obvious that the early afterglow x-ray lightcurve (minutes - hours) does not follow the previously expected self-similar decay seen at much later times. Rather, in about 60% of GRBs, a flat "plateau", lasting for $\sim 10^2 - 10^5$ s was observed in their x-ray lightcurve,[1,2] before it turns into the familiar self-similar decay, well modeled by the Blandford-McKee[3] solution.

Over the years, many attempts were made to explain this surprising result. Among the ideas discussed in the literature, are: (i) continuous energy injection that slows down the acceleration[1,4–6]; (ii) A two component jet model[7]; (iii) A forward shock emission in inhomogeneous media[8]; (iv) scattering by dust, or other modification of the ambient density by a gamma-ray trigger[9,10]; (v) A dominant reverse shock emission[11–13]; (vi) evolving microphysical parameters[9,14]; (vii) Viewing angle effect - jets viewed off-axis[8,15–17]; (viii) proto-magnetar that releases some of its energy at late times[18]; and (ix) forward shock emission, before the deceleration phase.[19] These plethora of models indicate the large uncertainty that exists in understanding this phenomenon. Furthermore, one thing in common for all these models, except for the last one, is that they all require some addition to the simple "fireball" model dynamics accompanied by synchrotron emission from shock-accelerated electrons.

The last suggestion, by Shen and Matzner[19] requires an explosion into a "wind" density profile (namely, $\rho(r) \propto r^{-2}$). It did not gain popularity, as (i) the deduced values of the Lorentz factor are lower than the 'fiducial' values, $\Gamma_i \gtrsim 100$; and (ii) the claim that this model can only account for a-chromatic afterglow, and can therefore explain only a sub-sample of the GRB population.[20] As we show here, these two claims are incorrect.

2. Measuring GRB Lorentz factor: Is there a contradiction?

To day, there are three main methods used to estimate the Lorentz factor of the expanding GRB jets. The first relies on the opacity argument: in order to avoid copious production of pairs that would prevent observations of > MeV emission one requires a high Lorentz factor. In particular, GeV emission seen by the LAT detector on board *Fermi* satellite in several bursts, require $\Gamma \gtrsim 100$.[21–24]

The second method requires identification of the onset of the self-similar expansion phase, which is accompanied by the formation and propagation of a reverse shock. For plausible parameters, emission from the reverse shock is expected mainly in the optical band, and thus an optical flash is considered as an indication for the transition to a self-similar motion. The time of this transition depends on the initial Lorentz factor, and is used to deduce its value.[25–29]

A third method of inferring the initial Lorentz factor is from quantifying the properties of the thermal emission (temperature and flux) observed during the prompt phase in a significant fraction of bright GRBs.[30–33] Indeed, within the framework of the classical GRB "fireball" model, a thermal component is unavoidable, as deep in the flow it is optically thick. The key is the adiabatic losses of the photons until they escape the plasma at the photosphere. If the photospheric radius is not much above the coasting radius, the thermal photons do not lose a large fraction of their energy, and a thermal component can be identified.[34]

In order to examine this issue, we looked at the 2nd *Fermi* catalogue.[35] Out of 186 GRBs in this catalogue, only 3 show evidence for a shallow decay phase in the LAT data[36]; only one (the hard-short GRB 090510) show any evidence for a decaying plateau in the *Swift*-XRT data. However, for this specific burst, the X-ray slope during the early afterglow ($0.69^{+0.05}_{-0.06}$) can only marginally identify it as having a plateau. We therefore conclude that for bursts that show high energy emission, no evidence for a plateau phase exists.

We next looked at bursts which show evidence for a strong thermal component, and appeared in.[37–39] Non of these showed any evidence for an X-ray plateau. Finally, we looked at bursts which we were interested in analyzing. These are bursts that do show evidence for an x-ray plateau, and for which the redshift is known, and optical data is available. Non of these bursts showed any evidence for a thermal emission during their prompt phase, or for high energy (> MeV) emission. We thus conclude that for bursts which show a plateau in their x-ray lightcurve, there is no indication for a high initial Lorentz factor, of $\Gamma_i \gtrsim 100$'s.

3. Dynamics and radiation

Within the context of the GRB "fireball" model, the expanding plasma jet undergoes 3 phases[40–42]: (i) an initial acceleration phase; due to light aberration, this phase is observed to last only a fraction of a second. (ii) A coasting phase, in which the Lorentz factor of the flow is approximately constant. For "typical" GRB parameters, this phase lasts ~few seconds. (iii) After the expanding plasma collects sufficient mass from the ambient medium (ISM), $m_{ISM} \gtrsim M_{ej}/\Gamma_i$, ($M_{ej}$ is the initially ejected mass), the flow begins its self-similar decay phase, which is well described by the Blandford-McKee[3] self-similar solution. During this phase, the Lorentz factor of the flow gradually decays. This is the phase responsible for the late time afterglow emission.

Once the flow becomes optically thin, the main radiation mechanism is synchrotron emission. Here we focus on emission from electrons accelerated to a power law distribution by the forward shock that exists in all phases, though we particularly focus on the coasting phase (ii) and late afterglow phase (iii). The accelerated electrons assume a power law distribution with power law index, p ($N_{el}(\gamma)d\gamma \propto \gamma^{-p}$). The resulting spectra is a well-known broken power law,[43,44] with 2 characteristic frequencies (omitting discussion on the self-absorption frequency, which is below the optical band is thus not relevant for the analysed signal): the peak frequency, $\nu_m^{ob.} \propto \Gamma B \gamma_{el}^2$, and the cooling frequency, $\nu_c^{ob.} \propto \Gamma^3/(B^3 r^2)$. Here, Γ is the jet (bulk) Lorentz factor, B is the magnetic field, γ_{el} is the characteristic Lorentz factor of the accelerated electrons (the minimum Lorentz factor above which a power law distribution exists), and r is the emission radius. The characteristic emission frequency of the electrons accelerated by the forward shock is ν_m, and ν_c is obtained by equating the radiative cooling time to the dynamical time. A third parameter, N_e is the total number of radiating electrons, is needed to determine the total observed flux (for bursts with known redshift).

The global spectral and temporal shapes depend on whether the cooling frequency ν_c is above or below the peak frequency, ν_m. When $\nu_c < \nu_m$ the system is in the "fast cooling" regime, where electrons lose nearly all of their energy within the dynamical time, and when $\nu_c > \nu_m$ it is in the "slow cooling". At a given observed frequency ν, there are therefore 6 possible regions, summarized as follows and marked [A] – [F]:

- "Fast cooling", $\nu_c < \nu_m$:

$$F_\nu = F_{\nu,\text{peak}} \times \begin{cases} \nu_c^{-1/3} \nu^{1/3} & \nu < \nu_c < \nu_m \ [A] \\ \nu_c^{1/2} \nu^{-1/2} & \nu_c < \nu < \nu_m \ [B] \\ \nu_m^{(p-1)/2} \nu_c^{1/2} \nu^{-p/2} & \nu_c < \nu_m < \nu \ [C] \end{cases} \quad (1)$$

- "Slow cooling", $\nu_m < \nu_c$:

$$F_\nu = F_{\nu,\text{peak}} \times \begin{cases} \nu_m^{-1/3} \nu^{1/3} & \nu < \nu_m < \nu_c \ [D] \\ \nu_m^{(p-1)/2} \nu^{-(p-1)/2} & \nu_m < \nu < \nu_c \ [E] \\ \nu_m^{(p-1)/2} \nu_c^{1/2} \nu^{-p/2} & \nu_m < \nu_c < \nu \ [F] \end{cases} \quad (2)$$

We adopt the standard assumption that the energy dissipated by the forward shock is used both in generating the magnetic field and in accelerating the electrons.

This assumption implies that the electrons characteristic Lorentz factor is linearly proportional to the bulk Lorentz factor, $\gamma_{el} \propto \epsilon_e \Gamma$, and similarly the energy density in the magnetic field, $B^2/8\pi = \epsilon_B u$, where u is the energy density of the material behind the shock and $\epsilon_B < 1$ is the fraction of post-shock thermal energy used in generating the magnetic field. This gives $B \propto \epsilon_B^{1/2} n^{1/2} \Gamma$.

In the literature, two scenarios are in frequent use in describing the ambient density profile. The first is a constant density interstellar medium (ISM). This scenario was thoroughly considered in the literature. It is easy to show that in this scenario, during the coasting phase, the flux continuously increases in all 6 regimes [A]–[F], as the expanding flow continuously accumulates particles from the ISM which are accelerated by the forward shock and radiate.

A second scenario (also in wide use) is that in which the GRB explosion occurs into a pre-ejected stellar wind with constant mass ejection rate and constant wind velocity. These imoly that the density drops as $\rho(r) \propto r^{-2}$. As we show below, under certain conditions, during the coasting phase the obtained lightcurve is ≈flat. We therefore focus here and below on this scenario.

Using the scaling relations derived above, it is straightforward to show that during the coasting phase where $\Gamma = cosnt$, $\nu_m \propto t^{-1}$ (following the decrease in the density with radius, which leads to a decrease in the magnetic field), and $\nu_c \propto t$ from a similar reason. During the decaying self-similar expansion, $\Gamma(r) \propto r^{-1/2}$, and a similar argument gives $\nu_m \propto t^{-3/2}$ and $\nu_c \propto t^{1/2}$. We thus find that both during the coasting and during the self-similar phases in a "wind" scenario, ν_m decreases with observed time, while ν_c increases. These behaviours are demonstrated (along side the 6 regions, [A] – [F]) in Figures 1 and 2.

The most relevant regions are regions [E] and [F]. Using the scaling relations of ν_m, ν_c and $N_e \propto r$, one obtains the scaling relations for these regions:

Table 1. Scaling relations of regions [E] and [F].

Region	Coasting phase	Self-similar decay phase
F ($\nu_c < \nu$)	$F_\nu \propto t^{(2-p)/2} \nu^{-p/2} \sim t^0$	$F_\nu \propto t^{(2-3p)/4} \nu^{-p/2} \sim t^{-1}$
E ($\nu < \nu_c$)	$F_\nu \propto t^{(1-p)/2} \nu^{-(p-1)/2} \sim t^{-0.5}$	$F_\nu \propto t^{(1-3p)/4} \nu^{-(p-1)/2} \sim t^{-1.25}$

Note: [a] Sample table footnote.

These results can now be confronted with the data. In region [F], which is always the earlier due to the rise of ν_c, one finds that at early times, the expected lightcurve is flat (if the power law index of the accelerated electrons is $p = 2$), which later decays as $F_\nu(t) \propto t^{-1}$. This is indeed what is observed in many GRBs that show a plateau. This model therefore provides an excellent explanation to the observed plateau phase. We note that as the optical band transient from region [F] to region [E] earlier than the x-ray band (see Figures on p. 3145), the optical lightcurve may very well decay during the X-ray plateau.

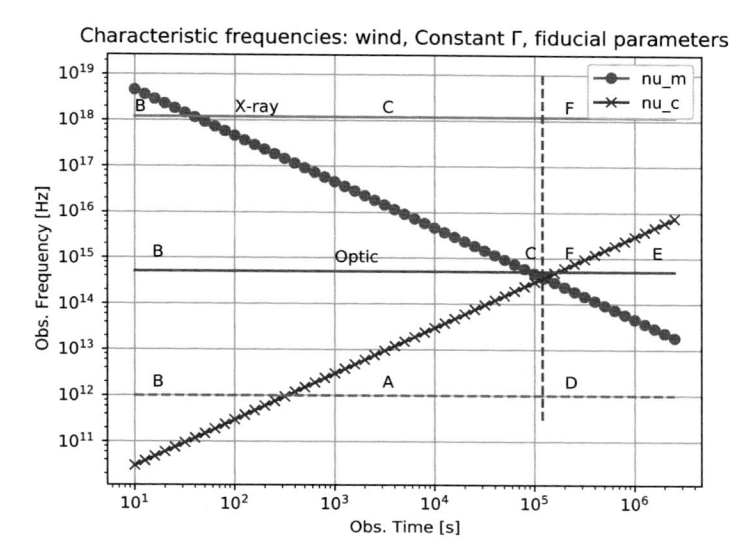

Fig. 1. Evolution of the characteristic synchrotron frequencies, ν_m and ν_c, calculated here for typical GRB parameters, during the coasting phase ($\Gamma_i = const$) for an explosion into a "wind" density environment, $\rho(r) \propto r^{-2}$. Marked are regions [A] – [F]. It is clear from the figure, that a given observed frequency change its regime in only one of two orders: Either $[B] \to [A] \to [D] \to [E]$ or $[B] \to [C] \to [F] \to [E]$.

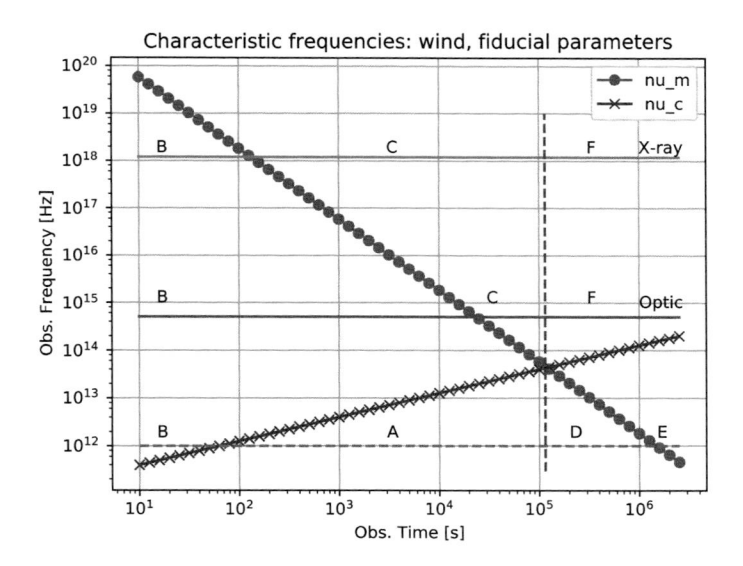

Fig. 2. Same as Figure 1, for evolution during the self-similar (decaying) expansion phase that follows the coasting phase.

4. Extracting information on the physical parameters

The excellent agreement between the theory and the data, calls for a simple interpretation according to which the transition from the plateau to the decay lightcurve marks the transition from the coasting to the self-similar expansion phases. For an explosion into a "Wind" environment, this transition time is related to the outflow parameters via

$$t_{tran}^{ob.} = (1+z)\frac{9E}{32\pi Ac^3\Gamma_i^4} \quad (3)$$

where A is the proportionality constant of the wind density ($\rho(r) = Ar^{-2}$), Γ_i is the initial (coasting) Lorentz factor, E is the isotropic-equivalent energy and z is the redshift. Thus, for bursts with known redshift, the transition time provides a direct information on the value of $A\Gamma_i^4$.

Furthermore, when the lightcurve is flat, the flow is in region [F], and the parametric dependence of the x-ray flux is $\nu F_\nu(x) \propto c^3 A\Gamma_i^4 \epsilon_e d_L^{-2}$, where d_L is the luminosity distance. Thus, for bursts with known redshift (hence energy), the transition time combined with the x-ray flux provides a direct measurement on the fraction of energy given to the accelerated electrons, ϵ_e.

A decaying optical flux accompanying the flat x-ray plateau implies that the optical frequency must be in region [E]. In this case, the flux at the optical (say, R)-band is $\nu F_\nu(R) = F_{\nu,peak}\nu_m^{1/2}\nu_R^{1/2}$. For power law index $p = 2$, this gives a parametric dependence connecting $A^{7/4}\Gamma_i^3\epsilon_B^{3/4}$. This implies that for a given density (a value of A), there is a single corresponding value of the magnetization ϵ_B (as well as of the coasting Lorentz factor, Γ_i). This can be used in the opposite direction: an additional knowledge of ϵ_B, such as equipartition, or some fraction of it, can be used to determine the ambient density and the Lorentz factor.

In a recent paper [Dereli-Begue et. al., submitted] we used this method to extract information about the physical parameters of GRB outflow, as well as their initial Lorentz factor. A very interesting result, is that for the sample of GRBs with x-ray plateau, the initial Lorentz factor is typically in the range $20 \leq \Gamma_i \leq 200$, smaller than the values inferred by other methods. As explained above, there is no contradiction, and the results obtained in fact extend the known range of Lorentz factors in GRB outflows.

References

1. B. Zhang, Y. Z. Fan, J. Dyks, S. Kobayashi, P. Mészáros, D. N. Burrows, J. A. Nousek and N. Gehrels, Physical Processes Shaping Gamma-Ray Burst X-Ray Afterglow Light Curves: Theoretical Implications from the Swift X-Ray Telescope Observations, *Astrophys. J.* **642**, 354 (May 2006).
2. G. P. Srinivasaragavan, M. G. Dainotti, N. Fraija, X. Hernandez, S. Nagataki, A. Lenart, L. Bowden and R. Wagner, On the Investigation of the Closure Relations for Gamma-Ray Bursts Observed by Swift in the Post-plateau Phase and the GRB Fundamental Plane, *Astrophys. J.* **903**, p. 18 (November 2020).

3. R. D. Blandford and C. F. McKee, Fluid dynamics of relativistic blast waves, *Physics of Fluids* **19**, 1130 (August 1976).
4. J. A. Nousek, C. Kouveliotou, D. Grupe, K. L. Page, J. Granot, E. Ramirez-Ruiz, S. K. Patel, D. N. Burrows, V. Mangano, S. Barthelmy, A. P. Beardmore, S. Campana, M. Capalbi, G. Chincarini, G. Cusumano, A. D. Falcone, N. Gehrels, P. Giommi, M. R. Goad, O. Godet, C. P. Hurkett, J. A. Kennea, A. Moretti, P. T. O'Brien, J. P. Osborne, P. Romano, G. Tagliaferri and A. A. Wells, Evidence for a Canonical Gamma-Ray Burst Afterglow Light Curve in the Swift XRT Data, *Astrophys. J.* **642**, 389 (May 2006).
5. J. Granot, A. Königl and T. Piran, Implications of the early X-ray afterglow light curves of Swift gamma-ray bursts, *Mon. Not. R. Astron. Soc.* **370**, 1946 (August 2006).
6. G. Ghisellini, G. Ghirlanda, L. Nava and C. Firmani, "Late Prompt" Emission in Gamma-Ray Bursts?, *Astrophys. J.* **658**, L75 (April 2007).
7. J. L. Racusin, S. V. Karpov, M. Sokolowski, J. Granot, X. F. Wu, V. Pal'Shin, S. Covino, A. J. van der Horst, S. R. Oates, P. Schady, R. J. Smith, J. Cummings, R. L. C. Starling, L. W. Piotrowski, B. Zhang, P. A. Evans, S. T. Holland, K. Malek, M. T. Page, L. Vetere, R. Margutti, C. Guidorzi, A. P. Kamble, P. A. Curran, A. Beardmore, C. Kouveliotou, L. Mankiewicz, A. Melandri, P. T. O'Brien, K. L. Page, T. Piran, N. R. Tanvir, G. Wrochna, R. L. Aptekar, S. Barthelmy, C. Bartolini, G. M. Beskin, S. Bondar, M. Bremer, S. Campana, A. Castro-Tirado, A. Cucchiara, M. Cwiok, P. D'Avanzo, V. D'Elia, M. Della Valle, A. de Ugarte Postigo, W. Dominik, A. Falcone, F. Fiore, D. B. Fox, D. D. Frederiks, A. S. Fruchter, D. Fugazza, M. A. Garrett, N. Gehrels, S. Golenetskii, A. Gomboc, J. Gorosabel, G. Greco, A. Guarnieri, S. Immler, M. Jelinek, G. Kasprowicz, V. La Parola, A. J. Levan, V. Mangano, E. P. Mazets, E. Molinari, A. Moretti, K. Nawrocki, P. P. Oleynik, J. P. Osborne, C. Pagani, S. B. Pandey, Z. Paragi, M. Perri, A. Piccioni, E. Ramirez-Ruiz, P. W. A. Roming, I. A. Steele, R. G. Strom, V. Testa, G. Tosti, M. V. Ulanov, K. Wiersema, R. A. M. J. Wijers, J. M. Winters, A. F. Zarnecki, F. Zerbi, P. Mészáros, G. Chincarini and D. N. Burrows, Broadband observations of the naked-eye γ-ray burst GRB080319B, *Nature* **455**, 183 (September 2008).
8. K. Toma, K. Ioka, R. Yamazaki and T. Nakamura, Shallow Decay of Early X-Ray Afterglows from Inhomogeneous Gamma-Ray Burst Jets, *Astrophys. J.* **640**, L139 (April 2006).
9. K. Ioka, K. Toma, R. Yamazaki and T. Nakamura, Efficiency crisis of swift gamma-ray bursts with shallow X-ray afterglows: prior activity or time-dependent microphysics?, *Astron. Astrophys.* **458**, 7 (October 2006).
10. L. Shao and Z. G. Dai, Behavior of X-Ray Dust Scattering and Implications for X-Ray Afterglows of Gamma-Ray Bursts, *Astrophys. J.* **660**, 1319 (May 2007).
11. Z. L. Uhm and A. M. Beloborodov, On the Mechanism of Gamma-Ray Burst Afterglows, *Astrophys. J.* **665**, L93 (August 2007).
12. F. Genet, F. Daigne and R. Mochkovitch, Can the early X-ray afterglow of gamma-ray bursts be explained by a contribution from the reverse shock?, *Mon. Not. R. Astron. Soc.* **381**, 732 (October 2007).
13. R. Hascoët, F. Daigne and R. Mochkovitch, The prompt-early afterglow connection in gamma-ray bursts: implications for the early afterglow physics, *Mon. Not. R. Astron. Soc.* **442**, 20 (July 2014).
14. A. Panaitescu, P. Mészáros, N. Gehrels, D. Burrows and J. Nousek, Analysis of the X-ray emission of nine Swift afterglows, *Mon. Not. R. Astron. Soc.* **366**, 1357 (March 2006).

15. D. Eichler and J. Granot, The Case for Anisotropic Afterglow Efficiency within Gamma-Ray Burst Jets, *Astrophys. J.* **641**, L5 (April 2006).
16. G. Oganesyan, S. Ascenzi, M. Branchesi, O. S. Salafia, S. Dall'Osso and G. Ghirlanda, Structured Jets and X-Ray Plateaus in Gamma-Ray Burst Phenomena, *Astrophys. J.* **893**, p. 88 (April 2020).
17. P. Beniamini, J. Granot and R. Gill, Afterglow light curves from misaligned structured jets, *Mon. Not. R. Astron. Soc.* **493**, 3521 (April 2020).
18. B. D. Metzger, D. Giannios, T. A. Thompson, N. Bucciantini and E. Quataert, The protomagnetar model for gamma-ray bursts, *Mon. Not. R. Astron. Soc.* **413**, 2031 (May 2011).
19. R. Shen and C. D. Matzner, Coasting External Shock in Wind Medium: An Origin for the X-Ray Plateau Decay Component in Swift Gamma-Ray Burst Afterglows, *Astrophys. J.* **744**, p. 36 (January 2012).
20. P. Kumar and B. Zhang, The physics of gamma-ray bursts and relativistic jets, *Phys. Rep.* **561**, 1 (February 2015).
21. J. H. Krolik and E. A. Pier, Relativistic motion in gamma-ray bursts, *Astrophys. J.* **373**, 277 (May 1991).
22. E. E. Fenimore, R. I. Epstein and C. Ho, The escape of 100 MeV photons from cosmological gamma-ray bursts, *àaps* **97**, 59 (January 1993).
23. E. Woods and A. Loeb, Empirical Constraints on Source Properties and Host Galaxies of Cosmological Gamma-Ray Bursts, *Astrophys. J.* **453**, p. 583 (November 1995).
24. Y. Lithwick and R. Sari, Lower Limits on Lorentz Factors in Gamma-Ray Bursts, *Astrophys. J.* **555**, 540 (July 2001).
25. P. Meszaros and M. J. Rees, Optical and Long-Wavelength Afterglow from Gamma-Ray Bursts, *Astrophys. J.* **476**, 232 (February 1997).
26. S. Kobayashi, T. Piran and R. Sari, Can Internal Shocks Produce the Variability in Gamma-Ray Bursts?, *Astrophys. J.* **490**, p. 92 (November 1997).
27. R. Sari and T. Piran, GRB 990123: The Optical Flash and the Fireball Model, *Astrophys. J.* **517**, L109 (June 1999).
28. A. Panaitescu and P. Kumar, Properties of Relativistic Jets in Gamma-Ray Burst Afterglows, *Astrophys. J.* **571**, 779 (June 2002).
29. S. Kobayashi and B. Zhang, Early Optical Afterglows from Wind-Type Gamma-Ray Bursts, *Astrophys. J.* **597**, 455 (November 2003).
30. A. Pe'er, F. Ryde, R. A. M. J. Wijers, P. Mészáros and M. J. Rees, A New Method of Determining the Initial Size and Lorentz Factor of Gamma-Ray Burst Fireballs Using a Thermal Emission Component, *Astrophys. J.* **664**, L1 (July 2007).
31. A. Mizuta and S. Nagataki, Photospheric Thermal Radiation from GRB Collapsar Jets, *International Journal of Modern Physics Conference Series* **8**, 225 (2012).
32. R. Hascoët, F. Daigne and R. Mochkovitch, Prompt thermal emission in gamma-ray bursts, *Astron. Astrophys.* **551**, p. A124 (March 2013).
33. G. V. Vereshchagin and I. A. Siutsou, Diffusive photospheres in gamma-ray bursts, *Mon. Not. R. Astron. Soc.* **494**, 1463 (May 2020).
34. A. Pe'er, B.-B. Zhang, F. Ryde, S. McGlynn, B. Zhang, R. D. Preece and C. Kouveliotou, The connection between thermal and non-thermal emission in gamma-ray bursts: general considerations and GRB 090902B as a case study, *Mon. Not. R. Astron. Soc.* **420**, 468 (February 2012).
35. M. Ajello, M. Arimoto, M. Axelsson, L. Baldini, G. Barbiellini, D. Bastieri, R. Bellazzini, P. N. Bhat, E. Bissaldi, R. D. Blandford, R. Bonino, J. Bonnell, E. Bottacini, J. Bregeon, P. Bruel, R. Buehler, R. A. Cameron, R. Caputo, P. A. Caraveo, E. Cavazzuti, S. Chen, C. C. Cheung, G. Chiaro, S. Ciprini, D. Costantin, M. Crnogorcevic,

S. Cutini, M. Dainotti, F. D'Ammando, P. de la Torre Luque, F. de Palma, A. Desai, R. Desiante, N. Di Lalla, L. Di Venere, F. Fana Dirirsa, S. J. Fegan, A. Franckowiak, Y. Fukazawa, S. Funk, P. Fusco, F. Gargano, D. Gasparrini, N. Giglietto, F. Giordano, M. Giroletti, D. Green, I. A. Grenier, J. E. Grove, S. Guiriec, E. Hays, J. W. Hewitt, D. Horan, G. Jóhannesson, D. Kocevski, M. Kuss, L. Latronico, J. Li, F. Longo, F. Loparco, M. N. Lovellette, P. Lubrano, S. Maldera, A. Manfreda, G. Martí-Devesa, M. N. Mazziotta, I. Mereu, M. Meyer, P. F. Michelson, N. Mirabal, W. Mitthumsiri, T. Mizuno, M. E. Monzani, E. Moretti, A. Morselli, I. V. Moskalenko, M. Negro, E. Nuss, M. Ohno, N. Omodei, M. Orienti, E. Orlando, M. Palatiello, V. S. Paliya, D. Paneque, M. Persic, M. Pesce-Rollins, V. Petrosian, F. Piron, S. Poolakkil, H. Poon, T. A. Porter, G. Principe, J. L. Racusin, S. Rainò, R. Rando, M. Razzano, S. Razzaque, A. Reimer, O. Reimer, T. Reposeur, F. Ryde, D. Serini, C. Sgrò, E. J. Siskind, E. Sonbas, G. Spandre, P. Spinelli, D. J. Suson, H. Tajima, M. Takahashi, D. Tak, J. B. Thayer, D. F. Torres, E. Troja, J. Valverde, P. Veres, G. Vianello, A. von Kienlin, K. Wood, M. Yassine, S. Zhu and S. Zimmer, A Decade of Gamma-Ray Bursts Observed by Fermi-LAT: The Second GRB Catalog, *Astrophys. J.* **878**, p. 52 (June 2019).
36. M. G. Dainotti, N. Omodei, G. P. Srinivasaragavan, G. Vianello, R. Willingale, P. O'Brien, S. Nagataki, V. Petrosian, Z. Nuygen, X. Hernandez, M. Axelsson, E. Bissaldi and F. Longo, On the Existence of the Plateau Emission in High-energy Gamma-Ray Burst Light Curves Observed by Fermi-LAT, *Astrophys. J.* **255**, p. 13 (July 2021).
37. H.-F. Yu, H. Dereli-Bégué and F. Ryde, Bayesian Time-resolved Spectroscopy of GRB Pulses, *Astrophys. J.* **886**, p. 20 (November 2019).
38. Z. Acuner, F. Ryde, A. Pe'er, D. Mortlock and B. Ahlgren, The Fraction of Gamma-Ray Bursts with an Observed Photospheric Emission Episode, *Astrophys. J.* **893**, p. 128 (April 2020).
39. H. Dereli-Bégué, A. Pe'er and F. Ryde, Classification of Photospheric Emission in Short GRBs, *Astrophys. J.* **897**, p. 145 (July 2020).
40. B. Paczynski, Gamma-ray bursters at cosmological distances, *Astrophys. J.* **308**, L43 (September 1986).
41. M. J. Rees and P. Meszaros, Relativistic fireballs - Energy conversion and time-scales, *Mon. Not. R. Astron. Soc.* **258**, 41P (September 1992).
42. M. J. Rees and P. Meszaros, Unsteady outflow models for cosmological gamma-ray bursts, *Astrophys. J.* **430**, L93 (August 1994).
43. G. B. Rybicki and A. P. Lightman, *Radiative processes in astrophysics* 1979.
44. R. Sari, T. Piran and R. Narayan, Spectra and Light Curves of Gamma-Ray Burst Afterglows, *Astrophys. J.* **497**, L17+ (April 1998).

Exploring the canonical behaviour of long Gamma-Ray Bursts using an intrinsic multi-wavelength afterglow correlation

S. R. Oates[a,*], J. L. Racusin[b], M. De Pasquale[c], D. Kocevski[d], M. J. Page[e],
A. J. Castro-Tirado[f,g], J. Gorosabel[g,h,i,†], A. A. Breeveld[e], N. P. M. Kuin[e] and P. J. Smith[e]

[a] School of Physics and Astronomy & Institute for Gravitational Wave Astronomy, University of Birmingham, B15 2TT, UK

[b] Astrophysics Science Division, NASA Goddard Space Flight Center, 8800 Greenbelt Road, Greenbelt, Maryland 20771, USA

[c] Dipartimento di Scienze Matematiche e Informatiche, Scienze Fisiche e Scienze della Terra (MIFT), Universitá di Messina - Viale F. Stagno d'Alcontres, 31 - 98166 Messina, Italy

[d] NASA Marshall Space Flight Center, Huntsville, AL

[e] Mullard Space Science Laboratory, University College London, Holmbury St. Mary, Dorking, Surrey, RH5 6NT, UK

[f] Instituto de Astrofísica de Andalucía (IAA-CSIC), Glorieta de la Astronomía s/n, E-18008, Granada, Spain

[g] Unidad Asociada Departamento de Ingeniería de Sistemas y Automática, E.T.S. de Ingenieros Industriales, Universidad de Málaga, Spain

[h] Unidad Asociada Grupo Ciencias Planetarias UPV/EHU-IAA/CSIC, Departamento de Física Aplicada I, E.T.S.

[i] Ingeniería, Universidad del País Vasco UPV/EHU, Bilbao, Spain

[†] deceased

[*] E-mail: s.r.oates@bham.ac.uk

In this conference proceeding we summarise our investigation of a correlation discovered between the afterglow luminosity (measured at restframe 200 s; log L_{200s}) and average afterglow decay rate (measured from restframe 200 s onwards; $\alpha_{>200s}$) of long duration Gamma-ray Burst (GRB) afterglows, found in both the optical/UV and X-ray afterglows. We examine the correlation in the X-ray light curves and find that it does not depend on the presence of specific features in the X-ray light curve. We test how the optical and X-ray parameters log $L_{O,200s}$, log $L_{X,200s}$, $\alpha_{O,>200s}$, $\alpha_{X,>200s}$ relate to each other and to parameters from the prompt emission phase. Using a Monte Carlo simulation, we explore whether these relationships are consistent with predictions of a basic standard afterglow model. We conclude that most of the correlations we observe are consistent with a common underlying physical mechanism producing GRBs and their afterglows regardless of their detailed temporal behaviour, but this basic model has difficulty explaining correlations involving $\alpha_{>200s}$. We therefore briefly discuss alternative more complex afterglow models.

Keywords: Gamma-ray bursts; correlations

1. Introduction

Gamma-ray bursts (GRBs) are intense flashes of gamma-rays that are usually accompanied by an afterglow, longer lived emission that may be detected at X-ray to radio wavelengths. Studies of single GRBs provide exceptional detail on the behaviour and physical properties of individual events. However, statistical investigations of large samples of GRBs aim to find common characteristics and correlations that link individual events and therefore provide insight into the mechanisms common to GRBs. Statistical investigations performed so far have found a number of trends and correlations within and linking the prompt gamma-ray emission and the afterglow emission e.g., Ref. 1–10.

In this conference proceeding, we focus on the discovery of a correlation, found in a sample of optical/UV afterglow light curves,[11] between the logarithmic brightness (log $L_{O,200s}$; measured at restframe 200 s and at a restframe wavelength 1600 Å), and their average decay rate ($\alpha_{>200s}$; measured from restframe 200 s onwards with a single power-law). This correlation has also been found at X-ray wavelengths.[12] To gain insight into the origin of the luminosity-decay correlation, we investigated the X-ray sample and how it relates to other GRB properties.[12,13] Ref. 12 discovered the log $L_{200s} - \alpha_{>200s}$ in the X-ray afterglows observed by the *Swift* X-ray Telescope (XRT[14]). Ref. 13 compared the parameters of the optical/UV log $L_{200s} - \alpha_{>200s}$ correlation with the equivalent values from the X-ray and also explored their relationship to properties of the prompt emission, namely the isotropic energy E_{iso} and the peak energy E_{peak}. In the following, we will provide a summary of these papers.

2. Sample Selection

The X-ray light curves were retrieved from the University of Leicester *Swift*-XRT Team GRB repository.[15,16] Ref. 12 selected X-ray afterglows of *Swift*/BAT detected GRBs, that were observed between December 2004 and March 2014, that had measured redshifts, had at least 3 light curve bins and started within a factor of restframe 200 s, t_{200s}. The final sample includes 246 GRBs; 237 long and 9 short. The count rate light curves were converted to flux density at 1 keV using the spectral index from the automated fits to the photon counting mode data, and then to intrinsic luminosity. All light curve fitting is performed in the count rate domain.

The Ref. 13 sample, used to compare the properties of the X-ray, optical afterglows together with their prompt emission parameters, consists of 48 long GRBs that overlap the Ref. 11 and Ref. 12 samples. The optical/UV luminosity light curves were produced at a common wavelength of 1600 Å.[11]

To measure luminosity at 200 s, log L_{200s}, for the optical/UV light curves we interpolated between 100 and 2000 s and for the X-ray we measured the luminosity at 200 s from the best-fit light curve model.[17] To obtain the average decay rate $\alpha_{>200s}$, a single power-law was fit to each optical/UV and X-ray light curve from 200 s onwards.

For some X-ray afterglows, an initial steep decay, associated with the tail of the prompt emission,[18] can contaminate the initial part of the X-ray light curve. Of the 246 X-ray light curves, the steep decay segment is found to contaminate 23 X-ray light curves at restframe 200 s. We identify a light curve segment to have a prompt origin if there is a steep to shallow transition with $\Delta\alpha > 1.0$. In these situations the average decay index is measured with a simple power-law fit to data beyond restframe 200 s and after the steep to shallow transition. In order to get a better estimate of the afterglow luminosity at restframe 200 s, we extrapolate back to restframe 200 s the first segment of the best-fit light curve that is not contaminated by the prompt emission (see also Ref. 12).

To compare the afterglow properties with the prompt emission properties we determined the isotropic energy E_{iso} and restframe peak energy, E_{peak} from the γ-ray emission, following Ref. 17. Of the 48 GRBs that overlap the optical and X-ray samples,[11,12] we determined E_{peak} for 44 GRBs and E_{iso} for 47 GRBs.

We determine the strength of the correlation using the IDL tool *r_correlate*, which measures the Spearman rank coefficient (R_{sp}), and its corresponding null hypothesis probability (p). We also use the partial Spearman rank correlation to test the dependence of each correlation on redshift.

We perform a linear regression analysis using the IDL routines *fitexy* and *sixlin*: *fitexy* is used when both parameters have errors, *sixlin* is used when we do not know the errors on one or both parameters. Since there are only a handful of GRBs with errors on the E_{iso} and E_{peak} parameters, we choose to discard errors in both parameters and use *sixlin* when determining the strength and significance of each correlation with one of these parameters involved.

3. Results

3.1. log $L_{X,200s} - \alpha_{X,>200s}$ *correlation*

Within the sample of 246 X-ray afterglow light curves we see evidence for a correlation between log $L_{X,200s}$ and $\alpha_{X,>200s}$, similar to that in the optical/UV.[11] The X-ray afterglow sample consists of long and short GRBs and the light curves are often more complex than the optical/UV, consisting of features such as plateaus and flares that may add scatter or influence the correlation. We test these effects by dividing the sample by specific characteristics and reproducing the same analyses. We report all of these tests and the final correlation in Table 1 and Fig. 1.

The first test is to determine if the log $L_{X,200s} - \alpha_{X,>200s}$ correlation is observed for both short and long GRBs. Separating GRBs in to long and short classes, we find that long GRBs are significantly correlated, but no significant correlation is found for the short GRBs. This suggests that their is some intrinsic difference in the afterglow properties of short and long GRBs, be it their environment or jet dynamics. For all further tests of the log $L_{X,200s} - \alpha_{X,>200s}$ correlation, we exclude short GRBs.

X-ray flares have been shown to have an internal rather than external shock origin and may be a potential source of contamination in measuring the log $L_{X,200s}$ and $\alpha_{X,>200s}$ parameters. We first separate those afterglows with X-ray flares (without removing flaring intervals) and those without flares, and find that the two samples show very similar correlation strengths and slopes, but with slightly more scatter in the sample with flares. We do not exclude GRBs with flares, instead we exclude the flaring intervals from the light curves and refit them to obtain log $L_{X,200s}$ and

$\alpha_{X,avg,>200s}$. Re-running the Spearman rank test, on the entire sample we find a tighter correlation. Henceforth, we therefore, continue our investigation using the flare-removed average decay fits.

The average decay rate may also be influenced by the plateau phase observed in some X-ray afterglows (e.g Ref. 17). For example, a light curve with an extremely long plateau (e.g. GRB 060729; Ref. 19) may have a shallower average decay, whereas GRBs without plateaus would be steeper. In addition Refs. 20, 21 have shown that there is a relationship between the time and flux of the end of the X-ray plateau, which could be another manifestation of the log $L_{200s} - \alpha_{>200s}$ correlation. We thus divide the X-ray sample in to those with and without plateaus and to determine if the correlation is still present in both sub-samples. The results in Table 1 indicate that the luminosity-average decay correlation is present and similarly significant in both sub-samples. This suggests that the plateau feature is not responsible for producing the correlation and is not solely responsible for regulating the average afterglow decay.

Table 1. Linear regression and correlation statistics for each test of the X-ray light curve sample. The partial Spearman rank coefficient tests the dependence of the given set of parameters on redshift. For the regular or partial Spearman rank coefficient, the corresponding null hypothesis is given to its right. This table is adapted from Table 2 in Ref. 12.

Sample	Parameters x-axis	Parameters y-axis	Spearman Rank	Null Hypothesis	Partial Spearman Rank	Null Hypothesis	Best fit linear regression Slope	Best fit linear regression Constant	Number in Sample
Short	log $L_{X,200s}$	$\alpha_{X,>200s}$	-0.07	> 0.10	0.11	> 0.10	$0.16^{+0.10}_{-0.39}$	$-3.40^{+11.16}_{-2.77}$	9
Long	log $L_{X,200s}$	$\alpha_{X,>200s}$	0.59	$\ll 10^{-6}$	0.59	$\ll 10^{-6}$	$0.27^{+0.04}_{-0.04}$	$-6.99^{+1.23}_{-1.10}$	237
Flares	log $L_{X,200s}$	$\alpha_{X,>200s}$	0.58	$\ll 10^{-6}$	0.56	$\ll 10^{-6}$	$0.30^{+0.07}_{-0.06}$	$-7.91^{+1.84}_{-2.17}$	134
No Flares	log $L_{X,200s}$	$\alpha_{X,>200s}$	0.59	$\ll 10^{-6}$	0.64	$\ll 10^{-6}$	$0.28^{+0.03}_{-0.04}$	$-7.27^{+1.28}_{-1.01}$	103
Plateau	log $L_{X,200s}$	$\alpha_{X,>200s}$	0.58	$\ll 10^{-6}$	0.55	$\ll 10^{-6}$	$0.26^{+0.05}_{-0.06}$	$-6.81^{+1.84}_{-1.43}$	156
No Plateau	log $L_{X,200s}$	$\alpha_{X,>200s}$	0.57	$\ll 10^{-6}$	0.61	$\ll 10^{-6}$	$0.26^{+0.06}_{-0.05}$	$-6.82^{+1.60}_{-1.83}$	81
Final	log $L_{X,200s}$	$\alpha_{X,>200s}$	0.59	$\ll 10^{-6}$	0.59	$\ll 10^{-6}$	$0.27^{+0.04}_{-0.04}$	$-6.99^{+1.23}_{-1.11}$	237

3.2. *Prompt emission and afterglow parameter comparison*

We now compare the parameters of the optical/UV and X-ray log $L_{200s} - \alpha_{>200s}$ correlations using the 48 GRBs that overlap both samples. The results are given in Table 2. Using the same GRBs for the optical and X-ray log $L_{200s} - \alpha_{>200s}$ correlation we find the slopes of the linear regressions are consistent at 1σ. When swapping the X-ray and optical/UV luminosity and decay parameters, i.e log $L_{O,200s}$ versus $\alpha_{X,>200s}$ and log $L_{X,200s}$ versus $\alpha_{O,>200s}$ we find similar strength relationships. Strong correlations are also observed when correlating log $L_{O,200s}$ vs log $L_{X,200s}$ and $\alpha_{O,>200s}$ vs $\alpha_{X,>200s}$.

In Table 2 we also provide the results of the comparison of the parameters of the optical/UV and X-ray luminosity-decay correlations with the prompt emission parameters: log E_{iso} and E_{peak}. Comparison of the optical/UV and X-ray luminosity with log E_{iso} indicates strong correlations and the slope of the linear regressions are consistent to within 1σ. We also provide the results of the comparison of log E_{iso}

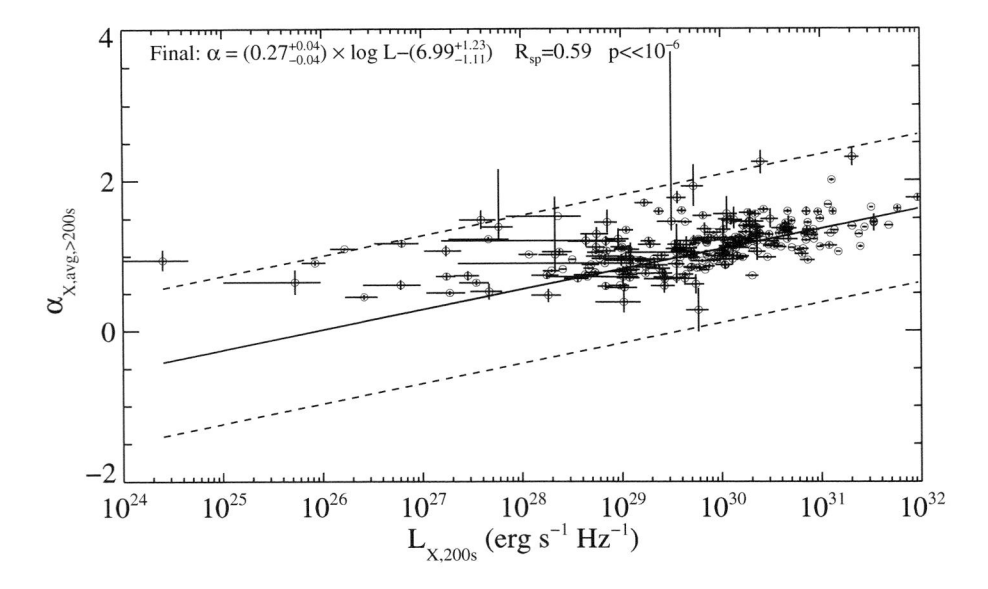

Fig. 1. Final average decay - luminosity correlation using the sample that includes flare correction and those only of long duration, with corrections and sub-sample optimisation described in §3. The solid line indicates the best fit regression, and the dashed lines indicates the 2σ deviation. This figure is reproduced from Fig. 9 of Ref. 12.

Table 2. For each pair of parameters examined, this table contains: the Spearman rank correlation coefficient with its associated null hypothesis; the coefficient of the partial Spearman rank with its associated null hypothesis; the slope and constant values provided by the best fit linear regression. We also provide the 1σ error of the Spearman rank coefficient. Table is a reproduction of Table 2 from Ref. 13.

Parameters		Spearman Rank	Null	Partial	Null	—Best fit linear regression—	
x-axis	y-axis	Coefficient	Hypothesis	Spearman Rank	Hypothesis	Slope	Constant
$\log L_{O,200s}$	$\log L_{X,200s}$	0.81 (0.05)	5.26×10^{-12}	0.70	2.85×10^{-8}	0.91 ± 0.22	1.04 ± 6.94
$\alpha_{O,>200s}$	$\alpha_{X,>200s}$	0.77 (0.07)	1.10×10^{-10}	0.75	1.27×10^{-9}	0.97 ± 0.10	0.25 ± 0.09
$\log L_{O,200s}$	$\alpha_{O,>200s}$	0.58 (0.11)	1.90×10^{-5}	0.50	2.85×10^{-4}	0.28 ± 0.04	-7.72 ± 1.31
$\log L_{X,200s}$	$\alpha_{X,>200s}$	0.69 (0.09)	8.03×10^{-8}	0.63	1.58×10^{-6}	0.26 ± 0.05	-6.71 ± 1.39
$\log L_{O,200s}$	$\alpha_{X,>200s}$	0.60 (0.12)	6.87×10^{-6}	0.52	1.53×10^{-4}	0.29 ± 0.03	-8.13 ± 1.08
$\log L_{X,200s}$	$\alpha_{O,>200s}$	0.65 (0.10)	5.58×10^{-7}	0.60	7.58×10^{-6}	0.32 ± 0.06	-8.70 ± 1.68
$\log E_{iso}$	$\alpha_{O,>200s}$	0.54 (0.12)	9.05×10^{-5}	0.44	1.96×10^{-3}	0.21 ± 0.05	-10.22 ± 2.57
$\log E_{iso}$	$\alpha_{X,>200s}$	0.57 (0.11)	3.12×10^{-5}	0.47	8.70×10^{-4}	0.21 ± 0.04	-9.60 ± 2.16
$\log E_{iso}$	$\log L_{O,200s}$	0.76 (0.06)	4.51×10^{-10}	0.66	4.59×10^{-7}	1.09 ± 0.13	-25.27 ± 6.92
$\log E_{iso}$	$\log L_{X,200s}$	0.83 (0.05)	5.04×10^{-13}	0.76	4.78×10^{-10}	1.10 ± 0.15	-27.81 ± 7.89
$\log E_{peak}$	$\alpha_{O,>200s}$	0.45 (0.13)	2.05×10^{-3}	0.38	1.20×10^{-2}	0.48 ± 0.17	-0.22 ± 0.41
$\log E_{peak}$	$\alpha_{X,>200s}$	0.48 (0.13)	9.22×10^{-4}	0.40	7.52×10^{-3}	0.48 ± 0.15	0.03 ± 0.36
$\log E_{peak}$	$\log L_{O \times 200s}$	0.66 (0.11)	1.16×10^{-6}	0.58	3.51×10^{-5}	2.97 ± 0.76	24.53 ± 1.95
$\log E_{peak}$	$\log L_{X,200s}$	0.75 (0.10)	4.74×10^{-9}	0.70	1.38×10^{-7}	2.97 ± 0.67	22.50 ± 1.73

with $\alpha_{O,>200s}$ and $\alpha_{X,>200s}$. The Spearman rank coefficients are smaller than those found between luminosity and $\log E_{iso}$, but do still indicate a correlation. Within 1σ the slopes of the linear regression for both the optical/UV and X-ray $\alpha_{>200s}$ versus $\log E_{iso}$ are consistent with each other. Similar results can are also found for the four optical/UV and X-ray parameters versus E_{peak}, see Table 2. However, the relationships involving E_{peak} are weaker in comparison to the relationships observed with log E_{iso}; consistent with that found by Ref. 6.

4. Discussion

The log $L_{200s} - \alpha_{>200s}$ correlation, observed in the optical/UV and X-ray light curves, suggests that the brightest afterglows decay more quickly than the fainter afterglows. This points towards a common underlying mechanism producing the afterglow emission in the X-ray and optical/UV afterglows. We can therefore generally exclude models that invoke different emission mechanisms that would result in the log $L_{200s} - \alpha_{>200s}$ correlation being observed in only one frequency band.

Pre-*Swift* observations of late time X-ray afterglows also seemed to suggest the brightest X-ray afterglows decay more quickly than fainter afterglows,[22–24] but a larger sample including some of the first *Swift* X-ray light curves[25] was not able to support previous claims (see also Ref. 12). In this analysis, the correlation between luminosity and temporal behaviour is investigated at a much earlier time, when there is greater spread in the luminosity distribution, and the average decay index is determined using almost the entire observed afterglow.

We also have shown that the X-ray and optical/UV log L_{200s} are correlated with log E_{iso} and E_{peak}. This is consistent with previous studies (e.g. Refs. 23, 26–28), in particular Refs. 6 and 29, who performed a similar study using early X-ray luminosity, 5−10 minutes after trigger. We have also shown that the optical/UV and X-ray $\alpha_{>200s}$ are correlated with log E_{iso} and E_{peak}. Altogether, these correlations indicate that the GRBs with the brightest, fastest, decaying afterglows also have the largest observed prompt emission energies and typically larger peak spectral energy.

We now investigate if these observations are consistent with the predictions of a basic standard afterglow model; an isotropic outflow with no reverse shock or energy injection. The standard afterglow model predicts different relationships between L, α and other parameters depending on the location and ordering of the synchrotron spectral frequencies relative to the observing bands. Therefore to obtain the expected relationships between various parameters for a sample of GRBs we performed a Monte Carlo simulation. Using 10^4 trials, we simulated the optical/UV (at 1600 Å) and X-ray (at 1 keV) flux densities for 48 GRBs using equation 8 of Ref. 30 and equations 4, 5 and 6 given in Ref. 31 for $F_{\nu,max}$, ν_m and ν_c. In this simulation we assume that all GRBs are produced in a constant density medium. To compute $F_{\nu,max}$, ν_m and ν_c we needed to determine values for the microphysical parameters. These were selected at random from log-normal distributions which had 3σ intervals ranging between: 0.01-0.3 for the fraction of energy given to the electrons, ϵ_e; $5 \times 10^{-4} - 0.5$ for the fraction of energy given to the magnetic field, ϵ_B, and $10^{-3} - 10^3 \text{cm}^{-2}$ for the density of the external medium. For the electron energy index p, we centred the distribution at 2.4, as determined by Ref. 32, however, we set the 1σ width to be 0.2 rather than 0.59. Since the closure relations fail for p values < 2, we re-selected p when $p < 2$ was selected. The value of p along with the position of ν_c relative to the observed band and redshift (selected from a uniform distribution with the range 0.5 - 4.5, a similar range as the observed sample) dictate the values of α, β and the k-correction (as given in Ref. 33).

For the 48 GRBs in each trial, we selected a prompt emission energy from a log-normal distribution with a 3σ range $10^{51} - 10^{54}$ erg; a range similar to that of the GRBs in this sample. We picked a random value between 10% and 99% for the efficiency, which we used to convert the prompt emission energy into kinetic energy. Once all the microphysical parameters, redshift and kinetic energy had been selected, we were then able to determine the position of ν_c and thus knew where it was in relation to ν_O and ν_X. With this information, we then calculated the value of the optical/UV and X-ray fluxes and converted these to luminosity. As a byproduct of calculating the optical/UV and X-ray luminosities, we also have simulated distributions for E_{iso} and α. Therefore we also produce predictions for comparisons that involve these parameters. For the parameters of 48 GRBs in each trial, we performed linear regression using the IDL routine *sixlin*, and we also calculated the Spearman rank coefficient. The results of the simulation can be found in Table 3.

Table 3. The Spearman rank coefficient and linear regression parameters as predicted by the synchrotron model for a sample of 48 GRBs. These values were computed with a Monte Carlo simulation with 10^4 trials. Table is a reproduction of Table 1 from Ref. 13.

Parameters		Simulated Spearman	—Best fit linear regression for simulation—	
x-axis	y-axis	Rank Coefficient	Slope	Constant
$\log L_{O,200s}$	$\log L_{X,200s}$	0.92 ± 0.0	0.82 ± 0.0	3.76 ± 1.25
$\alpha_{O,>200s}$	$\alpha_{X,>200s}$	0.74 ± 0.0	1.10 ± 0.1	0.04 ± 0.17
$\log L_{O,200s}$	$\alpha_{O,>200s}$	0.30 ± 0.14	0.04 ± 0.02	-0.31 ± 0.65
$\log L_{X,200s}$	$\alpha_{X,>200s}$	0.20 ± 0.14	0.04 ± 0.03	0.10 ± 0.78
$\log E_{iso}$	$\alpha_{O,>200s}$	0.06 ± 0.15	0.03 ± 0.06	-0.32 ± 2.91
$\log E_{iso}$	$\alpha_{X,>200s}$	0.09 ± 0.15	0.04 ± 0.06	-0.76 ± 3.13
$\log E_{iso}$	$\log L_{O,200s}$	0.51 ± 0.11	4.43 ± 1.03	-200.76 ± 54.10
$\log E_{iso}$	$\log L_{X,200s}$	0.54 ± 0.11	3.28 ± 0.71	-142.22 ± 37.33

In the basic standard afterglow model, the optical/UV and X-ray emission is produced by the same mechanism in an isotropic outflow, we would therefore expect to see relationships between $\log L_{O,200s}$ & $\log L_{X,200s}$ and $\alpha_{O,>200s}$ versus $\alpha_{X,>200s}$. Our observed relationships between these parameters can therefore be explained easily by the standard afterglow model and are fully consistent with the simulations. A relationship between $\log E_{iso}$ and $\log L_{200s}$ is also expected in the standard afterglow model, but the comparison of our observed relationship to the simulations suggests that the observed linear regression slope is less steep than predicted by the simulation. Furthermore, the relationships we observe, between $\log L_{200s}$ and $\alpha_{>200s}$, and log E_{iso} and $\alpha_{>200s}$, are not expected in the standard afterglow model and are not predicted by the simulations.

Since the standard afterglow does not succeed in fully predicting all of our observed correlations, it is likely that a more complex outflow model is required. This conclusion is similar to that drawn during the separate investigation of the optical/UV log $L_{200s} - \alpha_{>200s}$ decay correlation.[11]

4.1. *Alternative Models*

There are three main possibilities that could make the outflow complex enough to be able to reproduce the observed correlations. The first is that perhaps there is some mechanism or parameter that controls the amount of energy given to and distributed during the prompt and afterglow phases and that also regulates the afterglow decay rate. This should occur in such a way that for events with the largest gamma-ray isotropic energy, the energy given to the afterglow is released quickly, resulting in an initially bright afterglow which decays rapidly. Conversely, if the gamma-ray isotropic energy is smaller, then the afterglow energy is released slowly over a longer period, the afterglow will be less bright initially and decay at a slower rate.

The second possibility is that the correlations could be a geometric effect, perhaps the result of the observer's viewing angle. Jets viewed away from the jet-axis may have fainter afterglows that decay less quickly in comparison to afterglows

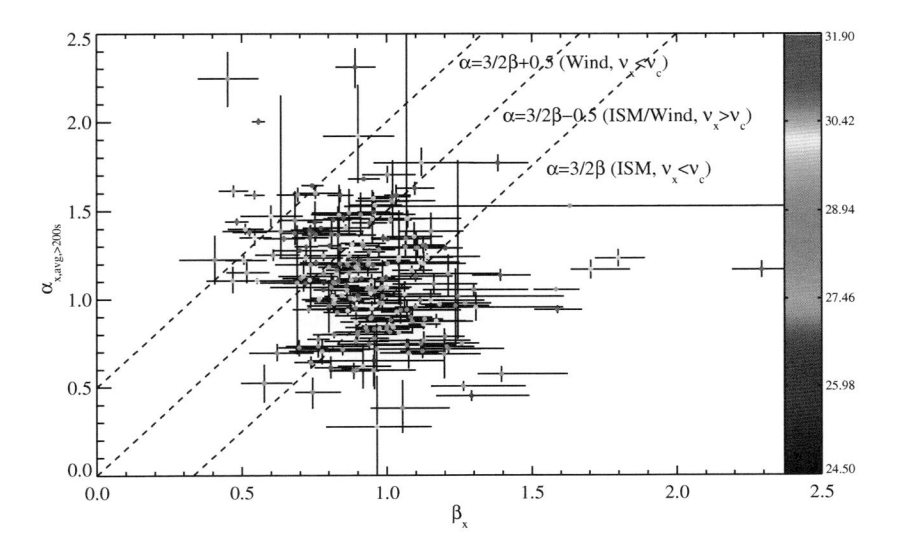

Fig. 2. The average temporal decay ($\alpha_{X,>200s}$) and average spectral energy index (β_X) are compared with log $L_{X,200s}$ (colour scale), demonstrating consistency and trends with the closure relations (dashed lines). The high luminosity (redder) points are roughly consistent with wind-like environments. This figure is reproduced from Fig. 15 of Ref. 12.

viewed closer to the centre of the jet (see Fig 3. of Ref. 4). Similarly, this will also affect the observed prompt emission, with jets viewed off-axis appearing to have lower isotropic energy and lower peak spectral energy.[34]

The third possibility could be related to the circumburst environment. The closure relations relate α and the spectral index β through different relationships depending on the ordering of the synchrotron spectral parameters and the density profile or the external medium. If the correlation is affected by the circumburst environment, we expect to see GRBs with the highest luminosities favouring a particular environment. No apparent correlation is observed in the optical/UV.[11] However in the X-ray (see Figure 2), the highest luminosity GRBs tend toward the lines demarcating the r^{-2} wind environment. The ambiguity in the $\nu_x > \nu_c$ cases prohibits us from making a strong statement on the role of circumburst environment, but it may be another possible contribution in that the initially brightest GRB afterglows may be more likely to live in wind-like environments (see also Ref. 35).

5. Conclusions

This proceeding has summarised the work presented in Refs. 12 and 13. We have shown that the correlation between luminosity (measured at restframe 200 s; log L_{200s}) and average decay rate (measured from 200 s; $\alpha_{>200s}$) is observed in the X-ray light curve sample as well as the optical/UV.[11] When we rerun the correlations with the GRBs that overlap the optical/UV and X-ray samples we find the luminosity-decay correlations are consistent. This suggests a single underlying mechanism producing the correlations in both bands and it is not dependent on their detailed temporal behaviour. We also show significant correlations between the logarithmic optical/UV and X-ray luminosity (log $L_{O,200s}$, log $L_{X,200s}$) and the optical/UV and X-ray decay indices ($\alpha_{O,>200s}$ and $\alpha_{X,>200s}$) and all four of these parameters are found to be correlated with the prompt emission parameters: isotropic energy (E_{iso}) and restframe peak spectral energy (E_{peak}). Together these correlations imply that the GRBs with the brightest afterglows in the X-ray and optical/UV bands, decay the fastest and they also have the largest observed prompt emission energies and typically larger peak spectral energy. This suggests that what happens during the prompt phase has direct implications on the afterglow.

We used a Monte Carlo simulation to examine whether the standard afterglow model is able to explain the observed correlations. Overall, observed correlations between the luminosities in both the X-ray and optical/UV bands and between the luminosities and the isotropic energy are consistent with the predictions of the simulation. However, observed relationships involving the average decay indices with either luminosity at 200 s or the isotropic γ-ray energy are not consistent with the simulation. We therefore suggest that a more complex afterglow or outflow model is required to produce all the observed correlations. This may be due to either a viewing angle effect or by some mechanism or physical property controlling the energy release within the outflow. The environment in which the GRB exploded may also contribute to the observed correlation.

Acknowledgements

This research has made use of data obtained from the High Energy Astrophysics Science Archive Research Center (HEASARC) and the UK Swift Science Data Centre provided by NASA's Goddard Space Flight Center and the University of Leicester, UK, respectively. MJP, AAB, NPMK and PJS acknowledge the support of the UK Space Agency.

References

1. L. Amati, F. Frontera, M. Tavani, J. J. M. in't Zand, A. Antonelli, E. Costa, M. Feroci, C. Guidorzi, J. Heise, N. Masetti, E. Montanari, L. Nicastro, E. Palazzi, E. Pian, L. Piro and P. Soffitta, Intrinsic spectra and energetics of BeppoSAX Gamma-Ray Bursts with known redshifts, *Astron. Astrophys.* **390**, 81 (July 2002).
2. G. Ghirlanda, G. Ghisellini and D. Lazzati, The Collimation-corrected Gamma-Ray Burst Energies Correlate with the Peak Energy of Their νF_ν Spectrum, *Astrophys. J.* **616**, 331 (November 2004).
3. M. G. Dainotti, V. F. Cardone and S. Capozziello, A time-luminosity correlation for γ-ray bursts in the X-rays, *Mon. Not. R. Astr. Soc.* **391**, L79 (November 2008).
4. A. Panaitescu and W. T. Vestrand, Taxonomy of gamma-ray burst optical light curves: Identification of a salient class of early afterglows, *Mon. Not. R. Astr. Soc.* **387**, 497 (June 2008).
5. M. G. Bernardini, R. Margutti, J. Mao, E. Zaninoni and G. Chincarini, The X-ray light curve of gamma-ray bursts: Clues to the central engine, *Astron. Astrophys.* **539**, p. A3 (March 2012).
6. P. D'Avanzo, R. Salvaterra, B. Sbarufatti, L. Nava, A. Melandri, M. G. Bernardini, S. Campana, S. Covino, D. Fugazza, G. Ghirlanda, G. Ghisellini, V. La Parola, M. Perri, S. D. Vergani and G. Tagliaferri, A complete sample of bright Swift Gamma-ray bursts: X-ray afterglow luminosity and its correlation with the prompt emission, *Mon. Not. R. Astr. Soc.* **425**, 506 (September 2012).
7. L. Li, E.-W. Liang, Q.-W. Tang, J.-M. Chen, S.-Q. Xi, H.-J. Lü, H. Gao, B. Zhang, J. Zhang, S.-X. Yi, R.-J. Lu, L.-Z. Lü and J.-Y. Wei, A Comprehensive Study of Gamma-Ray Burst Optical Emission. I. Flares and Early Shallow-decay Component, *Astrophys. J.* **758**, p. 27 (October 2012).
8. E.-W. Liang, L. Li, H. Gao, B. Zhang, Y.-F. Liang, X.-F. Wu, S.-X. Yi, Z.-G. Dai, Q.-W. Tang, J.-M. Chen, H.-J. Lü, J. Zhang, R.-J. Lu, L.-Z. Lü and J.-Y. Wei, A Comprehensive Study of Gamma-Ray Burst Optical Emission. II. Afterglow Onset and Late Re-brightening Components, *Astrophys. J.* **774**, p. 13 (September 2013).
9. E. Zaninoni, M. G. Bernardini, R. Margutti, S. Oates and G. Chincarini, Gamma-ray burst optical light-curve zoo: Comparison with X-ray observations, *Astron. Astrophys.* **557**, p. A12 (September 2013).
10. A. Panaitescu, W. T. Vestrand and P. Woźniak, Peaks of optical and X-ray afterglow light curves, *Mon. Not. R. Astr. Soc.* **433**, 759 (July 2013).
11. S. R. Oates, M. J. Page, M. De Pasquale, P. Schady, A. A. Breeveld, S. T. Holland, N. P. M. Kuin and F. E. Marshall, A correlation between the intrinsic brightness and

average decay rate of Swift/UVOT gamma-ray burst optical/ultraviolet light curves, *Mon. Not. R. Astr. Soc.* **426**, L86 (October 2012).
12. J. L. Racusin, S. R. Oates, M. de Pasquale and D. Kocevski, A Correlation between the Intrinsic Brightness and Average Decay Rate of Gamma-Ray Burst X-Ray Afterglow Light Curves, *Astrophys. J.* **826**, p. 45 (July 2016).
13. S. R. Oates, J. L. Racusin, M. De Pasquale, M. J. Page, A. J. Castro-Tirado, J. Gorosabel, P. J. Smith, A. A. Breeveld and N. P. M. Kuin, Exploring the canonical behaviour of long gamma-ray bursts using an intrinsic multiwavelength afterglow correlation, *Mon. Not. R. Astr. Soc.* **453**, 4121 (November 2015).
14. D. N. Burrows, J. E. Hill, J. A. Nousek, J. A. Kennea, A. Wells, J. P. Osborne, A. F. Abbey, A. Beardmore, K. Mukerjee, A. D. T. Short, G. Chincarini, S. Campana, O. Citterio, A. Moretti, C. Pagani, G. Tagliaferri, P. Giommi, M. Capalbi, F. Tamburelli, L. Angelini, G. Cusumano, H. W. Bräuninger, W. Burkert and G. D. Hartner, The Swift X-Ray Telescope, *Space Science Reviews* **120**, 165 (October 2005).
15. P. A. Evans, A. P. Beardmore, K. L. Page, L. G. Tyler, J. P. Osborne, M. R. Goad, P. T. O'Brien, L. Vetere, J. Racusin, D. Morris, D. N. Burrows, M. Capalbi, M. Perri, N. Gehrels and P. Romano, An online repository of Swift/XRT light curves of γ-ray bursts, *Astron. Astrophys.* **469**, 379 (July 2007).
16. P. A. Evans, A. P. Beardmore, K. L. Page, J. P. Osborne, P. T. O'Brien, R. Willingale, R. L. C. Starling, D. N. Burrows, O. Godet, L. Vetere, J. Racusin, M. R. Goad, K. Wiersema, L. Angelini, M. Capalbi, G. Chincarini, N. Gehrels, J. A. Kennea, R. Margutti, D. C. Morris, C. J. Mountford, C. Pagani, M. Perri, P. Romano and N. Tanvir, Methods and results of an automatic analysis of a complete sample of Swift-XRT observations of GRBs, *Mon. Not. R. Astr. Soc.* **397**, 1177 (August 2009).
17. J. L. Racusin, E. W. Liang, D. N. Burrows, A. Falcone, T. Sakamoto, B. B. Zhang, B. Zhang, P. Evans and J. Osborne, Jet Breaks and Energetics of Swift Gamma-Ray Burst X-Ray Afterglows, *Astrophys. J.* **698**, 43 (June 2009).
18. B. Zhang, Y. Z. Fan, J. Dyks, S. Kobayashi, P. Mészáros, D. N. Burrows, J. A. Nousek and N. Gehrels, Physical Processes Shaping Gamma-Ray Burst X-Ray Afterglow Light Curves: Theoretical Implications from the Swift X-Ray Telescope Observations, *Astrophys. J.* **642**, 354 (May 2006).
19. D. Grupe, C. Gronwall, X. Wang, P. W. A. Roming, J. Cummings, B. Zhang, P. Mészáros, M. D. Trigo, P. T. O'Brien, K. L. Page, A. Beardmore, O. Godet, D. E. vanden Berk, P. J. Brown, S. Koch, D. Morris, M. Stroh, D. N. Burrows, J. A. Nousek, M. McMath Chester, S. Immler, V. Mangano, P. Romano, G. Chincarini, J. Osborne, T. Sakamoto and N. Gehrels, Swift and XMM-Newton Observations of the Extraordinary Gamma-Ray Burst 060729: More than 125 Days of X-Ray Afterglow, *Astrophys. J.* **662**, 443 (June 2007).
20. M. G. Dainotti, R. Willingale, S. Capozziello, V. Fabrizio Cardone and M. Ostrowski, Discovery of a Tight Correlation for Gamma-ray Burst Afterglows with "Canonical" Light Curves, *Astrophys. J. Letters* **722**, L215 (October 2010).
21. M. G. Dainotti, V. Petrosian, J. Singal and M. Ostrowski, Determination of the Intrinsic Luminosity Time Correlation in the X-Ray Afterglows of Gamma-Ray Bursts, *Astrophys. J.* **774**, p. 157 (September 2013).
22. M. Boër and B. Gendre, Evidences for two Gamma-Ray Burst afterglow emission regimes, *Astron. Astrophys.* **361**, L21 (September 2000).
23. C. Kouveliotou, S. E. Woosley, S. K. Patel, A. Levan, R. Blandford, E. Ramirez-Ruiz, R. A. M. J. Wijers, M. C. Weisskopf, A. Tennant, E. Pian and P. Giommi, Chandra Observations of the X-Ray Environs of SN 1998bw/GRB 980425, *Astrophys. J.* **608**, 872 (June 2004).

24. B. Gendre and M. Boër, Decay properties of the X-ray afterglows of gamma-ray bursts, *Astron. Astrophys.* **430**, 465 (February 2005).
25. B. Gendre, A. Galli and M. Boër, X-Ray Afterglow Light Curves: Toward A Standard Candle?, *Astrophys. J.* **683**, 620 (August 2008).
26. M. De Pasquale, L. Piro, B. Gendre, L. Amati, L. A. Antonelli, E. Costa, M. Feroci, F. Frontera, L. Nicastro, P. Soffitta and J. in't Zand, The BeppoSAX catalog of GRB X-ray afterglow observations, *Astron. Astrophys.* **455**, 813 (September 2006).
27. M. Nysewander, A. S. Fruchter and A. Pe'er, A Comparison of the Afterglows of Short- and Long-duration Gamma-ray Bursts, *Astrophys. J.* **701**, 824 (August 2009).
28. D. A. Kann, S. Klose, B. Zhang, D. Malesani, E. Nakar, A. Pozanenko, A. C. Wilson, N. R. Butler, P. Jakobsson, S. Schulze, M. Andreev, L. A. Antonelli, I. F. Bikmaev, V. Biryukov, M. Böttcher, R. A. Burenin, J. M. Castro Cerón, A. J. Castro-Tirado, G. Chincarini, B. E. Cobb, S. Covino, P. D'Avanzo, V. D'Elia, M. Della Valle, A. de Ugarte Postigo, Y. Efimov, P. Ferrero, D. Fugazza, J. P. U. Fynbo, M. Gålfalk, F. Grundahl, J. Gorosabel, S. Gupta, S. Guziy, B. Hafizov, J. Hjorth, K. Holhjem, M. Ibrahimov, M. Im, G. L. Israel, M. Jelínek, B. L. Jensen, R. Karimov, I. M. Khamitov, Ü. Kiziloğlu, E. Klunko, P. Kubánek, A. S. Kutyrev, P. Laursen, A. J. Levan, F. Mannucci, C. M. Martin, A. Mescheryakov, N. Mirabal, J. P. Norris, J.-E. Ovaldsen, D. Paraficz, E. Pavlenko, S. Piranomonte, A. Rossi, V. Rumyantsev, R. Salinas, A. Sergeev, D. Sharapov, J. Sollerman, B. Stecklum, L. Stella, G. Tagliaferri, N. R. Tanvir, J. Telting, V. Testa, A. C. Updike, A. Volnova, D. Watson, K. Wiersema and D. Xu, The Afterglows of Swift-era Gamma-ray Bursts. I. Comparing pre-Swift and Swift-era Long/Soft (Type II) GRB Optical Afterglows, *Astrophys. J.* **720**, 1513 (September 2010).
29. R. Margutti, E. Zaninoni, M. G. Bernardini, G. Chincarini, F. Pasotti, C. Guidorzi, L. Angelini, D. N. Burrows, M. Capalbi, P. A. Evans, N. Gehrels, J. Kennea, V. Mangano, A. Moretti, J. Nousek, J. P. Osborne, K. L. Page, M. Perri, J. Racusin, P. Romano, B. Sbarufatti, S. Stafford and M. Stamatikos, The prompt-afterglow connection in gamma-ray bursts: a comprehensive statistical analysis of Swift X-ray light curves, *Mon. Not. R. Astr. Soc.* **428**, 729 (January 2013).
30. R. Sari, T. Piran and R. Narayan, Spectra and Light Curves of Gamma-Ray Burst Afterglows, *Astrophys. J. Letters* **497**, L17 (April 1998).
31. B. Zhang, E. Liang, K. L. Page, D. Grupe, B.-B. Zhang, S. D. Barthelmy, D. N. Burrows, S. Campana, G. Chincarini, N. Gehrels, S. Kobayashi, P. Mészáros, A. Moretti, J. A. Nousek, P. T. O'Brien, J. P. Osborne, P. W. A. Roming, T. Sakamoto, P. Schady and R. Willingale, GRB Radiative Efficiencies Derived from the Swift Data: GRBs versus XRFs, Long versus Short, *Astrophys. J.* **655**, 989 (February 2007).
32. P. A. Curran, R. L. C. Starling, A. J. van der Horst and R. A. M. J. Wijers, Testing the blast wave model with Swift GRBs, *Mon. Not. R. Astr. Soc.* **395**, 580 (May 2009).
33. E. Berger, S. R. Kulkarni and D. A. Frail, A Standard Kinetic Energy Reservoir in Gamma-Ray Burst Afterglows, *Astrophys. J.* **590**, 379 (June 2003).
34. E. Ramirez-Ruiz, J. Granot, C. Kouveliotou, S. E. Woosley, S. K. Patel and P. A. Mazzali, An Off-Axis Model of GRB 031203, *Astrophys. J. Letters* **625**, L91 (June 2005).
35. M. De Pasquale, S. Schulze, D. A. Kann, S. Oates and B. Zhang, Physical properties of rapidly decaying Afterglows, in *EAS Publications Series*, eds. A. J. Castro-Tirado, J. Gorosabel and I. H. Park, EAS Publications Series, Vol. 61, July 2013.

Kilonova emission observed so far: A comparison with AT2017gfo

A. Rossi

INAF - Osservatorio di Astrofisica e Scienza dello Spazio, via Piero Gobetti 93/3, 40129 Bologna, Italy
E-mail: andrea.rossi@inaf.it

AT2017gfo is the first kilonova (KN) that could be extensively monitored in time both photometrically and spectroscopically. Moreover, it is the first optical counterpart of a gravitational wave source and it is associated with the short gamma-ray burst GRB 170817A. Here I present our search for the fingerprints of AT2017gfo-like kilonova emissions in the optical/NIR light curves of 39 short GRBs with known redshift. Afterwards, I show how, for the first time, our results allow us to study separately the range of luminosity of the blue and red components of AT2017gfo-like kilonovae in short GRBs. With these results at hand, I show up to which redshift a KN can be followed up by some of the current and future observatories.

Keywords: Kilonovae; Gamma-ray bursts; Neutron stars

1. Introduction

For a long time only indirect evidence associated short Gamma-ray bursts (GRBs) to the merging of compact objects, but the simultaneous detection of the gravitational wave (GW) source GW170817[1] by aLIGO/AdVirgo[2,3] and the short Gamma-ray burst GRB 170817A[4–6] has provided the first direct evidence that at least a fraction of short GRBs is associated with the merging of two neutron stars (NSs). At the same time, the discovery of AT2017gfo, the optical counterpart of GW170817,[7] allowed us, for the first time, to follow-up spectroscopically the elusive astrophysical phenomena known as "kilonova",[8,9] i.e. a thermal emission powered by the radioactive decay of elements formed via r-process nucleosynthesis in the ejecta of the NS-NS merger e.g.,[10,11]. In particular, the observations are consistent with a kilonova characterised by a blue, rapidly decaying, component and a red, more slowly evolving one. Therefore, one can distinguish between the *blue* and *red* components, depending on whether the rest-frame effective wavelength is brighter in the optical or in the NIR, respectively.

In the following, we aim to further investigate the possible range of kilonova luminosity and identify possible new kilonova candidates, comparing the optical/NIR light curves of all short GRBs (sGRBs) with known redshift up to June 2019 with those of AT2017gfo.

2. Kilonovae known to date

Although AT2017gfo is the most outstanding and clear demonstration of the existence of kilonovae, the majority of the known kilonovae are associated to sGRBs, although often the association is not very strong. Among those, the most clear evidence was found in the optical counterparts of 6 sGRBs: 050709A,[12] 060614A,[13,14] 080503,[15,16] 130603B,[17,18] 150101B,[19] 160821B,[20–23] and 070809.[24] In addition to those, there are the magnetar-powered kilonovae identified by Gao *et al.*[16] (GRBs 050724, 070714B). Unfortunately, in the case of GRB 080503 the redshift could not be measured either via spectroscopy of the afterglow or of the host galaxy; in the case of GRB 070809 the redshift is not well defined. Recently, a new KN candidate has been found associated to GRB 200222A, although this claim is not secure.[25,26] Therefore, we define a golden sample that includes all 7 GRBs with kilonova candidates claimed in the literature that have accurate redshift.

Note that the evidence of kilonova in GRBs 050724 070714B has been found by modelling the X-rays and optical light curves with magnetar-powered KN model. These magnetar KN (MKN) are expected to be more luminous, have longer duration but also bluer than the the classical KN. It should also be noted that in all these possible kilonova identifications (but GRB 150101B), the emission was preceded by a bright GRB afterglow indicating an on-axis configuration, thus suggesting that the kilonova emission may exceed the afterglow luminosity even for on-axis GRBs.

3. Optical/NIR light curves of AT2017gfo and of short GRB afterglows

The sample of short GRBs consists of 39 objects within the redshift range $0.1 \leq z \leq 2.2$.[27] As described in,[27] to have a coverage from UV to NIR bands between ~ 1.5 and ~ 10.5 days after the GW trigger we built 3 early SEDs using photometric observations from the literature[7,28–34] and ten spectra of AT2017gfo[33,35] Data have been corrected for foreground Galactic extinction. In order to compare AT2017gfo with sGRB optical counterparts, we first built a set of rest-frame light curves of AT2017gfo for all the filters in which there are sGRB observations. Afterwards, we compared, in each filter, the optical and NIR luminosities of AT2017gfo with those of the sGRB counterparts in our selected sample.[27] We have distinguished between the *blue* and *red* components, depending on whether the rest-frame effective wavelength is below or above 9000 Å, respectively.

4. Possible new kilonova candidates

A kilonova is expected to show a shallow evolution close to its maximum brightness. Therefore, it can be distinguished from the standard afterglow behaviour, which has a constant power-law decay according to the standard fireball model.[36] In this context we considered a decay to be anomalously shallow when its decaying index is $\alpha < 0.75$; see also.[27] The blue component of GRB 090515 has a shallow decay in the first 24 hours and is just ∼ 2 times fainter than AT2017gfo at the same time. This is also true in the case of GRB 080905A, and thus may be compatible with a kilonova with a luminosity similar to the blue counterpart of GRB 090515. However, the error of the decay index is too large ($\alpha = 0.4 \pm 1.3$) and thus we do not consider this sGRB. We also identify possible shallow decay in the cases of 150423A and 150424A which however can be interpreted otherwise. In particular, the shallow decay of GRB 150423A is too early to be compared with AT2017gfo. A more detailed analysis, which consists in modelling together the optical and X-ray light curves, is needed to further investigate the presence of kilonova emission in all cases.

5. Constraints to the kilonovae luminosity

Considering the blue component spectral band, we observe a wide range in luminosity. In particular, we can exclude the presence of an AT2017gfo-like kilonova in two cases (GRBs 050509B and 061201). Few cases with an anomalous shallow decay, namely GRBs 050724, 060614, 070714B, and 150424A, are more than 10 times brighter than AT2017gfo. Note that in the case of GRBs 150423A and 150424A the optical and X-ray light curves are very similar to those of GRB 050724 and GRB 060614, which optical re-brightening is interpreted as magnetar-powered kilonova emission by.[16] In this case, the additional source of energy would explain why they are all much brighter than AT2017gfo.

On the contrary, all the kilonovae detected in the NIR (GRBs 050709, 130603B, 160821B), are no more than 3 times brighter or fainter than AT2017gfo after 2 days. Intriguingly, there are no NIR upper limits below AT2017gfo luminosity after ∼ 50 hours. In other words, in all cases when observations comparable to AT2017gfo NIR emission exist the kilonova counterpart has been detected. This suggests that all red kilonovae detected so far have similar luminosity, although we are aware that the numbers are not high enough for meaningful statistics.

6. Future perspectives

In Figure 1 I show how the peak luminosity of the blue KN changes with redshift, assuming the luminosity constraints found by[27] and summarized above. It shows that the search and follow-up of the electromagnetic (EM) counterparts will be possible during O4 and O5, like what has been done in the case GW 170817, provided hat the whole sky-map can be covered down to r∼ 21 mag. Facilities like, VST, will be advantaged, but should concentrate on the smaller skymaps of tens of sq. degrees, or the regions of higher probability, to maximize the return and their gain in depth.

The Binary neutron star horizon expected for the 3rd generation of GW interferometers will extend above z=1, with the bulk of events concentrated at $z < 0.5$. Although the increment in distance translates in a huge increment in the number of GW events, including BNS and their EM counterparts, the localization will not

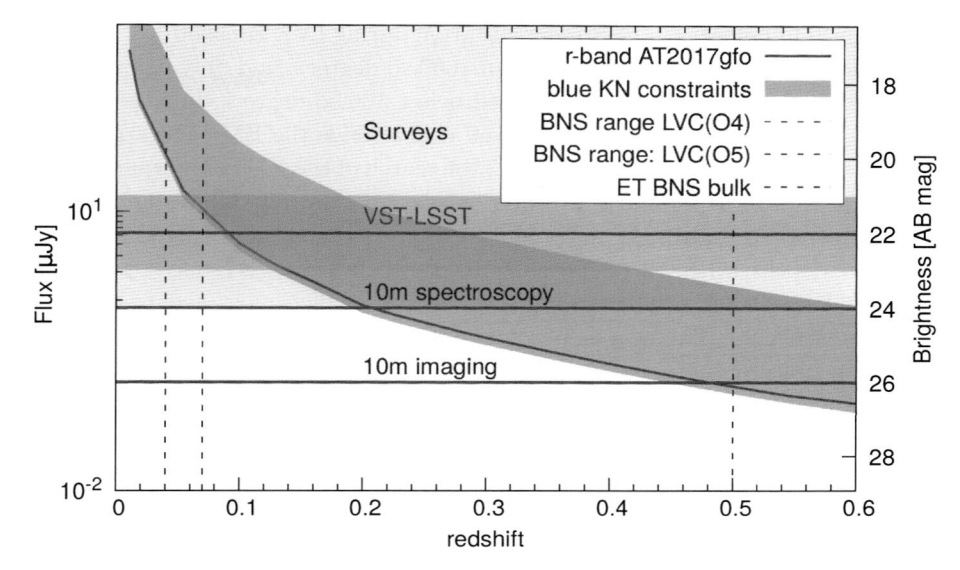

Fig. 1. Peak brightness of AT2017gfo in the r-band at different redshifts, within the constraints we derived for an AT2017gfo-like KN from the golden sample. The vertical line is the aLIGO/AVirgo detection limits for a BNS event during O4, O5 and ET. The last one is limited at $z \lesssim 0.5$ at which ET will be able to detect most of the GW signals from merging BNS. The horizontal lines are different detection limits for different class of telescopes with an exposure time of 10 min.

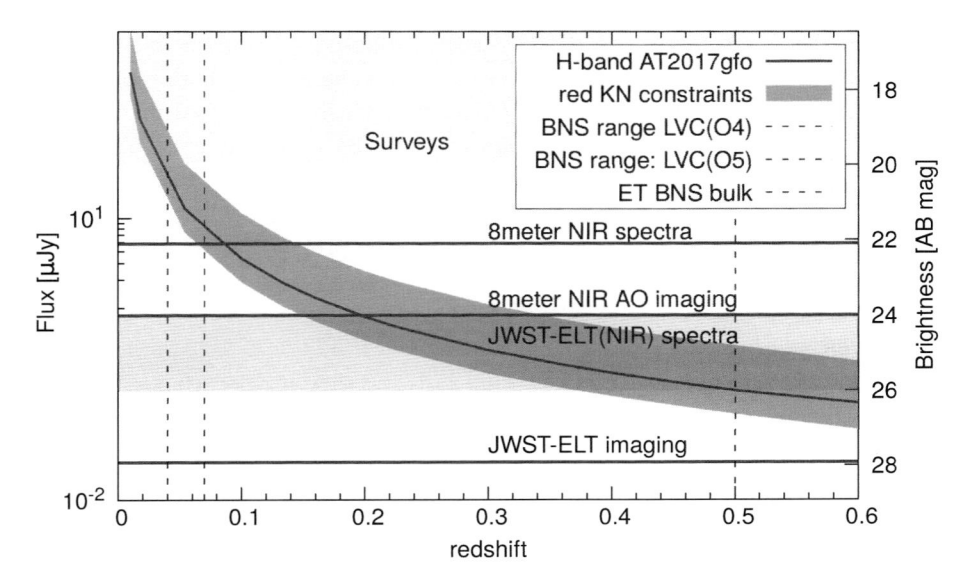

Fig. 2. The same as shown in Figure 1 but in the H-band.

improve much in respect to the present situation during LVK runs: 50% of all events will have localized with error of more than 1000 sq degrees, and only below redshift 0.2 at least 50% of events will be localized below 100 sq degrees. In this situation, what are the chances to find, follow-up and characterize the EM counterparts?

A shown in Figure 1, below redshift 0.2 the search of the EM counterpart can still be succesful thanks to the most advanced surveys if they capabilities and strategy will be adjusted to reach r 21 mags and beyond, perhaps sacrificing sky covergae to optimize depths, when this is possible. In particular, the VST telescope, or even better the Vera Rubin telescope, will be able to localize most events, or at list the brightest events. The search becomes difficult at higher redshifts, with only Vera Rubin able to successfully find the brightest events. On the contrary, once localized, the follow-up and characterization via spectroscopy will not be a problem, as the class of the 10m telescope has enough sensitivity and is well equipped for the follow-up.

More critical is the situation in the NIR, where no many facilities may be able to reach the necessary depth to successfully search and localize the EM counterpart. Still, the characterization will be guaranteed by the class of 8-10m and extremely large telescopes, together with the Nancy Roman space observatory. This situation is even more dramatic dramatic if we think that the blue kilonova is expected only if there is no prompt collapse in a black hole, and therefore the characteristic feature in common to both cases i.e., the red kilonova is the only that is always expected. One solution may be offered by a space observatory capable to detect the gama-ray signal and slew in the direction of the burst to localize its afterglow, like the current *Swift*, the future *SVOM* or the proposed *THESEUS* and *GAMOW* missions. In this case the bright afterglow can be localized up to high redshift. The only limitation is that only on-axis (or close) events will be followed up, being the emission collimated. However, it also means that all the sGRBs at $z < 0.5$ and many at $z < 1$ will be associated to a gravitational wave signal, allowing to measure both distance and redshift, constrain both masses and inclinations with implications n the cosmological studies and equation of state of the progenitor NS.

References

1. B. P. Abbott, R. Abbott, T. D. Abbott, F. Acernese, K. Ackley, C. Adams, T. Adams, P. Addesso, R. X. Adhikari, V. B. Adya and et al., GW170817: Observation of Gravitational Waves from a Binary Neutron Star Inspiral, *Physical Review Letters* **119**, p. 161101 (October 2017).
2. LIGO Scientific Collaboration, J. Aasi, B. P. Abbott, R. Abbott, T. Abbott, M. R. Abernathy, K. Ackley, C. Adams, T. Adams, P. Addesso and et al., Advanced LIGO, *Classical and Quantum Gravity* **32**, p. 074001 (April 2015).
3. F. Acernese, M. Agathos, K. Agatsuma, D. Aisa, N. Allemandou, A. Allocca, J. Amarni, P. Astone, G. Balestri, G. Ballardin and et al., Advanced Virgo: A second-generation interferometric gravitational wave detector, *Classical and Quantum Gravity* **32**, p. 024001 (January 2015).

4. A. Goldstein, P. Veres, E. Burns, M. S. Briggs, R. Hamburg, D. Kocevski, C. A. Wilson-Hodge, R. D. Preece, S. Poolakkil, O. J. Roberts, C. M. Hui, V. Connaughton, J. Racusin, A. von Kienlin, T. Dal Canton, N. Christensen, T. Littenberg, K. Siellez, L. Blackburn, J. Broida, E. Bissaldi, W. H. Cleveland, M. H. Gibby, M. M. Giles, R. M. Kippen, S. McBreen, J. McEnery, C. A. Meegan, W. S. Paciesas and M. Stanbro, An Ordinary Short Gamma-Ray Burst with Extraordinary Implications: Fermi-GBM Detection of GRB 170817A, *Astroph. J.* **848**, p. L14 (October 2017).
5. V. Savchenko, C. Ferrigno, E. Kuulkers, A. Bazzano, E. Bozzo, S. Brandt, J. Chenevez, T. J.-L. Courvoisier, R. Diehl, A. Domingo, L. Hanlon, E. Jourdain, A. von Kienlin, P. Laurent, F. Lebrun, A. Lutovinov, A. Martin-Carrillo, S. Mereghetti, L. Natalucci, J. Rodi, J.-P. Roques, R. Sunyaev and P. Ubertini, INTEGRAL Detection of the First Prompt Gamma-Ray Signal Coincident with the Gravitational-wave Event GW170817, *Astroph. J.* **848**, p. L15 (October 2017).
6. B. P. Abbott, R. Abbott, T. D. Abbott, F. Acernese, K. Ackley, C. Adams, T. Adams, P. Addesso, R. X. Adhikari, V. B. Adya and et al., Gravitational Waves and Gamma-Rays from a Binary Neutron Star Merger: GW170817 and GRB 170817A, *Astroph. J.* **848**, p. L13 (October 2017).
7. D. A. Coulter, R. J. Foley, C. D. Kilpatrick, M. R. Drout, A. L. Piro, B. J. Shappee, M. R. Siebert, J. D. Simon, N. Ulloa, D. Kasen, B. F. Madore, A. Murguia-Berthier, Y.-C. Pan, J. X. Prochaska, E. Ramirez-Ruiz, A. Rest and C. Rojas-Bravo, Swope Supernova Survey 2017a (SSS17a), the optical counterpart to a gravitational wave source, *Science* **358**, 1556 (December 2017).
8. L.-X. Li and B. Paczyński, Transient Events from Neutron Star Mergers, *Astroph. J.* **507**, L59 (November 1998).
9. B. D. Metzger, G. Martínez-Pinedo, S. Darbha, E. Quataert, A. Arcones, D. Kasen, R. Thomas, P. Nugent, I. V. Panov and N. T. Zinner, Electromagnetic counterparts of compact object mergers powered by the radioactive decay of r-process nuclei, *Mon. Not. R. Astron. Soc.* **406**, 2650 (Aug 2010).
10. D. Kasen, B. Metzger, J. Barnes, E. Quataert and E. Ramirez-Ruiz, Origin of the heavy elements in binary neutron-star mergers from a gravitational-wave event, *Nature* **551**, 80 (November 2017).
11. B. D. Metzger, T. A. Thompson and E. Quataert, A Magnetar Origin for the Kilonova Ejecta in GW170817, *Astroph. J.* **856**, p. 101 (April 2018).
12. Z.-P. Jin, K. Hotokezaka, X. Li, M. Tanaka, P. D'Avanzo, Y.-Z. Fan, S. Covino, D.-M. Wei and T. Piran, The Macronova in GRB 050709 and the GRB-macronova connection, *Nature Communications* **7**, p. 12898 (September 2016).
13. B. Yang, Z.-P. Jin, X. Li, S. Covino, X.-Z. Zheng, K. Hotokezaka, Y.-Z. Fan, T. Piran and D.-M. Wei, A possible macronova in the late afterglow of the long-short burst GRB 060614, *Nature Communications* **6**, p. 7323 (June 2015).
14. Z.-P. Jin, X. Li, Z. Cano, S. Covino, Y.-Z. Fan and D.-M. Wei, The Light Curve of the Macronova Associated with the Long-Short Burst GRB 060614, *Astroph. J.* **811**, p. L22 (October 2015).
15. D. A. Perley, B. D. Metzger, J. Granot, N. R. Butler, T. Sakamoto, E. Ramirez-Ruiz, A. J. Levan, J. S. Bloom, A. A. Miller, A. Bunker, H.-W. Chen, A. V. Filippenko, N. Gehrels, K. Glazebrook, P. B. Hall, K. C. Hurley, D. Kocevski, W. Li, S. Lopez, J. Norris, A. L. Piro, D. Poznanski, J. X. Prochaska, E. Quataert and N. Tanvir, GRB 080503: Implications of a Naked Short Gamma-Ray Burst Dominated by Extended Emission, *Astroph. J.* **696**, 1871 (May 2009).
16. H. Gao, B. Zhang, H.-J. Lü and Y. Li, Searching for Magnetar-powered Merger-novae from Short GRBS, *Astroph. J.* **837**, p. 50 (March 2017).

17. N. R. Tanvir, A. J. Levan, A. S. Fruchter, J. Hjorth, R. A. Hounsell, K. Wiersema and R. L. Tunnicliffe, A 'kilonova' associated with the short-duration γ-ray burst GRB 130603B, *Nature* **500**, 547 (August 2013).
18. E. Berger, W. Fong and R. Chornock, An r-process Kilonova Associated with the Short-hard GRB 130603B, *Astroph. J.* **774**, p. L23 (Sep 2013).
19. E. Troja, L. Piro, G. Ryan, H. van Eerten, R. Ricci, M. H. Wieringa, S. Lotti, T. Sakamoto and S. B. Cenko, The outflow structure of GW170817 from late-time broad-band observations, *Mon. Not. R. Astron. Soc.* **478**, L18 (July 2018).
20. Z.-P. Jin, X. Li, H. Wang, Y.-Z. Wang, H.-N. He, Q. Yuan, F.-W. Zhang, Y.-C. Zou, Y.-Z. Fan and D.-M. Wei, Short GRBs: Opening Angles, Local Neutron Star Merger Rate, and Off-axis Events for GRB/GW Association, *Astroph. J.* **857**, p. 128 (April 2018).
21. M. M. Kasliwal, O. Korobkin, R. M. Lau, R. Wollaeger and C. L. Fryer, Infrared Emission from Kilonovae: The Case of the Nearby Short Hard Burst GRB 160821B, *Astroph. J.* **843**, p. L34 (July 2017).
22. E. Troja, A. J. Castro-Tirado, J. Becerra González, Y. Hu, G. S. Ryan, S. B. Cenko, R. Ricci, G. Novara, R. Sánchez-Rámirez, J. A. Acosta-Pulido, K. D. Ackley, M. D. Caballero García, S. S. Eikenberry, S. Guziy, S. Jeong, A. Y. Lien, I. Márquez, S. B. Pand ey, I. H. Park, T. Sakamoto, J. C. Tello, I. V. Sokolov, V. V. Sokolov, A. Tiengo, A. F. Valeev, B. B. Zhang and S. Veilleux, The afterglow and kilonova of the short GRB 160821B, *Mon. Not. R. Astron. Soc.* **489**, 2104 (Oct 2019).
23. G. P. Lamb, N. R. Tanvir, A. J. Levan, A. de Ugarte Postigo, K. Kawaguchi, A. Corsi, P. A. Evans, B. Gompertz, D. B. Malesani, K. L. Page, K. Wiersema, S. Rosswog, M. Shibata, M. Tanaka, A. J. van der Horst, Z. Cano, J. P. U. Fynbo, A. S. Fruchter, J. Greiner, K. E. Heintz, A. Higgins, J. Hjorth, L. Izzo, P. Jakobsson, D. A. Kann, P. T. O'Brien, D. A. Perley, E. Pian, G. Pugliese, R. L. C. Starling, C. C. Thöne, D. Watson, R. A. M. J. Wijers and D. Xu, Short GRB 160821B: A Reverse Shock, a Refreshed Shock, and a Well-sampled Kilonova, *Astroph. J.* **883**, p. 48 (Sep 2019).
24. Z.-P. Jin, S. Covino, N.-H. Liao, X. Li, P. D'Avanzo, Y.-Z. Fan and D.-M. Wei, A kilonova associated with GRB 070809, *Nature Astronomy* , p. 461 (Oct 2019).
25. W. Fong, T. Laskar, J. Rastinejad, A. R. Escorial, G. Schroeder, J. Barnes, C. D. Kilpatrick, K. Paterson, E. Berger, B. D. Metzger, Y. Dong, A. E. Nugent, R. Strausbaugh, P. K. Blanchard, A. Goyal, A. Cucchiara, G. Terreran, K. D. Alexander, T. Eftekhari, C. Fryer, B. Margalit, R. Margutti and M. Nicholl, The Broadband Counterpart of the Short GRB 200522A at z = 0.5536: A Luminous Kilonova or a Collimated Outflow with a Reverse Shock?, *Astroph. J.* **906**, p. 127 (January 2021).
26. B. O'Connor, E. Troja, S. Dichiara, E. A. Chase, G. Ryan, S. B. Cenko, C. L. Fryer, R. Ricci, F. Marshall, C. Kouveliotou, R. T. Wollaeger, C. J. Fontes, O. Korobkin, P. Gatkine, A. Kutyrev, S. Veilleux, N. Kawai and T. Sakamoto, A tale of two mergers: constraints on kilonova detection in two short GRBs at z $\sim$ 0.5, *Mon. Not. R. Astron. Soc.* **502**, 1279 (March 2021).
27. A. Rossi, G. Stratta, E. Maiorano, D. Spighi, N. Masetti, E. Palazzi, A. Gardini, A. Melandri, L. Nicastro, E. Pian, M. Branchesi, M. Dadina, V. Testa, S. Brocato, S. Benetti, R. Ciolfi, S. Covino, V. D'Elia, A. Grado, L. Izzo, A. Perego, S. Piranomonte, R. Salvaterra, J. Selsing, L. Tomasella, S. Yang, D. Vergani, L. Amati and J. B. Stephen, A comparison between short GRB afterglows and AT2017gfo: shedding light on kilonovae properties, *arXiv e-prints* , p. arXiv:1901.05792 (Jan 2019).
28. N. R. Tanvir, A. J. Levan, C. González-Fernández, O. Korobkin, I. Mandel, S. Rosswog, J. Hjorth, P. D'Avanzo, A. S. Fruchter, C. L. Fryer, T. Kangas, B. Milvang-Jensen, S. Rosetti, D. Steeghs, R. T. Wollaeger, Z. Cano, C. M. Copperwheat,

S. Covino, V. D'Elia, A. de Ugarte Postigo, P. A. Evans, W. P. Even, S. Fairhurst, R. Figuera Jaimes, C. J. Fontes, Y. I. Fujii, J. P. U. Fynbo, B. P. Gompertz, J. Greiner, G. Hodosan, M. J. Irwin, P. Jakobsson, U. G. Jørgensen, D. A. Kann, J. D. Lyman, D. Malesani, R. G. McMahon, A. Melandri, P. T. O'Brien, J. P. Osborne, E. Palazzi, D. A. Perley, E. Pian, S. Piranomonte, M. Rabus, E. Rol, A. Rowlinson, S. Schulze, P. Sutton, C. C. Thöne, K. Ulaczyk, D. Watson, K. Wiersema and R. A. M. J. Wijers, The Emergence of a Lanthanide-rich Kilonova Following the Merger of Two Neutron Stars, *Astroph. J.* **848**, p. L27 (October 2017).

29. M. R. Drout, A. L. Piro, B. J. Shappee, C. D. Kilpatrick, J. D. Simon, C. Contreras, D. A. Coulter, R. J. Foley, M. R. Siebert, N. Morrell, K. Boutsia, F. Di Mille, T. W.-S. Holoien, D. Kasen, J. A. Kollmeier, B. F. Madore, A. J. Monson, A. Murguia-Berthier, Y.-C. Pan, J. X. Prochaska, E. Ramirez-Ruiz, A. Rest, C. Adams, K. Alatalo, E. Bañados, J. Baughman, T. C. Beers, R. A. Bernstein, T. Bitsakis, A. Campillay, T. T. Hansen, C. R. Higgs, A. P. Ji, G. Maravelias, J. L. Marshall, C. M. Bidin, J. L. Prieto, K. C. Rasmussen, C. Rojas-Bravo, A. L. Strom, N. Ulloa, J. Vargas-González, Z. Wan and D. D. Whitten, Light curves of the neutron star merger GW170817/SSS17a: Implications for r-process nucleosynthesis, *Science* **358**, 1570 (December 2017).

30. P. A. Evans, S. B. Cenko, J. A. Kennea, S. W. K. Emery, N. P. M. Kuin, O. Korobkin, R. T. Wollaeger, C. L. Fryer, K. K. Madsen, F. A. Harrison, Y. Xu, E. Nakar, K. Hotokezaka, A. Lien, S. Campana, S. R. Oates, E. Troja, A. A. Breeveld, F. E. Marshall, S. D. Barthelmy, A. P. Beardmore, D. N. Burrows, G. Cusumano, A. D'Aì, P. D'Avanzo, V. D'Elia, M. de Pasquale, W. P. Even, C. J. Fontes, K. Forster, J. Garcia, P. Giommi, B. Grefenstette, C. Gronwall, D. H. Hartmann, M. Heida, A. L. Hungerford, M. M. Kasliwal, H. A. Krimm, A. J. Levan, D. Malesani, A. Melandri, H. Miyasaka, J. A. Nousek, P. T. O'Brien, J. P. Osborne, C. Pagani, K. L. Page, D. M. Palmer, M. Perri, S. Pike, J. L. Racusin, S. Rosswog, M. H. Siegel, T. Sakamoto, B. Sbarufatti, G. Tagliaferri, N. R. Tanvir and A. Tohuvavohu, Swift and NuSTAR observations of GW170817: Detection of a blue kilonova, *Science* **358**, 1565 (December 2017).

31. S. Covino, K. Wiersema, Y. Z. Fan, K. Toma, A. B. Higgins, A. Melandri, P. D'Avanzo, C. G. Mundell, E. Palazzi, N. R. Tanvir, M. G. Bernardini, M. Branchesi, E. Brocato, S. Campana, S. di Serego Alighieri, D. Götz, J. P. U. Fynbo, W. Gao, A. Gomboc, B. Gompertz, J. Greiner, J. Hjorth, Z. P. Jin, L. Kaper, S. Klose, S. Kobayashi, D. Kopac, C. Kouveliotou, A. J. Levan, J. Mao, D. Malesani, E. Pian, A. Rossi, R. Salvaterra, R. L. C. Starling, I. Steele, G. Tagliaferri, E. Troja, A. J. van der Horst and R. A. M. J. Wijers, The unpolarized macronova associated with the gravitational wave event GW 170817, *Nature Astronomy* **1**, 791 (November 2017).

32. E. Troja, L. Piro, H. van Eerten, R. T. Wollaeger, M. Im, O. D. Fox, N. R. Butler, S. B. Cenko, T. Sakamoto, C. L. Fryer, R. Ricci, A. Lien, R. E. Ryan, O. Korobkin, S.-K. Lee, J. M. Burgess, W. H. Lee, A. M. Watson, C. Choi, S. Covino, P. D'Avanzo, C. J. Fontes, J. B. González, H. G. Khandrika, J. Kim, S.-L. Kim, C.-U. Lee, H. M. Lee, A. Kutyrev, G. Lim, R. Sánchez-Ramírez, S. Veilleux, M. H. Wieringa and Y. Yoon, The X-ray counterpart to the gravitational-wave event GW170817, *Nature* **551**, 71 (November 2017).

33. E. Pian, P. D'Avanzo, S. Benetti, M. Branchesi, E. Brocato, S. Campana, E. Cappellaro, S. Covino, V. D'Elia, J. P. U. Fynbo, F. Getman, G. Ghirlanda, G. Ghisellini, A. Grado, G. Greco, J. Hjorth, C. Kouveliotou, A. Levan, L. Limatola, D. Malesani, P. A. Mazzali, A. Melandri, P. Møller, L. Nicastro, E. Palazzi, S. Piranomonte, A. Rossi, O. S. Salafia, J. Selsing, G. Stratta, M. Tanaka, N. R. Tanvir, L. Tomasella,

D. Watson, S. Yang, L. Amati, L. A. Antonelli, S. Ascenzi, M. G. Bernardini, M. Boër, F. Bufano, A. Bulgarelli, M. Capaccioli, P. Casella, A. J. Castro-Tirado, E. Chassande-Mottin, R. Ciolfi, C. M. Copperwheat, M. Dadina, G. De Cesare, A. di Paola, Y. Z. Fan, B. Gendre, G. Giuffrida, A. Giunta, L. K. Hunt, G. L. Israel, Z.-P. Jin, M. M. Kasliwal, S. Klose, M. Lisi, F. Longo, E. Maiorano, M. Mapelli, N. Masetti, L. Nava, B. Patricelli, D. Perley, A. Pescalli, T. Piran, A. Possenti, L. Pulone, M. Razzano, R. Salvaterra, P. Schipani, M. Spera, A. Stamerra, L. Stella, G. Tagliaferri, V. Testa, E. Troja, M. Turatto, S. D. Vergani and D. Vergani, Spectroscopic identification of r-process nucleosynthesis in a double neutron-star merger, *Nature* **551**, 67 (November 2017).

34. P. S. Cowperthwaite, E. Berger, V. A. Villar, B. D. Metzger, M. Nicholl, R. Chornock, P. K. Blanchard, W. Fong, R. Margutti, M. Soares-Santos, K. D. Alexander, S. Allam, J. Annis, D. Brout, D. A. Brown, R. E. Butler, H.-Y. Chen, H. T. Diehl, Z. Doctor, M. R. Drout, T. Eftekhari, B. Farr, D. A. Finley, R. J. Foley, J. A. Frieman, C. L. Fryer, J. García-Bellido, M. S. S. Gill, J. Guillochon, K. Herner, D. E. Holz, D. Kasen, R. Kessler, J. Marriner, T. Matheson, E. H. Neilsen, Jr., E. Quataert, A. Palmese, A. Rest, M. Sako, D. M. Scolnic, N. Smith, D. L. Tucker, P. K. G. Williams, E. Balbinot, J. L. Carlin, E. R. Cook, F. Durret, T. S. Li, P. A. A. Lopes, A. C. C. Lourenço, J. L. Marshall, G. E. Medina, J. Muir, R. R. Muñoz, M. Sauseda, D. J. Schlegel, L. F. Secco, A. K. Vivas, W. Wester, A. Zenteno, Y. Zhang, T. M. C. Abbott, M. Banerji, K. Bechtol, A. Benoit-Lévy, E. Bertin, E. Buckley-Geer, D. L. Burke, D. Capozzi, A. Carnero Rosell, M. Carrasco Kind, F. J. Castander, M. Crocce, C. E. Cunha, C. B. D'Andrea, L. N. da Costa, C. Davis, D. L. DePoy, S. Desai, J. P. Dietrich, A. Drlica-Wagner, T. F. Eifler, A. E. Evrard, E. Fernandez, B. Flaugher, P. Fosalba, E. Gaztanaga, D. W. Gerdes, T. Giannantonio, D. A. Goldstein, D. Gruen, R. A. Gruendl, G. Gutierrez, K. Honscheid, B. Jain, D. J. James, T. Jeltema, M. W. G. Johnson, M. D. Johnson, S. Kent, E. Krause, R. Kron, K. Kuehn, N. Nuropatkin, O. Lahav, M. Lima, H. Lin, M. A. G. Maia, M. March, P. Martini, R. G. McMahon, F. Menanteau, C. J. Miller, R. Miquel, J. J. Mohr, E. Neilsen, R. C. Nichol, R. L. C. Ogando, A. A. Plazas, N. Roe, A. K. Romer, A. Roodman, E. S. Rykoff, E. Sanchez, V. Scarpine, R. Schindler, M. Schubnell, I. Sevilla-Noarbe, M. Smith, R. C. Smith, F. Sobreira, E. Suchyta, M. E. C. Swanson, G. Tarle, D. Thomas, R. C. Thomas, M. A. Troxel, V. Vikram, A. R. Walker, R. H. Wechsler, J. Weller, B. Yanny and J. Zuntz, The Electromagnetic Counterpart of the Binary Neutron Star Merger LIGO/Virgo GW170817. II. UV, Optical, and Near-infrared Light Curves and Comparison to Kilonova Models, *Astroph. J.* **848**, p. L17 (October 2017).

35. S. J. Smartt, T.-W. Chen, A. Jerkstrand, M. Coughlin, E. Kankare, S. A. Sim, M. Fraser, C. Inserra, K. Maguire, K. C. Chambers, M. E. Huber, T. Krühler, G. Leloudas, M. Magee, L. J. Shingles, K. W. Smith, D. R. Young, J. Tonry, R. Kotak, A. Gal-Yam, J. D. Lyman, D. S. Homan, C. Agliozzo, J. P. Anderson, C. R. Angus, C. Ashall, C. Barbarino, F. E. Bauer, M. Berton, M. T. Botticella, M. Bulla, J. Bulger, G. Cannizzaro, Z. Cano, R. Cartier, A. Cikota, P. Clark, A. De Cia, M. Della Valle, L. Denneau, M. Dennefeld, L. Dessart, G. Dimitriadis, N. Elias-Rosa, R. E. Firth, H. Flewelling, A. Flörs, A. Franckowiak, C. Frohmaier, L. Galbany, S. González-Gaitán, J. Greiner, M. Gromadzki, A. N. Guelbenzu, C. P. Gutiérrez, A. Hamanowicz, L. Hanlon, J. Harmanen, K. E. Heintz, A. Heinze, M.-S. Hernandez, S. T. Hodgkin, I. M. Hook, L. Izzo, P. A. James, P. G. Jonker, W. E. Kerzendorf, S. Klose, Z. Kostrzewa-Rutkowska, M. Kowalski, M. Kromer, H. Kuncarayakti, A. Lawrence, T. B. Lowe, E. A. Magnier, I. Manulis, A. Martin-Carrillo, S. Mattila, O. McBrien, A. Müller, J. Nordin, D. O'Neill, F. Onori, J. T. Palmerio, A. Pastorello,

F. Patat, G. Pignata, P. Podsiadlowski, M. L. Pumo, S. J. Prentice, A. Rau, A. Razza, A. Rest, T. Reynolds, R. Roy, A. J. Ruiter, K. A. Rybicki, L. Salmon, P. Schady, A. S. B. Schultz, T. Schweyer, I. R. Seitenzahl, M. Smith, J. Sollerman, B. Stalder, C. W. Stubbs, M. Sullivan, H. Szegedi, F. Taddia, S. Taubenberger, G. Terreran, B. van Soelen, J. Vos, R. J. Wainscoat, N. A. Walton, C. Waters, H. Weiland, M. Willman, P. Wiseman, D. E. Wright, L. Wyrzykowski and O. Yaron, A kilonova as the electromagnetic counterpart to a gravitational-wave source, *Nature* **551**, 75 (November 2017).
36. R. Sari, T. Piran and R. Narayan, Spectra and Light Curves of Gamma-Ray Burst Afterglows, *Astroph. J.* **497**, p. L17 (April 1998).

Neutrinos and gamma-ray production from proton-proton interactions in binary-driven hypernovae framework

S. Campion

Dipartimento di Fisica, Sapienza Università di Roma, P.le Aldo Moro 5,
Rome, 00185, Italy
E-mail: stefano.campion@roma1.infn.it
www.phys.uniroma1.it/fisica

ICRA, Dipartimento di Fisica, Sapienza Università di Roma, P.le Aldo Moro 5,
Rome, 00185, Italy

International Center for Relativistic Astrophysics Network, Piazza della Repubblica 10,
Pescara, 65122, Italy

J. D. Melon Fuksman

ICRA, Dipartimento di Fisica, Sapienza Università di Roma, P.le Aldo Moro 5,
Rome, 00185, Italy

International Center for Relativistic Astrophysics Network, Piazza della Repubblica 10,
Pescara, 65122, Italy
E-mail: david.melon@icranet.org

J. A. Rueda Hernandez

International Center for Relativistic Astrophysics Network, Piazza della Repubblica 10,
Pescara, 65122 , Italy,
E-mail: jorge.rueda@icra.it

ICRA, Dipartimento di Fisica, Università di Roma "La Sapienza", Piazzale Aldo Moro 5,
Roma, 00185, Italy

ICRANet-Ferrara, Dipartimento di Fisica e Scienze della Terra,
Università degli Studi di Ferrara, Via Saragat 1,
Ferrara, 44122, Italy

Dipartimento di Fisica e Scienze della Terra, Università degli Studi di Ferrara, Via Saragat 1,
Ferrara, 44122, Italy

INAF, Istituto de Astrofisica e Planetologia Spaziali, Via Fosso del Cavaliere 100,
Rome, 00133, Italy

In this paper we make a prediction on the intensity and energies of neutrinos and photons coming out from the decay chain of the π-meson and μ-lepton, produced by proton-proton inelastic interaction in energetic $\left(E_{\rm iso} \gtrsim 10^{52} \text{ erg}\right)$ long gamma-ray bursts (Long-GRBs), within the type I binary-driven hypernova (BdHN) framework.

Keywords: Long-GRBs BdHN; *pp* interaction; GeV-TeV ν/γ

1. Introduction

In the last years multi-messenger astronomy became a fundamental technique to get complementary informations from a single cosmic source. The aim of this technique is to connect different messengers, from the same source, emerging from the same process or from a different one an which are connected spatially and temporally. The advent of new facilities able to detect high-energy astrophysical sources, as gamma-ray bursts (GRBs) or active galactic nuclei (AGN), have been/is important for the development of this field of research.

In this paper we study the neutrino and photons emission emerging from the proton–proton inelastic interaction, for the specific model of binary driven hypernova (BdHN) of long GRB. The BdHN I progenitor is a binary system composed of a carbon-oxygen star (CO_{core}) and a neutron star (NS) companion, where the CO_{core} explosion as supernova (SN) triggers an accretion process onto the NS that, for orbital periods of a few minutes, leads to the formation a black hole (BH). Close to the *cavity* formed around the BH—due to the accretion and the collapse processes—an electron–positron plasma (created in the BH formation), during its isotropic and self-accelerating expansion, it engulfs different amounts of the ejecta baryons along different directions, leading to a direction-dependent proton Lorentz factor. The protons engulfed in the ejecta along the high-density direction ($\sim 10^{23}$ particle/cm^3) reach energies in the range $1.24 \lesssim E_p \lesssim 6.14$ GeV and interact with the ejecta unshocked protons. The protons engulfed along the low density direction, instead, reach energies ~ 1 TeV and interact with the low-density (~ 1 particle/cm^3) protons of the interstellar medium (ISM). The pp interactions, for both the density regions, give rise to γ/ν with energies $E_{\gamma,\nu} \leq 5$ GeV and $10 \leq E_{\gamma,\nu} \leq 10^3$ GeV, respectively, for which we calculate the spectra and luminosity.

1.1. *BdHN I: from MeV to GeV and TeV neutrinos*

There are two principal classes of GRBs (see Ref. 1 for the subdivision of long and short GRBs in seven different subclasses). The "short bursts" originate in the mergers of binaries composed of a neutron star (NS) accompanied either by another NS, or a white dwarf (WD) or a black hole (BH), or mergers of binary WDs. The "long bursts" split in four different subclasses, all of them originating from binaries which have been called *binary-driven hypernovae* (BdHNe) of type I, II, III and IV.[2] In this paper, we focus only on the BdHN of type I.

The progenitors of a BdHN system could be zero-age main-sequence (ZAMS) stars ($\gtrsim 10-12\ M_\odot$).[3,4] The core–collapse of one of the primary and the consequent formation of a NS at it's center, leads to a system composed by this new born NS and the secondary original star. The system then evolves through mass-transfer episodes and possibly multiple common-envelope epochs.[5] These binary interactions lead to the ejection of the outermost and lighter (H/He) outermost layers of the secondary star. At this stage, the binary is composed of a CO_{core} (or a helium star) and a NS companion.[3,6,7] The different types of BdHN are distinguishable by their final state. As regards the BdHN I, the evolution of the system proceed through the following steps. The CO$_{\text{core}}$ explodes as SN and forms a new NS (hereafter νNS) at its center. At the same time, the ejected material triggers a hypercritical accretion process onto the NS companion. For compact binaries (orbital periods $P \sim 5$ min), the accretion onto the NS brings to the formation of a BH by gravitational collapse (see Refs. 4, 7). This final system is called BdHN I[a], and it explain energetic long bursts with isotropic energy in gamma-rays $E_{\text{iso}} \gtrsim 10^{52}$ erg and peak energy $E_{p,i} \gtrsim 200$ keV. The observed occurrence rate of BdHN I ~ 1 Gpc^{-3} y^{-1}.[9]

1.1.1. *Baryonic content available for proton-proton interactions in a BdHN I*

Let's start to analyze now the structure of the baryonic matter present in the BdHN I. The three-dimensional simulations of this system,[2,7,10] pointed out that the SN ejecta, although starts expanding in a spherically symmetric way, becomes highly asymmetric by the accretion process onto the NS[7,10] and the BH formation.[11] Due to this morphology and distribution of baryonic matter around the binary component, the $e^{\pm}$–plasma created in the process of BH formation (see Refs. 12–15 for details on the creation and dynamics of the plasma), which expands isotropically from the newborn BH site, experiences a different dynamics along different directions.[16]

These studies have been specialized in the case where the $e^{\pm}$–plasma engulfs a limited amount of baryons, characterized by a *baryon load* parameter $B \lesssim 10^{-2}$. The *baryon load* is defined as $B \equiv M_b c^2/E_{e^+e^-}$, namely the ratio between the baryon rest-mass energy respect to the $e^{\pm}$ energy. Such low values of B allow the plasma to reach transparency with high Lorentz factor $\Gamma \sim 1/B \gtrsim 10^2$, needed to explain the gamma-ray prompt emission of the GRB. We denote with γ the Lorentz factor of a single particle, and with Γ the one of bulk motion.

In the direction pointing from the CO$_{\text{core}}$ to the accreting NS, outwards and lying on the orbital plane, the NS and the BH formation cave a region characterized by very poor baryon pollution, a *cavity* (see Refs. 7, 10, 11). In the other directions along the orbital plane, the $e^{\pm}$–plasma penetrates inside the SN ejecta at $\sim 10^{8}$–10^{10} cm, and evolves engulfing much larger amounts of baryons, finally reaching transparency at 10^{12} cm with $\Gamma \lesssim 4$.

In order to count the baryon mass engulfed by the $e^{\pm}$–plasma, the baryon load parameter is defined as $B \equiv M_b c^2/E_{e^+e^-}$, namely the ratio between the baryon rest-mass energy respect to the e^+e^- energy. For low baryon load values ($10^{-2} - 10^{-3}$), the transparency of the $e^{\pm}$–plasma occurs for high Lorentz factor $\Gamma \sim 1/B$. For high baryon load, as we will show, the transparency is reach with $\Gamma \sim 4$.

We are ready now to set up the properties of the incident and target protons. Therefore, in BdHN I we have, at least, two types of proton–proton interactions:

(I) Interaction of the protons with low $\Gamma \sim 7$ within the self-accelerated e^+e^-p–plasma that penetrates the SN ejecta, with the unshocked protons ahead the plasma expansion front, at rest inside the ejecta.

---

[a]We refer the reader to Refs. 2, 8 for details on the other BdHN systems, BdHN II–IV.

(II) Interaction of the protons with $\Gamma \sim 10^2$–10^3 engulfed in the self-accelerated e^+e^-p-plasma in the direction of least baryon density around the newborn BH, with the protons at rest of the interstellar medium (ISM), at a distance $\sim 10^{16}$ cm from the system (see e.g. Ref. 17 for details).

In Sec. 2, we consider the interaction in the high density region (interaction (I) above) and describe the processes connected with the interaction along this direction. In Sec. 3, we study the interaction occurring along the low density region (interaction (II) above). Since the energy range of the interacting and produced particles are different in the two regions, also the models and the approaches used to study the interaction and get the final results differs. Finally, in Sec. 4 we summarize the main results of this work.

2. pp interactions inside the high-density ejecta

In this section, we analyze the pp interaction occurring when the $e^+e^-\gamma$-plasma starts to expands along the high-density direction and to engulf the protons present in the SN ejecta, forming a $e^+e^-\gamma p$-plasma. Consequently these protons are accelerated and interact inelastically with the target protons ahead of them, still at rest. If the the kinematic energy threshold for the production of the resonance Δ^{++} is reached, the products of the scattering are: photons (from the decay of the π^0), two ν_μ and one ν_e—considering also their antiparticle—(from the decay of $\pi^\pm$ and, consequently, of the secondary created $\mu^\pm$).

In order to study this evolution of the system, we have performed relativistic hydrodynamic (RHD) simulations—performed with a one-dimensional implementation of the RHD module of the PLUTO code[18]—of the $e^\pm$-plasma dynamics inside the SN ejecta (see Ref. 16,19 for additional details), described by a system of partial differential equations in only radius and time coordinates. The simulation starts at the moment of BH formation, with initial conditions taken from the final configuration of the numerical simulations in Ref. 7:

(i) The SN remnant is obtained from the explosion of the CO_{core} of mass $M_{CO} = 11.15\ M_\odot$ evolved from a ZAMS star of $30\ M_\odot$. M_{CO} is composed by $2\ M_\odot$ for the mass of the νNS (collapsed iron core) and $9.15\ M_\odot$ conform the total ejecta mass (envelope mass).
(ii) The orbital period is $P \approx 5$ min, i.e. a binary separation $a \approx 1.5 \times 10^{10}$ cm.
(iii) The ejecta have negligible pressure, is considered to be in homologous expansion ($v(r) \propto r$) and at rest as seen from the expanding plasma.
(iv) The baryon load of the $e^\pm$-plasma is not isotropic since the baryon density is different along different directions. The density profile of the ejecta, at the BH formation time, decays with distance as a power-law, i.e. $\rho \propto (R_0 - r)^\alpha$ (see Ref. 7).
(v) The total isotropic energy of the $e^\pm$-plasma is set to $E_{e^+e^-} = 3.16 \times 10^{53}$ erg. This implies, according to the above ejecta properties, a baryon load parameter of $B = 51.75$.

The evolution from these initial conditions leads to the formation of a shock and to its subsequent expansion until reaching the outermost part of the SN.

We consider a protons energy distribution in the laboratory frame as a monochromatic function $J_p(E_p) \propto \delta(E_p - E_p^0)$ since, in the comoving frame, it can be represented by Maxwell–Boltzmann distribution. As one can guess from the energy conservation, the protons energy decrease very fast. Then we concentrate on the first stages of the expansion $(10^8 \lesssim r \lesssim 10^{10}$ cm$)$.

From the RHD simulations described above, we have extracted the quantities necessary for our calculations of the γ/ν spectra, namely the protons Lorentz factor at the shock front, γ_p, their energy, their density, n_{sh}, and the density of the unshocked protons, n_t.

In order to get these quantities, we have built a process that use the pressure inside the plasma, the protons Lorentz factor at the front and the protons mean–free–path λ_p to recognize the plasma front position and the possible interaction protons (above and below the front position).

From this procedure we got that the protons energy varies between the range $1.24 \leq E_p \leq 6.14$ GeV, which is high enough to produce secondary particles. The proton energy threshold to produce pions in the final state is, for the interaction $pp \to pn\pi^+$, $E_{p,\text{Th}} = 1228$ MeV and, for $pp \to pp\pi^0$, $E_{p,\text{Th}} = 1217$ MeV.

In the region of the expansion of the shock, at every radius, the average number density of the target protons $\langle n_t \rangle$ in the remnant varies in the range 5×10^{23} cm$^{-3} \lesssim n_t \lesssim 8 \times 10^{23}$ cm^{-3} (the higher value occurs in the beginning of the simulation, namely at the beginning of the expansion). The protons number density at the front of the expanding shell, $\langle n_{sh} \rangle$, does not vary much either; it is in the range $(0.5-9) \times 10^{25}$ cm^{-3} (the maximum value occurs in the region close to the initial radius of the expansion).

2.1. *Particles spectra*

We turn now to the describe how we have calculated the spectrum of the particles emerging form the π/μ decay[b]. For our low energy protons, the differential pp cross-section, $d\sigma(E_\pi, E_p)/dE_\pi$, is given in Ref. 20. We notice that the cross-section is different for the three types of pions π^+, π^-, π^0. The pions production rate can be computed as

$$Q_\pi(E_\pi) = cn_t \int_{E_\pi}^{E_p^{\max}} J_p(E_p) \frac{d\sigma(E_\pi, E_p)}{dE_\pi} dE_p, \qquad (1)$$

with $J_p(E_p)$ the monochromatic protons energy distribution, n_t the number density of the target protons.

---

[b]See Ref. 19 for more details on the calculations and for the plot of the particles spectra.

We denote with $\Phi_a = dN_a/dE_a$ the spectrum of the particle a, with N_a the particle number density per unit time[c].

The spectrum of photons emerging from π^0 decay is given by

$$\Phi_{\pi^0 \to \gamma\gamma}(E_\gamma) = 2 \int_{E^{\min}(E_\gamma)}^{E_\pi^{\max}} \frac{Q_\pi(E_\pi)}{\sqrt{E_\pi^2 - m_\pi^2 c^4}} dE_\pi, \qquad (2)$$

where $E^{\min}(E_\gamma) = E_\gamma + m_{\pi^0}^2 c^4/(4 E_\gamma)$ can be derived by the kinematics of the process and the factor 2 takes into account the two produced photons.

The spectrum of $\nu_{\mu(1)}$ is similarly given by

$$\Phi_{\pi \to \mu\nu_\mu}(E_{\nu_\mu}) = \frac{1}{\lambda} \int_{E^{\min}(E_{\nu_\mu})}^{E_\pi^{\max}} \frac{Q_\pi(E_\pi) \theta\left(\lambda - \frac{E_{\nu_\mu}}{E_\pi}\right)}{\sqrt{E_\pi^2 - m_\pi^2 c^4}} dE_\pi, \qquad (3)$$

where $E^{\min}(E_{\nu_\mu}) = E_{\nu_\mu}/\lambda + (\lambda/4)\left(m_\pi^2 c^4/E_{\nu_\mu}\right)$; $\lambda = 1 - r_\pi$, with $r_\pi = (m_\mu/m_\pi)^2$, is the maximum energy fraction that the neutrino emerging from the direct decay can take from the pion. The value $E_\pi^{\max}$ is calculated from the kinematics and results to be:

$$E_\pi^{\max}(E_p) = \gamma_{\mathrm{CM}}(E_p) \left[E_\pi^{\mathrm{CM}}(E_p) + \beta_{\mathrm{CM}}(E_p) p_f^{\mathrm{CM}}(E_p)\right], \qquad (4)$$

where CM indicate that the Lorentz factor, the momentum and the velocity are calculated in centre-of-mass frame.

Instead, the spectrum of the $\nu_{\mu(2)}$ are given by:

$$\Phi_{\pi \to \mu \to \nu_\mu/\nu_e}(E_\nu) = \int_{E^{\min}(E_\nu)}^{E_\pi^{\max}} \frac{Q_\pi(E_\pi)}{\sqrt{E_\pi^2 - m_\pi^2 c^4}} g\left(\frac{E_\nu}{E_\pi}\right) dE_\pi, \qquad (5)$$

where the functions $g(z)$ are derived in Ref. 21 and represent the ν spectra after the decay chain $\pi \to \mu \to \nu$.

The function $g(z)$ can be decomposed as the sum of an unpolarized spectrum, $g^0(z)$, plus a polarized one, $g^{\mathrm{pol}}(z)$ (see Appendix in Ref. 21). We have used the formula for the relativistic limits (given in that paper), $\beta_\pi \to 1$, which is well satisfied since the pions Lorentz factor assumes values $4.5 \leq \gamma_\pi \leq 34.5$. We have calculated the spectrum for both unpolarized and polarized case (see Ref. 19).

Altogether, the spectra of the different particles varies between values $10^{23} \leq E^2 dN_a/dE \leq 10^{31}$ erg/cm^3/s at energies $0.3 \leq E_a \leq 5$ GeV.

At this point, we can calculate the particle emissivity at every radius, ϵ_a^i, integrating over the energy of the particle a (from 0.3 to $E_\pi^{\max}$) its spectrum times E_a and, then, integrate ϵ_a^i over the volume V_i to get the total luminosity L_a. The interacting volume at the radius i is calculated as $V_i = 4\pi r_i^2 \lambda_i$, where λ_i is the mean-free path of the protons of energy E_p^i in the shell front. Finally, the total

---

[c]Henceforth we denote as $\nu_{\mu(1)}$ the muonic neutrino/antineutrino from the direct pion decay, $\pi \to \mu\nu_\mu$, and $\nu_{\mu(2)}$ the neutrino/antineutrino from the consequent muon decay, $\mu \to e\nu_\mu\nu_e$.

energy emitted for each particle a, is given integrating L_a over the entire emission time, namely (Δt_i, is the time the shell spends to cover the distance between r_{i-1} and r_i with the velocity β_i, $\Delta t_i \approx \Delta r_i/(c\beta_i)$):

$$\mathcal{E}_a \approx \sum_{i=2}^{n} L_a^i \times \Delta t_i = \sum_{i=2}^{n} L_a^i \times \frac{\Delta r_i}{c\beta_i}, \quad (6)$$

The total energy emitted in photons is $\sim 4 \times 10^{52}$ erg, while the different types of ν it varies between 0.5 and 3.5×10^{51} erg. Summing all the energy emitted for all the particle, we obtain a total energy release of 9.11×10^{51} erg, that is $\approx 2.9\%$ of the energy of initial energy of the $\gamma e^{\pm}$–plasma.

3. TeV protons interacting with the ISM

In this section, we now consider the interaction of incident protons engulfed by the $\gamma e^{\pm}$–plasma in the direction of the circumburst medium (CBM) with low baryon load—we assume here $B = 10^{-3}$—with target protons of the ISM. The interaction with the ISM—located at a distance between $10^{16} \leq r \leq 10^{17}$ cm from the BH site—occurs in a spherical shell. Thus in this case, the number density of the target is $n_{\text{ISM}} \sim 1$ cm^{-3} and the transparency is reached far away from the BH site, with ultra-relativistic Lorentz factor of up to $\gamma_p = \Gamma \sim 10^3$. Therefore, we adopt here that the incident protons have energies ~ 1 TeV.

The number of engulfed protons, N_p, is given by the ration between the isotropic energy of the $e^{\pm}$ times the baryon load over the protons mass. For $E_{e^+e^-} \sim 10^{53}$ erg and $B = 10^{-3}$, $N_p = 6.65 \times 10^{52}$.

Since the energy range differs from the previous case, for the computation of the particles spectrum here we have used the results obtained in Ref. 22, where a parameterization of the pp cross-section for high-energy protons and an analytic formula for the spectrum of the emerging particles is derived.

Following Ref. 22 and denoting $J_p(E_p)$ the protons energy distribution—in units cm^{-3} TeV^{-1}—in this case the production rate for the secondary particle a, $\Phi_a(E_a) \equiv dN_a/dE_a$ (for $E_p \geq 0.1$ TeV) is given by

$$\Phi_a(E_a) = c\,n_p \int_{E_a}^{\infty} \sigma_{\text{inel}}^{pp}(E_p) J_p(E_p) F_a(x, E_p) \frac{dE_p}{E_p}, \quad (7)$$

with n_p the target protons density (we assume it is 1 particles/cm^3), $\sigma_{\text{inel}}^{pp}(E_p)$ is the inelastic pp cross-section, $x \equiv E_a/E_p$ and F_a is the specific spectrum for the particle a derived in Ref. 22.[d]

---

[d] We notice that in Ref. 22 they do not distinguish between π^+ and π^-, as well as between ν and $\bar{\nu}$. So, differently from the low density/energy case, here we do not distinguish between ν and $\bar{\nu}$ too.

3.0.1. *Particles spectra*

Here the protons energy distribution is $J_p(E_p) = A\delta(E_p - E_p^0)$, with $E_p^0 = 1$ TeV and $A = N_p/V$, with N_p the number of interacting protons over the volume $V = 4\pi(r_2^3 - r_1^3)/3$, with $r_1 = 10^{16}$ cm and $r_2 = 10^{17}$ cm.

The total emitted energy for each particle a here is calculated as

$$\mathcal{E}_{tot,\, a} = \Delta t \sum_i \epsilon_a^i \times \Delta V_i = \epsilon_a\, \Delta t\, \Delta V, \tag{8}$$

where $\Delta V_i = 4/3\,\pi\left(r_i^3 - r_{i-1}^3\right)$, with $r_i = r_{i-1} + \delta s$—δs is the space covered by the protons with their velocities in one second.[e]

The luminosity is given by $L_a = \epsilon_a \times \Delta V_{\text{last shell}}$, where: ϵ_a the emissivity of the particle a calculated by Eq. (7), $\Delta V_{\text{last shell}} = 4/3\,\pi\left(r_2^3 - r_*^3\right)$ and $r_* = 10^{17} - \delta s$ cm and $r_2 = 10^{17}$ cm. $r_2 - r_*$ represents the last ISM shell where the accelerated protons interact—the protons spends $\Delta t = \Delta r/c\beta = 3 \times 10^6$ seconds to cross the entire ISM region and, then, it is useless to talk about total luminosity.

Then, the emissivity of all the secondary emerging particles from the pp interaction are given by substituting the $F_a(x, E_p)$ functions derived in Ref. 22 inside Eq. (7). We got the following results for: the total energy $\mathcal{E}_a$ emitted through all emitting region (calculated via Eq. (8)), the luminosity of the last emitting shell L_a and the particle energy for which we have the maximum value of the spectrum $E^2 dN_\gamma/dE$, $E_a^{\max}$:

(1) for photons: $\mathcal{E}_\gamma = 5.41 \times 10^{43}$ erg, $L_\gamma = 1.01 \times 10^{43}$ erg s^{-1} and $E_\gamma^{\max} = 91.62$ GeV;
(2) for muonic neutrino from direct pion decay $\left(\nu_{\mu^{(1)}}\right)$: $\mathcal{E}_{\nu_{\mu^{(1)}}} = 1.60 \times 10^{43}$ erg, $L_{\nu_{\mu^{(1)}}} = 3.01 \times 10^{42}$ erg s^{-1} and $E_{\nu_{\mu^{(1)}}}^{\max} = 44.72$ GeV;
(3) for muonic neutrino from muon decay $\left(\nu_{\mu^{(2)}}\right)$: $\mathcal{E}_{\nu_{\mu^{(2)}}} = 1.98 \times 10^{43}$ erg, $L_{\nu_{\mu^{(2)}}} = 3.71 \times 10^{42}$ erg s^{-1} and $E_{\nu_{\mu^{(2)}}}^{\max} = 63.9$ GeV.

From these results we deduce that the principal differences between the interactions considered in Sec. 2 and Sec. 3 resides in the density of the target particles in both interaction regions. Another, but less efficient, factor that has influence on the obtained results is the difference in the interacting protons energy, which is reflected onto the pp cross-section.

4. Summary, discussion and conclusions

In this work we have computed the photon and neutrino production via proton-proton interactions occurring within the BdHNe I scenario for energetic long GRBs, which we have recalled in Sec. 1. From the dynamics of the BdHN I formation process leads to a highly asymmetric SN ejecta around the newborn BH site. Therefore,

---

[e]Note that ϵ_a^i does not depend on the radius, $\epsilon_a^i = \epsilon_a$, and then $\Delta V = 4/3\,\pi\left(r_2^3 - r_1^3\right)$.

the $e^{\pm}$–plasma created in the BH formation process, during its isotropic expansion and self-acceleration, engulfs different amounts of matter of the surrounding SN ejecta, depending on the direction. Consequently, either the observation of the emitted particles are direction dependent.

In Sec. 2 we have studied the *pp* interaction along the high-density direction inside the SN ejecta. The secondary particles production occurs in the first ~ 1.5 s of the plasma expansion inside the ejecta. The $e^{\pm}$–plasma starts to expand inside the SN ejecta, engulfing protons and accelerating them to energies of a few GeV. For these low energetic protons, we adopted the cross-section given in Ref. 20. At later times, the energy of the protons is below the threshold for the production of secondary particles by *pp* inelastic scattering. The obtained results tell us that the neutrinos and photons have energies $E_{\nu_{\mu(1)}} \leq 2$ GeV and E_γ, $E_{\nu_{\mu(2)}}$, $E_{\nu_e} <$ 5 GeV, with associated total energy (integrated over the whole emitting region) of $\sim 10^{50}$–10^{51} erg.

In the second part, Sec. 3, we have studied the expansion of the plasma along the direction of low baryon load $(B = 10^{-3})$ (see, e.g., Refs. 1,23). Here, the expansion of the $\gamma e^{\pm}$–plasma along the low-density directions allows a self-acceleration of it that brings the engulfed protons to energies of up to $E_p \sim 1$ TeV ($\gamma_p \sim 10^3$). For these higher energetic protons we have followed the approach presented in Ref. 22, where the *pp* cross-section and the spectra of the emerging particles are parametrized. In this case, the secondary particles have energies $1 \leq E_a \leq 10^3$ GeV and the total emitted energy is $\sim 10^{43}$ erg.

We found also that the spectrum of the emerging particles follow approximately a cutoff power-law function (CPL) $f(E) \propto E^\alpha \exp E/E_c$, with spectral index $1 \leq \alpha < 3$, depending on the considered particle and the interaction region. The power-law term usually derives from the spectral index of the primary interacting protons (see, for example, Ref. 24), but since we considered a spherical expansion of the $\gamma e^{\pm} B$–plasma, and a monochromatic protons energy distribution (at each radius of the expansion), we deduce that the power-law term is intrinsic in the considered process. Instead, the exponential decay is explained by the kinematic of the process. Indeed a fraction of the parent proton energy is taken by the pion; for the direct pion decay, the $\nu_{\mu(1)}$ can take, at maximum, a fraction λ of the pion energy, while the muon can take, at maximum, the entire pion energy.

Now we try to give some numbers concerning the ν detection with Earth Detectors. In general, since GRB occur at cosmological distances and this makes neutrino detection very challenging because of the very low neutrino flux arriving to the Earth.

We can obtain order-of-magnitude estimate of the probability of detection of these neutrinos considering three detectors: SuperKamiokande (SK), Hyper-Kamiokande (HK) and IceCube (IC), calculating the detection horizon.[f] The

---

[f]For this purpose, we use the best experimental conditions, i.e. the peak neutrino luminosity and the corresponding neutrino energy.

number of neutrinos per-unit-time and per-unit-area that arrive to the detector is

$$\frac{d^2 N_\nu}{dS dt} = \frac{\mathcal{E}_\nu}{4\pi D^2 E_\nu^*}, \qquad (9)$$

where $\mathcal{E}_\nu$ is the total energy emitted during 1 s in neutrinos of energy E_ν, D is the luminosity distance to the source, $E_\nu^* = E_\nu/(1+z)$ is the redshifted neutrino energy, and z the source cosmological redshift.

The number of detectable neutrino, $N_\nu^{\rm det}$, is calculated as the number of neutrino per unit of time and area that arrives to the detector, given by Eq. (9), times the cross-section for the neutrino-nucleon interaction, $\sigma_{\nu N}$ (see, e.g. Ref. 25, 26), times the number of probable interacting baryon in the detector $N_b^{\rm det} = N_A \times M_{\rm int}$—where N_A is the Avogadro number and $M_{\rm int}$ the interacting mass inside the detector—times the integration time of the detector $T_{\rm int}$, that we set to 1 second (in agreement with the time-interval of the emission inside the ejecta):

$$N_\nu^{\rm det} = \frac{d^2 N_\nu}{dS dt} \times T_{\rm int} \times \sigma_{\nu N} \times N_b^{\rm det}, \qquad (10)$$

For the three considered detectors is $N_b^{\rm det} = N_A \times (22.5 \,{\rm kton}) = 1.35 \times 10^{34}$ baryons (for SK); $N_b^{\rm det} = (560 \,{\rm kton}) \times N_A = 3.37 \times 10^{35}$ baryons (for HK); for the *Deep Core Detector* of IC, the effective volume is a function of the neutrino energy: $N_b^{\rm det} = (10 \,{\rm Mton}) \times N_A = 6.022 \times 10^{36}$ baryons; $N_b^{\rm det} = (20 \,{\rm Mton}) \times N_A = 1.2044 \times 10^{37}$ baryons; $N_b^{\rm det} = (30 \,{\rm Mton}) \times N_A = 1.8066 \times 10^{37}$ baryons.

Now, using the relations and estimates above and considering the Hubble-Lemaître law, $cz = H_0 D_h$ (with $H_0 = 72$ km s^{-1} Mpc^{-1}), we can obtain the neutrino-detection horizon, D_h, i.e. the luminosity distance to the source for which we have $N_\nu^{\rm det} = 1$:

$$D_h = \frac{K H_0}{2c} + \frac{1}{2}\sqrt{\frac{K^2 H_0^2}{c^2} + 4K}, \qquad (11)$$

where $K = \mathcal{E}_\nu \sigma_{\nu N} T_{\rm int} N_b^{\rm det}/(12\pi E_\nu)$.

For the low energy neutrinos ($E_\nu \leq 2$ GeV, at the production site, i.e. in the source frame) there are additional considerations that decrease the probability to detect these neutrino, namely: 1) the fact that the energy need to be divided for the factor $1+z$ and that for low energetic ν the cross-section for $\nu-N$ interaction is very low—$\sim 10^{-39}$ cm^2 (see, for example, Ref. 25, 26); 2) for these low energies, there is much background noise by atmospheric neutrinos, created in the atmospheric showers by cosmic rays and solar neutrinos.

The high energetic neutrinos ($E_\nu \leq 10^3$ GeV) from the low-density region could be, in principle, more easily detected than the previous case since at these energies there is no background noise from atmospheric and solar neutrinos and the cross-section assumes higher values $\sigma_{\nu N} \sim 10^{-37}$ cm^2.

The calculations of the horizon distance through Eq. (11) give the following results that

(I) for the ν from the high density region, $0.2 \leq D_h \leq 11.12$ Mpc;
(II) for the ν from the low density region, $22 \leq D_h \leq 954$ pc.

In both cases, we obtained the higher values with the Deep Core of the IC detector, while the lower ones are for the SK detector. This analysis suggests that only the IceCube detector might detect the neutrinos here analyzed, i.e. neutrinos produced by pp interactions in the context of BdHNe I, especially the one coming from the high-density region, even if all of them have the right energy range of sensibility to detect our neutrinos.

References

1. R. Ruffini, J. Rueda, M. Muccino, Y. Aimuratov, L. Becerra, C. Bianco, M. Kovacevic, R. Moradi, F. Oliveira, G. Pisani et al., On the classification of GRBs and their occurrence rates, *The Astrophysical Journal* **832**, p. 136 (2016).
2. Y. Wang, J. A. Rueda, R. Ruffini, L. Becerra, C. Bianco, L. Becerra, L. Li and M. Karlica, Two Predictions of Supernova: GRB 130427A/SN 2013cq and GRB 180728A/SN 2018fip, *ApJ* **874**, p. 39 (March 2019).
3. J. A. Rueda and R. Ruffini, On the Induced Gravitational Collapse of a Neutron Star to a Black Hole by a Type Ib/c Supernova, *ApJ* **758**, p. L7 (October 2012).
4. L. Becerra, F. Cipolletta, C. L. Fryer, J. A. Rueda and R. Ruffini, Angular Momentum Role in the Hypercritical Accretion of Binary-driven Hypernovae, *ApJ* **812**, p. 100 (October 2015).
5. T. M. Tauris, N. Langer and P. Podsiadlowski, Ultra-stripped supernovae: Progenitors and fate, *MNRAS* **451**, 2123 (August 2015).
6. C. L. Fryer, J. A. Rueda and R. Ruffini, Hypercritical Accretion, Induced Gravitational Collapse, and Binary-Driven Hypernovae, *ApJ* **793**, p. L36 (October 2014).
7. L. Becerra, C. L. Bianco, C. L. Fryer, J. A. Rueda and R. Ruffini, On the Induced Gravitational Collapse Scenario of Gamma-ray Bursts Associated with Supernovae, *ApJ* **833**, p. 107 (December 2016).
8. J. A. Rueda, R. Ruffini and Y. Wang, Induced Gravitational Collapse, Binary-Driven Hypernovae, Long Gramma-ray Bursts and Their Connection with Short Gamma-ray Bursts, *Universe* **5**, p. 110 (May 2019).
9. R. Ruffini, J. A. Rueda, M. Muccino, Y. Aimuratov, L. M. Becerra, C. L. Bianco, M. Kovacevic, R. Moradi, F. G. Oliveira, G. B. Pisani and Y. Wang, On the Classification of GRBs and Their Occurrence Rates, *ApJ* **832**, p. 136 (December 2016).
10. L. Becerra, C. L. Ellinger, C. L. Fryer, J. A. Rueda and R. Ruffini, SPH Simulations of the Induced Gravitational Collapse Scenario of Long Gamma-Ray Bursts Associated with Supernovae, *ApJ* **871**, p. 14 (Jan 2019).
11. R. Ruffini, J. D. Melon Fuksman and G. V. Vereshchagin, On the Role of a Cavity in the Hypernova Ejecta of GRB 190114C, *ApJ* **883**, p. 191 (Oct 2019).
12. G. Preparata, R. Ruffini and S.-S. Xue, The dyadosphere of black holes and gamma-ray bursts, *A&A* **338**, L87 (October 1998).
13. R. Ruffini, J. D. Salmonson, J. R. Wilson and S.-S. Xue, On evolution of the pair-electromagnetic pulse of a charged black hole, *Astronomy and Astrophysics Supplement* **138**, 511 (September 1999).

14. R. Ruffini, J. D. Salmonson, J. R. Wilson and S. S. Xue, On the pair-electromagnetic pulse from an electromagnetic black hole surrounded by a baryonic remnant, *A&A* **359**, 855 (July 2000).
15. C. L. Bianco, R. Ruffini and S. S. Xue, The elementary spike produced by a pure e^+e^- pair-electromagnetic pulse from a Black Hole: The PEM Pulse, *A&A* **368**, 377 (March 2001).
16. R. Ruffini, Y. Wang, Y. Aimuratov, U. Barres de Almeida, L. Becerra, C. L. Bianco, Y. C. Chen, M. Karlica, M. Kovacevic, L. Li, J. D. Melon Fuksman, R. Moradi, M. Muccino, A. V. Penacchioni, G. B. Pisani, D. Primorac, J. A. Rueda, S. Shakeri, G. V. Vereshchagin and S.-S. Xue, Early X-Ray Flares in GRBs, *ApJ* **852**, p. 53 (January 2018).
17. L. Izzo, R. Ruffini, A. V. Penacchioni, C. L. Bianco, L. Caito, S. K. Chakrabarti, J. A. Rueda, A. Nandi and B. Patricelli, A double component in GRB 090618: A proto-black hole and a genuinely long gamma-ray burst, *A&A* **543**, p. A10 (July 2012).
18. A. Mignone, C. Zanni, P. Tzeferacos, B. Van Straalen, P. Colella and G. Bodo, The pluto code for adaptive mesh computations in astrophysical fluid dynamics, *The Astrophysical Journal Supplement Series* **198**, p. 7 (2011).
19. S. Campion, J. D. M. Fuksman and J. A. R. Hernandez, Neutrino production from proton-proton interactions in binary-driven hypernovae, *arXiv preprint arXiv:1910.10439* (2019).
20. S. R. Blattnig, S. R. Swaminathan, A. T. Kruger, M. Ngom and J. W. Norbury, Parametrizations of inclusive cross sections for pion production in proton-proton collisions, *Phys. Rev. D* **62**, p. 094030 (Oct 2000).
21. P. Lipari, Lepton spectra in the earth's atmosphere, *Astroparticle Physics* **1**, 195 (1993).
22. S. R. Kelner, F. A. Aharonian and V. V. Bugayov, Energy spectra of gamma rays, electrons, and neutrinos produced at proton-proton interactions in the very high energy regime, *Phys. Rev. D* **74**, p. 034018 (Aug 2006).
23. R. Ruffini, Y. Wang, Y. Aimuratov, U. B. de Almeida, L. Becerra, C. L. Bianco, Y. C. Chen, M. Karlica, M. Kovacevic, L. Li, J. D. M. Fuksman, R. Moradi, M. Muccino, A. V. Penacchioni, G. B. Pisani, D. Primorac, J. A. Rueda, S. Shakeri, G. V. Vereshchagin and S.-S. Xue, Early x-ray flares in GRBs, *The Astrophysical Journal* **852**, p. 53 (2018).
24. T. K. Gaisser, R. Engel and E. Resconi, *Cosmic rays and particle physics* (Cambridge University Press, 2016).
25. P. Zyla *et al.*, Review of Particle Physics, *PTEP* **2020**, p. 083C01 (2020).
26. Y. Hayato, A neutrino interaction simulation program library neut, *Acta Phys. Polon.* **40**, 2477 (2009).

General relativistic turbulence in spherically symmetric core-collapse supernovae simulations

L. Boccioli* and G. J. Mathews

Center for Astrophysics, Department of Physics, University of Notre Dame,
225 Nieuwland Science Hall, Notre Dame, IN 46556, USA
*E-mail: lbocciol@nd.edu

E. P. O'Connor

The Oskar Klein Centre, Department of Astronomy, Stockholm University, AlbaNova,
SE-106 91 Stockholm, Sweden

It is generally believed that General Relativity (GR) is of secondary importance in the explosion of core-collapse supernovae (CCSN). However, as 3D simulations are becoming more and more detailed, GR effects can be strong enough to change the hydrodynamics of the supernova and affect the explosion. Since a 3D simulation in full GR is computationally extremely challenging, it is valuable to modify simulations in a spherically symmetric spacetime to incorporate 3D effects. This permits exploration of the parameter dependence of CCSN with a minimum of computational resources. In this proceedings contribution we report on the formulation and implementation of general relativistic neutrino-driven turbulent convection in the spherically symmetric code GR1D. This is based upon *STIR*, a recently proposed Newtonian model based on mixing length theory. When the parameters of this model are calibrated to 3D simulations, we find that our GR formulation significantly alters the correspondence between progenitor mass and explosion vs. black-hole formation. We therefore believe that, going forward, simulating CCSNe in full GR is of primary importance.

Keywords: Supernovae - Simulations - Mixing Length Theory - General Relativistic Hydrodynamics

1. Introduction

This proceedings contribution is based on work published in Ref. [1]. Core-collapse supernovae (CCSNe) have been at the core of cutting-edge computational research for more than 50 years. Despite that, the details of the mechanisms driving the explosion still remain unknown, even though significant progress has been made since the first attempts at explaining CCSNe.[2–4]

Historically, one-dimensional (1D) spherically symmetric simulations were able to assess the crucial role of neutrinos in aiding the expansion of the shock through the so-called delayed neutrino-heating mechanism.[5,6] Two-dimensional (2D) simulations[7,8] and three-dimensional (3D) simulations,[9] have been only recently accessible thanks to the fast technological improvements of the last three decades.

Spherically symmetric simulations, however, have unfortunately, not led to self-consistent explosions of Fe-core CCSNe (which are the most common) since they involve all stars with masses > 11 $M_\odot$. On the other hand, there have been several simulations in 2D and 3D that have led to successful explosions.[10–16] However, 2D simulations have been recently shown[17] to favor explosions by an artificial enhancement of neutrino-heating behind the shock via an inverse turbulence cascade which is not present in 3D. Therefore, only 3D simulations can provide the final explanation as to what causes the explosion. However, despite the technological improvements of the last few decades, 3D simulations continue to present a difficult computational challenge, even for modern supercomputers.

In comparison, modern 1D simulations are significantly faster to run and are also more consistent across different codes.[18] In other words, when the initial conditions are the same, different groups obtain similar results. This guarantees a somewhat solid foundation, making 1D simulations an ideal tool to study how different input physics can affect the explosion of supernovae. To do that, first one needs to artificially trigger an explosion. In a recent paper Couch et al.[19] (hereafter CWO20) developed *STIR* (Simulated Turbulence In Reduced-dimensionality), a parametric model based upon Mixing Length Theory (MLT) that incorporates the effects of 3D turbulence in spherically symmetric simulations.

The simulations from CWO20 use Newtonian hydrodynamics and only partially include general relativistic effects through a General Relativistic Effective Potential (GREP) from Ref. [20], which is a common practice in the supernova community. However, we know that General Relativity (GR) plays an important role in the explosion of supernovae.[10,21] Hence, simulations in full GR are desirable, and in this proceedings contribution we summarize the extension of the *STIR* model to a general relativistic treatment.[1] Throughout the manuscript, we adopt natural units, i.e. $G = c = M_\odot = 1$.

2. Methods

2.1. *The STIR model of Couch et al. (2020)*

A detailed description of STIR can be found in Refs. 22, 23 and CWO20. There, it is shown that the effects of turbulence can be treated as a perturbation on the background fluid. After a Reynolds decomposition of the compressible Euler equations, and several other approximations valid in typical supernova thermodynamic environments, one arrives to the following equation describing the evolution of the turbulent kinetic energy:

$$\frac{\partial \rho v_{\text{turb}}^2}{\partial t} + \frac{1}{r^2}\frac{\partial}{\partial r}[r^2(\rho v_{\text{turb}}^2 v_r - \rho D_K \nabla v_{\text{turb}}^2)] \\ = -\rho v_{\text{turb}}^2 \frac{\partial v_r}{\partial r} + \rho v_{\text{turb}} \omega_{\text{BV}}^2 \Lambda_{\text{mix}} - \rho \frac{v_{\text{turb}}^3}{\Lambda_{\text{mix}}} , \quad (1)$$

where

$$\Lambda_{\mathrm{mix}} = \alpha_{\mathrm{MLT}} \frac{P}{\rho g}, \quad (2)$$

$$\omega_{\mathrm{BV}}^2 = g_{\mathrm{eff}} \left(\frac{1}{\rho} \frac{\partial \rho}{\partial r} - \frac{1}{\rho c_s^2} \frac{\partial P}{\partial r} \right). \quad (3)$$

In the above equations, ρ is the mass density, v_r is the radial velocity, Λ_{mix} is the mixing length, ω_{BV} is the Brunt-Väisälä frequency, c_s is the sound speed, D_K is a diffusion coefficient due to turbulence and g_{eff} is the magnitude of the local effective acceleration. For a fluid in hydrostatic equilibrium, g_{eff} simply reduces to the local gravitational acceleration g. More generally, however, in the rest frame one should take the acceleration of the fluid into account. Therefore, the total acceleration g_{eff} can be expressed as:

$$g_{\mathrm{eff}} = g - v_r \frac{\partial v_r}{\partial r}, \quad (4)$$

as described in CWO20.

The mixing length Λ_{mix} is the average distance that a convective element will travel before being mixed with (and increasing the internal energy of) the surrounding material. The Brunt-Väisälä frequency ω_{BV} is the rate at which the convective elements are rising. As one can notice from Eq. (3), ω_{BV}^2 can be either positive or negative: when $\omega_{\mathrm{BV}}^2 > 0$ the fluid is convectively unstable, i.e. convection is generated; when $\omega_{\mathrm{BV}}^2 < 0$ the fluid is convectively stable, i.e. convection is damped. Ultimately, the main parameter of the model is α_{MLT}, which scales the mixing length to the pressure scale height in Eq. (2). Typically $\alpha_{\mathrm{MLT}} \sim O(1)$.

The diffusion coefficient D_K is defined as:

$$D_K = \alpha_K v_{\mathrm{turb}} \Lambda_{\mathrm{mix}}. \quad (5)$$

Similar terms appear in the internal energy, electron fraction, and neutrino energy density evolution equations (for the complete set of hydrodynamic equations used in the model, (see Eqs. 25-29 and 33 in CWO20). Therefore, strictly speaking, *STIR* has 4 additional free parameters: α_K, α_e, α_{Ye}, α_ν. However, the convective motions are not very sensitive to the value of these parameters, so we set them to 1/6 for simplicity, consistent with the choices of Ref. [24] and CWO20.

In the next section we describe a general relativistic version of the model described above.

2.2. *STIR in General relativity*

The first attempts to create a general relativistic model for convection date back to Ref. [25]. We follow the same approach, but using a slightly different formalism.

All the simulations described here[1] were run with the open-source, spherically symmetric, general relativistic code GR1D.[26] The Boltzmann equation for neutrino transport is solved using an M1-scheme, with opacity tables generated using the open-source code NuLib.[27]

The metric evolved in GR1D is Schwarzchild-like:

$$ds^2 = g_{\mu\nu}x^\mu x^\nu \\ = -\alpha(r,t)^2 dt^2 + X(r,t)^2 dr^2 + r^2 d\Omega^2, \tag{6}$$

where α and X can be expressed as functions of a metric potential ϕ (which reduces to the Newtonian potential in the Newtonian limit) and the enclosed gravitational mass M_{grav}:

$$\alpha(r,t) = \exp[\phi(r,t)],$$
$$X(r,t) = \left(1 - \frac{2M_{\text{grav}}(r,t)}{r}\right)^{-1/2}. \tag{7}$$

For the present work, we first note that turbulence is mostly relevant far from the proto-neutron star (PNS) where GR effects can be treated as a perturbation. Therefore, one can simply make a few changes to the terms in Eq. (1) without having to re-derive the entire Reynold's decomposition. The expression for ω_{BV}^2, however, must be carefully re-derived. Far from the PNS, we invoke the following:

(1) replace the conserved variable ρ with its GR counterpart, i.e. $D = WX\rho$, where $W = (1-v^2)^{-1/2}$ and $v = Xv_r$;
(2) multiply the RHS of Eq. (1) by αX.
(3) multiply the spatial flux in Eq. (1) by α/X (see Ref. [26] for more details on the derivation of the hydrodynamic equations in GR1D).

The expression of ω_{BV}^2 can be derived using conservation of momentum for a convective eddy in a background fluid in hydrostatic equilibrium. The case of a fluid with non zero acceleration can be derived with ad-hoc corrections for general relativistic effects. The derivation can be found in Ref. [1], and it leads to:

$$\omega_{\text{BV}}^2 = \frac{\alpha^2}{\rho h X^2}\left(\frac{d\phi}{dr} - v\frac{\partial v}{\partial r}\right)\left(\frac{\partial \rho(1+\epsilon)}{\partial r} - \frac{1}{c_s^2}\frac{\partial P}{\partial r}\right), \tag{8}$$

where $v = Xv_r$.

The main difference between Eqs. (3) and (8) is the inclusion of $\partial \rho \epsilon / \partial r$ in the latter. In the gain region the internal energy decreases with radius, i.e. $\partial \rho \epsilon / \partial r < 0$. This decreases the magnitude of ω_{BV} and therefore the amount of turbulence that is generated. We will come back to this in Section 3.2

3. Results: Comparison with 3D simulations

3.1. *Results using an effective potential*

Inspired by the work of CWO20, we compare our GREP model to the mesa20_LR_v 3D simulation,[28] by using the same setup chosen by CWO20. That is, we simulate the collapse of a 20 $M_\odot$ progenitor from,[29] adopting the SFHo EOS[30] and assuming Nuclear Statistical Equilibrium (NSE) everywhere. The algorithm used in FLASH to solve the neutrino radiation transport closely resembles the one used in GR1D.[27] Additionally, the set of NuLib opacities we adopted is the same used by CWO20. Finally, we use 12 neutrino energy groups geometrically spaced up to ~250 MeV.

The upper panels of Figure 1 (modified from Ref. [1]) show the shock radius versus time and the turbulent velocity profile at ~135 ms post-bounce for our GREP model (to be compared to Figures 1 and 2 of CWO20). The main difference between our results using GR1D and the ones from CWO20 using FLLASH is that GR1D consistently gives larger values for the turbulent velocity at a given α_{MLT}. This then translates into larger shock radii at a given time. Except for these small differences, the agreement between the two models is very good, and both yield explosions for $\alpha_{\mathrm{MLT}} \gtrsim 1.2$.

When it comes to the comparison with the 3D results, however, our MLT-like model does not captures some features that are present in the 3D case. Specifically, the profile at ~135 ms post-bounce of the convective speed in 3D has a longer tail at 50-80 km. This has already been noticed by CWO20, and it is due to angular variations present in the 3D model, rather than a deeper convection extending in the region below the gain layer. In our model, convection shuts off at 80 km, as one would expect, since that is approximately the location of the gain layer. A more interesting difference is the lack of PNS convection at 25 km, not captured by our MLT-like model. A possible explanation for this is that STIR is not taking lepton number-driven convection into account, which is not easily tractable with MLT models, and therefore a more careful treatment of this type of convection might ease the discrepancy with the 3D results. We are currently working on adjusting some of the parameters of STIR deep inside the PNS to match the 3D result, and therefore analyze the impact of PNS convection on the explosion, but this goes beyond the scope of this conference proceedings.

3.2. *Results using GR*

One can compare the results obtained using the simple GREP approach with results in full GR. We show the results using full GR in the bottom panels of Figure 1, while the upper panels refer to the runs using our GREP model. The most important difference to point out is the range of α_{MLT} used in the GR and GREP simulations. To produce shock radii and turbulent velocities that are similar to the GREP results, the value of α_{MLT} that needs to be used in full GR is ~ 20% larger. The reason behind this increase in α_{MLT} lies in the expression of ω_{BV}. As pointed out in Section 2.2, including the internal energy gradient into eq. (8) is the main difference between the GREP and GR models.

In the gain region, where turbulent convection is most relevant, the gradient of the internal energy is negative. This decreases the magnitude of ω_{BV}^2, making the fluid more stable against convection. Including $\rho\epsilon$ in the definition of ω_{BV} is hence

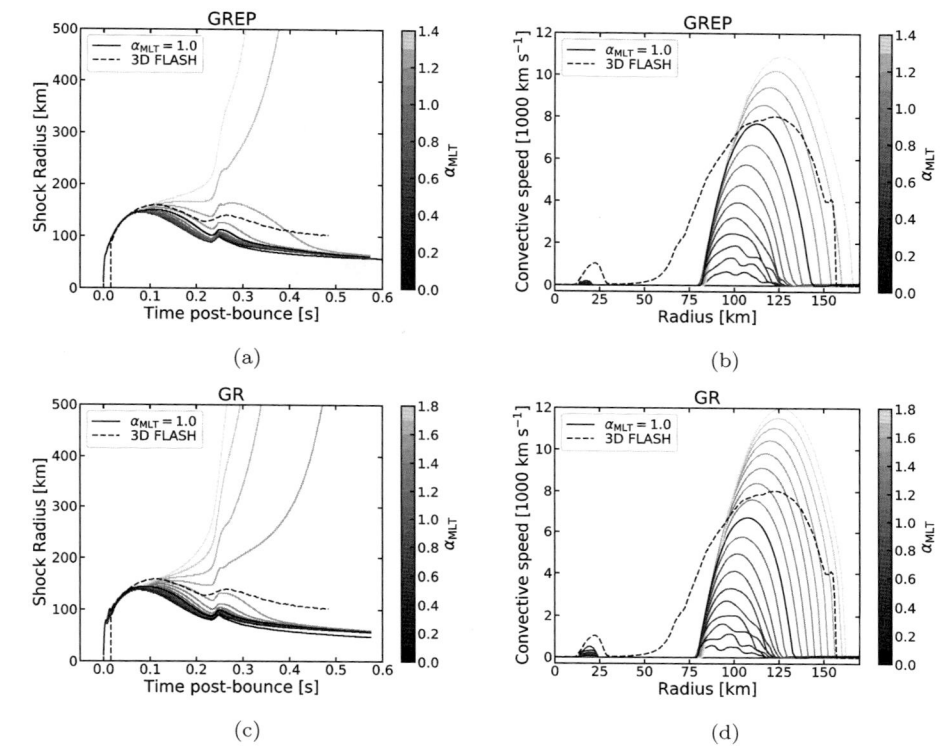

Fig. 1. The plots on the upper row were generated using our GREP model, while the plots on the bottom row were generated using full GR. Panels (a,c) show the time evolution of the shock radius for different values of the parameter α_{MLT}, and can be compared to Figure 2 from CWO20. Panels (b,d) show a snapshot at ~ 135 ms post bounce of v_{turb}, and can be compared to Figure 1 from CWO20. The dashed lines represent the 3D simulation from Ref. [28].

needed to realistically characterize turbulent convection. If one takes the form of ω_{BV} from Eq. (8) and implements it in the GREP model, the value of α_{MLT} needed to achieve an explosion increases, becoming comparable to the one used in the GR model.

3.3. *Progenitor Study*

In the previous Sections we summarized the validation of our turbulent convection model[1] by comparing it to the 3D results of Ref. [31]. In this section, we summarize the use[1] of our calibrated models to simulate the collapse and subsequent shock revival of 20 progenitors from Ref. [32]. We use three different values of α_{MLT}, for which the fraction of successful explosions is roughly between 25% and 80%.

Our GREP model generates results[1] that are compatible with the ones obtained by CWO20 shifted by $\Delta\alpha_{\mathrm{MLT}} \simeq 0.05$. If one compares the left panel of Figure 2 with Figure 6 from CWO20, it is clear that our model tends to yield explosions for slightly smaller values of α_{MLT}. This shift mainly depends on two differences between our model and the one from CWO20: (i) we used a finer resolution in space and energy; (ii) the numerical algorithms used to solve the hydrodynamic equations and the neutrino transport are different.

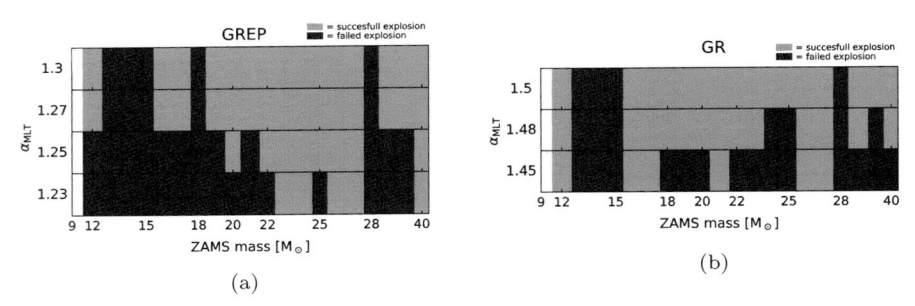

Fig. 2. Explosion pattern (modified from Ref. [1]) of CCSN for the GREP (left panel) and GR (right panel) models as a function of the Zero Age Main Sequence mass. Orange bands represent successful explosions (i.e. the shock has reached 500 km), while dark blue bands represent failed explosions.

Even more importantly, Figure 2 shows that a General Relativistic treatment of turbulent convection does not simply reproduce the results obtained by the GREP model. By looking at Figure 1 one might conclude that, since the value of α_{MLT} required to generate an explosion in GR is larger, using GR with larger values of α_{MLT} would produce the same patterns shown in the left panel of Fig. 2. However, that is not the case, and GR modifies the explosion pattern of CCSNe. To even more accurately characterize the differences between the patterns of explodability in the GR and GREP models, a systematic study with hundreds of progenitors and more values of α_{MLT} would be desired. That, however, is beyond the scope of this conference proceedings.

We can conclude from Figure 2 that general relativity changes which progenitors are more likely to explode. By focusing on the patterns associated with $\alpha_{\mathrm{MLT}} = 1.27$ and $\alpha_{\mathrm{MLT}} = 1.48$ one can see that, using the GREP model, the 24, 25 and 30 $M_\odot$ progenitors explode, whereas the 18 $M_\odot$ doesn't. In the GR model it is the exact opposite. It should be pointed out that the pattern of explodability generated by the GR model with $\alpha_{\mathrm{MLT}} = 1.48$ is intermediate between the results of CWO20 and Ref. [32]: (i) like the former (but unlike the latter), it shows failed explosions for low mass progenitors with M = 13-15 $M_\odot$; (ii) like the latter (and unlike the former) it shows that higher mass progenitors with M = 24-25 $M_\odot$ result in failed explosions.

It is worth mentioning that the explodability pattern obtained using the GR model with $\alpha_{\mathrm{MLT}} = 1.48$ cannot be reproduced by the GREP model. One can see that, from the left panel of Figure 2, for $\alpha_{\mathrm{MLT}} = 1.23$, the 25 $M_\odot$ progenitor fails, and all progenitors below 22 $M_\odot$ fail as well. This shows that the GREP model cannot produce successful explosions for progenitors with masses 15-18 $M_\odot$ and at the same time failed explosions of the 24-25 $M_\odot$ progenitors, like we see in the right panel of Figure 2. Notably, the GR model with $\alpha_{\text{MLT}} = 1.5$ reproduces the same pattern of explodability found in the GREP model with $\alpha_{\text{MLT}} = 1.27$ (with the only exception of the 18 $M_\odot$ progenitor). This tells us that: (i) the threshold between failed and successful explosions is a steep function of α_{MLT}; and (ii) GR can reproduce the GREP results for large values of α_{MLT} and large explosion fractions.

Overall, our results[1] have shown that including general relativistic effects can modify how turbulence behaves in a one-dimensional, MLT-like model. It is hard to predict if this effect will translate to multi-dimensional simulations, given the differences between 1D and multi-D. Nonetheless, these results suggest that GR (as opposed to GREP) can have a significant impact on the explosion of CCSNe. A detailed comparison between full-GR and Newtonian simulations, performed with 2D and 3D codes across multiple progenitors, will clarify whether this effect translates to higher dimensions, where turbulent convection is generated self-consistently.

4. Conclusions

In this proceedings contribution we have summarized our development[1] of extended *STIR*, the MLT-like model of CWO20, to a full general relativistic formalism. Our implementation of STIR in `GR1D` can reproduce the results of CWO20 when using the same GREP model that they developed. The GR version of STIR needs larger values of α_{MLT} to achieve shock dynamics that are similar to the ones obtained with a GREP model.[1] The reason behind this is that, as can be seen from Eq. (8), one needs to include the gradient of the internal energy gradient in the expression for ω_{BV}. This reduces the magnitude of ω_{BV}^2 in the gain region, which inhibits the generation of turbulence. The net result is that larger values of Λ_{mix} (and therefore of α_{MLT}) are needed to develop a convective mixing that is as strong as the one obtained without the inclusion of GR.

After comparing our model to the 3D results of Ref. [28], we simulated[1] the collapse and subsequent shock expansion of 20 different progenitors[32] for different values of α_{MLT}, for both the GREP and GR models. Our main finding[1] is that GR changes the pattern of explodability of CCSNe. Specifically, the 24 $M_\odot$ and the 25 $M_\odot$ progenitors need comparatively much larger values of α_{MLT} to explode with the GR model. This produces an explodability as a function of progenitor mass that is intermediate between the results of CWO20 and Ref. [32]. However, the GR model also shows, for values of α_{MLT} that yield large explosion fractions (i.e. $\alpha_{\text{MLT}} = 1.5$), an explodability that is compatible with the results obtained using the GREP model.

Acknowledgments

The authors would like to thank Sean Couch, Andre da Silva Schneider and Mackenzie Warren for fruitful discussions. Work at the University of Notre Dame supported by the U.S. Department of Energy under Nuclear Theory Grant DE-FG02-95-ER40934. EOC would like to acknowledge Vetenskapsrådet (the Swedish Research Council) for supporting this work under award numbers 2018-04575 and 2020-00452.

References

1. L. Boccioli, G. J. Mathews and E. P. O'Connor, General Relativistic Neutrino-driven Turbulence in One-dimensional Core-collapse Supernovae, *ApJ* **912**, p. 29 (May 2021).
2. S. A. Colgate and R. H. White, The Hydrodynamic Behavior of Supernovae Explosions, *ApJ* **143**, p. 626 (March 1966).
3. W. D. Arnett, Gravitational collapse and weak interactions, *Canadian Journal of Physics* **44**, 2553 (January 1966).
4. G. Sonneborn, B. Altner and R. P. Kirshner, The Progenitor of SN 1987A: Spatially Resolved Ultraviolet Spectroscopy of the Supernova Field, *ApJ* **323**, p. L35 (December 1987).
5. H. A. Bethe and J. R. Wilson, Revival of a stalled supernova shock by neutrino heating, *ApJ* **295**, 14 (August 1985).
6. S. W. Bruenn, Stellar core collapse - Numerical model and infall epoch, *ApJS* **58**, 771 (August 1985).
7. D. S. Miller, J. R. Wilson and R. W. Mayle, Convection above the Neutrinosphere in Type II Supernovae, *ApJ* **415**, p. 278 (September 1993).
8. M. Herant, W. Benz, W. R. Hix, C. L. Fryer and S. A. Colgate, Inside the Supernova: A Powerful Convective Engine, *ApJ* **435**, p. 339 (November 1994).
9. C. L. Fryer and M. S. Warren, Modeling Core-Collapse Supernovae in Three Dimensions, *ApJL* **574**, L65 (July 2002).
10. B. Müller, H.-T. Janka and A. Marek, A New Multi-dimensional General Relativistic Neutrino Hydrodynamics Code for Core-collapse Supernovae. II. Relativistic Explosion Models of Core-collapse Supernovae, *ApJ* **756**, p. 84 (September 2012).
11. E. J. Lentz, S. W. Bruenn, W. R. Hix, A. Mezzacappa, O. E. B. Messer, E. Endeve, J. M. Blondin, J. A. Harris, P. Marronetti and K. N. Yakunin, Three-dimensional Core-collapse Supernova Simulated Using a 15 $M_\odot$ Progenitor, *ApJL* **807**, p. L31 (July 2015).
12. H.-T. Janka, T. Melson and A. Summa, Physics of Core-Collapse Supernovae in Three Dimensions: A Sneak Preview, *Annual Review of Nuclear and Particle Science* **66**, 341 (October 2016).
13. S. W. Bruenn, E. J. Lentz, W. R. Hix, A. Mezzacappa, J. A. Harris, O. E. B. Messer, E. Endeve, J. M. Blondin, M. A. Chertkow, E. J. Lingerfelt, P. Marronetti and K. N. Yakunin, The Development of Explosions in Axisymmetric Ab Initio Core-collapse Supernova Simulations of 12-25 M Stars, *ApJ* **818**, p. 123 (February 2016).
14. E. P. O'Connor and S. M. Couch, Two-dimensional Core-collapse Supernova Explosions Aided by General Relativity with Multidimensional Neutrino Transport, *ApJ* **854**, p. 63 (February 2018).
15. B. Müller, T. M. Tauris, A. Heger, P. Banerjee, Y.-Z. Qian, J. Powell, C. Chan, D. W. Gay and N. Langer, Three-dimensional simulations of neutrino-driven core-collapse supernovae from low-mass single and binary star progenitors, *MNRAS* **484**, 3307 (April 2019).
16. A. Burrows, D. Radice, D. Vartanyan, H. Nagakura, M. A. Skinner and J. C. Dolence, The overarching framework of core-collapse supernova explosions as revealed by 3D FORNAX simulations, *MNRAS* **491**, 2715 (January 2020).

17. S. M. Couch and C. D. Ott, The Role of Turbulence in Neutrino-driven Core-collapse Supernova Explosions, *ApJ* **799**, p. 5 (January 2015).
18. E. O'Connor, R. Bollig, A. Burrows, S. Couch, T. Fischer, H.-T. Janka, K. Kotake, E. J. Lentz, M. Liebendörfer, O. E. B. Messer, A. Mezzacappa, T. Takiwaki and D. Vartanyan, Global comparison of core-collapse supernova simulations in spherical symmetry, *Journal of Physics G: Nuclear and Particle Physics* **45**, p. 104001 (sep 2018).
19. S. M. Couch, M. L. Warren and E. P. O'Connor, Simulating turbulence-aided neutrino-driven core-collapse supernova explosions in one dimension, *The Astrophysical Journal* **890**, p. 127 (feb 2020).
20. A. Marek, H. Dimmelmeier, H. T. Janka, E. Müller and R. Buras, Exploring the relativistic regime with Newtonian hydrodynamics: An improved effective gravitational potential for supernova simulations, *A&A* **445**, 273 (January 2006).
21. J. R. Wilson and G. J. Mathews, *Relativistic Numerical Hydrodynamics* (Cambridge University Press, 2003).
22. Q. A. Mabanta and J. W. Murphy, How Turbulence Enables Core-collapse Supernova Explosions, *ApJ* **856**, p. 22 (March 2018).
23. Q. A. Mabanta, J. W. Murphy and J. C. Dolence, Convection-aided Explosions in One-dimensional Core-collapse Supernova Simulations. I. Technique and Validation, *ApJ* **887**, p. 43 (December 2019).
24. B. Müller, M. Viallet, A. Heger and H.-T. Janka, The Last Minutes of Oxygen Shell Burning in a Massive Star, *ApJ* **833**, p. 124 (December 2016).
25. K. S. Thorne, Validity in General Relativity of the Schwarzschild Criterion for Convection, *ApJ* **144**, p. 201 (April 1966).
26. E. O'Connor and C. D. Ott, A new open-source code for spherically symmetric stellar collapse to neutron stars and black holes, *Classical and Quantum Gravity* **27**, p. 114103 (June 2010).
27. E. O'Connor, An Open-source Neutrino Radiation Hydrodynamics Code for Core-collapse Supernovae, *ApJS* **219**, p. 24 (August 2015).
28. E. P. O'Connor and S. M. Couch, Exploring Fundamentally Three-dimensional Phenomena in High-fidelity Simulations of Core-collapse Supernovae, *ApJ* **865**, p. 81 (October 2018).
29. R. Farmer, C. E. Fields, I. Petermann, L. Dessart, M. Cantiello, B. Paxton and F. X. Timmes, On Variations of Pre-Supernova Model Properties, *The Astrophysical Journal Supplement Series* **227**, p. 22 (dec 2016).
30. A. W. Steiner, M. Hempel and T. Fischer, Core-collapse Supernova Equations of State Based on Neutron Star Observations, *ApJ* **774**, p. 17 (September 2013).
31. S. M. Couch and E. P. O'Connor, High-resolution Three-dimensional Simulations of Core-collapse Supernovae in Multiple Progenitors, *ApJ* **785**, p. 123 (April 2014).
32. T. Sukhbold, T. Ertl, S. E. Woosley, J. M. Brown and H.-T. Janka, Core-Collapse Supernovae from 9 to 120 Solar Masses Based on Neutrino-Powered Explosions, *The Astrophysical Journal* **821**, p. 38 (April 2016).

Mountain formation by repeated, inhomogeneous crustal failure in a neutron star

A. D. Kerin[1] and A. Melatos[1,2]

[1] *School of Physics, University of Melbourne, Parkville, VIC 3010, Australia*
[2] *Australian Research Council Centre of Excellence for Gravitational Wave Discovery (OzGrav), University of Melbourne, Parkville, VIC 3010, Australia*

As a neutron star spins down mechanical strain accumulates in the solid crust up to and beyond the point of failure. To model the repeated macroscopic failure of the crust an idealised cellular automaton is developed, with nearest-neighbour interactions representing strain dissipation and redistribution, and including thermal losses. The probability distribution functions (PDFs) of the size and waiting times of failure events in the automaton are presented. The final failure event of a star's life occurs when the star spins down to $\approx (5\pm 3)\%$ of its birth frequency with implications for transient events e.g. rotational glitches. In addition the automaton is able to predict the star's mass-quadrupole moment and gravitational wavestrain at all points in the star's life, with relevance to future gravitational wave surveys such as those carried out with the Laser Interferometer Gravitational Wave Observatory (LIGO).

Keywords: Asteroseismology – gravitational waves – stars: evolution – stars: neutron – stars: rotation

1. Introduction

The mechanical failure of the crust of a rotating neutron star, and the associated creation of mountains, has been suggested as a source of continuous gravitational waves,[1-3] and transient events such as rotational glitches[4,5] and fast radio bursts.[6] No such gravitational waves have been observed despite multiple recent searches,[7-13] but theoretical arguments exist that the first detection is close.[2] It should be noted that other reasonable explanations for transients have been suggested, e.g. superfluid vortices in the context of glitches.[14,15]

The macroscopic, tectonic process by which the crust fails and mountains form is unknown.[16,17] By analogy with the Earth, one expects crustal failure to involve large-scale, inhomogeneous elements such as fault lines, plates, subduction zones, stress zones, and so on, even though the tensile properties of a neutron star's crust are likely to be different to those of terrestrial rocks (and indeed are not understood completely at present). Modelling has primarily focused on the microphysics of crustal failure.[18-22] In particular Ref. 19 found local cracking does not occur due to the extreme pressure and the crust material fails globally. There have been some investigations into the evolution of the whole star as it evolves through a quasistatic sequence of elastic equilibria.[23,24,31] However, these do not consider the impact of the stick-slip dynamics of repeated local failures involving inhomogenous tectonic features, e.g. tectonic plates, which lead to history dependent outcomes.

Here we present a model of local mountain formation caused by mechanical failure of the crust on macroscopic scales driven by spin down. The model describes the tectonics of crustal failure through a cellular automaton, similar in spirit to the block-and-spring automata used to describe the far-from-equilibrium, stick-slip dynamics of terrestrial earthquakes.[25] Section 2 deals with how the crust deforms due to spin down, the consequent strain build up, and the effects of repeated local failures. Section 3 briefly presents some of the results of this model, in particular the probability distribution functions (PDFs) of the heat dissipated in failure events and the time between events. Section 4 presents the gravitational wavestrain over time as a function of the automaton parameters. For simplicity we do not consider a magnetic field, which is unlikely to be important in ordinary neutron stars (although this may not be true in magnetars).

This paper summarises the key aspects of the model and its output as developed in Ref. 26. This summary borrows heavily from the structure and content of Ref. 26. Among other things, Figs. 1 and 2 are reproduced from the latter reference.

2. Tectonics of Mountain Formation

2.1. *Global deformation due to spin down*

A neutron star is composed of a superfluid core and a solid crystalline crust.[21,22,27–30] Other components, e.g. transitional layers containing nuclear pasta at the crust-core interface,[16] are neglected here for simplicity.

As a neutron star spins down the balance of centrifugal and gravitational forces changes and so does the equilibrium figure of the crust. We use the method of Ref. 31 to model the secular deformation due to spin down, which in turn allows for the calculation of the mechanical strain at every point in the crust. In Ref. 27 Eqs. (3)-(8) define a vector which describes the change in the star's equilibrium figure due to spin down from which the mechanical strain can be calculated, see also Eqs. (1)-(7) in Ref. 26.

2.2. *Local microscopic failure*

We propose that the strain built up over the course of spin down causes the crust to fail locally when strained beyond breaking, and that some fraction of the energy released from the strained crystal lattice of the crust causes the centre of mass of the failed section to move radially outwards, creating a mountain.

Estimates of the breaking strain of neutron star crust material vary many orders of magnitude, e.g. Ref. 32 found a breaking strain of $\sim 10^{-5}$ and the more recent results of Ref. 19 instead found a breaking strain of ~ 0.1. We follow the results of Ref. 19 and consider a breaking strain in the range 0.075 to 0.11. Additionally Ref. 19 found that the material fails in a global manner, i.e. local cracks do not form, but the simulation volume is $\sim 10^{11}$ fm^3 and the macroscopic crust likely behaves differently (see Sec. 2.3 in this paper and Sec. 2.3 in Ref. 26).

When the crust fails it deforms plastically. When a material is deformed plastically a fraction of the plastic work done, β, is dissipated as heat. The value of β depends on a variety of factors such as the material, current strain, strain rate, and deformation history.[33–37] As per Ref. 35 terrestrial metals such as copper and steel have $0.75 \lesssim \beta \lesssim 0.95$, however such metals are unlikely to be good analogues for neutron star crust material. It is extremely difficult to calculate a realistic value of β and we do not attempt to do so. Instead we conservatively set $\beta = 0.9$, taking the position that the significant majority of the plastic work done is dissipated as heat.

2.3. Repeated global failure: An automaton

Ref. 19 found, using a direct simulation of nucleonic crystal (neutron star crust material), that the material fails in a global sense. Due to the extreme pressure local failure, i.e. cracking, is not observed. However the simulation volume is $\sim 10^{11}$ fm^3 and the macroscopic crust likely behaves differently, as noted in Sec. 2.2. In reality there are likely to be macroscopic features like seismic faults. To model these stick-slip and stress-relax dynamics[25] we create an automaton.

We divide the crust into N discrete cells; cells are indexed by i, with $0 \leq i < N$, and have position (r_i, θ_i, ϕ_i). The half-annular shape of the cells (dictated by assumed symmetry) and their coordinates are discussed in detail in Sec. 2.3 and Appendix A of Ref. 26. Each cell is assigned a breaking strain, σ_i, uniformly randomly between 0.075 and 0.11, informed by the stress-strain curve calculated in Ref. 19. Strain is greatest at the base of the crust, so the elastic potential energy density is greatest there too. As such the strain of each cell is evaluated at the base of the crust.

Over the course of spin down the strain of each cell, γ_i, increases. We define failure as when a cell has strain equal to or greater than its breaking strain, $\gamma_i \geq \sigma_i$. A failed volume of material is less able to support mechanical loads and so shifts the load to the neighbouring volume.[38] To model this we implement a nearest-neighbours interaction. Upon failure adjacent cells receive a fraction of the strain "lost" by the failed cell, with

$$\gamma_{i\pm 1} \mapsto \gamma_{i\pm 1} + \frac{1}{3}D(1-A)\gamma_i, \tag{1}$$

$$\gamma_{N-1-i} \mapsto \gamma_{N-1-i} + \frac{1}{3}D(1-A)\gamma_i, \tag{2}$$

where $0 \leq D \leq 1$ and $0 \leq A \leq 1$ are constants of the automaton, and cells indexed by $i = 0$ and $i = N - 1$ are adjacent.[a] $(1-A)\gamma_i$ is the amount of strain "lost" by cell i upon failure. Some portion of the released strain, $D(1-A)\gamma_i$, is redistributed amongst cell i's nearest neighbours as per Eqs. (1) and (2). The remaining portion

---

[a]The cells closest to the North pole, $i = 0, N-1$, and South pole, $i = \lfloor N/2 \rfloor$ for N odd, or $i = N/2, N/2-1$ for N even, are adjacent to two cells not three. As such during strain redistribution Eq. (2) does not apply and Eq. (1) should be evaluated with a factor of 1/2 rather than 1/3.

of strain, $(1 − D)(1 − A)\gamma_i$, is converted into plastic work deforming the crust, i.e. moving cell i. After the strain of the failed cell's nearest neighbours is increased the failed cell's own strain is updated accordingly,

$$\gamma_i \mapsto A\gamma_i. \tag{3}$$

The quantity A is the fraction of strain a failed cell retains upon failure, and D is the fraction of strain released from the failed cell that is redistributed to the nearest neighbours. We call A and D the "dissipation" and "redistribution" parameters respectively.

In the failure process described above the crust is deformed plastically. The failed cell i is moved purely radially (θ_i and ϕ_i are unchanged) a distance Δr_i to model the plastic deformation,

$$r_i \mapsto r_i + \Delta r_i. \tag{4}$$

Δr_i is calculated by equating the energy associated with plastic deformation with the work done moving the cell against the gravitational-centrifugal potential a distance Δr_i. The potential is given by[31]

$$\Phi(\vec{r}) = -\pi G \rho_{\text{core}} \left[2R^2 - \frac{2r^2}{3} - \frac{4e^2 r^2}{15} P_2(\cos\theta) \right], \tag{5}$$

where G is the gravitational constant, ρ_{core} is the density of the fluid core, and e is the eccentricity of the ellipse defined by the meridional cross-section of the star.

In general the mechanical potential energy U stored in a body of volume V under a strain γ is given by the strain-energy formula

$$\frac{\mu \gamma^2}{2} = \frac{U}{V}, \tag{6}$$

where μ is the shear modulus of the material. The mechanical potential energy density of a given cell i is then $\mu \gamma_i^2/2$. As described above if a given cell i with strain γ_i fails then the amount of strain that is converted into plastic work is $(1 − A)(1 − D)\gamma_i$. We calculate Δr_i from

$$\frac{\mu(1-\beta)}{2}[(1-A)(1-D)\gamma_i]^2 = \Delta r_i \rho_{\text{crust}} \left. \frac{d\Phi(\vec{r})}{dr} \right|_{\vec{r}=\vec{r}_i}, \tag{7}$$

where ρ_{crust} is the density of the crust, and β is the coefficient of thermal dissipation. As per Sec. 2.2 we take the conservative position of $\beta = 0.9$, i.e. we assume the significant majority of the plastic work done on the crust during failure is dissipated as heat.

The state of each cell in the automaton is described by five numbers $[r_i(t_n), \theta_i(t_n), \phi_i(t_n), \gamma_i(t_n), \sigma_i(t_n)]$, which are updated at each time-step. Here the i index refers to the cell index and t_n corresponds to the time-step. The initial shape of the star is a Maclaurin spheroid with eccentricity $e = 0.1$, a representative value.

The specific steps of the automaton are given:

(1) Choose the values of A and D.
(2) Initialise $[r_i(t_0), \theta_i(t_0), \phi_i(t_0)]$.
(3) Randomly assign each cell a breaking strain in the range $0.075 \leq \sigma_i \leq 0.11$, and set $\gamma_i = 0$.
(4) Using the method of Ref. 31 calculate the deformation vectors and increase the strain of each cell for a small spin down of $\delta\Omega$ and the fiducial values below in Sec. 2.4.
(5) If a cell i has $\gamma_i \geq \sigma_i$ then it undergoes failure.
   (a) Redistribute the strain of failed cell i to its nearest neighbours as per Eqs. (1) and (2) synchronously, i.e. all cells with $\gamma_i \geq \sigma_i$ are identified and fail simultaneously before Eqs. (1) and (2) are applied.
   (b) Move cell i radially as per Eqs. (4) and (7).
   (c) Decrease the strain in cell i as per Eq. (3).
   (d) Assign to cell i a new breaking strain, uniformly randomly in the range $0.075 \leq \sigma_i \leq 0.11$.
   (e) Repeat the steps (5)(a) to (5)(e) until $\gamma_i < \sigma_i$ for all $0 \leq i < N$.
(6) Decrease Ω by $\delta\Omega$.
(7) Repeat from step (4) until one has $\Omega \leq \delta\Omega$.

2.4. *Fiducial parameters*

The fiducial values used for this automaton are: $\mu = 2.4 \times 10^{29}$ Jm^{-3}, total radius $R = 10.5$ km, crust-core radius $R' = 9.5$ km, $\rho_{\text{core}} = 6.38 \times 10^{17}$ kgm^{-3}, $\rho_{\text{crust}} = 10^{17}$ kgm^{-3}, total stellar mass of 1.4 solar masses, $\Omega(0)/2\pi = 800$ Hz, and $\dot{\Omega}(0)/2\pi = -1 \times 10^{-8}$ Hzs^{-1}. For $A = D = 0.5$ and the above fiducial values the failure of a cell on the equator with $\sigma_i = 0.1$ leads to $\Delta r_i \approx 0.04$ mm. For the purpose of calculating the gravitational wavestrain we consider a star that is a distance $d = 1$ kpc away from the Earth.

In this automaton we set $N = 400$. The typical angular velocity step per automaton time-step is $\delta\Omega = (1.25 \times 10^{-4})\Omega(0)$. To convert $\Omega(t)$ into time t in what follows, we use $\Omega(t) = \Omega(0)(1 + t/\tau)^{-1/2}$ where $\tau = -\Omega(0)/2\dot{\Omega}(0) = 4 \times 10^{10}$ s, is the electromagnetic spin-down timescale.

3. Event Statistics

The automaton allows for the location of every part of the crust to be known at every point in time over the course of the star's life. Additionally the time, location, and energy of failure events are tracked. Numerous observables are studied as functions of t in Ref. 26. In Sec. 3.1 we focus on the PDF of event sizes. The PDF of the time between one event and the next one (the waiting time) and the age of the star at which tectonic activity ceases are presented in Sec. 3.2, and the correlation between event size and waiting time is presented in Sec. 3.3.

3.1. Size PDF

Mechanical failure of the crust has been linked to multiple types of transient events such as rotational glitches,[4,5] soft gamma-ray repeaters[22,39,40] and fast radio bursts.[6] Testable models of the transients' statistics, such as the automaton presented here, are needed to differentiate between crustal failure and other viable explanations of the transients e.g. superfluid vortices in the context of rotational glitches.[14,41–44]

In the upper panel of Fig. 1 we present the PDFs for the heat dissipated in an event, i.e. its size, given as ΔE. The left-hand side of Eq. (7) gives the amount of energy done as plastic work on the crust not lost as heat. Thus multiplying by $\beta/(1-\beta)$ gives the energy that is dissipated as heat in a failure event. The qualitative form of the PDF is similar across parameter space, a tight peak with a tail in increasing ΔE. Close to $A = D = 0$ events are largest with $\langle \Delta E \rangle \approx 5.4 \times 10^{36}$ J and the tail is most strongly suppressed; events with $\Delta E > \langle \Delta E \rangle$ are relatively less likely than in other regions of parameter space. Close to $A = D = 1$ events are smallest with $\langle \Delta E \rangle \approx 1.9 \times 10^{33}$ J and the tail is much more pronounced; events with $\Delta E > \langle \Delta E \rangle$ are relatively more likely than in other regions of parameter space. The decrease in $\langle \Delta E \rangle$ with increasing A and D follows from Eq. (7). The change in the tail comes from larger A and D more easily facilitating avalanches. More frequent avalanches means larger events are more frequent. For larger A cells remain close to critical after failure, and are thus more prone to fail when a neighbour does. For larger D the nearest-neighbours interaction is simply stronger.

3.2. Waiting-time PDF

We define the waiting time of an event, Δt, as the time between that event and the next one. In the lower panel of Fig. 1 we present the PDFs of waiting time for a variety of values of A and D. There is a steep rise for small Δt with an approximately exponential tail for high Δt, the probability density peaks at $\Delta t \approx 0.1\tau$. Recall τ is the spin-down timescale as defined in Sec. 2.4. The waiting-time PDF is approximately exponential, with the peak at $\Delta t \approx 0.1\tau$ an artifact of time discretisation. The frequency decrement, $\delta\Omega$, is constant. Correspondingly the time-steps are small early in the star's life and large later on. As such short waiting-time events are restricted to early in the star's life whereas long waiting-time events can happen throughout. In contrast to the PDF of event sizes the PDF of waiting times is unaffected by A or D. This is because the driver of events is the rate of strain build up, which is governed by spin down and unaffected by A or D.

In order for failure to occur at all we find that the star must be born with an initial rotational frequency $\gtrsim 750$ Hz, consistent with the results of Ref. 27. However once failure does occur, it continues until the star is near totally spun down, $\approx 5 \pm 3\%$ of the birth frequency, i.e. $t/\tau \approx 100$ to 2500. This is because the only way for strain to exit the system is through failure events, it otherwise continually builds up.

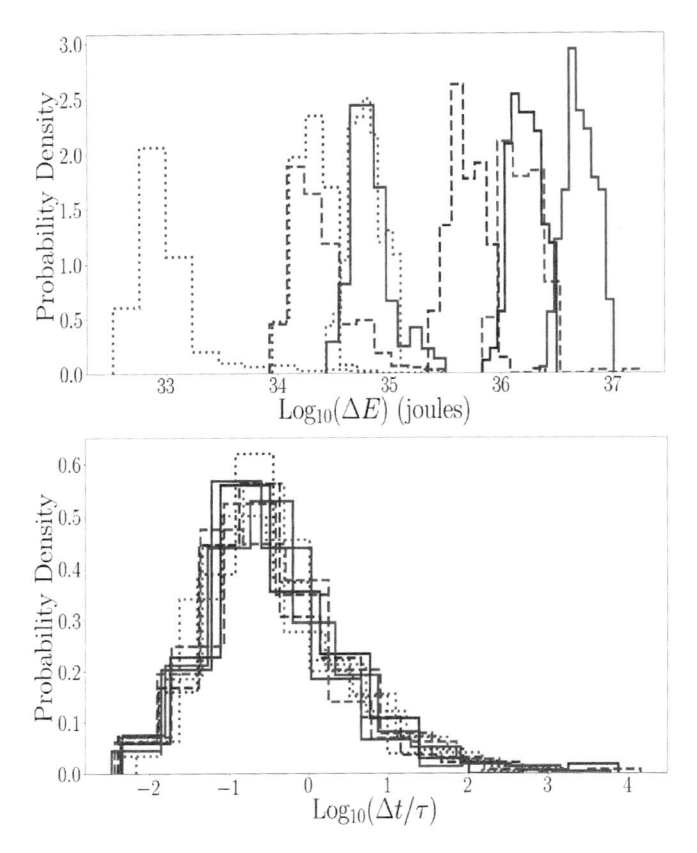

Fig. 1. Size PDFs, measured in joules, for a range of A and D (top panel). Waiting-time PDFs, measured in units of spin-down timescale, τ, for a range of A and D (bottom panel). In both panels red corresponds to $A = 0.1$, blue to $A = 0.5$ and green to $A = 0.9$. The solid lines correspond to $D = 0.1$, dashed to $D = 0.5$ and dotted to $D = 0.9$. Each PDF is constructed from all the events from five simulations. This figure is copied from Ref. 26.

3.3. *Size-waiting-time correlations*

Also of interest are the correlations between the size of an event and the waiting time (recall the waiting time is the time until the next event). We find that the Spearman rank coefficient is ≈ 0.3 uniformly across parameter space. On average larger events affect more of the crust and so, post-failure, cause a larger fraction of the crust to be further from failure, meaning that the average time until the next event is longer. However larger events do not necessarily affect more of the crust, due to the random breaking strains of cells, causing the correlation to be weak. Additionally it is possible for a large event to simply not involve the next-closest-to-failure cell and thus do nothing to delay the next event, further weakening the correlation.

4. Gravitational Radiation

Continuous gravitational waves are the subject of many recent, albeit unsuccessful, searches.[7-13] As such we are motivated to calculate the signal expected from possible sources. Here we consider an isolated spinning-down neutron star with mountains forming due to mechanical failure of the crust. Other potential sources of continuous waves include X-ray binaries[45] and accreting neutron stars.[46] In this model the location of every part of the crust, and the rotational frequency, is known for all of the star's life, so the gravitational wavestrain can be calculated at all times.

In Fig. 2 we plot the wavestrain over time from a neutron star. The two dynamical factors that determine the wavestrain are the changing failure-induced mass-quadrupole moment and the decaying rotational frequency, with $h_0 \propto Q\Omega(t)^2/d$, where h_0 is the gravitational wavestrain, Q is the mass-quadrupole moment, and d is the distance from Earth. At early times spin down is rapid, causing strain to accumulate quickly and many failures to occur, leading to a rapid increase in Q, thus causing the sharp initial rise in Fig. 2. As the star spins down $\dot{\Omega}(t)$ decreases, this slows the rate of mountain creation and causes Q to increase more slowly. At $t/\tau \approx 5$ to 10 the effect of increasing Q balances with the effect of decreasing $\Omega(t)$, causing the wavestrain reach its maximum value. After the peak in wavestrain the decreasing frequency leads to $h_0 \propto (1 + t/\tau)^{-1}$ for $t \gtrsim 10\tau$.

Similar to the size of events the wavestrain is largest near $A = D = 0$ peaking at $h_0 \approx 5 \times 10^{-28}$ and smallest near $A = D = 1$ peaking at $h_0 \approx 1.6 \times 10^{-31}$. Larger events create larger mountains and so lead to a greater wavestrain. Wavestrain reaches a maximum at $t/\tau \approx 5$ to 10, corresponding to $\Omega(t)/2\pi \approx 250$ to 320 Hz. There is no trend with A or D in when the wavestrain peaks. The timing of the peak

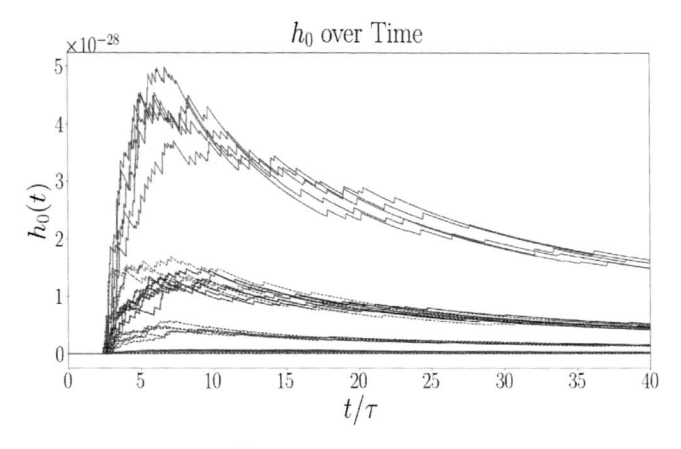

Fig. 2. Gravitational wavestrain, $h_0(t)$, as a function of time, t, in units of the spin-down timescale τ. Each line is the wavestrain of an individual run, of which there are five per value of (A, D). Red corresponds to $A = 0.1$, blue to $A = 0.5$ and green to $A = 0.9$. The solid lines correspond to $D = 0.1$, dashed to $D = 0.5$, dotted to $D = 0.9$. This figure is copied from Ref. 26.

is determined by the rate of events and spin down, neither of which is impacted by A or D.

It should be noted that spin down induced-failure is not the only potential source of mountains on neutron stars. Mountains may form on accreting stars[46] and r-mode oscillations may also lead to a detectable current-quadrupole gravitational wave signal.[47]

5. Conclusion

Electromagnetic spin down drives centrifugal crustal deformation and repeated crustal failure in rotation-powered pulsars. Crustal failure may be responsible for impulsive phenomena like rotational glitches.[4,5] It may also create mountains which lead to the continuous emission of gravitational radiation.[1–3] Molecular dynamics simulations reveal that the crust fails homogeneously, without cracking, under the high pressures on neutron stars.[19] However the simulations are conducted on picometre scales and cannot resolve inhomogeneities on macroscopic length scales (e.g. $\gtrsim 1$ m) such as tectonic plates, faults, and so on, which are seeded by dislocations and other impurities and grow under repeated failure. In this paper, we develop a phenomenological model in the form of a cellular automaton to capture - in a highly idealised form - some of the far-from-equilibrium physics of repeated failure.

We present an idealised cellular automaton to model the evolution of the crust as it both spins down secularly and deforms plastically due to mechanical failure. The secular deformation and strain build up are modelled using the method of Ref. 31. We make use of a nearest-neighbours interaction to model the redistribution and dissipation of strain and the plastic deformation following crustal failure, including the effects of thermal dissipation.

In this model the time, location and size of every failure event are known, as is position of every part of the crust at every point in time. This allows for a wide variety of observables to be predicted, e.g. total tectonic activity, rate of tectonic activity, and number of events. These observables, among others, are investigated in greater detail in Ref. 26. We find the ΔE PDF is qualitatively similar for all values of A and D, namely a tight peak with a tail in increasing ΔE. Events are largest near $A = D = 0$ with $\langle \Delta E \rangle \approx 5.4 \times 10^{36}$ J and smallest near $A = D = 1$ with $\langle \Delta E \rangle \approx 1.9 \times 10^{33}$ J. The gravitational wavestrain follows a similar pattern due to larger events creating larger mountains. The maximum emitted wavestrain in the star's life is greatest near $A = D = 0$ with $h_0 \approx 5 \times 10^{-28}$ and smallest near $A = D = 1$ with $h_0 \approx 1.6 \times 10^{-31}$. In contrast we find that the waiting-time PDF is insensitive to A and D.

The key predictions of this model are (i) in order for failure to occur at all the star must be born spinning $\gtrsim 750$ Hz, consistent with the results of Ref. 27, (ii) once the first failure has occurred failures will continue until $\Omega(t) \approx (0.05 \pm 0.03)\Omega(0)$, and (iii) there is a weak positive correlation (Spearman rank coefficient ≈ 0.3) between the size of an event and the time until the next one.

We plan to improve this calculation in future. Refs. 23 and 24 extend the formalism of Ref. 31. These extensions account for the stratification of the star i.e. they allow for the consideration of a star of multiple variously dense layers, rather than requiring a two component crust-core formulation, additionally they model perturbations from chemical equilibrium.

References

1. K. Riles, Gravitational waves: Sources, detectors and searches, *Progress in Particle and Nuclear Physics* **68**, 1 (2013).
2. G. Woan, M. Pitkin, B. Haskell, D. Jones and P. Lasky, Evidence for a minimum ellipticity in millisecond pulsars, *The Astrophysical Journal Letters* **863**, p. L40 (2018).
3. B. Reed, A. Delbel and C. Horowitz, Modeling the galactic neutron star population for use in continuous gravitational wave searches, *arXiv preprint arxiv:2104.007711* (2021).
4. M. Ruderman, Crust-breaking by neutron superfluids and the vela pulsar glitches, *The Astrophysical Journal* **203**, 213 (1976).
5. J. Middleditch, F. E. Marshall, Q. D. Wang, E. V. Gotthelf and W. Zhang, Predicting the starquakes in psr j0537–6910, *The Astrophysical Journal* **652**, p. 1531 (2006).
6. A. G. Suvorov and K. D. Kokkotas, Young magnetars with fracturing crusts as fast radio burst repeaters, *Monthly Notices of the Royal Astronomical Society* **488**, 5887 (2019).
7. B. Abbott, B. P, R. Abbott, T. Abbott, S. Abraham, F. Acernese, K. Ackley, C. Adams, R. X. Adhikari, V. B. Adya, C. Affeldt *et al.*, Narrow-band search for gravitational waves from known pulsars using the second ligo observing run, *Physical Review D* **99**, p. 122002 (2019).
8. B. Abbott, R. Abbott, T. Abbott, S. Abraham, F. Acernese, K. Ackley, C. Adams, R. Adhikari, V. Adya, C. Affeldt *et al.*, Directional limits on persistent gravitational waves using data from advanced ligo's first two observing runs, *Physical Review D* **100**, p. 062001 (2019).
9. B. Abbott, R. Abbott, T. Abbott, S. Abraham, F. Acernese, K. Ackley, C. Adams, R. Adhikari, V. Adya, C. Affeldt *et al.*, Search for gravitational waves from scorpius x-1 in the second advanced ligo observing run with an improved hidden markov model, *Physical Review D* **100**, p. 122002 (2019).
10. B. Abbott, R. Abbott, T. Abbott, S. Abraham, F. Acernese, K. Ackley, C. Adams, R. Adhikari, V. Adya, C. Affeldt *et al.*, Searches for continuous gravitational waves from 15 supernova remnants and fomalhaut b with advanced ligo, *The Astrophysical Journal* **875**, p. 122 (2019).
11. B. Abbott, R. Abbott, T. Abbott, S. Abraham, F. Acernese, K. Ackley, C. Adams, R. X. Adhikari, V. B. Adya, C. Affeldt *et al.*, Searches for gravitational waves from known pulsars at two harmonics in 2015–2017 ligo data, *The Astrophysical Journal* **879**, p. 10 (2019).
12. R. Abbott, T. Abbott, S. Abraham, F. Acernese, K. Ackley, A. Adams, C. Adams, R. Adhikari, V. Adya, C. Affeldt *et al.*, Gravitational-wave constraints on the equatorial ellipticity of millisecond pulsars, *The Astrophysical journal letters* **902**, p. L21 (2020).
13. M. A. Papa, J. Ming, E. V. Gotthelf, B. Allen, R. Prix, V. Dergachev, H.-B. Eggenstein, A. Singh and S. J. Zhu, Search for continuous gravitational waves from the

central compact objects in supernova remnants cassiopeia a, vela jr., and g347. 3–0.5, *The Astrophysical Journal* **897**, p. 22 (2020).
14. P. Anderson and N. Itoh, Pulsar glitches and restlessness as a hard superfluidity phenomenon, *Nature* **256**, 25 (1975).
15. L. Warszawski and A. Melatos, Gross–pitaevskii model of pulsar glitches, *Monthly Notices of the Royal Astronomical Society* **415**, 1611 (2011).
16. M. Caplan and C. Horowitz, Colloquium: Astromaterial science and nuclear pasta, *Reviews of Modern Physics* **89**, p. 041002 (2017).
17. F. Gittins, N. Andresson and D. Jones, Modelling neutron stars, *arXiv preprint arXiv:2009.12794* (2021).
18. C. Horowitz and J. Hughto, Molecular dynamics simulation of shear moduli for coulomb crystals, *arXiv preprint arXiv:0812.2650* (2008).
19. C. Horowitz and K. Kadau, Breaking strain of neutron star crust and gravitational waves, *Physical Review Letters* **102**, p. 191102 (2009).
20. A. Chugunov and C. Horowitz, Breaking stress of neutron star crust, *Monthly Notices of the Royal Astronomical Society: Letters* **407**, L54 (2010).
21. C. Horowitz, J. Hughto, A. Schneider and D. Berry, Neutron star crust and molecular dynamics simulation, *arXiv preprint arXiv:1109.5095* (2011).
22. D. Baiko and A. Chugunov, Breaking properties of neutron star crust, *Monthly Notices of the Royal Astronomical Society* **480**, 5511 (2018).
23. E. Giliberti, M. Antonelli, G. Cambiotti and P. Pizzochero, Incompressible analytical models for spinning-down pulsars, *Publications of the Astronomical Society of Australia* **36** (2019).
24. E. Giliberti, G. Cambiotti, M. Antonelli and P. Pizzochero, Modelling strains and stresses in continuously stratified rotating neutron stars, *Monthly Notices of the Royal Astronomical Society* **491**, 1064 (2020).
25. R. Burridge and L. Knopoff, Model and theoretical seismicity, *Bulletin of the seismological society of america* **57**, 341 (1967).
26. A. Kerin and A. Melatos, Mountain formation by repeared, inhomogeneous crustal failure in a neutron star, *Submitted to the Monthly Notices of the Royal Astronomical Society* (2021).
27. F. Fattoyev, C. Horowitz and H. Lu, Crust breaking and the limiting rotational frequency of neutron stars, *arXiv preprint arXiv:1804.04952* (2018).
28. A. I. Chugunov, Neutron star crust in voigt approximation: general symmetry of the stress–strain tensor and an universal estimate for the effective shear modulus, *Monthly Notices of the Royal Astronomical Society: Letters* **500**, L17 (2020).
29. A. Kozhberov and D. Yakovlev, Deformed crystals and torsional oscillations of neutron star crust, *Monthly Notices of the Royal Astronomical Society* **498**, 5149 (2020).
30. A. A. Kozhberov, Breaking stress of coulomb crystals in the neutron star crust, *arXiv preprint arXiv:2011.04397* (2020).
31. L. M. Franco, B. Link and R. I. Epstein, Quaking neutron stars, *The Astrophysical Journal* **543**, p. 987 (2000).
32. R. Smoluchowski, Frequency of pulsar starquakes, *Physical Review Letters* **24**, p. 923 (1970).
33. D. Rittel, On the conversion of plastic work to heat during high strain rate deformation of glassy polymers, *Mechanics of Materials* **31**, 131 (1999).
34. P. Rosakis, A. Rosakis, G. Ravichandran and J. Hodowany, A thermodynamic internal variable model for the partition of plastic work into heat and stored energy in metals, *Journal of the Mechanics and Physics of Solids* **48**, 581 (2000).

35. D. Macdougall, Determination of the plastic work converted to heat using radiometry, *Experimental mechanics* **40**, 298 (2000).
36. J. Hodowany, G. Ravichandran, A. Rosakis and P. Rosakis, Partition of plastic work into heat and stored energy in metals, *Experimental mechanics* **40**, 113 (2000).
37. G. Ravichandran, A. J. Rosakis, J. Hodowany and P. Rosakis, On the conversion of plastic work into heat during high-strain-rate deformation, in *AIP conference proceedings*, (1)2002.
38. R. V. R. Hertzberg and J. Hertberg, *Deformation and Fracture mechanics of engineering materials*, 5 edn. (John Wiley and Sons Inc, 2013).
39. D. Kaplan, S. Kulkarni, M. Van Kerkwijk, R. Rothschild, R. Lingenfelter, D. Marsden, R. Danner and T. Murakami, Hubble space telescope observations of sgr 0526–66: New constraints on accretion and magnetar models, *The Astrophysical Journal* **556**, p. 399 (2001).
40. K. Hurley, S. Boggs, D. Smith, R. Duncan, R. Lin, A. Zoglauer, S. Krucker, G. Hurford, H. Hudson, C. Wigger *et al.*, An exceptionally bright flare from sgr 1806–20 and the origins of short-duration γ-ray bursts, *Nature* **434**, 1098 (2005).
41. L. Warszawski and A. Melatos, Knock-on processes in superfluid vortex avalanches and pulsar glitch statistics, *Monthly Notices of the Royal Astronomical Society* **428**, 1911 (2013).
42. W. Fulgenzi, A. Melatos and B. Hughes, Radio pulsar glitches as a state-dependent poisson process, *Monthly Notices of the Royal Astronomical Society* **470**, 4307 (2017).
43. A. Melatos, G. Howitt and W. Fulgenzi, Size-waiting-time correlations in pulsar glitches, *The Astrophysical Journal* **863**, p. 196 (2018).
44. J. B. Carlin and A. Melatos, Autocorrelations in pulsar glitch waiting times and sizes, *Monthly Notices of the Royal Astronomical Society* **488**, 4890 (2019).
45. G. Ushomirsky, L. Bildsten and C. Cutler, Gravitational waves from low-mass x-ray binaries: A status report, in *AIP Conference Proceedings*, (1)2000.
46. G. Ushomirsky, C. Cutler and L. Bildsten, Deformations of accreting neutron star crusts and gravitational wave emission, *Monthly Notices of the Royal Astronomical Society* **319**, 902 (2000).
47. N. Andersson and K. D. Kokkotas, The r-mode instability in rotating neutron stars, *International Journal of Modern Physics D* **10**, 381 (2001).

Gravitational waves from neutrino mass generating phase transitions

Nobuchika Okada

Department of Physics and Astronomy, University of Alabama,
Tuscaloosa, Alabama 35487, USA

Osamu Seto*

Institute for the Advancement of Higher Education, Hokkaido University,
Sapporo 060-0817, Japan, and
Department of Physics, Hokkaido University, Sapporo 060-0810, Japan
* E-mail: seto@particle.sci.hokudai.ac.jp

Some particle physics models with an additional $U(1)$ gauge interaction are interesting because those address the origin of neutrino masses. We show that, in a wide class of models, such an extra $U(1)$ gauge symmetry breaking in the early universe can be first-order phase transition and hence generate a detectable amplitude of stochastic gravitational wave radiation in future experiments. We also discuss the parameter dependence and a possible UV completion.

Keywords: Gravitational waves; Beyond the standard model.

1. Introduction

The detection of gravitational waves (GWs) provides information on the evolution of the Universe at an early stage. Cosmological GWs could originate from, for instance, quantum fluctuations during inflationary expansion[1] and phase transitions.[2,3] The first-order phase transition in the early Universe is one of the promising sources of GWs stochastic background.[4–6] After a first-order phase transition, the dynamics of bubble collision[7–11] and subsequent turbulence of the plasma[12–16] and sonic waves generate GWs.[17–19] These might be within the reach of future space interferometer experiments such as the Big Bang Observer (BBO)[20] and DECi-hertz Interferometer Observatory (DECIGO)[21]; or even ground-based detectors such as Advanced LIGO (aLIGO),[22] and Einstein Telescope (ET),[23] if the transition temperature is below $\mathcal{O}(10^7)$ GeV.[24–26]

One of the important open questions in particle physics is the origin of nonvanishing neutrino masses established by various neutrino oscillation phenomena. The most attractive idea for explaining the tiny neutrino masses is the so-called seesaw mechanism with heavy Majorana right-handed (RH) neutrinos N_R.[27–30] From analogy to the fact that masses of gauge bosons and fermions in the standard model (SM) of particle physics are generated by the breakdown of the electroweak SM gauge symmetry, it is natural to suppose that the masses of heavy RH neutrinos are also generated by developing the vacuum expectation value (VEV) of a Higgs field which breaks a certain symmetry at a high energy scale.

Our Universe has undergone several phase transitions since its birth. The well-known examples are the quark-hadron, aka QCD, transition and the electroweak phase transition. Other promising transitions would be associated with the generation of RH neutrino Majorana masses, and the breakdown of the Great Unified Theory (GUT) gauge symmetry.

The spectrum of stochastic GWs produced by the first-order electroweak phase transition with an extended Higgs sector has been investigated due to interest in the electroweak baryogenesis.[4–6] Among GWs generated by an extra $U(1)$ symmetry breaking,[31–41] one of the simplest and the most promising symmetry is the gauged $U(1)_{B-L}$ (baryon number minus lepton number) symmetry,[42–45] since the SM also poses the $B-L$ symmetry as an accidental global symmetry. In the standard $U(1)_{B-L}$ charge assignment, three RH neutrinos must be introduced to satisfy the conditions for cancellation of the gauge and gravity anomaly. The $U(1)_{B-L}$ may come from a larger GUT symmetry.

In the case that the $U(1)_{B-L}$ symmetry breaking takes place at an energy scale higher than the TeV scale, it is very difficult for any collider experiments to address the mechanism of the symmetry breaking and the RH neutrino mass generation. On the other hand, GWs from the first-order phase transition associated with the spontaneous $U(1)_{B-L}$ gauge symmetry breaking can probe the mechanism. This is what we point out here. For GWs generated by a TeV scale $U(1)_{B-L}$ phase transition, see literature.[32,33,38]

First, we investigate GWs from the first-order phase transition associated with the spontaneous $U(1)_{B-L}$ gauge symmetry breaking within the minimal Higgs model[39] and a non-minimal Higgs model.[35] We show that the first-order phase transition of the Higgs $B-L$ potential can generate a sufficiently large GWs amplitude to be detected in future experiments.

Next, we consider an ultraviolet (UV) completion of such an extra $U(1)$ extended SM. A primary candidate for the completion is an $SO(10)$ GUT model, in which the extra $U(1)$ gauge group along with the SM gauge group is embedded, and all the SM fermions and RH neutrinos in each generation are also unified into a single **16** representation of $SO(10)$ (see, for example, a review[46] and references therein). Among several possible paths of symmetry breaking from the $SO(10)$ to the SM gauge group, we consider the following two step breaking. The first breaking $SO(10)$ into $SU(5) \times U(1)$ takes place at a very high scale $M_{SO(10)}$. As the second step, the $SU(5)$ breaks to the SM gauge group at a scale $M_{SU(5)} \simeq 10^{16}$ GeV. We show that the parameter set compatible with $SO(10)$ unification can produce a detectable GWs spectrum.[41]

This paper is organized as follows: In the next section, we describe the minimal and non-miminal $U(1)_{B-L}$ model and then derive the resultant GWs spectrum by estimating the latent heat and the transition timescale of the phase transition. In Sect. 3, after we describe the outline for the $SO(10)$ unification of the $U(1)$ extended SM based on the gauge group of $SU(3)_C \times SU(2)_L \times U(1)_Y \times U(1)_X$.

through an intermediate path with the $SU(5) \times U(1)_X$ unification, we compute the GWs spectrum generated by the first-order phase transition of $U(1)_X$ and present the resultant GWs spectrum for various sets of the model parameters. The last section is devoted to our summary.

2. Gravitational waves from $U(1)_{B-L}$ phase transition

After we briefly summarize the properties of GWs produced by a first-order phase transition in the early Universe, we show the amplitude and the spectrum of GWs from the first-order phase transition associated with the spontaneous $U(1)_{B-L}$ gauge symmetry breaking within the minimal Higgs model[39] and a non-minimal Higgs model.[35]

2.1. *Scalar potential parameters related to the GW spectrum*

We consider the following two types of tree-level scalar potential. One is the potential for the minimal model:

$$V_0(\Phi_2) = -M_{\Phi_2}^2 \Phi_2 \Phi_2^\dagger + \frac{1}{2}\lambda_2(\Phi_2\Phi_2^\dagger)^2, \quad (1)$$

and the other is a non-minimal form with two Higgs fields:

$$V_0(\Phi_1, \Phi_2) = \frac{1}{2}\lambda_1(\Phi_1\Phi_1^\dagger)^2 + \frac{1}{2}\lambda_2(\Phi_2\Phi_2^\dagger)^2 + \lambda_3 \Phi_1\Phi_1^\dagger(\Phi_2\Phi_2^\dagger)$$
$$+ M_{\Phi_1}^2 \Phi_1\Phi_1^\dagger - M_{\Phi_2}^2 \Phi_2\Phi_2^\dagger - A(\Phi_1\Phi_1\Phi_2^\dagger + \Phi_1^\dagger\Phi_1^\dagger\Phi_2). \quad (2)$$

The subscript i of Φ_i stands for the $B-L$ charge of each Φ_i field. Here, M_{Φ_i}, λ_i, and A are real positive parameters. We omit the SM Higgs field part and its interaction terms because of those little importance. The Yukawa interactions of N_R are given by

$$\mathcal{L}_{Yukawa} \supset -\sum_{i=1}^{3}\sum_{j=1}^{3} Y_D^{ij}\overline{l_L^i} H N_R^j - \frac{1}{2}\sum_{k=1}^{3} Y_{N^k} \Phi_2 \overline{N_R^k{}^C} N_R^k + \text{H.c.}, \quad (3)$$

where the first term is the neutrino Dirac Yukawa coupling, and the second is the Majorana Yukawa couplings. Once the Higgs field Φ_2 develops a nonzero VEV, the $U(1)$ gauge symmetry is broken and the Majorana mass terms of the RH neutrinos and the mass of the extra gauge boson are generated. After the electroweak symmetry breaking, tiny neutrino masses are generated through the seesaw mechanism. The experimental bounds on the extra gauge boson are derived as the LEP constraint $m_{Z'}/g_{B-L} \gtrsim 6$ TeV[47,48] and the LHC Run 2 constraints $m_{Z'} \gtrsim 3.9$ TeV[49–52] for $g_{B-L} \simeq 0.7$.

In order to realize a first-order phase transition, the magnitude of the cubic term in the scalar potential

$$V(\varphi) \sim m^2\varphi^2 - E\varphi^3 + \lambda\varphi^4, \quad (4)$$

is crucial, where φ is defined as $\Phi = \varphi/\sqrt{2}$. There are two possibilities of the origin of the cubic term: One case is that the effective cubic term is induced as loop thermal corrections, and the other is that the term exists in the tree level potential. The cases (1) and (2) above are representative samples of each case. The former corresponds to the case of thermal correction and the later does to the tree level model respectively.

In calculation of the phase transition, we include one-loop corrections to the scalar potential for zero temperature $\Delta V_{1-\text{loop}}(\varphi)$ and that for a finite temperature T given by

$$\Delta V_T(\varphi) = \sum_s g_s \frac{T^4}{2\pi^2} J_B(m_s^2(\varphi)/T^2) - \sum_f g_f \frac{T^4}{2\pi^2} J_F(m_f^2(\varphi)/T^2)$$
$$+ \sum_v g_v \frac{T^4}{2\pi^2} J_B(m_v^2(\varphi)/T^2), \tag{5}$$

where g_i, with $i = s$ (scalars), f (fermions) and v (vectors) denotes the number of internal degrees of freedom, $m_i(\varphi)$ are φ dependent masses for i-th particles. $J_{B(F)}$ is an auxiliary function in thermal corrections.[53,54] As is well known, $J_B(x^2)$ is expressed as

$$J_B(x^2) \simeq -\frac{\pi^4}{45} + \frac{\pi^2}{12}x^2 - \frac{\pi}{6}(x^2)^{3/2} + ..., \tag{6}$$

at the high temperature expansion. The third term induces the effective cubic term that could make the transition of the first order even if the tree level potential does not contain a cubic term as in the potential (1).

For our numerical calculations, we have implemented our models into the public code `CosmoTransitions`,[55] where both zero- and finite-temperature one-loop effective potentials with the corrections for resummation,

$$V_{\text{eff}}(\varphi, T) = V_0(\varphi) + \Delta V_{1-\text{loop}}(\varphi) + \Delta V_T(\varphi, T), \tag{7}$$

have been calculated in the $\overline{\text{MS}}$ renormalization scheme. Here, as a caveat, we note that there is a long-standing open problem of gauge dependence on the use of the effective Higgs potential. Our results are also subjects of this issue[56,57] and should be regarded as a reference value.

By using `CosmoTransitions`, we find the bounce solution of φ and the bounce action for the transition, the bubble nucleation temperature $T_\star$,[58] and the latent heat energy density ϵ in the radiation dominated Universe. With the bounce solution and action, we obtain the dimensionless transition timescale

$$\frac{\beta}{H_\star} \simeq T\frac{dS}{dT}\bigg|_{T_\star} = T\frac{d(S_E^3/T)}{dT}\bigg|_{T_\star}, \tag{8}$$

with

$$\beta \equiv -\frac{dS}{dt}\bigg|_{t_\star}, \tag{9}$$

from the bounce action[10] in the four-dimensional Minkowski space S and in the three-dimensional Euclidean space S_E^3. Here, $t_\star$ is the bubble nucleation time.

2.2. *The GW spectrum*

There are three main processes and mechanisms of GWs production: bubble collisions, turbulence and sound waves after bubble collisions. The resulting spectrum of the generated background GWs is given by

$$\Omega_{GW}(f) = \Omega_{GW}^{\text{coll}}(f) + \Omega_{GW}^{\text{sw}}(f) + \Omega_{GW}^{\text{turb}}(f), \qquad (10)$$

in terms of the density parameter Ω_{GW}. The three terms on the right side indicate the GW produced by bubble collisions, sound waves, and turbulence, respectively. We adopt the fitting formula of spectrum commonly adopted in literature[4–6] as well as our papers.[35,39,41]

We only show predicted GWs spectra for our benchmark points of the minimal Higgs model (1) with expected sensitivities of various future experiments,[59] while one may find the similar spectrum of GWs in non-minimal model.[35] One benchmark point $(g_{B-L}, v_2, \lambda_2) = (0.44, 4\,\text{TeV}, 1.5 \times 10^{-4})$ is shown by the green curve, while the other $(g_{B-L}, v_2, \lambda_2) = (0.46, 3.8 \times 10^3\,\text{TeV}, 4.0 \times 10^{-4})$ is shown by the red curve in Fig. 1. The green curve point is similar to the lowest energy case satisfying the LHC limit. An approximate relationship can be seen that f_{peak} is proportional to the VEV of Φ_2, v_2. Next, we discuss the resulting GWs spectrum gauge coupling dependency. The GWs spectrum for various values of the $B - L$ gauge coupling constant for the fixed value of $v_2 = 10$ TeV and $\lambda_2 = 0.002$ is shown in Fig. 2. We have found a mild dependence for the frequency but the amplitude is quite sensitive. The largest amplitude is obtained for $0.35 \lesssim g_{B-L} \lesssim 0.4$. Here, we note that the GWs amplitude in Figs. 1 and 2 have been re-evaluated with taking the suppression effect due to the short-lasting sonic wave[60–64] into account and smaller than previous estimations.[39]

3. UV completion by SO(10)

3.1. *From $U(1)_{B-L}$ to $U(1)_X$*

We consider the UV completion of the $U(1)$ extended SM by $SO(10)$ GUT via the intermediate step of $SU(5) \times U(1)_X$ unification. To realize this partial unification, we generalize $U(1)_{B-L}$ of the minimal $B - L$ model to $U(1)_X$, under which the charge of an SM field is defined as a linear combination of its hyper-charge and $B - L$ charge, $q_X = Yx + Q_{B-L}$, with x being a real constant.[65,66] The particle content of this model is listed in Table 1. Except for the introduction of the new parameter x, the model properties are quite similar to those of the minimal $B - L$ model, which is realized as the special case of $x = 0$. Another limit $|x| \gg 1$ is called a "hyper-charge oriented" case.[67–69]

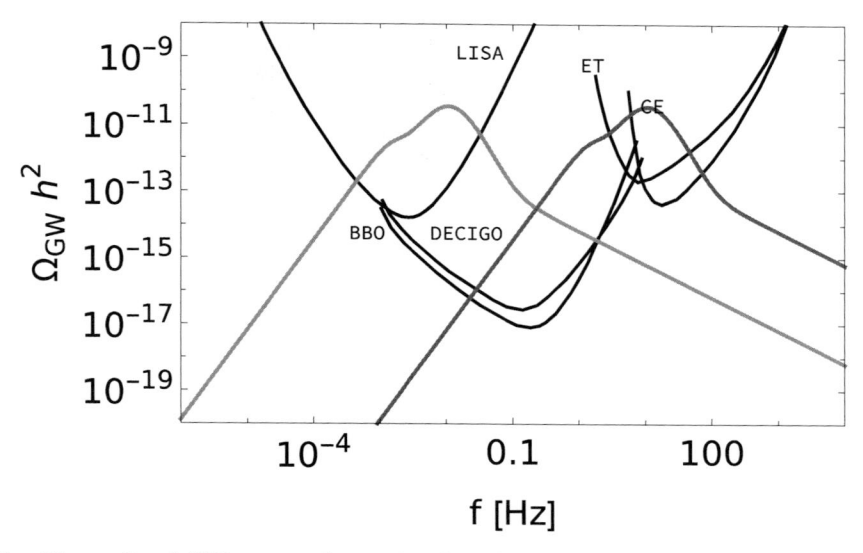

Fig. 1. The predicted GWs spectra for two benchmark points are shown. The expected sensitivities of each indicated experiments[59] are shown by black solid curves.

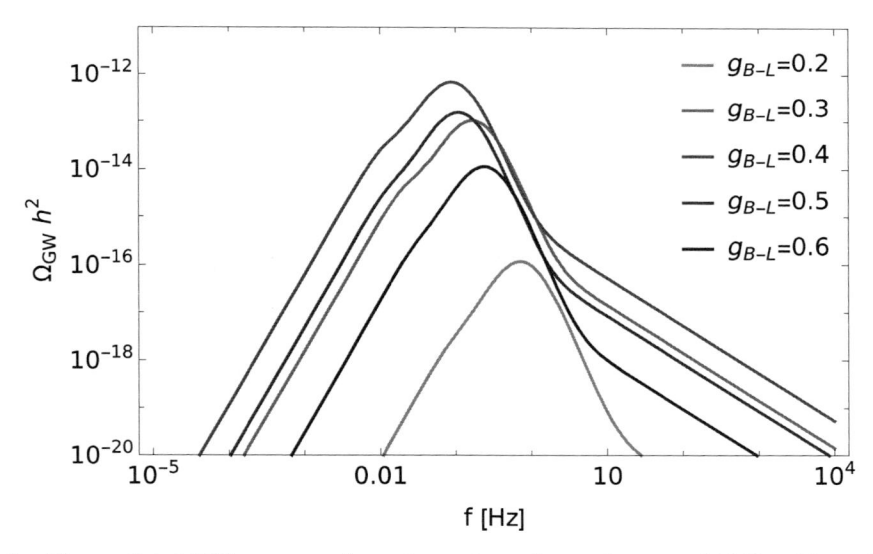

Fig. 2. The predicted GWs spectrum for various values of g_{B-L} for $v_2 = 10$ TeV and $\lambda_2 = 0.002$.

3.2. $SU(5) \times U(1)_X$ unification

3.2.1. $SU(5) \times U(1)_X$ embedding

We now consider the embedding,

$$SU(5) \times U(1)_X \supset SU(3)_C \times SU(2)_L \times U(1)_Y \times U(1)_X. \tag{11}$$

Table 1. The particle content of the minimal $U(1)_X$ model. In addition to the SM particle content ($i = 1, 2, 3$), three RH neutrinos N_R^i ($i = 1, 2, 3$) and one $U(1)_X$ Higgs field Φ_2 are introduced.

	$SU(3)_C$	$SU(2)_L$	$U(1)_Y$	$U(1)_X$
q_L^i	3	2	$\frac{1}{6}$	$\frac{1}{6}x + \frac{1}{3}$
u_R^i	3	1	$\frac{2}{3}$	$\frac{2}{3}x + \frac{1}{3}$
d_R^i	3	1	$-\frac{1}{3}$	$-\frac{1}{3}x + \frac{1}{3}$
ℓ_L^i	1	2	$-\frac{1}{2}$	$-\frac{1}{2}x - 1$
e_R^i	1	1	-1	$-x - 1$
N_R^i	1	1	0	-1
H	1	2	$-\frac{1}{2}$	$-\frac{1}{2}x$
Φ_2	1	1	0	-2

As in the standard $SU(5)$ GUT,[70] the charge conjugation of RH down quarks and left-handed leptons are embedded in $\mathbf{5^*}$ representation of $SU(5)$, while left-handed quarks, the charge conjugation of RH up quarks, and the charge conjugation of RH charged leptons are embedded in $\mathbf{10}$ representation:

$$\mathbf{5^*} \supset d_R^{iC} \oplus \ell_L^i, \qquad \mathbf{10} \supset q_L^i \oplus u_R^{iC} \oplus \ell_R^{iC}. \qquad (12)$$

This is possible for $x = -4/5$ and hence the $SU(5)$ unification leads to a quantization of $U(1)_X$ charge.[71]

3.2.2. Gauge coupling unification to $SU(5)$

A simple setup to achieve the unification of the three SM gauge couplings is to introduce two pairs of vector-like quarks ($Q + \bar{Q}$ and $D + \bar{D}$) with TeV scale masses, M_Q and M_D, respectively. Their representations are listed in Table 2. In the presence of the exotic quarks, the SM gauge couplings are successfully unified at $M_{SU(5)} \simeq 10^{16}$ GeV.[72-78] This unification scale corresponds to the proton lifetime of $\tau_p \simeq 10^{38}$ yr, which is much longer than the current experimental lower limit of $\tau(p \to \pi^0 e^+) \simeq 10^{34}$ yr reported by the Super-Kamiokande collaboration.[79]

Table 2. Representations of the vector-like quarks.

	$SU(3)_C$	$SU(2)_L$	$U(1)_Y$	$U(1)_X$
Q	3	2	$\frac{1}{6}$	$\frac{1}{5}$
$\bar{Q}$	3^*	2	$-\frac{1}{6}$	$-\frac{1}{5}$
D	3	1	$-\frac{1}{3}$	$\frac{3}{5}$
$\bar{D}$	3^*	1	$\frac{1}{3}$	$-\frac{3}{5}$

We show the gauge coupling unification by solving the renormalization group (RG) equations of the SM gauge couplings including the contributions of exotic quarks Q and D also into the beta function coefficients. Our results are shown in Fig. 3. We set the vector-like quark masses to be $M_Q = M_D = 1.5$ TeV, which satisfy the latest LHC bounds.[80,81] We find that three SM gauge couplings are successfully unified at $M_{\text{SU}(5)} \simeq 2.24 \times 10^{16}$ GeV. We will discuss the RG evolution for g_χ in the next subsection.

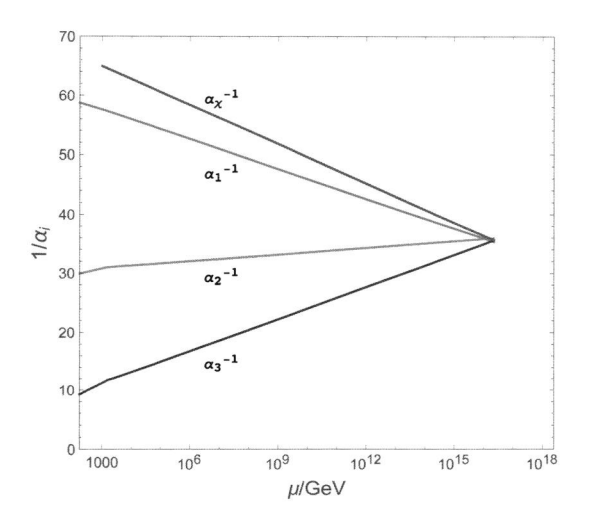

Fig. 3. The RG evolution of the gauge couplings of the $U(1)$ extended SM with the vector-like quarks. Three SM gauge couplings are unified at $M_{\text{SU}(5)} \simeq 2.24 \times 10^{16}$ GeV. The results for the case of $M_{\text{SU}(5)} = M_{\text{SO}(10)}$.

3.3. *SO(10) unification*

The $SU(5) \times U(1)_X$ can be embedded into $SO(10)$. The decomposition of several $SO(10)$ multiplets to $SU(5) \times U(1)_X$ is given by[82]:

$SO(10) \supset SU(5) \times U(1)_X$

$\mathbf{10} = \mathbf{5}(-2/5) + \mathbf{5}^*(2/5),$

$\mathbf{16} = \mathbf{1}(1) + \mathbf{5}^*(-3/5) + \mathbf{10}(1/5),$

$\mathbf{45} = \mathbf{1}(0) + \mathbf{10}(-4/5) + \mathbf{10}^*(4/5) + \mathbf{24}(0),$

$\mathbf{126} = \mathbf{1}(2) + \mathbf{5}^*(2/5) + \mathbf{10}(6/5) + \mathbf{15}^*(-6/5) + \mathbf{45}(-2/5) + \mathbf{50}^*(2/5).$

The SM fermions and RH neutrinos are embedded in **16** representation. The SM Higgs doublet (H) is embedded in **10** representation,[a] while the $U(1)_X$ Higgs field (Φ_2) is in **126** representation. Exotic quarks $D + \bar{D}$ in $(\mathbf{5}, 3/5) + (\mathbf{5}^*, -3/5)$ are embedded in $\mathbf{16}^* + \mathbf{16}$ multiplets in the $SO(10)$ GUT, while $Q + \bar{Q}$ in $(\mathbf{10}, 1/5) + (\mathbf{10}^*, -1/5)$ are embedded in $\mathbf{16} + \mathbf{16}^*$ multiplets. Similarly to the embedding of

---

[a]To be precise, for deriving realistic SM fermion mass matrices, the SM Higgs doublet is identified with a linear combination of $SU(2)_L$ doublets in **10** and **126** representations. See Eq. (15) for the Yukawa coupling in the $SO(10)$ GUT.

$U(1)_Y$ into $SU(5)$, the $SO(10)$ GUT normalization of $U(1)_X$ is given by

$$g_X = \sqrt{\frac{5}{8}} g_\chi, \qquad\qquad Q_X = \sqrt{\frac{5}{8}} Q_\chi. \qquad (13)$$

For simplicity, we assume the $SO(10)$ symmetry breaking to the $U(1)_X$ extended SM by non-zero vacuum expectation values (VEVs) of $\langle \mathbf{1}(0) \rangle$ and $\langle \mathbf{24}(0) \rangle$ in a **45**-representation Higgs field:

$$SO(10) \xrightarrow[\langle \mathbf{1}(0) \rangle]{} SU(5) \times U(1)_X \xrightarrow[\langle \mathbf{24}(0) \rangle]{} SU(3)_C \times SU(2)_L \times U(1)_Y \times U(1)_X. \qquad (14)$$

The final $U(1)_X$ breaking can be realized by a non-zero VEV of $\Phi_2^\dagger = \mathbf{1}(2) \subset \mathbf{126}$ Higgs field. The Yukawa interactions for the SM fermions are given by

$$\mathcal{L}_{\text{Yukawa}} \supset Y_{10} \mathbf{16}_f \mathbf{16}_f \mathbf{10}_H + Y_{126} \mathbf{16}_f \mathbf{16}_f \mathbf{126}_H^\dagger, \qquad (15)$$

where $\mathbf{16}_f$ is a fermion multiplet (the generation index is suppressed), and $\mathbf{10}_H$ and $\mathbf{126}_H$ are Higgs fields. Referring the above decomposition, one can see that the VEV of $\mathbf{1}(2) \subset \mathbf{126}$ Higgs breaks the $U(1)_X$ symmetry and generates Majorana masses of RH neutrinos in $\mathbf{16}_f$ through the Yukawa coupling Y_{126} in Eq. (15).

3.4. *Gauge coupling unification to $SO(10)$*

After the successful unification of the SM gauge groups to $SU(5)$ at $M_{\text{SU}(5)}$ we consider the unification of $SU(5) \times U(1)_\chi \to SO(10)$ at $M_{\text{SO}(10)}$. The simplest case is $M_{\text{SU}(5)} = M_{\text{SO}(10)}$, then the running coupling $g_\chi(\mu)$ is determined so as to satisfy the unification condition $g_\chi(M_{\text{SU}(5)}) = g_i(M_{\text{SU}(5)})$ ($i = 1, 2, 3$). The result is shown in the left-handed panel of Fig. 3. For a case of $M_{\text{SU}(5)} < M_{\text{SO}(10)}$, we need to solve the RG evolution of g_5 and g_χ in the energy range of $M_{\text{SU}(5)} < \mu < M_{\text{SO}(10)}$. We omit discussion of those cases here, however, we have shown that the unification of $SU(5) \times U(1)_\chi$ into $SO(10)$ is possible.

3.5. *The GW spectrum*

First, we show the dependence of the GWs spectrum on the energy scale of symmetry breaking, or equivalently, the VEV (v_2) scale. In Fig. 4 we show the GWs spectrum for different symmetry breaking scales for a fixed value of $\lambda_2 = 6 \times 10^{-4}$. As expected, the peak frequency becomes higher, as the symmetry breaking occurs at higher energies. The black solid curves denote the expected sensitivities of each indicated experiment: LISA, DECIGO, BBO, ET, and Cosmic Explore (CE). The expected sensitivity curves for each experiment were based on one of the latest results.[59]

Next, we study how the $U(1)_X$ Higgs quartic coupling and Yukawa coupling affect the resultant GWs spectrum. As a Yukawa coupling increases, the peak amplitude decreases with the peak frequency increasing. This is because fermion loops generate only thermal mass term and not an effective trilinear term in the thermal potential (5), which weakens the first order phase transition. Assuming the hierarchy among the Yukawa couplings as $Y_{N_3} \equiv Y_N \gg Y_{N_2}, Y_{N_1}$, for simplicity, we show in Fig. 5 the GWs spectrum for various values of Y_N and λ_2 for $g_\chi = 0.463$ and $v_2 = 1$ PeV.

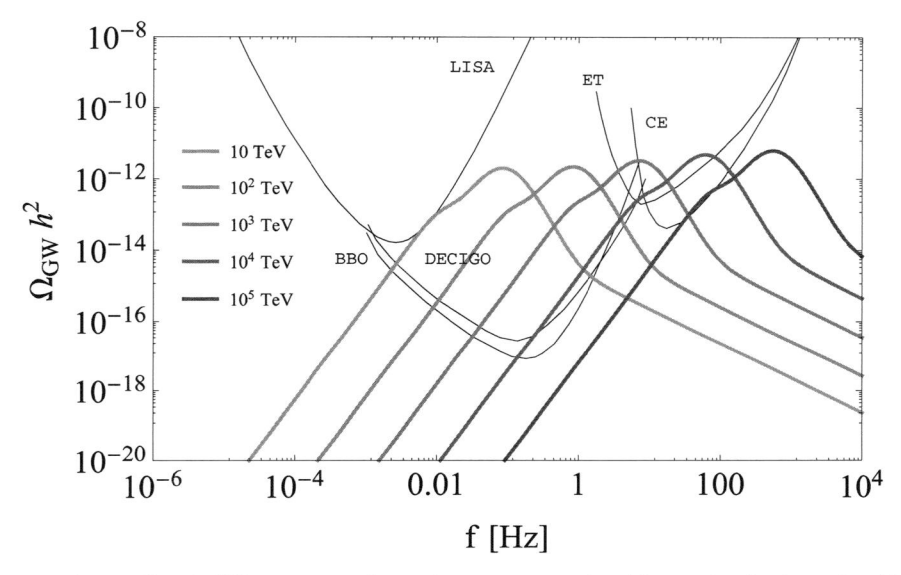

Fig. 4. The predicted GWs spectrum for various symmetry breaking scales for $\lambda_2 = 6 \times 10^{-4}$. The difference of the symmetry breaking scale is indicated by colors as shown in the legends. The expected sensitivities of each indicated experiments[59] are shown by black solid curves.

4. Summary

In this paper, we have considered the $U(1)_X$ extended SM and studied the spectrum of stochastic GWs generated by the first-order phase transition associated with the extra $U(1)_X$ symmetry breaking in the early Universe. This breaking is responsible for the generation of Majorana masses of RH neutrinos and may be surveyed by the GWs spectrum.

We also have shown a UV completion of the $U(1)_X$ extended SM by an $SO(10)$ GUT. We have found that the first-order phase transition triggered by this extra $U(1)$ symmetry breaking can be strong enough to generate GWs with a detectable size of amplitude if the $U(1)_X$ Higgs quartic coupling is small enough and the symmetry breaking scale (the bubble nucleation temperature $T_\star$) is smaller than about 10^5 (10^4) TeV.

We have also clarified the dependence of the resultant GWs spectrum on the RH neutrino Majorana Yukawa couplings, in other words, the mass scale of RH neutrinos. It can be seen as the reduction of the amplitude and the shift of peak

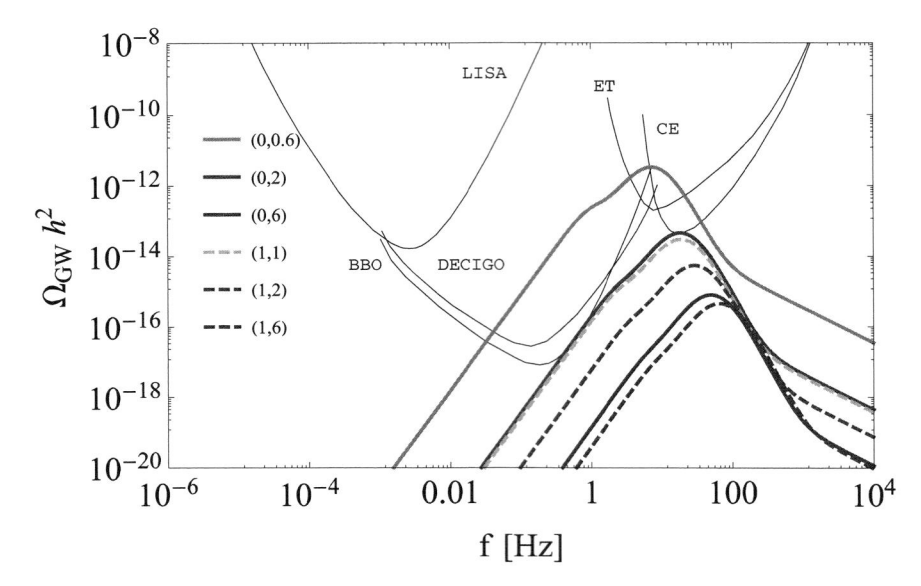

Fig. 5. The predicted GWs spectrum for various values of Y_N and λ_2 for $g_\chi = 0.463$ and $v_2 = 1$ PeV. Parameters in the legend denote $(Y_N, \lambda_2 \times 10^3)$.

frequency of GWs background, which is very similar to the effect of the variation of the $U(1)_X$ Higgs quartic coupling nevertheless.

Acknowledgments

We thank Taiki Hasegawa and Hikaru Uchida for collaboration which results were in part based on. This work is supported in part by the U.S. DOE Grant No. DE-SC0012447 (N.O.), the Japan Society for the Promotion of Science (JSPS) KAKENHI Grants No. 19K03860, No. 19H05091, No. 19K03865, and No. 21H00060. (O.S.).

References

1. A. A. Starobinsky, JETP Lett. **30**, 682 (1979) [Pisma Zh. Eksp. Teor. Fiz. **30**, 719 (1979)].
2. E. Witten, Phys. Rev. D **30**, 272 (1984).
3. C. J. Hogan, Mon. Not. Roy. Astron. Soc. **218**, 629 (1986).
4. C. Caprini and D. G. Figueroa, Class. Quant. Grav. **35**, 163001 (2018).
5. A. Mazumdar and G. White, Rept. Prog. Phys. **82**, no. 7, 076901 (2019).
6. C. Caprini, M. Chala, G. C. Dorsch, M. Hindmarsh, S. J. Huber, T. Konstandin, J. Kozaczuk, G. Nardini, J. M. No, K. Rummukainen, P. Schwaller, G. Servant, A. Tranberg and D. J. Weir, JCAP **03**, 024 (2020).
7. M. S. Turner and F. Wilczek, Phys. Rev. Lett. **65**, 3080 (1990).
8. A. Kosowsky, M. S. Turner and R. Watkins, Phys. Rev. D **45**, 4514 (1992).
9. A. Kosowsky, M. S. Turner and R. Watkins, Phys. Rev. Lett. **69**, 2026 (1992).

10. M. S. Turner, E. J. Weinberg and L. M. Widrow, Phys. Rev. D **46**, 2384 (1992).
11. A. Kosowsky and M. S. Turner, Phys. Rev. D **47**, 4372 (1993).
12. M. Kamionkowski, A. Kosowsky and M. S. Turner, Phys. Rev. D **49**, 2837 (1994).
13. A. Kosowsky, A. Mack and T. Kahniashvili, Phys. Rev. D **66**, 024030 (2002).
14. A. D. Dolgov, D. Grasso and A. Nicolis, Phys. Rev. D **66**, 103505 (2002).
15. G. Gogoberidze, T. Kahniashvili and A. Kosowsky, Phys. Rev. D **76**, 083002 (2007).
16. C. Caprini, R. Durrer and G. Servant, JCAP **0912**, 024 (2009).
17. M. Hindmarsh, S. J. Huber, K. Rummukainen and D. J. Weir, Phys. Rev. Lett. **112**, 041301 (2014).
18. M. Hindmarsh, S. J. Huber, K. Rummukainen and D. J. Weir, Phys. Rev. D **92**, 123009 (2015).
19. M. Hindmarsh, Phys. Rev. Lett. **120**, 071301 (2018).
20. G. M. Harry, P. Fritschel, D. A. Shaddock, W. Folkner and E. S. Phinney, Class. Quant. Grav. **23**, 4887 (2006); Erratum: [Class. Quant. Grav. **23**, 7361 (2006)].
21. N. Seto, S. Kawamura and T. Nakamura, Phys. Rev. Lett. **87**, 221103 (2001).
22. G. M. Harry [LIGO Scientific Collaboration], Class. Quant. Grav. **27**, 084006 (2010).
23. M. Punturo *et al.*, Class. Quant. Grav. **27**, 194002 (2010).
24. C. Grojean and G. Servant, Phys. Rev. D **75**, 043507 (2007).
25. P. S. B. Dev and A. Mazumdar, Phys. Rev. D **93**, 104001 (2016).
26. C. Balazs, A. Fowlie, A. Mazumdar and G. White, Phys. Rev. D **95**, 043505 (2017).
27. P. Minkowski, Phys. Lett. **67B**, 421 (1977).
28. T. Yanagida, Conf. Proc. C **7902131**, 95 (1979).
29. M. Gell-Mann, P. Ramond, and R. Slansky, Conf. Proc. C **790927**, 315 (1979).
30. R. N. Mohapatra and G. Senjanovic, Phys. Rev. Lett. **44**, 912 (1980).
31. R. Jinno, K. Nakayama and M. Takimoto, Phys. Rev. D **93**, 045024 (2016).
32. R. Jinno and M. Takimoto, Phys. Rev. D **95**, 015020 (2017).
33. W. Chao, W. F. Cui, H. K. Guo and J. Shu, Chin. Phys. C **44**, no. 12, 123102 (2020).
34. K. Hashino, M. Kakizaki, S. Kanemura, P. Ko and T. Matsui, JHEP **1806**, 088 (2018).
35. N. Okada and O. Seto, Phys. Rev. D **98**, 063532 (2018).
36. K. Hashino, R. Jinno, M. Kakizaki, S. Kanemura, T. Takahashi and M. Takimoto, Phys. Rev. D **99**, no. 7, 075011 (2019).
37. V. Brdar, A. J. Helmboldt and J. Kubo, JCAP **1902**, 021 (2019).
38. C. Marzo, L. Marzola and V. Vaskonen, Eur. Phys. J. C **79**, no. 7, 601 (2019).
39. T. Hasegawa, N. Okada and O. Seto, Phys. Rev. D **99**, no. 9, 095039 (2019).
40. N. Haba and T. Yamada, Phys. Rev. D **101**, no. 7, 075027 (2020).
41. N. Okada, O. Seto and H. Uchida, PTEP **2021**, no. 3, 033B01 (2021).
42. J. C. Pati and A. Salam, Phys. Rev. D **8**, 1240-1251 (1973).
43. A. Davidson, Phys. Rev. D **20**, 776 (1979).
44. R. N. Mohapatra and R. E. Marshak, Phys. Rev. Lett. **44**, 1316 (1980) [Erratum-ibid. **44**, 1643 (1980)].
45. R. E. Marshak and R. N. Mohapatra, Phys. Lett. B **91**, 222 (1980).
46. T. Fukuyama, Int. J. Mod. Phys. A **28**, 1330008 (2013).
47. M. Carena, A. Daleo, B. A. Dobrescu and T. M. P. Tait, Phys. Rev. D **70**, 093009 (2004).
48. J. Heeck, Phys. Lett. B **739**, 256 (2014).
49. N. Okada and S. Okada, Phys. Rev. D **93**, 075003 (2016).
50. N. Okada and S. Okada, Phys. Rev. D **95**, 035025 (2017).
51. N. Okada and O. Seto, Mod. Phys. Lett. A **33**, 1850157 (2018).
52. S. Okada, Adv. High Energy Phys. **2018**, 5340935 (2018).
53. M. L. Bellac, *Thermal Field Theory*, Cambridge University Press (1996).

54. J. I. Kapusta and C. Gale, *Finite-Temperature Field Theory: Principles and Applications*, Cambridge University Press (2011).
55. C. L. Wainwright, Comput. Phys. Commun. **183**, 2006 (2012).
56. C. L. Wainwright, S. Profumo and M. J. Ramsey-Musolf, Phys. Rev. D **86**, 083537 (2012).
57. C. W. Chiang and E. Senaha, Phys. Lett. B **774**, 489 (2017).
58. S. J. Huber and T. Konstandin, JCAP **0809**, 022 (2008).
59. K. Schmitz, JHEP **01**, 097 (2021).
60. J. Ellis, M. Lewicki and J. M. No, JCAP **1904**, 003 (2019).
61. J. Ellis, M. Lewicki, J. M. No and V. Vaskonen, JCAP **1906**, 024 (2019).
62. D. Cutting, M. Hindmarsh and D. J. Weir, Phys. Rev. Lett. **125**, no. 2, 021302 (2020).
63. M. Hindmarsh and M. Hijazi, JCAP **1912**, no. 12, 062 (2019).
64. J. Ellis, M. Lewicki and J. M. No, JCAP **07**, 050 (2020).
65. T. Appelquist, B. A. Dobrescu and A. R. Hopper, Phys. Rev. D **68** 035012 (2003).
66. S. Oda, N. Okada and D. s. Takahashi, Phys. Rev. D **92**, no. 1, 015026 (2015).
67. N. Okada, S. Okada and D. Raut, Phys. Rev. D **95** no. 5, 055030 (2017).
68. S. Oda, N. Okada, D. Raut and D.-s. Takahashi, Phys. Rev. D **97** no. 5, 055001 (2018).
69. N. Okada, S. Okada and Q. Shafi, Phys. Lett. B **810**, 135845 (2020).
70. H. Georgi and S. L. Glashow, Phys. Rev. Lett. **32**, 438 (1974).
71. N. Okada, S. Okada and D. Raut, Phys. Lett. B **780**, 422 (2018).
72. U. Amaldi, W. de Boer, P. H. Frampton, H. Furstenau and J. T. Liu, Phys. Lett. B **281**, 374 (1992).
73. J. L. Chkareuli, I. G. Gogoladze and A. B. Kobakhidze, Phys. Lett. B **340**, 63 (1994).
74. J. L. Chkareuli, I. G. Gogoladze and A. B. Kobakhidze, Phys. Lett. B **376**, 111 (1996).
75. D. Choudhury, T. M. P. Tait and C. E. M. Wagner, Phys. Rev. D **65**, 053002 (2002).
76. D. E. Morrissey and C. E. M. Wagner, Phys. Rev. D **69**, 053001 (2004).
77. I. Gogoladze, B. He and Q. Shafi, Phys. Lett. B **690**, 495 (2010).
78. H. Y. Chen, I. Gogoladze, S. Hu, T. Li and L. Wu, Eur. Phys. J. C **78**, no. 1, 26 (2018).
79. K. Abe *et al.* [Super-Kamiokande Collaboration], Phys. Rev. D **95**, no. 1, 012004 (2017).
80. A. M. Sirunyan *et al.* [CMS Collaboration], JHEP **1808**, 177 (2018).
81. A. M. Sirunyan *et al.* [CMS Collaboration], Phys. Rev. D **100**, no. 7, 072001 (2019).
82. R. Slansky, Phys. Rept. **79**, 1 (1981).

Efficiency of registration of chirp bursts and signals of collapsing stars by the Euro-Asian network of GW interferometers

V. N. Rudenko[1,2,3], S. L. Andrusenko[3], D. P. Krichevskiy[1,3], G. D. Manucharyan[1,3]

[1]*Sternberg Astronomical Institute, Lomonosov State University,*
Universitetskii prospect 13, Moscow, 119234, Russia
[2]*Faculty of Physics, Lomonosov Moscow State University,*
Leninskie Gory, Moscow 119991 Russia
[3]*Bauman Moscow State Technical University, Physics Department,*
2-nd Baumanskaya street 5, building 1, Moscow, 105005, Russia

In this report, we evaluate the performance of the proposed Euro-Asian network (EAN) of gravitational wave (GW) interferometers, which is planned taking into account the location of one of the detectors at the RAS Novosibirsk Scientific Center. EAN is formed by four detectors: VIRGO, KAGRA, LIGO India and Novosibirsk. The efficiency of this configuration is calculated based on typical numerical criteria for wide area networks.[1] One of the key criteria is the accuracy of reconstructing the parameters of GW bursts, which links the calculation of this criterion to a specific class of astrophysical sources. We present results for calculations performed for the chirp signals from the of relativistic binaries inspiral and for signals from rotating collapsing stars. Maximizing the integral criterion we find the optimal orientation of the Novosibirsk detector, which is specified by the angle between the south direction and the bisector of the Michelson arms of the GW interferometer.

Keywords: Gravitational waves; Network of detectors; Binary merger; gravitational collapse

1. Introduction

In September 2015, the first direct registration of a gravitational-wave burst from the merger of a relativistic binary, whose components were evaluated as black holes (BH), took place. The detection of this event was carried out using LIGO detectors.[2] After there were several other similar registrations. A qualitative step was the registration by three detectors (including a similar interferometer VIRGO in Europe) GW170814 burst from the merger of BH binary ($M = 30M_\odot$) from the distance of 540 Mps,[3] which allowed to reduce the localization zone of the source on the celestial sphere by an order of magnitude, up to $\sim 60\ deg^2$. A gravitational wave (GW) signal from neutron stars (NS) merger was registered, coinciding with GRB170817A gamma burst (with $1.7\ s$ delay).[4] One of the most recent significant steps is the registration of gravitational waves from the neutron star – black hole binaries coalescence.[5] All these facts allow to claim confidently real occurrence of a new gravitational-wave channel of astrophysical information and heuristic value of multi-messenger astronomy, i.e. strategy of parallel observation of transients on detectors of different physical nature. However, there is still no observation of gravitational waves from supernova as well as significant coincidence between

LIGO/VIGRO data and neutrino detectors like NOvA[6] and IceCube[7] experiments. Gravitational waves from core-collapse supernovae can serve as an important source of information about the processes occurring during a given event.[8]

In this context, we continue the discussion of a European-Asian network (EAN)[9] which consists of four antennas in the northern hemisphere: VIRGO in Italy, KAGRA in Japan, LIGO-India in India and the planned new additional antenna in Novosibirsk. In order to assess the scientific feasibility and efficiency of such a network the calculation of its main characteristics was performed in the approach developed in Refs. 1, 10.

Here we consider two sources of gravitational wave signals: inspiral of a relativistic binary and collapsing stars at the protoneutron star stage which is subjected to rotational instabilities. For both sources we define the optimal orientation angle of possible detector in Novosibirsk by maximizing the integral effiency criteria.

Table 1 shows the coordinates of the detectors in question. The detector orientation angle γ is defined as the angle between the southward direction at the detector location and the bisector of the angle formed by its arms, measured counterclockwise.

Table 1. Detector data; all angles given in degrees.

Detector	Latitude l	Longitude L	Orientation γ
VIRGO	43.6	-10.5	206.5
KAGRA	36.4	-137.3	163.3
LIGO India	19.6	-77.0	254.0
Novosibirsk	55.0	-82.9	to be defined

It's worth noting that in addition to the planning Novosibirsk interferometer, today a project of search for neutrino and gravitational correlations using the OGRAN gravitational detector and the BUST neutrino telescope is being developed in Russia.[11]

2. Criteria of a network

To estimate efficiency of a network of ground based detectors it's necessary to construct power patterns of individual components and the whole network. Here we review the basic information necessary for construction of the pattern and calculation of the criteria.

In the long wavelength approximation (the GW wavelength is much larger than the interferometer arm length L) the detector response can be evaluated as

$$h(t) = \frac{\delta L}{L} = F_+(\theta, \varphi, \psi) h_+(t) + F_\times(\theta, \varphi, \psi) h_\times(t), \qquad (1)$$

where $F_+(\theta, \varphi, \psi)$, $F_\times(\theta, \varphi, \psi)$ are the antenna pattern functions for the two polarizations, which are functions of the polar angle θ and the azimuth angle φ of the spherical coordinate system (XY is the detector plane) and the polarization angle of the GW ψ.

Antenna pattern functions have the following form (in the coordinate frame, which basis vectors, coincide with the direction of the detector arms):

$$F_+ = \frac{1}{2}(1 + \cos^2\theta)\cos 2\varphi \cos 2\psi - \cos\theta \sin 2\varphi \sin 2\psi, \qquad (2)$$

$$F_\times = \frac{1}{2}(1 + \cos^2\theta)\cos 2\varphi \sin 2\psi + \cos\theta \sin 2\varphi \cos 2\psi. \qquad (3)$$

In Ref. 12 it's shown that for a network of N detectors network antenna power pattern P^N:

$$P^N = \sum_{k=1}^{4}(F_{+,k}^2 + F_{\times,k}^2). \qquad (4)$$

In order to choose the optimal detector angle in Novosibirsk, we use 3 independent criteria presented in Refs. 1, 10. These three criteria form an integral criterion, which is to be maximized by changing the orientation of the Novosibirsk detector, to find the most effective angle.

2.1. *Polarization criterion I*

Criterion I characterizes ability of the network to assess the polarization of the received GW. Following Ref. 1 we define + and × integral functions for a network of four detectors:

$$F^N = \frac{1}{2}\sqrt{F_1^2 + F_2^2 + F_3^2 + F_4^2}, \qquad (5)$$

where N - stands for a network function and $F_1...F_4$ all either correspond to the + or × polarization. Obviously F^N depend on the polarization angle of ψ.

Calculation of I is carried out in dominant polarization frame (DPF).[13] In DPF for each point on the celestial sphere $(\alpha; \delta)$ (in equatorial coordinate system point is defined by right ascension $\alpha \in [-\pi; \pi]$ and declination $\delta \in [-\frac{\pi}{2}; \frac{\pi}{2}]$) a polarization angle that maximizes the network factor F_+^N and minimizes $F_\times^N$ is chosen. Consequently, for this direction $(\alpha; \delta)$ the condition $F_+^N \geq F_\times^N$ is valid. The condition of approximate equality of factors $F_\times^N$ and F_+^N has to be kept, i.e. $\frac{F_\times^N}{F_+^N} \approx 1$. This means that the gravity detector network will be sensitive to both gravity wave polarizations. It follows that a minimum difference of $|F_\times^N - F_+^N|$ should be sought for all $(\alpha; \delta)$. This leads to the quantitative formulation of the polarization criterion I[1]:

$$I = \left(\frac{1}{4\pi}\oiint |F_+^N(\alpha;\delta) - F_\times^N(\alpha;\delta)|^2 d\Omega\right)^{-1/2}, \qquad (6)$$

where averaging of $|F_\times^N - F_+^N|$ over celestial sphere takes place ($d\Omega$ - solid angle). The bigger is I the smaller is the averaged difference $|F_\times^N - F_+^N|$.

2.2. Localization criterion D

Criterion D characterizes the ability of a network to define angular position of a source. In astrometry the problem of a source localization on celestial sphere of a radiation source is solved by a method of triangulation. Triangulation is based on the difference in time between the registration of signals by network detectors. The further apart the detectors are, the greater the time delay is. To maximize the source location accuracy on the celestial sphere, the telescopes should be placed as far apart from each other as possible. According to Ref.,[1] for a network of four detectors D is calculated as the area of the triangle formed by the three detectors in the network, which has the largest area among all possible combinations. If O - the center of the Earth, A, B, C - points where the detectors are located, the area of the corresponding triangle:

$$S_{ABC} = 1/2|[\overrightarrow{AC}, \overrightarrow{AB}]| = 1/2|[\overrightarrow{OC} - \overrightarrow{OA}; \overrightarrow{OB} - \overrightarrow{OA}]|. \quad (7)$$

2.3. Parameters reconstruction criterion R

Criterion R characterizes the possibility of reconstruction the parameters of the signal of a known analytical form. According to the Maximum likelihood estimation in the additive Gaussian noise background model, the parameters of the received signal are evaluated by the Rao-Cramer bound. The best possible estimates are obtained using the Fisher information matrix $\Gamma_{\alpha\beta}$[14] in accordance with the formula

$$\Gamma_{\alpha\beta} = Re\left\{ 4 \int_{f_{min}}^{f_{max}} \frac{\overline{\partial_\alpha \tilde{h}(f)} \partial_\beta \tilde{h}(f)}{S_n(f)} df \right\}, \quad (8)$$

where $\tilde{h}(f)$ is the Fourier image of response of the detector, the line above the Fourier image of response represents the complex conjugate, and $S_n(f)$ is the spectral noise density of a single detector. In this paper we assume for simplicity that all detectors have the same noise properties presented in.[15]

Rao-Cramer bound determines the best possible accuracy of parameter P estimation[14]:

$$\delta P^2 = \left(\Gamma_N^{-1}\right)_{PP}, \quad (9)$$

where $\Gamma_N = \sum_{i=1}^{N} \Gamma_i$, i.e. the Fisher information matrix for detector network, is the sum of the corresponding detector matrices constituting the network. The inverse value of the celestial-averaged relative error is a numerical expression of criterion R:

$$R = \left(\frac{1}{4\pi} \oiint \left(\frac{\delta P}{P}\right)^2 d\Omega \right)^{-1/2} = \left\langle \frac{\delta P}{P} \right\rangle^{-1}. \quad (10)$$

Maximization of criterion R leads to the minimum relative error averaged over the celestial sphere in the estimation of the parameter.

2.4. Integral criterion C

Integral criterion C is used to compare different configurations of a network:

$$C = \sqrt{\left(\frac{I}{I_{max}}\right)^2 + \left(\frac{D}{D_{max}}\right)^2 + \left(\frac{R}{R_{max}}\right)^2}. \qquad (11)$$

Criteria I, D and R together define a three-dimensional space that can be used to define a point which describes a particular configuration. Maximization of C by orientation angle of the detector in Novosibirsk gives the optimal orientation angle and leads to values $I(\gamma_{Nsk}^{max}) = I_{max}$, $D(\gamma_{Nsk}^{max}) = D_{max}$ and $R(\gamma_{Nsk}^{max}) = R_{max}$ (from the definition it's clear $C_{max} = 1$).

3. Sources

3.1. Binary inspiral

As a first typical source of gravitational radiation we consider inspiral of a relativistic binary. For our purposes a rather simplified Newtonian form of gravitational chirp signal, which does not take into account post-Newtonian corrections is sufficient[16]:

$$h(t) = \frac{4}{d_L}\sqrt{F_+^2 + F_\times^2}\frac{G^{5/3}}{c^4}\mathcal{M}^{5/3}(\pi f)^{2/3}\cos(\Phi + \Psi), \qquad (12)$$

$$\mathcal{M} = \mu^{3/5}M^{2/5}, \qquad (13)$$

$$\Phi = -2\left(\frac{c^3(T-t)}{5GM}\right)^{5/8}, \qquad (14)$$

$$f = \frac{1}{\pi M}\left[\frac{5}{256}\frac{c^5 M}{G(T-t)}\right]^{3/8}, \qquad (15)$$

where $\mathcal{M}$ is the chirp mass of a system, d_L is the distance to the source, Φ is the phase, f is the frequency, Ψ is the initial phase, M and μ is the total and reduced masses of the binary system, T is the moment of coalescence.

3.2. Collapsing star

As a second source of gravitational radiation we consider a core-collapse supernovae. During the core-collapse there exist many mechanisms of gravitational waves radiation on different stages of the process.[17] As Fisher matrix approach (8) requires analytical form of the signal we have considered gravitational waves from long-lived rotational instabilities of a proto-neutron star. If the key result of this instabilities is bar deformation that the radiation can be simulated by radiation from a rotating cylinder (axis of rotation is a bisector of the cylinder axis) with a Gaussian exponent which is introduced phenomenologically to take into account finiteness of the signal:

$$h(t) = \sqrt{F_+^2 + F_\times^2}\frac{GM\omega^2 L^2}{3c^4 r}(1-3\varepsilon^2)e^{-\frac{4(t-t_0)^2}{t_0^2}}\cos(2\omega t + \phi), \quad (16)$$

$$\phi = \pi + \tan^{-1}\frac{F_+}{F_\times}, \quad (17)$$

where G is Newtonian constant of gravitation, c – speed of light, M – mass of the source, L – length of the cylinder, R – radius of the cylinder, ω – source angular frequency, t_0 – characteristic signal length and parameter $\varepsilon = \frac{R}{L}$ characterizes the degree of deformation and is used for calculation of criterion R (10). Gravitational radiation carries away energy from the system so ω decreases over time. However for typical values of source parameters[17] $\omega = 2\pi \times 700$ rad/s, $L = 20$ km, $R = 5$ km, $M = M_\odot$ and $t_0 = 1$ s calculation of gravitational waves luminosity via Einstein's formula[18]:

$$L_{GW} = \frac{G}{5c^5}\left\langle \sum_{j,k=1}^{3}\dddot{Q}_{jk}\left(t-\frac{r}{c}\right)\dddot{Q}_{jk}\left(t-\frac{r}{c}\right)\right\rangle, \quad (18)$$

where Q_{jk} – reduced quadrupole moment and dot denotes time derivative, leads to $\frac{\Delta\omega}{\omega} \sim 10^{-7}$, so we consider ω to be constant.

4. Numerical results and conclusions

To define the optimal orientation angle of possible Novosibirsk detector for the to sources in question we maximize the integral criterion C (11). We have chosen the following typical values for the first source parameters: a binary neutron star with masses of $1.4M_\odot$, without spins, located at a distance of 1 Gpc from the Earth and with an orbital plane perpendicular to the line-of-sight. The results of numerical integration are presented in Figure 1. Criterion D in our approximation does not depend on the orientation angle of the detector in Novosibirsk. The most sensitive to changes in orientation angle is criterion I. The maximum value of integral criterion C is achieved at $\gamma_{Nsk}^{max} = 13°$.

In the case of gravitational collapse the strain $h(t)$ is expected to be several orders of magnitude less than for binary coalescence ($h \sim 10^{-22} - 10^{-20}$ at 10 kpc) so we can't assume isotropic distribution of sources over the celestial sphere. Instead we integrate over the Milky Way disk (neglecting the fact that the sensitivity may be sufficient for detection of the signal from several nearby galaxies). Due to rotation of the Earth antenna pattern functions F_+ and $F_\times$ depend on time (and consequently $P = P(t)$, $\phi = \phi(t)$) thus we average functions of time over 24 hours which also makes analytical calculation of Fourier image $\tilde{h}(f)$ in (8) possible. The parameters of a source are those ones from Section 3.2. The calculation results are shown in Figure 2. Again I is again the most sensitive criterion to changes of orientation angle. The maximum value of integral criterion C is achieved at $\gamma_{Nsk}^{max} = 40°$.

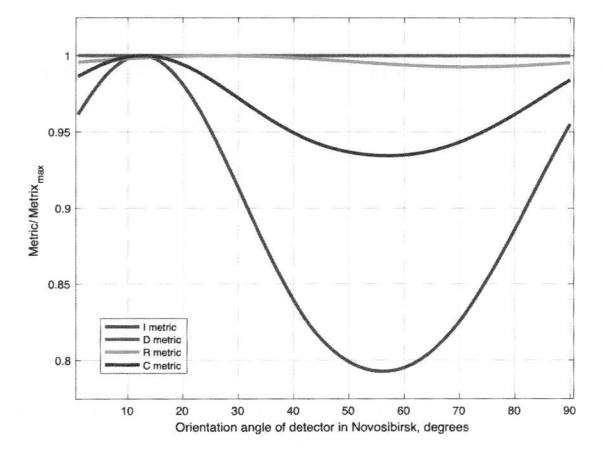

Fig. 1. Dependence of all criteria on orientation angle of detector in Novosibirsk for binary inspiral.

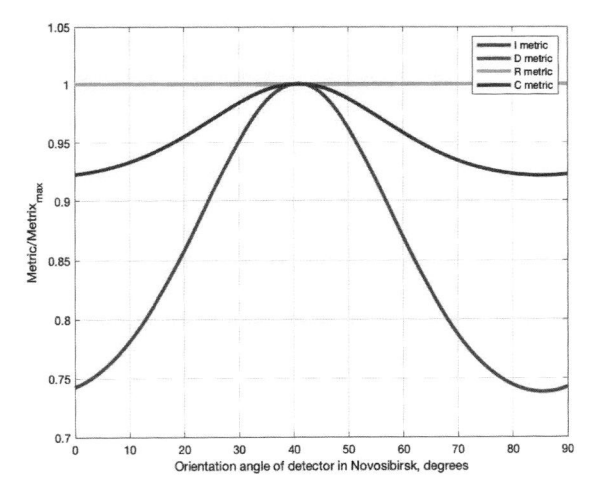

Fig. 2. Dependence of all criteria on orientation angle of detector in Novosibirsk for gravitational collapse.

The final choice of the orientation depends on the most topical problems at the time of construction of the detector in Novosibirsk. To conclude we notice that the choice of the source is a limitation of this work, because more significant physics is encrypted in a more complex structure of the signal from the core collapse, but such signals are model-dependent and do not have an analytical form (e.g.[19]), which does not allow using them within the framework of this approach.

The obtained result shows that in one specific network it is impossible to indicate the orientation of the interferometer in Novosibirsk, which would be optimal both for GW signals from the coalescence of relativistic binaries and for signals from collapses. This is despite the fact that the collapse model with the stage of rotating cylindrical bar instability is closest to the picture of a merging bynaries at the inspiral stage. At the moment, it is possible to recommend the choice of an averaged orientation with an appropriate estimate of the loss in the accuracy of estimating the parameters of the received signals.

Acknowledgments

The authors are grateful to Prof. A.N.Morozov and Prof. V.O Gladyshev from the Fundamental Physics Faculty of Bauman Moscow Technical University for stimulation of this analysis. This work was supported by the grant RFBR 19-29-11010.

References

1. P. Raffai et al., Optimal networks of future gravitational-wave telescopes, *Class. Quantum Grav.* **30**, p. 155004 (2013).
2. B. P. Abbott et al., Observation of gravitational waves from a binary black hole merger, *Phys. Rev. Lett.* **116**, p. 061102 (Feb 2016).
3. B. P. Abbott et al., Gw170814: A three-detector observation of gravitational waves from a binary black hole coalescence, *Phys. Rev. Lett.* **119**, p. 141101 (Oct 2017).
4. B. P. Abbott et al., Gw170817: Observation of gravitational waves from a binary neutron star inspiral, *Phys. Rev. Lett.* **119**, p. 161101 (Oct 2017).
5. R. Abbott et al., Observation of gravitational waves from two neutron star–black hole coalescences, *ApJL* **915**, p. L5 (jun 2021).
6. M. A. Acero et al., Search for multimessenger signals in nova coincident with ligo/virgo detections, *Phys. Rev. D* **101**, p. 112006 (Jun 2020).
7. D. Veske et al., Multi-messenger searches via IceCube's high-energy neutrinos and gravitational-wave detections of LIGO/Virgo, *PoS* **ICRC2021**, p. 950 (2021).
8. C. L. Fryer and K. C. B. New, Gravitational Waves from Gravitational Collapse, *Living Rev. Relativ.* **14**, p. 1 (2011).
9. V. Rudenko, S. Andrusenko, D. Krichevskiy and G. Manucharyan, Gw interferometer euro-asian network: Detection characteristics for signals of known shape, *Universe* **6**, p. 140 (2020).
10. Y.-M. Hu et al., Global optimization for future gravitational wave detector sites, *Class. Quantum Grav.* **32**, p. 105010 (apr 2015).
11. V. N. Rudenko, Y. M. Gavrilyuk, A. V. Gusev, D. P. Krichevskiy, S. I. Oreshkin, S. M. Popov and I. S. Yudin, Gravitational wave detector ogran as multi-messenger project of ras-msu, *International Journal of Modern Physics A* **35**, p. 2040007 (2020).
12. L. S. Finn, Aperture synthesis for gravitational-wave data analysis: Deterministic sources, *Physical Review D* **63**, p. 102001 (2001).
13. S. Klimenko et al., Localization of gravitational wave sources with networks of advanced detectors, *Phys. Rev. D* **83**, p. 102001 (May 2011).
14. B. Kocsis, Z. Haiman, K. Menou and Z. Frei, Premerger localization of gravitational-wave standard sirens with lisa: Harmonic mode decomposition, *Phys. Rev. D* **76**, p. 022003 (Jul 2007).
15. LIGO, (2009), LIGO Document T0900288-v3.
16. L. S. Finn and D. F. Chernoff, Observing binary inspiral in gravitational radiation: One interferometer, *Phys. Rev. D* **47**, 2198 (Mar 1993).

17. S. E. Gossan *et al.*, Observing gravitational waves from core-collapse supernovae in the advanced detector era, *Phys. Rev. D* **93**, p. 042002 (Feb 2016).
18. L. D. Landau and E. M. Lifshitz, *The Classical Theory of Fields: Volume 2* (Butterworth-Heinemann, 1980).
19. H. Dimmelmeier *et al.*, Gravitational wave burst signal from core collapse of rotating stars, *Phys. Rev. D* **78**, p. 064056 (Sep 2008).

Joint analysis method on gravitational waves and low-energy neutrinos to detect core-collapse supernovae

O. Halim

Istituto Nazionale di Fisica Nucleare (INFN) sez. di Trieste, Italy
E-mail: odysse.halim@ts.infn.it

C. Casentini

Istituto Nazionale di Astrofisica - Istituto di Astrofisica e Planetologia Spaziali (INAF -IAPS),
Rome, Italy

M. Drago

Università di Roma La Sapienza, I-00185 Roma, Italy,
INFN, Sezione di Roma, I-00185 Roma, Italy

V. Fafone

University of Rome Tor Vergata, Rome, Italy,
INFN sez. di Roma Tor Vergata, Rome, Italy

K. Scholberg

Department of Physics, Duke University, Durham, NC, USA

C. F. Vigorito

University of Turin, Italy,
INFN sez. di Torino, Italy

G. Pagliaroli

Gran Sasso Science Institute (GSSI), L'Aquila, Italy,
INFN sez. di LNGS, Assergi, Italy

Core-collapse supernovae produce copious low-energy neutrinos and are also predicted to radiate gravitational waves. These two messengers can give us information regarding the explosion mechanism. The gravitational wave detection from these events are still elusive even with the already advanced detectors. Here we give a concise and timely introduction to a new method that combines triggers from GW and neutrino observatories; more details shall be given in a forthcoming paper.[1]

Keywords: Multimessenger, supernova, core-collapse, low-energy neutrino, gravitational wave.

1. Introduction

Core-collapse supernovae (CCSNe) are expected to produce multimessenger signals such as neutrinos, gravitational waves (GWs), as well as multi-wavelength electromagnetic waves.[2,3] Low-energy neutrinos (LENs) are expected to be produced by these events, with the average energy ~ 10 MeV and these LENs are from the majority of the total energy budget ($\sim 10^{53}$ erg) of the CCSNe.

LENs from a CCSN have been successfully detected with the observation of SN1987A in Large Magellanic Cloud by Kamiokande-II,[4] IMB,[5] and Baksan.[6] Today, there are several LEN detectors waiting for these astrophysical events such as Super-Kamiokande[7] (Super-K), LVD,[8] KamLAND,[9] and IceCube[10] with the horizon up to the edge of our galaxy and beyond. These detectors are in fact in a multi-detector collaboration for this effort to produce low-latency alerts under SuperNova Early Warning System (SNEWS).[11,12]

Moreover, the era of multimessenger astronomy involving GWs has just begun with the detection of the binary neutron star merger.[13] Recently, GW search has been in the phase of O3 data taking, which is done by LIGO[14] detectors (4-km arm in Hanford and Livingston USA), Virgo[15] detector (3-km arm in Cascina Italy), and KAGRA[16] (3-km arm in Gifu Prefecture, Japan in the latest period of O3). In total, the GW science data taking has been done for 3 observing runs (O1, O2, and O3) from 2015 to 2020, and currently the detectors undergo improvements in order to be more sensitive for O4 (expected in August 2022). CCSNe are expected to produce GW signals with broad physical processes.[17–20] Detecting GWs from these sources will enable us to study the physical processes. As we will see later on, the detection capability of GWs could be improved by multimessenger search involving LENs.

Here, we provide a timely description of a strategy to combine GWs and LENs for a multimessenger search following the chart in Fig. 1. More details discussion will be given in a forthcoming paper,[1] which has just been accepted by JCAP. This method is based on our previous works.[21,22] We construct a time-coincident strategy and test it with the simulated signals for both GW and LEN data.

In our strategy, we use the `coherent WaveBurst` (cWB) pipeline[23–26] for GW data analysis from simulations. This is a model-agnostic algorithm pipeline that is used to search GWs from CCSNe.[27] Moreover, we also simulate LEN signals arriving in several neutrino detectors and analyse them[a]. At this stage, we use a new approach (introduced in[22]) for neutrino analysis in order to exploit the temporal behaviour of CCSNe. In the next step, we perform a temporal-coincidence analysis between the two messengers. Different messenger data are analysed separately and then combined together for possible GW-LEN signals. This could be interesting for online networks such as SNEWS or offline search for sub-threshold signals.

This paper is organised as follows. In Sec. 2, we discuss the emission models for each messenger. Then, in Sec. 3, the data and analysis by our strategy will be presented. In the end, we show the implementation of our strategy in Sec. 4.

---

[a]Note that we employ no detailed neutrino-detector simulation.

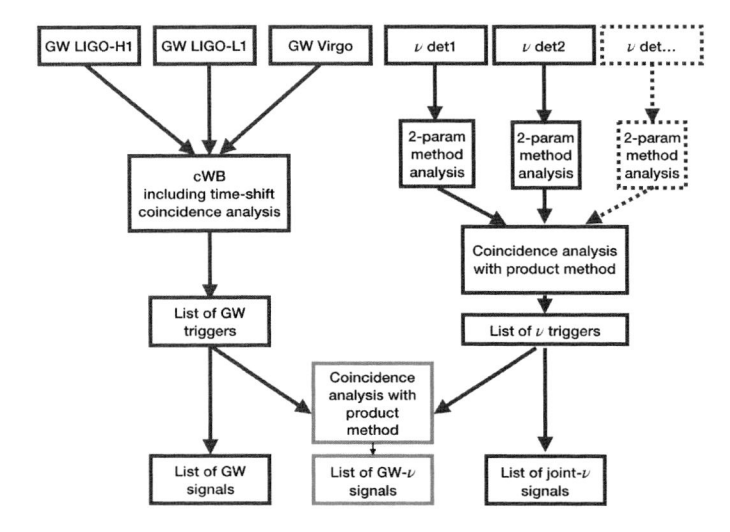

Fig. 1. The schematic view of the multimessenger GW-LEN strategy.

2. Messengers from Core-Collapse Supernovae

A CCSN is expected to produce a $O(10\,\text{ms} - 1\,\text{s})$ GW burst and an impulsive $O(10 - 30\,\text{s})$ emission of $O(10\,\text{MeV})$ LENs[28][b], which highly depend on the CCSN initial conditions: progenitor mass, rotation, etc. Thus, it would be ideal to perform a simultaneous GW-LEN analysis from *the same numerical simulation*. Unfortunately, no simultaneous GW-LEN numerical simulations have provided successful CCSN explosion, or if there are, the simulations can only provide both signals for the first half of a second, until the explosion. Meanwhile, the LEN emission duration is expected to last about 10 seconds. Therefore, we combine the currently available GW signals and LEN signals from different simulations with similar progenitor masses, and handle them as if they are from the simultaneous simulation.

2.1. *Gravitational Wave Emission*

We provide the detail of our GW waveforms in Tab. 1. We use the GW signals from the 3D neutrino-radiation hydrodynamics simulations of Radice *et al.*[30] (named as "Rad") with the various zero age main sequence masses in order to have the successful explosions from the low-mass and the failed explosions from the high-mass. Besides, we also take into account models with rapid rotation and high magnetic field which produce much stronger GWs. In this case, we take GW waveforms from two simulations: the Dimmelmeier[31] ("Dim") and the Scheidegger[32] ("Sch"). The stellar progenitors of Dim and Sch have strong rotation and magnetic field. These constraints make the models less favourable to happen than the neutrino-radiation

---

[b]These signals could also be emitted by "failed" SNe.[29]

mechanism.[27,28,33] Nevertheless, we would not rule out any models since we have not yet detected any CCSN GWs. Thus, we try to cover as broad as possible the uncertainty band from theoretical predictions: the lower limit is from the Rad model, and the upper limit is from the Dim and the Sch models.

Table 1. Waveforms from the considered CCSN simulations. In the columns: emission type and reference, waveform identifier, waveform abbreviation for this manuscript, progenitor mass, angle-averaged root-sum-squared strain h_rss, frequency when the GW energy spectrum peaks, and emitted GW energy.

Waveform Family	Waveform Identifier	Abbr.	Mass $M_\odot$	h_rss @10 kpc $\left[10^{-22} \frac{1}{\sqrt{\mathrm{Hz}}}\right]$	f_peak [Hz]	E_GW $[10^{-9} M_\odot c^2]$
Radice[30]	s25	Rad25	25	0.141	1132	28
3D simulation;	s13	Rad13	13	0.061	1364	5.9
h_+ & $h_\times$; (Rad)	s9	Rad9	9	0.031	460	0.16
Dimmelmeier[31]	dim1-s15A2O05ls	Dim1	15	1.052	770	7.685
2D simulation;	dim2-s15A2O09ls	Dim2	15	1.803	754	27.880
h_+ only; (Dim)	dim3-s15A3O15ls	Dim3	15	2.690	237	1.380
Scheidegger[32]	sch1-R1E1CA$_L$	Sch1	15	0.129	1155	0.104
3D simulation;	sch2-R3E1AC$_L$	Sch2	15	5.144	466	214
h_+ & $h_\times$; (Sch)	sch3-R4E1FC$_L$	Sch3	15	5.796	698	342

2.2. Low-energy Neutrino Emission

Similar to the previous emission, we consider two models for the LEN emissions. First, we take the signals from the numerical simulations of Hüdepohl obtained for a progenitor of $11.2 M_\odot$; without the collective oscillations,[34] with the time-dependent neutrino luminosities, and average energies. The simulation provides the first 7.5 seconds of the neutrino emission with the analytical extension in order to reach 10 seconds of the signal. The average LEN energies from before collapse up to the simulated 0.5 s after bounce are (c.f. Table 3.4 of Ref.[34]): $\langle E_{\nu_e}\rangle = 13$ MeV, $\langle E_{\bar\nu_e}\rangle = 15$ MeV and $\langle E_{\nu_x}\rangle = 14.6$ MeV.

Second, we also use a parametric model for neutrino emission from Pagliaroli et al.,[35] focusing on the best-fit emission from SN1987A data and the model provides the average energies of $\langle E_{\nu_e}\rangle = 9$ MeV, $\langle E_{\bar\nu_e}\rangle = 12$ MeV and $\langle E_{\nu_x}\rangle = 16$ MeV. This signal has a temporal structure:

$$F(t, \tau_1, \tau_2) = (1 - e^{-t/\tau_1})e^{-t/\tau_2}, \qquad (1)$$

where τ_1 and τ_2 are parameters governing the emission, representing the rise and decay timescales of the neutrino signal. The best-fit values on these parameters are ~ 0.1 s and ~ 1 s.[36]

Here, we consider only the main interaction channel for water and scintillator detectors: the inverse beta decay (IBD) $\bar\nu_e + p \to n + e^+$. We also consider standard MSW neutrino oscillations on the flux $\Phi_{\bar\nu_e}$ at the detectors. The flux is an admixture of the unoscillated flavor fluxes at the source, i.e. $\Phi_{\bar{\nu}_e} = P \cdot \Phi_{\bar{\nu}_e} + (1-P)\Phi_{\bar{\nu}_x}$. Here, P describes the survival probability for the $\bar{\nu}_e$. The value of $P \simeq 0$ is for the Inverted Hierarchy (IH), while $P \simeq 0.7$ is for the Normal Hierarchy (NH). The expected number of IBD events can be seen in Tab. 2 with the reference distance of 10 kpc.

Table 2. Average number of IBD events for a CCSN exploding at 10 kpc for the considered models detected by Super-K,[7] LVD,[8] and KamLAND,[9] with the assumed energy thresholds (E_{thr}).

Model (identifier)	Progenitor Mass	Super-K ($E_{\text{thr}} = 6.5$ MeV)	LVD ($E_{\text{thr}} = 7$ MeV)	KamLAND ($E_{\text{thr}} = 1$ MeV)
Pagliaroli[35] (SN1987A)	$25\,M_\odot$	4120	224	255
Hüdepohl[34] (Hud)	$11.2\,M_\odot$	2620	142	154

3. Data and Analysis Strategy

Here, we will discuss the data and analysis for GWs, for LENs, and for a combined multimessenger search. We consider a conservative threshold on global false alarm rate (FAR) of 1/1000 years.

3.1. *Gravitational Wave Analysis*

We employ the cWB[37,38,c] algorithm for the GW data analysis, a widely used software in the LIGO-Virgo-KAGRA collaborations; which is also used for the study of CCSN targeted-search.[27,39] The cWB software does not need any waveform templates; it combines coherently the excess energy of the data from the involved GW detectors. A maximum likelihood analysis is used to search for the GW candidates and their parameters. The significance is estimated comparing foreground the detection statistics ρ (of the candidates) with a background distribution from the time-shift procedure. We simulate Gaussian noise with a spectral sensitivity based on the expected Advanced LIGO[40] and Advanced Virgo detectors.[41,42] We simulate ~ 16 days of data and ~ 20 years of background livetime.

Waveforms from the models in Sec. 2.1 have been simulated for several distances: 5, 15, 20, 50, 60, 700 kpc. In terms of sky direction, for the shorter distances (5, 15, 20) we use the Galactic model given in,[43] whereas for the longer (50 and 60 kpc) distances we take fixed directions, either towards the Large or Small Magellanic Clouds, and additionally for the 700 kpc we use the Andromeda direction. We focus

---

[c]cWB home page, https://gwburst.gitlab.io/;
public repositories, https://gitlab.com/gwburst/public
documentation, https://gwburst.gitlab.io/documentation/latest/html/index.html.

mainly on the 5-60 kpc distances for the multimessenger analysis, while the distance between 60 and 700 kpc are used for the efficiency curve[d]. We inject 1 GW signal per 100 seconds, wide enough for two consecutive waveforms. In terms of sky positions, we apply ~ 2500 different realizations over all the sky direction for each distance and model.

We choose a threshold of 864 per day for GW candidates to be used for our multimessenger analysis, to satisfy the requirement of the combined FAR of 1/1000 years. The efficiency curves for each distance can be seen in Fig. 2 as the ratio of the number of recovered injections ($\text{FAR}_{\text{GW}} < 864/\text{day}$) to the ~ 2500 total injections.

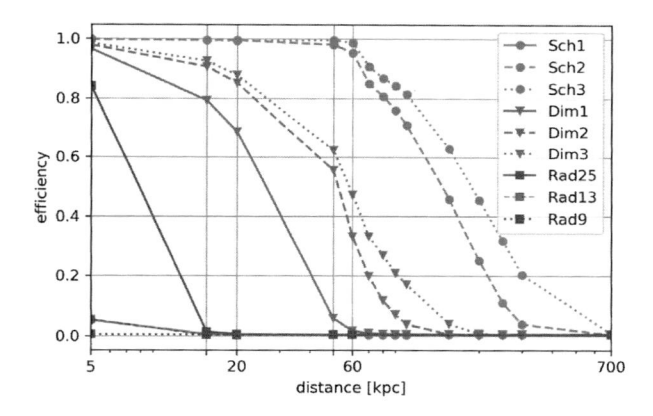

Fig. 2. Efficiency curve of GW search from Advanced LIGO and Advanced Virgo detectors for the various models in Tab. 1, given a FAR threshold of 864/day. Sch1-3 are for the Scheidegger model with different frequency peaks, Dim1-3 are for the Dimmelmeier model with different h_{rss} values, and Rad1-3 are for the Radice model with different progenitor masses

3.2. *Neutrino Analysis: Expanding the Neutrino Detection Horizon*

The standard LEN analysis for CCSNe[44–46] employs a binning in a time series data set with a sliding time window of $w = 20$ seconds. The group of events in a bin is called a *cluster* and the number of events in a cluster is called multiplicity m. We can assume the multiplicity distribution of background events follows a Poisson distribution. For each i-th cluster, we calculate the *imitation frequency* (f^{im}), which is correlated with the significance, defined as,

$$f_i^{\text{im}}(m_i) = N \times \sum_{k=m_i}^{\infty} P(k), \qquad (2)$$

---

[d]For the simulations between 60 and 700 kpc, we use the Andromeda position, though no known astronomical objects are expected around that area.

where $P(k)$ is the Poisson term: the probability in which a cluster of multiplicity k is simply due to the background,

$$P(k) = \frac{(f_{\text{bkg}}w)^k e^{-f_{\text{bkg}}w}}{k!}, \qquad (3)$$

with $N = 8640$ is the total number of bins in one day, calculated from the 10-s overlapping window between two consecutive bins, to tackle the boundary problems. This f^{im} is basically called FAR in the GW community.

From our previous work,[47] we can exploit the temporal behavior of LEN signals with an additional cluster parameter called $\xi_i \equiv \frac{m_i}{\Delta t_i}$, with Δt_i as the i-th cluster duration: the time difference between the last and the first event. Clearly, Δt_i has a maximum value of the bin width itself, which is 20 seconds. A cluster is considered when $m_i \geq 2$, thus $\xi_i \geq 0.1$.

Previous work[47] uses ξ as a cut value. In this work we develop further in order improve the estimation of the imitation frequency. Particularly, it is formulated a new modified **2-parameter** (m and ξ) imitation frequency, called F^{im}:

$$F_i^{\text{im}}(m_i, \xi_i) = N \times \sum_{k=m_i}^{\infty} P(k, \xi_i), \qquad (4)$$

where the term $P(k, \xi_i)$ is the joint probability of a cluster with multiplicity k **and** ξ_i substituting $P(k)$ previously (Eq. 3). Finally, it is convenient to write (see c.f. App. A of[1] and c.f. Sec. 7.1. of[21] for more detail),

$$F_i^{\text{im}}(m_i, \xi_i) = N \times \sum_{k=m_i}^{\infty} P(k) \int_{\xi=\xi_i}^{\infty} \text{PDF}(\xi \geq \xi_i | k) d\xi. \qquad (5)$$

Fig. 3 shows the ξ probability density function (PDF) for the Super-K detector (as an example). The black solid line represents the PDF of ξ values due to the background, i.e. $\text{PDF}(\xi|k)$.

We simulate ~ 10 years of background data for each neutrino detector with the assumption that the background frequencies f_{bkg}: 0.012 Hz for Super-K,[46] 0.015 Hz for KamLAND,[48] and 0.028 Hz for LVD.[44] Moreover, the CCSN simulated signals (see Sec. 2) are injected into the background data for each detector model (the starting times are simultaneous with the GW injections, with reasonable time delay due to detectors' positions) and for each source distance. These clusters are extracted via the Monte Carlo method and the injection rate is 1 per day.

The clusters are considered signal candidates if their standard $f^{\text{im}} \leq 1/\text{day}$, which has been set in order to reach the global FAR of 1/1000 years. The efficiency for each distance D can be defined as,

$$\eta(D) = \frac{N_{\text{r,s}}(D)}{N_{\text{inj,s}}(D)}, \qquad (6)$$

where $N_{\text{r,s}}$ is the number of candidates and $N_{\text{inj,s}}$ is the total number of injections. With the recipes up to now, the efficiency curves can be constructed (see Fig. 4).

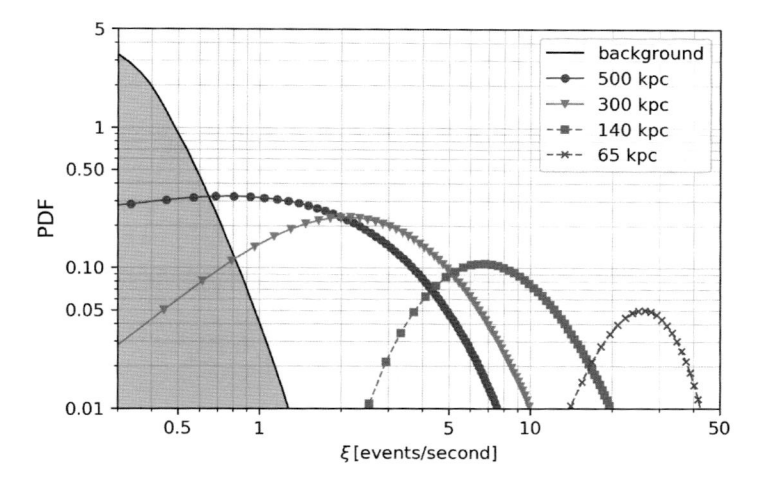

Fig. 3. PDF of ξ values for background (black line) and signal clusters (colored-lines) for different distances in the case of the Super-K detector. Data are from.[47]

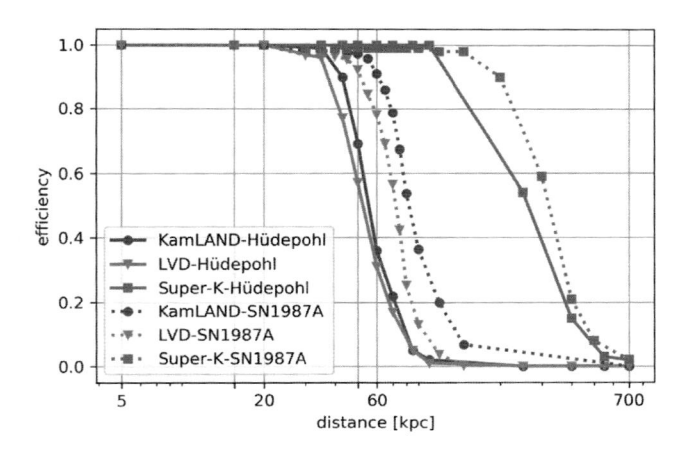

Fig. 4. The efficiency curves of LEN detectors for the Hud (continuous lines) and SN1987A (dashed lines). The imitation frequency threshold is 1/day.

3.3. Multimessenger Analysis

The ultimate goal of our work is to construct a multimessenger analysis, combining both LEN and GW data sets (green boxes in Fig. 1). We simply perform a temporal-coincidence analysis between the GW and LEN lists and the statistical significance can be estimated by the combination of its FAR. The joint coincidences are defined as "CCSN candidates".

The FAR_{GW} is acquired via the time-shifting method (Sec. 3.1) while, the FAR_ν from LEN is obtained by the product method based on SNEWS[11] i.e.,

$$\text{FAR}_\nu = \text{Nd} \times w_\nu^{\text{Nd}-1} \prod_{i=1}^{\text{Nd}} F_i^{\text{im}}, \tag{7}$$

where Nd is the number of LEN detectors, w_ν is the time window of coincidence analysis, and F_i^{im} is the 2-parameter imitation frequency of the clusters.

All in all, the multimessenger FAR_{glob} from "CCSN candidates" can be written[e],

$$\text{FAR}_{\text{glob}} = \text{Net} \times w_c^{\text{Net}-1} \prod_{X=1}^{\text{Net}} \text{FAR}_X, \tag{8}$$

where Net is the number of sub-networks, w_c is the temporal coincidence window between GW and LEN, and FAR_X is the *false-alarm-rate* ($X = \{\nu, \text{GW}\}$). Thus, the *false-alarm-probability* taking into account Poisson statistics can be written,

$$\text{FAP} = 1 - e^{-\text{FAR} \times \text{livetime}}, \tag{9}$$

where "livetime" is the common observing time among the network.

Eq. 8 and 9 are used to compare the performance of our 2-parameter method (Eq. 5) with the standard 1-parameter method (Eq. 2). This performance is discussed as efficiency values, analogous with Eq. 6. For the multimessenger step, we define a "detection" in a network when $\text{FAP} \geq 5\sigma$[f].

4. Results

Here, we discuss the results of our method. First, we mention the single-detector neutrino analysis performance. Next, we show the sub-network of neutrino detectors. Finally, we provide the global network of GW-LEN multimessenger analysis.

4.1. *Improvement of the Single-Detector LEN Analysis*

We work our method on the simulated single-detector data for KamLAND, LVD, and Super-K. To show the improvement, we discuss in the following, as a leading example, the case of the KamLAND detector. We consider a CCSN at 60 kpc with the LEN profile following SN1987A model (the first row of Tab. 2). We perform a 10 years of KamLAND simulated background data and we inject randomly the simulated LENs with the rate of 1/day, thus, 3650 total injections.

All clusters, either due to background or injections, are plotted in Fig. 5 in a ξ vs multiplicity plane. Blue crosses represents the clusters due to injections while the yellow inverted-triangles are due to background. Because of the statistical Poisson fluctuation in the Monte Carlo simulation method, the injection clusters may have

---

[e]Thorough discussion on the choice of coincidence analysis can be seen in.[21]
[f]$5\sigma \approx 5.7 \times 10^{-7}$

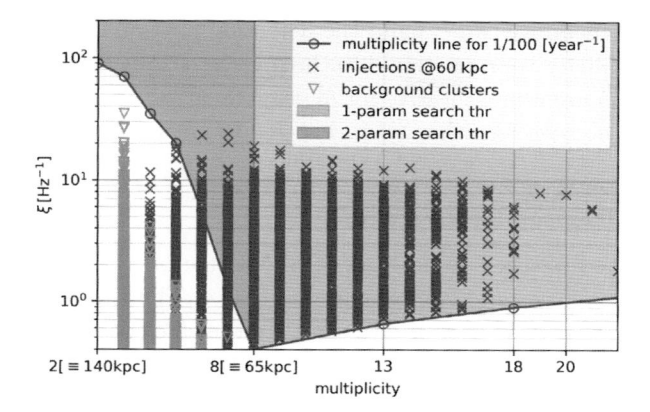

Fig. 5. The ξ-multiplicity map for KamLAND with the simulated background (yellow-triangle) and injection (blue-cross) clusters generated with the SN1987A model at 60 kpc.

various multiplicity values. Besides, background events are also fluctuating in this 20-sec window.

We estimate the associated imitation frequency (or FAR$_\nu$[g]) for each recovered cluster. This imitation frequency in 1-parameter analysis is a function of only the cluster multiplicity via Poisson statistics. To satisfy the SNEWS requirement of FAR$_\nu \leq 1/100$ year, the multiplicity threshold is 8. This means clusters should lie on the green area of Fig. 5 to satisfy the standard 1-parameter requirement. This limit on the multiplicity could be understood as a KamLAND horizon for CCSN search of $\simeq 65$ kpc with the model based on SN1987A, in fact it is the average multiplicity for this CCSN configuration: $\langle m_i \rangle = 8$.

On the other hand, the imitation frequency of our 2-parameter method requires each cluster to satisfy the requirement of both multiplicity and the ξ value following Eq. 4. That equation gives us the red line in Fig. 5 for FAR$_\nu = 1/100$ years[h] required for the 2-parameter method. All clusters above the red line pass the 2-parameter method requirement. This also relax the requirement allowing multiplicity lower than 8 as long as a specific ξ value is satisfied. Thus, the red area in Fig. 5 represents the improvement area of our 2-parameter method comparing with the 1-parameter. In addition, it is clear from the figure that all simulated background clusters (yellow triangles) are well below the red threshold line.

Quantitatively, Fig. 5 shows an increase of the detection efficiency with details given in the first row of Tab. 3. The KamLAND efficiency at 60 kpc is improved from 73% by the standard 1-parameter method to 83% by our 2-parameter method. Moreover, we mention also that there are 75198 noise triggers in this data set and none of them have FAR lower than 1/100 years for both methods. The efficiency

---

[g]As previously stated in Sec. 3.2, the imitation frequency is actually the FAR. So, FAR$_\nu$ is imitation frequency for KamLAND data, either f^{im} or F^{im} depending on the context.
[h]The threshold corresponding to the current SNEWS requirement.

increase could also mean we can expand the detection horizon of the detector since the expected multiplicity is proportional to the inverse of squared-distance[i]. The results for KamLAND are representative for all the scenarios we investigated. Similar improvements can be seen for other scenarios (see c.f. App. C of[1]).

4.2. The LEN Detector Sub-Network

We apply our method for the sub-network of LEN detectors: KamLAND and LVD, since their efficiency curves are compatible; see Fig. 4. The threshold for LEN detector network is 5σ in FAP_ν (Eq. 9). We compare the efficiencies in the second and third row of Tab. 3.

Table 3. Efficiency (η) comparison between 1-parameter and 2-parameter method for analysis of KamLAND (with the SN1987A model) and KamLAND-LVD (with the Hud model) and for $FAP_\nu > 5\sigma$.

Analysis	Model	Distance [kpc] [$> 5\sigma$]	η_{1param} [$> 5\sigma$]	η_{2param}
KamLAND	SN1987A	60	2665/3654=72.9%	3026/3654=82.8%
KamLAND-LVD	Hud	50	47/108=43.5%	59/108=54.6%
KamLAND-LVD	Hud	60	19/107=17.8%	28/107=26.2%

At a distance of 50 kpc with a $FAR_\nu \leq 1/100$ years, we can detect 12% and 26% CCSNe for LVD and KamLAND, respectively. Meanwhile, if the detectors are in a network looking for coincidences within w_ν, it is possible to recover $\sim 43\%$ with 5σ threshold. When we start using 2-parameter method taking into account the ξ distribution for each detector, this efficiency grows to $\sim 55\%$.

Analogously, for CCSNe at 60 kpc, the signals with $FAR_\nu \leq 1/100$ years can be detected only 3% and 7% for LVD and KamLAND. Whereas, as a network this efficiency increases to 18% and to 26% for 1-parameter and 2-parameter method, respectively for 5σ threshold.

In order to quantify the result, we will mention the results for the SN1987A model with a CCSN at 60 kpc recovered by the LVD-KamLAND network. The improvement in efficiency is from 85% to 93%. These results can be compared with first row of Tab. 3 for the single detector analysis.

4.3. The Multimessenger Network

In the multimessenger network, the temporal coincidence window is $w_c = 10$ seconds between GW and LEN lists. We use the 5σ threshold to claim a multimessenger

---

[i]The number of events is basically a flux.

"detection" of injected signals. We focus on emphasizing the improvement of combining GWs and LENs, which means when the detection efficiency of both LEN and GW detectors is less than 100%. In other words, it is to combine detectors with comparable detection efficiencies. The horizon of the GW network is highly influenced by the assumed GW emission model, see Fig. 2. In this case, the Dim2 model (see Tab. 1) has the GW detection horizon comparable with the LVD and KamLAND detectors, which is more or less the Large Magellanic Cloud distance. Thus, we perform the method for the global network of LIGO-Virgo, LVD, and KamLAND. Results for other GW models can be seen in c.f. App. B of.[1]

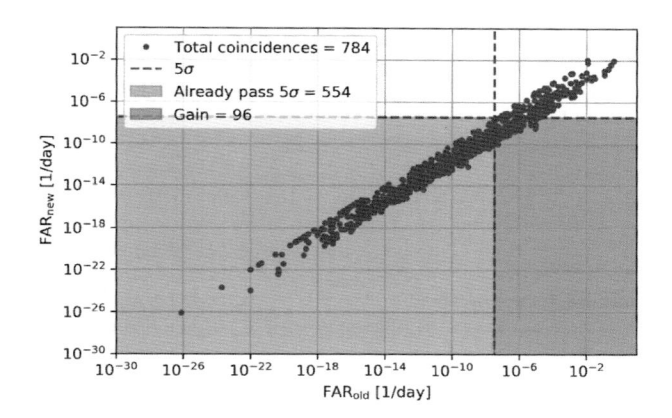

Fig. 6. The joint FAR of GW-LEN candidates obtained with the 2-parameter method (FAR$_{new}$ y-axis) vs the 1-parameter (FAR$_{old}$ x-axis) with the **KamLAND** (SN1987A-model) and HLV (Dim2-model) at 60 kpc.

For the coincidence analysis of KamLAND detector with the HLV (Hanford, Livingston, Virgo) GW network, we can see the FAR comparison in Fig. 6 for the case of CCSNe at 60 kpc and with the LENs from SN1987A model and the GW from Dim2 model. The magenta dashed-line is 5σ significance threshold. Either FAR$_{old}$ or FAR$_{new}$ values lower than this line mean they pass 5σ. Thus, all clusters (blue dots) lie on the green area are recovered by the 1-parameter method. While, the red area is the improvement: the clusters recovered by the 2-parameter but not by the 1-parameter. The first row of Tab. 4 gives us the efficiency of the 1-parameter and the 2-parameter method. This yields an additional $\sim 12\%$ of signals from the 2-parameter that are discarded by the 1-parameter.

The cWB performs and analyses 2346 GW injections, and out of that, 784 of them have FAR$_{GW}$ < 864/day. These candidates' significances are far too low to be even taken as *sub-threshold* triggers. Then, temporal coincidence analysis is performed with the input of these GW triggers and the list of LEN clusters. There are 554 coincident candidates that pass 5σ ($\sim 71\%$ of the GW triggers) with the

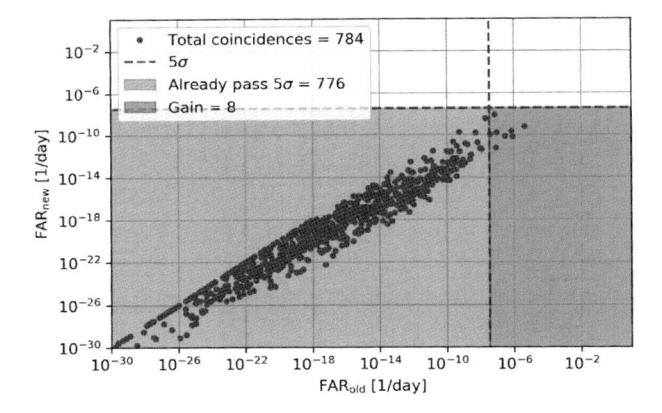

Fig. 7. The joint FAR of GW-LEN candidates obtained with the 2-parameter method (FAR$_{\rm new}$ y-axis) vs the 1-parameter (FAR$_{\rm old}$ x-axis) with the **KamLAND-LVD** (SN1987A-model) and HLV (Dim2-model) at 60 kpc.

Table 4. Efficiency comparison of the 1-parameter ($\eta_{\rm 1param}$) and the 2-parameter ($\eta_{\rm 2param}$) method for Fig. 6 (upper row) and 7 (lower row). The first column indicates the specific network of detectors and models. The second column shows the GW results with the threshold on the FAR$_{\rm GW}<864$/day). The third and last columns are the efficiency with $>5\sigma$ significance.

Network & Type of Injections	Recovered FAR$_{\rm GW}<864$/d	$\eta_{\rm 1param}$ [$>5\sigma$]	$\eta_{\rm 2param}$ [$>5\sigma$]
HLV-KAM (Dim2-SN1987A)	784/2346= 33.4%	554/784= **70.7%**	650/784= **82.9%**
HLV-KAM-LVD (Dim2-SN1987A)	784/2346= 33.4%	776/784= **99.0%**	784/784= **100%**

standard 1-parameter method. However, if we employ the new 2-parameter method, we can get additional 110 recovered signals. This means the efficiency increases to $\sim 83\%$ (the first row of Tab. 4).

We also study further this method involving the LVD detector to be in the triple-detector configuration. We show the result in Fig. 7 and quantitative summary in the second row of Tab. 4. The improvement of our method seems less evident. This is clear due to the fact that the efficiency cannot go beyond the maximum value of 33.4%, where all the GW triggers from cWB are coincident with the list of LEN clusters with $>5\sigma$ significance.

We then provide the result by using the Hud model in exchange of the SN1987A model. The FARs can be seen in Fig. 8 and the efficiency values in Tab. 5. This 2-parameter method gives us $\sim 7\%$ more recovered signals. We found that on average, the FARs the injections are $O(10^3)$ smaller with the 2-parameter than the 1-parameter for both emission models.

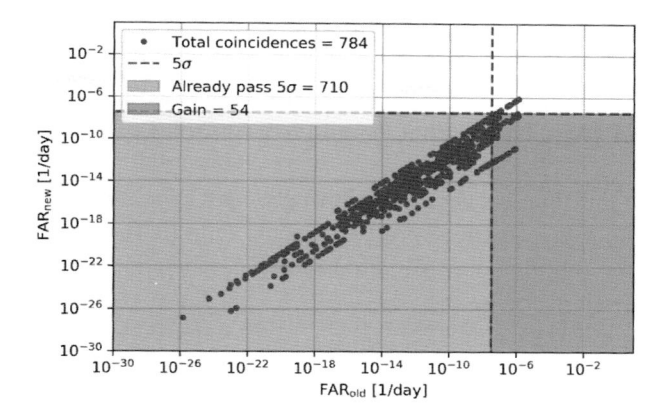

Fig. 8. The joint FAR of GW-LEN candidates obtained with the 2-parameter method (FAR$_{\text{new}}$ y-axis) vs the 1-parameter (FAR$_{\text{old}}$ x-axis) with the KamLAND-LVD (**Hud-model**) and HLV (Dim2-model) at 60 kpc.

Table 5. Efficiency comparison of the 1-parameter (η_{1param}) and the 2-parameter (η_{2param}) method for Fig. 8. The columns are analogous to Table 4.

Network & Type of Injections	Recovered FAR$_{\text{GW}}$ < 864/d	η_{1param} [> 5σ]	η_{2param} [> 5σ]
HLV-KAM-LVD (Dim2-Hud)	784/2346= 33.4%	710/784= **90.6%**	764/784= **97.5%**

All in all, let us summarize the results. Fig. 2 for Dim2 model shows that the GW network HLV, by applying a threshold FAR$_{\text{GW}} \leq 864$/day, recovers about $\sim 33\%$ of the injected signals at 60 kpc. Notice that these GW triggers are far from statistically significant and clearly 0% passes a 5σ threshold. With this global network analysis and with our 2-parameter method, the multimessenger detection efficiency grows to $\sim 33\%$. If taking into account the weaker emission like Hud model, the detection efficiency arrives at the value of $33.4\% \cdot 97.5\% = 32.6\%$.

5. Conclusion

This paper is a timely description of the multimessenger strategy to combine GWs and LENs to search for CCSNe. More detail results will be discussed in a forthcoming paper[1] that has been accepted by JCAP.

Various models of GW and LEN emissions have been considered and used for a set of simultaneous injections into the background from the considered detectors. The data are then analysed with our proposed 2-parameter method comparing with the standard 1-parameter method. The performance is exercised at the level of efficiency estimation between these two methods for various analysis steps.

In general a multimessenger analysis can give a better efficiency to low-significant signals.

We highlight the improvement of the neutrino analysis with the ξ parameter in terms of FAR and FAP. This method could be of interest of the online alert system like SNEWS2.0.

All in all, the multimessenger campaign between GWs and LENs with the proposed method can increase the overall efficiency. Due to the higher sensitivity in LEN detectors, we can also do a targeted search in the (hopefully near) future to search for GWs from CCSNe.

Acknowledgement

The authors gratefully acknowledge the support of the NSF for the provision of computational resources. The work of GP is partially supported by the research grant number 2017W4HA7S "NAT-NET: Neutrino and Astroparticle Theory Network" under the program PRIN 2017 funded by the Italian Ministero dell'Istruzione, dell'Università e della Ricerca (MIUR).

References

1. O. Halim, C. Casentini, M. Drago, V. Fafone, K. Scholberg, C. F. Vigorito and G. Pagliaroli, Multimessenger analysis strategy for core-collapse supernova search: Gravitational waves and low-energy neutrinos (2021), arXiv:2107.02050.
2. G. Pagliaroli, F. Vissani, E. Coccia and W. Fulgione, Neutrinos from supernovae as a trigger for gravitational wave search, *Phys. Rev. Lett.* **103**, p. 031102 (Jul 2009).
3. I. Leonor, L. Cadonati, E. Coccia, S. D'Antonio, A. D. Credico, V. Fafone, R. Frey, W. Fulgione, E. Katsavounidis, C. D. Ott, G. Pagliaroli, K. Scholberg, E. Thrane and F. Vissani, Searching for prompt signatures of nearby core-collapse supernovae by a joint analysis of neutrino and gravitational wave data, *Classical and Quantum Gravity* **27**, p. 084019 (apr 2010).
4. K. Hirata *et al.*, Observation of a neutrino burst from the supernova sn1987a, *Phys. Rev. Lett.* **58**, 1490 (Apr 1987).
5. R. M. Bionta *et al.*, Observation of a neutrino burst in coincidence with supernova 1987a in the large magellanic cloud, *Phys. Rev. Lett.* **58**, p. 1494 (1987).
6. E. Alexeyev *et al.*, Detection of the neutrino signal from sn 1987a in the lmc using the inr baksan underground scintillation telescope, *Physics Letters B* **205**, 209 (1988).
7. Y. Fukuda *et al.*, The super-kamiokande detector, *Nucl. Instrum. Meth.* **A501**, 418 (2003).
8. M. Aglietta *et al.*, The most powerful scintillator supernovae detector: Lvd, *Il Nuovo Cimento A Series 11* **105**, 1793 (1992), cited By 103.
9. F. Suekane *et al.*, An overview of the kamland 1-kiloton liquid scintillator2004. arXiv:physics/0404071.
10. M. Aartsen *et al.*, The icecube neutrino observatory: Instrumentation and online systems, *Journal of Instrumentation* **12**, P03012 (mar 2017).
11. P. Antonioli *et al.*, SNEWS: The supernova early warning system, *New Journal of Physics* **6**, 114 (sep 2004).
12. S. A. Kharusi *et al.*, SNEWS 2.0: a next-generation supernova early warning system for multi-messenger astronomy, *New Journal of Physics* **23**, p. 031201 (mar 2021).

13. B. P. Abbott *et al.*, Multi-messenger observations of a binary neutron star merger*, *The Astrophysical Journal* **848**, p. L12 (oct 2017).
14. J. Aasi *et al.*, Advanced LIGO, *Class. Quant. Grav.* **32**, p. 074001 (2015).
15. F. Acernese *et al.*, Advanced Virgo: a second-generation interferometric gravitational wave detector, *Class. Quant. Grav.* **32**, p. 024001 (2015).
16. T. Akutsu *et al.*, Overview of KAGRA: Detector design and construction history (2020), arXiv:2005.05574.
17. C. D. Ott, The gravitational-wave signature of core-collapse supernovae, *Classical and Quantum Gravity* **26**, p. 063001 (feb 2009).
18. E. Abdikamalov, G. Pagliaroli and D. Radice, Gravitational waves from core-collapse supernovae (2020), arXiv:2010.04356.
19. J. Powell and B. Müller, Three-dimensional core-collapse supernova simulations of massive and rotating progenitors, *Mon. Not. Roy. Astron. Soc.* **494**, 4665 (2020).
20. M. Szczepanczyk, J. Antelis, M. Benjamin, M. Cavaglia, D. Gondek-Rosinska, T. Hansen, S. Klimenko, M. Morales, C. Moreno, S. Mukherjee, G. Nurbek, J. Powell, N. Singh, S. Sitmukhambetov, P. Szewczyk, J. Westhouse, O. Valdez, G. Vedovato, Y. Zheng and M. Zanolin, Detecting and reconstructing gravitational waves from the next galactic core-collapse supernova in the advanced detector era (2021), arXiv:2104.06462.
21. O. Halim, Searching for core-collapse supernovae in the multimessenger era: Low energy neutrinos and gravitational waves, PhD thesis, Gran Sasso Science Institute (GSSI)2020.
22. O. Halim *et al.*, Expanding core-collapse supernova search horizon of neutrino detectors, *Journal of Physics: Conference Series* **1468**, p. 012154 (feb 2020).
23. S. Klimenko and G. Mitselmakher, A wavelet method for detection of gravitational wave bursts, *Classical and Quantum Gravity* **21**, S1819 (sep 2004).
24. S. Klimenko *et al.*, A coherent method for detection of gravitational wave bursts, *Classical and Quantum Gravity* **25**, p. 114029 (may 2008).
25. M. Drago, Search for transient gravitational wave signals with unknown waveform in the ligo virgo network of interferometric detectors using a fully coherent algorithm, PhD thesis, Università degli Studi di Padova2010.
26. V. Necula, S. Klimenko and G. Mitselmakher, Transient analysis with fast wilson-daubechies time-frequency transform (jun 2012).
27. B. P. Abbott *et al.*, Optically targeted search for gravitational waves emitted by core-collapse supernovae during the first and second observing runs of advanced ligo and advanced virgo, *Phys. Rev. D* **101**, p. 084002 (Apr 2020).
28. H.-T. Janka, Explosion mechanisms of core-collapse supernovae, *Annual Review of Nuclear and Particle Science* **62**, 407 (2012).
29. E. O'Connor and C. D. Ott, Black Hole Formation in Failing Core-Collapse Supernovae, *Astrophys. J.* **730**, p. 70 (2011).
30. D. Radice, V. Morozova, A. Burrows, D. Vartanyan and H. Nagakura, Characterizing the Gravitational Wave Signal from Core-Collapse Supernovae, *Astrophys. J. Lett.* **876**, p. L9 (2019).
31. H. Dimmelmeier *et al.*, Gravitational wave burst signal from core collapse of rotating stars, *Phys. Rev. D* **78**, p. 064056 (Sep 2008).
32. S. Scheidegger, R. Kaeppeli, S. C. Whitehouse, T. Fischer and M. Liebendoerfer, The Influence of Model Parameters on the Prediction of Gravitational wave Signals from Stellar Core Collapse, *Astron. Astrophys.* **514**, p. A51 (2010).
33. S. Woosley and A. Heger, The Progenitor stars of gamma-ray bursts, *Astrophys. J.* **637**, 914 (2006).

34. L. Hüdepohl, Neutrinos from the formation, cooling and black hole collapse of neutron stars, PhD thesis, Technische Universität München2014.
35. G. Pagliaroli *et al.*, Improved analysis of sn1987a antineutrino events, *Astroparticle Physics* **31**, 163 (2009).
36. F. Vissani, G. Pagliaroli and M. L. Costantini, A parameterized model for supernova electron antineutrino emission and its applications, *J. Phys. Conf. Ser.* **309**, p. 012025 (2011).
37. S. Klimenko, G. Vedovato, M. Drago, F. Salemi, V. Tiwari, G. A. Prodi, C. Lazzaro, K. Ackley, S. Tiwari, C. F. Da Silva and G. Mitselmakher, Method for detection and reconstruction of gravitational wave transients with networks of advanced detectors, *Phys. Rev. D* **93**, p. 042004 (2016).
38. M. Drago, V. Gayathri, S. Klimenko, C. Lazzaro, E. Milotti, G. Mitselmakher, V. Necula, B. O'Brian, G. A. Prodi, F. Salemi, M. Szczepanczyk, S. Tiwari, V. Tiwari, G. Vedovato and I. Yakushin, Coherent waveburst, a pipeline for unmodeled gravitational-wave data analysis (2021), arXiv:2006.12604.
39. B. P. Abbott *et al.*, First targeted search for gravitational-wave bursts from core-collapse supernovae in data of first-generation laser interferometer detectors, *Phys. Rev. D* **94**, p. 102001 (Nov 2016).
40. B. P. Abbott *et al.*, Prospects for observing and localizing gravitational-wave transients with Advanced LIGO, Advanced Virgo and KAGRA, *Living Rev. Rel.* **23**, p. 3 (2020).
41. J. Aasi *et al.*, Advanced LIGO, *Class. Quant. Grav.* **32**, p. 074001 (2015).
42. F. Acernese *et al.*, Advanced Virgo: A second-generation interferometric gravitational wave detector, *Class. Quant. Grav.* **32**, p. 024001 (2015).
43. M. J. Szczepańczyk, Multimessenger astronomy with gravitational waves from core-collapse supernovae, PhD thesis, Embry-Riddle Aeronautical University2018.
44. N. Agafonova *et al.*, Implication for the core-collapse supernova rate from 21 years of data of the large volume detector, *Astrophys. J.* **802**, p. 47 (2015).
45. M. Ikeda *et al.*, Search for supernova neutrino bursts at super-kamiokande, *Astrophys. J.* **669**, 519 (2007).
46. K. Abe *et al.*, Real-time supernova neutrino burst monitor at super-kamiokande, *Astropart. Phys.* **81**, 39 (2016).
47. C. Casentini *et al.*, Pinpointing astrophysical bursts of low-energy neutrinos embedded into the noise, *JCAP* **1808**, p. 010 (2018).
48. K. Eguchi *et al.*, First results from kamland: Evidence for reactor antineutrino disappearance, *Phys. Rev. Lett.* **90**, p. 021802 (Jan 2003).

A cryogenic and superconducting inertial sensor for the Lunar Gravitational–Wave Antenna, the Einstein Telescope and Selene-physics

F. Badaracco*, J. V. van Heijningen and E. C. Ferreira

Centre for Cosmology, Particle Physics and Phenomenology, Université catholique de Louvain, Louvain-La-Neuve, B-1348, Belgium
* E-mail: francesca.badaracco@uclouvain.be
http://www.uclouvain.be/

A. Perali

School of Pharmacy, Physics Unit, SuperNano Laboratory, University of Camerino, 62032 - Camerino (MC), Italy
http://www.supermaterials.org

INAF - Sezione di Camerino, Via Gentile III da Varano, 27, 62032 - Camerino (MC) - Italy

The Lunar Gravitational–Wave Antenna is a proposed low–frequency gravitational–wave detector on the Moon surface. It will be composed of an array of high-end cryogenic superconducting inertial sensors (CSISs). A cryogenic environment will be used in combination with superconducting materials to open up pathways to low–loss actuators and sensor mechanics. CSIS revolutionizes the (cryogenic) inertial sensor field with a modelled displacement sensitivity at 0.5 Hz of 3 orders of magnitude better than the current state–of–the–art. It will allow the Lunar Gravitational–Wave Antenna to be sensitive below 1 Hz, down to 1 mHz and it will also be employed in the forthcoming Einstein Telescope—a third-generation gravitational–wave detector which will make use of cryogenic technologies and that will have an enhanced sensitivity below 10 Hz. Moreover, CSIS seismic data could also be employed to obtain new insights about the Moon interior and what we can call the Selene-physics.

Keywords: Inertial sensor, Superconducting, Cryogenic, Seismic sensor, Lunar science, Lunar gravitational-wave antenna, Einstein Telescope

1. Introduction

The development of the Cryogenic Superconducting Inertial Sensor (CSIS) originates in the Einstein Telescope (ET) framework. ET will need a highly precise sensor to monitoring motion effects caused by the low–vibration cooling applied to its penultimate suspension stage, which indeed will operate at cryogenic temperatures and in vacuum.[1] Because of its extreme sensitivity and capability of working at cryogenic temperatures, CSIS will also be deployed on the Moon, exploiting it as a detector to reveal gravitational waves (GWs). The Lunar Gravitational–Wave Antenna (LGWA)[2] aims to exploit Moon's response to passing GWs and its resulting

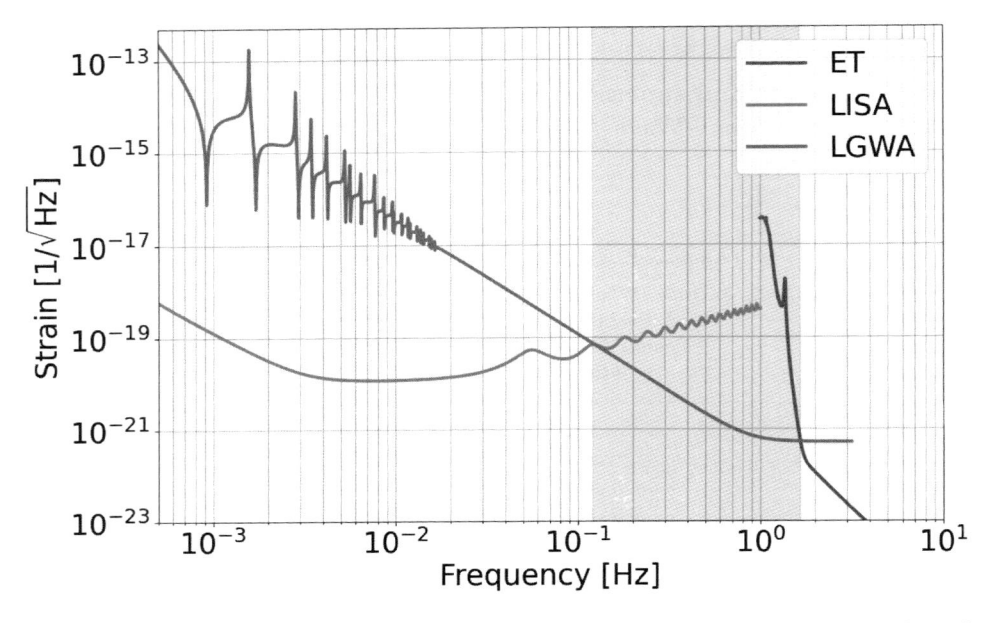

Fig. 1. Comparison in strain sensitivity between three future GW detectors. The notch–peak structures in the LGWA curve around 1–10 mHz result from the response of the Moon to passing GWs. Combining the performance of CSIS with the expected surface motion due to the lunar response yields the LGWA strain sensitivity. The grey rectangle highlights the gap that LGWA would bridge. See Ref.[2] for more info about the LGWA sensitivity curve.

surface motion. It will employ an array of 4 CSISs which can be regarded as the readout of a detector constituted by the Moon. The seismic data that LGWA would record will be used to study the Moon interior, its seismicity and its formation. This field of study is addressed as Selene-physics (the geophysics of the Moon).

LGWA will bridge the sensitivity gap between ET and the Laser Interferometer Space Antenna (LISA)[3] (see Fig. 1) between 0.12 and 1.5 Hz.

Improving detector sensitivity in the low–frequency band (below 10 Hz) entails a huge technical effort: Earth–bound GW detectors, like ET, are limited by the Newtonian noise,[4] while LGWA poses some difficulties deriving from deploying, assembling and powering the necessary instruments on the Moon.

The three detectors of which the sensitivity curves are shown in Fig. 1 are in development to extend our ability to detect GWs at lower frequencies. Signals of binary systems of (super–)massive black holes are found at these frequencies. Additionally, it will allow us to observe binary neutron stars already hours before the final merging.[5,6] Release of early warnings for the Electromagnetic (EM) follow–up will then be possible. The longer the observational time, the better the parameter estimation will be, also allowing to perform the sky–localization solely with the aid of LGWA (by exploiting the rotation of the Moon around the Earth). Polarization measurements and general relativity tests will also be possible.[2] Finally, it is impossible to know, but exciting to imagine what kinds of unknown can be detected once we open up that low–frequency band.

2. A technical design for CSIS

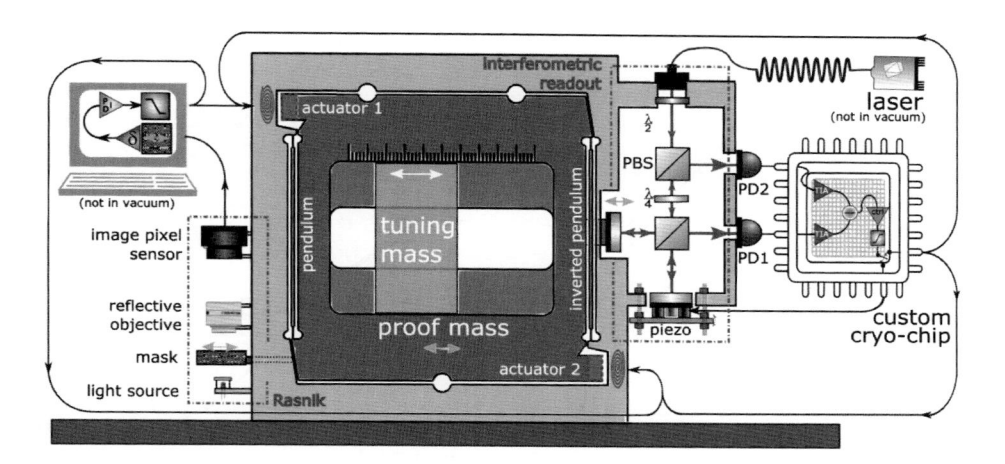

Fig. 2. Design of the CSIS sensor. We can identify four main parts: two readouts (highlighted by green dotted rectangles), spiral actuators (orange and red) and the proof mass (at the center). In Sec. 2 more details about the actuators and the proof mass are provided, while the two readouts are described in Secs. 3 and 4.

The design of CSIS is presented in Fig. 2. We can identify its four main parts: the Rasnik readout, the interferometric readouts, the two actuators on either side of the proof mass, and the niobium monolithic sensor mechanics. The latter will be the core of our sensor: a 1 kg mass suspended in a Watt's linkage configuration[7] (a combination of a pendulum and an inverted one) fabricated by Electrical Discharge Machining (EDM). The monolithic design allows to avoid having separate mechanical parts which would cause thermal dissipation.[8] Moreover, in Fig. 2 we see a tuning mass that will serve to adjust the resonance frequency of the sensor.

At cryogenic temperatures we can dramatically reduce the thermal noise, especially by employing materials that are superconductive (T_c = 9.2 K). At $\sim$ 5 K the mechanical Q–factor of a niobium CSIS will be of the order of 10^4 (see Ref.[9]), which is a significant improvement with respect to the room temperature version. Concerning LGWA, permanent shadow zones (of the order of several km) on the Moon are a convenient way to provide low and stable temperatures (<40 K).[10] This will make less challenging reaching the temperatures where the niobium behaves as a superconductor.

The actuators of Fig. 2 will constitute of a thin layer of niobium deposited on a ceramic substrate and then attached to the sensor frame. By applying a current

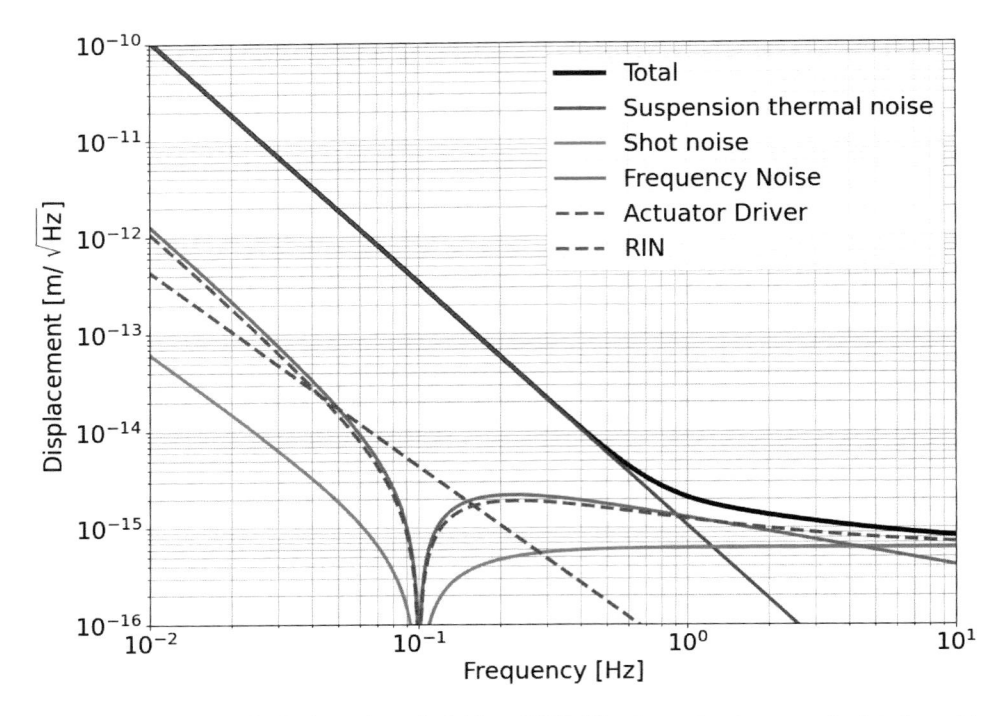

Fig. 3. Sensitivity and relative noises of niobium CSIS. The thermal noise was calculated considering a Q–factor of 10^4 and a temperature of 5 K. The other noises where calculated based on Ref.[9], where RIN is referring to the Relative Intensity Noise of the laser source of the interferometric readout and the actuator driver is calculated following Eq. 1.

to the spiral coil, a magnetic field will be created. Thanks to the Meissner effect, it will be expelled from the niobium of the proof mass, thus exerting a force on it.

To calculate CSIS sensitivity of Fig. 3, we need to take into account also the noise produced by the actuator driver:

$$n_{AD} = \frac{\beta V_{DAC}}{R_s m \omega^2}, \qquad (1)$$

where m is the mass, R_s is the sampling resistance (which determines the current into the actuator), V_{DAC} is the DAC voltage noise and β is the coil response value based on the latest simulations.

Another important advantage of employing a superconducting material is that it will avoid the thermal dissipation due to the eddy currents. This was a significant problem for the room temperature sensor version, where voice coils were employed to actuate the proof mass. In this way, the mechanical Q–factor was found to be highly limited by viscous damping associated with eddy currents induced on the moving metal surfaces by the voice coil stray field. The two readouts in Fig. 2 will be instead described in the next two sections.

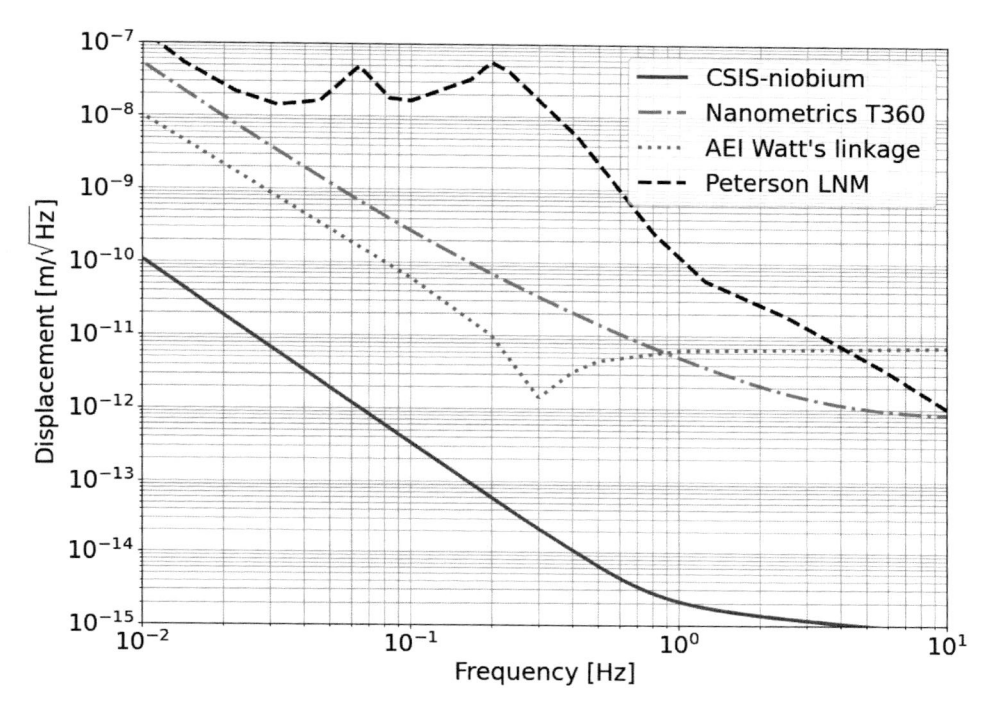

Fig. 4. Sensitivity of CSIS made of niobium compared to that of the most sensitive seismic sensors available. The Peterson's Low Noise Model (LNM) is depicted for comparison.

Thanks to its monolithic design, the employment of a material with a high Q-factor and thanks to two different readouts, CSIS will be able to reach sensitivities of $2\,\mathrm{fm}/\sqrt{\mathrm{Hz}}$ at 1 Hz (see Fig. 3). This is a factor 3000 better than the most sensitive seismic sensors (see Fig. 4, where the Peterson's Low Noise Model (LNM)[11] is depicted for comparison).

3. Interferometric readout

The interferometric readout that will be implemented in CSIS is based on that of Ref.[12] and it can be seen on the right side of Fig. 2 and in Fig. 6. It can be described as a simple Michelson interferometer with one more beamsplitter that allows to read the light coming back towards the laser. This second beamsplitter is needed to remove the common noise (such as intensity fluctuations in the laser power) by taking the differential signal between the two outputs. In this way, we can reach a shot noise limited sensitivity. The subtraction will be performed by a chip designed to work at cryogenic temperatures using CMOS technology.

The differential signal (see Fig. 5) will be fed through a control filter to the actuators which will dynamically lock the proof mass. This results in highly reduced relative motion between the proof mass and its frame and increased readout dynamic range. Moreover, keeping the differential signal as close as possible to a fixed working point ensures optimal subtraction of the common noises. Indeed, in the room temperature version, it was found that the the desired shot-noise-limit performance was not yet achieved.[13] The reason was that there was still some residual motion of the proof mass, thus resulting in a sub-optimal subtraction of the two photodiodes signals. To solve this, we can use a second control loop to reduce as much as possible the residual motion of the proof mass: the Rasnik readout.

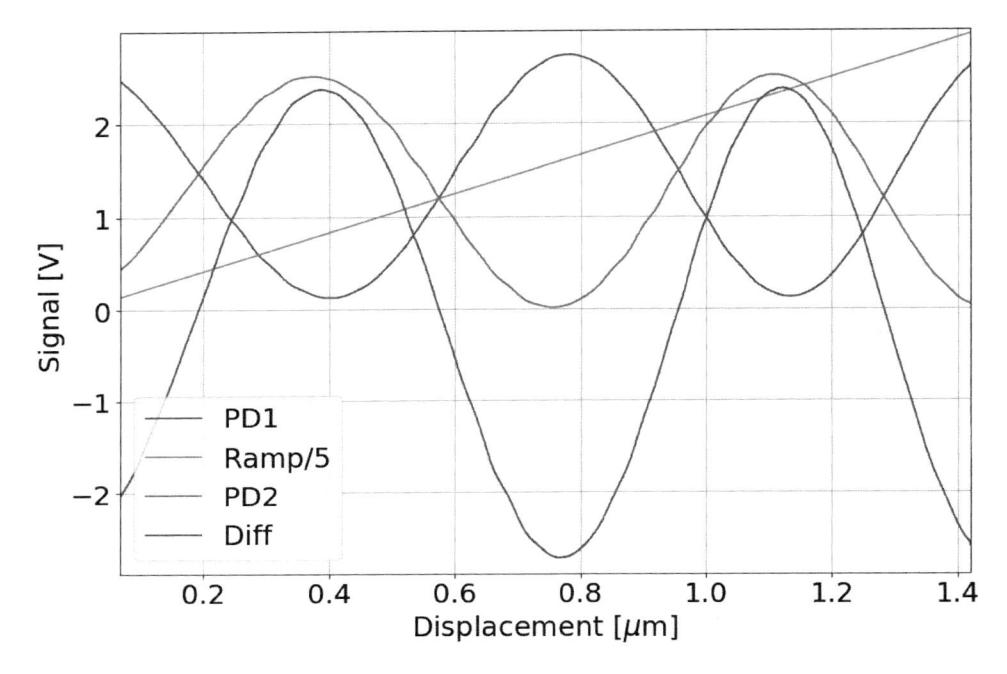

Fig. 5. Interference fringes obtained with a 1538 nm laser and moving one of the mirrors by injecting a ramp signal in its piezo actuator (PK44M3B8P2-Thorlabs). Using the known wavelength we find a piezo conversion factor of $96.1\,\text{nm}\,\text{V}^{-1}$. The minima and maxima are not exactly separated by the same distance probably due to non-linearities of the piezo actuator. The working points of the control loop are at 0 V of the differential signal.

Polarizing optics divert all the available power onto the photodiodes, avoiding dumping part of it. This is a important feature when working at cryogenic temperatures and it also means less shot noise for given injected power. Indeed, in Tab. 1 we can compare the powers received by the photodiodes and the overall shot noise when polarizing and non-polarizing optics are used. The total shot noise expected in the interferometer output depends on the amount of power falling on the photodiodes as $\text{SN}_i \propto 1/\sqrt{P_i}$. The total shot noise is then $\text{SN}_{\text{tot}} = \sqrt{\text{SN}_{\text{PD}_1}^2 + \text{SN}_{\text{PD}_2}^2}$.

We thus get a factor $\sqrt{3}$ of reduction in the shot noise when polarizing optics are employed with respect to the non-polarizing optics case.

Table 1. Comparison of interferometric readout outputs and shot noise without and with polarizing optics for a given input power P_0.

	power on PD1	power on PD2	SN_{tot}
previous configuration[12]	$P_0/4$	$P_0/8$	$\propto \sqrt{12/P_0}$
with polarizing optics	$P_0/2$	$P_0/2$	$\propto \sqrt{4/P_0}$

Fig. 6. Readout interferometer set up (laser on the bottom and photodiodes on the right). The arrows represent the light polarization: the green arrow right after the half wave plate (AHWP05M-1600-Thorlabs) is the linearly polarized light along the transmission axis of the polarizing beamsplitter (PBS104-Thorlabs), which, after passing through a quarter wave plate (AQWP05M-1600-Thorlabs), becomes circularly polarized (pink arrow). Reflection on the mirrors then reverses the handedness (yellow arrow). The second passage through the quarter wave plate with reversed handedness produces a linear polarization rotated by 90° degrees, which allows the light to be reflected by the polarizing beamsplitter instead of being transmitted.

4. Rasnik readout

The control loop driven by the Rasnik readout will have a larger dynamic range, capable of damping the proof mass resonance and thus reducing the proof mass residual motion. A Rasnik uses a back-lit chessboard mask which has its image projected via an objective on a pixel camera. The mask moves with the proof mass to which it is attached. The image that is recorded by the camera is then fed to a processing unit which performs a 2-dimensional Fourier transform. This transform will show a peak because of the many periodically spaced black-white transitions in the chessboard image. This peak shifts according to the motion of the mask and a peak fitting algorithm returns then the Rasnik displacement measurement. The obtained sensitivity is 7 pm/$\sqrt{\text{Hz}}$ and a sub-pm/$\sqrt{\text{Hz}}$ sensitivity is expected given the implementation of certain improvements.[14] The beauty of this system is that its dynamic range is only dependent on the chessboard mask dimensions, which can be designed arbitrarily large.

5. Final remarks

The development of highly sensitive inertial sensors in the GW community opens the path to new GW detector concepts like LGWA, but also to the possibility of studying the Moon in more detail, giving rise to Selene-physics.

CSIS is the product of R&D in the ET community and it is the perfect candidate to be employed as readout in LGWA. It will reach a sensitivity of a few fm/$\sqrt{\text{Hz}}$ from 0.5 Hz onwards and, therefore, it will become the most sensitive inertial sensor capable of working at cryogenic temperatures in the low–frequency band.

References

1. ET Steering Committee Editorial Team, ET design report update 2020, *ET-0007A-20* (2020).
2. J. Harms *et al.*, Lunar Gravitational-wave Antenna, *The Astrophysical Journal* **910**, p. 1 (Mar 2021).
3. K. Danzmann and the LISA study team, LISA: laser interferometer space antenna for gravitational wave measurements, *Classical and Quantum Gravity* **13**, A247 (November 1996).
4. J. Harms, Terrestrial gravity fluctuations, *Living Reviews in Relativity* **22** (October 2019).
5. M. L. Chan, C. Messenger, I. S. Heng and M. Hendry, Binary neutron star mergers and third generation detectors: Localization and early warning, *Physical Review D* **97** (June 2018).
6. S. Grimm and J. Harms, Multiband gravitational-wave parameter estimation: A study of future detectors, *Physical Review D* **102** (July 2020).
7. J. Liu, L. Ju and D. G. Blair, Vibration isolation performance of an ultra-low frequency folded pendulum resonator, *Physics Letters A* **228**, 243 (April 1997).
8. A. Bertolini, R. DeSalvo, F. Fidecaro, M. Francesconi, S. Marka, V. Sannibale, D. Simonetti, A. Takamori and H. Tariq, Mechanical design of a single-axis monolithic accelerometer for advanced seismic attenuation systems, *Nuclear Instruments and Methods in Physics Research Section A: Accelerators, Spectrometers, Detectors and Associated Equipment* **556**, 616 (January 2006).
9. J. V. van Heijningen, A fifty-fold improvement of thermal noise limited inertial sensitivity by operating at cryogenic temperatures, *Journal of Instrumentation* **15**, P06034 (June 2020).
10. D. A. Paige, M. A. Siegler, J. A. Zhang, P. O. Hayne, E. J. Foote, K. A. Bennett, A. R. Vasavada, B. T. Greenhagen, J. T. Schofield, D. J. McCleese, M. C. Foote, E. DeJong, B. G. Bills, W. Hartford, B. C. Murray, C. C. Allen, K. Snook, L. A. Soderblom, S. Calcutt, F. W. Taylor, N. E. Bowles, J. L. Bandfield, R. Elphic, R. Ghent, T. D. Glotch, M. B. Wyatt and P. G. Lucey, Diviner lunar radiometer observations of cold traps in the moon's south polar region, *Science* **330**, 479 (October 2010).

11. J. Peterson, Observation and modeling of seismic background noise, *Open-file report* **93-322** (1993).
12. M. B. Gray, D. E. McClelland, M. Barton and S. Kawamura, A simple high-sensitivity interferometric position sensor for test mass control on an advanced ligo interferometer, *Optical and Quantum Electronics* **31**, 571 (1999).
13. J. V. van Heijningen, Turn up the bass! Low-frequency performance improvement of seismic attenuation systems and vibration sensors for next generation gravitational wave detectors, *PhD thesis, Vrije Universiteit* (2018).
14. H. van der Graaf *et al.*, The ultimate performance of the rasnik 3-point alignment system, *arXiv:2104.03601v4* (2021).

Space gravitational wave antenna DECIGO and B-DECIGO

S. Kawamura[1,2,*] and the DECIGO working group

[1] *Physics department, Nagoya University, Nagoya, Aichi, 464-8602, Japan*
[2] *The Kobayashi-Maskawa Institute for the Origin of Particles and the Universe, Nagoya University, Nagoya, Aichi, 464-8602, Japan*
E-mail: kawamura@u.phys.nagoya-u.ac.jp

Deci-hertz Interferometer Gravitational Wave Observatory (DECIGO) is the future mission that aims to detect gravitational waves between 0.1 Hz and 10 Hz. DECIGO has four clusters, and one cluster of DECIGO consists of three differential Fabry-Perot interferometers with three drag-free spacecraft. Among various science targets of DECIGO, the detection of primordial gravitational waves is crucial. We are now updating the DECIGO design to ensure the detection of the primordial gravitational waves. We aim to launch B-DECIGO first at the earliest in 2032 as a pathfinder mission of DECIGO. B-DECIGO will not only establish the necessary technologies for DECIGO, but also accomplish a variety of important sciences.

Keywords: DECIGO; B-DECIGO; interferometer; primordial gravitational wave

1. Introduction

Since the first detection of gravitational waves by LIGO and Virgo[1] in 2015, gravitational waves from various sources such as black hole binary, neutron star binary,[2] intermediate-mass black hole binary,[3] and black hole/neutron star binary coalescences[4] have been detected by LIGO and Virgo. Especially the neutron star binary coalescence was accompanied by short gamma-ray burst[5] and electromagnetic-wave observations of the afterglow.[6]

In the future, gravitational wave astronomy will be further developed by the third-generation ground-based detectors, such as Einstein Telescope (ET)[7] and Cosmic Explorer (CE),[8] as well as space detectors, such as LISA.[9] Ground-based detectors aim to detect gravitational waves above 10 Hz, while LISA aims below 0.1 Hz. Detection of gravitational waves from compact star binaries between the two frequency bands is useful because it can play a role of follow-up of the gravitational waves already detected by LISA, as well as a role of a predictor of the gravitational waves to be detected by the ground-based detectors. Furthermore, this mid-frequency band has the potential of establishing a deep and effective window for gravitational waves coming from various sources, not only because expected gravitational-wave signals are larger at lower frequencies, but also the confusion limiting noise caused by irresolvable gravitational wave signals coming from white dwarf binaries.

One of the future missions, aiming at detecting gravitational waves in this mid-frequency (between 0.1 Hz and 10 Hz), is Deci-hertz Interferometer Gravitational Wave Observatory (DECIGO).[10,11] In this paper, pre-conceptual design and aimed science of DECIGO are explained in sections 2 and 3. Then the necessary update of the DECIGO design is described in section 4. In section 5, B-DECIGO, which is a pathfinder mission of DECIGO with solid scientific targets, is explained. Finally, in section 6, conclusions are summarized.

2. Design of DECIGO

The concept of DECIGO was born in 2001. At that time, the main science target was the direct measurement of the acceleration of the Universe. Since then, we have elaborated the design of DECIGO by implementing Fabry-Perot arm cavities, and finally, we established a pre-conceptual design of DECIGO.

As shown in Fig. 1, one cluster of DECIGO consists of three differential Fabry-Perot interferometers with three drag-free spacecraft. Each spacecraft has two floating mirrors, which are shared by two interferometers. The relative position of the mirror with respect to the spacecraft is measured by local position sensors attached to the spacecraft, and the position signals are fed back to the thrusters attached to the spacecraft to control the position of the spacecraft. The distance between the two spacecraft is 1,000 km. Laser light illuminating the interferometers has a wavelength of 515 nm and a power of 10 W. The mirrors have a radius of 0.5 m and a mass of 100 kg. The Fabry-Perot cavities have a finesse of 10. There are four clusters altogether placed separately, with two clusters at the same place in the heliocentric Earth-trail orbit, as shown in Fig. 2. The separation of the spacecraft is useful to increase the angular resolution of the sources, while placing the two clusters at the same place is useful to take correlation measurements to detect stochastic gravitational-wave background, such as primordial gravitational waves.

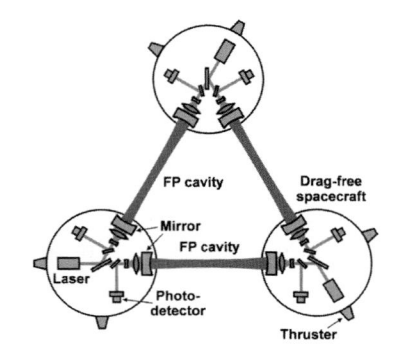

Fig. 1.   Pre-conceptual design of DECIGO.

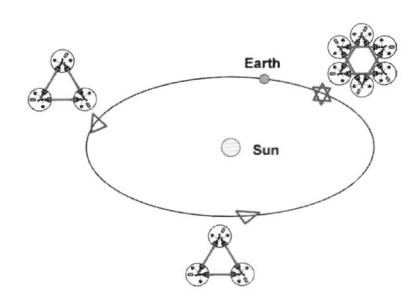

Fig. 2. Orbit of DECIGO.

3. Science of DECIGO

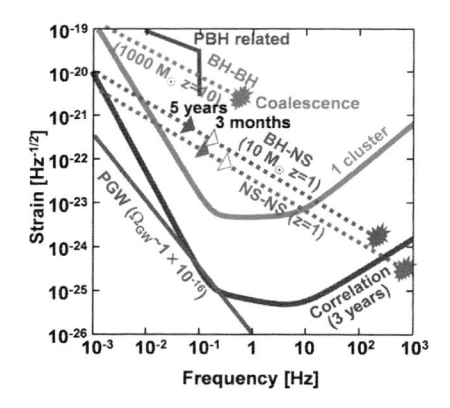

The target sensitivity of DECIGO and expected gravitational-wave signals from various sources are shown in Fig. 3. The target sensitivity of one cluster of DECIGO is $4 \times 10^{-24}\,\text{Hz}^{-1/2}$ around 1 Hz. The sensitivity is limited by radiation pressure noise below 0.1 Hz and shot noise above 10 Hz. The shot-noise-limited sensitivity decreases above the cavity pole frequency, about 10 Hz, because the gravitational wave signals are canceled by the long storage time of the light in the arm cavities.

One cluster of DECIGO can detect gravitational waves coming from a large number of black hole binaries, for example, 1,000-solar-mass black holes at a redshift of $z = 10$ with a high signal-to-noise ratio. This could reveal the formation mechanism of intermediate-mass black holes. DECIGO can also detect gravitational waves from a large number of neutron star binaries, for example, at a redshift of $z = 1$ with a good signal-to-noise ratio. This can provide a prediction of the exact time and location of neutron star binary coalescences for ground-based gravitational-wave detectors as well as both terrestrial and space electromagnetic-wave observatories.[12]

Fig. 3. Target sensitivity of DECIGO and expected gravitational wave signals.

This could also lead to the direct measurement of the acceleration of the expansion of the Universe, because it could cause a phase delay of gravitational wave signals.[10,13,14] This could provide reliable information about dark energy. DECIGO can also detect gravitational waves from, for example, about ten solar-mass black hole and neutron star binaries at a redshift of $z = 1$. This could provide a factor of 10^4 more precise test for the general theory of relativity.[15] In addition, DECIGO could detect gravitational waves coming from density fluctuations at the beginning of the Universe, which could have produced primordial black holes as candidates of dark matters.[16] DECIGO also has a variety of other science targets.[17-20]

The target sensitivity of DECIGO can be improved to 7×10^{-26} Hz$^{-1/2}$ around 1 Hz by taking a correlation of two clusters st the same place for three years. This could enable detection of the primordial gravitational waves and revelation of the true inflation mechanism.[21] Moreover, DECIGO could observe a parity violation between the two circular polarizations,[22] separate the tensor, scalar, and vector modes of gravitational waves,[23] and reveal the thermal history after the inflation.[24,25] The design sensitivity of DECIGO was established more than ten years ago in such a way that DECIGO could detect the primordial gravitational waves corresponding to normalized energy of $\Omega_{GW} = 2 \times 10^{-15}$, which was the upper limit of the primordial gravitational waves at that time. However, analysis based on the observations by the Planck satellite lowered the upper limit of Ω_{GW} to 1×10^{-16}. As a result, the DECIGO sensitivity became no longer good enough to detect the primordial gravitational waves.

4. Update of DECIGO design and target sensitivity

We are currently updating the design parameters of DECIGO, so that the new target sensitivity, determined by the updated design parameters, could ensure detection of the primordial gravitational waves with a good margin. We take the following three steps for the update. (1) For a given radius of the mirror, the cavity length, reflectivity of the mirrors, and laser power are optimized for the best signal-to-noise ratio, considering only the quantum noise as the noise source of DECIGO. (2) The same optimization is performed, considering other noise sources, such as the thermal noise of the mirrors. (3) The design and the corresponding sensitivity are updated, considering practical issues, such as the constraints of the mirror size.

We have completed the first step so far. For a given radius of the mirrors, we used a set of the three free design parameters (the cavity length, reflectivity of the mirrors, and laser power) to calculate the signal-to-noise ratio for the primordial gravitational waves. In the process of the calculation, optical loss due to the diffraction of the light, determined by the radius of the mirrors and the cavity length, was properly considered.[26] The signal-to-noise ratio was calculated between 0.1 Hz and 1 Hz, assuming that the confusion limiting noise caused by gravitational waves coming from extra-galactic white dwarf binaries does not exist above 0.1 Hz. The laser power of 100 W at the maximum was assumed to be available, although the default design of the laser power for DECIGO is 10 W. The result of the optimization is shown in Fig. 4.[27] It indicates that by increasing the radius of the mirror from 0.5 m (default value) to 1 m, the cavity length can be extended from 1,000 km (default value) to about 5,000 km. This results in the improvement of the signal-to-noise ratio from 1.6 to about 100 with also the optimized reflectivity of the mirrors and laser power. It should be noted that in this optimization, the mass of the mirror is maintained to be constant, 100 kg (default value), even with the increased radius of the mirrors by shortening the thickness of the mirrors. We are now doing the same kind of optimization considering other noise sources, such as the thermal noise of the mirrors.

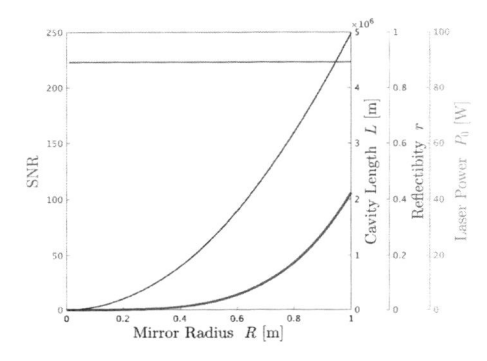

Fig. 4. Optimization of the cavity length, reflectivity of the mirrors, and laser power for a given radius of the mirrors in terms of the best signal-to-noise ratio.[27]

We are also investigating the possibility of implementing the quantum locking technique with an optical spring to DECIGO. We found that the quantum locking with an optical spring could improve the signal-to-noise ratio of the quantum noise to the primordial gravitational waves from 1.6 to 214 without changing the mirror size.[28,29]

5. B-DECIGO

We aim to launch B-DECIGO[30] at the earliest in 2032 before DECIGO. B-DECIGO can play a role in demonstrating the required technologies for DECIGO as well as a role of a real gravitational wave detector. B-DECIGO consists of three differential Fabry-Perot interferometers with three drag-free spacecraft. The distance between two spacecraft is 100 km, which is one-tenth of that of DECIGO. The laser wavelength is the same as that of DECIGO, and the laser power is 1 W (one-tenth of that of DECIGO). The mirror radius is 0.15 m (one-third of that of DECIGO), and the mass is 30 kg (one-third of that of DECIGO). The finesse of the arm cavities is 100 (ten times larger than that of DECIGO). B-DECIGO has one cluster, and the orbit is still under consideration.

The target sensitivity of B-DECIGO is shown in Fig. 5. The target sensitivity of B-DECIGO is lower than that of DECIGO approximately by a factor of ten. Since it has only one cluster, the correlation between the two clusters is not available. Although we cannot expect to detect the primordial gravitational waves, B-DECIGO can still bring us a variety of science.[31] It is expected to predict the timing of the neutron star binary coalescences together with the location of the source 100 times a year. It could reveal the origin of about 30 solar-mass black holes. It could estimate the parameter of compact star binaries much better than before. B-DECIGO could also demonstrate the method of removing the foreground gravitational wave signals coming from neutron star binaries, which is necessary for DECIGO. It could also demonstrate the technologies required to realize DECIGO, such as the Fabry-Perot cavities in space and drag-free system.

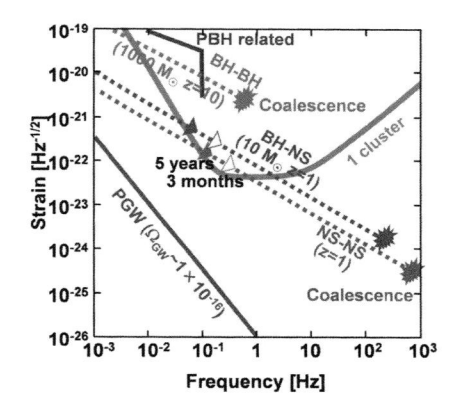

Fig. 5. Target sensitivity of B-DECIGO and expected gravitational wave signals.

6. Conclusions

DECIGO will accomplish a variety of outstanding sciences, including direct observation of the primordial gravitational waves. We are now investigating the improvement of target sensitivity of DECIGO to ensure the detection of the primordial gravitational waves. B-DECIGO will not only accomplish a variety of important sciences but also establish the necessary technologies for DECIGO.

Acknowledgments

This work was supported by the Japan Society for the Promotion of Science (JSPS) KAKENHI, grant number JP19H01924.

References

1. B. P. Abbott, et al., *Phys. Rev. Lett.* **116** (2016) 061102.
2. B. P. Abbott, et al., *Phys. Rev. Lett.* **119** (2017) 161101.
3. R. Abbott, et al., *Phys. Rev. Lett.* **125** (2020) 101102.
4. R. Abbott, et al., *Astrophys. J. Lett.* **915:L5** (2021).
5. A. Goldstein, et al., *ApJ* **848** (2017) L14.
6. D. A. Coulter, et al., *Science* **358** (2017) 1556.
7. M. Punturo, et al., *Class. Quantum Grav.* **27** (2010) 194002.
8. B. P. Abbott, et al., *Class. Quantum Grav.* **34** (2017) 044001.
9. K. Danzmann, et al., *Nature Physics* **11** (2015) 613.
10. N. Seto, S. Kawamura, and T. Nakamura, *Phys. Rev. Lett.* **87** (2001) 221103.
11. S. Kawamura, et al., *Int. J. Mod. Phys. D* **28** (2019) 1845001.
12. R. Takahashi and T. Nakamura, *Astrophys. J.* **596** (2003) L231.
13. A. Nishizawa, et al., *Phys. Rev. D* **85** (2012) 044047.
14. A. Nishizawa, A. Taruya, and S. Saito, *Phys. Rev. D* **83** (2011) 084045.
15. K. Yagi and T. Tanaka, *Prog. Theor. Exp. Phys.* **123** (2010) 1069.
16. R. Saito and J. Yokoyama, *Phys. Rev. Lett.* **102** (2009) 161101.
17. N. Seto, *Astrophys. J.* **677** (2008) L55.
18. M. Kakizaki, S. Kanemura, and T. Matsui, *Phys. Rev. D* **92** (2015) 115007.
19. S. Hou, et al., *Phys. Rev. D* **103** (2021) 044005.
20. A. Piórkowska-Kurpas, et al., *ApJ* **908** (2021) 196.
21. S. Kuroyanagi, T. Chiba, and N. Sugiyama, *Phys. Rev. D* **79** (2009) 103501.
22. N. Seto, *Phys. Rev. D* **75** (2007) 061302(R).
23. A. Nishizawa, A. Taruya, and S. Kawamura, *Phys. Rev. D* **81** (2010) 104043.
24. S. Kuroyanagi, K. Nakayama, and J. Yokoyama, *Prog. Theor. Exp. Phys.* (2015) 013E02.
25. K. Nakayama, et al., *Phys. Rev. D* **77**, 124001.
26. S. Iwaguchi, et al., *Galaxies* **9** (2021) 9010009.
27. T. Ishikawa, et al., *Galaxies* **9** (2021) 9010014.
28. R. Yamada, et al., *Phys. Lett. A* **384** (2020) 126626.
29. R. Yamada, et al., *Phys. Lett. A* **402** (2021) 127365.
30. T. Nakamura, et al., *Prog. Theor. Exp. Phys.* (2016) 093E01.
31. S. Isoyama, H. Nakano, and T. Nakamura, *Prog. Theor. Exp. Phys.* (2018) 073E01.

Summary of the parallel session GW2

Dongfeng Gao*, Wei-Tou Ni†, Jin Wang‡, Ming-Sheng Zhan§, and Lin Zhou¶

Wuhan Institute of Physics and Mathematics, APM, Chinese Academy of Sciences, Wuhan 430071, China
*dfgao@wipm.ac.cn
†wei-tou.ni@wipm.ac.cn
‡wangjin@wipm.ac.cn
§mszhan@wipm.ac.cn
¶lzhou@wipm.ac.cn

This article summarizes the talks in the session GW2 of *the Sixteenth Marcel Grossmann Meeting on Recent Developments in Theoretical and Experimental General Relativity, Gravitation, and Relativistic Field Theories*, 5-10 July, 2021, on *Mid-frequency (0.1-10 Hz) gravitational waves: Sources and detection methods* with a review on strain power spectral density amplitude of various mid-frequency gravitational wave projects/concepts and with extended summaries on the progress of ZAIGA project and on the conceptual study of AMIGO.

Keywords: Mid-frequency gravitational waves; Earth-based gravitational wave detectors; Moon-based gravitational wave detectors; Space-borne gravitational wave detectors

1. Introduction

The mid-frequency GW (Gravitational Wave) band (0.1-10 Hz) between the LIGO-Virgo-KAGRA detection band and LISA-TAIJI/TIANQIN detection band is rich in GW sources. In addition to the intermediate BH (Black Hole) Binary coalescence, it can also come from the inspiral phase of stellar-mass coalescence and from compact binaries falling into intermediate BHs. Detecting mid-frequency GWs enables us to study the compact object population, to test general relativity and beyond-the-Standard-Model theories, to explore the stochastic GW background and so on. In addition to DECIGO and BBO, the detection proposals under study include AEDGE, AIGSO, AION, AMIGO, DO, ELGAR, GLOC, INO, LGWA, MAGIS, MIGA, SOGRO, TIAGO, TOBA, ZAIGA, etc. Great advances have accumulated since MG15.

In the GW2 parallel session on 7 July 2021, there were ten talks.[1–10] First, an outlook of the mid-frequency GW detection and AMIGO were reviewed[1] followed by three talks on the mid-frequency astrophysical/cosmological sources and their propagation through the inhomogeneous universe for the GW observations from the Earth, the Moon and the Space.[2–4] The next two talks were on the Lunar Gravitational-Wave Antenna (LGWA) and its sensor development.[5,6] The last four talks were on Earth-based detectors TOBA,[7] ZAIGA[8] and AION,[9] and space-borne detectors AEDGE,[9] DECIGO[10] and B-DECIGO.[10]

Although there have been activities across all GW frequency spectrum,[11] current activities on GW detection are largely in the high-frequency band (10 Hz-10 kHz) of LIGO-Virgo-KAGRA and low-frequency band (0.1 mHz-100 mHz) of LISA-TAIJI/TIANQIN together with PTAs (300 pHz-100 nHz) and CMB polarization observations (1 aHz-10 fHz). Nevertheless, activities in the mid-frequency GW band have increased steadily since last decade. In the 2030s, ET and Cosmic Explorer will be deployed in the high-frequency band; LISA and TAIJI/TIANQIN will be deployed in the mHz low-frequency band. To complete the map, some mid-frequency GW detectors are desired to be deployed also. Table 1 lists the strain power spectral density (psd) amplitude at 0.1 Hz, 1 Hz and 10 Hz for various mid-frequency GW detectors together with the strain psd amplitude for ET at 1 Hz & 10 Hz and Cosmic Explorer at 10 Hz, and the strain psd amplitude for LISA at 0.1 Hz and for & TAIJI & TIANQIN at 0.1 Hz, 1 Hz and 10 Hz.

Harms et al.[31] have discussed ground-based GW detector concepts to extend the present ground-based interferometers' detection spectral range to middle-frequency band 0.1–10 Hz. They find that although there are no fundamental limits to the detector sensitivity in this band, the technical limits for the Newtonian-noise cancellation from infrasound and seismic surface fields are challenging to overcome.[31,32] Newtonian noise needs to be measured and subtracted. ET and Cosmic Explorer need to deal with this issue to certain extent and their sensitivity extends only down to 1 Hz and 5 Hz amplitudes respectively. ET is listed at 10 Hz and 1 Hz and Cosmic Explorer is listed at 10 Hz in Table 1 for comparison. On the lower frequency side, LISA, TAIJI and TIANQIN are listed for comparison. For space missions, local gravity noise (Newtonian noise needs to be compensated, and/or measured and subtracted. Due to the success of LISA Pathfinder mission,[33,34] this issue is largely solved.

The goal on the strain psd noise of ET at 1 Hz is $\sim 1 \times 10^{-21}\text{Hz}^{-1/2}$, while that of LISA at 0.1 Hz is $4 \times 10^{-20}\text{Hz}^{-1/2}$. Any new mid-frequency proposals aiming at a starting time after ET and LISA turn-on can keep these sensitivities in mind for their designs.

In Section 2, we discuss and review sources and scientific goals for mid-frequency GW detection. In Section 3, we discuss Earth-based detectors and summarize the TOBA, AION and ZAIGA talks. In Section 4, we discuss Moon-based detectors and summarize the LGWA and GLOC talks. In Section 5, we discuss space-borne GW detectors and summarize the AEDGE, AMIGO, DECIGO and B-DECIGO talks.

2. Sources and Scientific Goals

The general scientific goals of mid-frequency GW detectors are:

(i) to bridge the spectral gap between high-frequency and first-generation low-frequency GW sensitivities for detecting intermediate mass BH coalescence;

(ii) to detect inspiral phase and predict time of stellar-mass binary black hole coalescence together with neutron star coalescence or neutron star-black hole

Table 1. Strain power spectral density (psd) amplitude at 0.1 Hz, 1 Hz and 10 Hz for various mid-frequency GW detectors. In the first column, [E] means Earth-based, [M] means Moon-based, and [S] means space-borne. All units are in $\text{Hz}^{-1/2}$.

GW detector or detector concept	Method of GW detection	Strain psd amplitude at 0.1 Hz	Strain psd amplitude at 1 Hz	Strain psd amplitude at 10 Hz
ET[12][E]	Micheson Interferometry with Fabry-Perot Cavities	n.a.	1×10^{-21}	1×10^{-24}
CE[13][E]	Micheson Interferometry with Fabry-Perot Cavities	n.a.	n.a.	6×10^{-25}
LISA[14][S]	TDI interferometry	4×10^{-20}	4×10^{-19}	n.a.
TAIJI[15][S]	TDI interferometry	3.3×10^{-20}	3.3×10^{-19}	3.3×10^{-18}
TIANQIN[16][S]	TDI interferometry	1.5×10^{-20}	3.5×10^{-20}	4×10^{-19}
aSOGRO[17][E]	SQUID capacitance-bridge transducer	5×10^{-20}	3×10^{-21}	1×10^{-21}
TOBA[18][E]	Torsion Bar	1×10^{-19}	8×10^{-20}	5×10^{-20}
ELGAR/MIGA[19][E]	Laser-Linked Atom Interferometry	3×10^{-19}	5×10^{-22}	5×10^{-22}
MAGIS-1 km[20][E]	Laser-Linked Atom Interferometry	n.a.	1×10^{-21}	n.a.
AION-1 km[21][E]	Laser-Linked Atom Interferometry	n.a.	1×10^{-21}	n.a.
ZAIGA[22][E]	Laser-Linked Atom Interferometry	1.4×10^{-18}	2.4×10^{-21}	1.2×10^{-21}
LGWA[23][M]	Inertial sensors with station location measurements	1×10^{-20}	1×10^{-20}	n.a.
GLOC[24][M]	Micheson Interferometry with with Fabry-Perot Cavities	n.a.	1×10^{-23}	1×10^{-24}
AEDGE[25][S]	Laser-Linked Atom Interferometry	3.5×10^{-23}	3×10^{-23}	n.a.
AIGSO[26][S]	Atom Interferometry	7×10^{-19}	1×10^{-20}	3×10^{-22}
INO-d[27][S]	Clocks with laser link	$1 - 2 \times 10^{-18}$	$1 - 2 \times 10^{-18}$	$1 - 2 \times 10^{-18}$
b-AMIGO[28][S]	Michelson X0/X TDI	5.5×10^{-21}	3×10^{-21}	6×10^{-21}
AMIGO[28][S]	Michelson X0/X TDI	4.3×10^{-21}	1×10^{-21}	2.3×10^{-21}
e-AMIGO[28][S]	Michelson X0/X TDI	4.3×10^{-21}	5×10^{-22}	8.5×10^{-22}
TIANGO[29][S]	TDI Interferometry	1×10^{-21}	4×10^{-22}	4×10^{-22}
DO-Conservative[30][S]	TDI Interferometry	1.5×10^{-22}	1.3×10^{-22}	3×10^{-22}
DO-Optimal[30][S]	TDI Interferometry	4×10^{-23}	2×10^{-23}	4×10^{-23}
B-DECIGO[10][S]	Fabry-Perot arm cavities	1.5×10^{-22}	5×10^{-23}	8×10^{-23}
DECIGO 1 cluster[10][S]	Fabry-Perot arm cavities	1.5×10^{-23}	5×10^{-24}	8×10^{-23}
DECIGO 3-year correlation[10][S]	Fabry-Perot arm cavities	3×10^{-25}	7×10^{-26}	3×10^{-25}

coalescence for ground interferometers, e.g., the inspiral GWs from sources like GW150914;[35]

(iii) to detect compact binary inspirals for studying stellar evolution and galactic population;

(iv) to detect middle frequency GWs from compact binaries falling into intermediate mass BHs for multi-band observation with ground-based GW detectors;[36]

(v) to study the compact object population and to estimate/explore the astrophysical stochastic background from stellar object inspirals;

(vi) to determine Supermassive Black Hole properties using GW radiation from surrounding stellar-mass BH binaries;[3,37]

(vii) to test general relativity and beyond-the-standard-model theories.

In subsection 2.1, the goal (vi) will be discussed. General treatments on astrophysical GW sources and associated goals for detection in the middle-frequency GW bands can be found in Refs. [35, 36, 38, 39]. In subsection 2.2, Generation, propagation and detection of GWs in inhomogeneous universe will be discussed. In section 3-5, specific scientific goals for individual detector will be stated.

2.1. *Determination of Supermassive Black Hole properties using GW radiation from surrounding stellar-mass BH binaries*[3,37]

With space-borne gravitational-wave observatories, one may use stellar-mass BH binary as a signal carrier to probe modulations induced by a central supermassive BH (SMBH) to further place constraints on the SMBH's properties. As an example, Yu and Chen[3,36] showed that the de Sitter precession of the inner stellar-mass binary's orbital angular momentum around the angular momentum of the outer orbit would be detectable when the precession period is comparable to the duration of observation, typically a few years. The precession could be combined with the Doppler shift arising from the outer orbital motion to determine the mass of the SMBH and the outer orbital separation with percent-level accuracy. Joint detection with Earth-based detector would extend the detection threshold to a precession period to ~ 100 yr.

2.2. *Generation, propagation and detection of GWs in inhomogeneous universe*

In the talk, Fier *et al.*[2,40] presented their recent studies on GWs produced by remote compact astrophysical sources. To describe such GWs properly, Fier *et al.* introduced three scales, the typical wavelength of GWs, the scale of the cosmological perturbations, and the size of the observable universe. For GWs to be detected by the current and foreseeable detectors, they can be well approximated as high-frequency GWs. The spatial, traceless, and Lorentz gauge conditions can be imposed simultaneously to simplify the field equations, even when the background is not vacuum, as long as the high-frequency GW approximation is valid. Fier *et al.* developed the geometrical optics approximation to such GWs, and calculated the gravitational integrated Sachs-Wolfe effects due to the presence of the cosmological scalar and tensor perturbations to read out explicitly the dependence of the amplitude, phase and luminosity distance of the GWs.

3. Earth-Based Detectors – TOBA, AION and ZAIGA

Earth is noisy for strain measurement. From 10 Hz to 10 kHz, vibration noise needs to be suppressed. This issue is basically solved by active and passive vibration isolation after decades of research and development. In the mid-frequency band of GW detection on Earth, the Newtonian noise (the gravity gradient noise) cannot be suppressed. It needs to be measured and subtracted. TOBA uses torsion bars, and AION and ZAIGA use atom interferometry to measure the Newtonian noise and subtract it.

3.1. *TOBA*

TOBA (TOrsion-Bar Antenna) is a mid.-frequency gravitational-wave antenna. It is formed by two bar-shape test masses, each suspended as a torsion pendulum. Tidal effect originated by incoming gravitational wave will be detected as differential angular motion of these two bars. The fundamental sensitivity is $10^{-19}\text{Hz}^{-1/2}$ at 0.1 Hz frequency band, assuming 10-m scale cryogenic detector at 4 K with the rotations of the bars measured with Fabry–Perot cavities at the end of the bars.[7,18] Though this sensitivity is not comparable with space antennae, it is sufficient to observe some intermediate-mass black-hole inspirals in our universe. Also, operation on ground is advantageous in development time and cost. The Phase-III prototype is to complete the demonstration of noise reduction reaching a sensitivity of about $10^{-15}\text{Hz}^{-1/2}$ at 0.1 Hz. Measuring the terrestrial gravity fluctuation with a sensitivity of about or below $10^{-15}\text{Hz}^{-1/2}$ at 0.1 Hz is useful for two geophysical purpose – earthquake early warning and Newtonian noise reduction for GW detection.

3.2. *AION*

AION (Atom Interferometer Observatory and Network) is a proposed experimental programme using cold strontium atoms to search for ultra-light dark matter, to explore gravitational waves in the mid-frequency, and to probe other frontiers in fundamental physics. AION has 3 stages of development, AION-10 m, AION-100 m and AION-1 km in parallel to MAGIS-10 m, MAGIS-100 m and MAGIS-1 km. AION would share many technical features with the MAGIS experimental programme, and synergies would flow from operating AION in a network with MAGIS, as well as with other atom interferometer experiments such as MIGA, ZAIGA and ELGAR.[9,21]

3.3. *ZAIGA*

ZAIGA (the Zhaoshan long-baseline Atom Interferometer Gravitation Antenna) is a proposed underground long-baseline atom interferometer (AI) facility (see Fig. 1), aiming for experimental research on gravitation and related problems.[22] It is located in the mountain named Zhaoshan which is about 80 km southeast to Wuhan city.

ZAIGA will consist of gravitational wave detection (ZAIGA-GW), dark matter detection (ZAIGA-DM), high-precision test of the equivalence principle (ZAIGA-EP), clock-based gravitational red-shift measurement (ZAIGA-CE-R), rotation measurement and gravitomagnetic effect (ZAIGA-RM), and geological and geophysical measurement (ZAIGA-GG). The first stage of the project (2021-2025) will include building a vertical 300-meter long tunnel to interrogate three 10-meter atom interferometers and atomic clocks (aiming for ZAIGA-EP, ZAIGA-DM and ZAIGA-CE-R), and building a horizontal 1.5-km long tunnel (aiming for ZAIGA-RM and ZAIGA-GG). Depending on the performance in the first stage, the second stage of the project will construct an array of 1-km arm-length horizontal triangular tunnels and be dedicated to ZAIGA-GW.

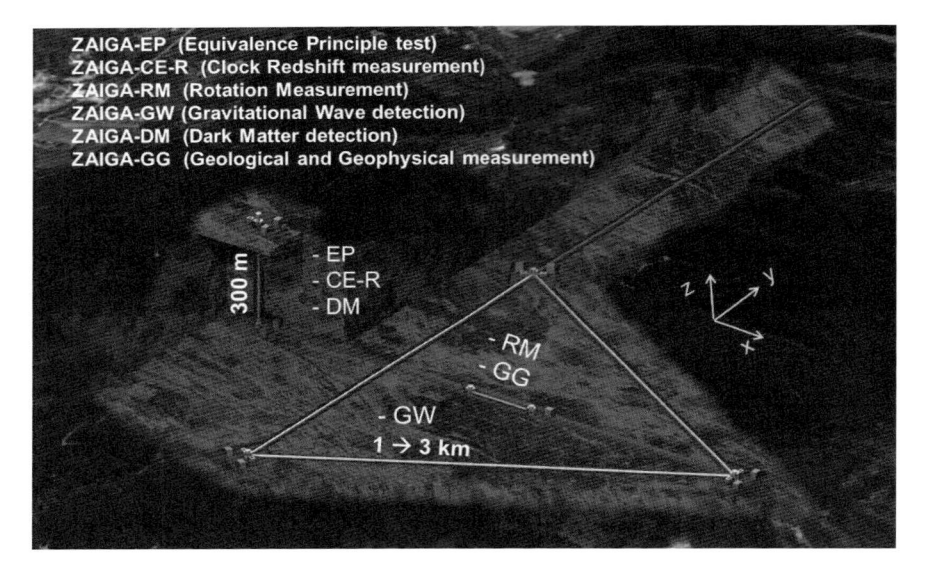

Fig. 1. Schematic diagram of ZAIGA design.

The site exploration started immediately after the ZAIGA plan was put forward. Relevant work for site exploration keeps on going now. The following progress on the technical and theoretical aspects of ZAIGA has also been made.

In the past three years, with our 10-m dual-species atom interferometer, we carried out a joint mass-energy test of the equivalence principle (EP), by using rubidium atoms with specified mass and internal energy.[41] By extending the four-wave double-diffraction Raman transition method (4WDR) to ^{85}Rb and ^{87}Rb atoms with different angular momenta, we can measure their differential gravitational acceleration. The Eötvös parameter, η, of the four paired combinations ($^{85}Rb|F = 2\rangle -^{87} Rb|F = 1\rangle$, $^{85}Rb|F = 2\rangle -^{87} Rb|F = 2\rangle$, $^{85}Rb|F = 3\rangle -^{87} Rb|F = 1\rangle$ and $^{85}Rb|F = 3\rangle -^{87} Rb|F = 2\rangle$) were measured to be $\eta_1 = (1.5 \pm 3.2) \times 10^{-10}$,

$\eta_2 = (-0.6 \pm 3.7) \times 10^{-10}$, $\eta_3 = (-2.5 \pm 4.1) \times 10^{-10}$ and $\eta_4 = (-2.7 \pm 3.6) \times 10^{-10}$, respectively. The violation parameters of mass and internal energy are constrained to $\eta_0 = (-0.8 \pm 1.4) \times 10^{-10}$ and $\eta_E = (0.0 \pm 0.4) \times 10^{-10}$. This work opens a door for joint tests of two attributes beyond the traditional pure mass or energy tests of EP with quantum systems. It also provides us a firm technical foundation for our proposed ZAIGA-EP experiment. For the rotation measurement, Yao *et al.* in our group has improved the precision of the measurement by one-order of magnitude recently and keep on advancing the precision and accuracy.[42]

Recently, a theoretical study on the possibility of detecting the ultralight scalar dark matter (DM) with ZAIGA was completed.[43] Starting with a popular scalar DM model, where the DM field is assumed to linearly couple to the standard model fields through five coupling parameters, the DM candidate can be detected by determining whether the five coupling parameters are zero or not. The solution to the DM field contains a background oscillation term and a local exponential fluctuation term. The DM signals in ZAIGA has been calculated. For a pair of AIs vertically separated by 300 meters, the DM-induced differential phase consists of three contributions, coming from the DM-induced changes in atomic internal energy levels, atomic masses and the gravitational acceleration. For a pair of AIs horizontally separated by several kilometers, the signal comes only from the DM-induced changes in atomic internal energy levels. The constraints on five DM coupling parameters for ZAIGA-DM have been estimated. It turns out that the proposed constraints would complement the MICROSCOPE space experiment[44] and would be several orders of magnitude better in higher-mass parametric regions. It also clearly shows the advantages and disadvantages of the two configurations of ZAIGA-DM. For the vertical configuration, the advantage is that all the five DM coupling parameters can be constrained, and the disadvantage is that the arm-length is not easy to extend. For the horizontal configuration, the advantage is that the arm-length is relatively easy to extend, and the disadvantage is that only two DM parameters can be constrained. For other type of DM candidates, the relevant studies are in progress.

4. Moon-Based Detectors – LGWA and GLOC

Moon is much quieter seismologically and does not have an atmosphere. This makes Moon itself a possible good detector by monitoring its surface motion excited by GWs. This also makes an interferometer GW detector based on the Moon possible.

4.1. *Lunar Gravitational-Wave Antenna*[5, 23]

One of the first concepts proposed for the detection of gravitational waves by Joseph Weber is to monitor the quadrupolar vibrations of elastic bodies excited by GWs. At laboratory scale, these experiments became known as resonant-bar detectors, which form an important part of the history of GW detection. Due to the dimensions of these bars, the targeted signal frequencies were in the kHz range. It was also Weber who suggested to monitor vibrations of Earth and Moon to search for gravitational waves in the mHz band. His Lunar Surface Gravimeter was deployed on the Moon in 1972 by the Apollo 17 crew. A design error made it impossible to carry out the intended search for GWs, but the idea remains intriguing. Harms et al.[5,23] have proposed a new concept, the Lunar Gravitational-Wave Antenna (LGWA), based on Weber's idea. LGWA would have a rich GW and multi-messenger science case with galactic binaries and more massive black-hole binaries. It would also serve as a high-precision geophysical station shedding light on the interior structure of the Moon, the mechanisms of moonquakes, and the Moon's formation history. The key component is a next-generation, high-sensitivity seismometer to be deployed on the Moon. For its most sensitive realization, LGWA would have to be deployed in a permanent shadow near the south or north pole of the Moon to benefit from the natural cryogenic environment. This would improve the sensitivity of the seismometer and also provide a lower-noise environment due to the absence of thermally induced seismic events that were observed by the Apollo seismometers. Powering of the seismic stations and data transfer pose additional challenges for such a deployment.

4.1.1. Inertial sensors for the LGWA[6]

The core of LGWA will be composed of an array of high-end seismic sensors: CSIS (Cryogenic Superconducting Inertial Sensor) on the Moon's surface. A cryogenic environment will be used in combination with superconducting materials to open up pathways to low-loss actuators and sensor mechanics.

CSIS revolutionizes the (cryogenic) inertial sensor field by obtaining a displacement sensitivity at 0.5 Hz of 3 orders of magnitude better than current state-of-art. It will allow LGWA to be sensitive below 1 Hz, down to 1 mHz. It will also be employed in the forthcoming Einstein Telescope (ET) - a third-generation gravitational-wave detector that will make use of cryogenic technologies and will have an enhanced sensitivity below 10 Hz. Moreover, CSIS seismic data could also be employed to get new insights about the Moon's interior... and the selenphysics (the Moon's geophysics). A technical design for CSIS with both interferometric readout and Rasnik readout is presented at the meeting.

4.2. GLOC (Gravitational-Wave Lunar Observatory for Cosmology)[4,24]

Taking advantage of the vacuum environment and the low seismic activities of the Moon, GLOC proposes to build a full laser-interferometric triangle-shape GW detector with 40 km arm length to explore fundamental cosmology and multi-band, multi-messenger astrophysics from the Moon. The speaker focused on goals that are unique to GLOC, and compare the detection landscape of the elusive intermediate-mass black holes between GLOC and other prominent space-based missions, 3G detectors and deci-Hertz concepts.

5. Space-Borne GW Detectors

The space environments are much quieter in terms of the gravity gradient noise consideration as compared to the Earth and Moon environments. It is so quiet that the major gravity gradient noise comes from local environments inside the spacecraft. In space, the GW strains propagating to the detector are measured above the geodetic motion or the desired controlled motion/position of the spacecraft. For spacecraft to follow geodesics, one needs to perform drag-free control. For spacecraft to follow desired motion/position over the geodetic motion, one needs to actuate acceleration on the geodetic motion in addition to basic drag-free control. LISA Pathfinder launched on December 3, 2015 has completely met the LISA drag-free noise requirement and has successfully demonstrated the first generation drag-free technology requirement for space detection of GWs.[33,34]

Many space GW detection proposals need to use constant/equal arm configurations. They are AEDGE,[9,25] AIGSO,[26,45] DECIGO/B-DECIGO,[10] etc. AIGSO has 10 km arm length, the shortest arm length among these mission proposals. The calculated actuation acceleration needed to maintain such orbits for AIGSO is around 10 pm s^{-2}.[45,46]

In the mission of LISA Pathfinder, different levels of force and torque authority were implemented, from the nominal configuration with x-force authority (on the sensitive line-of-sight axis) of 1100 pm s^{-2} to the URLA configuration levels, with x-force authority of 26 pm s^{-2}.[47] The published LPF differential acceleration noise floor is established by measurements in this configuration. Specifically, LISA Pathfinder demonstrated that when a constant out of the loop force with amplitude of 11.2 pN was applied to the sensitive axis of TM1 (Test Mass 1) for reducing the gravitational imbalance between the TMs, this force does not introduce significant noise or calibration errors.[47] Basically, the accelerometer part of the constant-arm technology is already demonstrated by LISA Pathfinder for AIGSO.

B-DECIGO has a nominal arm length of 100 km, DECIGO 1,000 km, and AMIGO 10,000 km. The actuation accelerations needed are respectively 10, 100, and 1000 times more than AIGSO. While the actuation accelerations needed for constant arm implementation of b-DECIGO and DECIGO is still basically in the LISA Pathfinder nominal configuration range, the actuation accelerations for constant arm AMIGO is one order larger. On what noise level could the actuation accelerations be done is an issue that needs to be studied and demonstrated carefully for AMIGO. A suggestion is to use an additional test mass (i.e. a pair) to alternate with the original one.[46,48]

GW space missions do not usually require large communication capacity. The deployment to 2-4 degrees behind or ahead of the Earth orbit is no more complicated as to L1 or L2 Sun-Earth Lagrange points. We hereby provide *an example for taking less than a week to reach the (pre)-science orbits.* A last-stage launch from 300 km LEO (Low Earth Orbit) to an eccentric Hohmann orbit with apogee 262931 km (The period of this Hohmann transfer orbit is about 6 days.) (Fig. 2). It takes 3 days (half an elliptic orbit) for this transfer from perigee to apogee (Fig. 2. (b)). This apogee can be designed to be the closest encounter point with respect to Earth of the center of mass of the 3 S/C traced back in time geodetically of the 2-degree-behind-the-Earth formation. From here, a Δv_1's of about 1.6 km/s are needed to allow the 3 S/C to enter their respective (pre-) science orbits (Fig. 2. (c)) when the calibration, commissioning and various science operations can be started. For example, it is the AMIGO-S-2-4deg orbit for AMIGO and the time epoch to reach the 2-degree-behind-the-Earth point is 2030-Jan-1st 12:00:00.[48] (AMIGO-Earth-like solar orbits with the AMIGO formation varying between 2 and 4 degrees behind the Earth orbit starting at epoch JD2462503.0 (2030-Jan-1st 12:00:00) in J2000 mean-equatorial solar-system-barycentric coordinate system.) There are similar orbit configurations for other time epochs and for ahead of the Earth situations. For ahead of the Earth situations, the apogees of the Hohmann orbits need to be on the other side of the Earth.

In the following, we summarize AEDGE,[9] AMIGO,[1] and DECIGO and B-DECIGO[10] in our session.

5.1. *AEDGE*[9,25]

Atomic Experiment for Dark Matter and Gravity Exploration (AEDGE) is a concept for a space experiment using cold atoms to search for ultra-light dark matter, and to detect gravitational waves in the mid-frequency band. It will also complement other planned searches for dark matter, and exploit synergies with other gravitational wave detectors. Examples are given in the talk of how its gravitational-wave measurements could explore the assembly of super-massive black holes, first-order phase transitions in the early universe and cosmic strings.[9,25] AEDGE will be based upon technologies now being developed for terrestrial experiments using cold atoms, and will benefit from the space experience obtained with, e.g., LISA and cold atom experiments in microgravity.

5.2. *AMIGO*

In 2017, a middle-frequency GW mission AMIGO (Astrodynamical Middle-frequency Interferometric GW Observatory) with arm length 10000 km was proposed to have significant sensitivity in this frequency band 0.1 Hz-10 Hz to bridge the gap between the ground detection sensitivity and the LISA sensitivity and yet to be a first-generation candidate for space GW missions.[51] The basic mission concept is in Ref. [51]. Stellar-size black hole inspirals[35] such as the ones like GW150914 will be sure sources of AMIGO. The AMIGO observation of the inspiral phase of these sources will enable us to predict the coalescence time precisely for the ground multi-messenger observations.

In [48], first studies on possible schemes of implementation of AMIGO were presented. Both the solar orbit and earth orbit options together with deployment

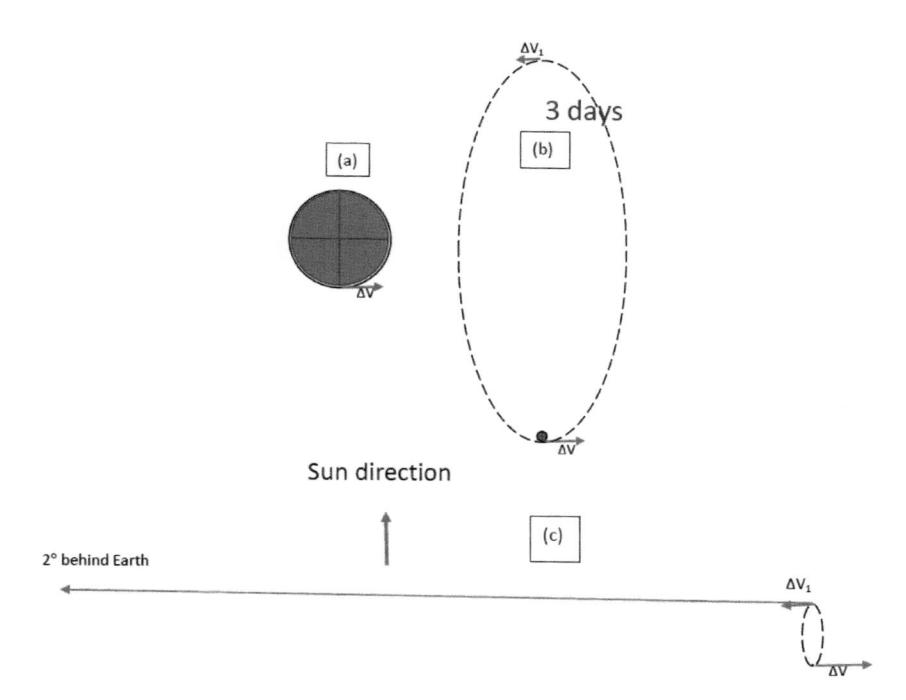

Fig. 2. An option for taking less than a week from launch to reaching the (pre-)science orbit for AMIGO-S-2-4 deg. (a) Launch to 300 km LEO (Low Earth Orbit) parking orbit. (b) A last-stage launch from 300 km LEO to an eccentric Hohmann orbit with apogee 262931 km (The period of this Hohmann transfer orbit is about 6 days.); It takes 3 days (half an elliptic orbit) for this transfer from perigee to apogee. (c) This apogee is designed to be the closest encounter point with respect to Earth of the center of mass of the 3 S/C traced back in time geodetically of the 2-degree-behind-the-Earth AMIGO formation]. From here, Δv_1's of about 1.6 km/s are needed to allow the 3 S/C to enter their respective (pre-)science orbits reaching 2-degree-behind-the-Earth at 2030-Jan-1st 12:00:00.[28,49,50]

strategy were discussed. The first-generation TDIs (Time Delay Interferometry's) for all orbit options studied were calculated and found that all the heliocentric orbit options satisfy the frequency-noise suppression requirement, but the geocentric orbit options do not satisfy the requirement. From this study, the heliocentric option is preferred. The issue on feasibility of constant equal-arm implementation was studied. For the solar-orbit options, the acceleration to maintain a constant equal-arm formation can be designed to be less than 15 nm/s^2 with the thruster requirement in the 15 μN range.[46,48] AMIGO would be a good place to test and implement the constant equal-arm option. Fuel requirement, thruster noise requirement and test mass acceleration actuation requirement were considered.

In [28], the core noise requirements on position noises and acceleration noises were updated. From these design white position noises and acceleration noises, the GW sensitivities (Fig. 3) were obtained for the first-generation Michelson X TDI configuration of b-AMIGO (baseline AMIGO), AMIGO, and e-AMIGO (enhanced

AMIGO). In Fig. 3, the sensitivities for the corresponding AMIGO-5's (50,000 km nominal arm length) are also shown. Steps to implement the AMIGO mission concept were indicated in view of the current technology development.

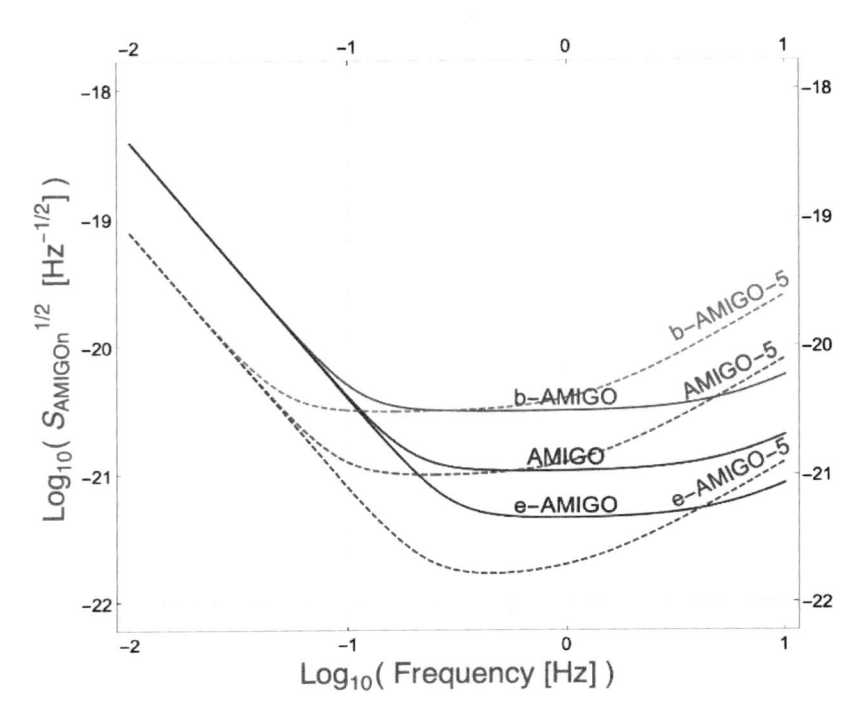

Fig. 3. Strain power spectral density (psd) amplitude vs. frequency for various AMIGO-5 proposals as compared to AMIGO proposals. The solid lines are for AMIGO's (10,000 km nominal arm length); the dashed lines are for AMIGO-5's (50,000 km nominal arm length).[28]

5.3. *DECIGO and B-DECIGO*[10]

DECIGO was conceived in 2001 with the main scientific target to directly measure the acceleration of the Universe. The design has been elaborated with laser Fabry-Perot arm cavities. DECIGO consists of four clusters with each cluster having three differential Fabry-Perot interferometers with three drag-free spacecraft forming an equilateral triangle of nominal arm cavity length 1000 km. Lasers illuminating the cavity have power 10 W and wavelength 515 nm. The current design has main mirrors with diameter 1 m and mass 100 kg forming cavities of finesse 10. The four clusters also form a nearly equilateral triangle in the heliocentric orbits with two clusters in Earth-trailing orbits. The other two clusters are separated from each other and from the near-Earth clusters by 120 degrees in the heliocentric orbits. The DECIGO team recognized that "... analysis based on the observations by the Planck satellite lowered the upper limit of GW to 1×10^{-16} As a result, the DECIGO sensitivity became no longer good enough to detect the primordial gravitational waves". Nevertheless, with target sensitivity the best among all the present mid-frequency concepts (Table 1), it may still bring us some clues on the very early universe, e.g. revealing the thermal history after the inflation[52,53] etc.

The design of B-DECIGO is down-scaled from DECIGO, consisting of one cluster with three spacecraft separated from each other by 100 km. The arm cavity mirrors have diameter of 0.3 m with mass of 30 kg, and cavity finesse of 100. The laser wavelength is 515 nm and laser power 1 W. With target strain psd amplitude about one order higher than DECIGO, it serves as a pathfinder for DECIGO, and with the noise sensitivity well enough, it is also a good probe to the many mid-frequency GW sources discussed in section 2. DECIGO team aim to launch B-DECIGO at the earliest in 2032.

6. Discussion and Outlook

Middle frequency band (0.1-10 Hz) is important for GW detection to bridge the gap between high-frequency GW detection and low-frequency GW detection for various scientific goals. We have seen various proposals. It is hopeful to have some mid-frequency GW detectors in the 2030s to do multiband astronomy and multi-messenger astronomy.

Acknowledgements

This work was supported by the Strategic Priority Research Program of the Chinese Academy of Sciences under grant No. XDB21010100, and by the National Key Research and Development Program of China under Grant No. 2016YFA0302002.

References

1. W.-T. Ni, Outlook of the Mid-frequency GW Detection and AMIGO, GW2 Parallel session talk of the MG16 Meeting (2021).
2. J. Fier, X. Fang, B. Li, S. Mukohyama, A. Wang, and T. Zhu, Generation, propagation and detection of GWs in inhomogeneous universe, GW2 Parallel session talk of the MG16 Meeting (2021).
3. H. Yu and Y. Chen, Direct Determination of Supermassive Black Hole Properties with Gravitational-Wave Radiation from Surrounding Stellar-Mass Black Hole Binaries, GW2 Parallel session talk of the MG16 Meeting (2021).
4. K. Jani, Fundamental Cosmology & Multi-band, Multi-messenger Astrophysics from the Moon, GW2 Parallel session talk of the MG16 Meeting (2021).
5. J. Harms, Lunar Gravitational-Wave Antenna, GW2 Parallel session talk of the MG16 Meeting (2021).
6. F. Badaracco, J. van Heijningen, E. Camilo Ferreira, and A. Perali, A cryogenic & superconducting inertial sensor for the Lunar Gravitational Wave Antenna and for selenphysics, GW2 Parallel session talk of the MG16 Meeting (2021), Proceedings of MG16, accepted.

7. M. Ando, S. Takano, C. P. Ooi, Y. Oshima, and Y. Michimura, TOBA: A Ground-Based Mid.-Frequency Gravitational-Wave Antenna, GW2 Parallel session talk of the MG16 Meeting (2021).
8. D. Gao on behalf of the ZAIGA collaboration, Recent progress on ZAIGA, GW2 Parallel session talk of the MG16 Meeting (2021).
9. M. Lewicki, AION and AEDGE: Gravitational physics with atom interferometry, GW2 Parallel session talk of the MG16 Meeting (2021).
10. S. Kawamura and DECIGO working group, Space gravitational wave antenna DECIGO and B-DECIGO, GW2 Parallel session talk of the MG16 Meeting (2021), Proceedings of MG16, accepted.
11. K. Kuroda, W.-T. Ni and W.-P. Pan, Gravitational waves: Classification, methods of detection, sensitivities, and sources, Int. J. Mod. Phys. D 24, 1530031 (2015); also in One Hundred Years of General Relativity: From Genesis and Empirical Foundations to Gravitational Waves, Cosmology and Quantum Gravity, Chap. 10, ed. W.-T. Ni (World Scientific, Singapore, 2017).
12. ET sensitivities, http://www.et-gw.eu/index.php/etsensitivities.
13. M. Evans et al., A Horizon Study for Cosmic Explorer: Science, Observatories, and Community, CE-P2100003-v7, arXiv:2109.09882 [astro-ph.IM].
14. LISA mission sensitivities, https://www.elisascience.org/articles/lisa-mission/first-gravitational-wave-observatory-space/sensitivity.
15. W.-H. Ruan, Z.-K. Guo, R.-G. Cai, and Y.-Z. Zhang, Taiji program: Gravitational-wave sources, Int. J. Mod. Phys. A 35, 2050075 (2020); arXiv:1807.09495.
16. J. Luo, L.-S. Chen, H.-Z. Duan et al., TianQin: A space-borne gravitational wave detector, Class. Quantum Grav. 33, 035010 (2016).
17. H. J. Paik, M. V. Moody and R. S. Norton, SOGRO – Terrrestrial full-tensor detector for mid-frequency gravitational waves, Int. J. Mod. Phys. D 29, 1940001 (2020).
18. T. Shimoda, S.Takano, C. P. Ooi, N. Aritomi, A. Shoda, Y. Michimura, and M. Ando, Torsion-bar antenna: A ground-based mid-frequency and low-frequency gravitational wave detector, Int. J. Mod. Phys. D 29, 1940003 (2020), arXiv:1812.01835.
19. B. Canuel et al., ELGAR – a European Laboratory for Gravitation and Atom-interferometric Research, Class. Quantum Grav. 37, 225017 (2020).
    B. Canuel et al., Exploring gravity with the MIGA large scale atom interferometer, Sci. Rep. 8, 14064 (2018).
20. MAGIS-100 collaboration, Matter-wave Atomic Gradiometer Interferometric Sensor (MAGIS-100), Quantum Sci. Technol. 6, 044003 (2021), arXiv:2104.02835.
21. L. Badurina, E. Bentine, D. Blas, K. Bongs, D. Bortoletto, AION: An Atom Interferometer Observatory and Network, JCAP 05, 011 (2020), arXiv:1911.11755v1 [astro-ph.CO].
22. M.-S. Zhan, J. Wang, W.-T. Ni et al., ZAIGA: Zhaoshan Long-baseline Atom Interferometer Gravitation Antenna, Int. J. Mod. Phys. D 29, 1940005 (2020), arXiv:1903.09288 [physics.atom-ph].
23. J. Harms et al., Lunar Gravitational-wave Antenna, Astrophys. J., 910, 1 (2021).
24. K. Jani and A. Loeb, Gravitational-Wave Lunar Observatory for Cosmology, arXiv:2007.08550.
25. Y. A. El-Neaj et al., AEDGE: Atomic Experiment for Dark Matter and Gravity Exploration in Space, EPJ Quantum Technology 7, 6 (2020), arXiv:1908.00802.
26. D. Gao, J. Wang, and M. Zhan, Atomic Interferometric Gravitational-Wave Space Observatory (AIGSO), Commun. Theor. Phys. 69, 37 (2018).
27. T. Ebisuzaki, H. Katori, J. Makino, A. Noda, H. Shinkai, T. Tamagawa, INO: Interplanetary network of optical lattice clocks, Int. J. Mod. Phys. D 29, 1940002 (2020), arXiv:1809.10317.

28. W.-T. Ni, Core noise requirements, and GW sensitivities of AMIGO, arXiv:2106.12432 [gr-qc; astro-ph.IM].
29. K. A. Kuns, H. Yu, Y. Chen, and R. X. Adhikari, Astrophysics and cosmology with a deci-hertz gravitational-wave detector: TianGO, *Phys. Rev. D* **102**, 043001 (2020), arXiv:1908.06004 [gr-qc, astro-ph.CO, astro-ph.HE].
30. Manuel Arca Sedda *et al.*, The missing link in gravitational-wave astronomy, *Experimental Astronomy* **51**, 1427 (2021).
31. J. Harms, B. J. J. Slagmolen, R. X. Adhikari *et al.*, Low-frequency terrestrial gravitational-wave detectors, *Phys. Rev. D* **88**, 122003 (2013).
32. J. Harms, Terrestrial gravity fluctuations, *Living Rev. Relativity* **18**, 3 (2015) (DOI 10.1007/lrr-2015-3).
33. M. Armano, H. Audley, G. Auger *et al.*, Sub-Femto-g Free Fall for Space-Based Gravitational Wave Observatories: LISA Pathfinder Results, *Phys. Rev. Lett.* **116**, 231101 (2016).
34. M. Armano, H. Audley and J. Baird *et al.*, Beyond the Required LISA Free-Fall Performance: New LISA Pathfinder Results down to 20 μHz, *Phys. Rev. Lett.* **120**, 061101 (2018).
35. A. Sesana, Prospects for multiband gravitational-wave astronomy after GW150914, *Phys. Rev. Lett.* **116**, 231102 (2016).
36. X. Chen and W.-B Han, Extreme-mass-ratio inspirals produced by tidal capture of binary black holes, *Communications Physics* **1**, 53 (2018) and references therein.
37. H. Yu and Y. Chen, Direct Determination of Supermassive Black Hole Properties with Gravitational-Wave Radiation from Surrounding Stellar-Mass Black Hole Binaries, *Phys. Rev. Lett.* **126**, 021101 (2021).
38. I. Mandel, A. Sesana, and A. Vecchio, The astrophysical science case for a decihertz gravitational-wave detector, *Class. and Quantum Grav.* **35**, 054004 (2018), and references therein.
39. Manuel Arca Sedda *et al.*, The Missing Link in Gravitational-Wave Astronomy: Discoveries waiting in the decihertz range, *Class. Quantum Grav.* **37**, 215011 (2020), arXiv:1908.11375.
40. J. Fier, X. Fang, B. Li, S. Mukohyama, A. Wang, and T. Zhu, Gravitational wave cosmology I: High frequency approximation, *Phys. Rev. D* **103**, 123021 (2021).
41. L. Zhou *et al.*, Joint mass-and-energy test of the equivalence principle at the 10^{-10} level using atoms with specified mass and internal energy, *Phys. Rev. A* **104**, 022822 (2021).
42. Z.-W. Yao *et al.*, Self-alignment of a large-area dual-atom-interferometer gyroscope using parameter-decoupled phase-seeking calibrations, *Phys. Rev. A* **103**, 023319 (2021).
43. W. Zhao, X. Mei, D. Gao, J. Wang, and M.-S. Zhan, Ultralight scalar dark matter detection with ZAIGA, arXiv: 2110.11564.
44. P. Touboul, G. Métris, M. Rodrigues, Y. Andréc and A. Robert, The MICROSCOPE space mission to test the Equivalence Principle, *Comptes Rendus Physique*, **21**, 139 (2020), and references therein.
45. G. Wang, D. Gao, W.-T. Ni, J. Wang and M.-S. Zhan, Orbit design for space atom-interferometer AIGSO, *Int. J. Mod. Phys. D* **29**, 1940004 (2020).
46. G. Wang, W.-T. Ni, and A.-M. Wu, Orbit design and thruster requirement for various constant-arm space mission concepts for gravitational-wave observation, *Int. J. Mod. Phys. D* **29**, 1940006 (2020), arXiv:1908.05444 [gr-qc].
47. M. Armano, H. Audley, J. Baird *et al.*, LISA Pathfinder Performance Confirmed in an Open-Loop Configuration: Results from the Free Fall Actuation Mode, *Phys. Rev. Lett.* **123**, 111101 (2019).

48. W.-T. Ni, G. Wang, and A.-M. Wu, Astrodynamical middle-frequency interferometric gravitational wave observatory AMIGO: Mission concept and orbit design, *Int. J. Mod. Phys. D* **29**, (2020) 1940007, arXiv:1909.04995 [gr-qc].
49. A.-M. Wu, W.-T. Ni and G. Wang, Deployment Simulation for LISA Gravitational Wave Mission, IAC-17-A2.1.4, 68th International Astronautical Congress, 25-29 September 2017, Adelaide, Australia (2017).
50. A.-M. Wu *et al.*, Deployment of AMIGO, paper in preparation.
51. W.-T. Ni, Gravitational Wave (GW) Classification, Space GW Detection Sensitivities and AMIGO (Astrodynamical Middle-frequency Interferometric GW Observatory), Proceedings of Joint Meeting of 13th International Conference on Gravitation, Astrophysics and Cosmology, and 15th Italian-Korean Symposium on Relativistic Astrophysics, Ewha Womans University, Seoul, Korea, July 3-7, 2017, *EPJ Web of Conferences* **168**, 01004 (2018); arXiv:1709.05659 [gr-qc].
52. S. Kuroyanagi, K. Nakayama, and J. Yokoyama, Prospects of determination of reheating temperature after inflation by DECIGO, *Prog. Theor. Exp. Phys.*, 013E02 (2015).
53. K. Nakayama *et al.*, Space-based gravitational-wave detectors can determine the thermal history of the early Universe, *Phys. Rev. D* **77**, 124001 (2008).

Salient features of the optimised PyCBC IMBH search

Koustav Chandra and Archana Pai

Department of Physics, Indian Institute of Technology Bombay, Powai, Mumbai 400 076, India

V. Villa-Ortega and T. Dent

IGFAE, Campus Sur, Universidade de Santiago de Compostela, 15782 Spain

C. McIsaac, I. W. Harry and G. S. Cabourn Davies

University of Portsmouth, Portsmouth, PO1 3FX, United Kingdom

K. Soni

Inter-University Centre for Astronomy and Astrophysics, Pune 411007, India

Matched-filter based PyCBC searches have successfully detected $\sim \mathcal{O}(50)$ compact binary merger signals in the LIGO-Virgo data. While most PyCBC searches have been designed to detect stellar-mass binaries, we present here a new search that is optimised to detect short-duration gravitational wave (GW) signals emitted by intermediate-mass black hole mergers. When applied to the first half of the third observation run data, the optimised search re-identified the intermediate mass black hole (IMBH) binary event, GW190521, with a false alarm rate of 1 in 727 yrs, significantly lower than the previous PyCBC search result of 1 in 0.94 yr. Analysis of simulated signals from IMBH binaries with generically spinning components shows an increase in sensitivity by a factor of 1.2 to 3 over previous PyCBC searches.

Keywords: Gravitational Waves, Matched-Filtering, Intermediate-Mass Black Holes

1. Introduction

Coalescing compact binaries are amongst the primary sources of gravitational wave (GW) with frequencies accessible to current second-generation ground-based GW interferometers. Detection of $\sim \mathcal{O}(50)$ stellar-mass binary mergers (the majority being the binary black holes) has already ushered us into the age of observational strong-field gravity. They have so far given us unique insights into the black hole population that we hardly knew existed, with one of them being the first confirmed detection of a massive black hole system GW190521 with a remnant IMBH.[1,2]

GW190521 was observed in the first half of the third observing run of the Advanced LIGO and Advanced Virgo detectors. The compact binary merger event lasted for ~ 0.1 s in the detector band and had barely any observable pre-merger phase of the signal, clearly reflecting the binary's high total mass. The detailed Bayesian parameter estimation showed the merger event to be consistent with the merger of two black holes in a mildly precessing orbit, with component masses of $85^{+21}_{-14}\,M_\odot$ and $66^{+17}_{-18}\,M_\odot$ and a remnant black hole of $142^{+28}_{-16}\,M_\odot$ falling in the mass range of intermediate-mass black holes.[1] The merger event producing this remnant was detected by a search sensitive to generic transient at high confidence with a false alarm rate of $< 1/4900$ years.[3]

Traditionally, the unmodeled GW transient search for short-duration GW signals is performed using the coherent waveburst (cWB) search[4] which is built on the rationale that a GW signal from a compact binary coalescence (CBC), chirp or not, is expected to be a transient waveform and it will produce some localised excess of energy if projected in the time-frequency plane. Therefore, identifying such an excess coherently across two or more detectors should give a strong indication of a GW event. Together with this, model-based matched-filter searches, such as PyCBC[5–9] and GstLAL,[10] targeting generic binaries have also been used for the IMBH binary searches in the LIGO-Virgo data (ADD O1-O2 and O3 paper link).

While unmodeled cWB searches are tuned to look for short-duration signals,[11] the standard matched-filter-based searches were not. The lack of *optimisation* towards IMBH binary signals made them suffer from the "look-elsewhere" effect. Further, improvements in the sensitivity of the detectors at low frequencies[12–14] before the beginning of the third observing run of Advanced LIGO and Advanced Virgo (O3) motivated us to adapt our matched-filter algorithms to the target search space. Here, we will summarise the salient features of one of the optimised templated searches, namely PyCBC-IMBH that was developed and deployed for the IMBH binary search. This optimised search was used together with other search pipelines to look for IMBH binaries in the O3 run, and the reader can find the results of it in.[15] For complete information on the algorithm itself, we direct the reader to the optimised PyCBC IMBH search paper.[16]

2. The Optimised PyCBC-IMBH Search

Below we summarise the salient features of the optimised PyCBC-IMBH search.[16]

Data cleaning: The gravitational wave strain data is often plagued with loud background noise, which can significantly hamper the search sensitivity.[17] Thus, we begin our analysis by windowing out very high amplitude excursions ($> 50\sigma$ deviation from Gaussian noise) in the whitened data.[6] Since empirically, these loud noise transients tend to be correlated with neighbouring quieter noise transients, we also *discard* any LIGO triggers which are either 1s before or 2.5s after the centre of the gating window.[16]

Template bank: After this data cleaning process, we use matched-filtering to detect the target signals hidden in the detector noise.[5,18,19] We assume that our target signals are well-modelled and deterministic, and to a good approximation, we can consider them to be buried in wide-sense stationary Gaussian noise. However, the binary's parameters are not known a priori, forcing us to use a discrete bank of filter waveforms, aka templates. Our bank of templates is designed to intercept the dominant quadrupolar harmonics of a non-precessing binary.[20] Specifically, we use the reduced-order representation of the spinning effective one-body model, SEOBNRv4,[21,22] for our templates, and we *constrain* ourselves to binaries with redshifted (detector frame) total mass between $100 - 600 M_\odot$.[16] Additionally, our templates have a minimum component mass of $40 M_\odot$ and a mass ratio between 1/1 and 1/10. We do not use relatively lower mass ratios in the templates as binaries with low mass ratios emit gravitational wave signals with significantly higher subdominant harmonics that are not modelled by our waveform approximant. We also don't include any templates with a duration less than 0.07 s., measured from a fixed starting frequency of 15 Hz, to reduce the false alarms arising from short-duration noisy transients. Since information on the spins of IMBH binaries is lacking, we allow our templates to have dimensionless spin components along the orbital angular momentum to be between ±0.998. The reader can find additional details about the template bank in.[16]

Although our search targets non-precessing binaries, we expect our search to retain its sensitivity towards moderately precessing binaries, mainly because our target systems are relatively short-lived within the detector bandwidth.[23,24] Furthermore, we also expect our search to be equally sensitive to binaries with low eccentricity as the emission of gravitational waves will circularise the binary system before the merger, and because of the shortness of our templates and the detector bandwidth, we will only be able to intercept the last few cycles of IMBH binary's inspiral.[25]

Time-phase consistency between detectors: Single-detector triggers are identified based on peaks in the matched filter signal-to-noise ratio (SNR) time series. Unfortunately, our detector data is polluted with several non-stationary instrumental artefacts that are not loud enough to be gated out during data pre-processing. Technically, this makes our search a detection problem in non-Gaussian noise. Having a network of simultaneously operating similar sensitivity detectors help a lot as we can demand that the time difference between triggers at different detectors is consistent with an astrophysical signal, i.e. within the light-travel time up to expected uncertainty. Besides, if the trigger is due to a GW signal, then it must share consistent phase and amplitude characteristics. Hence the *coincidence test* significantly reduces the number of noisy artefacts that is picked up by the search.

Signal consistency tests: But there can be chance coincidences between noise triggers. So, before the coincidence test is performed, there is a need to differentiate a signal from a glitch at the single detector level. We do this in multiple stages. We begin by only considering the loudest trigger within a pre-determined window of time to reduce false alarms, and we subject these triggers to two different signal-consistency tests: the χ_r^2-test[26] and the $\chi_{r,sg}^2$-test.[27] The former checks if the morphology of the triggers matches with that of the best-matched template, while the latter checks for any excess power beyond the maximum frequency of the template. The output of these two tests is used to amend the trigger SNR to reduce the apparent loudness of a noise trigger as the target signal will return values closer to unity. We also account for any short-term non-stationarity of the detector noise that can lead to wrongful estimation of the trigger SNR.[28–30]

Given our target space, our search is susceptible to short but loud noise triggers motivating us to use stricter discriminators. We chose to discard any trigger with $\chi_r^2 > 10$ or with short-term power spectral density (PSD) measure of over ten times the expectation from stationary noise.[16]

Event significance and ranking: We subject the surviving single-detector triggers to the coincidence test and assign each *multi-detector candidate* a rank based on their response to the coincidence test.[8,9] Our candidate events can be coincidentally observed either in one of the possible two detector combinations or in all three detectors. This is because we analyse all possible two and three detector combinations. Finally, a statistical significance is assigned to each of these candidates by comparing its rank against simulated background noise that is generated by finding fictitious coincidences between detector data.[6] We achieve this by shifting the pivot detector(s) data with respect to a fixed reference detector by a time that is considerably larger than the light-travel time between the detectors. By repeating this procedure, we produce more than 10^4 years worth of noise background.

In the next section, we provide details of how the PyCBC algorithm benefits from the optimisation made.

3. Summary of Sensitivity Comparison

To quantify the benefit of our restricted analysis, we compared the sensitivity of our optimised search against existing PyCBC-based searches with overlapping parameter space.[16] We compared the PyCBC-IMBH search against the PyCBC-broad and the PyCBC-BBH search. The former looks for binaries consisting of either neutron stars or black holes or both, while the latter is a "focused" search for binary black hole (BBH) covering a restricted range of masses. We resort to an injection campaign for the comparison. This involved adding simulated signals to real GW data from the first half of the third observing run (O3a) run as part of the analysis without any physical actuation and then estimate the sensitivity of each of the searches in terms of sensitive volume time $\langle VT \rangle$.[31,32] Our simulated signals mimicked those from generically spinning BBH with detector frame total mass between $100 - 600 M_\odot$ and having a mass ratio between $1/1 - 1/10$. The signals themselves were either the dominant quadrupolar mode or the full symphony emitted by such binaries. We found that the PyCBC-IMBH search is $\sim 1.2 - 3$ times more sensitive than the PyCBC-broad search and is $\sim 1.1 - 12.6$ times more sensitive than the PyCBC-BBH search at a false alarm rate threshold of 1 in 100 years.

We also compare our search against two other searches, namely cWB and GstLAL-IMBH, that were used by the LIGO Scientific, Virgo & Kagra collaboration (LVK) to look for IMBH binaries in O3 run.[15] For this purpose, we utilise the results of the injection campaign that were used by the LVK to place upper limits on the merger rate density for a discrete set of IMBH binaries. The dataset is publicly

Table 1. Summary of the single pipeline sensitive volume-time $\langle VT \rangle$. Here, M_T is the total source frame mass of the binary and $q = m_2/m_1 \leq 1$ denotes the mass ratio of the binary. χ_{eff} is the mass-weighted combination of the spins parallel to the orbital angular momentum $\vec{L}$ while χ_{P} captures the average amount of precession exhibited by a generically precessing system over many cycles defined at reference frequency of 11 Hz during the inspiral.

M_T ($M_\odot$)	q	χ_{eff}	χ_{P}	$\langle VT \rangle_{\text{PyCBC}}[\text{Gpc}^3\text{yr}]$	$\langle VT \rangle_{\text{cWB}}[\text{Gpc}^3\text{yr}]$	$\langle VT \rangle_{\text{GstLAL}}[\text{Gpc}^3\text{yr}]$
120	1/2	0.00	0.00	11.51	8.93	8.18
120	1/4	0.00	0.00	4.64	3.54	3.04
120	1/5	0.00	0.00	3.11	2.42	2.06
120	1/7	0.00	0.00	1.67	1.24	1.05
120	1/10	0.00	0.00	0.82	0.60	0.51
150	1/2	0.00	0.00	11.95	9.96	7.40
200	1	0.00	0.00	14.84	12.76	10.27
200	1/2	0.00	0.00	10.35	9.47	6.56
200	1/4	0.00	0.00	3.90	3.69	1.93
200	1/7	0.00	0.00	1.34	1.29	0.53
220	1/10	0.00	0.00	0.57	0.60	0.22
250	1/4	0.00	0.00	2.99	2.83	1.80
300	1/2	0.00	0.00	6.27	5.86	5.38
350	1/6	0.00	0.00	0.72	0.75	0.44
400	1	0.00	0.00	4.82	4.55	4.29
400	1/2	0.00	0.00	3.08	3.33	2.68
400	1/3	0.00	0.00	1.68	1.94	1.29
400	1/4	0.00	0.00	1.11	1.22	0.70
400	1/7	0.00	0.00	0.44	0.47	0.20
440	1/10	0.00	0.00	0.20	0.20	0.09
500	2/3	0.00	0.00	1.87	1.97	1.45
600	1	0.00	0.00	0.90	0.79	0.50
600	1/2	0.00	0.00	0.65	0.81	0.34
800	1	0.00	0.00	0.15	0.14	0.11
200	1	0.80	0.00	38.54	29.60	30.99
400	1	0.80	0.00	18.08	15.88	16.07
600	1	0.80	0.00	4.97	5.35	4.03
800	1	0.80	0.00	0.89	0.88	0.37
200	1	-0.80	0.00	10.07	9.28	6.39
400	1	-0.80	0.00	1.90	1.86	1.66
600	1	-0.80	0.00	0.22	0.22	0.11
800	1	-0.80	0.00	0.04	0.05	0.03
200	1	0.51	0.42	26.38	20.88	19.42
200	1/2	0.14	0.42	13.97	12.36	9.01
200	1/4	0.26	0.42	7.67	7.65	4.13
200	1/7	0.32	0.42	3.35	3.59	1.44
400	1	0.51	0.42	10.53	9.38	9.19
400	1/2	0.14	0.42	4.96	5.42	4.24
400	1/4	0.26	0.42	2.58	3.63	1.88
400	1/7	0.32	0.42	1.11	1.79	0.65
600	1	0.51	0.42	2.44	2.49	1.72
600	1/2	0.14	0.42	1.12	1.45	0.58
800	1	0.51	0.42	0.10	0.18	0.01

available at https://dcc.ligo.org/LIGO-P2100179/public, and it contains details about the parameters of each of the injections and also their associated p-value as reported by the contributing searches. The signals themselves were numerically simulated and are designed to imitate GWs from a representative population of IMBH binaries with generic spins. Additional details about the injections can be found in.[15]

To estimate $\langle VT \rangle$ using the publicly available dataset, we start off by calculating the number of signals that are recovered by each of three contributing searches. We do this by considering only those injections whose p-value is less than the minimum p-value of the loudest noise trigger, namely that of 200214_224526 in the.[15] This trigger has a minimum p-value of 9.2×10^{-2} and was only reported by the weakly model-dependent cWB search. The $\langle VT \rangle$ is then given by

$$\langle VT \rangle = \frac{N_\text{rec}}{N_\text{total}} \langle VT \rangle_\text{total} \qquad (1)$$

where the first term denotes the fraction of injections that are recovered below the p-value threshold while the second term denotes the total spacetime volume covered by a given injection set.

We tabulate the results of this analysis for each of the three pipelines for each simulated IMBH binary in Table 1. Amplitude and phase errors arising from detector calibration have not been included in the analysis, but a statistical uncertainty of 4%-7% is expected. We find that the PyCBC-IMBH search has higher sensitivity as compared to the GstLAL-IMBH for all of the mass bins and is comparably sensitive (if not better for most of the symmetric and/or relatively low total mass bins) to cWB search.

The latter can be understood as follows. As discussed in Sec. 2, the PyCBC-IMBH search uses only the dominant multipole templates in matched filtering. Hence, the sensitivity drops with a decrease in mass ratio as compared to the cWB search. This is because a decrement in mass ratio corresponds to an increase in the contribution coming from the sub-dominant harmonics. The cWB search being a weakly modelled search, is oblivious to this effect and hence has higher sensitivity than template-based searches. Furthermore, if one compares the sensitivity of a given search for a given total mass but decreasing mass ratio, one will observe that the search performance degrades owing to an overall decrease in the intrinsic luminosity of the system involved.

Concerning the total mass of a binary, the PyCBC search tends to have higher sensitivity for relatively lower total mass as signals from such systems tend to have a longer inspiral within the detector bandwidth, thus allowing for a larger SNR. At higher total mass, the cWB search has higher sensitivity because of its efficient signal-noise discriminators, which allow it to distinguish the signal from noisy transients better, thus allowing for a relatively lower p-value and hence greater sensitivity. This also explains why the PyCBC search has a poorer performance for a system with a given mass distribution but having a relatively anti-aligned spin.

GW signals from a significantly precessing binary can have a notably suppressed inspiral right before the merger, causing a characteristic sine-Gaussian morphology. The search summarised here uses non-precessing quadrupolar templates meaning the SNR recovered would be lower and the χ_r^2 higher owing to mismatch with templates.

4. Conclusion

Here, we summarise the salient features of the optimisation made to the existing PyCBC search to target short-duration GWs from massive BBHs. This optimisation enabled us to improve the search performance and re-detect the event GW190521 with improved statistical significance. We also compare the sensitivity of PyCBC-IMBH with other searches used for the detection of IMBH binaries using the public data.

Detection of IMBH and its subsequent studies has the potential to provide valuable insight into the BBH population. Hence searches like this are going to be increasingly important. While we are primarily concerned here with detection of IMBH binaries, this type of search can be used to detect highly red-shifted BBHs which we expect to see in the next few years with the advent of third-generation GW observatories like the Einstein Telescope and Cosmic Explorer. Thus, the future of this field is quite exciting!

Acknowledgments

KC is extremely grateful to the organisers of the conference for hosting such a wonderful meeting in challenging circumstances. We thank Gayathri V. and Keith Riles for their comments on an earlier draft of this proceeding. The authors are grateful for the computational resources and data provided by the LIGO Laboratory which is funded by National Science Foundation Grants No. PHY-0757058 and No. PHY-0823459. The open data is available in the Gravitational Wave Open Science Center (https://www.gw-openscience.org/), a service of LIGO Laboratory, the LIGO Scientific Collaboration and the Virgo Collaboration. The authors also acknowledge the use of the IUCAA LDG cluster, Sarathi, for computational/numerical work. KC acknowledges the MHRD, Government of India, for the fellowship support. AP's research is supported by SERB-Power-fellowship grant SPF/2021/000036, DST, India. VVO and TD acknowledge financial support from Xunta de Galicia (Centro singular de investigación de Galicia accreditation 2019-2022), by European Union ERDF, and by the "María de Maeztu" Units of Excellence program MDM-2016-0692 and the Spanish Research State Agency. GSCD and IWH acknowledge the STFC for funding through grant ST/T000333/1. CM was supported by the STFC through the DISCnet Centre for Doctoral Training. KS acknowledges the Inter-University Centre of Astronomy and Astrophysics (IUCAA), India, for the fellowship support.

We want to thank all of the essential workers who put their health at risk during this ongoing COVID-19 pandemic. Without their support, we would not have completed this work. We offer condolences to people who have lost their family members during this pandemic.

References

1. R. Abbott *et al.*, GW190521: A Binary Black Hole Merger with a Total Mass of $150M_\odot$, *Phys. Rev. Lett.* **125**, p. 101102 (2020).
2. R. Abbott *et al.*, Properties and Astrophysical Implications of the 150 $M_\odot$ Binary Black Hole Merger GW190521, *Astrophys. J. Lett.* **900**, p. L13 (2020).
3. M. Szczepańczyk *et al.*, Observing an intermediate-mass black hole GW190521 with minimal assumptions, *Phys. Rev. D* **103**, p. 082002 (2021).
4. S. Klimenko *et al.*, Method for detection and reconstruction of gravitational wave transients with networks of advanced detectors, *Phys. Rev. D* **93**, p. 042004 (2016).
5. B. Allen, W. G. Anderson, P. R. Brady, D. A. Brown and J. D. E. Creighton, FIND-CHIRP: An Algorithm for detection of gravitational waves from inspiraling compact binaries, *Phys. Rev. D* **85**, p. 122006 (2012).
6. S. A. Usman *et al.*, The PyCBC search for gravitational waves from compact binary coalescence, *Class. Quant. Grav.* **33**, p. 215004 (2016).
7. T. Dal Canton and I. W. Harry, Designing a template bank to observe compact binary coalescences in Advanced LIGO's second observing run, *arXiv e-prints* (5 2017).
8. A. H. Nitz, T. Dent, T. Dal Canton, S. Fairhurst and D. A. Brown, Detecting binary compact-object mergers with gravitational waves: Understanding and Improving the sensitivity of the PyCBC search, *Astrophys. J.* **849**, p. 118 (2017).
9. G. S. Davies, T. Dent, M. Tápai, I. Harry, C. McIsaac and A. H. Nitz, Extending the PyCBC search for gravitational waves from compact binary mergers to a global network, *Phys. Rev. D* **102**, p. 022004 (2020).
10. C. Messick *et al.*, Analysis Framework for the Prompt Discovery of Compact Binary Mergers in Gravitational-wave Data, *Phys. Rev. D* **95**, p. 042001 (2017).
11. B. P. Abbott *et al.*, Search for intermediate mass black hole binaries in the first and second observing runs of the Advanced LIGO and Virgo network, *Phys. Rev. D* **100**, p. 064064 (2019).
12. D. Davis *et al.*, LIGO detector characterization in the second and third observing runs, *Class. Quant. Grav.* **38**, p. 135014 (2021).
13. R. P. Fisher, G. Hemming, M.-A. Bizouard, D. A. Brown, P. F. Couvares, F. Robinet and D. Verkindt, Dqsegdb: A time-interval database for storing gravitational wave observatory metadata, *SoftwareX* **14**, p. 100677 (2021).
14. B. P. Abbott *et al.*, A guide to LIGO–Virgo detector noise and extraction of transient gravitational-wave signals, *Class. Quant. Grav.* **37**, p. 055002 (2020).
15. The LIGO Scientific Collaboration, the Virgo Collaboration and the KAGRA Collaboration, Search for intermediate mass black hole binaries in the third observing run of Advanced LIGO and Advanced Virgo, *arXiv e-prints*, p. arXiv:2105.15120 (May 2021).
16. K. Chandra, V. Villa-Ortega, T. Dent, C. McIsaac, A. Pai, I. W. Harry, G. S. C. Davies and K. Soni, An optimized PyCBC search for gravitational waves from intermediate-mass black hole mergers, *Phys. Rev. D* **104**, p. 042004 (2021).
17. M. Cabero *et al.*, Blip glitches in Advanced LIGO data, *Class. Quantum Grav.* **36**, p. 155010 (2019).

18. B. Sathyaprakash and S. Dhurandhar, Choice of filters for the detection of gravitational waves from coalescing binaries, *Phys. Rev. D* **44**, 3819 (1991).
19. B. J. Owen, Search templates for gravitational waves from inspiraling binaries: Choice of template spacing, *Phys. Rev. D* **53**, 6749 (1996).
20. P. Ajith et al., Inspiral-merger-ringdown waveforms for black-hole binaries with non-precessing spins, *Phys. Rev. Lett.* **106**, p. 241101 (2011).
21. A. Bohé, S. Marsat and L. Blanchet, Next-to-next-to-leading order spin–orbit effects in the gravitational wave flux and orbital phasing of compact binaries, *Class. Quant. Grav.* **30**, p. 135009 (2013).
22. M. Pürrer, Frequency domain reduced order model of aligned-spin effective-one-body waveforms with generic mass-ratios and spins, *Phys. Rev. D* **93**, p. 064041 (2016).
23. I. Harry, S. Privitera, A. Bohé and A. Buonanno, Searching for Gravitational Waves from Compact Binaries with Precessing Spins, *Phys. Rev. D* **94**, p. 024012 (2016).
24. K. Chandra, V. Gayathri, J. C. Bustillo and A. Pai, Numerical relativity injection analysis of signals from generically spinning intermediate mass black hole binaries in Advanced LIGO data, *Phys. Rev. D* **102**, p. 044035 (2020).
25. A. Ramos-Buades, S. Tiwari, M. Haney and S. Husa, Impact of eccentricity on the gravitational wave searches for binary black holes: High mass case, *Phys. Rev. D* **102**, p. 043005 (2020).
26. B. Allen, χ^2 time-frequency discriminator for gravitational wave detection, *Phys. Rev. D* **71**, p. 062001 (2005).
27. A. H. Nitz, Distinguishing short duration noise transients in LIGO data to improve the PyCBC search for gravitational waves from high mass binary black hole mergers, *Class. Quant. Grav.* **35**, p. 035016 (2018).
28. T. Venumadhav, B. Zackay, J. Roulet, L. Dai and M. Zaldarriaga, New binary black hole mergers in the second observing run of Advanced LIGO and Advanced Virgo, *Phys. Rev. D* **101**, p. 083030 (2020).
29. T. Venumadhav, B. Zackay, J. Roulet, L. Dai and M. Zaldarriaga, New search pipeline for compact binary mergers: Results for binary black holes in the first observing run of Advanced LIGO, *Phys. Rev. D* **100**, p. 023011 (2019).
30. S. Mozzon, L. Nuttall, A. Lundgren, T. Dent, S. Kumar and A. Nitz, Dynamic Normalization for Compact Binary Coalescence Searches in Non-Stationary Noise, *Class. Quant. Grav.* **37**, p. 215014 (2020).
31. R. Biswas, P. R. Brady, J. D. E. Creighton and S. Fairhurst, The Loudest event statistic: General formulation, properties and applications, *Class. Quant. Grav.* **26**, p. 175009 (2009), [Erratum: Class. Quant. Grav. 30, 079502 (2013)].
32. B. P. Abbott et al., Upper Limits on the Rates of Binary Neutron Star and Neutron Star–black Hole Mergers From Advanced Ligo's First Observing run, *Astrophys. J. Lett.* **832**, p. L21 (2016).

Matter shells modifying gravitational wave signals

Monos Naidoo*, Nigel T. Bishop and Petrus J. van der Walt

Department of Mathematics, Rhodes University,
Grahamstown, 6140, South Africa
*E-mail: monos.naidoo@gmail.com
www.ru.ac.za

As detections of mergers of compact bodies begin to flow in, and as we enter an era of precision GW measurements, our understanding of compact bodies, their physics and that of the surrounding astrophysical environment, will continue to grow and at times even be challenged. The need to revise the mass bounds of compact bodies such as BHs and NSs and the possibility of the existence of GW echoes are just some of consequences of the first few years of GW detection. In previous work, using linearised perturbation theory, we made the novel finding that a dust shell will cause a GW to be modified both in magnitude and phase, but without any energy being transferred to or from the dust. We extend our analysis to matter shells surrounding compact body mergers and to intervening matter in cosmology. Instead of only monochromatic GW sources, as we used in our initial investigation, we also consider burst-like GW sources. The thin density shell approach is modified to include thick shells by considering concentric thin shells and integrating. Solutions are then found for these burst-like GW sources using Fourier transforms. In the context of cosmology, apart from the gravitational redshift, the effects are too small to be measurable. We show that GW echoes that are claimed to be present in the LIGO data of certain events, could not have been caused by a matter shell. We do find, however, that matter shells surrounding BBH mergers, BNS mergers, and CCSNe could make modifications of order a few percent to a GW signal. These modifications are expected to be measurable in GW data with current detectors if the event is close enough and at a detectable frequency; or in future detectors with increased frequency range and amplitude sensitivity.

Keywords: Gravitational waves; Gravitational wave echoes; Bondi-Sachs; Matter shell; Linearized perturbation theory.

1. Introduction

Claims have been made that echoes have been detected in the LIGO data of the binary black hole (BBH) merger GW150914,[1,2] and also from the binary neutron star (BNS) merger GW170917.[3] It has been postulated that various exotic compact objects (ECOs) may cause echoes in a gravitational wave (GW) signal and that these may be the cause of the echoes claimed to be observed. These claims have been contested,[4,5] sparking a debate and responses in defense of the claims[6,7] with further substantiations.[3,8] A number of ECO scenarios have been investigated. At the quantum level, Hawking's information paradox suggests Planck-scale modifications of black hole horizons (firewalls[9]) and other modifications to black hole structure (fuzzballs[10]). Dark matter particles have been suggested surrounding star-like objects.[11] Other postulates include stars with interiors consisting of self-repulsive, de Sitter spacetime, surrounded by a shell of ordinary matter (gravastars[12]). Then there are Boson stars, which are macroscopic objects made up of scalar fields.[13] All these objects are compact bodies mimicking black holes, but without a horizon. One consequence of these horizonless structures is that ingoing gravitational waves produced in a merger may reflect multiple times off effective radial potential barriers. The gravitational waves may be, in effect, trapped between effective radial potential barriers causing the waves to be 'bounced' off these barriers several times with wave packets leaking out to infinity at regular times. These gravitational wave signals, 'trailing' the main (outward bound) signal are referred to as gravitational wave echoes.[14–16]

Whilst much of the discussion around gravitational wave echoes has been within the context of 'new physics'[17–23] (beginning with[14]), the possibility that the echoes may be a consequence of the astrophysical environment should also be investigated. One such scenario is the effect of a matter shell surrounding the gravitational wave source. This case was considered using numerical methods in,[24] and was also mentioned in our previous work on the effects of matter on GW propagation.[25]

Echoes from the astrophysical environment were considered in,[26] by placing a massive shell that is not infinitely thin. This was a generalisation of the approach of[27] which was based on an infinitely thin shell. As we have shown in our paper[25] the case for a thin shell can be generalised to that of a thick shell by considering several concentric thin shells and integrating[26] showed that the deviation from Schwarzschild ringdown in their astrophysical estimations were relatively small except for a large mass which indicated that for the majority of astrophysical scenarios the effect would be relatively small. However they did note that considerations of dark matter around black holes (or compact body mergers) would leave some parametric freedom for echoes as well,[24] studied both the combination of contributions of modifications of the Schwarzschild geometry near the surface, and a nonthin shell of matter surrounding the compact body/merger. They found that a massive shell at a distance could be distinguished from the purely Schwarzschild evolution of perturbations. However, for the situation of new physics near the surface of a compact object, (a wormhole in their case), the strong echoes of the surface dominate the echoes of the distant shell. Furthermore, they found that it would take an extraordinarily large mass, located sufficiently close to the wormhole, to lead to discernable changes in the main echoes of the surface and that these changes would be relatively small. The interaction of GWs with matter has also been studied in cosmology,[28,29] with the objective of using GW observations to constrain the properties of dark matter.

In previous work,[25] we showed that a thin spherical dust shell surrounding a gravitational wave source, causes the gravitational wave to be modified both in magnitude and phase, but without any energy being transferred to or from the dust. That work suggests the possibilty of GW echoes. In Sec. 2 we describe the problem considered in this scenario, the assumptions made and the key results.

The solution of[25] is for a monochromatic GW source. A general waveform may be decomposed into a sum of Fourier components, and the technical details are given in Sec. 3. The decomposition is implemented within a Matlab script using the Fast Fourier Transform, and validation results are reported in this section.

Secs. 4 and 5 are about the astrophysics of the various scenarios considered. In[30] we investigated whether a matter shell could explain the echoes that may exist in the LIGO data of GW150914 and GW170817. It was found that the shell would need to have such a large mass that it would constitute a black hole and this is discussed in Sec. 4. Our results show that if GW echoes are confirmed in another GW event, and with a relative magnitude and delay time similar to that of GW150914 and GW170817, then a matter shell would not be a viable explanation, so strengthening the case that an ECO would have been observed.

A key factor in determining the echo properties of a matter shell is the echo delay time, which in the cases above was of order 1s. If the echo delay time is much smaller, order 1ms or smaller, then shell properties that are physically acceptable could lead to measurable effects; however, the short delay time would mean that the effect would not appear as an echo in the usual sense, but rather as a modification to the original signal. Examples of such signal modifications are given in Sec. 5.1 for a matter shell around an event like GW150914; in Sec. 5.2 for black hole quasinormal mode signal following a binary neutron star merger; and in Sec. 5.3 for the case of core collapse supernovae (CCSNe).

Our conclusions are discussed in Sec. 6.

2. Effect of a shell of matter on a GW

In[25] we considered the scenario of a thin shell of matter surrounding a gravitational wave source such as a compact binary merger, as shown schematically in Fig. 1. The spacetime around the GW source in[25] would be otherwise empty except for the surrounding shell of matter. Confining the investigation to a thin shell does not preclude the case of a thick shell. Results can easily be applied to a series of concentric thin shells and then integrated to give the effect for a thick matter shell. The EOS is taken, as a start, to be that of dust. The results show that the shell modifies the outgoing GWs in both phase and magnitude without contradicting previous results about energy transfer. The problem is set up within the Bondi-Sachs formalism for the Einstein equations with coordinates based on outgoing null hypersurfaces.[31,32] The null hypersurfaces, are labelled by the coordinate $x^0 = u$, the angular coordinates by x^A ($A = 2, 3$) and the surface area radial coordinate by $x^1 = r$. The angular coordinates (e.g. spherical polars (θ, ϕ)) label the null ray generators of a hypersurface $u = $ constant. The Bondi-Sachs metric then describes a general spacetime, which may be written as

$$ds^2 = -\left(e^{2\beta}\left(1 + \frac{W}{r}\right) - r^2 h_{AB} U^A U^B\right) du^2 - 2e^{2\beta} du dr$$
$$- 2r^2 h_{AB} U^B du dx^A + r^2 h_{AB} dx^A dx^B, \tag{1}$$

where, $h^{AB}h_{BC} = \delta^A_C$. The condition that r is a surface area coordinate implies $\det(h_{AB}) = \det(q_{AB})$, where, q_{AB} is a unit sphere metric (e.g. $d\theta^2 + \sin^2\theta d\phi^2$).

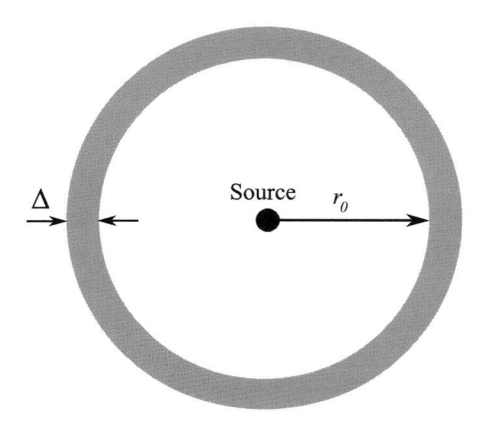

Fig. 1. The problem of a GW source which is surrounded by a spherical shell of mass M_S located between $r = r_0$ and $r = r_0 + \Delta$, where r is the distance from the source.

The GW strain far from the source is written $\mathcal{H}_{M0} = r(h_+ + ih_\times)$, where $h_+, ih_\times$ are the usual polarization modes in the TT gauge. Now suppose that, in the absence of the matter shell,

$$\mathcal{H}_{M0} = \Re(H_{M0}\exp(2i\pi fu))\,{}_2Z_{2,2}, \qquad (2)$$

where f is the frequency (assumed to be monochromatic) of the GWs; H_{M0} is a constant determined by the physics of the GW source; and ${}_2Z_{2,2}$ is a spin-weighted spherical harmonic related to the usual ${}_sY_{\ell,m}$ as specified in.[33,34] Then, as found in,[25] the introduction of a spherical shell around the GW source of mass M_S, radius r_0 and thickness Δ modifies the wave strain to:

$$\mathcal{H} = \Re\left(H_{M0}\left(1 + \frac{2M_S}{r_0} + \frac{iM_S}{\pi r_0^2 f} + \frac{iM_S e^{-4i\pi r_0 f}}{4\pi r_0^2 f}\right.\right.$$
$$\left.\left. + \mathcal{O}\left(\frac{M_S\Delta}{r_0^2}, \frac{M_S}{r_0^3 f^2}\right)\right)\exp(2i\pi fu)\right){}_2Z_{2,2}. \qquad (3)$$

Each of the terms containing M_S in Eq. (3) represents a correction to the wave strain in the absence of the shell.[25] The first correction, $2M_S/r_0$, is part of the gravitational red-shift effect, the main consequence of which is a reduction in the frequency; this effect is well-known, and henceforth we will assume that GW waveforms to be considered have allowed for this effect. The second term, $iM_S/(\pi r_0^2 f)$, is out of phase with the leading terms $1 + 2M_S/r_0$ and hence represents a phase shift of the GW. This term, to $\mathcal{O}(M_S)$, does not change the magnitude of $\mathcal{H}$ and hence has no effect on the energy of the GW. The presence of $e^{-4i\pi r_0 f}$ in the third term describes a change in the magnitude of $\mathcal{H}$, as verified in.[25] In this context, the modified signal would then be interpreted as an echo of the main signal. The echo varies from the main signal in both magnitude and phase, with the magnitude of the echo described by

$$R = \frac{M_S}{4\pi r_0^2 f} \qquad (4)$$

relative to the original signal.

3. Solution for a burst-like GW source using Fourier transforms

The time-delay of the echo is $2r_0$, but the echo's magnitude depends on the wave frequency f. The GW sources reported to date are not monochromatic but are burst-like. Such a source may be decomposed into its Fourier components and Eq. (3) applied to each component, and the echo signal obtained by summing over the transformed components. Because the magnitude of the transformation is frequency-dependent, the echo signal will have a form more complicated than simply a time-delay and magnitude change to the original signal. This effect is now analyzed.

We replace $\Re(H_{M0}\exp(2i\pi f u))$ in Eq. (2) by $h(u)$ defined in the interval $u_0 \leq u \leq u_{N-1}$; and then construct a discrete representation of $h(u)$, $h_k = h(u_k)$ ($k = 0, \cdots, N-1$), with the u_k on a regular grid, i.e. $u_{k+1} - u_k = \delta$ for $k = 0, \cdots, N-2$. Note that if the highest frequency that needs to be resolved is f_m, then N should be chosen so that $(u_{N-1} - u_0)/(N-1) < 1/(2f_m)$, i.e. to satisfy the Nyquist condition. The discrete Fourier transform[35] of $\{h_k\}$ is

$$H_n = \sum_{k=0}^{N-1} h_k \exp\left(\frac{2\pi ikn}{N}\right) \quad \text{with inverse} \quad h_k = \frac{1}{N}\sum_{n=0}^{N-1} H_n \exp\left(\frac{-2\pi ikn}{N}\right). \qquad (5)$$

Then defining $H_{2,n}$ and $H_{3,n}$ to be coefficients in the transform domain of the second (phase-shift) and third (echo) terms of Eq. (3), we have

$$H_{2,n} = \frac{iM_S H_n}{\pi r_0^2 f_n}, \quad H_{3,n} = \frac{iM_S H_n \exp(-4\pi i r_0 f_n)}{4\pi r_0^2 f_n}, \quad n = 1, \cdots, \frac{N}{2},$$

$$H_{2,n} = H_{2,N-n}^*, \quad H_{3,n} = H_{3,N-n}^*, \quad n = \frac{N}{2}+1, \cdots, N-1,$$

$$H_{2,0} = H_{3,0} = 0, \qquad (6)$$

where * denotes the complex conjugate, and where we have used the condition that, in the time domain, all quantities are real. It is being assumed that N is even, and normally $N = 2^m$ (with m an integer) for convenience when using the fast Fourier transform; further

$$f_n = \frac{n(N-1)}{N(u_{N-1} - u_0)}. \qquad (7)$$

Then $h_{2,k}, h_{3,k}$ are found on applying the inverse discrete Fourier transformation.

A Matlab script that implements the calculation of the previous paragraph is available as Supplementary Material in.[30] The script was checked by applying it to a monochromatic signal $h(u) = \Re(-i\exp(2\pi i f u))$. The errors $e_{2,k}$ in $h_{2,k}$ and $e_{3,k}$ in $h_{3,k}$ are

$$e_{2,k} = \left|h_{2,k} - \Re\left(iM_S/(\pi r_0^2 f)\exp(2i\pi f u)\right)\right|$$
$$e_{3,k} = \left|h_{3,k} - \Re\left(iM_S/(4\pi r_0^2 f)e^{-4\pi i r_0 f}\exp(2i\pi f u)\right)\right|. \qquad (8)$$

For the case $u_0 = 0$ms, $u_{N-1} = 100$ms, $f = 1$kHz, $r_0 = 1.25$ms ($\approx$km), and $M_S = 0.25$ms ($\approx M_\odot$), we found:

$$\begin{array}{ccc} N & \|e_{2,k}\| & \|e_{3,k}\| \\ 2^9 & 4.0 \times 10^{-4} & 1.6 \times 10^{-3} \\ 2^{15} & 1.6 \times 10^{-6} & 2.7 \times 10^{-5} \\ 2^{21} & 2.4 \times 10^{-8} & 4.3 \times 10^{-7} \end{array} \qquad (9)$$

where $\|e_k\|$ is defined to be

$$\|e_k\| = \sqrt{\frac{\sum_{k=0}^{N-1} e_k^2}{N}}. \qquad (10)$$

Thus the errors are tending to zero, and N can be chosen so as to attain a desired accuracy. Note that an error of order machine precision is achieved for special values of the frequency $f = k(N-1)/N/(u_{N-1} - u_0)$ with k an integer; in this case we would have that the cyclic assumption of the discrete Fourier transform would be satisfied, i.e. $u_i = u_{i+N}$.

4. Could matter shells explain the GW echo claims?

In,[1] the first of the tentative search for echoes, the authors find evidence for the existence of echoes in the first detection event[36] **GW150914**. They find further comparable evidence for echoes from the events GW151012[37] (then referred to as LVT151012) and GW151226.[38] The references report a number of echo events for GW150914, with the first occurring at about 0.3s after merger; therefore, if caused by a matter shell, the radius would be about 45,000km. The magnitude of the echo was about 0.0992 times that of the original signal. Using 132Hz for the frequency, which is its value when the amplitude was at its maximum at the end of the merger phase, and applying Eq. (4) gives $M_S \simeq 740{,}000 M_\odot$. Such a mass within a radius of 45,000km would constitute a black hole, so the scenario of an echo caused by a shell can be discounted for GW150914.

Extending their investigations to the first BNS detection **GW170817**,[39] the authors of[1] find evidence again of the existence of echoes in the postmerger event.[3] The echo was reported to occur at frequency $f_{echo} \simeq 72$ Hz, approximately 1.0 sec after the BNS merger event. The inspiral signal is at 72Hz about 4.0s before merger, so if the reported echo is caused by a matter shell it must have a radius of about

2.5s$\simeq$ 750,000km. Assuming that the magnitude of the echo signal must be at least 0.01× that of the original signal and applying Eq. (4), it follows that for the echo to be caused by a shell it would have a mass of approximately $10^7 M_\odot$. Now, a mass of $10^7 M_\odot$ inside a radius of 750,000km would constitute a black hole, so the scenario of an echo caused by a shell can be discounted for GW170817.

The above two examples illustrate the general difficulty of producing a GW echo by means of a matter shell. An echo, in the usual sense, is a repeat of the original signal after a short time delay, which in practice must be at least hundreds of ms, corresponding to a shell radius of at least $\sim$ 20,000km. Now, Eq. (4) shows that the shell mass $M_S = 4\pi R r_0^2 f$ which, for expected values of the frequency f, will be large – either implying a black hole and thus not feasible, or requiring an unexpected astrohysical scenario. A much smaller shell radius would avoid these difficulties, but the effect of the shell would be seen as a modification of the original signal, rather than as an echo. Some possible scenarios are presented in the next section.

5. GW events and matter shells

5.1. *GW150914 in the presence of a matter shell*

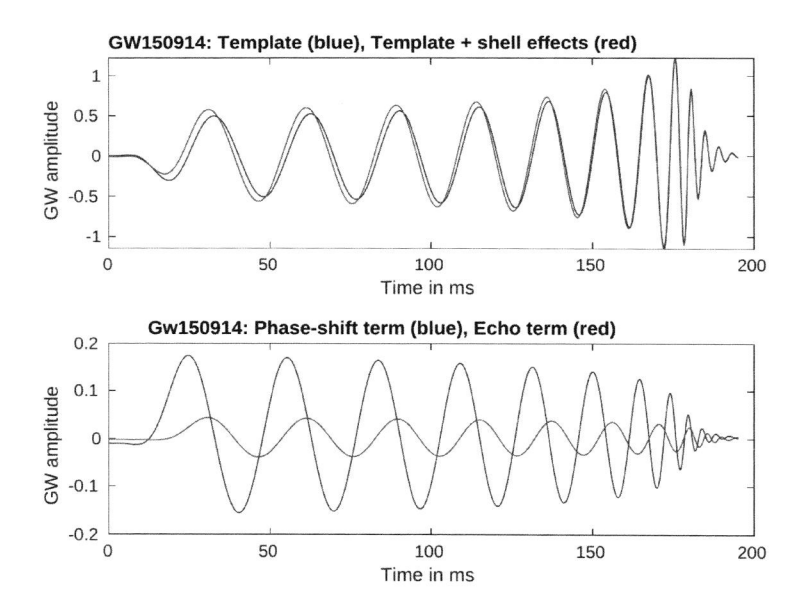

Fig. 2. The effect of a matter shell of radius 3ms (about 900km) and mass 0.3ms (about $60 M_\odot$) on the signal of GW150914. The top panel shows the original signal in blue, and the original signal plus modifications due to the shell in red. The lower panel shows the modifications due to the phase-shift term in blue, and due to the echo term in red.

Although a matter shell could not explain the echoes that might exist in GW150914 data, we now investigate how a hypothetical matter shell might modify the signal from a binary black hole merger. We consider the example case of a shell at radius 3ms (about 900km) and of mass 0.3ms (about $60M_\odot$) and the signal of GW150914[40–42] (Of course, the astrophysical evidence does not suggest the existence of such a shell). The results are shown in Fig. 2. The top panel shows that there is a small but noticeable modification to the template signal, particularly at early times; this is because the frequency is lower at early times and so the modification effects are larger. The bottom panel shows the contributions of the phase-shift term (h_2, blue) and the echo term (h_3, red); it is noticeable that, unlike the template signal, these terms decrease in magnitude as the frequency increases with time.

The accuracy of the results presented in Fig. 2 is limited since the formalism used in[25] assumed a weak field GW source, which is not the case for two black holes at merger. In particular, GWs reflected by the shell would be partially absorbed by the black holes, so reducing the magnitude of the echo contribution to the GW signal.

5.2. *Binary Neutron Star (BNS) mergers*

BNS GW events that have been observed include GW170817[43] and GW190425.[44] Of these, GW170817 was at a higher signal to noise ratio and the event was observed post-merger in the electromagnetic spectrum,[45] indicating that the post-merger object contained a large amount of free matter; we will therefore focus on this event.

The relevant source parameters reported for the event are[46,47]: total mass $M_1 + M_2 = 2.74 M_\odot$, and radii $R_1 = 10.8$km, $R_2 = 10.7$km. The reported GW signal increased in amplitude and frequency until 500Hz, at which stage the signal finished; i.e. the signal was observed during the inspiral phase, but ended as the two objects started to merge. The merger probably produced a central remnant of a neutron star or a black hole, in which case GWs in the lowest quasinormal mode would have been produced; however, the frequency of these GWs would be about 1.5 to 3kHz for a neutron star, or about 6kHz for a $2M_\odot$ black hole, which is outside the sensitivity band of the LIGO detectors.

In order to estimate the possible effect of matter on GWs emitted from a central remnant, we consider the model of a spherical shell of mass $M_S = 0.7 M_\odot$ and radius $r_0 = 25$km around a GW source at either 6kHz or 2kHz. We find that the phase-shift term $2iM_S/(r_0^2 \nu)$ evaluates to

$$\frac{iM_S}{r_0^2 \pi f} = 0.0263i \text{ or } 0.0788i, \tag{11}$$

for 6kHz or 2kHz, respectively. The echo effect would be 1/4 of the above values, and the delay would be 0.1667ms, which is the same as the wave period (at 6kHz),

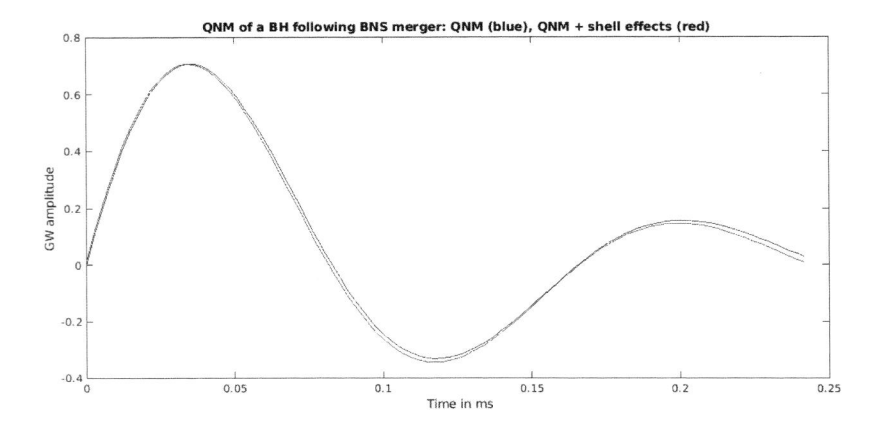

Fig. 3. The effect of a matter shell of radius 25km and mass $0.7M_\odot$ on a quasinormal mode (QNM) signal of a $2M_\odot$ remnant of a binary neutron star merger. The original signal is in blue, and the original signal plus modifications due to the shell is in red.

or less than a wave period (at 2kHz). Thus, in the future if GW detectors in the kHz band are operational and if a BNS event occurs at high signal to noise ratio, then shell effects would affect the GW signal in a measurable way, although the small delay time means that it would be difficult to disentangle the echo and phase-shift effects from the main signal. The modifications to the quasinormal mode signal are illustrated in Fig. 3. However, there are a number of caveats that should be noted:

- The model in[25] assumed that the shell is static, but the aftermath of a BNS meger will be highly dynamical.
- The hypothesis of a shell forming is not supported by a detailed numerical simulation; indeed, since the system started as an inspiral, the matter outside the remnant should have a ring-like structure. Thus, the matter effects could be much smaller than shown in Eq. (11) for an observer on the axis of rotation of the system.
- The comment at the end of Sec. 5.1 about absorption of GWs by a black hole applies here.

So the quantitative values in Eq. (11) should be interpreted as indicative of the order of magnitude of the interaction of GWs with matter, rather than as precise estimates. It should also be noted that if the numerical modeling includes all the matter, and if the simulation run period includes the quasinormal mode ringdown, then shell effects would already be included in the simulation.

5.3. *Core collapse supernovae*

We next turn our attention to an anticipated candidate of detectable GW waves: core collapse supernovae (CCSNe). Whilst BBH and BNS mergers are currently the only GW events picked up by LIGO and VIRGO, supernovae are expected to produce, under certain conditions, GW waves detectable by the current generation of interferometers or those on the horizon. For now, all detection of supernovae have been confined to electromagnetic detection. Photons originate at the outer edge of a star and hence provide only limited information on the interior regions. The detection of GWs which are the result of the aspherical motion of the inner regions will provide a wealth of information on these regions and the mechanism leading to the supernova explosion, where all the four fundamental forces of nature are involved.

Whilst the central engines and inner regions of CCSNe have yet to be fully understood, there exist several studies of their progenitors and the subsequent evolution and detection.[48–51] For stars of mass larger than $8M_\odot$, evolution normally proceeds through several stages of core burning and then to core collapse once nuclear fusion halts when there are no further burning processes to balance the gravitational attraction. Typically, these cores are iron cores, with the critical mass signalling the onset of core collapse ranging from $1.3M_\odot$ to $1.7M_\odot$. The core breaks into two during the collapse, with the inner core of $0.4M_\odot$ to $0.6M_\odot$ in sonic contact and collapsing homologously and the outer core collapsing supersonically. The inner core reaches supranuclear densities of $\sim 2 \times 10^{14} \text{g/cm}^3$ where the nuclear matter stiffens, resulting in a bounce of the inner core. The resulting shock wave is launched into the collapsing outer core. However, the shock loses energy to dissociation of iron nuclei, stalling at ~ 150 km within ~ 10 ms after formation. Many computationally demanding simulations exist[52–54] for generation of GWs from CCSNe.

5.3.1. *Model for the GW modifications due to matter around the inner core*

Ref.[54] presents GW waveforms from simulations of CCSNe for various zero age main sequence (ZAMS) masses in the range $9M_\odot, \cdots, 60M_\odot$. The GW signal starts with an initial burst of duration about 50ms and frequency about 100Hz, followed by a quiescent period. We model this part of the waveform as

$$\begin{aligned} h_+ + ih_\times &\sim \sin(0.2\pi u)\sin(0.02\pi u)\,_2Z_{2,2}\,, \quad 0 \le u \le 50 \\ h_+ + ih_\times &= 0\,, \quad 50 \le u \le 100\,. \end{aligned} \qquad (12)$$

GWs are generated by aspherical motions in the inner core, commencing just after the bounce. The inner core is surrounded by the outer core, treated as a thick matter shell, and we now model its modifications to the GW signal. The shell has an inner radius r_{in}, an outer radius r_{out}, and density at $r = r_{in}$ of ρ_0 with density fall-off $\rho \propto r^{-1-a}$ with $1/2 \le a \le 2$. The effect of the whole shell is obtained by decomposing it into thin shells and then integrating. The result for the echo term is not a simple analytic expression and will be evaluated numerically. However, the phase shift term does give a simple analytic result

$$\int_{r_{in}}^{r_{out}} \frac{iM_s}{r^2 \pi f} dr = i \int_{r_{in}}^{r_{out}} \frac{4\pi r^2 \rho_0 (r_{in})^{1+a}}{r^{1+a} r^2 \pi f} dr = \frac{4i\rho_0 r_{in}}{af}\left(1 - \left(\frac{r_{in}}{r_{out}}\right)^a\right), \qquad (13)$$

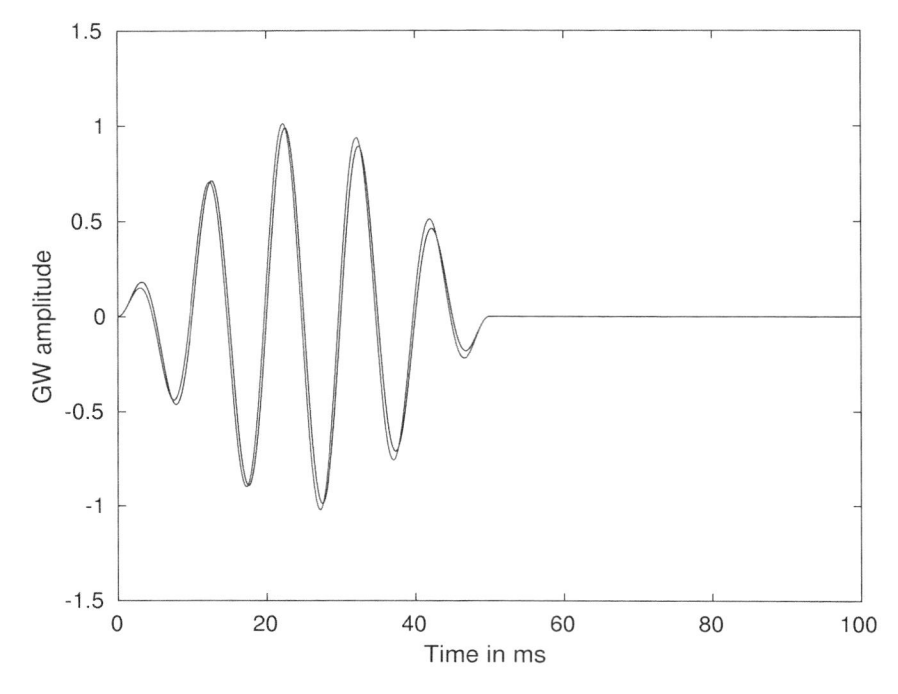

Fig. 4. The effect on the initial burst in a CCSNe GW signal of a matter shell extending from a radius 30km to the shock boundary at 150km. The original signal is in blue, and the signal plus modifications is shown in red.

where f is the GW frequency. Fig. 4 shows the original signal given by Eq. (12) in blue, and the original signal plus shell modifications in red, for the case $r_{in} = 0.1$ms (≈ 30km), $r_{out} = 0.5$ms (≈ 150km), $a = 1$, and $\rho_0 = 0.05/\text{ms}^2$ ($\approx 0.75 \times 10^{12} \text{g/cm}^3$). These values model: the inner core as a proto-neutron star (PNS) of radius 30km, and whose oscillations generate the GWs; the shock boundary as having a radius of 150km; and the density at the inner radius ($\approx 0.75 \times 10^{12} \text{g/cm}^3$) at a couple of orders below the supranuclear density. For this model, Eq. (13) evaluates to $0.16i$, and the total mass of the shell to $0.503 M_\odot$.

There is some uncertainty in the parameter values that should be used in modeling the matter shell around the inner core. The simple form of Eq. (13) shows how varying the parameters would change the magnitude of the shell effect.

6. Conclusion

There are astrophysical scenarios which can be regarded as comprising a shell of matter around a GW source, and this paper has investigated in what way the GW signal would be affected. The investigation started with GW events for which echoes have been claimed to exist in the LIGO data, and it was found that such echoes could not be caused by a matter shell. Thus, an unambiguous observation of GW echoes in the future would favour the existence of ECOs.

We investigated the effect of matter shells in three specific example cases. The first was a binary black hole merger analogous to GW150914, surrounded by a hypothetical matter shell at radius 900km and mass $60M_\odot$. Astrophysically, such a shell is highly unlikely to exist, but this case is useful as it well illustrates some of the features of the shell effects on the waveform. The next case considered was the quasinormal mode signal from the remnant of a binary neutron star merger like GW170917. In this case, it is known that there is a substantial amount of matter around the remnant, although the extent to which the shell model is appropriate is unclear. The final case considered was that of a core collapse supernova. Although GWs from such events have not been observed, they are regarded as potential sources; and here it is clear that the proto neutron star, in which the GWs are generated, is surrounded by shells of matter. Of the three cases, the core collapse supernova is that which yielded the largest shell modifications to the GWs, and for which the predictions are most reliable.

The effects of matter shells are small but measurable if the signal to noise ratio is sufficiently high. As GW observations become more accurate, through both hardware developments and, as time passes, the increasing chance of observing nearby events, these effects will need to be taken into account.

Acknowledgments

This work was supported by the National Research Foundation, South Africa, under grant numbers 118519 and 114815.

References

1. J. Abedi, H. Dykaar and N. Afshordi, Echoes from the Abyss: Tentative evidence for Planck-scale structure at black hole horizons, *Phys. Rev. D* **96**, p. 082004 (2017).
2. R. S. Conklin, B. Holdom and J. Ren, Gravitational wave echoes through new windows, *Phys. Rev. D* **98**, p. 044021 (Aug 2018).
3. J. Abedi and N. Afshordi, Echoes from the Abyss: A highly spinning black hole remnant for the binary neutron star merger GW170817, *JCAP* **11**, p. 010 (2019).
4. G. Ashton, O. Birnholtz, M. Cabero, C. Capano, T. Dent, B. Krishnan, G. D. Meadors, A. B. Nielsen, A. Nitz and J. Westerweck, Comments on: "Echoes from the abyss: Evidence for Planck-scale structure at black hole horizons" (12 2016).
5. J. Westerweck, A. Nielsen, O. Fischer-Birnholtz, M. Cabero, C. Capano, T. Dent, B. Krishnan, G. Meadors and A. H. Nitz, Low significance of evidence for black hole echoes in gravitational wave data, *Phys. Rev. D* **97**, p. 124037 (2018).
6. J. Abedi, H. Dykaar and N. Afshordi, Echoes from the Abyss: The Holiday Edition!, *arXiv e-prints*, p. arXiv:1701.03485 (January 2017).
7. J. Abedi, H. Dykaar and N. Afshordi, Comment on: "Low significance of evidence for black hole echoes in gravitational wave data", *arXiv e-prints*, p. arXiv:1803.08565 (March 2018).

8. J. Abedi and N. Afshordi, Echoes from the Abyss: A Status Update, *arXiv e-prints*, p. arXiv:2001.00821 (January 2020).
9. A. Almheiri, D. Marolf, J. Polchinski and J. Sully, Black Holes: Complementarity or Firewalls?, *JHEP* **02**, p. 062 (2013).
10. O. Lunin and S. D. Mathur, AdS/CFT duality and the black hole information paradox, *Nucl. Phys. B* **623**, 342 (2002).
11. G. F. Giudice, M. McCullough and A. Urbano, Hunting for Dark Particles with Gravitational Waves, *JCAP* **10**, p. 001 (2016).
12. P. O. Mazur and E. Mottola, Gravitational vacuum condensate stars, *Proc. Nat. Acad. Sci.* **101**, 9545 (2004).
13. S. L. Liebling and C. Palenzuela, Dynamical Boson Stars, *Living Rev. Rel.* **20**, p. 5 (2017).
14. V. Cardoso, E. Franzin and P. Pani, Is the gravitational-wave ringdown a probe of the event horizon?, *Phys. Rev. Lett.* **116**, p. 171101 (2016), [Erratum: Phys. Rev. Lett. 117, 089902 (2016)].
15. V. Cardoso, S. Hopper, C. F. B. Macedo, C. Palenzuela and P. Pani, Gravitational-wave signatures of exotic compact objects and of quantum corrections at the horizon scale, *Phys. Rev. D* **94**, p. 084031 (2016).
16. V. Cardoso and P. Pani, Tests for the existence of black holes through gravitational wave echoes, *Nature Astron.* **1**, 586 (2017).
17. H. Nakano, N. Sago, H. Tagoshi and T. Tanaka, Black hole ringdown echoes and howls, *Progress of Theoretical and Experimental Physics* **2017** (Jul 2017).
18. A. Testa and P. Pani, Analytical template for gravitational-wave echoes: Signal characterization and prospects of detection with current and future interferometers, *Phys. Rev. D* **98**, p. 044018 (2018).
19. Y.-T. Wang, Z.-P. Li, J. Zhang, S.-Y. Zhou and Y.-S. Piao, Are gravitational wave ringdown echoes always equal-interval?, *Eur. Phys. J. C* **78**, p. 482 (2018).
20. P. Bueno, P. A. Cano, F. Goelen, T. Hertog and B. Vercnocke, Echoes of Kerr-like wormholes, *Phys. Rev. D* **97**, p. 024040 (2018).
21. A. Maselli, S. H. Völkel and K. D. Kokkotas, Parameter estimation of gravitational wave echoes from exotic compact objects, *Phys. Rev. D* **96**, p. 064045 (2017).
22. C. Barceló, R. Carballo-Rubio and L. J. Garay, Gravitational wave echoes from macroscopic quantum gravity effects, *JHEP* **05**, p. 054 (2017).
23. R. Carballo-Rubio, F. Di Filippo, S. Liberati and M. Visser, Phenomenological aspects of black holes beyond general relativity, *Phys. Rev. D* **98**, p. 124009 (2018).
24. R. A. Konoplya, Z. Stuchlík and A. Zhidenko, Echoes of compact objects: New physics near the surface and matter at a distance, *Phys. Rev. D* **99**, p. 024007 (Jan 2019).
25. N. T. Bishop, P. J. van der Walt and M. Naidoo, Effect of a low density dust shell on the propagation of gravitational waves, *Gen. Rel. Grav.* **52**, p. 92 (2020).
26. E. Barausse, V. Cardoso and P. Pani, Can environmental effects spoil precision gravitational-wave astrophysics?, *Phys. Rev. D* **89**, p. 104059 (2014).
27. P. Leung, Y. Liu, W. Suen, C. Tam and K. Young, Quasinormal modes of dirty black holes, *Phys. Rev. Lett.* **78**, 2894 (1997).
28. G. Goswami, G. K. Chakravarty, S. Mohanty and A. R. Prasanna, Constraints on cosmological viscosity and self-interacting dark matter from gravitational wave observations, *Phys. Rev. D* **95**, p. 103509 (May 2017).
29. G. Baym, S. P. Patil and C. J. Pethick, Damping of gravitational waves by matter, *Phys. Rev. D* **96**, p. 084033 (Oct 2017).

30. M. Naidoo, N. T. Bishop and P. J. van der Walt, Modifications to the signal from a gravitational wave event due to a surrounding shell of matter, *arXiv e-prints*, p. arXiv:2102.00060 (January 2021).
31. H. Bondi, M. G. J. van der Burg and A. W. K. Metzner, Gravitational waves in general relativity VII. Waves from axi-symmetric isolated systems, *Proc. R. Soc. London* **A269**, 21 (1962).
32. R. Sachs, Gravitational waves in general relativity VIII. Waves in asymptotically flat space-time, *Proc. Roy. Soc. London* **A270**, 103 (1962).
33. N. T. Bishop and L. Rezzolla, Extraction of gravitational waves in numerical relativity, *Living Rev. Relativ.* **19**, p. 1 (Oct 2016).
34. N. T. Bishop, Linearized solutions of the Einstein equations within a Bondi-Sachs framework, and implications for boundary conditions in numerical simulations, *Class. Quantum Grav.* **22**, 2393 (2005).
35. W. H. Press, B. P. Flannery, S. A. Teukolsky and W. T. Vetterling, *Numerical Recipes*, 2nd edn. (Cambridge University Press, New York, 1992).
36. B. Abbott et al., Observation of Gravitational Waves from a Binary Black Hole Merger, *Phys. Rev. Lett.* **116**, p. 061102 (2016).
37. A. H. Nitz, C. Capano, A. B. Nielsen, S. Reyes, R. White, D. A. Brown and B. Krishnan, 1-OGC: The first open gravitational-wave catalog of binary mergers from analysis of public Advanced LIGO data, *Astrophys. J.* **872**, p. 195 (2019).
38. B. P. Abbott et al., GW151226: Observation of Gravitational Waves from a 22-Solar-Mass Binary Black Hole Coalescence, *Phys. Rev. Lett.* **116**, p. 241103 (2016).
39. B. Abbott, R. Abbott, T. Abbott, F. Acernese, K. Ackley, C. Adams, T. Adams, P. Addesso, R. Adhikari, V. Adya and et al., Gw170817: Observation of gravitational waves from a binary neutron star inspiral, *Physical Review Letters* **119** (Oct 2017).
40. B. P. Abbott et al., A guide to LIGO–Virgo detector noise and extraction of transient gravitational-wave signals, *Class. Quant. Grav.* **37**, p. 055002 (2020).
41. G. W. O. S. Center, GW150914 Template Data https://www.gw-openscience.org/GW150914data.
42. G. W. O. S. Center, Binary Black Hole Signals in LIGO Open Data https://losc.ligo.org/s/events/GW150914/LOSC_Event_tutorial_GW150914.html.
43. B. Abbott et al., GW170817: Observation of Gravitational Waves from a Binary Neutron Star Inspiral, *Phys. Rev. Lett.* **119**, p. 161101 (2017).
44. B. Abbott et al., GW190425: Observation of a Compact Binary Coalescence with Total Mass $\sim 3.4 M_\odot$, *Astrophys. J. Lett.* **892**, p. L3 (2020).
45. B. P. Abbott et. al., Multi-messenger Observations of a Binary Neutron Star Merger, *Astrophys. J. Lett.* **848**, p. L12 (2017).
46. B. Abbott et al., Observing gravitational-wave transient GW150914 with minimal assumptions, *Phys. Rev. D* **93**, p. 122004 (2016), [Addendum: Phys.Rev.D 94, 069903 (2016)].
47. B. Abbott et al., GW170817: Measurements of neutron star radii and equation of state, *Phys. Rev. Lett.* **121**, p. 161101 (2018).
48. B. Müller, Hydrodynamics of core-collapse supernovae and their progenitors, *Astrophysics* **6**, p. 3 (2020).
49. E. Abdikamalov, G. Pagliaroli and D. Radice, Gravitational Waves from Core-Collapse Supernovae (10 2020).
50. S. E. Woosley, A. Heger and T. A. Weaver, The evolution and explosion of massive stars, *Rev. Mod. Phys.* **74**, p. 1015 (November 2002).

51. S. Woosley and A. Heger, Nucleosynthesis and Remnants in Massive Stars of Solar Metallicity, *Phys. Rept.* **442**, 269 (2007).
52. H. Andresen, B. Müller, E. Müller and H.-T. Janka, Gravitational Wave Signals from 3D Neutrino Hydrodynamics Simulations of Core-Collapse Supernovae, *Mon. Not. Roy. Astron. Soc.* **468**, 2032 (2017).
53. H. Andresen, E. Müller, H. Janka, A. Summa, K. Gill and M. Zanolin, Gravitational waves from 3D core-collapse supernova models: The impact of moderate progenitor rotation, *Mon. Not. Roy. Astron. Soc.* **486**, 2238 (2019).
54. D. Radice, V. Morozova, A. Burrows, D. Vartanyan and H. Nagakura, Characterizing the Gravitational Wave Signal from Core-Collapse Supernovae, *Astrophys. J. Lett.* **876**, p. L9 (2019).

Odd-dimensional gravitational waves from a binary system on a three-brane

D. V. Gal'tsov[a,*] and M. Khlopunov[a,b,†]

[a] *Faculty of Physics, Lomonosov Moscow State University,
Moscow, 119899, Russia*
[b] *Institute of Theoretical and Mathematical Physics, Lomonosov Moscow State University,
Moscow 119991, Russia*
E-mail: [*] *galtsov@phys.msu.ru,* [†] *khlopunov.mi14@physics.msu.ru*

We consider gravitational radiation in the presence of non-compact extra dimensions. If their number is odd, all spacetime becomes odd-dimensional and formation of gravitational radiation becomes non-trivial because of violation of the Huygens principle. Gravitational waves travel with the speed of light, while the full retarded gravitational field of a localized source propagates with all velocities lower or equal to the speed of light, so special care is needed to extract radiation. Here we consider a simplified model consisting of two point masses moving on a three-brane embedded in five-dimensional bulk. Particles are assumed to interact through a massless scalar field living on the same brane, while gravitational radiation is emitted into the full five-dimensional space. We use the Rohrlich-Teitelboim approach to radiation, extracting the radiative component of the retarded gravitational field via splitting of the energy-momentum tensor. The source term consists of the local contribution from the particles and the non-local contribution from the scalar field stresses. The latter is computed using the DIRE approach to the post-Newtonian expansions. In the non-relativistic limit, we find an analog of the quadrupole formula containing the integral over the full history of motion, preceding the retarded moment of time. We compute gravitational radiation and study the orbit evolution of the non-relativistic circular binary system on the brane.

Keywords: Extra dimensions, Huygens principle, gravitational radiation, brane

1. Introduction

Gravitational radiation in the higher-dimensional spacetimes has become an intriguing problem in the last twenty years due to development of the gravity theories with large extra dimensions.[1-4] Recent successes of the gravitational-wave astronomy give us the new tool for exploring extra dimensions.[5-10] Some constraints on their size, number and geometry have already been extracted.[11-16] Another new tool relevant to extra dimensions is shadow of a black hole.[17-19]

With regard to the theoretical study of multidimensional radiation, then in the majority of literary sources only radiation in even space-time dimensions is studied,[20-24] while the odd dimensions were discussed mainly in the more academic context of the problem of radiation reaction.[25-28] Huygens principle violation in odd dimensions[29-31] leads to significant difference of field propagation in even and odd dimensions. In both cases, signal from the instantaneous flash reaches the observation point in time required to propagate with the speed of light. However, in odd dimensions, after the arrival of the primary signal an endless tail is observed which is not the case in the even dimensions. Mathematically, this is related to the localisation of the odd-dimensional retarded Green's functions not only on the light cone, but also inside it:

$$G_{\text{ret}}^{2\nu+1}(x) = \frac{(-1)^\nu}{(2\pi)^\nu} \frac{d^{\nu-1}}{(rdr)^{\nu-1}} \frac{\theta(t)\,\theta(t^2-r^2)}{\sqrt{t^2-r^2}}, \quad \nu \in \mathbb{N}, \qquad (1)$$

where $t = x^0$, and $r = |\mathbf{x}|$. The odd-dimensional gravitational radiation of the non-relativistic binary systems has been studied[32] using the effective field theory formalism,[33,34] which is insensitive to the dimensionality of spacetime. But since it is based on the Fourier decompositions, the obtained analog of the quadrupole formula does not contain any information about the gravitational field in the wave zone and does not reveal the role of the tail in the formation of the gravitational-wave signal. So here we consider five-dimensional radiation essentially using the space-time picture.

2. The setup

We consider a simplified model of a binary system whose motion is confined inside the four-dimensional subspace (brane). Particles interact with each other only through the massless scalar field localised on the same brane, while gravitational radiation is five-dimensional. Our localisation mechanism is purely kinematical: if the initial conditions are restricted to the brane, and the mediator scalar field is four-dimensional, the system remains in the brane forever. Such a system admits the stable elliptical orbits, and the interaction field is free from tails, providing us with a simple setup to study the features of the odd-dimensional gravitational radiation related to the Huygens principle violation.

Gravitational radiation of such a system can be described by the linearised theory on the Minkowski background without use of the quadratic part of the Ricci tensor corresponding to the gravitational stresses.[35] However, one still needs to take into account the scalar field stresses corresponding to the energy of the particles interaction:

$$\Box \bar{h}_{MN}(x) = -2\kappa_5 \left[T^{\text{P}}_{MN}(x) + T^{\text{F}}_{MN}(x) \right], \quad \partial^M \bar{h}_{MN} = 0, \qquad (2)$$

$$T^{\text{P}}_{MN}(x) = \delta^\mu_M \delta^\nu_N \sum_{a=1}^{2} m_a \int d\tau_a\, \dot{z}_{a\mu} \dot{z}_{a\nu}\, \delta^{(4)}(x-z_a)\delta(x^4), \qquad (3)$$

$$T^{\text{F}}_{MN}(x) = \frac{1}{4\pi} \delta^\mu_M \delta^\nu_N \left(\partial_\mu \varphi \partial_\nu \varphi - \frac{1}{2}\eta_{\mu\nu} \partial^\alpha \varphi \partial_\alpha \varphi \right) \delta(x^4), \qquad (4)$$

where $M, N = \overline{0,4}$ and $\mu, \nu = \overline{0,3}$, and $\eta_{MN} = \text{diag}(-1,1,1,1,1)$. Here, $z_a^\mu(\tau_a)$ are the world lines of the particles and $\dot{z}_a^\mu = dz_a^\mu/d\tau_a$, m_a are their masses, and κ_5 is the five-dimensional gravitational constant. We assume that the brane lies in the $x^4 = 0$ hypersurface.

The effective energy-momentum tensor of the gravitational field, by analogy with the four-dimensional theory,[36] is given by

$$t_{MN}^{\text{rad}}(x) = \frac{1}{4\kappa_5} \left\langle \partial_M \bar{h}_{ij}^{\text{TT}} \partial_N \bar{h}_{ij}^{\text{TT}} \right\rangle, \quad i,j = \overline{1,4}, \tag{5}$$

where a periodic motion of the source is assumed, and bracket $\langle \ldots \rangle$ denotes averaging over the period. In Eq. (5), we use the metric deviations in the transverse-traceless gauge

$$h_{0M}^{\text{TT}} = 0, \quad h_{ii}^{\text{TT}} = 0, \quad \partial^j h_{ij}^{\text{TT}} = 0, \tag{6}$$

in which gravitational waves have five independent polarisations. Namely, polarisations of the plane wave propagating along the x^3-coordinate are presented by the matrix

$$\bar{h}_{ij}^{\text{TT}} = \begin{pmatrix} h_+ - \frac{1}{2}h_\circ & h_\times & 0 & h_{14} \\ h_\times & -h_+ - \frac{1}{2}h_\circ & 0 & h_{24} \\ 0 & 0 & 0 & 0 \\ h_{14} & h_{24} & 0 & h_\circ \end{pmatrix}, \tag{7}$$

where the "cross" and "plus" polarisations are the same as in the four-dimensional theory[35, 36]

$$h_+ = \frac{1}{2}(h_{11} - h_{22}), \quad h_\times = h_{12}, \tag{8}$$

and $h_\circ$ is the "breathing" mode[7]

$$h_\circ = \frac{2}{3}h_{44} - \frac{1}{3}(h_{11} + h_{22}). \tag{9}$$

The brane-living observer would detect only three of them – the standard "plus" and "cross", and the "breathing" polarisation, corresponding to the uniform shrinking and stretching of the probe masses circle lying in the plane orthogonal to the wave propagation direction.[7] We find that the breathing polarisation is non-vanishing even when both the source and an observer live on the brane.

3. Point particles contribution

To calculate the point particles contribution into the gravitational radiation we use the Rohrlich-Teitelboim definition of radiation[37–39] (see also[40–43]) based on the Lorentz-invariant decomposition of the on-shell energy-momentum tensor of the retarded field in the far zone. The Lorentz-invariant distance from the particle trajectory $z^M(\tau)$,

$$\hat{\rho} \equiv \hat{v}^M \hat{X}_M, \quad \hat{\rho} \xrightarrow{r \gg |\mathbf{z}|} r \tag{10}$$

is equivalent to the spatial distance from the system to the observation point. Here, the following notations are used:

$$\hat{X}^M = x^M - z^M(\hat{\tau}) \equiv \hat{\rho}\hat{c}^M, \quad \hat{c}^M \hat{v}_M = 1, \quad \hat{c}^2 = 0, \tag{11}$$

$$\hat{v}^M = v^M(\hat{\tau}), \quad v^M = \frac{dz^M}{d\tau}, \tag{12}$$

and $\hat{\tau}$ is the retarded proper time defined as

$$\left(x^M - z^M(\hat{\tau})\right)^2 = \hat{X}^2 = 0, \ x^0 \geq z^0(\hat{\tau}). \tag{13}$$

Then, in D dimensions, the on-shell energy-momentum tensor can be expanded in the inverse powers of $\hat{\rho}$ as follows

$$T^{MN} = T^{MN}_{\text{Coul}} + T^{MN}_{\text{mix}} + T^{MN}_{\text{rad}} \tag{14}$$

$$T^{MN}_{\text{Coul}} \sim \frac{A^{MN}}{\hat{\rho}^{2D-4}}, \quad T^{MN}_{\text{mix}} \sim \frac{B^{MN}}{\hat{\rho}^{2D-5}} + \ldots + \frac{C^{MN}}{\hat{\rho}^{D-1}}, \quad T^{MN}_{\text{rad}} \sim \frac{D^{MN}}{\hat{\rho}^{D-2}}. \tag{15}$$

Here, the most short-range part T^{MN}_{Coul} is the energy-momentum tensor of the Coulomb part of the field; T^{MN}_{mix} is the mixed part, which is absent in $D = 3$ and consists of more that one term in $D > 4$. The remaining long-range part of the energy-momentum tensor T^{MN}_{rad} has the properties allowing one to associate it with the energy-momentum flux carried by the emitted part of the field. Indeed, it is separately conserved $\partial_M T^{MN}_{\text{rad}} = 0$; it is proportional to the direct product of two null vectors $T^{MN}_{\text{rad}} \sim \hat{c}^M \hat{c}^N$, corresponding to the propagation of the associated energy-momentum flux exactly with the speed of light $\hat{c}_M T^{MN}_{\text{rad}} = 0$. Finally, it falls down as $T^{MN}_{\text{rad}} \sim 1/r^{D-2}$ and gives positive definite energy-momentum flux through the distant sphere of the area $\sim r^{D-2}$.

These properties hold both in even and odd dimensions. However, due to the Huygens principle violation, in odd dimensions the emitted part of the energy-momentum tensor T^{MN}_{rad} depends on the entire history of the source's motion preceding the retarded time $\hat{\tau}$, while in even ones it is completely determined by the state of the source at this moment. Also, due to the form of the energy-momentum tensor (5), which is the bilinear expression of the field derivatives, one can define its emitted part, by analogy with that of the energy-momentum tensor

$$(\partial_M \bar{h}^{\text{TT}}_{ij})^{\text{rad}} \sim 1/\hat{\rho}^{D/2-1}. \tag{16}$$

Therefore, the radiated energy flux through the distant $(D-2)$-dimensional sphere of radius r is given as

$$W_D = \int T^{0i}_{\text{rad}} \, n^i \, r^{D-2} \, d\Omega_{D-2}, \tag{17}$$

where $d\Omega_{D-2}$ is the angular element, and $n^i = x^i/r$ is a unit spacelike vector in the observation direction.

Considering the gravitational radiation from the non-relativistic binary system we demonstrate that to find the non-relativistic approximation of the emitted part of the gravitational field produced by point particles one have to introduce, besides the small particles velocities $|\mathbf{v}| \ll 1$, another small parameter

$$\mathbf{s}(\tau) = \frac{\mathbf{z}(\hat{\tau}) - \mathbf{z}(\tau)}{\hat{\tau} - \tau}, \quad \lim_{\tau \to \hat{\tau}} \mathbf{s}(\tau) = \hat{\mathbf{v}}, \quad |\mathbf{s}| \sim |\mathbf{v}|, \tag{18}$$

which is of order of particles velocities for any moment of proper time. Then, we find the point particles contribution into the gravitational radiation from the binary system as

$$(\partial_M \bar{h}_{ij}^{\mathrm{P}})^{\mathrm{rad}} = -\frac{\mu \kappa_5 \bar{c}_M}{2^{3/2} \pi^2 r^{3/2}} \int_{-\infty}^{\bar{\tau}} d\tau \frac{\dot{a}_i v_j + 2 a_i a_j + v_i \dot{a}_j}{(\bar{\tau} - \tau)^{1/2}}, \quad \bar{c}_M = [-1, \mathbf{n}], \tag{19}$$

where $z^i = z_2^i - z_1^i$ is the relative coordinate of the system, $\mu = m_1 m_2/(m_1 + m_2)$ is its reduced mass, and $\bar{\tau} = t - r$ is the retarded proper time calculated up to the leading order. Note that the emitted part of the gravitational field (19) is proportional to the null vector $\bar{c}_M$ leading to the corresponding energy-momentum tensor (5) being proportional to the direct product of two null vectors, in accordance with the Rohrlich-Teitelboim approach, and depends on the history of the system's motion preceding the retarded time $\bar{\tau}$.

4. Scalar field contribution

The scalar field stresses contribution into the gravitational radiation is calculated by use of the DIRE approach to the post-Newtonian expansions.[44] It is based on the splitting of the spacetime into the near zone, whose size is of order of the characteristic wavelength of gravitational radiation $\mathcal{R} = \mathcal{S}/|\mathbf{v}| \sim \lambda_{\mathrm{GW}}$ ($\mathcal{S}$ is the characteristic size of the binary system), and the radiation zone being exterior to the near zone.

In our calculations we assume that the observation point is in the radiation zone, the retardation of the scalar field inside the near zone is negligible, and that the energy-momentum density of the scalar field is non-vanishing only in the near zone being large enough due to the slow motion of the particles. Then, we arrive at the scalar field contribution into the gravitational radiation in the form

$$(\partial_M \bar{h}_{ij}^{\mathrm{F}})^{\mathrm{rad}} = -\frac{\mu \kappa_5 \bar{c}_M}{2^{5/2} \pi^2 r^{3/2}} \int_{-\infty}^{\bar{\tau}} d\tau \frac{\ddot{a}_i z_j + 2 \dot{a}_i v_j + 2 a_i a_j + 2 v_i \dot{a}_j + z_i \ddot{a}_j}{(\bar{\tau} - \tau)^{1/2}}. \tag{20}$$

As the point particles contribution (19), this expression is proportional to the null vector $\bar{c}_M$ and depends on the history of the particles motion.

Combining the point-like (19) and the non-local scalar field (20) contributions, we find the emitted part of the total gravitational field of the binary system:

$$(\partial_M \bar{h}_{ij}^{\mathrm{TT}})^{\mathrm{rad}} = -\frac{\kappa_5 \bar{c}_M}{2^{5/2} \pi^2 r^{3/2}} \int_{-\infty}^{\bar{\tau}} d\tau \frac{\dddot{Q}_{ij}^{\mathrm{TT}}}{(\bar{\tau} - \tau)^{1/2}}, \quad Q_{ij} = \mu \left[z_i z_j - \frac{1}{4} \delta_{ij} z_k z_k \right]. \tag{21}$$

As in the four-dimensional theory,[36] it is determined by the transverse-traceless part of the quadrupole moment of the binary system but now depends on the history of motion.

Therefore, using the Eqs. (5) and (17) we obtain the five-dimensional analog of the quadrupole formula for the angular distribution of the gravitational radiation power

$$\frac{dW_5}{d\Omega_3} = \frac{\kappa_5}{128\pi^4} \langle \mathcal{A}_{ij}^{\text{TT}} \mathcal{A}_{ij}^{\text{TT}} \rangle, \quad \mathcal{A}_{ij}^{\text{TT}} = \int_{-\infty}^{\bar{\tau}} d\tau \frac{\dddot{Q}_{ij}^{\text{TT}}}{(\bar{\tau} - \tau)^{1/2}}. \tag{22}$$

depending on the entire history of the binary system's motion preceding the retarded time $\bar{\tau}$. Recently, the analogous formula was obtained by use of the spectral decompositions of the retarded Green's functions,[45] which are insensitive to the dimensionality of the spacetime, and can be considered as a confirmation of our result.

5. Binary system on a circular orbit

As the simplest application of the obtained five-dimensional quadrupole formula, we consider the gravitational radiation from the non-relativistic binary system on the circular orbit. Integrating the angular distribution (22), we find the total gravitational radiation power of the system on the circular orbit

$$W_5^{\text{circ}} = \frac{5}{9\pi} \kappa_5 \mu^2 R_s^4 \omega_s^7, \tag{23}$$

where R_s is the orbital radius of the system, and ω_s is its frequency of the orbital motion. Also, using the energy conservation law

$$\frac{dE_{\text{tot}}}{dt} = -W_5^{\text{circ}}, \tag{24}$$

where E_{tot} is the total mechanical energy of the point particles, we analyse the quasi-circular orbit shrinking of the binary system arriving at the evolution laws for the orbital frequency and radius

$$\omega_s(t) = \left(\frac{9\pi}{55\kappa_5}\right)^{3/11} (\sqrt{\mu} g_1 g_2)^{-2/11} (t_{\text{coal}} - t)^{-3/11}, \tag{25}$$

$$R_s(t) = R_0 \left(\frac{t_{\text{coal}} - t}{t_{\text{coal}} - t_0}\right)^{2/11}, \tag{26}$$

where t_{coal} is the moment of time corresponding to the coalescence of the binary system $R_s \to 0$, $\omega_s \to \infty$, and $R_s(t_0) = R_0$. Note that the obtained Eqs. (25) and (26) differ significantly from their four-dimensional analogs

$$\omega_s^{\text{4D}}(t) \sim (t_{\text{coal}} - t)^{-3/8}, \quad R_s^{\text{4D}}(t) \sim (t_{\text{coal}} - t)^{1/4}, \tag{27}$$

what could be expected, given the five-dimensional nature of gravity and infinite size of extra dimension in our model.

Acknowledgements

The work of M. Kh. was supported by the "BASIS" Foundation Grant No. 20-2-10-8-1. The work of D.G. was supported by the Russian Foundation for Basic Research on the project 20-52-18012, and the Scientific and Educational School of Moscow State University "Fundamental and Applied Space Research".

References

1. N. Arkani-Hamed, S. Dimopoulos and G. R. Dvali, The Hierarchy problem and new dimensions at a millimeter, *Phys. Lett. B* **429**, 263 (1998).
2. L. Randall and R. Sundrum, A Large mass hierarchy from a small extra dimension, *Phys. Rev. Lett.* **83**, 3370 (1999).
3. L. Randall and R. Sundrum, An Alternative to compactification, *Phys. Rev. Lett.* **83**, 4690 (1999).
4. G. R. Dvali, G. Gabadadze and M. Porrati, 4D gravity on a brane in 5D Minkowski space, *Phys. Lett. B* **485**, 208 (2000).
5. A. O. Barvinsky and S. N. Solodukhin, Echoing the extra dimension, *Nucl. Phys. B* **675**, 159 (2003).
6. C. Deffayet and K. Menou, Probing Gravity with Spacetime Sirens, *Astrophys. J. Lett.* **668**, L143 (2007).
7. D. Andriot and G. Lucena Gómez, Signatures of extra dimensions in gravitational waves, *JCAP* **06**, 048 (2017) [erratum: *JCAP* **05**, E01 (2019)].
8. H. Yu, Z. C. Lin and Y. X. Liu, Gravitational waves and extra dimensions: a short review, *Commun. Theor. Phys.* **71**, no. 8, 991 (2019).
9. O. K. Kwon, S. Lee and D. D. Tolla, Gravitational Waves as a Probe of the Extra Dimension, *Phys. Rev. D* **100**, 084050 (2019).
10. M. Corman, C. Escamilla-Rivera and M. A. Hendry, Constraining extra dimensions on cosmological scales with LISA future gravitational wave siren data, *JCAP* **02**, 005 (2021).
11. L. Visinelli, N. Bolis and S. Vagnozzi, Brane-world extra dimensions in light of GW170817, *Phys. Rev. D* **97**, no. 6, 064039 (2018).
12. K. Pardo, M. Fishbach, D. E. Holz and D. N. Spergel, Limits on the number of spacetime dimensions from GW170817, *JCAP* **07**, 048 (2018).
13. K. Chakravarti, S. Chakraborty, K. S. Phukon, S. Bose and S. SenGupta, Constraining extra-spatial dimensions with observations of GW170817, *Class. Quant. Grav.* **37**, no. 10, 105004 (2020).
14. S. Chakraborty, K. Chakravarti, S. Bose and S. SenGupta, Signatures of extra dimensions in gravitational waves from black hole quasinormal modes, *Phys. Rev. D* **97**, no. 10, 104053 (2018).
15. K. Chakravarti, S. Chakraborty, S. Bose and S. SenGupta, Tidal Love numbers of black holes and neutron stars in the presence of higher dimensions: Implications of GW170817, *Phys. Rev. D* **99**, no. 2, 024036 (2019).
16. A. K. Mishra, A. Ghosh and S. Chakraborty, Constraining extra dimensions using observations of black hole quasi-normal modes, [arXiv:2106.05558 [gr-qc]].
17. S. Vagnozzi and L. Visinelli, Hunting for extra dimensions in the shadow of M87*, *Phys. Rev. D* **100**, no. 2, 024020 (2019).
18. I. Banerjee, S. Chakraborty and S. SenGupta, Silhouette of M87*: A New Window to Peek into the World of Hidden Dimensions, *Phys. Rev. D* **101**, no. 4, 041301 (2020).
19. J. C. S. Neves, Constraining the tidal charge of brane black holes using their shadows, *Eur. Phys. J. C* **80**, no. 8, 717 (2020).

20. B. P. Kosyakov, Exact solutions of classical electrodynamics and the Yang-Mills-Wong theory in even-dimensional space-time, *Theor. Math. Phys.* **119**, 493 (1999).
21. V. Cardoso, O. J. C. Dias and J. P. S. Lemos, Gravitational radiation in D-dimensional space-times, *Phys. Rev. D* **67**, 064026 (2003).
22. V. Cardoso, M. Cavaglia and J. Q. Guo, Gravitational Larmor formula in higher dimensions, *Phys. Rev. D* **75**, 084020 (2007).
23. A. Mironov and A. Morozov, Radiation beyond four space-time dimensions, *Theor. Math. Phys.* **156**, 1209 (2008).
24. B. P. Kosyakov, Electromagnetic radiation in even-dimensional spacetimes, *Int. J. Mod. Phys. A* **23**, 4695 (2008).
25. D. V. Galtsov, Radiation reaction in various dimensions, *Phys. Rev. D* **66**, 025016 (2002).
26. P. O. Kazinski, S. L. Lyakhovich and A. A. Sharapov, Radiation reaction and renormalization in classical electrodynamics of point particle in any dimension, *Phys. Rev. D* **66**, 025017 (2002).
27. Y. Yaremko, Self-force in 2+1 electrodynamics, *J. Phys. A* **40**, 13161 (2007).
28. E. Shuryak, H. U. Yee and I. Zahed, Self-force and synchrotron radiation in odd space-time dimensions, *Phys. Rev. D* **85**, 104007 (2012).
29. J. Hadamard, *Lectures on Cauchy's Problem in Linear Partial Differential Equations* (Dover Publications, New York, 2014).
30. R. Courant and D. Hilbert, *Methods of Mathematical Physics: Partial Differential Equations*, Wiley Classics Library (Wiley, New York, 2008).
31. D. Ivanenko and A. Sokolov, *Sov. Phys. Dokl.* **36**, 37 (1940); *Classical Field Theory* (State Publishing House of Technical and Theoretical Literature, Moscow, 1951) (in Russian) [*Klassische Feldtheorie* (Akademie-Verlag, Berlin, 1953)].
32. V. Cardoso, O. J. C. Dias and P. Figueras, Gravitational radiation in d>4 from effective field theory, *Phys. Rev. D* **78**, 105010 (2008).
33. W. D. Goldberger and I. Z. Rothstein, An Effective field theory of gravity for extended objects, *Phys. Rev. D* **73**, 104029 (2006).
34. W. D. Goldberger, Les Houches lectures on effective field theories and gravitational radiation, [arXiv:hep-ph/0701129 [hep-ph]].
35. S. Weinberg, *Gravitation and Cosmology*, (Wiley, New York, 1972).
36. M. Maggiore, *Gravitational Waves. Vol. 1: Theory and Experiments*, (OUP, Oxford, 2007).
37. F. Rohrlich, The definition of electromagnetic radiation, *Nuovo Cim* **21**, 811 (1961).
38. F. Rohrlich, *Classical Charged Particles* (World Scientific, Singapore, 2007).
39. C. Teitelboim, Splitting of the maxwell tensor - radiation reaction without advanced fields, *Phys. Rev. D* **1**, 1572 (1970) [erratum: *Phys. Rev. D* **2**, 1763 (1970)].
40. D. V. Gal'tsov and P. Spirin, Radiation reaction reexamined: Bound momentum and Schott term, *Grav. Cosmol.* **12**, 1 (2006).
41. B. P. Kosyakov, Radiation in electrodynamics and in Yang-Mills theory, *Sov. Phys. Usp.* **35**, 135 (1992).
42. P. A. Spirin, Massless field emission in the space-time of extra dimensions, *Grav. Cosmol.* **15**, 82 (2009).
43. D. V. Gal'tsov and M. Khlopunov, Synchrotron radiation in odd dimensions, *Phys. Rev. D* **101**, no. 8, 084054 (2020).
44. M. E. Pati and C. M. Will, PostNewtonian gravitational radiation and equations of motion via direct integration of the relaxed Einstein equations. 1. Foundations, *Phys. Rev. D* **62**, 124015 (2000).
45. Y. Z. Chu, Electromagnetic and Gravitational Radiation in All Dimensions: A Classical Field Theory Treatment, [arXiv:2107.14744 [gr-qc]].

Developments in numerical relativity and gravitational wave observations

Nigel T. Bishop

Department of Mathematics (Pure and Applied), Rhodes University,
Makhanda 6139, South Africa
E-mail: n.bishop@ru.ac.za
www.ru.ac.za

This paper provides a summary of the fourteen talks that were presented in the session GW4 on various aspects of numerical relativity and computation concerning gravitational waves.

Keywords: Numerical relativity, gravitational waves

1. Introduction

A total of fourteen talks were presented over two days, covering a number of different topics within numerical relativity and computation concerning gravitational waves (GWs). Since the authors of each talk are publishing their work in these Proceedings or elsewhere, the purpose of this article is not to present any of the technical details of the talks. Rather, this session summary is aimed at presenting an overview of, and background information about, the various topics covered. As such, it is intended to be accessible to those working on other aspects of general realativty and astrophysics.

2. Inclusion of null infinity

Numerical relativity simulations of events such as compact object mergers, are normally carried out in a finite region, and the GW emission is estimated from the geometry near the outer boundary. However, because of the nonlinear nature of the Einstein equations, GWs are unambiguously defined only at future null infinity. Now the Einstein equations have the property that they can be compactified in a radial null direction and remain regular, so there are numerical approaches that compute GWs at future null infinity. The method commonly utilized is known as characteristic extraction, in which geometric data near the outer boundary of a merger simulation is used to provide boundary data to a characteristic code, i.e. one in which the spacetime is foliated by outgoing null cones. An alternative approach uses hyperboloidal slicing, in which the spacetime slices are spacelike in the central region, and become asymptotically null in the far region; however, this approach is less developed and has not yet produced gravitational waveforms.

Giannakopoulos et al.[1,2] presented results concerning the well-posedness of the Einstein equations in characteristic coordinates. In partial differential equation (PDE) theory, well-posedness in the standard L_2 norm is characterized by a system that is strongly (or symmetric) hyperbolic. However, it was shown that the characteristic Einstein equations form a PDE system that is only weakly hyperbolic. Further, it was demonstrated, using numerical examples, that weak hyperbolicity can have the effect of reducing the order of convergence of a code from that expected from considerations of the truncation error.

Gautam et al.[3] discussed a dual foliation formulation on hyperboloidal slices. There has been much effort over many years to implement a successful hyperboloidal scheme, but there remain problems of instability and of the need to regularize quantities that can become unbounded at null infinity. The essential idea presented is that these problems can be resolved by making a nonlinear change of variables, and the approach has been tested and shown to work in the special case of spherical symmetry. The approach is currently being extended to the general case, and if successful, this would be a significant achievement.

3. Surrogate models

Surrogate models have become an essential tool in searches in detector data for GWs from binary black hole mergers. Numerical relativity provides the most accurate waveforms, but they are computationally expensive and can take over a month for a single waveform. Since the merger phase space has, in principle, up to 7 dimensions, it is not feasible to populate it with numerical relativity waveforms. A surrogate waveform can be regarded as a mapping from (a restricted part of) the merger phase space to give a waveform. The quality of the model depends on how the mapping function is parametrized, and then fixing the parameter values so as to be consistent with known numerical relativity waveforms.

Islam et al.[4] reported a surrogate model for waveforms produced when the orbit is eccentric rather than circular. Eccentricity has long been neglected in waveform calculations, because it is well known that the reaction to GW emission damps out eccentricity at a rate that is much faster than that of the inspiral. However, there are possible astrophysical scenarios which could lead to the orbit being eccentric near merger, and the identification of such an event would be significant in terms of the understanding of formation channels of binary black hole systems. The model reported is restricted, at this stage, to non-spinning equal-mass black hole binary systems.

4. Effect of matter on GW propagation

As GWs pass through matter, some energy will be transferred to the matter causing the GW to be attenuated, but in astrophysical scenarios this effect is so small that it has been completely negelcted. However, recent work has shown that matter can affect GW propagation in other ways, i.e. as a phase shift or as an echo. The possibility of a GW echo is interesting because there are (controversial) reports that echoes have been observed in GW data, caused by the remnant being some form of exotic compact object (ECO).

Naidoo et al.[5] applied a model of a GW source inside a shell of matter to GW events for which there are claims of echo observations. It was shown that any echo could not have been produced by the effect of a matter shell, since if it were the shell would have to be so massive as to constitute a black hole. Thus, confirmation of an echo in GW data would provide evidence in favour of the ECO hypothesis. However, it was also shown that there are astrophysical events, such as a binary neutron star merger and especially a core collapse supernova, for which the echo and phase-shift effects would alter the GW signal sufficiently for the difference to be measurable.

5. Hadron-quark phase transition in a binary neutron star merger

During the merger of two neutron stars, the matter becomes denser than nuclear matter and with a temperature of order $10^{12}\,°K$, and it is feasible that a phase transition from hadronic matter to quark matter may occur. Such a phase transition would change the effective equation of state, and therefore would affect the motion of the matter and thus the emitted GW signal.

Hanauske et al.[6] considers whether a hadron-quark phase transition could lead to an observational signature of the event in the GW signal.[7–10] Computational models for a number of possible post-merger scenarios are constructed, and results obtained for the GW signal in runs to about 20ms. The results show that an increase in the frequency of the post-merger GW signal would indicate the occurrence of a phase transition.

6. Alternative theories of gravity

General relativity is consistent with every observation and experiment to date. However, there are reasons for investigating alternative theories. General relativity is not consistent with quantum mechanics, so it needs to be modified in a way that would affect its properties at a very small scale. On the other hand, at the very large scale of cosmology, the issues of the unknown nature of dark matter and dark energy may be resolved by using an alternative theory. Clearly, any alternative theory would need to be consistent with observations including those by LIGO/Virgo, and that motivates the need to calculate GW emission from compact object coalescence in the theory.

Lim et al.[11] reported the construction of a numerical code for an effective field theory with a Lagrangian that is that of general relativity plus terms that are quadratic in the Ricci tensor. The resulting field equations involve up to 4th order derivatives. The code uses the harmonic gauge, and is restricted to the case of spherical symmetry. It has been tested with initital data that is Minkowski or Schwarzschild plus noise, and has been shown to be stable and convergent.

Khlopunov et al.[12] calculates the GW emission due to a system of two point masses on a 3-brane embedded in a 5-dimensional spacetime, using analytical methods. In the non-relativistic limit, a generalization of the quadrupole formula is obtained.

7. GW memory

The memory effect in GW theory is well-known. Consider a system of free particles, each particle being at rest relative to the others, in a region of spacetime that can be regarded as initially Minkowskian. Supose that the particles are now perturbed by GWs, and that afterwards the spacetime region is again Minkowskian. Then the particles will be at rest relative to each other, but in general the positions of the particles relative to each other will have changed.

Grant et al.[13,14] generalizes the memory concept to the case that the particles have initial relative velocity and acceleration (due to forces other than gravity), and obtains formulas in terms of the GWs and non-radiative quantities for the memory-like changes to these quantities. In the case of zero relative velocity and acceleration, the formulas reduce to what is already known.

8. Searches for intermediate mass black hole (IMBH) mergers in GW data

IMBHs are usually defined as being in the mass range $10^2 M_\odot \leq M \leq 10^5 M_\odot$. They are less massive than the supermassive black holes at galactic centres, and too massive to have been formed by stellar collapse, because the pair instability gap means that stellar collapse cannot produce a black hole in the mass range $50 M_\odot \lesssim M \lesssim 130 M_\odot$. The event GW190521 is estimated to have been caused by the merger of black holes with approximate masses $85 M_\odot$ and $66 M_\odot$ yielding a remnant with mass about $142 M_\odot$, providing conclusive evidence for the existence of IMBHs. This observation has motivated searches that focus on identifying IMBH events in LIGO/Virgo data.

PyCBC is a free and open software package used to search for GW events in detector data. Chandra et al.[15] reported a PyCBC-based search that is optimized to identify IMBH events. The search re-identified GW190521 with a much better false alarm rate than that of the original search.

Gayathri et al.[16] presented, on behalf of the LIGO, Virgo and KAGRA collaborations, the results of their searches for IMBH events in the observing period O3.

9. Searches for a GW signal of a spinning neutron star

An object spinning with frequency f, unless it is exactly axisymmetric, emits GWs at frequency $2f$. Pulsars are spinning neutron stars that emit regular radio pulses, and thus have rotational frequencies that are accurately determined. However, searches for GW signals from a number of pulsars have not yielded any positive result, and have only been able to place upper bounds on the magnitude of such signals. It is well-known that glitches occur in the radio pulses, indicating that some form of deformation is occurring in the neutron star. Thus it can be expected that there are periods of time during which the neutron star would be emitting GWs, but when such periods occur and their duration is not known.

Fesik et al.[17,18] presented a method for localising a long-duration signal in GW data, that is, to estimate the start time and duration of the signal. The method applies when the signal duration is much longer than the wave period, so more than a few hours. This knowledge can then be used to improve the signal-to-noise ratio of the recovered signal.

10. Machine learning

In recent years, the use of machine learning has become more and more commonplace throughout science, and this certainly includes applications to GW calculations and GW data analysis. The key advantages of machine learning are that: (a) in many circumstances it has proven to be remarkably accurate; and (b) there are now a number of software packages available, so from a user perspective, implementation can be straightforward. A common application of machine learning is the construction of a function that maps an input vector $\mathbf{x}$ to an output vector $\mathbf{y}$, i.e $\mathbf{y} = \mathcal{F}(\mathbf{x})$. We need to know the expected output $\mathbf{z}_i$ in a number of cases, and then construct $\mathcal{F}$ by minimizing the error $||\mathbf{z}_i - \mathbf{y}_i||$; this process is called *training* the network, and the quality of the network is described by the magnitude of the error, particularly for data points that are not used in the training.

Mishra[19] applied machine learning to search for a coherent WaveBurst in GW detector data. The network is trained on calculated waveforms of binary black hole mergers; the complete waveform is not used, but rather certain statistics representing the waveform are calculated, and these are used for the training. The resulting network is reported to improve the detection of binary black hole merger events by between 15% and 25%.

Field et al.[20,21] use machine learning to determine orbital dynamics of binary black hole systems from GW measurements. The system is written in the form of a universal differential equation, $\dot{\mathbf{x}} = \mathcal{F}(\mathbf{x})$, where $\mathbf{x}$ is a vector with components representing various aspects of the system dynamics. Once a choice of $\mathcal{F}$ is made, $\mathbf{x}$ is determined and then the quadrupole formula is applied to find the emitted GWs. Given observed (or numerically calculated) GW data from a binary black hole system, the next step is network training, i.e. to find $\mathcal{F}$ by minimizing the mismatch between this data and that associated with the choice made for $\mathcal{F}$. It was found that this model makes quite accurate waveform predictions outside the time interval over which the model is trained.

References

1. Thanasis Giannakopoulos, Nigel T. Bishop, David Hilditch, Denis Pollney and Miguel Zilhao, *Hyperbolicity of General Relativity in null foliations*, Book of Abstracts, p. 325 (2021).
2. Thanasis Giannakopoulos, David Hilditch and Miguel Zilhao, *Hyperbolicity of General Relativity in Bondi-like gauges*, Phys. Rev. D **102**, 064035 (2020).
3. Shalabh Gautam, Alex Vañó-Viñuales, Edgar Gasperin, David Hilditch and Sukanta Bose, *Einstein Field Equations in Spherical Symmetry on Hyperboloidal Slices: Dual Foliation Formulation*, Book of Abstracts, p. 324 (2021).
4. Tousif Islam, Vijay Varma, Jackie Lodman, Scott Field, Gaurav Khanna, Mark Scheel, Harald Pfeiffer, David Gerosa and Lawrence Kidder, *Eccentric binary black hole surrogate models for the gravitational waveform andremnant properties: comparable mass, nonspinning case*, Book of Abstracts, p. 328 (2021).
5. M Naidoo, Nigel T. Bishop and Petrus van der Walt, *Matter shells modifying gravitational wave signals*, Book of Abstracts, p. 328, and in these Proceedings (2021).
6. Matthias Hanauske, Gloria Montana, Lukas Weih and Luciano Rezzolla, *Gravitational-wave signatures of the hadron-quark phase transition in binary compact star mergers*, Book of Abstracts, p. 326 (2021).
7. M. Hanauske and L. R. Weih, *Neutron star collisions and gravitational waves*, Astronomische Nachrichten **342**, 788 (June 2021).
8. L. R. Weih, M. Hanauske and L. Rezzolla, *Postmerger Gravitational-Wave Signatures of Phase Transitions in Binary Mergers*, Physical review letters **124**, p. 171103 (May 2020).
9. E. R. Most, L. J. Papenfort, V. Dexheimer, M. Hanauske, S. Schramm, H. Stöcker and L. Rezzolla, *Signatures of Quark-Hadron Phase Transitions in General-Relativistic Neutron-Star Mergers*, Physical review letters **122**, p. 061101 (February 2019).
10. G. Montaña, L. Tolós, M. Hanauske and L. Rezzolla, *Constraining twin stars with GW170817*, Physical Review D **99**, p. 103009 (May 2019).
11. Hyun Lim and Aaron Held, *Dynamics of Quadratic Gravity in Spherical Symmetry*, Book of Abstracts, p. 323 (2021).
12. Mikhail Khlopunov and Dmitry Galtsov, *Odd-dimensional gravitational waves from the binary system on three-brane*, Book of Abstracts, p. 329, and in these Proceedings (2021).
13. Alexander Grant and David Nichols, *Memory-like effects due to relative velocity and acceleration*, Book of Abstracts, p. 327 (2021).
14. Alexander Grant and David Nichols, *Persistent gravitational wave observables: Curve deviation in asymptotically flat spacetimes*, https://arxiv.org/abs/2109.03832 (2021).
15. Koustav Chandra, Veronica Villa-Ortega, Thomas Dent, Connor McIsaac, Archana Pai, Ian Harry, Gareth Davies and Kanchan Soni, *An optimised PyCBC search for gravitational waves from intermediate-mass black hole mergers*, Book of Abstracts, p. 324, and in these Proceedings (2021).
16. V. Gayathri, The LIGO Scientific Collaboration, The Virgo Collaboration and The KAGRA Collaboration, *Intermediate mass black hole search in LIGO-Virgo's third observing period*, Book of Abstracts, p. 325 (2021).
17. Liudmila Fesik and Maria Alessandra Papa, *Localisation of a long-duration gravitational wave signal in time*, Book of Abstracts, p. 327 (2021).
18. Liudmila Fesik and Maria Alessandra Papa, *The detectability of long-duration gravitational wave signals*, Book of Abstracts, p. 327 (2021).

19. Tanmaya Mishra, *Optimization of model independent gravitational wave search using machine learning*, Book of Abstracts, p. 326 (2021).
20. Scott Field, Brendan Keith and Akshay Khadse, *Learning orbital dynamics of binary black hole systems from gravitational wave measurements*, Book of Abstracts, p. 323 (2021).
21. Brendan Keith, Akshay Khadse and Scott E. Field, *Learning orbital dynamics of binary black hole systems from gravitational wave measurements*, Phys. Rev. Research **3**, 043101 (2021).

Insights into the Galactic Center environment from VHE gamma-ray observations with ground-based facilities

C. Fruck*

Physics Department, Technical University Munich,
James-Franck-Str. 1, 85748, Garching, Germany
E-mail: cfruck@ph.tum.de
www.ph.tum.de

The dynamic center of our galaxy is known to host a source of TeV gamma rays since the very beginning of the 21st century and a link to the supermassive black hole at the Galactic Center has been speculated on ever since. But not only the point-like source, spatially coincident with SgrA*, can be observed from the ground using the Imaging Air Cherenkov Telescope technique, but also diffuse emission from the vicinity, spanning more than one degree along the Galactic plane and emitting a remarkably hard energy spectrum, reaching energies well beyond 10 TeV.

Recent observations by the H.E.S.S., MAGIC and VERITAS facilities have enabled detailed studies of the dynamics of high-energy particles in Galactic Center region that indicate a link between the diffuse component and central point-like gamma-ray source. These studies suggest the presence of a powerful cosmic-ray accelerator in close proximity to SgrA*. This could potentially even be one of the long-sought-after Galactic PeVatrons, needed in order to explain the cosmic-ray spectrum up to the the feature called 'knee' at around 10^{15} eV.

Keywords: Galactic Center, SMBH, VHE gamma-ray astronomy

1. Introduction

The Milky Way Galaxy falls into the category of bared spiral galaxies, with a moderate star forming rate within the spiral arms and a significantly lower star forming rate inside the bar and bulge, towards its dynamic center. The bar and bulge span 1.5 and 4.4 kpc in size, respectively, while the the galactic disk extends over more than 30 kpc. A much smaller region at the center of the Galactic bulge contains a much higher density of young stars when compared to the surrounding regions. Such a high star-formation rate can only be maintained by a high density of molecular gas in this region, which is referred to as the Central Molecular Zone (CMZ) of the Milky Way Galaxy. The high star formation rate inside the CMZ is also the reason for the high density of high energy astrophysical phenomena being observed in this area of the sky. Those include pulsar wind nebulae (PWN), supernova remnants (SNR)[1] and presumably also millisecond pulsars (MSP).[2] All those types of

---

*Now at: Deutsches Zentrum für Luft- und Raumfahrt, Institut für Physik der Atmosphäre, Oberpfaffenhofen, Germany

objects can potentially accelerate charged particles to TeV energies and beyond, which can in turn produce very high energy (VHE) gamma rays through secondary processes like Bremsstrahlung or inverse Compton scattering in case of electrons or deep inelastic scattering in case of protons.

Another potential source of VHE gamma rays is the strong accumulation of dark matter (DM) that is expected around the Galactic Center (GC).[3] Some models predict DM particles to interact or decay with gamma-rays in the final state. The high expected DM density at the GC, paired with its relative proximity makes it one of the prime observational targets for indirect DM searches.[4] Strong foregrounds from astrophysical sources on the other hand complicate the search.

At the very center of the Milky Way Galaxy's rotation, spanning less than a 0.1 pc in size, resides the so-called S-star cluster with numerous O and B-type stars, whose rapid movement can be traced over a time scale of years with high resolution observations in the infrared.[5] The velocity of these stars and the tight elliptical orbits around a common dynamical center allow to quantify the central mass concentration, $\approx 4.4 \cdot 10^6 \, M_\odot$, and to exclude nearly all other explanations, except for the presence of a super-massive black hole (SMBH) at the dynamic center of our galaxy.[5] This mass concentration is spatially consistent with the point-like radio source SgrA*,[6] thus probably caused by non-thermal emission from the vicinity of the black hole (BH). The gravitational radius of such a BH would be

$$r_G = \frac{2\,G\,M}{c^2} = 1.3 \cdot 10^{12} \text{cm} \approx 10\,\mu\,\text{arcsec}, \quad (1)$$

which is within reach for the most ambitious very-long-baseline interferometry (VLBI) campaigns, such as the *Event Horizon Telescope* (EHT) that utilizes a global network of radio telescopes.[7]

SgrA* is also visible in X-ray,[8] adding further evidence for non-thermal processes being at work and the acceleration of charged particles to high energies. In radio, infrared, as well as in X-rays, SgrA* shows minute to day-scale variability, changing its brightness over several orders of magnitude.[9,10] These observations indicate that the site of emission of non-thermal radiation must be comparable to the size of the BH itself and thus likely located in close proximity to the event horizon. Also from X-ray observations, echoes on the scale of tens of parsecs have been identified within the surrounding structures of dense gas. These are believed to stem from past very strong X-ray flares caused by SgrA*, now visible as echoes that can be seen traveling through the surrounding environment over a time scale of several years.[11] Another hint for an episode in the more distant past of strongly increased intensity of acceleration of high energy charged particles at the Galactic Center are the giant bubble-like structures found in X-rays[12] and gamma rays,[13] extending far outside the galactic disk in both directions. These structures can not be directly linked to SgrA* with certainty, but could potentially be the result of increased accretion activity onto the GC black hole.

2. VHE Gamma-Ray Observations from the Ground

The very dense and active astrophysical environment within the CMZ and especially the link between the SMBH, the closest to Earth by a large margin) and non-thermal processes visible in radio and X-ray, make the GC a very interesting target for observations in gamma rays. The *Fermi* large area telescope (LAT) in low earth orbit since 2008 is the most sensitive all-sky detector for gamma-rays in the energy range between 100 MeV and about 1 TeV.[14] While the GC hosts strong sources found also in the the *Fermi* source catalog, including a point source coincident with SgrA*,[15] the spatial resolution in the energy range around 10 GeV below is rather poor, while the effective collection area needed to cope with the low flux above that energy, is way large than the only about 1 m^2 offered by *Fermi*.

This is where ground-based facilities come into play, that in fact predate *Fermi* by more than a decade. The most successful class of ground-based instruments for observations in the very high energy (VHE) range between about 50 GeV and 100 TeV are so-called imaging air Cherenkov telescopes (IACTs). IACTs detect short ($\approx$ 3 ns long) and faint (hundred to a couple of ten thousand photons collected by the telescope) flashes of Cherenkov light produced in extensive air showers produced by gamma-rays interacting with the atmosphere generating charged leptons. These Cherenkov light flashes, mostly generated in the lower stratosphere and high troposphere, illuminate an area of several ten thousand m^2 on the ground at sea level. The light is collected by optical telescopes with simple geometry but large mirror area and fast as well as sensitive cameras, capable of time resolution on the order of nanoseconds. The reconstruction of the original direction of the VHE photons is strongly helped by employing stereoscopy and observing the same event with two or more telescopes placed within the light pool. The technique was pioneered by the Whipple[16] and HEGRA[17] instruments, but became a more established branch of astronomy with the next generation of telescopes. The three most important of those installations are the H.E.S.S.,[18] MAGIC[19] and VERITAS[20] experiments, located in Namibia, La Palma and the US, respectively.

The first detection of the GC in VHE gamma rays was already made with Whipple in 2004,[21] quickly followed up by detections with H.E.S.S. (2004)[22] and MAGIC (2006).[23] Later deep observations by H.E.S.S. have reveled further details of the GC VHE emission. In 2006, after subtracting the point sources at SgrA* and G0.9+0.1, the presence of diffuse emission throughout the CMZ has been reveled, spanning about 200 pc in width along the Galactic plane. The emission has been attributed to high energy protons interacting with the dense molecular clouds in the region.[24] The position estimate of the Galactic Center point source could be greatly refined, far below the gamma-ray PSF of the instrument. This lead to the exclusion of the SNR SgrA East as other potential source apart from SgrA*.[25] The spectral shape of the GC point source has been measured with high precision, yielding an index of around 2.2 and an exponential cut off at $\approx$ 10 TeV.[26]

3. Recent Observational Results

The recent increased interest that the GC received in VHE gamma rays has been sparked by the discovery of a gas cloud in 2011, on a highly eccentric orbit towards SgrA* in infrared, that led to speculations about a potential increase in accretion rate and possibly also flaring activity of the non-thermal emission of the object.[27] The pericenter passage was predicted to happen in 2013/14 with possible effects on the accretion rate around the time or later.[28] These revelations lead to a multi-year observation campaign by MAGIC, starting in 2012 and leading to a publication of the results covering the first four years of monitoring the gamma-ray source.[29] No variability of the GC point source has been detected until 2015, neither at energies above 1 TeV, nor at higher energies above 10 TeV, where some hadronic emission models predict a much faster reaction of the gamma-ray flux to newly injected particles compared to lower energy gamma rays.[30]

In 2016 the H.E.S.S. collaboration probed the extended emission from the Galactic Ridge in great detail, reveling that in contrast to the spectrum of the point-source, the gamma-ray spectrum emitted by this region reaches more than 30 TeV in energy without a hint for a cut-off.[31] Assuming proton-proton interactions as source for the emission, proton energies would thus not cut off before reaching around 1 PeV in energy. Another important finding from those observations is that the flux density of protons required to explain the observed gamma-ray emission profile, under the assumption of a density profile of molecular gas from CO emissions, best fits a $1/r$ shape, where r is the distance from the location of SgrA*.[31] Such an observation is compatible with cosmic rays (CRs) being accelerated in the vicinity of SgrA* and undergoing diffusion processes on their path away from the source. Combining both of those observations provides evidence that the GC might indeed host a Galactic PeVatron, potentially even linked to the SMBH SgrA*.

These findings were largely confirmed in 2020 by a new analysis of a large set of MAGIC data collected around the GC and CMZ. A new data analysis tool (SkyPrism[32]) for extended sources that allows fitting of 2D spatial models to gamma-ray sky maps binned in energy, similar to what is done by the *Fermi* tools,[33] was utilized for this analysis. This way individual energy spectra for 3 point-like (SgrA*, the PWN G0.9+01 and a recently discovered source inside the Galactic Radio Arc) and one extended source (the diffuse Galactic Ridge emission) could be extracted.[34] The energy spectrum of the diffuse component, in contrast to earlier findings by H.E.S.S., in this case shows a 2σ hint for a cut-off at around 20 TeV. It should however be noted that the regions probed and the methods used differ for both results. While the H.E.S.S. analysis extracted events from a cut anulus with inner radius of 0.1 and outer radius of 0.4 degrees around SgrA* and excluding the Arc source ("pacman" region),[31] the MAGIC analysis used a CS radio map that extends about 1.4 degrees and 0.8 along the Galactic plane as spatial template for this emission component.[34] Earlier in 2018 in second H.E.S.S publication concerning the gamma-ray emission from the CMZ, a similar extraction region has been used for the spectrum of the diffuse component, showing a spectral shape compatible to the one found with MAGIC, exhibiting a similar downward trend above 10 TeV but not further commenting on it. Also the roughly $1/r$ spatial profile of the underlying proton flux density has been confirmed by MAGIC,[34] tending to somewhat higher values of α (≈ 1.2), especially when assuming an underlying constant CR-sea component in addition to the $1/r^\alpha$ profile.

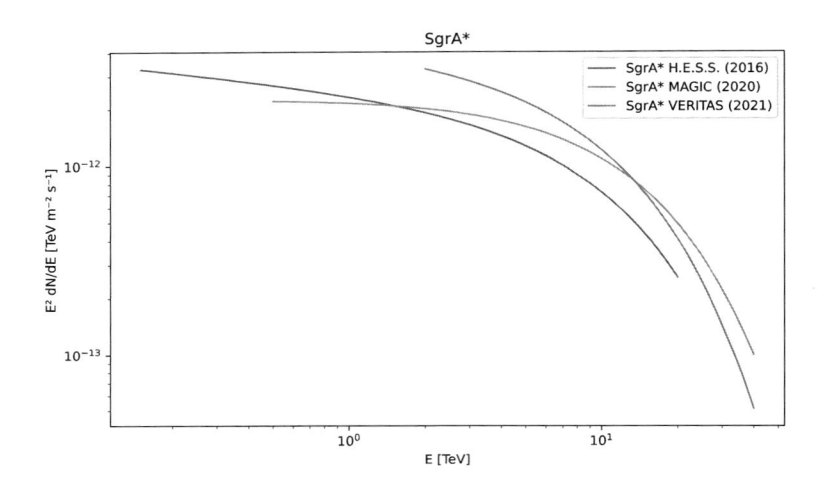

Fig. 1. Best fit SEDs of the point source coincident with SgrA* measured with H.E.S.S.,[31] MAGIC[34] and VERITAS.[35]

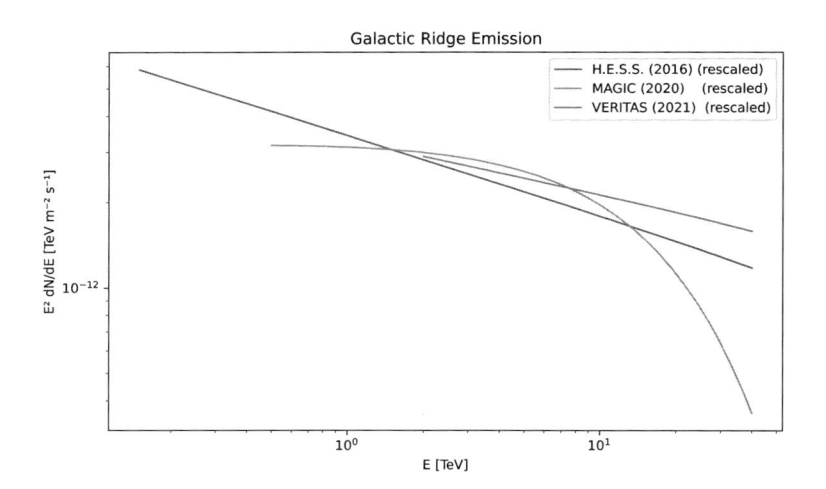

Fig. 2. Best fit SEDs of the Galactic Ridge emission measured with H.E.S.S.,[1] MAGIC[34] and VERITAS.[35]

The latest results of the current VERITAS GC observation campaign have been published in 2021, showing a nearly 10 y light curve of SgrA*, without a hint for variability, neither at energies above 2 TeV, nor above 5 TeV.[35] This study also presented an energy spectrum of the diffuse emission from the CMZ, extracted from Circular regions along the Galactic plane, but avoiding close proximity to SgrA*. Despite the complementary nature compared to the "pacman" region probed by H.E.S.S. (2016)[31] and the overlap with H.E.S.S. (2018)[1] and MAGIC (2020),[34] here no hint for a cut-off has been detected, with the spectrum continuing with an index around -2.2 until 30 TeV.

The best-fit spectral energy distributions (SEDs) from recent observations of the Galactic Center region[1,31,34,35] are illustrated in Figures 1 (spectrum of SgrA*) and 2 (Galactic Ridge). The SEDs measured for the Galactic Ridge have been slightly re-scaled in flux for better comparison, as not all correspond to the exact same extraction region. The Galactic Ridge spectra measured with H.E.S.S. and VERITAS have been fitted with a power law, while the MAGIC spectrum corresponds to a power law with exponential cut-off.

4. Conclusions and Outlook

The VERITAS result[35] highlights once more that the debate about the nature of the GC gamma-ray source and and CR accelerator is still open and further observations are necessary in order to gain even better insight to the underlying physics. It is unclear weather the current generation of Cherenkov telescopes are sufficient for the task at hand, or if new discoveries will mainly rely on the next generation of IACTs, the telescopes of the Cherenkov Telescope Array (CTA) currently under construction.[36] Also instruments utilizing the water Cherenkov technique like the recently commissioned HAWC[37] and LHAASO[38] could play an important role in the future. While on one hand lacking the angular resolution, those instruments do not suffer from the limited field of view of IACTs and can accumulate vast amounts of data with relatively low irreducible background. This makes them perfectly suited for putting the GC and CMZ into context with the larger scale emission from the rest of the Galactic plane. Being located on the northern hemisphere, HAWC and LHAASO themselves are not ideally suited for the task, but the upcoming Southern Wide-Field Gamma-Ray Observatory (SWGO) might well be.[39]

References

1. H. E. S. S. Collaboration *et al.*, Characterising the VHE diffuse emission in the central 200 parsecs of our Galaxy with H.E.S.S., *Astronomy and Astrophysics* **612**, p. A9 (April 2018).
2. R. Bartels, S. Krishnamurthy and C. Weniger, Strong Support for the Millisecond Pulsar Origin of the Galactic Center GeV Excess, *Physical Review Letters* **116**, p. 051102 (February 2016).
3. O. Y. Gnedin and J. R. Primack, Dark Matter Profile in the Galactic Center, *Physical Review Letters* **93**, p. 061302 (August 2004).

4. L. Bergström, P. Ullio and J. H. Buckley, Observability of gamma rays from dark matter neutralino annihilations in the Milky Way halo, *Astroparticle Physics* **9**, 137 (August 1998).
5. R. Genzel, F. Eisenhauer and S. Gillessen, The Galactic Center massive black hole and nuclear star cluster, *Reviews of Modern Physics* **82**, 3121 (December 2010).
6. K. Y. Lo, D. C. Backer, R. D. Ekers, K. I. Kellermann, M. Reid and J. M. Moran, On the size of the galactic centre compact radio source: diameter <20 AU, *Nature* **315**, 124 (May 1985).
7. D. Castelvecchi, How to hunt for a black hole with a telescope the size of Earth, *Nature* **543**, 478 (March 2017).
8. F. K. Baganoff *et al.*, Rapid X-ray flaring from the direction of the supermassive black hole at the Galactic Centre, *Nature* **413**, 45 (September 2001).
9. D. Haggard, M. Nynka, B. Mon, N. d. l. C. Hernandez, M. Nowak, C. Heinke, J. Neilsen, J. Dexter, P. C. Fragile, F. Baganoff, G. C. Bower, L. R. Corrales, F. C. Zelati, N. Degenaar, S. Markoff, M. R. Morris, G. Ponti, N. Rea, J. Wilms and F. Yusef-Zadeh, Chandra Spectral and Timing Analysis of Sgr A\ast's Brightest X-Ray Flares, *The Astrophysical Journal* **886**, p. 96 (November 2019).
10. T. Do *et al.*, Unprecedented Near-infrared Brightness and Variability of Sgr A\ast, *The Astrophysical Journal* **882**, p. L27 (September 2019).
11. M. Clavel, R. Terrier, A. Goldwurm, M. R. Morris, G. Ponti, S. Soldi and G. Trap, Echoes of multiple outbursts of Sagittarius A* revealed by Chandra, *Astronomy & Astrophysics* **558**, p. A32 (October 2013).
12. P. Predehl *et al.*, Detection of large-scale X-ray bubbles in the Milky Way halo, *Nature* **588**, 227 (December 2020).
13. M. Su, T. R. Slatyer and D. P. Finkbeiner, Giant Gamma-Ray Bubbles from Fermi-Lat: Active Galactic Nucleus Activity or Bipolar Galactic Wind?, *The Astrophysical Journal* **724**, 1044 (November 2010).
14. W. B. Atwood *et al.*, The large area telescope on the fermi gamma-ray space telescope mission, *The Astrophysical Journal* **697**, 1071 (May 2009).
15. S. Abdollahi *et al.*, Fermi Large Area Telescope Fourth Source Catalog, *The Astrophysical Journal Supplement Series* **247**, p. 33 (March 2020).
16. J. e. a. Kildea, The Whipple Observatory 10m gamma-ray telescope, 1997–2006, *Astroparticle Physics* **28**, 182 (October 2007).
17. H. Collaboration *et al.*, First Results on the Performance of the HEGRA IACT Array, *arXiv:astro-ph/9704098* (April 1997).
18. W. Benbow, The Status and Performance of H.E.S.S., *AIP Conference Proceedings* **745**, 611 (February 2005).
19. J. Aleksić *et al.*, The major upgrade of the MAGIC telescopes, Part I: The hardware improvements and the commissioning of the system, *Astroparticle Physics* **72**, 61 (January 2016).
20. N. Park, Performance of the VERITAS experiment, in *Proceedings of The 34th International Cosmic Ray Conference — PoS(ICRC2015)*, (SISSA Medialab, August 2016).
21. K. Kosack *et al.*, TeV Gamma-Ray Observations of the Galactic Center, *The Astrophysical Journal* **608**, p. L97 (May 2004).
22. F. Aharonian *et al.*, Very high energy gamma rays from the direction of Sagittarius A*, *Astronomy and Astrophysics* **425**, L13 (October 2004).
23. J. Albert *et al.*, Observation of Gamma Rays from the Galactic Center with the MAGIC Telescope, *The Astrophysical Journal* **638**, p. L101 (January 2006).

24. F. Aharonian et al., Discovery of very-high-energy gamma-rays from the Galactic Centre ridge, *Nature* **439**, 695 (February 2006).
25. HESS Collaboration et al., Localizing the VHE gamma-ray source at the Galactic Centre, *Monthly Notices of the Royal Astronomical Society* **402**, 1877 (March 2010).
26. F. Aharonian et al., Spectrum and variability of the Galactic center VHE gamma-ray source HESS J1745–290, *Astronomy & Astrophysics* **503**, 817 (September 2009).
27. S. Gillessen et al., A gas cloud on its way towards the supermassive black hole at the Galactic Centre, *Nature* **481**, 51 (January 2012).
28. S. Gillessen et al., New Observations of the Gas Cloud G2 in the Galactic Center, *The Astrophysical Journal* **763**, p. 78 (January 2013).
29. M. L. Ahnen et al., Observations of Sagittarius A* during the pericenter passage of the G2 object with MAGIC, *Astronomy & Astrophysics* **601**, p. A33 (May 2017).
30. D. R. Ballantyne, M. Schumann and B. Ford, Modelling the time-dependence of the TeV gamma-ray source at the Galactic Centre, *Monthly Notices of the Royal Astronomical Society* **410**, 1521 (January 2011).
31. H. E. S. S. collaboration et al., Acceleration of petaelectronvolt protons in the Galactic Centre, *Nature* **531**, 476 (March 2016).
32. I. Vovk, M. Strzys and C. Fruck, Spatial likelihood analysis for MAGIC telescope data - From instrument response modelling to spectral extraction, *Astronomy & Astrophysics* **619**, p. A7 (November 2018).
33. Fermi Science Support Development Team, Fermitools: Fermi Science Tools, *Astrophysics Source Code Library*, p. ascl:1905.011 (May 2019).
34. V. A. Acciari et al., MAGIC observations of the diffuse gamma-ray emission in the vicinity of the Galactic center, *Astronomy & Astrophysics* **642**, p. A190 (October 2020).
35. C. B. Adams et al., VERITAS Observations of the Galactic Center Region at Multi-TeV Gamma-Ray Energies, *The Astrophysical Journal* **913**, p. 115 (June 2021).
36. J. Knödlseder, The Cherenkov Telescope Array, *arXiv:2004.09213 [astro-ph]* (April 2020).
37. A. U. Abeysekara et al., The 2HWC HAWC Observatory Gamma-Ray Catalog, *The Astrophysical Journal* **843**, p. 40 (June 2017).
38. X. Bai et al., The Large High Altitude Air Shower Observatory (LHAASO) Science White Paper, *arXiv:1905.02773 [astro-ph]* (May 2019).
39. P. Abreu et al., The Southern Wide-Field Gamma-Ray Observatory (SWGO): A Next-Generation Ground-Based Survey Instrument for VHE Gamma-Ray Astronomy, *arXiv:1907.07737 [astro-ph]* (July 2019).

The TAIGA experiment

M. Tluczykont

Institut für Experimentalphysik, Universität Hamburg, Hamburg, D-22 761 Germany
martin.tluczykont@physik.uni-hamburg.de

I.I. Astapov

National Research Nuclear University MEPhI, Moscow, 115409 Russia

A.K. Awad

Institut für Experimentalphysik, Universität Hamburg, Hamburg, D-22 761 Germany

P.A. Bezyazeekov

Research Institute of Applied Physics, Irkutsk State University, Irkutsk, 664003 Russia

M. Blank

Institut für Experimentalphysik, Universität Hamburg, Hamburg, D-22 761 Germany

E.A. Bonvech

Skobeltsyn Institute of Nuclear Physics, Moscow State University, Moscow, 119991 Russia

A.N. Borodin

Joint Institute for Nuclear Research, Dubna, Moscow oblast, 141980 Russia

A.V. Bulan

Skobeltsyn Institute of Nuclear Physics, Moscow State University, Moscow, 119991 Russia

M. Brückner

Deutsches Elektronen-Synchrotron DESY, Zeuthen, 15738 Germany

N.M. Budnev

Research Institute of Applied Physics, Irkutsk State University, Irkutsk, 664003 Russia

A. Chiavassa

Physics Department of the University of Torino and Istituto Nazionale di Fisica Nucleare,
Torino, 10125 Italy

D.V. Chernov

Skobeltsyn Institute of Nuclear Physics, Moscow State University, Moscow, 119991 Russia

A.N. Dyachok

Research Institute of Applied Physics, Irkutsk State University, Irkutsk, 664003 Russia

A.R. Gafarov

Research Institute of Applied Physics, Irkutsk State University, Irkutsk, 664003 Russia

A.Yu. Garmash

Novosibirsk State University, Novosibirsk, 630090 Russia

Budker Institute of Nuclear Physics, Siberian Branch, Russian Academy of Sciences, Novosibirsk, 630090 Russia

V.M. Grebenyuk

Joint Institute for Nuclear Research, Dubna, Moscow oblast, 141980 Russia

Dubna University, Dubna, Moscow oblast, 141980 Russia

O.A. Gress

Research Institute of Applied Physics, Irkutsk State University, Irkutsk, 664003 Russia

E. Gress

Research Institute of Applied Physics, Irkutsk State University, Irkutsk, 664003 Russia

T.I. Gress

Research Institute of Applied Physics, Irkutsk State University, Irkutsk, 664003 Russia

O.G. Grishin

Research Institute of Applied Physics, Irkutsk State University, Irkutsk, 664003 Russia

A.A. Grinyuk

Joint Institute for Nuclear Research, Dubna, Moscow oblast, 141980 Russia

D. Horns

Institut für Experimentalphysik, Universität Hamburg, Hamburg, D-22 761 Germany

A.L. Ivanova

Novosibirsk State University, Novosibirsk, 630090 Russia

Research Institute of Applied Physics, Irkutsk State University, Irkutsk, 664003 Russia

N.N. Kalmykov

Skobeltsyn Institute of Nuclear Physics, Moscow State University, Moscow, 119991 Russia

V.V. Kindin

National Research Nuclear University MEPhI, Moscow, 115409 Russia

S.N. Kiryuhin

Research Institute of Applied Physics, Irkutsk State University, Irkutsk, 664003 Russia

R.P. Kokoulin

National Research Nuclear University MEPhI, Moscow, 115409 Russia

K.G. Kompaniets

National Research Nuclear University MEPhI, Moscow, 115409 Russia

E.E. Korosteleva

Skobeltsyn Institute of Nuclear Physics, Moscow State University, Moscow, 119991 Russia

V.A. Kozhin

Skobeltsyn Institute of Nuclear Physics, Moscow State University, Moscow, 119991 Russia

E.A. Kravchenko

Novosibirsk State University, Novosibirsk, 630090 Russia

Budker Institute of Nuclear Physics, Siberian Branch, Russian Academy of Sciences, Novosibirsk, 630090 Russia

A.P. Kryukov

Skobeltsyn Institute of Nuclear Physics, Moscow State University, Moscow, 119991 Russia

L.A. Kuzmichev

Skobeltsyn Institute of Nuclear Physics, Moscow State University, Moscow, 119991 Russia

A.A. Lagutin

Altai State University, Barnaul, Altai krai, 656049 Russia

M. Lavrova

Joint Institute for Nuclear Research, Dubna, Moscow oblast, 141980 Russia

E. Lemeshev

Research Institute of Applied Physics, Irkutsk State University, Irkutsk, 664003 Russia

B.K. Lubsandorzhiev

Institute for Nuclear Research, Russian Academy of Sciences, Moscow, 117312 Russia

N.B. Lubsandorzhiev

Skobeltsyn Institute of Nuclear Physics, Moscow State University, Moscow, 119991 Russia

A.D. Lukanov

Institute for Nuclear Research, Russian Academy of Sciences, Moscow, 117312 Russia

D.S. Lukyantsev

Research Institute of Applied Physics, Irkutsk State University, Irkutsk, 664003 Russia

R.R. Mirgazov

Research Institute of Applied Physics, Irkutsk State University, Irkutsk, 664003 Russia

R. Mirzoyan

Max Planck Institute for Physics, Munich, 80805 Germany

Research Institute of Applied Physics, Irkutsk State University, Irkutsk, 664003 Russia

R.D. Monkhoev

Research Institute of Applied Physics, Irkutsk State University, Irkutsk, 664003 Russia

E.A. Osipova

Skobeltsyn Institute of Nuclear Physics, Moscow State University, Moscow, 119991 Russia

A.L. Pakhorukov

Research Institute of Applied Physics, Irkutsk State University, Irkutsk, 664003 Russia

A. Pan

Joint Institute for Nuclear Research, Dubna, Moscow oblast, 141980 Russia

L.V. Pankov

Research Institute of Applied Physics, Irkutsk State University, Irkutsk, 664003 Russia

A.D. Panov

Skobeltsyn Institute of Nuclear Physics, Moscow State University, Moscow, 119991 Russia

A.A. Petrukhin

National Research Nuclear University MEPhI, Moscow, 115409 Russia

D.A. Podgrudkov

Skobeltsyn Institute of Nuclear Physics, Moscow State University, Moscow, 119991 Russia

V.A. Poleschuk

Research Institute of Applied Physics, Irkutsk State University, Irkutsk, 664003 Russia

E.G. Popova

Skobeltsyn Institute of Nuclear Physics, Moscow State University, Moscow, 119991 Russia

A. Porelli

Deutsches Elektronen-Synchrotron DESY, Zeuthen, 15738 Germany

E.B. Postnikov

Skobeltsyn Institute of Nuclear Physics, Moscow State University, Moscow, 119991 Russia

V.V. Prosin

Skobeltsyn Institute of Nuclear Physics, Moscow State University, Moscow, 119991 Russia

V.S. Ptuskin

Pushkov Institute of Terrestrial Magnetism, Ionosphere and Radio Wave Propagation, Russian Academy of Sciences, Troitsk, Moscow, 142190 Russia

A.A. Pushnin

Research Institute of Applied Physics, Irkutsk State University, Irkutsk, 664003 Russia

R.I. Raikin

Altai State University, Barnaul, Altai krai, 656049 Russia

A.Y. Razumov

Skobeltsyn Institute of Nuclear Physics, Moscow State University, Moscow, 119991 Russia

G.I. Rubtsov

Institute for Nuclear Research, Russian Academy of Sciences, Moscow, 117312 Russia

E.V. Ryabov

Research Institute of Applied Physics, Irkutsk State University, Irkutsk, 664003 Russia

Y.I. Sagan

Joint Institute for Nuclear Research, Dubna, Moscow oblast, 141980 Russia

Dubna University, Dubna, Moscow oblast, 141980 Russia

V.S. Samoliga

Research Institute of Applied Physics, Irkutsk State University, Irkutsk, 664003 Russia

I. Satyshev

Joint Institute for Nuclear Research, Dubna, Moscow oblast, 141980 Russia

Yu.A. Semeney

Research Institute of Applied Physics, Irkutsk State University, Irkutsk, 664003 Russia

A.A. Silaev

Skobeltsyn Institute of Nuclear Physics, Moscow State University, Moscow, 119991 Russia

A.A. Silaev(junior)

Skobeltsyn Institute of Nuclear Physics, Moscow State University, Moscow, 119991 Russia

A.Yu. Sidorenkov

Institute for Nuclear Research, Russian Academy of Sciences, Moscow, 117312 Russia

A.V. Skurikhin

Skobeltsyn Institute of Nuclear Physics, Moscow State University, Moscow, 119991 Russia

A.V. Sokolov

Novosibirsk State University, Novosibirsk, 630090 Russia

Budker Institute of Nuclear Physics, Siberian Branch, Russian Academy of Sciences, Novosibirsk, 630090 Russia

Y. Suvorkin

Research Institute of Applied Physics, Irkutsk State University, Irkutsk, 664003 Russia

L.G. Sveshnikova

Skobeltsyn Institute of Nuclear Physics, Moscow State University, Moscow, 119991 Russia

V.A. Tabolenko

Research Institute of Applied Physics, Irkutsk State University, Irkutsk, 664003 Russia

A.B. Tanaev

Research Institute of Applied Physics, Irkutsk State University, Irkutsk, 664003 Russia

B.A. Tarashansky

Research Institute of Applied Physics, Irkutsk State University, Irkutsk, 664003 Russia

M. Ternovoy

Research Institute of Applied Physics, Irkutsk State University, Irkutsk, 664003 Russia

L.G. Tkachev

Joint Institute for Nuclear Research, Dubna, Moscow oblast, 141980 Russia

Dubna University, Dubna, Moscow oblast, 141980 Russia

N. Ushakov

Institute for Nuclear Research, Russian Academy of Sciences, Moscow, 117312 Russia

A. Vaidyanathan

Novosibirsk State University, Novosibirsk, 630090 Russia

P.A. Volchugov

Skobeltsyn Institute of Nuclear Physics, Moscow State University, Moscow, 119991 Russia

N.V. Volkov

Altai State University, Barnaul, Altai krai, 656049 Russia

D. Voronin
Institute for Nuclear Research, Russian Academy of Sciences, Moscow, 117312 Russia

R. Wischnewski
Deutsches Elektronen-Synchrotron DESY, Zeuthen, 15738 Germany

I.I. Yashin
National Research Nuclear University MEPhI, Moscow, 115409 Russia

A.V. Zagorodnikov
Research Institute of Applied Physics, Irkutsk State University, Irkutsk, 664003 Russia

D.P. Zhurov
Research Institute of Applied Physics, Irkutsk State University, Irkutsk, 664003 Russia

Irkutsk National Research Technical University, Irkutsk, Russia

The Tunka Advanced Instrument for Gamma-ray and cosmic ray Astrophysics (TAIGA) is a hybrid experiment for the measurement of Extensive Air Showers (EAS) with good spectral resolution in the TeV to PeV energy range. In this domain, the long-sought Pevatrons can be detected. Currently the hybrid TAIGA detector combines two wide angle shower front Cherenkov light sampling timing arrays (HiSCORE and Tunka-133), two 4m class, 10° aperture Imaging Air Cherenkov Telescopes (IACTs) and 240 m^2 surface and underground charged particle detector stations. Our goal is to introduce a new hybrid reconstruction technique, combining the good angular and shower core resolution of HiSCORE with the gamma-hadron separation power of imaging telescopes. This approach allows to maximize the effective area and simultaneously to reach a good gamma-hadron separation at low energies (few TeV). At higher energies, muon detectors are planned to enhance gamma-hadron separation. During the commissioning phase of the first and second IACT, several sources were observed. First detections of known sources with the first telescope show the functionality of the TAIGA IACTs. Here, the status of the TAIGA experiment will be presented, along with first results from the current configuration.

Keywords: Gamma-rays: experiments; Observations: Crab Nebula.

1. Introduction

TAIGA stands for Tunka Advanced Instrument for Gamma-ray and cosmic ray Astrophysics, and is a hybrid instrument designed to access the gamma-ray energy range from approx. 1 TeV to several 100s of TeV. The experiment is located at an altitude of 675m above sea level on the site of the Tunka-133[1] cosmic ray array (51°48'35"N, 103°04'02"E). Observations in this energy range are motivated by several questions of Astroparticle and particle physics. The presence of cosmic ray (CR) accelerators within our Galaxy can be inferred from observations of diffuse and extended gamma-ray emission in the High-Energy (HE)[2] and Very-High-Energy (VHE) range[3–5] e.g. These Gamma-ray emissions result from the decay of neutral pions, which are produced in interactions of the accelerated cosmic rays with the ambient interstellar medium, i.e. molecular gas clouds, which effectively act as CR tracers.[6] The gamma-ray energy range from 10 TeV to few 100 TeV is crucial for the search for the Galactic Pevatrons, which accelerate cosmic ray particles up to knee-energies (approx. 3 PeV proton energy). Due to the typical inelasticity of hadronic interactions, the cutoff energy of Pevatrons in the gamma-ray regime is located at energies of several 100 TeV. Hard gamma-ray spectra in this energy range are much less ambiguously attributable to the hadronic rather than leptonic emission mechanism, because the cross-section for inverse Compton scattering drops with increasing energy (Klein-Nishina regime). Recent neutrino observations[7] and the detection of gamma-rays at ultra high energies by LHAASO[8] emphasize the potential of the search for the Galactic Pevatrons. The detection of Pevatrons, and their spectroscopic, and morphological resolution in their cutoff energy regime are the main physics goals of TAIGA.

Beyond 10^{17} eV, the origin of CR is assumed to be extra-Galactic (EG). Due to the development of intergalactic pair cascades, the accelerators of EG cosmic rays (EGCR) might exhibit a halo-like gamma-ray emission. Furthermore, one can expect an enhancement of EGCR from the local galactic supercluster.[9] The intergalactic pair cascades from that direction could create an anisotropic gamma-ray emission, observable with a wide field of view.

In the energy range of 100 TeV to several PeV, absorption due to pair creation becomes relevant also for Galactic sources. The attenuation of Galactic gamma-ray signals via production of e^+e^--pairs reaches a maximum around 100 TeV from the Galactic interstellar radiation field (IRF) and at 2 PeV from the cosmic microwave background (CMB).[10] This opens up the possibility to measure the density of the IRF, provided the distance of the emitting object is known. At PeV energies, the relevant field is the CMB, which is universal and very well known. Therefore, a possibility might exist to measure distances from a CMB absorption feature, i.e. cutoff in energy spectra of the most energetic Galactic gamma-ray sources. Another variable comes into play when considering the possibility of photon/axion conversion[11] or photon/hidden-photon oscillations,[12] because axions and hidden-photons could propagate without interaction, reconvert to photons, thus reducing the attenuation effect by pair production. Another fundamental effect on the attenuation by pair production might be the modification of the e^+e^- pair production threshold due to Lorentz Invariance violation. In a more direct way, other, non-thermal, dark matter candidates (e.g. wimpzillas) with masses ranging from 10^{12} GeV to 10^{16} GeV can be searched for in the energy range considered.

Furthermore, the chemical composition of Cosmic rays can be measured with TAIGA in the transition range from a Galactic to extragalactic origin ($\approx 10^{15}$ eV to 10^{17} eV) and in the energy range above, where the composition of cosmic rays is still poorly understood.[13] Furthermore, TAIGA will allow measurements of cosmic ray anisotropies beyond 100 TeV primary energy. Finally, observations of EAS can also address fundamental questions of particle physics such as measurements of the proton-proton cross-section, or the search for quark-gluon plasma.

2. The TAIGA Experiment

In the TAIGA experiment, a hybrid approach using different detection techniques is used. While both Cherenkov photon and particle identification are used, the term hybrid also, and foremostly, refers to the hybrid Cherenkov technique. The angle-integrating air shower timing array TAIGA-HiSCORE is combined with the imaging air Cherenkov Telescopes TAIGA-IACT. The timing array is a cost effective method for the instrumentation of very large detector areas, and it provides good angular, core position, and energy resolution in the energy range above few 10s of TeV. The IACTs provide the air shower image shape for good gamma-hadron separation. When used in stand alone mode (i.e. no stereo), one IACT can detect air showers at a distance of 300 m - and more - from the shower core. Both detector components together provide the most relevant key parameters: direction and core from HiSCORE-TAIGA and image shape (width, length) from IACT-TAIGA. Placed at a distance of about 600 m from each other, 4 IACTs can cover a HiSCORE array of more than 1 km² area. It has been shown that using such a hybrid approach with only few IACTs per km², combined with a HiSCORE array, achieves a competitive gamma-hadron separation in the energy range above 10 TeV.[14] At energies higher than 100 TeV, the measurement of the muon component of the EAS using particle detectors on the surface and underground will enhance the gamma-hadron separation further.

Currently, TAIGA consists of a total of 120 HiSCORE stations deployed on an area of 1 km², and two 4 m class imaging air Cherenkov telescopes (IACTs) with a 10° aperture. A third IACT is planned for 2022. The distance between the IACTs was chosen as 300 m in the prototype phase of TAIGA. In future, distances of up to 600 m are planned. Additionally, scintillator stations for charged particle detection with a total surface of 240 m² are deployed above and below ground for the measurement of the muon component of EAS. The layout of the TAIGA-HiSCORE and TAIGA-IACT components is shown in Figure 1. The current TAIGA pilot array is used for a proof of principle of the detector concept. In future, an optimized array layout will take advantage of the hybrid method, that allows larger separations between the individual IACTs.

2.1. *TAIGA-HiSCORE*

HiSCORE is an array of angle-integrating air Cherenkov detector stations, distributed over an area of approximately 1 km². As shown in Figure 1, the stations are arranged in rows offset to each other with inter-station distances of 75 m to 150 m. Each station consists of 4 8 inch (and 10 inch) photomultiplier tubes (PMTs, ElectronTubes and Hamamatsu) with a segmented Winston cone (Alanod 4300UP foil), resulting in a light sensitive area of 0.5 m² per station. The viewing cone of

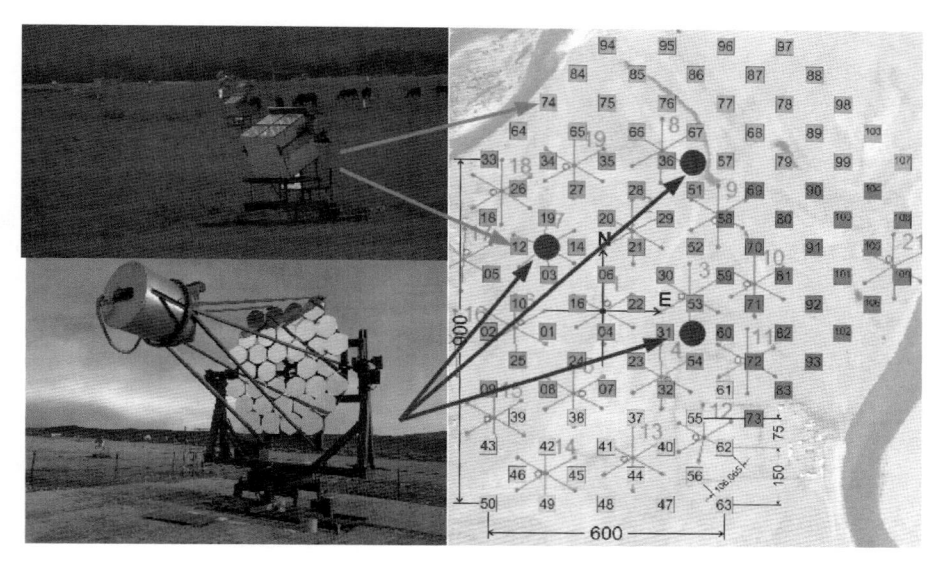

Fig. 1. Layout of the TAIGA-HiSCORE array. Only the HiSCORE and IACT components are shown. The first two IACTs were deployed from 2016 to 2019. The third IACT will be deployed until 2022. The HiSCORE array currently consists of 89 stations and will be extended to 120 stations by the end of 2021.

one station has a diameter of 60°, resulting in an effective field of view of 0.6 sr. An analog summator sums up the signals of all four channels. The sum is used for triggering, and the individual channels are read out with a DRS 4-based 9-channel readout board at a sampling rate of 2 GHz. Four anode signals and four dynode signals (low gain channel) are read out. Channel number 9 is used for time synchronization, based on the sampling of a 100 MHz clock signal. This custom time-synchronization was cross checked with the WhiteRabbit system. It could be verified that the time synchronization works on a level of 0.2 ns relative timing accuracy.[15,16] Each detector station is connected to the central DAQ via optical fibre. The signal traces are processed to extract the amplitude and the timing (half-rise-time, full width half maximum). Based on these parameters, the air shower arrival direction, core impact position, and energy are reconstructed using the methods developed for Tunka-133 and HiSCORE.[1,16,17] Monte Carlo simulations were used to evaluate the detector performance, resulting in resolutions for core position (O(15 m)), energy (20%), and direction (0.1°). Moreover, the serendipituous discovery of a pulsed signal from the CATS lidar onboard the international space station allowed to verify the absolute pointing of the experiment.

2.2. *TAIGA-IACT*

Currently, two IACTs are in operation on the TAIGA site. A third IACT is under construction. The TAIGA IACTs are based on a Davies-Cotton design, with

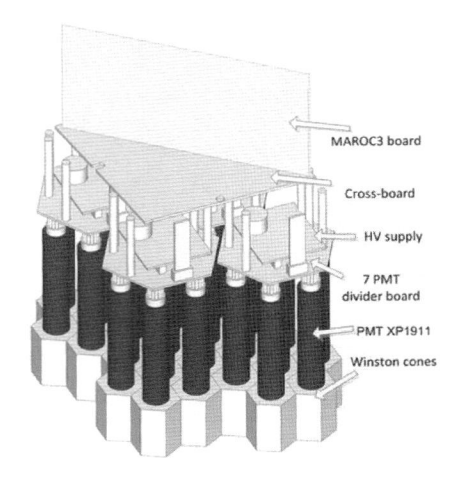

Fig. 2. Layout of a camera cluster of 28 PMTs. The high voltage is supplied to subgroups of 7 pixels. Each cluster is equipped with a MAROC-3 ASIC board.

a tesselated mirror dish of 34 facets with 60 cm diameter each, resulting in a mirror area of about 10 m². Each axis of the alt-az dish mount mechanics is driven by a stepper motor equipped with shaft-encoders for pointing positioning. Additionally, a sky-CCD system is used for pointing calibration. A verification of the absolute pointing accuracy of 0.02°, was carried out by the measurement of the anode current in the central camera PMT-pixel in a drift-scan accross a known bright star position.[18] The PMT camera of IACT-1 consists of 560 XP1911 PMTs (diameter 19mm). The second IACT is equipped with 595 PMTs. Both cameras have a field of view of 9.6° and are placed at the focal point at 4.75 m distance from the respective dishes. For enhanced light collection, and noise suppression from stray light, a Winston Cone plate is attached to the PMT camera plane. The PMTs are organized in clusters of 28 pixels (see Figure 2). All channels are read out with a 64 channel ASIC MAROC-3 board. The board provides a fast shaper which is used for triggering and a slow shaper which is used for read out. The camera electronics for the first two TAIGA-IACT cameras are described elsewhere.[19,20]

Air shower event images, such as shown in Figure 3, are reconstructed using the pixel amplitude distributions in the camera, either based on classical moment analysis,[21] or more advanced machine learning algorithms.[22]

2.3. TAIGA Muon array

The TAIGA-Muon array[23] consists of scintillation counters on a total area of currently 240 m². The muon detector stations are distributed above and below ground. In a future stage, a 5 times larger instrumented area is planned. Each TAIGA muon detector consists of four triangular sectors of scintillator material. The sectors are connected with wavelength shifting bars that guide the light to small PMTs (FEU-85). Measurements of cosmic rays have yielded an average cosmic ray muon amplitude of 31p.e.±20%. The TAIGA-Muon array develops its power

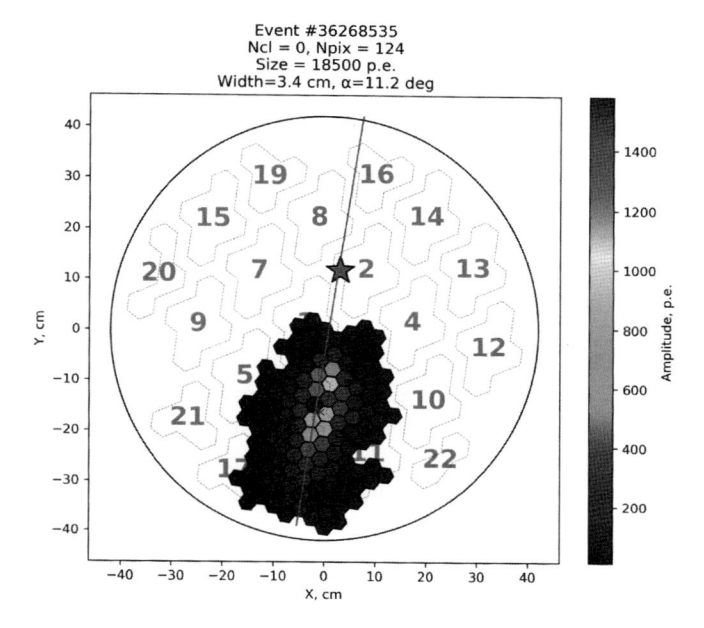

Fig. 3. Real data event for IACT1. The numbered shapes correspond to the above described clusters. The star shows the direction of the air shower event as reconstructed by the HiSCORE array. The total amplitude summed over pixels (size) is 18500 photoelectrons (p.e.). The alpha angle of the major axis is 11.2 degrees, and the measured image with (second image moment) is 0.41 degrees.

at higher energies, starting at about 100 TeV, where the measurement of the muon component of EAS helps in discriminating hadrons from gamma-rays, as well as identifying the nature of the hadronic cosmic rays.

2.4. *Hybrid technique*

A large instrumented detector area is key for accessing very high energies from few TeV to several 100s of TeV. Using only IACTs and the well-established stereoscopic technique requires a large number of channels per instrumented km^2, because firstly, each IACT has a large number of camera channels, and secondly, the IACTs cannot be placed too far away from each other, in order to detect the same EAS in at least two IACTs for stereoscopic reconstruction. As opposed to that, the instrumentation of large areas with a timing array such as HiSCORE is more cost effective, requiring considerably lower number of channels per km^2. However, while gamma-hadron separation is possible with HiSCORE alone to a certain degree (and improving with increasing energy[17]), the separation power stays below the quality reached with IACTs. Therefore, TAIGA implements a novel hybrid technique, taking advantage of the strengths of both Cherenkov techniques. The effective area is maximized using the timing array principle, and the gamma-hadron separation is optimized using the IACTs. More specifically, the strong points of HiSCORE are the directional and core position resolution. The strength of the IACTs is the image shape. The IACTs can be placed so far apart from each other, that each IACT is operated in monoscopic mode, meaning that the Cherenkov lightpool of one air shower event only hits one IACT, as shown in Figure 4. Without requiring a stereoscopic trigger, the effective area of each IACT can be fully exploited and only 4 IACTs are needed in order to cover an area of the order of $1\,\text{km}^2$. The loss of reconstruction quality when using the IACTs in monoscopic mode as compared to stereoscopic mode can be recuperated using the information of the HiSCORE array on angular and core position, as illustrated in Figure 5. The major axis of the IACT image in that Figure is pointing towards the core position, which cannot be reconstructed with the IACT alone, but is provided by the HiSCORE array. For comparison, a classical method for hadron suppression in stereoscopic systems is to use the mean scaled width parameter, for which the core position is reconstructed stereoscopically and the image widths of all IACTs are scaled according to MC-expectation. A similar parameter in TAIGA is the hybrid scaled width, which is the image width from one IACT, scaled with the MC-expectation for the given image size and using the core position and direction as reconstructed by HiSCORE. It was shown that the hybrid scaled width achieves competitive rejection power.[14] As opposed to stereoscopic systems, this method does not suffer from deteriorating core impact resolution at large distances (over the full HiSCORE array, the core resolution is the same) and also does not require closely spaced IACTs. The sensitivity of the air Cherenkov components of the TAIGA experiment was estimated using MC-simulations and is shown in Figure 6.

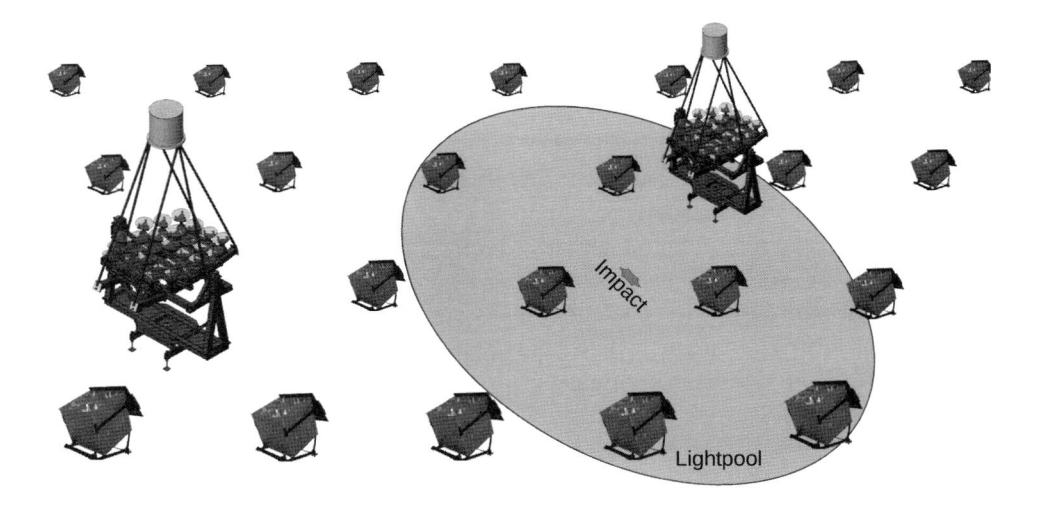

Fig. 4. Schematical drawing of the principle of hybrid operation.

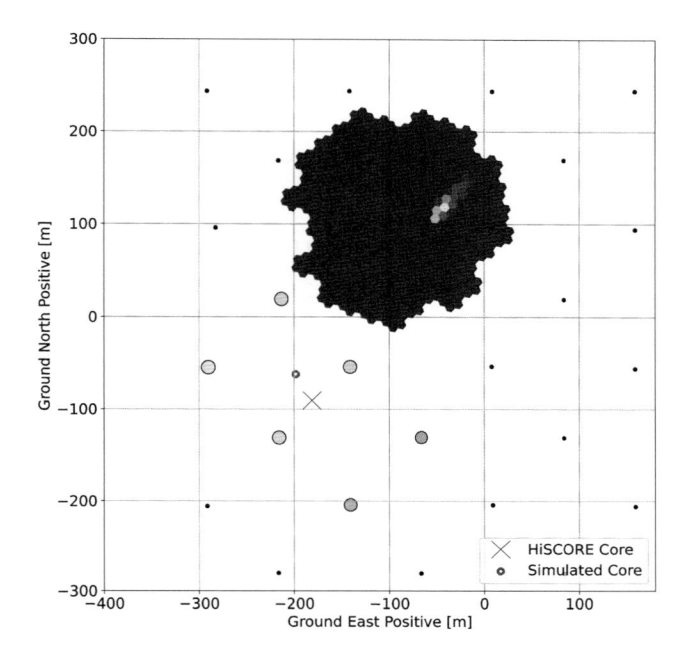

Fig. 5. Simulated hybrid event: as explained in Figure 4, the EAS impact position is reconstructed using the HiSCORE array. The major IACT image axis projected to the ground reference frame (not drawn) is pointing towards the position of the reconstructed core impact position.

3. First results

3.1. *TAIGA-HiSCORE*

The angle integrating HiSCORE array was installed in several stages since 2016. The performance of the array was estimated using from MC-simulations and real data. The relative angular and core position resolutions using a subdivision of the array into subarrays (chessboard method) could be reproduced in simulations, verifying the expected performance of TAIGA-HiSCORE.[24] The relative station timing is calibrated using stationary light sources and air shower data. A fast moving source in the field of view of the array turned out to be the CATS Lidar onboard the international space station. This light source could be used to verify time synchronization and absolute array pointing.[15,16] As compared to the Tunka-133 array, the measurement of the cosmic ray energy spectrum could be extended to lower energies with TAIGA-HiSCORE, as indicated in Figure 7.

3.2. *TAIGA-IACT*

The MC detector simulation for the TAIGA-IACTs is done using two simulation chains: a custom MC simulation chain, and an adaptation of the *sim_telarray* package.[25] The image pixel photoelectron scale is calibrated using an LED illuminating

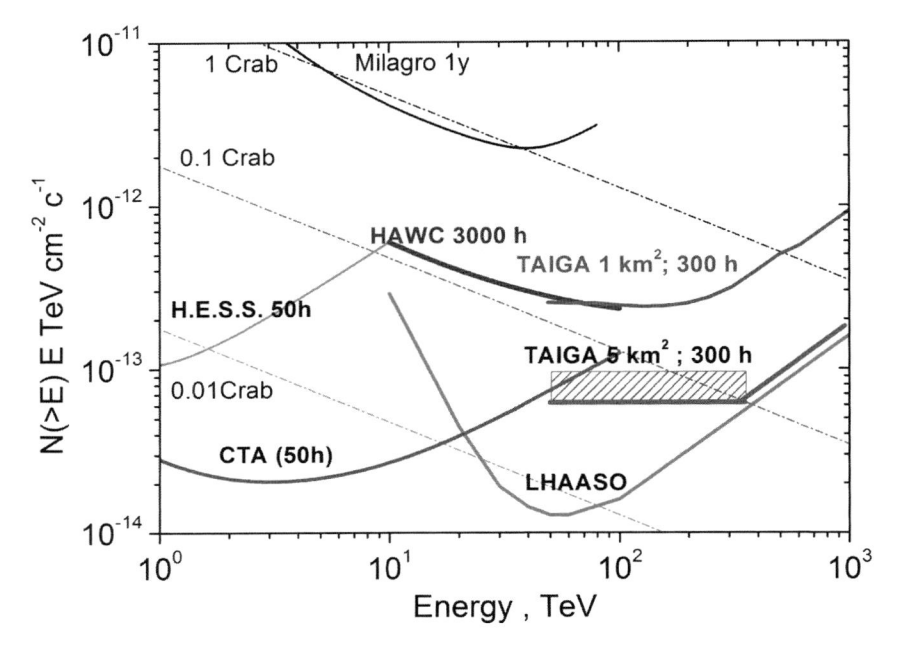

Fig. 6. Sensitivity of the TAIGA experiment for 300 hours of observations in hybrid mode (without muon detectors). A comparison to sensitivities of other experiments is not straight forward, since also the angular and spectroscopic resolutions play an important role for measurements of the morphology and spectra of astrophysical objects. TAIGA has a relative energy resolution of better than 20% and an angular resolution of the order of 0.1°.

the whole PMT camera. Raw data are processed using two independent reconstruction chains to obtain air shower images (amplitude distributions of all pixels for each event). Four different high-level analyses, based on the robust Hillas-parameters, were applied to these image data. Figure 8 shows a comparison of the amplitude distributions of the second-hottest pixel in real data and simulation. A comparison of simulated and real image width is shown in Figure 9. The simulations describe real data reasonably well.

After commissioning of the first TAIGA-IACT, our primary goal was to demonstrate that the IACT is operational. For this purpose, observations of the standard candle, the Crab Nebula, were carried out. After weather quality selection, a total data set of 40.5 h is obtained for analysis. Observations were taken in the wobble mode (Wobble offset 1.2deg). The position of the Crab Nebula inside the IACT camera is taken as the on-source region and the background was estimated from off-source regions at identical distances to the camera center, from the same dataset. The distribution of the alpha angle between the major image axis and the position of the Crab Nebula inside the camera is shown in Figure 10. Selecting events with an image size of at least 120 p.e., a clear excess can be observed. With a zenith angle of 31deg, and taking into accout the altitude of the observation level, the efficiency

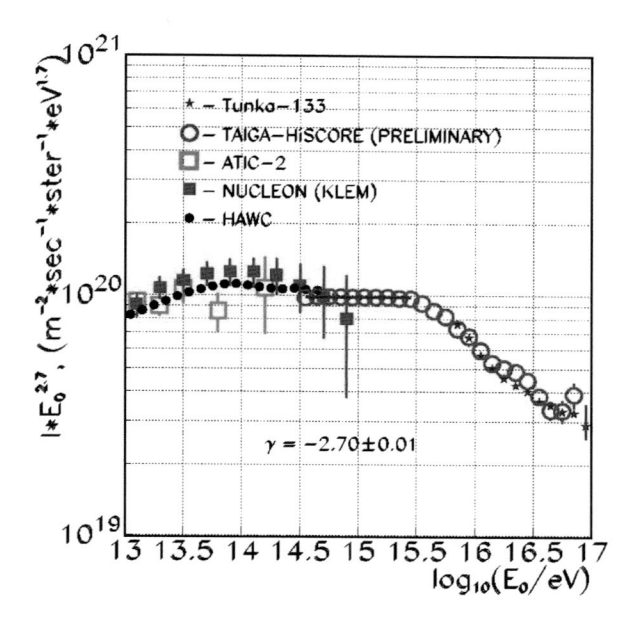

Fig. 7. The all-particle cosmic ray spectrum measured with TAIGA-HiSCORE, compared to different measurements by other experiments.

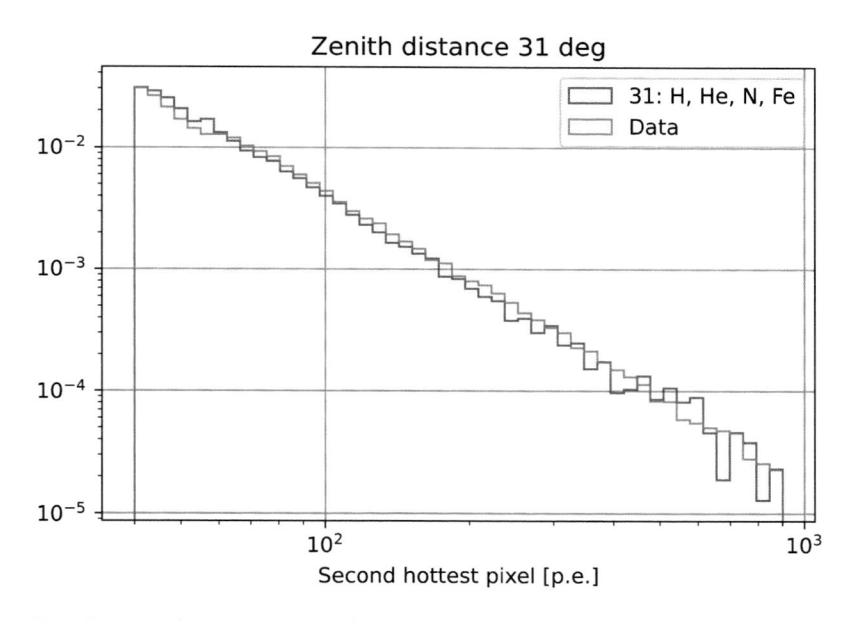

Fig. 8. Distribution of the amplitude of the second-hottest pixel in IACT-1. Data are shown in light grey, simulations are shown in dark grey.

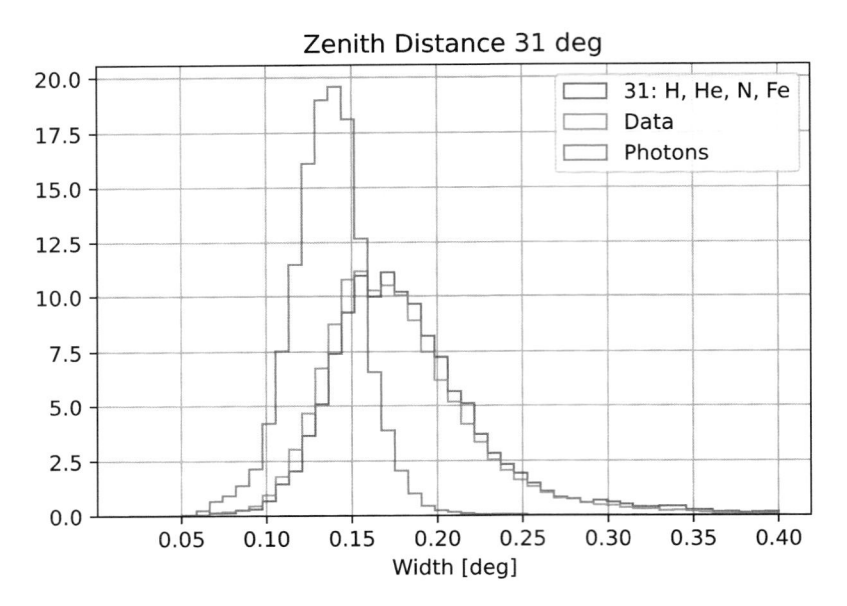

Fig. 9. Distribution of the image width for MC and real data.

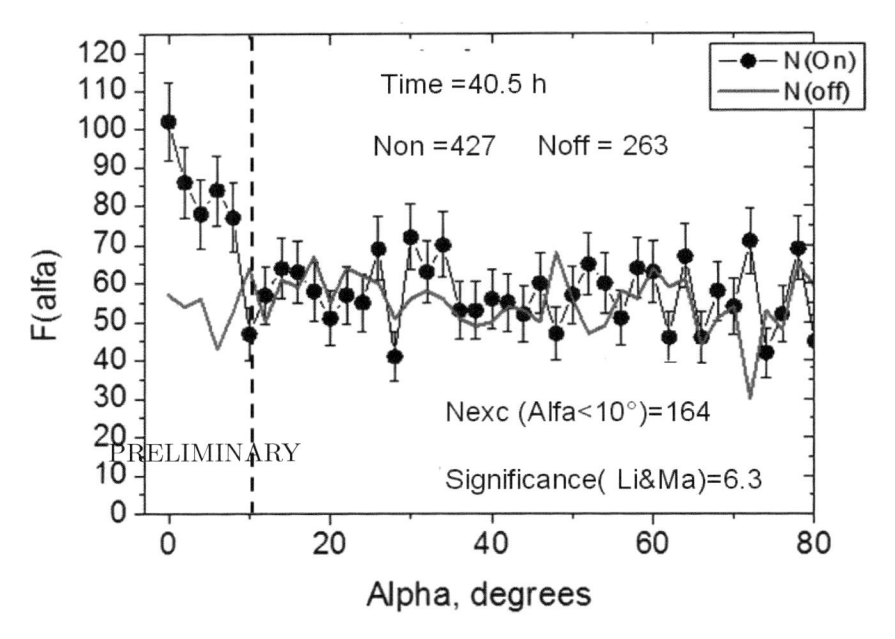

Fig. 10. Distribution of the alpha angle for all runs of a dataset of 42 hours from the Crab Nebula. These preliminary results are currently being finalized to be included in an upcoming journal publication.

of the optical system, and the cuts applied, the energy threshold of this data set is 4.5 TeV . The significance[26] of the observed excess is 6.3 σ (using a cut on alpha smaller than 10deg).

4. Conclusion

The novel hybrid technique of the TAIGA pilot array combines the angle integrating air Cherenkov timing techinque with 4 m class imaging air Cherenkov telescopes, taking advantage of the strengths of both techniques, i.e. large instrumented areas with the HiSCORE array, and gamma-hadron separation from image shape using the IACTs. Additionally, a scintillator detector for particle detection above and below ground will allow the measurement of the muon component, for improved gamma-hadron separation at higher energies. The expected sensitivity of the future 5 km^2 stage is in the region of 10^{-13} photons cm^{-2}s^{-1}. First stages of the 3 TAIGA detector components are in operation. Monte Carlo simulations were compared to real data, showing a good understanding of the detecots. Observations of the Crab Nebula for 40.5 h above 4.5 TeV resulted in an excess of 6.3 σ.

Acknowledgments

The work was performed at the UNU "Astrophysical Complex of MSU-ISU" (agreement 13.UNU.21.0007). The work is supported by Russian Foundation for Basic Research (grants 19-52-44002, 19-32-60003), the Russian Science Foundation (grant 19-72-20067 (Section D,E), the Russian Federation Ministry of Science and High Education (projects FZZE-2020-0017, FZZE-2020-0024), by the Deutsche Forschungsgemeinschaft (DFG, TL 51/6-1) and by the Helmholtz Association (HRJRG-303) and by European Union's Horizon 2020 programme (No. 653477). D.H., M.T, A.K.A. and M.B. acknowledge support by the Deutsche Forschungsgemeinschaft (DFG, German Research Foundation) under Germany's Excellence Strategy — EXC 2121 "Quantum Universe" — 390833306.

References

1. S. F. Berezhnev, D. Besson, N. M. Budnev, A. Chiavassa, O. A. Chvalaev, O. A. Gress, A. N. Dyachok, S. N. Epimakhov, A. Haungs, N. I. Karpov, N. N. Kalmykov, E. N. Konstantinov, A. V. Korobchenko, E. E. Korosteleva, V. A. Kozhin, L. A. Kuzmichev, T. Collab.) et al., *Nucl. Instrum. Methods* **692**, p. 98 (2012).
2. S. D. Hunter, D. L. Bertsch, J. R. Catelli, T. M. Dame, S. W. Digel, B. L. Dingus, J. A. Esposito, C. E. Fichtel, R. C. Hartman, G. Kanbach, D. A. Kniffen, Y. C. Lin, H. A. Mayer-Hasselwander, P. F. Michelson, C. von Montigny, R. Mukherjee, P. L. Nolan, E. Schneid, P. Sreekumar, P. Thaddeus and D. J. Thompson, *The Astrophysical Journal* **481**, 205 (May 1997).
3. A. A. Abdo, B. Allen, D. Berley, E. Blaufuss, S. Casanova, C. Chen, D. G. Coyne, R. S. Delay, B. L. Dingus, R. W. Ellsworth and et al., *The Astrophysical Journal* **658**, p. L33–L36 (Feb 2007).

4. F. Aharonian, A. G. Akhperjanian, A. R. Bazer-Bachi, B. Behera, M. Beilicke, W. Benbow, D. Berge, K. Bernlöhr, C. Boisson, O. Bolz and et al., *Astronomy & Astrophysics* **481**, p. 401–410 (Jan 2008).
5. A. Abramowski, F. Aharonian, F. A. Benkhali *et al.*, *Nature* **531**, p. 476–479 (Mar 2016).
6. S. Gabici and F. A. Aharonian, *The Astrophysical Journal* **665**, p. L131–L134 (Aug 2007).
7. T. Glauch, in *Proceedings of the 3rd International Symposium on Cosmic Rays and Astrophysics (ISCRA-2021), 8–10 June 2021*.
8. Z. Cao, F. Aharonian, Q. An *et al.*, *Nature* **594**, p. 33–36 (2021).
9. T. Kneiske and D. Horns, in *38th COSPAR Scientific Assembly*,
10. I. V. Moskalenko, T. A. Porter and A. W. Strong, *Astr. Phys. J. L.* **640**, L155 (April 2006).
11. F. D. Steffen, *European Physical Journal C* **59**, 557 (January 2009).
12. H.-S. Zechlin, D. Horns and J. Redondo, in *American Institute of Physics Conference Series (2008)*, eds. F. A. Aharonian, W. Hofmann and F. Rieger.
13. L. Anchordoqui, M. T. Dova, A. Mariazzi, T. McCauley, T. Paul, S. Reucroft and J. Swain, *Ann. Phys. (N.Y.)* **314**, p. 145 (2004), hep-ph/0407020.
14. M. Kunnas, PhD thesis, University of Hamburg (2017), https://ediss.sub.uni-hamburg.de/handle/ediss/7582.
15. O. Gress, I. Astapov, N. Budnev, P. Bezyazeekov, A. Bogdanov, V. Boreyko, M. Brückner, A. Chiavassa, O. Chvalaev, A. Dyachok, T. Gress, S. Epimakhov, E. Fedoseev, A. Gafarov, N. Gorbunov, V. Grebenyuk, (TAIGA Collab.) *et al.*, *Nucl. Instrum. Methods A* **845**, p. 367 (2017).
16. A. Porelli, D. Bogorodskii, M. Brückner, N. Budnev, O. Chvalaev, A. Dyachok, S. Epimakhov, T. Eremin, O. Gress, T. Gress, D. Horns, A. Ivanova, S. Kiruhin, E. Konstantinov, E. Korosteleva, M. Kunnas *et al.*, *J. Phys.: Conf. Ser.* **632**, p. 012041 (2015).
17. D. Hampf, M. Tluczykont and D. Horns, *Nucl. Instrum. Methods A* **712**, p. 137 (2013).
18. D. Zhurov, in *Proceedings of the 36th International Cosmic Ray Conference (ICRC2019)*.
19. N. Lubsandorzhiev, I. Astapov, P. Bezyazeekov, V. Boreyko, A. Borodin, M. Brueckner, N. Budnev, A. Chiavassa, A. Dyachok, O. Fedorov, A. Gafarov, A. Garmash, N. Gorbunov, V. Grebenyuk, O. Gress, T. Gress, (TAIGA collab.) *et al.*, in *Proceedings of the 35th International Cosmic Ray Conference (ICRC2017)*.
20. N. Lubsandorzhiev, in *Proceedings of the 36th International Cosmic Ray Conference (ICRC2019)*.
21. A. M. Hillas, in *Proceedings of the 19th International Cosmic Ray Conference (1985)*.
22. R. Parsons and S. Ohm, *Eur. Phys. J. C* **80**, p. 363 (2020).
23. I. I. Yashin, I. I. Astapov, N. S. Barbashina, A. G. Bogdanov, V. Boreyko, N. M. Budnev, M. Büker, M. Bruckner, A. Chiavassa, O. B. Chvalaev, A. V. Gafarov, N. Gorbunov, V. Grebenyuk, O. A. Gress, A. Grinyuk, O. G. Grishin, (TAIGA collab.) *et al.*, *J. Phys.: Conf. Ser.* **675**, p. 032037 (2016).
24. M. Tluczykont, O. Gress, E. Korosteleva, L. Kuzmichev, A. Pakhorukov, A. Porelli, V. Prosin, L. Sveshnikova, R. Wischnewski, I. Astapov, P. Bezyazeekov, V. Boreyko, A. Borodin, M. Brueckner, N. Budnev, A. Chiavassa, (TAIGA Collab.) *et al.*, in *Proceedings of the 35th International Cosmic Ray Conference (ICRC2017)*.
25. K. Bernlöhr, *Astropart. Phys.* **30**, p. 149 (2008).
26. T. Li and Y. Ma, *Astrophys. J.* **272**, p. 317 (1983).

Science perspectives of the Southern Wide-field Gamma-ray Observatory (SWGO)

K.L. Engel* for the SWGO Collaboration

Department of Physics, University of Maryland, College Park; 4150 Campus Dr, College Park, MD, USA 20742
*E-mail: klengel@umd.edu

We outline the science case for SWGO, the Southern Wide-field Gamma-ray Observatory, an air-shower array planned for construction at a high-altitude site in the Southern Hemisphere. This next-generation, wide-field-of-view, gamma-ray survey instrument will be sensitive to gamma rays from $\sim$ 100 GeV to beyond 100 TeV energies and, due to its location and features, will be complementary to other gamma-ray observatories such as HAWC, LHAASO, and CTA. SWGO's scientific endeavors will cover a broad range of exciting topics, such as monitoring the transient sky at very high energies, unveiling Galactic and extragalactic particle accelerators, probing particle physics beyond the Standard Model, and the characterization of the cosmic ray flux. With its novel design, SWGO stands poised to provide the world's best sensitivity across many facets of our exciting field.

Keywords: Instrumentation: detectors; gamma rays: general

1. Introduction

With an abundance of "paradigm-shifting" discoveries in the field of high-energy particle astrophysics in the last decade, it is critical for the continued growth of these topics and movement into potential new discovery space that there be facilities in both hemispheres capable of continuously surveying the gamma-ray sky in the time and space domains. Ideally, such an instrument would have a very wide field of view, making it capable of providing transient alerts to the astrophysics community in addition to having an abundance of archival data for performing follow-ups from other notifications. It is also important that this new facility be ground-based, collecting information from extensive air showers, as necessitated by the declining flux emitted by cosmic sources at very-high energies. We believe that the Southern Wide-field Gamma-ray Observatory (SWGO), a water-Cherenkov facility to be located in the Southern Hemisphere, fills this pivotal role within the astrophysics and high-energy particle physics communities.

The complementarity between IACTs and a wide-field-of-view ground-based particle array such as that outlined herein is summarized by Table 1, from the Science Case White Paper for a wide-field-of-view gamma-ray observatory in the Southern Hemisphere.[1]

This work is intended to highlight endeavors presented in Ref. 1, as well as additional efforts since the time of that document's publication, and is the collective work of the whole of the SWGO Collaboration.

Table 1. Comparison of typical performance of current and planned IACT arrays and ground particle arrays for gamma-ray astronomy. See Ref. 1 for details.

	IACT Arrays	Ground-particle Arrays
Field-of-view	3°–10°	90°
Duty cycle	10%–30%	>95%
Energy range	30 GeV – >100 TeV	∼500 GeV – >100 TeV
Angular resolution	0.05°–0.02°	0.4°–0.1°
Energy resolution	∼7%	60%–20%
Background rejection	>95%	90%–99.8%

2. The Southern Wide-field Gamma-ray Observatory (SWGO) Concept

SWGO is a proposed future water Cherenkov experiment in the Southern Hemisphere for the ground-based detection of astrophysical gamma rays. The core unit will use the water-Cherenkov technique to observe intensive air showers from primary particles incident on the Earth's atmosphere and would be the most sensitive gamma-ray observatory in the Southern Hemisphere above 10 TeV, with expected sensitivity up to PeV energies. With an array of such detections, similar to the operational mode of the HAWC Observatory in the Northern Hemisphere,[2] the energy and direction of the incident gamma ray that produced the shower can be determined.

The exact design of SWGO is potentially dependent on site choice, with water access, construction costs, and infrastructure feasibility all playing deciding roles in addition to compatibility with science-driven main design goals. The aim of the design such a next-generation observatory, no matter the specifics, is to achieve roughly an order of magnitude higher sensitivity over the current-generation of instruments like HAWC.[1]

Being the most sensitive observatory in the Southern Hemisphere above ∼ 20 TeV (as seen in Figure 1) would make SWGO an ideal complement not only to Northern Hemisphere observatories, but also to CTA South. It's complementarity with Northern Hemisphere observatories is well visualized by comparing SWGO's projected field of view with that of the HAWC Observatory, shown in Figure 2. By placing SWGO in the Southern Hemisphere, we would have a prime view to monitor sources and source regions previously inaccessible or mostly in accessible to HAWC, such as the Galactic Center and the Magellanic Clouds, as well as more ideal viewing of source regions such as the Fermi Bubbles.

3. The Core Science Case

The following list is just an overview of the science we intend to do with SWGO once built, with promising sensitivity studies currently being conducted on all fronts.

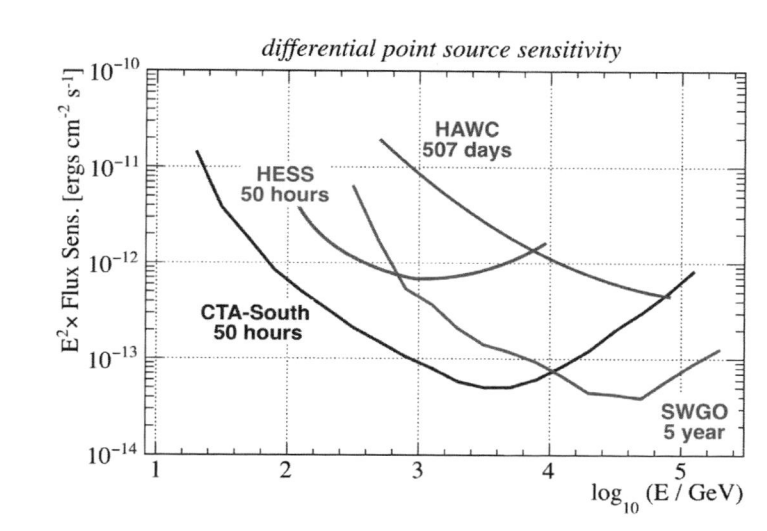

Fig. 1. The five-year differential point-source sensitivity of SWGO, anticipated to bbe the best in the Southern sky above tens of TeV. Figure from Ref. 3.

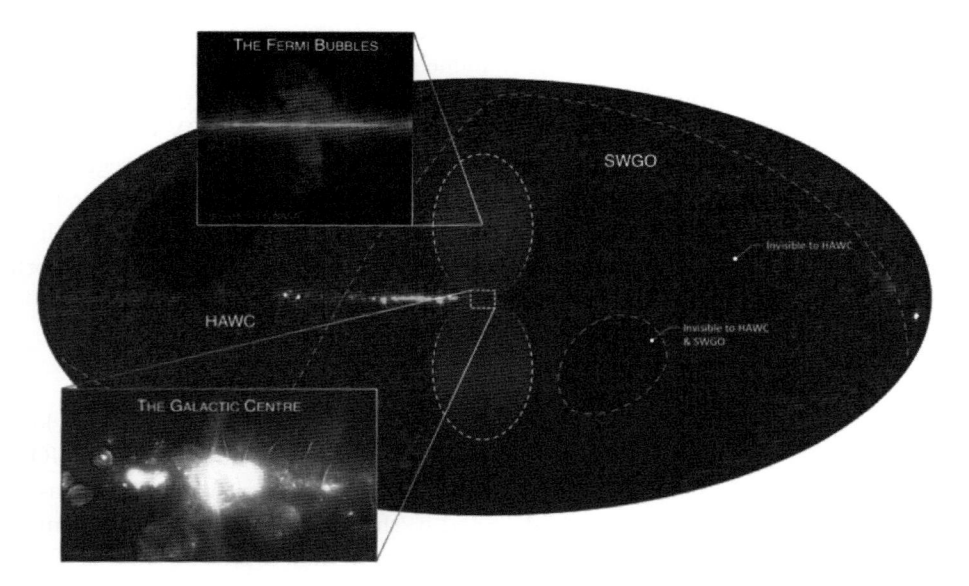

Fig. 2. Sky coverage of SWGO in Galactic coordinates (red dashed line) overlaid on the HAWC significance map containing over 50 sources. Figure from Ref. 3.

The core science cases of SWGO, as enumerated in Ref. 1, are:

- Detection of short-timescale phenomena[4]— low-energy threshold for detection of short-timescale (<1 hr) transient events down to 100 GeV

- Search for PeVatrons[5]— Improved sensitivity up to a few 100s of TeV to search for PeV Galactic particle accelerators
- Pulsar Wind Nebulae (PWNe) and Gamma-ray halos[6]— Unique potential for accessing the high-energy end of the Galactic population
- Dark matter and diffuse emission[7,8]— Unique access to the Galactic Center and Halo at the high-energy end of the spectrum
- Cosmic rays[9]— Unique complement to LHAASO for anisotropy studies, with the capability to reach low angular scale. Additionally, good muon tagging implies good mass resolution for composition studies up to the *knee*

3.1. *The High-Energy Transient Sky*

There are four key targets of interest in the high-energy transient sky—gravitational waves (GWs), fast radio bursts (FRBs), high-energy neutrinos, and gamma-ray bursts (GRBs)—to which the applied properties of SWGO will be a unique advantage for observing.

3.1.1. *Gravitational Waves*

GRB 170817A and the subsequent kilonova emission associated with binary-neutron-star (BNS) merger GW 170817 launched the field of GW multimessenger astronomy. SWGO's wide field of view and large, unbiased duty cycle would allow the recording of real-time, high-energy gamma-ray data for all GW events falling into its field of view. This would provide coverage of high-uncertainty regions, locate very-high-energy counterparts, and search for currently unmodeled burst-like GW signals. SWGO could even provide real-time notifications to other Southern Hemisphere telescopes and observatories, *e.g.,* CTA, so that they might perform detailed follow-up observations.

3.1.2. *Fast Radio Bursts*

Monitoring approaches by IACTs of FRBs are less than ideal as the duty cycle of FRBs is poorly constrained. A wide-field-of-view survey instrument like SWGO is therefore ideal for Galactic FRB follow-ups to provide constraints on gamma-ray emission in coincidence with bursts detected in the radio domain, as well as monitoring for repeaters. Simulation studies have also predicted that 60–70% of FRBs are located in the Southern Hemisphere, so SWGO's location will be incredibly advantageous for the study of these objects.

3.1.3. *High-Energy Neutrinos*

As evidence for the interaction of high-energy hadronic particles, high-energy neutrinos are crucial in the search for sources of high-energy cosmic-ray accelerators, but a multimessenger approach is necessary to determine the source of the astrophysical flux of high-energy neutrinos. This multimessenger approach, towards which SWGO's large, unbiased duty cycle will be an invaluable tool, greatly aids neutrino studies as high-energy gamma-ray observations allow precise localization of the emission region, allowing for not only the identification of their astrophysical source, but also information about overall source energetics and energy- and time-dependent power output.

3.1.4. *Gamma-Ray Bursts*

Although electromagnetic emission from GRBs is widely observed down to the radio, the VHE domain remains largely uncharted. The transient and unpredictable nature of GRBs combined with intrinsic alert delays by X-ray satellites, makes it difficult for IACTs to observe GRBs rapidly enough to catch the prompt-to-early afterglow phases in which very-high-energy emission is either rarely, or as yet not observed. However, SWGO's wide field of view, large, unbiased duty cycle, and sensitivity $\lesssim 1$ TeV would allow for the monitoring of all nearby GRBs inside its field of view, increasing the number of observations without the need for external triggers, in addition to the benefits of its archival data analysis (see Figure 3). Additionally, follow-ups in SWGO's energy range would potentially allow for the discrimination between proposed emission scenarios— a longstanding topic of great interest within the field.

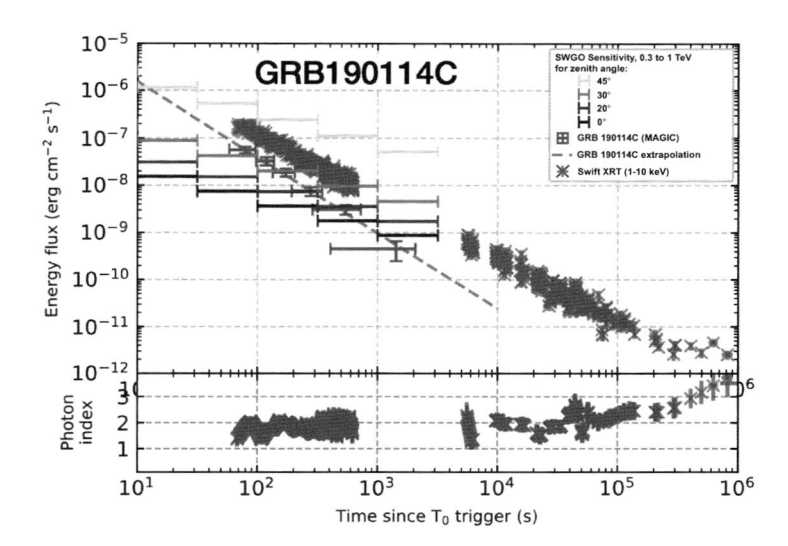

Fig. 3. SWGO's sensitivity to a GRB like GRB 190114C, including results from the MAGIC telescopes for comparison. Figure adapted from Ref. 10.

3.2. Galactic Particle Acceleration

The study of very-high-energy gamma rays is one of the most powerful methods to search the Galactic plane for astrophysical particle accelerators, including PeVatrons— sources able to accelerate hadrons up to the "knee" of the cosmic-ray spectrum. With its large energy range, excellent sensitivity above 10 TeV, and ideal design features, SWGO will be able to isolate Galactic PeVatrons from the background of softer gamma-ray sources. Its design means that SWGO is well equipped to handle the source confusion, diffuse gamma-ray backgrounds, and spatially extended emission regions that typically complicate these kinds of analyses, making its sensitivity to astrophysical particle accelerators in the local Galactic neighborhood one of the greatest strengths of the proposed observatory. From this, we are enthusiastic that SWGO will be the optimal instrument to discover sources such as the microquasar SS433.[11] Such assets will also allow SWGO to identify hard-spectrum sources for long-term observation with CTA, as well as complement the coverage provided of the Northern Hemisphere by HAWC and LHAASO.

3.3. Pulsar Wind Nebulae and Gamma-Ray Halos

First observed by HAWC,[12] the all-sky observations of which SWGO is capable will allow the testing of large gamma-ray halos as potential sources of the observed positron excess. Studying gamma rays from such potential positron sources provides crucial input to the positron excess puzzle. SWGO will survey nearby pulsars (age $< 10^6$ yr; see Figure 4) in the Southern Hemisphere, where its wide field of view is ideal for measuring gamma-ray halos around the co-located pulsar wind nebulae (PWNe), including from millisecond pulsars not (yet) discovered with current instruments. The large extents of these gamma-ray halos allow us to study the propagation of particles within them in unprecedented detail, unveiling the properties of the accelerators and the medium around them.

3.4. The Extragalactic Very-High-Energy Sky

Several models currently exist to explain the spectra of Active Galactic Nuclei (AGN) from radio to very-high-energy gamma rays, with additional data needed to unravel the mechanisms at work in these extreme environments. The very-high-energy extragalactic sky is dominated by Blazars, radio-loud AGN with jets oriented near our line of sight, whose second power-spectrum peak in the gamma rays has a much debated origin. SWGO is expected to be able to detect very-high-energy blazars at both short and long time scales, as well as perform searches in an unbiased way over the full Southern sky due to its near-continuous duty cycle. Such observations will provide information on the intergalactic magnetic field, radiative processes and acceleration mechanisms, periodicity, and beyond-the-Standard-Model physics. SWGO's characteristics are also ideal for the crucial evaluation of the significance of neutrino-blazar flare correlations, such as implied by observations of TXS 0506+056.[13]

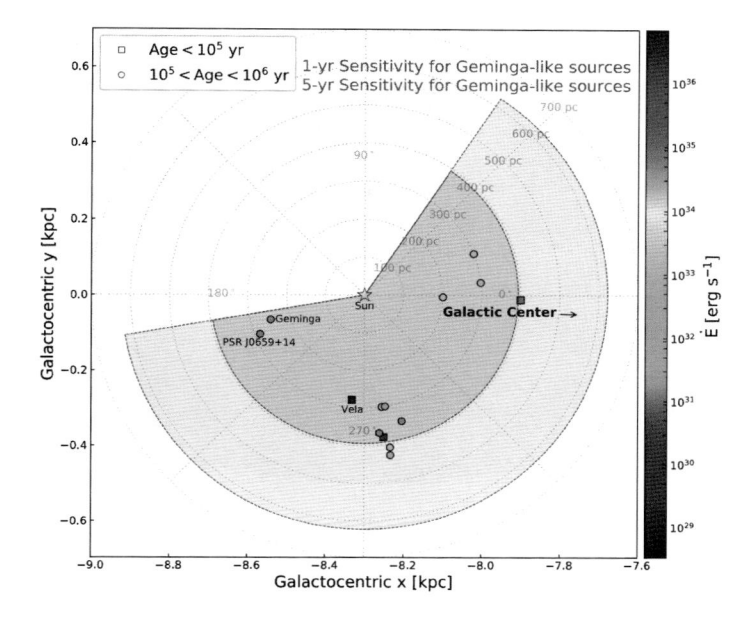

Fig. 4. Pulsars, age $< 10^6$ yr., within 500 pc, showing the one-year (red) and five-year (blue) sensitivity of SWGO to Geminga-like sources at these locations. Figure from Ref. 1.

3.5. *Physics Beyond the Standard Model*

Returning to the sky that we would expect to see with SWGO in Figure 5, one can see that SWGO would have access to several prominent dark matter targets that cannot be seen, or cannot be seen well, by HAWC in the Northern Hemisphere, such as the Galactic Center, the Magellanic Clouds, and a population of dwarf galaxies recently discovered with optical surveys like DES.

3.5.1. *WIMP Searches with Cosmic Gamma Rays*

Dark matter annihilation is theorized to produce Standard Model particles through weak interactions which, in turn, produce gamma rays, mainly via pion decay but also through inverse Compton scattering of photons off produced electron-positron pairs. Weakly Interacting Massive Particles, or WIMPs, are promising dark matter candidates with $E_{CM} \sim 100$ GeV. Their masses can range from ~ 5–100 TeV, but the heaviest particles, $m_\chi > 10$ TeV, that can only be searched for with an instrument with a high sensitivity, are best probed with an indirect experiment like SWGO. Heavy dark matter (100 TeV–100 PeV) is also theorized beyond the WIMP model, where SWGO's wide field of view and sensitivity to the highest energies will make it a crucial player in searching for indirect signals from dark matter.

The Galactic Center is the closest dense region of dark matter and, as seen in Figure 5, SWGO's location in the Southern Hemisphere will allow this to be a prime

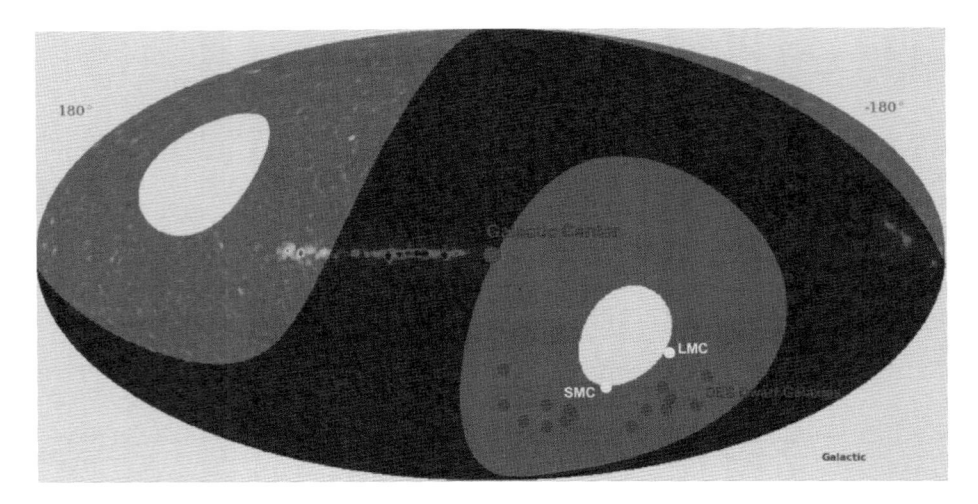

Fig. 5. HAWC skymap with SWGO view (shaded) overlaid. Figure from Andrea Albert.

target for observations. This is also an opportunity to highlight the complementarity of SWGO with the *Fermi*-LAT and CTA. Combined, these experiments will explore thermal WIMPs from 5 GeV–100 TeV.[14] There is an overlap in mass between experiments, which will allow for multiple potential detections, but it is SWGO that extends the reach of such studies up to 100 TeV— one of many exciting reasons to build SWGO.

3.5.2. *Axion-Like Particles*

As SWGO will have its best sensitivity at the highest energies, we can also look for Axion-like particles (ALPs), a generalization of the axion and a well-motivated dark matter candidate. Gamma rays from AGN can convert to ALPs in magnetic fields in the environment through which they propagate. These particles can travel unattenuated through the extragalactic background light (EBL) and convert back into gamma rays in the Milky Way's magnetic field. This conversion results in a high-energy tail in the observed energy spectrum—as seen in Figure 6—to which SWGO would be sensitive.

3.5.3. *Dark Matter Searches in Dwarf Galaxies*

We can also look for dark matter annihilation gamma rays from dwarf galaxies, many of which have recently been discovered by optical surveys in the Southern Hemisphere, making them prime targets for SWGO. These dwarf spheroidals (dSphs) are dark-matter-rich Milky Way satellites that are nearby and essentially background-free. With its wide field of view and large duty cycle, SWGO will observe dozens of dSphs every day, giving us the ideal survey of the sources needed

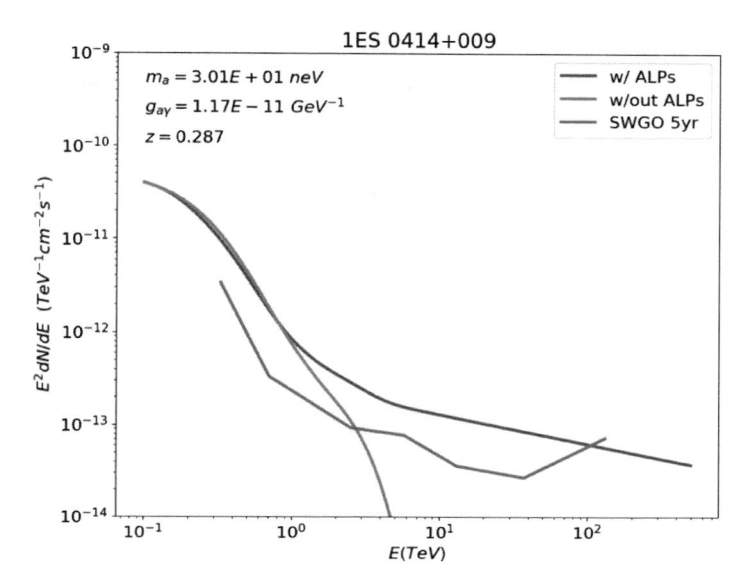

Fig. 6. ALP conversions could produce sharp spectral features in the observed spectrum of extragalactic sources which would require good energy resolution and large event statistics to resolve well. Figure from Ref. 1.

to place strong constraints on dark matter annihilation and decay. Unlike similar experiments, SWGO will have archival data at all locations within its field of view, which means if a new dwarf is discovered, there is already data on it to be analyzed with no time delay to collect it, such as might be experienced with IACTs.

3.5.4. *Lorentz Invariance Violation*

If Lorentz Invariance is violated, then gamma rays above an energy threshold ($E_{LIV}^{(n)}$) rapidly decay into e^+e^- pairs, so seeing a photon at the highest energies will set a limit on the energy scale of Lorentz Invariance Violation (LIV)— The current highest gamma-ray energy observed is 1,140 TeV seen by LHAASO.[15] SWGO's sensitivity up to several PeV would allow gamma rays to be probed for this signature of LIV at the highest energies ever observed. The detection of multiple PeV gamma rays will provide the world-leading constraints on LIV.

3.5.5. *Primordial Black Holes*

Primordial Black Holes (PBHs) are black holes created in the early Universe with masses ranging from the Planck mass to supermassive black holes. PBHs in some mass ranges are candidates to constitute some of the observed dark matter in the Galaxy. PBHs evaporate through Hawking Radiation, with this evaporation increasing substantially towards the end of their lives, producing a burst of very-high-energy gamma rays. As these are transient sources with a runaway emission,

SWGO's wide field of view and large duty cycle make it an optimal instrument with which to observe PBHs of initial mass $m_{PBH} \sim 5 \times 10^{14}$ g. The expected limits are 30 times better than the data-based limits currently placed by HAWC,[16] as shown in Figure 7.

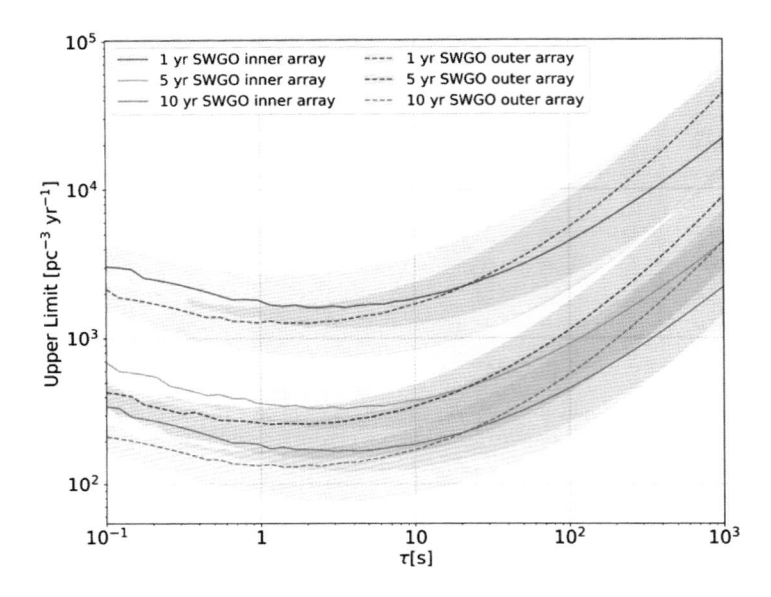

Fig. 7. The expected limits on the local burst rate density of PBHs. Figure from Ref. 17.

3.6. *Cosmic Rays*

The main feature in the energy spectrum of Galactic cosmic rays is the so-called "knee", which is characterized by a steepening of the spectral index from ~ -2.7 to ~ -3.1 at about 3 PeV. Understanding the origin of the "knee" is the key for a comprehensive theory of the origin of cosmic rays up to the highest observed energies. SWGO is uniquely suited to detect sources of cosmic rays with energies in excess of 1 PeV—expected to produce very-high-energy gamma rays above 100 TeV[18–21]— and measure any cutoffs in their spectra that indicate the maximum energy to which they are able to accelerate particles. With its wide aperture and its almost 100% duty cycle, SWGO will be able to gather significantly larger electron event statistics than IACTs, which may help in extending the electron spectrum further than the 20 TeV already measured, potentially revealing more details of the local source distribution. Additionally, the large sky coverage of SWGO would enable the search for anisotropy in the electron arrival direction at different angular scales, which would provide additional very relevant information for the understanding of Galactic particle acceleration and cosmic-ray transport.

4. Looking Forward

As a ground-based cosmic-gamma-ray observatory sensitive up to PeV energies, SWGO would be the most sensitive gamma-ray observatory in the Southern Hemisphere above 10 TeV, with complementarities among both Northern Hemisphere observatories, as well as other Southern Hemisphere observatories. With its wide field of view, near 100% duty cycle, ad high-energy reach, SWGO will provide the world's best sensitivity to emission from high-energy transients, propagation of particles within gamma-ray halos, PeVatrons in the galactic plane, several dark matter candidates, and Lorentz Invariance Violation.

References

1. A. Albert *et al.*, Science Case for a Wide Field-of-View Very-High-Energy Gamma-Ray Observatory in the Southern Hemisphere (2 2019).
2. A. U. Abeysekara *et al.*, Measurement of the Crab Nebula at the Highest Energies with HAWC, *Astrophys. J.* **881**, p. 134 (2019).
3. P. Abreu *et al.*, The Southern Wide-Field Gamma-Ray Observatory (SWGO): A Next-Generation Ground-Based Survey Instrument for VHE Gamma-Ray Astronomy (7 2019).
4. F. Schüssler and K. Satalecka, All-Sky time domain astrophysics with Very High Energy Gamma rays, *BAAS* **51**, p. 357 (May 2019).
5. P. Cristofari, A. Albert, A. Carraminana, S. Casanova, B. Dingus, M. Duvernois, N. Fraija, H. Fleischhack, J. Goodman, T. Greenshaw, J. Harding, A. Haungs, B. Hona, P. Huentemeyer and V. Joshi, Where are the pevatrons? (05 2019).
6. H. Fleischhack, A. Albert, C. Alvarez, R. Arceo, H. A. A. Solares, J. F. Beacom, R. Bird, C. A. Brisbois, K. S. Caballero-Mora, A. Carraminana, S. Casanova, P. Cristofari, P. Coppi, B. L. Dingus, M. A. DuVernois, K. L. Engel, J. A. Goodman, T. Greenshaw, J. P. Harding, B. Hona, P. H. Huentemeyer, H. Li, T. Linden, K. Malone, J. Martinez-Castro, M. A. Mostafa, M. U. Nisa, C. Riviere, F. S. Greus, A. Sandoval, A. J. Smith, W. Springer, T. Sudoh, K. Tollefson, A. Zepeda and H. Zhou, Pulsars in a Bubble? Following Electron Diffusion in the Galaxy with TeV Gamma Rays, *BAAS* **51**, p. 311 (May 2019).
7. A. Viana, Searching for TeV Dark Matter in the Milky Way Galactic Center, *BAAS* **51**, p. 308 (May 2019).
8. A. Albert, K. S. Caballero, P. M. Chadwick, B. L. Dingus, K. L. Engel, J. A. Goodman, T. Greenshaw, J. P. Harding, P. Huentemeyer, J. S. Lapington, J. Lundeen, J. Martinez-Castro, M. U. Nisa, H. Schoorlemmer, K. Tollefson, A. Viana and A. Zepeda, Searching for Sources of TeV Particle Dark Matter in the Southern Hemisphere, *BAAS* **51**, p. 202 (May 2019).
9. Fraija, A. Albert, J. C. Arteaga-Velazquez, H. A. Ayala Solares, K. S. Caballero-Mora, P. Cristofari, G. Di Sciascio, J. C. Diaz-Velez, M. A. DuVernois, K. L. Engel, A. Galvan-Gamez, J. A. Garcia-Gonzalez, T. Greenshaw, J. P. Harding, A. Haungs, O. Martinez-Bravo, J. Martinez, M. A. Mostafa, I. Torres, A. Zepeda and H. Zhou, Cosmic rays in the TeV to PeV primary energy range, *Astro2020: Decadal Survey on Astronomy and Astrophysics* **2020**, p. 459 (May 2019).
10. V. A. Acciari *et al.*, Teraelectronvolt emission from the γ-ray burst GRB 190114C, *Nature* **575**, 455 (2019).

11. A. U. Abeysekara *et al.*, Very high energy particle acceleration powered by the jets of the microquasar SS 433, *Nature* **562**, 82 (2018), [Erratum: Nature 564, E38 (2018)].
12. A. U. Abeysekara *et al.*, Extended gamma-ray sources around pulsars constrain the origin of the positron flux at Earth, *Science* **358**, 911 (2017).
13. D. Van Eijk, Tau Neutrinos in IceCube, KM3NeT and the Pierre Auger Observatory, *SciPost Phys. Proc.* **1**, p. 030 (2019).
14. A. Viana, H. Schoorlemmer, A. Albert, V. de Souza, J. P. Harding and J. Hinton, Searching for Dark Matter in the Galactic Halo with a Wide Field of View TeV Gamma-ray Observatory in the Southern Hemisphere, *JCAP* **12**, p. 061 (2019).
15. Z. Cao *et al.*, Exploring Lorentz Invariance Violation from Ultra-high-energy Gamma Rays Observed by LHAASO (6 2021).
16. A. Albert *et al.*, Constraining the Local Burst Rate Density of Primordial Black Holes with HAWC, *JCAP* **04**, p. 026 (2020).
17. R. López-Coto, M. Doro, A. de Angelis, M. Mariotti and J. P. Harding, Prospects for the Observation of Primordial Black Hole evaporation with the Southern Wide Field of View Gamma-ray Observatory (3 2021).
18. N. Fraija, E. Aguilar-Ruiz, A. Galván-Gámez, A. Marinelli and J. A. de Diego, Study of the PeV neutrino, γ-rays, and UHECRs around the lobes of Centaurus A, *MNRAS* **481**, 4461 (December 2018).
19. P. Cristofari, A. Albert, A. Carramiñana, S. Casanova, B. L. Dingus, M. A. DuVernois, N. Fraija, H. Fleischhack, J. A. Goodman and T. Greenshaw, Where are the pevatrons?, in *BAAS*, May 2019.
20. N. Fraija, M. Araya, A. Galván-Gámez and J. A. de Diego, Analysis of Fermi-LAT observations, UHECRs and neutrinos from the radio galaxy Centaurus B, *JCAP* **2019**, p. 023 (August 2019).
21. J. Holder, E. Amato, R. Bandiera, R. Bird, A. Bulgarelli, V. V. Dwarkadas, N. Giglietto, P. Goldoni, J. Hinton and B. Hnatyk, Understanding the Origin and Impact of Relativistic Cosmic Particles with Very-High-Energy Gamma-rays, in *BAAS*, May 2019.

Laue lenses:
Focusing optics for hard X/soft Gamma-ray astronomy

L. Ferro*, M. Moita, P. Rosati, R. Lolli, C. Guidorzi and F. Frontera

Department of Physics and Earth Science, University of Ferrara,
Via Giuseppe Saragat 1, Ferrara (FE), 44122, Italy
*E-mail: frrlsi@unife.it
www.fst.unife.it

E. Virgilli, E. Caroli, N. Auricchio, J. B. Stephen, C. Labanti, F. Fuschino and R. Campana

OAS of Bologna, INAF,
Via Piero Gobetti 93/3, Bologna (BO), 40129, Italy
www.oas.inaf.it

C. Ferrari

Institute of Materials for Electronics and Magnetism (IMEM), CNR,
Parco Area delle Scienze 37/A, Parma (PR), 43124, Italy
www.imem.cnr.it

S. Squerzanti

INFN of Ferrara,
Via Giuseppe Saragat 1, Ferrara (FE), 44122, Italy
www.fe.infn.it

M. Pucci

National Institute of Optics (Istituto Nazionale di Ottica, CNR-INO), CNR,
Largo Enrico Fermi 6, Firenze (FI), 50125, Italy
www.ino.cnr.it

S. del Sordo and C. Gargano

IASF of Palermo, INAF,
Via Ugo La Malfa 153, Palermo (PA), 90146, Italy
www.ifc.inaf.it

Hard X-/soft Gamma-ray astronomy is a key field for the study of important astrophysical phenomena such as the electromagnetic counterparts of gravitational waves, gamma-ray bursts, black holes physics and many more. However, the spatial localization, imaging capabilities and sensitivity of the measurements are strongly limited for the energy range >70 keV due to the lack of focusing instruments operating in this energy band. A new generation of instruments suitable to focus hard X-/ soft Gamma-rays is necessary to shed light on the nature of astrophysical phenomena which are still unclear due to the limitations of current direct-viewing telescopes. Laue lenses can be the answer to those needs. A Laue lens is an optical device consisting of a large number of properly oriented crystals which are capable, through Laue diffraction, of concentrating the radiation into the common Laue lens focus. In contrast with the grazing incidence telescopes commonly used for softer X-rays, the transmission configuration of the Laue lenses allows us to obtain a significant sensitive area even at energies of hundreds of keV. At the University of Ferrara we are actively working on the modelization and construction of a broad-band Laue lens. In this work we will present the main concepts behind Laue lenses and the latest technological developments of the TRILL (Technological Readiness Increase for Laue Lenses) project, devoted to the advancement of the technological readiness of Laue lenses by developing the first prototype of a lens sector made of cylindrical bent crystals of Germanium.

Keywords: Hard X/soft Gamma-ray astronomy; Laue Lenses; Focusing Telescopes.

1. Laue lenses: A new way to look at the X-ray/Gamma sky

Laue lenses are innovative X and Gamma-ray optics based on the Bragg's law of diffraction in crystals[1]:

$$2d_{hkl} \sin \theta_B = n \frac{hc}{E} \quad (1)$$

Where θ_B is the Bragg's angle, which is the angle between the diffraction planes of the crystal and the diffracted beam, d_{hkl} is the inter-planar spacing of diffraction planes of the crystal with Miller indexes (hkl), E is the energy of the diffracted photon, n is the diffraction order and hc corresponds to $12.4 \text{ keV} \cdot \text{Å}$.

The crystals can be arranged in such a way that the X-ray beam can be reflected by a thin, superficial layer of the crystal (Bragg geometry, or Reflection geometry) or it can cross the whole crystal and be transmitted over it (Laue geometry, or Transmission geometry).

Optics based on Bragg's law of diffraction in Laue configuration can be of great interest in the astrophysical context because (1) Bragg's diffraction is effective up to energies of few MeV and (2) the transmission configuration can be exploited to increase the effective area of the optics.

A Laue lens, indeed, is exactly based on this concept. A Laue lens can be visualized as a spherical cap of radius R covered by crystal tiles oriented in such a way that the the radiation coming from the sky is transmitted through the crystals and sent to the focal point. The focal distance of the lens f is equal to half the curvature radius of the spherical cap[2] (Fig. 1).

There are different configurations for the crystals on the cap which can be chosen to optimize the effective area in different ways; the simplest one, which is the configuration we are using for our prototypes, is to place the crystals in concentric rings at a distance r from the axis of the lens. From the Bragg's equation, we can see that the centroid of the energy spectrum of the photons diffracted by each ring can be expressed as[2]:

$$E = \frac{hc}{2d_{hkl}} \sin\left[\frac{1}{2} \arctan\left(\frac{f}{r}\right)\right] \sim \frac{hc}{d_{hkl}} \frac{f}{r} \quad (2)$$

Where the approximation holds for small Bragg's angle, which is the case of hard X and Gamma rays. Higher energy photons are diffracted from crystals in the inner region of the lens, while lower energy photons interact with the outermost regions

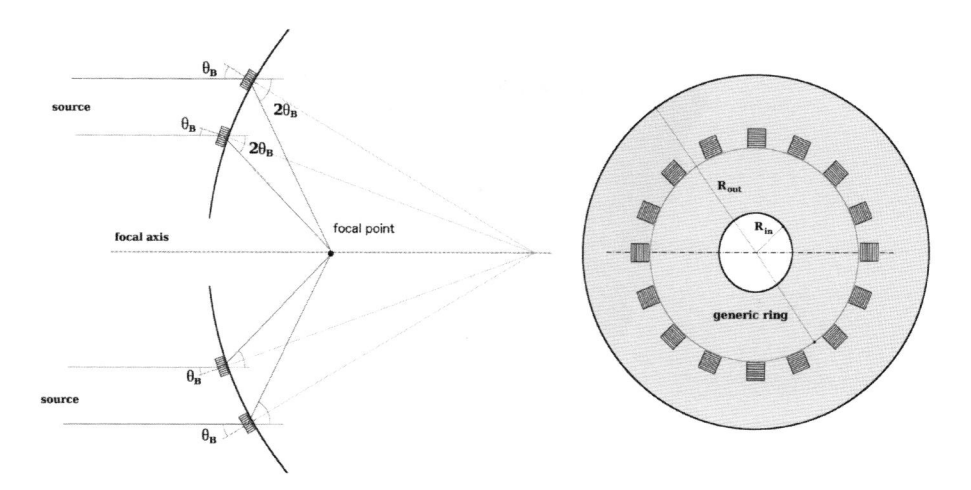

Fig. 1. Side and top view of a Laue lens. The crystals are positioned on a spherical support in such a way that the radiation coming from the sky, parallel to the optical axis of the lens, interacts with the crystals and is focused. The diffraction planes of the crystals are oriented in such a way that the angle between them and the incoming X-ray beam is equal to the Bragg's angle θ_B, so the angle between the diffracted beam and the incoming beam is $2\theta_B$. The focal lens is equal to half the curvature radius of the spherical cap.

of the optics (Fig. 2). With Laue lenses, we expect to be able to build a lightweight (<150 kg), stable optics which will enable real concentration of high energy radiation up to 600 keV at a focal distance of 20 m. Thanks to the unprecedented imaging capabilities of Laue lenses, we will be able to obtain a Point Spread Fuction (PSF) with a width of ∼30 arcsec in the energy band 50 keV - 600 keV. Comparing this with one of today's most advanced high energy instruments, the IBIS aboard INTEGRAL, whose PSF is of about 12 arcmin we can immediately understand the quantum leap in imaging capabilities that would be brought by an instrument such as a Laue lens, which will also allow us to make spectroscopy and even X-ray Compton polarimetry with an unprecented quality.

2. Bent perfect crystals

Several types of crystals can be used to build a Laue lens and the imaging capabilities and effective area of the optics are strictly related to the physical and chemical nature of the chosen crystals. Two are the families of crystals that we considered for our applications: perfect crystals and mosaic crystals.

A perfect crystal is a crystal in which the lattice plane are all oriented in the same direction. The rocking curve of the crystal has a Gaussian shape and it centered on the position satisfying Bragg's equation. The Full Width at Half Maximum (FWHM) of the rocking curve is called Darwin width.[1] A mosaic crystal, instead, can be seen as made up by microscopic perfect crystals, called *crystallites*, whose

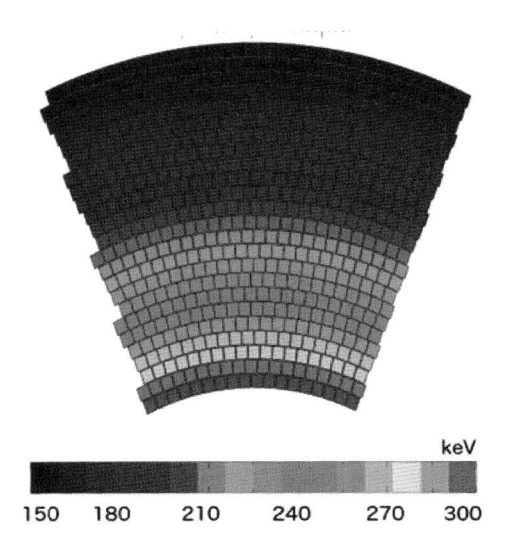

Fig. 2. In a spherical Laue lens, all the crystals at the same radial distance from the center of the lens are sensitive to the same energy range, so by nesting multiple rings it is possible to build a broad-band Laue lens. The highest energies are focused by the innermost crystals, while the lower energies are focused by the outermost crystals.

diffraction planes are misaligned around an average direction following a Gaussian distribution. The FWHM of the distribution of the cristallites is called *mosaicity* of the crystal.[1] The presence of a distribution of cristallites increases the passband of the crystals, however it also generates an effect called *mosaic defocusing*, which enlarges the PSF.

With the past HAXTEL project,[3] flat mosaic crystals of copper crystals were successfully used to build a prototype of a short-focal Laue lens. However they show some evident limits:

- Flat crystals don't have true concentration capability: they can redirect X-ray beams, however the size of the image produced by a flat crystal is comparable to the cross section of the crystal itself. This can be a problem especially in the case of long-focal lenses, for which very small crystals would be required to obtain an adequately small image.
- Flat crystals, expecially of the perfect type, show a very narrow passband.[1] Even though they can work perfectly for a narrow band Laue lens, the reduced pass-band is a problem for a broadband Laue lens, since it can be responsible of a very uneven variation of the effective area of the instrument.
- The diffraction efficiency for flat crystals cannot be higher than 50%.[1] This comes from the fact that the photon traversing the crystal have the same probability of undergoing an even or odd number of diffraction processes, limiting the maximum efficiency theoretically achievable.

The use of bent crystals allow us to overcome those limitations. A bent crystal is a crystal in which the average direction of the diffraction planes varies inside the volume of the crystals according to a definite curvature radius. If a crystal is cilindrically bent, which is the easiest type of curvature configuration attainable, then it acts as a concentrator along the bent direction, focusing the radiation coming from an astrophysical source to a focal distance equal to half the curvature radius of the crystal itself.[4] This allows us both to shrink the cross section of the image in a region smaller than size of the crystal tile, and to increase the energy passband of each crystal (Fig. 3).

This holds true both for perfect and mosaic crystals, however bent perfect crystals have some interesting properties which can make them particularly interesting for a Laue lens.

Bending a perfect crystal to a chosen curvature radius induce an internal secondary curvature on specific diffraction planes in a way related to the primary curvature radius of the crystal.[5] In this way, the average direction of the diffraction planes varies continuously inside the crystal, slightly increasing their angular spread, whose average value is called *quasi-mosaicity* of the crystal.[6]

According to the dynamical theory of diffraction in bent perfect crystals, the bending of a perfect crystal can also increase the reflectivity of the bent planes above the limit of 50%.[5] This can be explained intuitively in the following way: since the diffraction planes are curved, the probability that the beam crossing the crystal

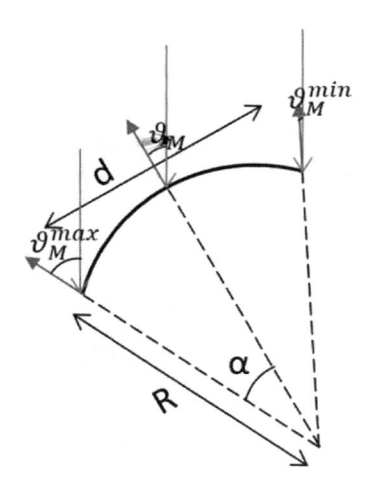

Fig. 3. Explanation of the concentration effect given by cylindrical bent crystal: due to the fact that the crystal is bent, the average direction of the diffraction planes (red arrows) varies continuously inside the crystals, which means that the Bragg's angle of the incoming radiation (blue arrows) changes accordingly. The result is that the X-ray beam is concentrated and that the crystal's energy pass-band is enlarged of a quantity which depends on the length of the focusing direction d of the crystal, its curvature radius R and its average diffracted energy.

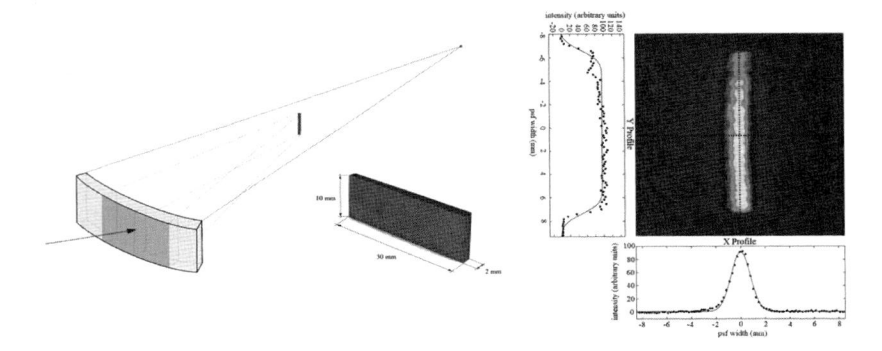

Fig. 4. Right: Schematics of the concentration effect of one cylindrical bent, 30×10 mm² crystals such as the one used in our tests. The radiation (in red) is concentrated along the focusing direction and the image is produced at a distance equal to half the curvature radius of the crystal. Left: Experimental image of a concentrated 150 keV X-ray beam obtained at the LARIX Facility. The area of the crystal is of 30×10 cm², while the area of the image is of 0.1×10 cm², which means that the beam was concentrated in an area 30 times smaller than the size of the crystal itself.

undergoes further diffractions gets reduced in a significant way. Experimental results suggest that an increase of the reflection efficiency can be effectively achieved.[7]

A crystal can be curved in an elastic way, by applying mechanical clamps to its surface, or in a plastic way, by subjecting it to a permanent deformation.[8] A mechanical bending of the crystal can bring some excessive complications for an astrophysical Laue lens, since adding further mechanical parts would increase the weight of the optics, the complexity of the design and the opacity to radiation, so crystals permanently bent are required for this type of applications.

Different methods to obtain a self-standing, cylindrical curvature have been studied and the surface lapping technique, developed at the IMEM/CNR in Parma, is one of the methods that reached a good technological maturity[9].[10] This technique consists in inducing a controlled damage by lapping one of the surfaces of the crystals, which generates an internal strain able to bend the crystal in self-standing way. The parameters of the lapping process, such as the grain of the machine, the sanding time and the final thickness of the crystals after the lapping procedure, can be set to bend the crystals to the desired curvature radius. The process can be paired with an etching process which can be used to reduce an excess of the curvature radius. By combining both methods, the curvature radius of the crystal can be fine-tuned in a very precise way. The focusing capabilities and the pass-band increase of crystals bent by surface lapping have been experimentally confirmed at our facility.[11]

For our prototype of Laue lens, we aim to use bent perfect crystals of Silicon and Germanium. Past tests done with mosaic GaAs(220) crystals curved to a radius of 40 m showed that bent crystals are able to focus high energy X-rays (Fig. 4). Now that the focusing capabilities of bent crystals has been widely assessed, we are moving to perfect Si(111) and Ge(111). According to the dynamical theory of diffraction, the (111) planes will show the properties of increased efficiency described by Malgrange's theory of bent perfect crystals.

3. The TRILL project

The TRILL project (Technological Readiness Level Increase for Laue Lenses) is a project funded by the Italian Space Agency (ASI) for the increase of the Technological Readiness Level (TRL) of technologies with a potential use in future space missions. The aim of the TRILL project is to increase the TRL of a Laue lens in all its aspects, from the production of the crystals, to their integration on the lens itself, to the performance testing using an adequate spectroscopic-imager detectors used as focal plane detectors.

To build our first prototype of Laue lens, we decided for a modular approach: the full Laue lens in divided in spherical sectors called *petals* and each petal is then divided in smaller *modules*. Every module can host some tenth of crystals (Fig. 5). Aim of the TRILL project is to build 4 modules of a Laue lens and join them together in a first prototype of a subsector of a petal.

The TRILL project is structured on the following main tasks:

(1) To define a reliable and repeatable way to bend the crystals with no deterioration of their properties. To avoid distortion on the PSF of the single crystals, it is crucial that the curvature radius of the bent Si and Ge crystals is as uniform as possible and within an accuracy of ± 2 m from the desired curvature radius of 40 m.

(2) To find the best materials and bonding method to build a module of Laue lens. To reach the desired PSF size of 30 arcsec, we need that the crystal tiles are

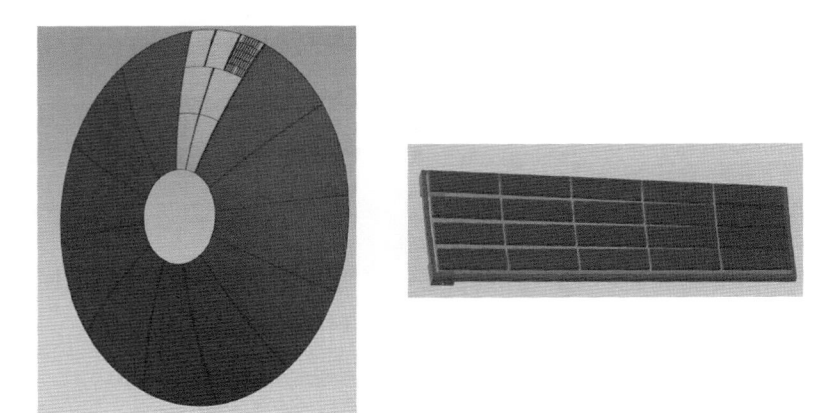

Fig. 5. Left: Schematic CAD model of a full Laue lens. The lens is divided in spherical sectors, called petals (red), and each petal is divided in a series of modules (cyan). The crystals are fixed on each module. Right: CAD model of a module of Laue lens, with 20 crystals on top.

set with an accuracy better than 10 arcsec, which requires us to find a very fine way to position the crystals.

(3) To find a way to join the modules together in one single piece. The modules will be connected in a way that will grant the possibility to adjust the position of each piece in an active way, to allow us to correct the position of the modules whenever required.

In this section, we illustrate the status of advancement of each of those 3 tasks.

The manufacturing of the crystals is done at the CNR/IMEM in Parma. Here, the crystals of Silicon and Germanium that we want to use for our prototypes are cut from wafers to obtain $30 \times 10 \times 2$ mm^3 tiles. Each tile is then bent via surface lapping to the desired curvature radius of 40 m. The procedure in the past was first tested on mosaic GaAs(220) crystals with a mosaicity of 13 arcsec. From those previous tests, we discovered that there is range of values for the crystal curvature radius for which the distortion of the image induced by a distorted curvature radius is completely masked by the mosaic defocusing effect. This allows us to reduce the constraints on the accuracy of the curvature radius of the crystals according to the value of the angular dispersion of the diffractive planes.

In the case of perfect Ge(220) crystals, the lapping procedure generates a mosaic structure on the diffraction planes of the crystals, which acquire a mosaicity of ∼5 arcsec. Given this value of mosaicity, if the curvature radius of the crystals is within ±2 m from the nominal value of 40 m, the induced distortion on the PSF is negligible.

Last tests on Ge(220) gave very promising results: the values of the curvature radius of this first sample of 38 Ge(220) crystals were in the range [37.9 ± 0.9;

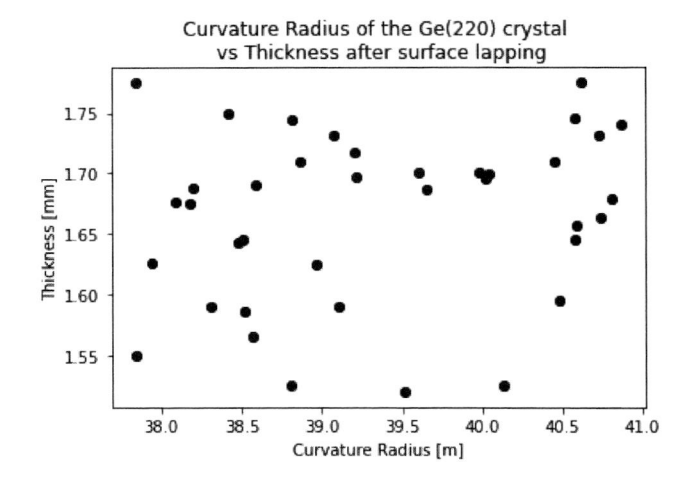

Fig. 6. Curvature radius of the sample of 38 bent crystals of Ge(220) vs their thickness after the surface lapping procedure. All the curvature radius are in the limit ±2 m from the nominal curvature radius of 40 m.

40.9 ± 0.7] m, which means that every crystal is suitable for our applications. The average value of the curvature radii distribution is of 39.3 ± 0.2 m, with a standard deviation of 1 m (Fig. 6).

The lapping procedure, however, removes part of the material and the thickness of the crystals gets significantly decreased. The final thickness of the crystals after the lapping procedure is in the interval [1.520 ± 0.005; 1.775 ± 0.005] mm, with an average value of (1.665 ± 0.002) mm (Fig. 6).

The module assembly is the second, crucial task of the TRILL project. The crystals will be bonded on an adequate substrate. Ray-tracing simulations of a full Laue lens made by bent perfect crystals of Ge(111) allowed us to establish that it is necessary a positioning accuracy of the crystals'diffracting planes <10 arcsec to obtain the desired PSF accuracy of 30 arcsec for the full lens. Given that the focal length of the lens is of 20 m, this required accuracy translates in a positional accuracy of the crystals of the order of few microns, which means that high precision bonding techniques are required to integrate the crystal on the support of the prototype.

Currently each Laue lens module consists of a glass trapezoid substrate on which the crystals are glued with a low-shrinkage UV-curable glue. Each substrate is made of clear quartz, chosen due to its transparency and its low CTE. The substrate is shaped as an isosceles trapezium with bases 68 mm and 56 mm long, while the height is 183 mm. Given that the cross section of the crystals is 30×10 mm^2 and that the spacing between the crystals glued on the substrate will be of about 1 mm, each glass support can hold about 30 crystals. The surfaces of the substrate was bent to a curvature radius of 40 mm, the same of the crystals, at the National Institute of Optics of the National Research Council, in Florence. The substrate is hold in vertical position by an INVAR steel frame.

The crystals are positioned on the glass substrate using a motorized hexapod with six degrees of freedom: three translations and three rotations. The hexapod has a accuracy of the order of 1 micron on the translational movements and of 2×10^{-5} radians on the rotations (Fig. 7, left).

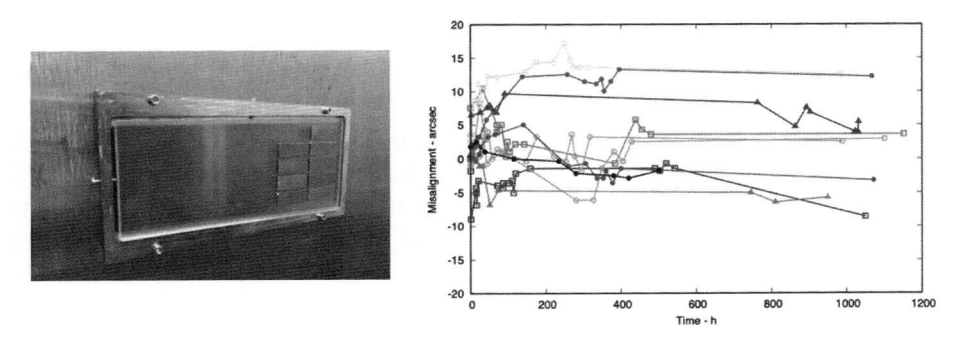

Fig. 7. Left: Laue lens module with nine crystals glued on top. The steel frame supporting the glass substrate is visible. Right: Misalignment of the crystals vs time from bonding.

Fig. 8. CAD model of the four Laue lens module assembled. The module will be connected to a steel frame by means of micrometric screws.

The glue currently used to bond the crystals to the glass substrate is the *DYMAX OP-61-LS*, an UV curable, single component optical adhesive. This glue was choosen for its very low linear shrinkage of 0.03% of its length and for its high viscosity, which makes it suitable for a vertical bonding.

The crystals are glued with the following procedure: (1) the crystal is positioned on the hexapod and oriented to the proper Bragg's angle, then (2) a small drop of glue is deposited on the substrate with a glue dispenser, (3) the crystal is then put in contact with the glue and the position is fine tuned to correct eventual slight change in the position of the crystal, (4) the glue is cured with an UV lamp and finally (5) the crystal is released from the hexapod.

The position of the crystals is then tested immediately after the bonding and also when some time has passed. We found that the misalignment of the crystals after 50 days from bonding is within the interval +15/-10 arcsec (Fig. 7, right). These first results are quite good, since we are starting to get close to our target of <10 arcsec misalignment. However at the moment this technique shows some problems of stability in time and repeatability. In particular, we are studying a better way to measure the quantity of glue deposited on the substrate and to control the illumination uniformity of the UV light used for the curing process.

The last task, i.e. the study of a way to assemble the modules together, is currently in study phase. At the moment, we plan to join the modules together by building a metal support frame in which the different modules will be fixed with high precision micrometric screws (Fig. 8). The screws will be set in position by using miniaturized piezoelectric motors, which will allow us to actively change the orientation of the module in any moment and to reduce as much as possible the effect that external solicitation can have on the final alignment of the prototype and, latter, of the full Laue lens itself.

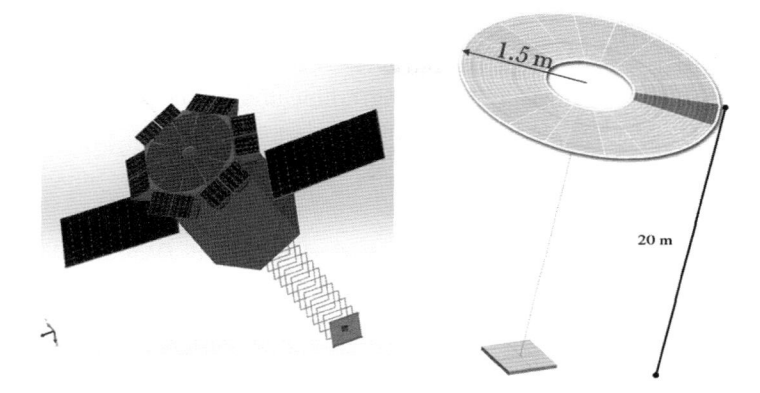

Fig. 9. Left: Representation of ASTENA's in-flight configuration. The Laue lens is shown on the top of spacecraft, in red. Right: Schematic representation of NFT. NFT will be made by a Laue lens optics with 3 m of diameter and 20 m of focal length. The focal plane detector will be a CZT spectral-imager detector.

The next step of the TRILL project will be to start the production of the bent Si(111) and Ge(111) crystals, to further optimize the bonding process and build the 4 modules and, finally, to assemble the modules together.

4. The NFT aboard ASTENA

Our studies on Laue lenses, including the TRILL project, are oriented to develop the technology for building the Narrow Field Telescope (NFT) on-board ASTENA, the Advanced Surveyor for Transient Events and Nuclear Astrophysics, a concept mission that we proposed for the ESA Call "Voyage 2050"[12].[13] The Narrow Field Telescope will be a revolutionary hard X/soft Gamma-ray focusing telescope working in the energy band 50-700 keV based on the technology of Laue lenses (Fig. 9). The NFT will be made by a Laue lens optics of 3 m of diameter with 20 m focal length. The lens will be made by about 19500 crystal tiles of perfect Si(111) and Ge(111) of size $30\times10\times2$ mm^3, bent to a curvature radius of 40 m. In the context of the TRILL project, we will then test the capabilities of the crystals that will be used for the lens and define the construction method for the whole lens.

The assumed focal plane detector will be a pixelated CdZnTe spectral-imager detector, with a size of $8\times8\times8$ cm^3, a pitch of 300 μm and an efficiency >80% in the whole energy band of NFT.

The combination between the characteristics of the optics and the detector will grant NFT of an unprecedented angular resolution in the sub-MeV energy range of 30 arcsec and a point source localization accuracy <10 arcsec, with a Field of View of 4 arcmin. NFT will bring a leap in sensitivity of two order of magnitude with respect to the best current instruments working in the same energy bands, opening a new range of possibilities for high energy astronomical observations.

Acknowledgements

This work is partly supported by the AHEAD-2020 Project grant agreement 871158 of the European Union's Horizon 2020 Programme and by the ASI-INAF agreement no. 2017-14-H.O "Studies for future scientific missions".

References

1. W. H. Zachariasen, *Theory of X-ray Diffraction in Crystals* (Wiley, 1945).
2. F. Frontera and P. V. Ballmoos, Laue gamma-ray lenses for space astrophysics:status and prospects (2011).
3. F. Frontera, G. Loffredo, A. Pisa, F. Nobili, V. Carassiti, F. Evangelisti, L. Landi, S. Squerzanti, E. Caroli, J. B. Stephen, K. H. Andersen, P. Courtois, N. Auricchio, L. Milani and B. Negri, Focusing of gamma-rays with Laue lenses: first results, in *Space Telescopes and Instrumentation 2008: Ultraviolet to Gamma Ray*, eds. M. J. L. Turner and K. A. Flanagan (SPIE, 2008).
4. E. Virgilli, F. Frontera, V. Valsan, V. Liccardo, V. Carassiti, S. Squerzanti, M. Statera, M. Parise, S. Chiozzi, F. Evangelisti, E. Caroli, J. Stephen, N. Auricchio, S. Silvestri, A. Basili, F. Cassese, L. Recanatesi, V. Guidi, V. Bellucci, R. Camattari, C. Ferrari, A. Zappettini, E. Buffagni, E. Bonnini, M. Pecora, S. Mottini and B. Negri, The laue project and its main results (2014).
5. A. Authier and C. Malgrange, Diffraction Physics, *Acta Crystallographica Section A* **54**, 806 (Nov 1998).
6. R. Camattari, V. Guidi, V. Bellucci and A. Mazzolari, The 'quasi-mosaic' effect in crystals and its applications in modern physics, *Journal of Applied Crystallography* **48** (08 2015).
7. V. Bellucci, V. Guidi, R. Camattari and I. Neri, Calculation of diffraction efficiency for curved crystals with arbitrary curvature radius, *Journal of Applied Crystallography* **46** (04 2013).
8. R. K. Smither, K. A. Saleem, D. E. Roa, M. A. Beno, P. von Ballmoos and G. K. Skinner, High diffraction efficiency, broadband, diffraction crystals for use in crystal diffraction lenses, *Experimental Astronomy* **20**, 201 (December 2005).
9. C. Ferrari, E. Buffagni, E. Bonnini and A. Zappettini, X-ray diffraction efficiency of bent GaAs mosaic crystals for the LAUE project, in *Optics for EUV, X-Ray, and Gamma-Ray Astronomy VI*, eds. S. L. O'Dell and G. Pareschi, Society of Photo-Optical Instrumentation Engineers (SPIE) Conference Series, Vol. 88612013.
10. E. Buffagni, E. Bonnini, C. Ferrari, E. Virgilli and F. Frontera, X-ray characterization of curved crystals for hard x-ray astronomy, in *EUV and X-ray Optics: Synergy between Laboratory and Space IV*, eds. R. Hudec and L. Pina, Society of Photo-Optical Instrumentation Engineers (SPIE) Conference Series, Vol. 95102015.
11. E. Virgilli, F. Frontera, P. Rosati, E. Bonnini, E. Buffagni, C. Ferrari, J. B. Stephen, E. Caroli, N. Auricchio, A. Basili and S. Silvestri, Focusing effect of bent GaAs crystals for γ-ray Laue lenses: Monte Carlo and experimental results, *Experimental Astronomy* **41**, 307 (February 2016).
12. F. Frontera, E. Virgilli, C. Guidorzi, P. Rosati, R. Diehl, T. Siegert, C. Fryer, L. Amati, N. Auricchio, R. Campana, E. Caroli, F. Fuschino, C. Labanti, M. Orlandini, E. Pian, J. B. Stephen, S. Del Sordo, C. Budtz-Jorgensen, I. Kuvvetli, S. Brandt, R. M. C. da Silva, P. Laurent, E. Bozzo, P. Mazzali and M. D. Valle, Understanding the origin of the positron annihilation line and the physics of supernova explosions, *Experimental Astronomy* **51**, 1175 (Jun 2021).

13. C. Guidorzi, F. Frontera, G. Ghirlanda, G. Stratta, C. G. Mundell, E. Virgilli, P. Rosati, E. Caroli, L. Amati, E. Pian, S. Kobayashi, G. Ghisellini, C. Fryer, M. D. Valle, R. Margutti, M. Marongiu, R. Martone, R. Campana, F. Fuschino, C. Labanti, M. Orlandini, J. B. Stephen, S. Brandt, R. C. d. Silva, P. Laurent, R. Mochkovitch, E. Bozzo, R. Ciolfi, L. Burderi and T. Di Salvo, A deep study of the high–energy transient sky, *Experimental Astronomy* **51**, 1203 (Jun 2021).

ASTENA: A mission concept for a deep study of the transient gamma-ray sky and for nuclear astrophysics

E. Virgilli[1,2,*], F. Frontera[1,3], P. Rosati[1,3,4], C. Guidorzi[1,3,4], L. Ferro[3], M. Moita[3],
M. Orlandini[1], F. Fuschino[1,2], R. Campana[1,2], C. Labanti[1], E. Marchesini[1],
E. Caroli[1], N. Auricchio[1], J. B. Stephen[1], C. Ferrari[5], S. Squerzanti[4], S. Del Sordo[6],
C. Gargano[6] and M. Pucci[7]
on behalf of the ASTENA Collaboration

[1] *INAF - OAS di Bologna, Via Piero Gobetti 93/3, I-40129 Bologna, Italy*
[2] *INFN Sezione di Bologna Viale C. Berti Pichat, 6/2 – 40127 Bologna, Italy*
[3] *Dept. of Physics and Earth Science, Univ. of Ferrara, Via Saragat 1, I-44122, Ferrara, Italy*
[4] *Istituto Nazionale di Fisica Nucleare, INFN-Sezione di Ferrara, 44122 Ferrara, Italy*
[5] *CNR-IMEM Institute, Parco Area delle Scienze 37/A, 43124 Parma, Italy*
[6] *INAF/IASF-Palermo, Via Ugo La Malfa 153, 90146 Palermo, Italy*
[7] *CNR - Istituto Nazionale di Ottica - Largo Fermi 6, 50125 Firenze, Italy*
* E-mail: enrico.virgilli@inaf.it

Gamma-ray astronomy is a branch whose potential has not yet been fully exploited. The observations of elemental and isotopic abundances in supernova (SN) explosions are key probes not only of the stellar structure and evolution but also for understanding the physics that makes Type-Ia SNe as standard candles for the study of the Universe expansion properties. In spite of its crucial role, nuclear astrophysics remains a poorly explored field mainly for the typical emission lines intensity which are vanishing small and requires very high sensitivities of the telescopes. Furthermore, in spite that the Galactic bulge-dominated intensity of positron annihilation line at 511 keV has been measured, its origin is still a mystery due to the poor angular resolution and insufficient sensitivity of the commonly employed instrumentation in the sub-MeV energy domain. To answer these scientific issues a jump in sensitivity and angular resolution with respect to the present instrumentation is required. Conceived within the EU project AHEAD, a new high energy mission, capable of tackling the previously mentioned topics, has been proposed. This concept of mission named ASTENA (Advanced Surveyor of Transient Events and Nuclear Astrophysics), includes two instruments: a Wide Field Monitor with Imaging and Spectroscopic (WFM-IS, 2 keV - 20 MeV) capabilities and a Narrow Field Telescope (NFT, 50 - 700 keV). Thanks to the combination of angular resolution, sensitivity and large FoV, ASTENA will be a breakthrough in the hard X and soft gamma–ray energy band, also enabling polarimetry in this energy band. In this talk the science goals of the mission are discussed, the payload configuration is described and expected performances in observing key targets are shown.

Keywords: Soft gamma-rays; hard x-ray telescope; Focusing gamma rays; Bragg diffraction; bent crystals.

1. Introduction

Within the H2020 European program AHEAD,[1,2] (integrated Activities for High Energy Astrophysics Domain) devoted to the assessment of future gamma-ray experiments, a Scientific Advisory Group recommended the prime scientific questions that might be addressed by a future space mission operating in the gamma-ray energy domain. The high-priorities themes resulted to be the nuclear astrophysics and

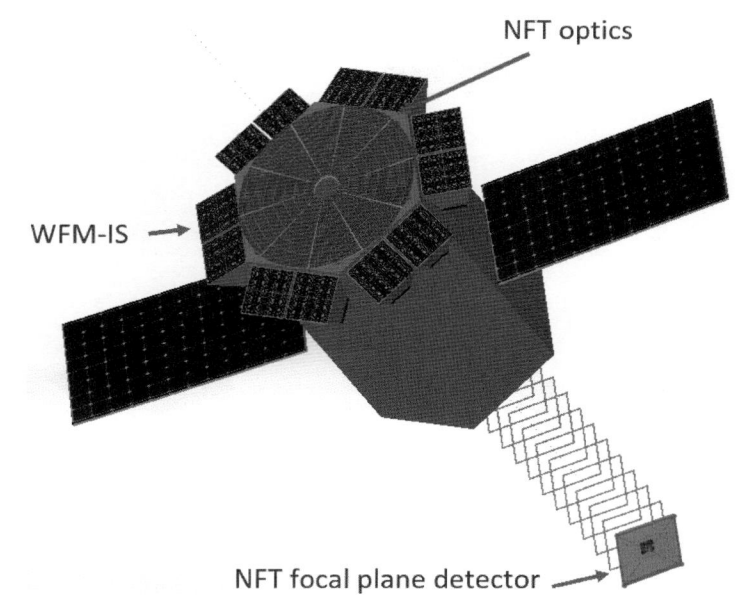

Fig. 1. Drawing of the ASTENA mission. The NFT (in red) is a 20 m focal length Laue lens made with bent Germanium and Silicon crystals. At the focal distance is positioned a focal plane detector (blue) which is a solid state device made with 4 layers of Cadmium Zinc Telluride. The focal distance is achieved through a deployable mast which at launch is fully enclosed in the spacecraft and in operative condition extends from the bottom of the spacecraft for 15 m, which is a reasonable distance for the stability of an extendable structure. The WFM-IS composed of 12 Position Sensitive Detectors (PSDs) distributed around the NFT and oriented 15 degrees two by two outwards with respect to the Laue lens axis in order to extend the FoV of the overall instrument.

the study of the transient sky. According to those themes, the ASTENA (Advanced Surveyor for Transient Events and Nuclear Astrophysics) has been designed. The ASTENA concept mission, which is shown in Fig. 1, is a broad energy pass-band experiment composed by two complementary instruments. The first is a Wide Field Monitor with Imaging and Spectrometric capabilities (WFM-IS) with an outstanding broad energy pass-band from 2 keV to 20 MeV. It consists on 12 coded mask cameras deployed in a circular pattern around the hexagonal spacecraft and oriented at 15 degrees with respect to the spacecraft axis. The overall Field of View (FoV) of the instrument is ∼2 steradians. The second instrument is a narrow FoV (few arcminutes) telescope based on a Laue lens with a geometric area of ∼7 m^2 and 20 m focal length, capable to focus photons in the broad energy pass-band 50 - 700 keV on a solid state detector. The Narrow Field Telescope (NFT) represents a technological breakthrough as its optics, based on the diffraction from bent crystals, provides an unprecedented sensitivity with respect to any other mission flown and operative in the same energy pass-band. At launch, we expect to keep the WFM-IS cameras and the focal plane detector stored within the cylindrical spacecraft

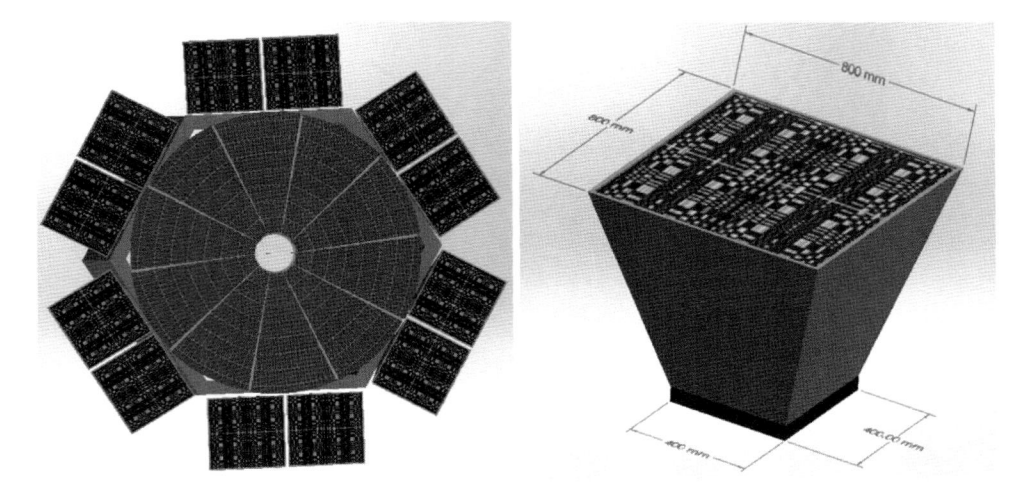

Fig. 2. Left: Top view of the instruments on board ASTENA. The 12 PSD of the WFM/IS are coupled 2 by two and are positioned around the hexagonal structure of the spacecraft. Each PSD is surmounted by a coded mask which ensures the imaging capability up to 150 keV. The red part is the broad energy pass-band Laue with 15 m focal length. Right: Detail of one PSD in which is visible the coded mask and the collimator surrounding the instrument. At the bottom (dark profile) is visible the detection plane made with scintillator bars which are coupled with SDDs (see text for the explanation of the instrument working principle).

whose diameter is 1.5 m and the length is 5 m. In the operational configuration an extendable boom brings the focal plane detector 15 m apart from the bottom of the spacecraft while a mechanism discloses and tilts the coded mask cameras at their nominal position and angle. In the following currently on-going project called AHEAD2020 the mission concept is being refined and optimized. The mission has been proposed in the ESA call "Voyage 2050"[3] as a future medium class mission for hard X-/soft gamma-ray astrophysics.[4,5] The final recommendation of the Senior Committee has confirmed the key importance of the high energy observations from space with high sensitivity and capable of enabling spectro-polarimetry based on new technologies, particularly in synergy with gravitational wave astronomy for resolving some of the fundamental questions still unanswered in astrophysics related to the nucleosynthesis in explosive events or to the accretion mechanism on compact sources.

2. The ASTENA configuration

The ASTENA mission concept builds on the complementarity between the two instruments on board. The WFM-IS is composed by 12 coded mask cameras equipped with Position Sensitive Detectors (visible in Fig.2 - left) (PSDs) distributed two by two around the hexagonal spacecraft envelope. Each pair of PSDs in the same hexagon side is co-aligned and directed towards the same direction which is radially tilted outwards of 15 degrees with respect to the satellite axis. Each PSD has a size

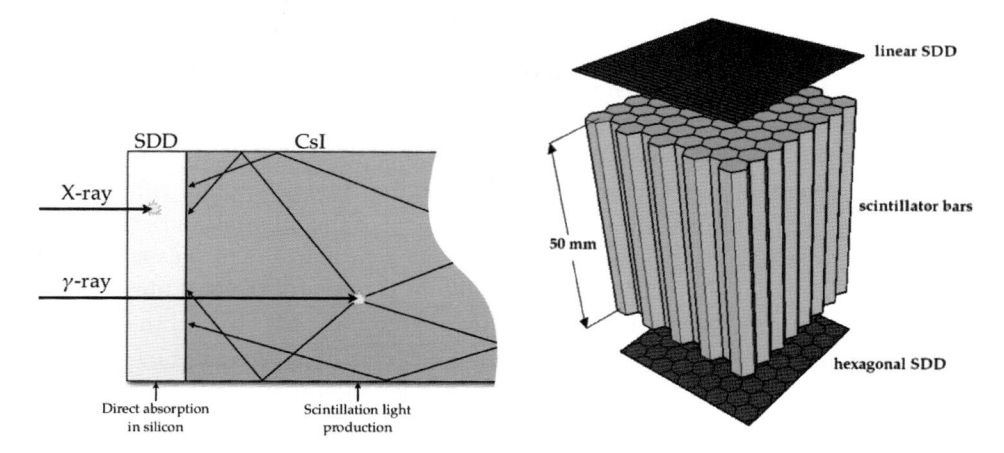

Fig. 3. Left: working principle of the WFM-IS. An hexagonal scintillator bar (cyan) is coupled at both ends (only one end is visible in the picture) with an SDD (yellow). The low energy radiation (< 30 keV) is directly absorbed in the SDD while higher energy photons pass through the SDD and interact in the scintillator bar. The scintillation light, which is produced at some distance from the surface of the scintillator bar and is reflected by the lateral surfaces, is collected by the two SDDs. The comparison between the two signals allows for the determination of the depth of interaction. Right: disposition of the scintillator bars (cyan) and of the top and bottom SDDs (grey). The top SDD is equipped with an array of linear anodes therefore the charge collected provides information only in one direction. In the bottom SDD the anodic structure has a hexagonal shape in order to fully exploit this geometry which minimizes the directional bias for polarimetric measurements, if compared with a detector with square (cubic) pixelization (voxelization).

of 43×42 cm^2 and is made of ~ 6500 scintillator bars with hexagonal cross section (5 mm between flat sides) and 50 mm long. Both ends of the scintillator bars are optically coupled with two Silicon Drift Detectors (SDDs) 400 μm thick. The instrument is based on the same detection principle of the X and Gamma-ray Imager and Spectrometer (XGIS) on board the THESEUS mission[6] which was proposed as 5th medium-class mission for the ESA Cosmic Vision Programme (M5).

The detection principle (see Fig. 3) is based on a different interaction of the radiation with the system, depending on the energy of the interacting photons. Low energy photons (< 30 keV) are directly absorbed in the SDD while photons with higher energy pass through the SDD and interact in the scintillator bar. The scintillation light, which is produced at some distance from the ends of the scintillator bars, is reflected by the lateral surfaces which are properly polished and wrapped in order to reflect as much as possible the light produced, and it is collected by the two SDDs optically coupled at both ends of the bar. For high energy photons (>30 keV) the detector is position sensitive with a 3-D resolution given that the position of interaction of the gamma-ray photon along the bar can be reconstructed by comparing the signal collected from the two opposed SDDs. The top SDDs (those facing the sky) have the dual purpose of directly detecting the low energy photons (below few tens of keV) and of collecting the scintillation light emitted by the scintillator bar when photons with higher energy pass through them. They have a linear anodic structure therefore are sensitive only to one direction (X or Y) with spatial resolution of 1.25 mm. Given that each pair of PSDs placed at the same side of the spacecraft have perpendicular anodes, they behave like a 2-D detector. Instead, the bottom SDD has hexagonal shape and it is used to get the 3-D position sensitivity. In this way we can minimize the background through the Compton kinematics reconstruction of the trajectory of the photons and exploit the polarimetric capability of the instrument. Different scintillator materials as Cesium Iodide (CsI(Tl)), Gadolinium Aluminium Gallium Garnet (GAGG), Lutetium Yttrium Orthosilicate (LYSO(Ce)) are under investigation in order to find the optimal properties to fit the instrument requirements. Each PSD is surmounted by a double scale[7] square coded mask with side of 80 cm at a distance of 70 cm from the detector plane (see Fig. 2 - right). The double scale enables imaging with Point Source Location Accuracy (PSLA) of 1 arcmin for a 7σ signal for photons with energy < 30 keV and PSLA of 5 arcmin for photons in the energy range 30 - 150 keV. In Fig. 4 (left) the PSLA as a function of the significance of the observation for different configurations of the WFM-IS is reported, compared with required PSLA of 1 arcminute. In Fig. 4 (right) the integrated sensitivity of the overall WFM-IS is reported as a function of the integration time, divided in three relevant pass-bands according to the different detection principle employed (2 - 10 keV: direct detection in the SDDs, 30 - 150 keV: interaction with the scintillator bars, 150 keV - 10 MeV: uncollimated interaction in the scintillator bar). Above 150 keV the coded mask is transparent to radiation and an effective imaging capability can be enabled through two features: 1. by exploiting the Compton kinematics for the photon direction reconstruction and 2. by taking advantage of the different measured photon intensity from the 6 blocks which are - in general - differently oriented with respect to the direction of the observed event, except for perfectly on-axis sources. With these configuration the instrument can provide a FoV of $\sim$2 sr with an angular resolution of a few arcmin and an unprecedented energy pass-band of 2 keV - 20 MeV which has never been achieved so far with a single device.

The second instrument is a 20 m long focal length Laue lens based on bent crystals made with Germanium and Silicon. The crystals are distributed in 43 concentric rings and, according to the spherical geometry and to the Bragg law, the lower energies are reflected from outer rings while inner rings are responsible for focusing the higher energies. The size of the crystals have been chosen to be 30 × 10 mm^2, the longer dimension being the focusing direction. In the other direction, no concentration is expected due to the cylindrical curvature of the tiles. The cross section of the tiles has been chosen in order to tile the overall geometric area with a moderate number of crystals ($\sim$19500) by minimizing the amount of uncovered area (the optics filling factor results above 85%). Depending on the energy to be diffracted the crystal thickness is optimized in order to maximize the diffraction efficiency. For both materials the 111 planes are assumed in order to exploit the

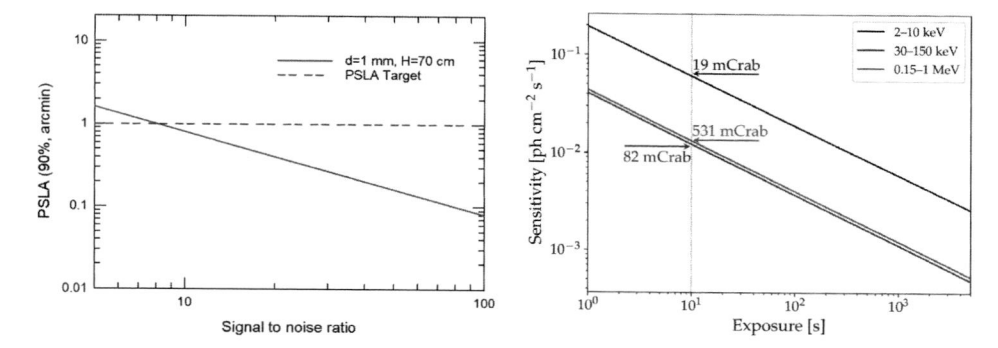

Fig. 4. Left: Point Source Location Accuracy (PSLA) for the WFM-IS as a function of the signal to noise ratio. The parameter d is the distance between the anodes of the top SDDs. The requird PSLA is also shown (green dashed line) Right: Integrated continuum sensitivity expressed in photons/cm^2/s as a function of the exposure time for the three significant energy pass-bands acquired for direct absorption in the SDDs (black curve, 2 - 10 keV), through the scintillation bars (30 - 150 keV, blue curve) and as a Compton detector with no coded mask (150 keV - 1 MeV, red curve).

so called secondary curvature of the diffraction planes induced in crystals for some crystallographic orientation (including the 111) allowing to achieve a throughput which overcomes the limitation of the 50% of the incident beam, which is the limit of mosaic and flat perfect crystals.

Orders of diffraction higher than the fundamental are being considered in the simulations in order to maximize the effective area, particularly in the energy range 500 - 520 keV (at the expenses of the effective area at lower energies) in order to increase the sensitivity at the energy of interest for the detection of the weak e$^+$/e$^-$ annihilation line from the Galactic center (see Sect. 3 for further details). At 20 m from the optics is placed the focal plane detector which is kept at the correct position with a deployable mast. The detector is made with 4 layers of Cadmium Zinc Telluride (CZT) with cross section 80×80 mm^2 each with a thickness of 20 mm. The detector has a 3-D spatial resolution of about 300 μm in all directions. This is achievable with a proper disposition of the anodes on the top and bottom of each CZT layer. Thanks to the overall detector thickness its detection efficiency is greater than 80% at 600 keV with energy resolution of 1% at 511 keV.

The NFT continuum sensitivity which has been derived at Low Earth Orbit (LEO) by comparison with the background measured by the Spectrometer on-board INTEGRAL SPI[8] is reported in Fig. 6 (top). The curve has been estimated for an integration time of 10^5 s and at 3σ confidence level. For comparison, in the plot has been reported a number of past and present experiments exploiting the direct view principle (equipped with coded masks or collimators) or using focusing telescopes. The energy band in which it is estimated is $\Delta E = E/2$, except in the band from 50 keV to 62.5 keV, in which the energy band linearly increases from $\Delta E = E/4$ to $\Delta E = E/2$, due to the absence of crystals diffracting energies

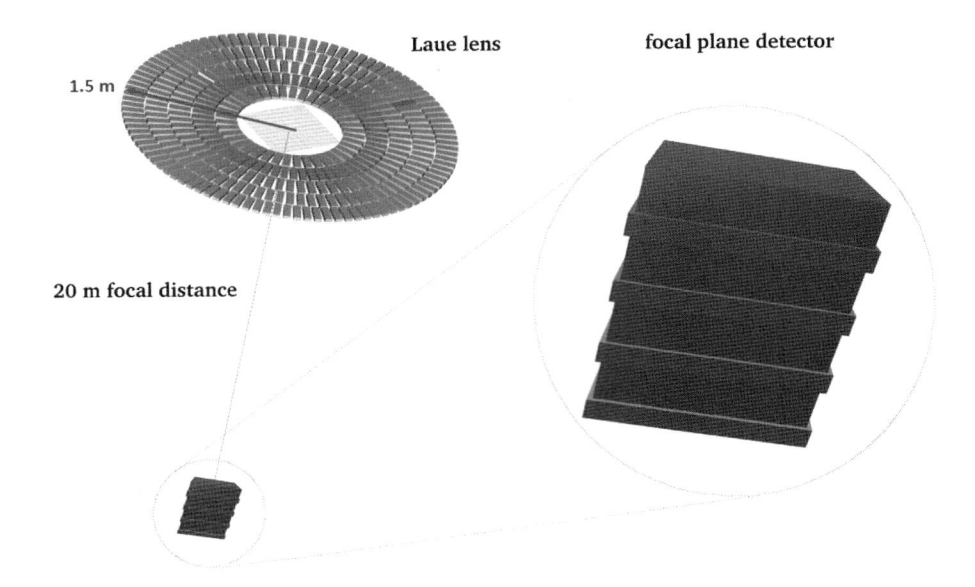

Fig. 5. Left: The optics of the NFT composed by 43 rings of crystal tiles made with Silicon and Germanium. The optics has a radius of 1.5 m for a total geometric area of about 7 m^2. At 20 m from the Laue lens is placed the focal plane detector. Right: a Geant4 drawing of the main components of the focal plane detector which is made of 4 layers of a solid state Cadmium Zinc Telluride (CZT, dark grey) with 3-D spatial resolution, spectral and polarimetric capabilities.

below 50 keV. Uncertainties in the realization of the optics have been also taken into account. The curvature radius of the crystals have been considered within 5% of the nominal radius and the mounting accuracy of about 10 arcseconds with respect to the nominal positioning. The presence of such deviations from the nominal lens realization requirements have effects on the size of the PSF and, ultimately, on the focusing power of the Laue lens. This unprecedented sensitivity is achieved thanks to the use of bent crystals with optimized thickness. Figure 6 (bottom) shows the sensitivity at measuring the flux of emission lines, at 3σ confidence level and for 10^5 s integration time. An intrinsic FWHM of 2 keV has been considered for the lines (e.g. see [9] for the 158 keV line from SN2014J). The narrow line sensitivity is about 1 order of magnitude better than SPI on board INTEGRAL at 511 keV. These values of sensitivities are mainly due to the use of bent crystals, to the transmission geometry and to the focal length that allows for an unprecedented large collecting area.

Laue optics have the great advantage of drastically reducing the instrumental background as the photons are mainly collected into an area of a few mm^2. The drawback is that, as far as the source moves out of the focal axis, the diffracted image spreads over a larger area generating ring-shaped images for coma aberrations. Through ray-tracing and Monte Carlo simulations it has been estimated that,

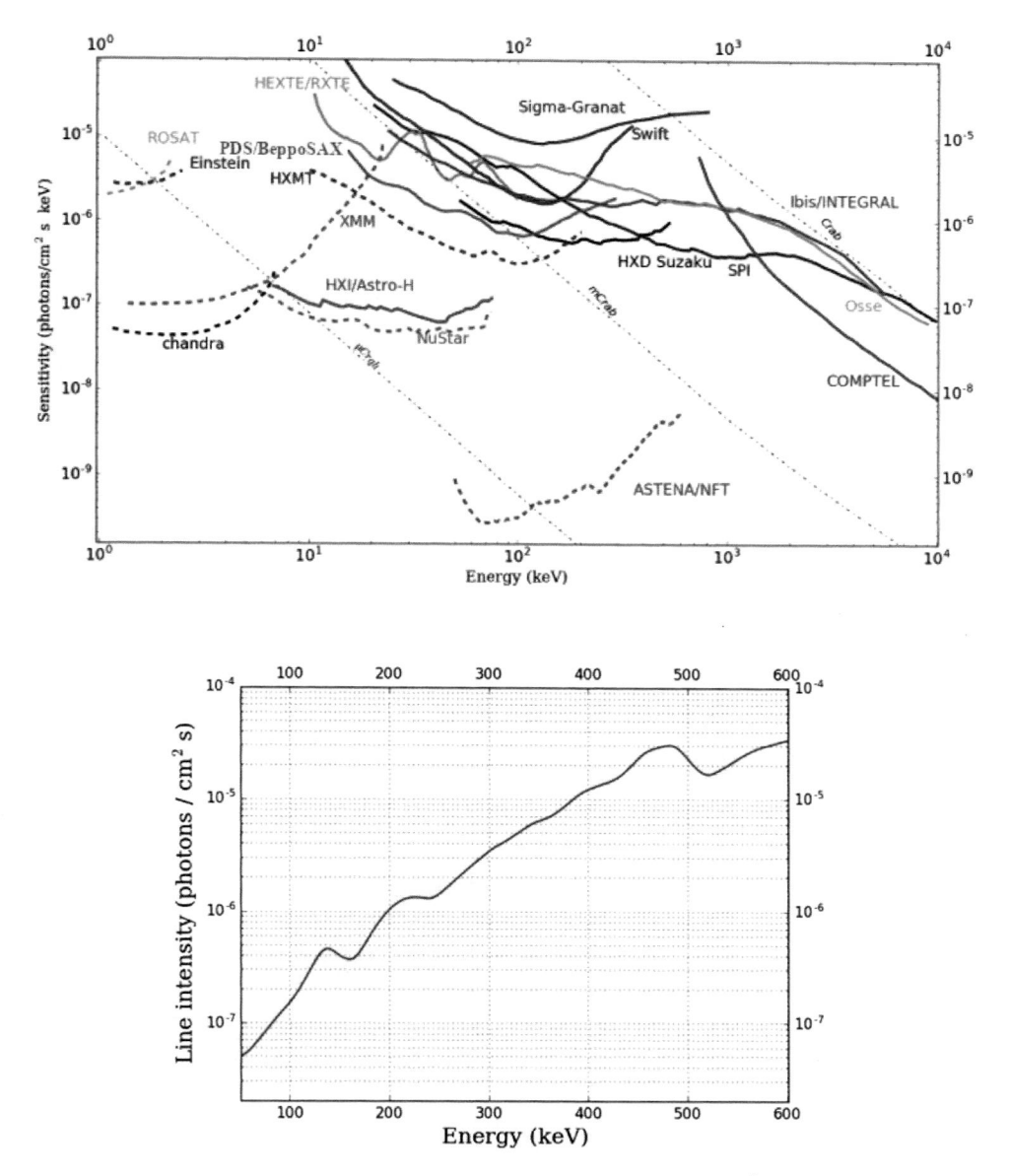

Fig. 6. Top: NFT continuum sensitivity at 3σ confidence level and in 10^5 s of observation time, with $\Delta E = E/2$, except in the band 50 to 62.5 keV, where ΔE linearly increases from $\Delta E = E/4$ to $\Delta E = E/2$, compared with the sensitivity at the same significance and with the same integration time of other missions or experiments (dashed lines represent other focusing experiment, continuum curves correspond to direct view instruments). Bottom: Expected line sensitivity for the NFT, calculated for an integration time of 10^5 s, at 3σ confidence level.

with the defined optics dimension and crystal size, photons from off-axis sources (>4 arcmin) are scattered into a broad detection area.[10] This reduces the benefits of the focusing process. Therefore the FOV of the NFT has been fitted with the PSLA of the WFM-IS in order to exploit the sensitivity of the former for nearly on-axis sources with the excellent broad-band survey capabilities of the latter.

3. Key science with ASTENA

For some relevant scientific key subjects that can be tackled with the instruments on board ASTENA see [10, 11]. Here we summarize these subjects. As mentioned in Sect. 1 the main objectives of the ASTENA mission concept are mainly two. First, ASTENA intends to investigate the intriguing key questions related to the gamma-ray lines in astrophysics. Furthermore, the high sensitivity of the on board instruments joined with the large pass-band of the WFM-IS and their polarimetric capabilities would make ASTENA an ideal tool for shading light in the transient sky, providing also an important contributions to the multi-messenger synergy.

3.1. *The transient sky observed with ASTENA*

The discovery of the Gravitational Wave (GW) event GW170817[12] and its electromagnetic counterpart GRB170817A[13–16] marked the birth of the multi-messenger study of the transient sky. In the near future, this plural effort will solve fundamental astrophysics and cosmological questions. Furthermore, it will boost the discovery of sources of known and unknown classes of transients. Short GRBs represent the main class of transient which has been already confirmed to be associated with powerful GW events.

Polarization level in the range 30 - 80% of the prompt emission of the GRBs has been claimed for a few dozens events (a summary of the properties of the events can be found in [17, 18]) but, due to the limited statistical significance of the results, their confirmation is not definitive. These uncertainties are mainly due to the lack of sensitivity of the instruments used as gamma-ray polarimeters. A significant detection could probe the geometry of the magnetic field and its intensity which are precious information for shedding light into the jet composition and dissipation mechanism. Thanks to its polarimetric capabilities, along with a large detection area and broad pass-band, the WFM-IS would be the ideal instrument to measure the degree of polarization of the prompt emission, to perform a detailed time-resolved study and to evaluate the dependence of the polarization degree with energy.

Instruments capable of measuring the electromagnetic counterpart of GW events have a crucial importance for different reasons. Firstly, they can independently confirm the astrophysical nature of a GW trigger, particularly for the faintest events. Furthermore, since present interferometers have large uncertainties in the sky localization, a high sensitive wide FoV instrument like the WFM-IS could provide the localization of the order of 1 arcmin with the possibility of performing followup observation with a soft gamma-ray telescope with an unprecedented sensitivity and angular resolution as the NFT.

It must be mentioned that with the launch of the Laser Interferometer Space Antenna (LISA) a plethora of GW events from stellar mass BH binaries will be detected in the mHz regime with a sky localization of the order of 1 deg^2. Such detections will work as alert for the observation of the same events at higher frequencies weeks/months later (with an accuracy of the order of tens of seconds) from ground interferometers. Thanks to the large FoV and to the PSLA of the WFM-IS will be possible to point in advance the instrument for the detection of the prompt hard X-ray counterpart of the event as well as the detection of the delayed hard X-ray emission through the NFT.

After the discovery of the GRB afterglow, till now this emission has been observed almost in all energy bands from IR to the soft X-ray regime up to ~ 10 keV. Afterglow detection in the 0.1–10 GeV, in the sub-TeV (100–440 GeV) and in the TeV energy regions have been reported.[19,20] One of the most important open issues that have still to be settled is the afterglow emission in the sub-MeV/MeV region which is almost completely undetected except for some events detected above few tens of keV[21–23] This is mainly due to the low flux emitted in this energy band, joined with the lack of sensitivity for the present instrumentation. From the prompt emission detected with the WFM-IS and though a fast repointing it would be possible, thanks to the sensitivity of the NFT, to measure the hard x-ray afterglow as well as its polarization level.

3.2. *Nuclear astrophysics with ASTENA*

In spite of its importance for understanding the inner regions of the astrophysical sources emitting hard X and mainly gamma-rays, nuclear astrophysics is still a theoretical field and almost experimentally unexplored, mainly due to observational limits. The reason is that present instrumentation in the hard-X and gamma-ray regime has absent or crude imaging capability and low sensitivity, compared with instruments in other wavelengths. One of the most relevant open issues in astrophysics is the origin of the 511 keV positron annihilation line observed from the Galactic Center (GC). Discovered in the seventies[24] neither the origin of the gamma emission, nor the responsible for the positron production have been found. The 511 keV annihilation line still represents a puzzle mainly due to the limitation of both sensitivity and angular resolution of current instruments operative in the 0.5 MeV region. To date, the best mapping of the line was obtained through SPI on-board INTEGRAL.[25] A variety of potential astrophysical sources responsible of the 511 keV signal and/or of the production of the positrons have been proposed, including type Ia supernovae,[26] GRBs,[27] microquasars,[28] low-mass X-ray binaries,[29] and neutron star mergers.[30] The high number of X–ray sources in the GC suggests the possibility that the 511 keV line is due to the emission of a number of discrete - unresolved - sources. The detection of a transient 0.5 MeV emission from V404 Cygni[31] is in

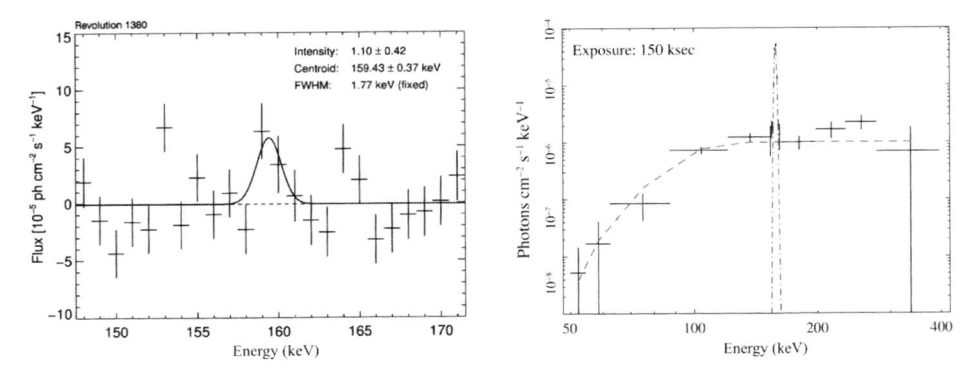

Fig. 7. Left: the 158 keV line due to the ^{56}Ni decay as observed from SN2014J as with the SPI on board INTEGRAL 3 weeks after the explosion. Reprinted from [9]. Right: the same line as observed with the NFT onboard ASTENA with 150 ks integration time. The simulated data (black points) consists of a continuum modeled with an absorbed power-law (red dashed line) with spectral index $\alpha = 0$ normalization 10^{-6} ph/cm^2/s @ 1 keV plus a Gaussian (red dot-dashed line) centered at 158 keV with σ=0.75 keV and normalization 1.1×10^{-4} ph/cm^2/s.

favour of this hypothesis. It is also believed that the 511 keV observed map would only represent the annihilation sites and not the positron sources. The propagation of the positrons away from the source could be the cause of a general broadening which originates the diffuse 511 keV emission. No point sources of annihilation radiation have yet been detected in the GC. Nevertheless, the angular resolution of INTEGRAL/SPI does not provide any definitive information about structure in the emission, even with several years of integrated data.[32] Under these considerations it is clear that observations of the GC with much higher angular resolution than that achievable with SPI aboard INTEGRAL together with high sensitive instruments are required in order to distinguish and localize - if any - discrete source of annihilation radiation.

Another topic under study that is worth to be mentioned is related to the nucleosynthesis of heavy elements in Type-Ia supernovae (SNe-Ia). Gamma-rays escaping the ejecta of SN-Ia can be used as tools for studying both the structure of the exploding star and the characteristics of the explosion. One of the key points is to estimate the amount of ^{56}Ni which is probably the most important physical parameter underlying the observed correlation of SNe-Ia luminosities with their light curves. The only direct way to estimate this amount is through the decay chain ^{56}Ni $\rightarrow$ ^{56}Co $\rightarrow$ ^{56}Fe. The decay produces gamma-rays that ultimately power the optical light curve of the SN-Ia. Most models predict that the ejected material is not transparent to gamma-rays at least for tens of days since the explosion. As the ejecta proceeds, it becomes gradually more transparent to gamma-rays. Contrarily to the expectations, only two weeks after SN2014J through SPI/INTEGRAL observations, the characteristic gamma-ray lines 158 keV and 812 keV from the ^{56}Ni decay have been detected [9] and later confirmed at 5σ confidence level also with

ISGRI/INTEGRAL.[33] The early observations of gamma-rays from ^{56}Ni support the hypotesis of the presence of this element at the star surface. The intensity of the gamma-ray spectra mainly depends on the mass and distribution of the nickel mass. High sensitivity measurements focused at particular narrow lines would shed light on the SNe-Ia explosion mechanism and, ultimately to the correct distribution and mass of ^{56}Ni.

As an example of performances with ASTENA, in Fig. 7 we show the 158 keV line detected with SPI/INTEGRAL from SN2014J[9] for an exposure time of 150 ks. The estimated line intensity of $(1.1\pm 0.4) \times 10^{-4}$ ph/cm^2/s corresponds to a detection confidence level of 2.5σ. For comparison, with the same integration time, a spectrum consisting of a Gaussian profile (centroid energy 158 keV, $\sigma = 0.75$ keV) superposed to a continuum described by a power-law with spectra slope $\alpha=0$ and normalization 10^{-6} ph/cm^2/s @ 1 keV has been simulated in order to estimate how it could be observed with the NFT aboard ASTENA. The same significance achieved by SPI in 150 ks is obtained in ~ 1 ks.

4. Conclusions

Future missions for hard X-ray astrophysics require higher sensitivity than current instrumentation and capability of observing the sky in a broad energy pass-band. Such features will be crucial for solving some of the most important open issues. In addition, hard-X and soft gamma-ray polarimetry, which are still in their infancy, will play a crucial role in combination with spectroscopy, timing and imaging, providing information about the degree and the direction of polarization of the incident radiation. Particularly in hard X-rays, whose emission comes directly from the central engine of the sources, polarimetry is a powerful tool for investigating the magnetic field and the distribution of matter around astrophysical objects. Moreover, today hard X-/gamma-ray astrophysics suffers from the absence of devices that allow the radiation to be focused, the only method through which it is possible to increase the signal to noise of the observations and to suppress the instrumental background.

The ASTENA mission concept includes two complementary instruments through which it is possible to carry out both polarimetry and imaging in the hard X-ray regime. The WFM-IS is an array of 12 monitors that can effectively work in an unprecedented energy pass-band for a single instrument (2 keV - 20 MeV) thanks to the coupling of SDDs a and scintillator bars. Thanks to the adoption of a double scale coded mask, the instrument enables localization accuracy of about 1 arcmin and 5 arcmin in the energy pass-bands < 30 keV and 30 - 150 keV, respectively. With this location accuracy, the WFM-IS is in complete synergy with the second instrument on board, the NFT: for the first time a focusing optics based on a Laue lens will be operative in a broad pass-band and with a FoV of a 4-5 arcminutes and an angular resolution of a few tens of arcseconds. Thanks to its focusing capability it provides an outstanding sensitivity for detecting source polarization[34] and both for the continuum and for nuclear lines. The unprecedented broad pass band and the large FoV of the WFM-IS will allow to make surveys and to detect faint transient sources, including GRBs. The NFT, with its deep sensitivity for nearly on-axis sources, will be the ideal tool for followup observations of detected transient events.

In this work we have presented the ASTENA mission concept and details on both instruments aboard. We have described some key science issues that can be tackled with ASTENA as a stand-alone experiment and in synergy with other experiments, including its contribution to the multi-messenger astrophysics. We expect that a mission like ASTENA will be a breakthrough in general astrophysics and in particular for answering the questions that are still central in high energy astrophysics.

Acknowledgements

This work has been partially supported with the financial contribution from the ASI-INAF agreement n. 2017-14-H.0 "Studi per future missioni scientifiche", the ASI-INAF agreement n. 2018-10-H.1-2020 "HERMES Technologic Pathfinder", and the AHEAD EU Horizon 2020 project (Integrated Activities in the High Energy Astrophysics Domain), grant agreement n. 871158.

References

1. L. Piro, L. Natalucci and Ahead Consortium, AHEAD: Integrated Activities in the High Energy Astrophysics Domain, in *Exploring the Hot and Energetic Universe: The first scientific conference dedicated to the Athena X-ray observatory*.
2. L. Piro, The Activities for the High-Energy Astrophysics Domain (AHEAD), in *Whereabouts and Physics of the Roaming Baryons in the Universe*.
3. F. Favata, G. Hasinger, L. J. Tacconi, C. S. Arridge and K. S. O'Flaherty, Introducing the Voyage 2050 White Papers, contributions from the science community to ESA's long-term plan for the Scientific Programme, *Experimental Astronomy* **51**, 551 (June 2021).
4. F. Frontera, E. Virgilli, C. Guidorzi, P. Rosati, R. Diehl, T. Siegert, C. Fryer, L. Amati, N. Auricchio, R. Campana, E. Caroli, F. Fuschino, C. Labanti, M. Orlandini, E. Pian, J. B. Stephen, S. Del Sordo, C. Budtz-Jorgensen, I. Kuvvetli, S. Brandt, R. M. Curado da Silva, P. Laurent, E. Bozzo, P. Mazzali and M. Della Valle, Understanding the origin of the positron annihilation line and the physics of the supernova explosions, *White paper in response to Voyage 2050 long term planning of ESA science programme* **1**, p. 20 (Oct 2019).
5. C. Guidorzi, F. Frontera, G. Ghirlanda, G. stratta, C. Mundell, E. Virgilli, P. Rosati, E. Caroli, L. Amati, E. Pian, S. Kobayashi, G. Ghisellini, C. Fryer, M. Della Valle, E. Margutti, M. Marongiu, R. Martone, R. Campana, F. Fuschino, C. Labanti, M. Orlandini, J. B. Stephen, S. Brandt, R. M. Curado da Silva, L. P., M. R., E. Bozzo, R. Ciolfi, L. Burderi and T. Di Salvo, Deeper and broder: future observations in the X-/gamma-ray band of known and unknown, *White paper in response to Voyage 2050 long term planning pf ESA science programme* **1**, p. 20 (Oct 2019).
6. L. Amati, P. O'Brien, D. Götz, E. Bozzo, C. Tenzer *et al.*, The THESEUS space mission concept: science case, design and expected performances, *Advances in Space Research* **62**, 191 (July 2018).

7. G. K. Skinner and J. E. Grindlay, Coded masks with two spatial scales, *Astronomy and Astrophysics* **276**, p. 673 (September 1993).
8. G. Vedrenne, J. P. Roques, V. Schönfelder, P. Mandrou, G. G. Lichti, A. von Kienlin, B. Cordier, S. Schanne, J. Knödlseder, G. Skinner, P. Jean, F. Sanchez, P. Caraveo, B. Teegarden, P. von Ballmoos, L. Bouchet, P. Paul, J. Matteson, S. Boggs, C. Wunderer, P. Leleux, G. Weidenspointner, P. Durouchoux, R. Diehl, A. Strong, M. Cassé, M. A. Clair and Y. André, SPI: The spectrometer aboard INTEGRAL, *Astronomy and Astrophysics* **411**, L63 (November 2003).
9. R. Diehl, T. Siegert, W. Hillebrandt, S. A. Grebenev, J. Greiner, M. Krause, M. Kromer, K. Maeda, F. Röpke and S. Taubenberger, Early ^{56}Ni decay gamma rays from SN2014J suggest an unusual explosion, *Science* **345**, 1162 (September 2014).
10. F. Frontera, E. Virgilli, C. Guidorzi, P. Rosati, R. Diehl, T. Siegert, C. Fryer, L. Amati, N. Auricchio, R. Campana, E. Caroli, F. Fuschino, C. Labanti, M. Orlandini, E. Pian, J. B. Stephen, S. Del Sordo, C. Budtz-Jorgensen, I. Kuvvetli, S. Brandt, R. M. C. da Silva, P. Laurent, E. Bozzo, P. Mazzali and M. D. Valle, Understanding the origin of the positron annihilation line and the physics of supernova explosions, *Experimental Astronomy* **51**, 1175 (June 2021).
11. C. Guidorzi, F. Frontera, G. Ghirlanda, G. Stratta, C. G. Mundell, E. Virgilli, P. Rosati, E. Caroli, L. Amati, E. Pian, S. Kobayashi, G. Ghisellini, C. Fryer, M. D. Valle, R. Margutti, M. Marongiu, R. Martone, R. Campana, F. Fuschino, C. Labanti, M. Orlandini, J. B. Stephen, S. Brandt, R. C. d. Silva, P. Laurent, R. Mochkovitch, E. Bozzo, R. Ciolfi, L. Burderi and T. Di Salvo, A deep study of the high-energy transient sky, *Experimental Astronomy* **51**, 1203 (June 2021).
12. B. P. Abbott, LIGO Scientific Collaboration and Virgo Collaboration, GW170817: Observation of Gravitational Waves from a Binary Neutron Star Inspiral, *prl* **119**, p. 161101 (October 2017).
13. A. von Kienlin, C. Meegan and A. Goldstein, GRB 170817A: Fermi GBM detection., *GRB Coordinates Network* **21520**, p. 1 (January 2017).
14. V. Connaughton, GBM-LIGO Group, L. Blackburn, M. S. Briggs, J. Broida, E. Burns, J. Camp, T. Dal Canton, N. Christensen, A. Goldstein, R. Hamburg, C. M. Hui, P. Jenke, D. Kocevski, N. Leroy, T. Littenberg, J. McEnery, R. Preece, J. Racusin, P. Shawhan, K. Siellez, L. Singer, J. Veitch, P. Veres and C. Wilson-Hodge, LIGO/Virgo G298048: Fermi GBM trigger 170817.529 and LIGO single IFO trigger, *GRB Coordinates Network* **21506**, p. 1 (August 2017).
15. A. Goldstein, P. Veres, E. Burns, M. S. Briggs, R. Hamburg, D. Kocevski, C. A. Wilson-Hodge, R. D. Preece, S. Poolakkil, O. J. Roberts, C. M. Hui, V. Connaughton, J. Racusin, A. von Kienlin, T. Dal Canton, N. Christensen, T. Littenberg, K. Siellez, L. Blackburn, J. Broida, E. Bissaldi, W. H. Cleveland, M. H. Gibby, M. M. Giles, R. M. Kippen, S. McBreen, J. McEnery, C. A. Meegan, W. S. Paciesas and M. Stanbro, An Ordinary Short Gamma-Ray Burst with Extraordinary Implications: Fermi-GBM Detection of GRB 170817A, *ApJ Letter* **848**, p. L14 (October 2017).
16. V. Savchenko, C. Ferrigno, E. Kuulkers, A. Bazzano, E. Bozzo, S. Brandt, J. Chenevez, T. J. L. Courvoisier, R. Diehl, A. Domingo, L. Hanlon, E. Jourdain, A. von Kienlin, P. Laurent, F. Lebrun, A. Lutovinov, A. Martin-Carrillo, S. Mereghetti, L. Natalucci, J. Rodi, J. P. Roques, R. Sunyaev and P. Ubertini, INTEGRAL Detection of the First Prompt Gamma-Ray Signal Coincident with the Gravitational-wave Event GW170817, *ApJ Letter* **848**, p. L15 (October 2017).
17. M. L. McConnell, High energy polarimetry of prompt GRB emission, *New Astronomy Review* **76**, 1 (February 2017).

18. R. Gill, M. Kole and J. Granot, GRB Polarization: A Unique Probe of GRB Physics, *Galaxies* **9**, p. 82 (October 2021).
19. H. Abdalla, R. Adam, F. Aharonian, F. Ait Benkhali, E. O. Angüner, M. Arakawa, C. Arcaro, C. Armand, H. Ashkar, M. Backes, V. Barbosa Martins, M. Barnard, Y. Becherini, D. Berge, K. Bernlöhr, E. Bissaldi, R. Blackwell, M. Böttcher, C. Boisson, J. Bolmont, S. Bonnefoy, J. Bregeon, M. Breuhaus, F. Brun, P. Brun, M. Bryan, M. Büchele, T. Bulik, T. Bylund, M. Capasso, S. Caroff, A. Carosi, S. Casanova, M. Cerruti, T. Chand, S. Chandra, A. Chen, S. Colafrancesco, M. Curyło, I. D. Davids, C. Deil, J. Devin, P. deWilt, L. Dirson, A. Djannati-Ataï, A. Dmytriiev, A. Donath, V. Doroshenko, J. Dyks, K. Egberts, G. Emery, J. P. Ernenwein, S. Eschbach, K. Feijen, S. Fegan, A. Fiasson, G. Fontaine, S. Funk, M. Füßling, S. Gabici, Y. A. Gallant, F. Gaté, G. Giavitto, L. Giunti, D. Glawion, J. F. Glicenstein, D. Gottschall, M. H. Grondin, J. Hahn, M. Haupt, G. Heinzelmann, G. Henri, G. Hermann, J. A. Hinton, W. Hofmann, C. Hoischen, T. L. Holch, M. Holler, D. Horns, D. Huber, H. Iwasaki, M. Jamrozy, D. Jankowsky, F. Jankowsky, A. Jardin-Blicq, I. Jung-Richardt, M. A. Kastendieck, K. Katarzyński, M. Katsuragawa, U. Katz, D. Khangulyan, B. Khélifi, J. King, S. Klepser, W. Kluźniak, N. Komin, K. Kosack, D. Kostunin, M. Kreter, G. Lamanna, A. Lemière, M. Lemoine-Goumard, J. P. Lenain, E. Leser, C. Levy, T. Lohse, I. Lypova, J. Mackey, J. Majumdar, D. Malyshev, V. Marandon, A. Marcowith, A. Mares, C. Mariaud, G. Martí-Devesa, R. Marx, G. Maurin, P. J. Meintjes, A. M. W. Mitchell, R. Moderski, M. Mohamed, L. Mohrmann, C. Moore, E. Moulin, J. Muller, T. Murach, S. Nakashima, M. de Naurois, H. Ndiyavala, F. Niederwanger, J. Niemiec, L. Oakes, P. O'Brien, H. Odaka, S. Ohm, E. de Ona Wilhelmi, M. Ostrowski, I. Oya, M. Panter, R. D. Parsons, C. Perennes, P. O. Petrucci, B. Peyaud, Q. Piel, S. Pita, V. Poireau, A. Priyana Noel, D. A. Prokhorov, H. Prokoph, G. Pühlhofer, M. Punch, A. Quirrenbach, S. Raab, R. Rauth, A. Reimer, O. Reimer, Q. Remy, M. Renaud, F. Rieger, L. Rinchiuso, C. Romoli, G. Rowell, B. Rudak, E. Ruiz-Velasco, V. Sahakian, S. Sailer, S. Saito, D. A. Sanchez, A. Santangelo, M. Sasaki, R. Schlickeiser, F. Schüssler, A. Schulz, H. M. Schutte, U. Schwanke, S. Schwemmer, M. Seglar-Arroyo, M. Senniappan, A. S. Seyffert, N. Shafi, K. Shiningayamwe, R. Simoni, A. Sinha, H. Sol, A. Specovius, M. Spir-Jacob, Ł. Stawarz, R. Steenkamp, C. Stegmann, C. Steppa, T. Takahashi, T. Tavernier, A. M. Taylor, R. Terrier, D. Tiziani, M. Tluczykont, C. Trichard, M. Tsirou, N. Tsuji, R. Tuffs, Y. Uchiyama, D. J. van der Walt, C. van Eldik, C. van Rensburg, B. van Soelen, G. Vasileiadis, J. Veh, C. Venter, P. Vincent, J. Vink, H. J. Völk, T. Vuillaume, Z. Wadiasingh, S. J. Wagner, R. White, A. Wierzcholska, R. Yang, H. Yoneda, M. Zacharias, R. Zanin, A. A. Zdziarski, A. Zech, A. Ziegler, J. Zorn, N. Żywucka, F. de Palma, M. Axelsson and O. J. Roberts, A very-high-energy component deep in the gamma-ray burst afterglow, *Nature* **575**, 464 (November 2019).
20. MAGIC Collaboration, V. A. Acciari, S. Ansoldi, L. A. Antonelli, A. Arbet Engels, D. Baack, A. Babić, B. Banerjee, U. Barres de Almeida, J. A. Barrio, J. Becerra González, W. Bednarek, L. Bellizzi, E. Bernardini, A. Berti, J. Besenrieder, W. Bhattacharyya, C. Bigongiari, A. Biland, O. Blanch, G. Bonnoli, Ž. Bošnjak, G. Busetto, A. Carosi, R. Carosi, G. Ceribella, Y. Chai, A. Chilingaryan, S. Cikota, S. M. Colak, U. Colin, E. Colombo, J. L. Contreras, J. Cortina, S. Covino, G. D'Amico, V. D'Elia, P. da Vela, F. Dazzi, A. de Angelis, B. de Lotto, M. Delfino, J. Delgado, D. Depaoli, F. di Pierro, L. di Venere, E. Do Souto Espiñeira, D. Dominis Prester, A. Donini, D. Dorner, M. Doro, D. Elsaesser, V. Fallah Ramazani, A. Fattorini, A. Fernández-Barral, G. Ferrara, D. Fidalgo, L. Foffano, M. V. Fonseca, L. Font, C. Fruck, S. Fukami, S. Gallozzi, R. J. García López, M. Garczarczyk, S. Gasparyan, M. Gaug, N. Giglietto,

F. Giordano, N. Godinović, D. Green, D. Guberman, D. Hadasch, A. Hahn, J. Herrera, J. Hoang, D. Hrupec, M. Hütten, T. Inada, S. Inoue, K. Ishio, Y. Iwamura, L. Jouvin, D. Kerszberg, H. Kubo, J. Kushida, A. Lamastra, D. Lelas, F. Leone, E. Lindfors, S. Lombardi, F. Longo, M. López, R. López-Coto, A. López-Oramas, S. Loporchio, B. Machado de Oliveira Fraga, C. Maggio, P. Majumdar, M. Makariev, M. Mallamaci, G. Maneva, M. Manganaro, K. Mannheim, L. Maraschi, M. Mariotti, M. Martínez, S. Masuda, D. Mazin, S. Mićanović, D. Miceli, M. Minev, J. M. Miranda, R. Mirzoyan, E. Molina, A. Moralejo, D. Morcuende, V. Moreno, E. Moretti, P. Munar-Adrover, V. Neustroev, C. Nigro, K. Nilsson, D. Ninci, K. Nishijima, K. Noda, L. Nogués, M. Nöthe, S. Nozaki, S. Paiano, J. Palacio, M. Palatiello, D. Paneque, R. Paoletti, J. M. Paredes, P. Peñil, M. Peresano, M. Persic, P. G. Prada Moroni, E. Prandini, I. Puljak, W. Rhode, M. Ribó, J. Rico, C. Righi, A. Rugliancich, L. Saha, N. Sahakyan, T. Saito, S. Sakurai, K. Satalecka, K. Schmidt, T. Schweizer, J. Sitarek, I. Šnidarić, D. Sobczynska, A. Somero, A. Stamerra, D. Strom, M. Strzys, Y. Suda, T. Surić, M. Takahashi, F. Tavecchio, P. Temnikov, T. Terzić, M. Teshima, N. Torres-Albà, L. Tosti, S. Tsujimoto, V. Vagelli, J. van Scherpenberg, G. Vanzo, M. Vazquez Acosta, C. F. Vigorito, V. Vitale, I. Vovk, M. Will, D. Zarić and L. Nava, Teraelectronvolt emission from the gamma-ray burst GRB 190114C, *Nature* **575**, 455 (November 2019).

21. E. Maiorano, N. Masetti, E. Palazzi, F. Frontera, P. Grandi and et al., The puzzling case of GRB 990123: multiwavelength afterglow study, *Astronomy and Astrophysics* **438**, 821 (August 2005).
22. C. Kouveliotou, J. Granot, J. L. Racusin, E. Bellm, G. Vianello, S. Oates, C. L. Fryer, S. E. Boggs, F. E. Christensen, W. W. Craig, C. D. Dermer, N. Gehrels, C. J. Hailey, F. A. Harrison, A. Melandri, J. E. McEnery, C. G. Mundell, D. K. Stern, G. Tagliaferri and W. W. Zhang, NuSTAR Observations of GRB 130427A Establish a Single Component Synchrotron Afterglow Origin for the Late Optical to Multi-GeV Emission, *ApJ Letter* **779**, p. L1 (December 2013).
23. A. Martin-Carrillo, L. Hanlon, M. Topinka and et al., GRB 120711A: An intense INTEGRAL burst with long-lasting soft γ-ray emission and a powerful optical flash, *Astronomy and Astrophysics* **567**, p. A84 (Jul 2014).
24. I. Johnson, W. N. and R. C. Haymes, Detection of a Gamma-Ray Spectral Line from the Galactic-Center Region, *Astrophysical Journal* **184**, 103 (August 1973).
25. J. Knödlseder and GRI Consortium, GRI: The Gamma-Ray Imager Mission, in *The Obscured Universe. Proceedings of the VI INTEGRAL Workshop (2007)*,
26. E. Kalemci, S. E. Boggs, P. A. Milne and S. P. Reynolds, Searching for Annihilation Radiation from SN 1006 with SPI on INTEGRAL, *ApJ Letter* **640**, L55 (March 2006).
27. G. Bertone, A. Kusenko, S. Palomares-Ruiz, S. Pascoli and D. Semikoz, Gamma-ray bursts and the origin of galactic positrons, *Physics Letters B* **636**, 20 (April 2006).
28. N. Guessoum, P. Jean and N. Prantzos, Microquasars as sources of positron annihilation radiation, *Astronomy and Astrophysics* **457**, 753 (October 2006).
29. N. Prantzos, Astrophysical gamma-ray lines: A probe of stellar nucleosynthesis and star formation, in *5th INTEGRAL Workshop on the INTEGRAL Universe (2004)*,
30. R. Bartels, F. Calore, E. Storm and C. Weniger, Galactic binaries can explain the Fermi Galactic centre excess and 511 keV emission, *MNRAS* **480**, 3826 (November 2018).
31. T. Siegert, R. Diehl, J. Greiner, M. G. H. Krause, A. M. Beloborodov, M. C. Bel, F. Guglielmetti, J. Rodriguez, A. W. Strong and X. Zhang, Positron annihilation signatures associated with the outburst of the microquasar V404 Cygni, *Nature* **531**, 341 (March 2016).

32. L. Bouchet, J. P. Roques and E. Jourdain, On the Morphology of the Electron-Positron Annihilation Emission as Seen by Spi/integral, *Astrophysical Journal* **720**, 1772 (Sep 2010).
33. J. Isern, P. Jean, E. Bravo, J. Knödlseder and et al., Gamma-ray emission from SN2014J near maximum optical light, *Astrophysical Journal* **588**, p. A67 (Apr 2016).
34. M. Moita, M. Ferro, U. Frontera, O. Caroli, R. Virgilli, P. Stephen, F. Curado da Silva, P. Maia and A. Del Sordo, "Polarimetric prospects of a new hard X-/soft gamma-ray space mission for next decades", these proceedings.

Polarimetric prospects of a new hard X-soft gamma-ray space mission for next decades

M. Moita*, L. Ferro and F. Frontera

*Dept. of Physics and Earth Science,
University of Ferrara, Ferrara, Italy*
E-mail: mmoita@fe.infn.it

E. Caroli, E. Virgilli and J. B. Stephen

*OAS of Bologna INAF Bologna,
Bologna, Italy*

R. M. Curado da Silva and M. Maia

*LIP-Laboratório de Instrumentação e Física Experimental de Partículas,
Coimbra, Portugal*

S. del Sordo

*IASF-Palermo INAF Palermo,
Palermo, Italy*

The measurement of the polarization of the high-energy photons from cosmic sources has now become a key observational parameter for understanding the emission mechanisms and the geometry of the active regions involved. Therefore, a mandatory requirement for new instrumentation in this energy regime will provide high sensitivity for polarimetric measurements associated with spectroscopy and imaging.

In this perspective, the Advanced Surveyor of Transient Events and Nuclear Astrophysics (ASTENA) mission, which includes two main instruments: the Wide field monitor (WFM-IS), with a large effective area and a wide energy passband (2 keV – 20 MeV); and the Narrow Field Telescope (NFT), with a broad energy passband (50–600 keV) with focusing capabilities based on the use of an advanced Laue lens; will both provide high sensitivity for polarimetric measurements. Furthermore, both instruments will include spectometers with a good 3D spatial resolution allowing to perform 3D Compton polarimetry, increasing the possibilities to optimize the event selection. Herein, we report on the results of a Monte Carlo study devoted to optimize the configuration of both instruments, in particular, the modulation factor (Q), the events detection efficiency (Eff) and the Minimum Detectable Polarization (MDP).

Keywords: Polarimetry, Gamma-ray detectors, Space instrumentation, Compton scattering.

1. Introduction

Polarimetry of high-energy sources is a key observational parameter for a better understanding of the emission mechanisms and geometry of a wide number of cosmic objects and events such as GRBs, pulsars, binary black holes and active galactic nuclei, whose emissions are expected to be polarized. The field of hard

X-ray polarimetry has been quite active in the last two decades: missions such as INTEGRAL, AstroSat and POLAR have provided some important scientific inputs in understanding emission mechanism and geometry in X-ray pulsars,[1-3] magnetic field structure in Pulsar Wind Nebula (PWN),[1,4] disk-jet interplay in black hole X-ray binaries (XRBs)[5,6] and hard X-ray emission mechanism in GRB prompt emission.[7-9] Though these results are marred with large uncertainties and a firm conclusion is not possible, most of these findings are extremely interesting as they pose new challenges to the existing theories. One interesting and common feature in all these measurements is a systematic increase in polarization within the hard X-ray band which makes this energy regime extremely promising for polarimetry experiments.[10]

As a part of the European project AHEAD (integrated Activities in the High Energy Astrophysics Domain), a new concept of high energy mission named ASTENA (Advanced Surveyor of Transient Events and Nuclear Astrophysics) has been proposed and accepted for feasibility and performance study.[11] In the current AHEAD 2020 project, which is a continuation of AHEAD, we deepen the feasibility study of ASTENA and increase our knowledge on the potential performances of the instruments on board concerning spectral, imaging and, particularly in this context, polarization capabilities. In this work we present the results of a study that aims to reliably and realistically evaluate the performance in terms of polarimetry that can be achieved with the ASTENA and to optimize the design of the detection units to achieve this aim taking into account the requirements.

2. ASTENA

The ASTENA configuration is described in,[12] and it is shown in Fig. 1. Its main properties are summarized in Table 1. The instrumentation on board consists of a Wide Field Monitor–Imaging Spectrometer (WFM-IS) with a 2 keV–20 MeV passband, and a Narrow Field Telescope (NFT) with a 50–600 keV passband.

Table 1. Summary of the main properties of the WFM-IS and of the NFT on board ASTENA.

	WFM-IS	NFT
Energy pass-band	2 keV – 20 MeV	50 – 600 keV
Total useful area[a]	~ 5800 cm^2 (< 30 keV) ~ 6700 cm^2 (30–150 keV) ~ 13800 cm^2 (>200 keV)	7 m^2 (projected)
Field of View	2 sr	4 arcmin
Angular resolution	6 arcmin	~ 30 arcsec HPD
Point source localization accuracy	1 arcmin	< 10 arcsec
3σ, **Continuum Sensitivity** (ph/cm^2 s keV)	1×10^{-4} (10 s, 30–150 keV)	1.2×10^{-9} (10^5 s, 225–375 keV)
3σ, 10^5 s **Line sensitivity** (ph/cm^2 s)	-	5×10^{-7} (178 keV)

Note: [a]Total geometric area through the mask or collimator.

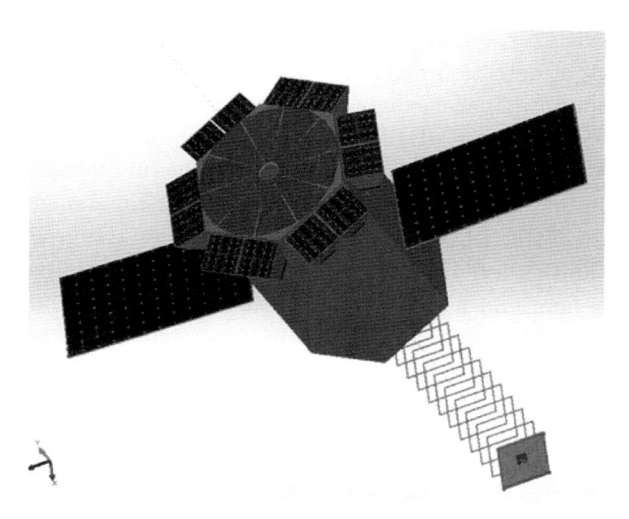

Fig. 1. The ASTENA satellite in inflight configuration. The WFM/S modules surround the NFT Laue lens (front), while its focal plane is positioned 20 m apart by a booming structure (back).

The NFT is a Laue lens focusing telescope with a 3 m diameter and 20 m focal length, composed by a large number of crystal tiles in transmission configuration, that are disposed in such a way that they concentrate the incident radiation onto a common focal spot.[13] The lens proposed for the NFT is made of ∼19500 bent crystal tiles of Si(111) and Ge(111), with 40 m curvature radius (within 5% uncertainty). The crystal tiles have a 30×10 mm^2 cross section, and an optimized thickness vs. energy for maximizing the diffraction efficiency, with the condition of a maximum thickness of 5 mm. The crystals are disposed on 43 rings, with an outermost ring radius of 149 cm and an innermost of 18 cm, ensuring an energy passband of 50 keV (outermost rings) to 600 keV (innermost rings). Current Monte Carlo simulations, ray-trace analyses and laboratory experiments evaluated that an angular resolution of 0.5 arcmin can be achieved, with a useful FOV of approximately 4 arcmin.[14]

Concerning the NFT focal plane detector, the adopted configuration consists of 4 layers of drift strip detectors of CdZnTe,[15] each layer with a cross section a 80×80 mm^2 and a thickness of 20 mm. This configuration will ensure a detection efficiency higher than 80% in the entire energy band of the NFT, a spectroscopy response of 1% @ 511 keV and fine spatial resolution (0.2–0.3 mm) in three dimensions,[16] allowing the correct sampling of the Point Spread Function (PSF) of the lens, that is of the order of a few mm^2. Thanks to the unprecedented sensitivity that can be achieved with the Laue lens focusing technique and the high segmentation level the focal plane detector, NFT is expected to provide fine polarization measurements.

The WFM-IS consists of an array of 12 units, two units on each side of the hexagon surrounding the NFT, accommodated as shown in Fig. 1. All the units are offset by 15 deg with respect to the axis of the NFT. Each WFM-IS unit consists of a 40 × 40 array of detection elements, each made of a scintillator bar (CsI(TI) or similar) 5 cm long, with an hexagonal cross section of about 75 mm^2, viewed by two Silicon Drift Detectors (SDD) 0.4 mm thick, one on the top (side of entrance of the celestial photons) and other on the bottom. The functioning principle of this detector is similar to that adopted for the X-Gamma-ray Imaging Spectrometer (XGIS) aboard the THESEUS mission concept.[17] It has the great advantage of a very broad passband (2 keV–20 MeV), a 3-D position sensitivity to energy losses in the scintillator bars and a very low intrinsic background. The hexagonal cross section of the bars, which allows us to obtain a low geometric systematic effect in the polarization measurements, associated with the 3D position sensitivity of the detector makes the WFM-IS suitable for fine polarization measurements.[11]

3. Compton Polarimetry with ASTENA

In the hard X- and soft γ-rays regime the measurement of the polarization status of a photon beam rely on the Compton scattering mechanism. The detectors on-board ASTENA provide the segmentation needed to offer an efficient method to measure the linear polarisation of incoming photons using Compton scattering because, with a coincidence event logic, each element/pixel can act at the same time both as a scattering element and as a detection unit allowing to record the pairs of events that provide polarimetric information: one is the Compton scattering of the incoming photon, the other is the interaction by Compton or photoelectric effect of the secondary photon.[10]

The cross-section of a hard X-ray photon to interact with a free electron is given by the Compton scattering cross-section described by the Klein–Nishina equation[18]:

$$\frac{d\sigma}{d\Omega} = \frac{r_0^2 \varepsilon^2}{2} \left(\frac{1}{\varepsilon} + \varepsilon - 2\sin^2\theta \cos^2\varphi \right) \quad (1)$$

where r_0^2 is the classic electron radius, $\varepsilon = E'/E$ the ratio between the energy of the scattered photon and the energy of the incoming photon, θ is the scattering angle of the scattered photon measured from the direction of the incident photon, and φ is the azimuth scattering angle with respect to the electric vector of the incident photon. On a segmented detector the distribution of the azimuthal angle measured on a large sample of data has a sinusoidal behavior with period π

$$N(\phi) = a_0(1 + a_1 \cos(2(\phi - a_2 + \pi/2))) \quad (2)$$

where a_0 is the normalization constant, $Q = a_1$ the modulation factor, and $P = a_2$ the polarization angle which are obtained from a fit to the data. This distribution is the called "modulation curve", which is built dividing the scattering map on a fixed number of angular sectors, covering 360°, and integrating the counts inside each angular sector. The aperture of the angular sectors should be chosen taking into account the discretization level of the detector (i.e., the pixel dimensions) and the counts statistics. Because of the segmented nature of the detector, the integration of count inside a defined angular sector should take into account effects due to pixels that lie across their borders. Methods to account for these pixels are, for example, that of distributing uniformly the pixel counts proportionally to the area of the pixel intercepted by two adjacent angular sectors. For the analyses performed the number of bins of the azimuthal distribution was optimized for each instrument since it affects the shape of the modulation curve.

In the characterization of a polarimeter it is important to describe its response not only to polarized, but also to unpolarized signals. For a perfectly uniform and symmetric instrument the modulation curve from a 0% polarized signal should be totally flat. However, the detector geometry introduces an asymmetry that is important to correct the signal from this component. We correct the measured modulation curve from the instrument response to a unpolarized signal by applying the following expression for each angle bin:

$$N_{corr}(\phi) = \frac{N_p(\phi)}{N_{np}(\phi)} N_{np}^{max} \qquad (3)$$

where $N_{corr}(\phi)$ is the corrected azimuthal distribution, $N_p(\phi)$ is the polarized azimuthal distribution, $N_{np}(\phi)$ the non polarized modulation azimuthal distribution, and N_{np}^{max} the maximum of the non polarized azimuthal distribution. In practice, the systematic uncertainty in the polarization measurement will be estimated from the results of an extensive on-ground calibration campaign of the instruments, using both polarized and unpolarized monochromatic beams of gamma rays.

The minimum detectable polarization (MDP) of an instrument for a given celestial source type is an essential parameter to estimate its polarimetric potential. For a space polarimeter in a background dominated environment, the MDP with a 99% confidence level, is given by[19]:

$$MDP = \frac{4.29}{A.\epsilon.S_F.Q_{100}} \sqrt{\frac{A.\epsilon.S_f + B}{T}} \qquad (4)$$

where, A is the effective area, ϵ is the events' efficiency, S_F is the source flux over the selected energy band (photons cm^{-2} s^{-1}), B is the background noise count rate (counts/s), T is the observation time (s) and Q_{100} is the polarimetric modulation factor for a 100% polarized source.

High polarimetric performance for hard X/soft γ-rays can be achieved fulfilling the following requirements: high scattering efficiency, fine spatial resolution, and fine spectroscopy. These characteristics allow a large flexibility in scattered events selection, and therefore several event filter can be implemented to optimize the modulation factor and the event efficiency, and consequently improve the MDP.

4. Polarimetric Analyses for a Monochromatic Source

4.1. *NFT*

In order to fulfil the requirements on the ASTENA NFT, and following the knowhow acquired by both experiments on CdTe/CZT detectors used as scattering polarimeter and development on 3D CZT spectrometers,[20] a simple model of the NFT focal plane has been implemented using MEGALib tools.[21] Using the MEGAlib/Geomega package, we implement a numerical model made of a stack of 4 thick layers of CZT separated by a layer (10 mm thick) of a PCB type mixture passive material, representative of the read-out front-end electronics board (Fig. 2). Each CZT layer is 20 mm thick and 80 mm × 80 mm wide. The CZT layers were divided in voxels with dimensions 0.25 x 0.25 x 0.25 mm^3 each. The spectroscopic response of the detector is simply modeled by a relationship derived from measurements on CZT drift strips spectrometers.[22] In all the performed simulation runs, we set the low energy threshold to 5 keV, that is a reasonable value at room temperature as demonstrated by the same experimental results.

The Laue lens configuration will impinge an almost monochromatic beam for each crystal ring on the detector, each one having a small inclination angle with respect to the axis of the lens, ranging from 0.4° (at the energy of 600 keV, corresponding to the inner radius) to 4.5° (at the energy of 50 keV, corresponding to the external radius). This will produce rings of photons with similar energy hitting the detector inside a PSF. We know from previous experiments that an off-axis beam introduce geometric effects on the detector that affect the modulation factor.[23] However, since the Laue lens presents a 180° symmetry, for each beam there will be a symmetric beam with opposite off-axis angle. This configuration will correct any possible systematic error due to the off-axis beam and the results will be similar as we impinge an on-axis beam on the detector. In fact, a systematic study was performed in order to validate this assumption. We evaluated the modulation factor by varying the number of pair of symmetric off-axis beams from 1 to 128, obtaining a distribution of values for the modulation factor with a standard deviation of 0.02 from the central value which is comparable with the error on the values of the modulation factor. To simulate a full Laue lens would require ∼20000 beams, each with its off-axis angle, however, by taking into account the aforementioned results, we decided to use instead a Gaussian cone shape beam, 20 m from the detector, which produce a Gaussian shape PSF with a FWHM of 0.15 cm on the top of the detector. This will simplify the simulation code and speed up the simulations without compromising the result.

To ensure the quality of the selected events we perform a check by Compton kinematics – by evaluating the energy of the two first interactions and the corresponding scattering angle we ensure that it corresponds to the expected values and the event can be selected as a "good event". This also can be done for multiple interactions, by using the energy of the first interaction, the sum of the following interactions

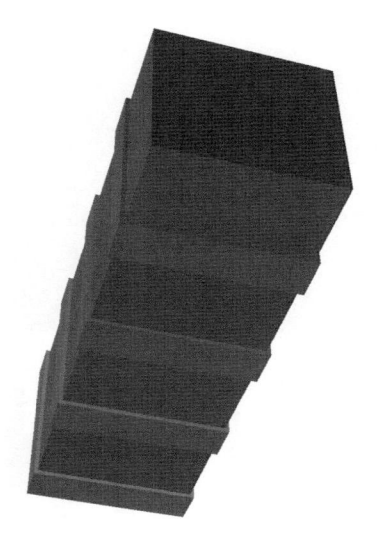

Fig. 2. Monte Carlo model of the the NFT focal plane. The gray volumes represent the segmented CZT spectrometer, while the green ones represent the readout electronics boards.

and the scattering angle from the first and second interaction. This method ensures that all the events selected are true Compton events and have polarimetric information on it. This method also removes the double events that occur in neighbour pixels. These type of events can introduce anomalies because the scattering angle is difficult to know. Since we consider the interaction in the center of pixel these types of events will be considered as a ∼90° scattering event (high polarimetric information). However, if the interactions occur near the edges of the pixels the scattering angle can be ∼0° (low polarimetric information).

Due to the focusing properties of the NFT we know that the first interaction is always inside the PSF. These allows a further correction since we only select the events which complies with this condition. This will reduce the background or any spurious events that occur in the detector.

After the selections, the scattering maps and modulation curves are drawn. To correct the systematic effects introduced by the detector geometry we also simulate an unpolarized source in the same conditions as the polarized source and we corrected the distributions with equation 3. As an example Fig. 3 presents the scattering maps obtained for a 300 keV unpolarized beam and for a 100% polarized beam with a polarization vector direction of 60°. By diving the scattering maps into 24 bins we achieved the azimuthal distributions presented in Fig. 3, below each scattering map. The corrected modulation curve is presented in Fig. 4. The corrected curve is then fitted with equation 2 to get the modulation factor and the polarization angle.

In Fig. 5 it is presented the modulation factor as function of the energy for the NFT focal plane for monochromatic beams ranging from 100 to 600 keV. These

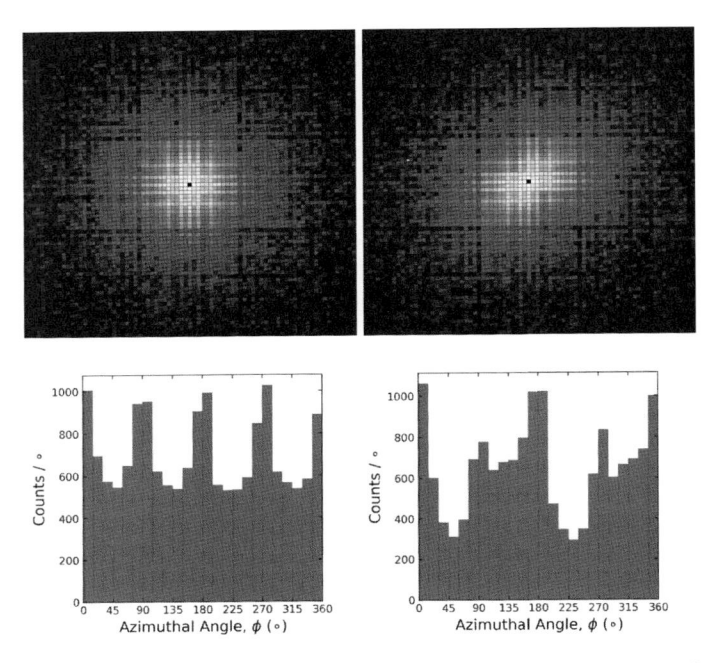

Fig. 3. Scattering maps and azimuthal distributions obtained for an unpolarized (left) and 100% polarized (right) beam. The beam energy is 300 keV and the polarization vector direction is 60° for the 100% polarized case.

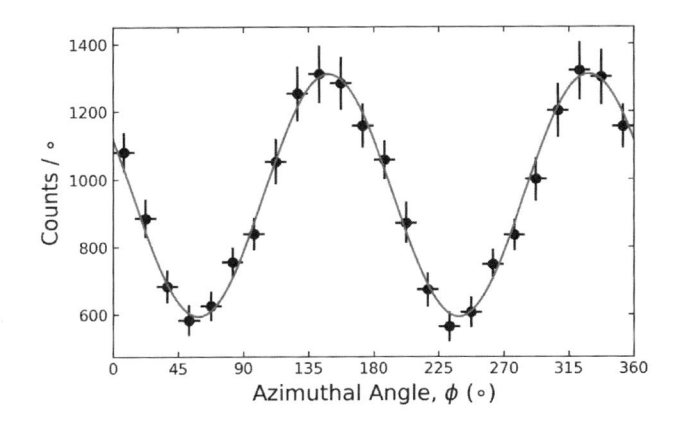

Fig. 4. Corrected modulation curve obtained when we apply the correction in Eq. (3) on the histograms of Fig. 3.

results showed that the NFT Focal Plane Detector (FPD) has potential to perform polarimetric analysis in the whole energy range presenting modulation factors >0.2. As expected, the best modulation factor is obtained at energies ∼300 keV.

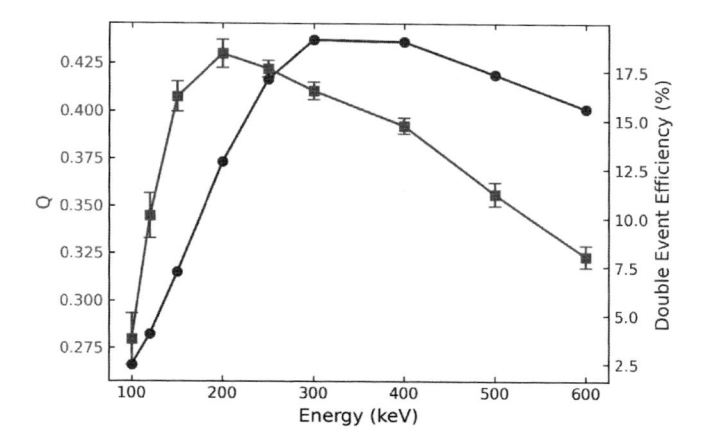

Fig. 5. NFT modulation factor and event efficiency as function of the energy.

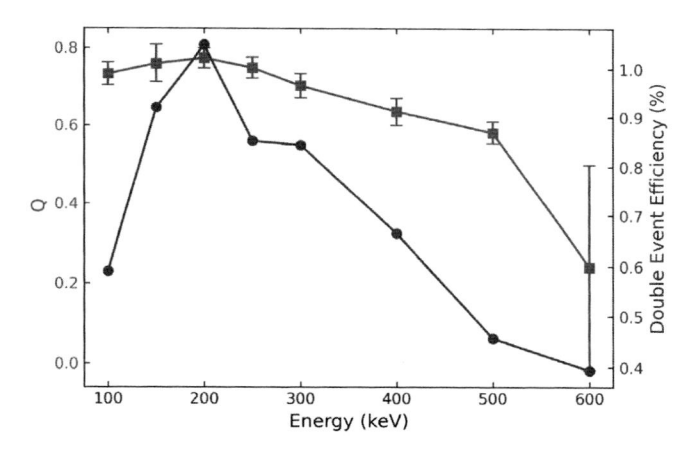

Fig. 6. NFT modulation factor and event efficiency as function of the energy for events with scattering angles of ∼90°.

The percentage of selected events shows its maximum at ∼200 keV where the Compton cross section prevails over the other interactions in the CZT.

Due to the highly segmented detector we can also select events that maximize the modulation factor like events with scattering angles ∼90° (along the detector axis). By making a selection in the Z coordinates we ensure that all the events have ∼90°. In Fig. 6 it is shown the modulation factor as a function of the energy taking account this selection. As can be seen, there is a big increase of the modulation factor when compared with the results without selection. The modulation factor reaches values near ∼0.8 for energies ∼200 keV. However the efficiency is very affected and reduced to values below ∼1%.

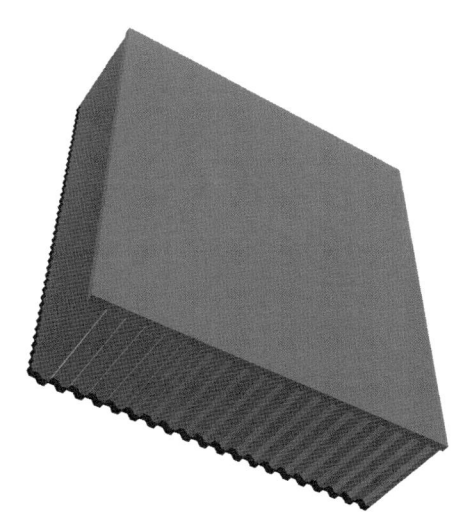

Fig. 7. A geometry sketch of the the WFM-IS unit. The green volume represent the CsI scintillators, while the gray ones represent the Si SDDs, light gray on top and dark gray on bottom.

4.2. *WFM-IS*

The Monte Carlo model of one WFM-IS unit is presented in Fig. 7. It consists of an hexagonal 40x40 array of CsI scintillators (for a total of 205 bars), with a distance between contiguous centres across hexagon flat sides of 5 mm, and a length of 50 mm. To mimic the depth resolution of the detector we segmented the bars in 10 segments of 5 mm each. On the top the detector has a linear SDD, 0.4 mm thick, and, on bottom an hexagonal single anode SDD, 0.4 mm thick, with a distance between hexagon flat sides of 5 mm. To construct the full WFM-IS we copied 12 units and placed along an hexagonal configuration, 2 units in each hexagon side, with a distance from the center (lens axis) of 1.5 m.

Since the WFM-IS is a wide field instrument, the beam used for the simulations was a far point source. For the WFM-IS we do not know were the beam undergoes the first interaction, all the scintillating bars will be scattering and absorbing elements, so we selected the events that comply the Compton kinematics and we corrected the signal data with the unpolarized data. In Fig. 8 the scattering maps are shown for a 500 keV unpolarized and 100% polarized source.

A systematic study was performed using monochromatic sources from 125 keV to 5 MeV. Fig. 9 shows the modulation factor and efficiency obtained for one WFM-IS unit and the full WFM-IS. As can be seen, for energies below 1 MeV the modulation factor shows values >0.2, however for energies above 1 MeV the modulation factor drops drastically becoming impossible to get polarization results. The reason for this is that for energies > 1 MeV both the theoretic value of the modulation factor and the efficiency of the Compton process drop significantly.[10] When comparing

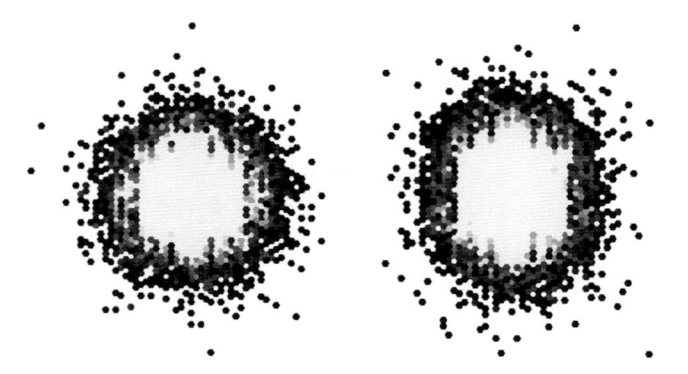

Fig. 8. Scattering maps obtained for a 500 keV unpolarized (left) and 100% polarized (right) beam with the WFM-IS unit. The polarization vector direction is 0° for the 100% polarized case.

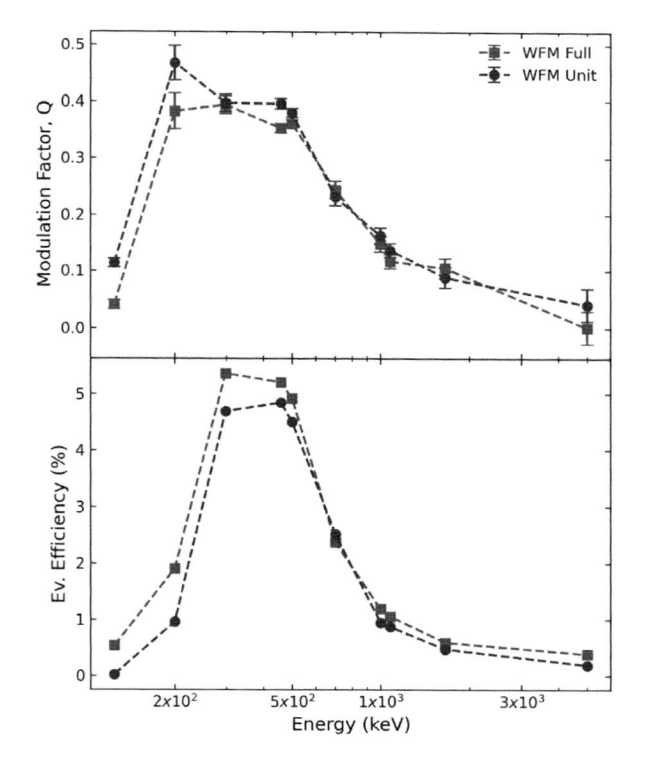

Fig. 9. Modulation factor (top) and event efficiency (bottom) as function of the energy for one WFM-IS unit and for the full WFM-IS.

the results for one WFM-IS unit and for the full WFM-IS the results of the modulation factor are similar, however the event efficiency increases when using the full WFM-IS.

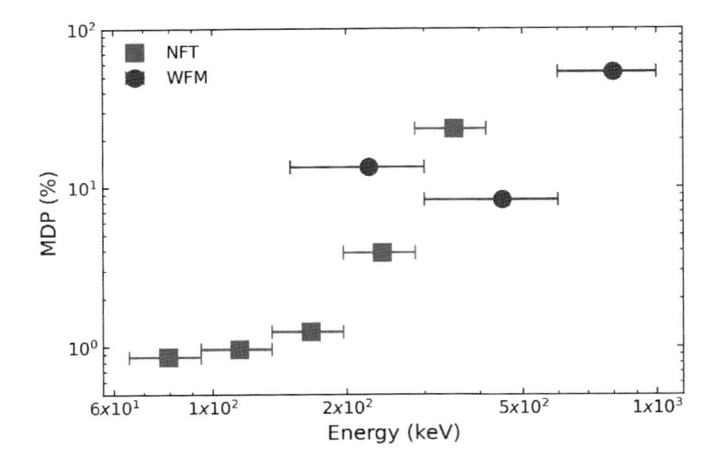

Fig. 10. Minimum detectable polarization (MDP) versus energy for a 100 mCrab source when observing with NFT and WFM-IS for 100 ks.

5. Polarimetric Sensitivity of ASTENA

In order to estimate the potential MDP of the ASTENA mission in a LEO (low Earth orbit) when observing a Crab type source, we simulated a source with a power law spectrum (normalization at 1 keV: 10.74 photons keV^{-1} s^{-2} cm^{-2}; photon index: 2.17) for each instrument individually and obtained the modulation factor and event efficiency. The simulated energy range was in accordance with the instrument energy passband: for the NFT 65 – 600 keV; and for the WFM-IS 150 keV – 1 MeV. As before, we simulated an on-axis Gaussian cone beam to mimic the 1.5 mm diameter of the Lens PSF for the NFT and a on-axis far source for the WFM-IS.

The background components were modeled in detail also using the MEGAlib environment tools for both NFT and WFM-IS using the works.[24–28] Background simulations were performed for both instruments individually and, to determine the real background for polarimetric analyses, we also performed the same selection process as the data. First we checked the events by Compton kinematics and, for the NFT data, we check if the first interaction is inside the PSF.

The effective area of the NFT was computed analytically as the product of the geometrical area of the instrument and the reflection efficiency of the lens[14] times the effective area for the WFM-IS was estimated using MEGAlib simulations.

The calculated MDP as a function of the energy when observing a 100 mCrab source for 100 ks is presented in Fig. 10. As can be seen, for energies < 200 keV the NFT presents MDP values ∼1%. However, above that energy it starts to substantially degrade because of the decrease of effective area of the Laue lens. For energies above 300 keV the WFM-IS presents a better MDP than the NFT meaning that the instruments can complement each other in energy bands.

6. Conclusions

In the next missions for medium energy astrophysics, polarimetry will be a fundamental requirement for the solution of important scientific problems related to the nature and geometry of the high energy cosmic sources emission. The ASTENA mission, under study as part of the European project AHEAD 2020, thanks to the high efficient, fine spectral resolution and high segmentation of the detectors onboard will be able to make polarimetry a standard way of observation by definitively opening this observation window also in the field of hard X- and soft γ-rays.

In this work we presented the results of an ongoing study which aims at a reliable and realistic evaluation of the performance in terms of polarimetry achievable with ASTENA, and obtain information for optimizing the design of the detection systems. The results show that the NFT will be able to achieve unprecedented polarametric capabilities for energies between 60 - 300 keV, while the WFM-IS will be capable to provide polarimetric measurements up to 1 MeV. ASTENA polarimetric performances show that such instruments hold the potential to address gamma-ray polarimetry with high sensitivity and contribute to expanding this new astrophysics knowledge window.

Acknowledgements

This work has been partially supported with the financial contribution from the ASI-INAF agreement n. 2017-14-H.0 "Studi per future missioni scientifiche", the ASI-INAF agreement n. 2018-10-H.1-2020 "HERMES Technologic Pathfinder", and the AHEAD EU Horizon 2020 project (Integrated Activities in the High Energy Astrophysics Domain), grant agreement n. 871158.

References

1. S. V. Vadawale, Chattopadhyay *et al.*, Phase-resolved X-ray polarimetry of the Crab pulsar with the AstroSat CZT Imager, *Nature Astronomy* **2**, p. 50–55 (2018).
2. M. Forot, P. Laurent, I. A. Grenier, C. Gouiffès and F. Lebrun, Polarization of the crab pulsar and nebula as observed by the INTEGRAL/IBIS telescope, *The Astrophysical Journal* **688**, L29 (nov 2008).
3. E. Jourdain and J.-P. Roques, 2003–2018 monitoring of the crab nebula polarization in hard x-rays with INTEGRAL SPI, *The Astrophysical Journal* **882**, p. 129 (sep 2019).
4. A. J. Dean, D. J. Clark, J. B. Stephen, V. A. McBride, L. Bassani, A. Bazzano, A. J. Bird, A. B. Hill, S. E. Shaw and P. Ubertini, Polarized gamma-ray emission from the crab, *Science* **321**, 1183 (2008).
5. P. Laurent, J. Rodriguez, J. Wilms, M. Cadolle Bel, K. Pottschmidt and V. Grinberg, Polarized gamma-ray emission from the galactic black hole cygnus x-1, *Science* **332**, p. 438–439 (Mar 2011).
6. E. Jourdain, J. P. Roques, M. Chauvin and D. J. Clark, Separation of two contributions to the high energy emission of cygnus x-1: Polarization measurements with INTEGRAL SPI, *The Astrophysical Journal* **761**, p. 27 (nov 2012).

7. S.-N. Zhang, M. Kole *et al.*, Detailed polarization measurements of the prompt emission of five gamma-ray bursts, *Nature Astronomy* **3**, 258 (Mar 2019).
8. T. Chattopadhyay, S. V. Vadawale, E. Aarthy, N. P. S. Mithun, V. Chand, A. Ratheesh, R. Basak, A. R. Rao, V. Bhalerao, S. Mate, A. B., V. Sharma and D. Bhattacharya, Prompt emission polarimetry of gamma-ray bursts with the AstroSat CZT imager, *The Astrophysical Journal* **884**, p. 123 (Oct 2019).
9. D. Götz, P. Laurent, F. Lebrun, F. Daigne and Ž. Bošnjak, Variable polarization measured in the prompt emission of grb 041219a using ibis on board INTEGRAL, *The Astrophysical Journal* **695**, L208 (Apr 2009).
10. T. Chattopadhyay, Hard x-ray polarimetry – an overview of the method, science drivers and recent findings (2021).
11. F. Frontera, "understanding the origin of the positron annihilation line and the physics of the supernova explosions".
12. F. Frontera, E. Virgilli, C. Guidorzi, P. Rosati, R. Diehl, T. Siegert, C. Fryer, L. Amati, N. Auricchio, R. Campana, E. Caroli, F. Fuschino, C. Labanti, M. Orlandini, E. Pian, J. B. Stephen, S. Del Sordo, C. Budtz-Jorgensen, I. Kuvvetli, S. Brandt, R. M. C. da Silva, P. Laurent, E. Bozzo, P. Mazzali and M. D. Valle, Understanding the origin of the positron annihilation line and the physics of supernova explosions, *Experimental Astronomy* **51**, 1175 (June 2021).
13. F. Frontera and P. von Ballmoos, Laue Gamma-Ray Lenses for Space Astrophysics: Status and Prospects, *X-Ray Optics and Instrumentation, 2010. Special Issue on X-Ray Focusing: Techniques and Applications, id.215375* **2010** (2010).
14. E. Virgilli, V. Valsan, F. Frontera, E. Caroli, V. Liccardo and J. B. Stephen, Expected performances of a Laue lens made with bent crystals, *Journal of Astronomical Telescopes, Instruments, and Systems* **3**, p. 044001 (October 2017).
15. I. Kuvvetli, C. Budtz-Jørgensen, E. Caroli and N. Auricchio, CZT drift strip detectors for high energy astrophysics, *Nuclear Instruments and Methods in Physics Research A* **624**, 486 (December 2010).
16. I. Kuvvetli, C. Budtz-Jørgensen, A. Zappettini, N. Zambelli, G. Benassi, E. Kalemci, E. Caroli, J. B. Stephen and N. Auricchio, A 3D CZT high resolution detector for x- and gamma-ray astronomy, in *High Energy, Optical, and Infrared Detectors for Astronomy VI*, eds. A. D. Holland and J. Beletic (SPIE, 2014).
17. R. Campana, F. Fuschino, C. Labanti, L. Amati, S. Mereghetti, M. Fiorini, F. Frontera, G. Baldazzi, P. Bellutti and et al., The X-Gamma Imaging Spectrometer (XGIS) onboard THESEUS, *Mem. Soc. Astron. Italiana* **89**, p. 137 (2018).
18. O. Klein and Y. Nishina, Über die Streuung von Strahlung durch freie Elektronen nach der neuen relativistischen Quantendynamik von Dirac, *Zeitschrift für Physik* **52**, 853 (1929).
19. M. C. Weisskopf, E. H. Silver, H. L. Kestenbaum, K. S. Long and R. Novick, A precision measurement of the X-ray polarization of the Crab Nebula without pulsar contamination., *The Astrophysical Journal* **220**, L117 (March 1978).
20. L. Abbene *et al.*, Recent advances in the development of high-resolution 3d cadmium–zinc–telluride drift strip detectors, *Journal of Synchrotron Radiation* **27**, 1564 (2020).
21. A. Zoglauer, Megalib: Medium energy gamma-ray astronomy library.
22. I. Kuvvetli, Development of cdznte detector systems for space applications, PhD thesis, Technical University of Denmark 2003.
23. R. M. C. da Silva *et al.*, Polarimetry study with a CdZnTe focal plane detector, *IEEE Transactions on Nuclear Science* **58**, 2118 (2011).

24. T. Mizuno, T. Kamae, G. Godfrey, T. Handa, D. J. Thompson, D. Lauben, Y. Fukazawa and M. Ozaki, Cosmic-ray background flux model based on a gamma-ray large area space telescope balloon flight engineering model, *The Astrophysical Journal* **614**, p. 1113–1123 (Oct 2004).
25. M. Kole, M. Pearce and M. Muñoz Salinas, A model of the cosmic ray induced atmospheric neutron environment, *Astroparticle Physics* **62**, 230 (2015).
26. E. Churazov, S. Sazonov, R. Sunyaev and M. Revnivtsev, Earth X-ray albedo for cosmic X-ray background radiation in the 1–1000 keV band, *Monthly Notices of the Royal Astronomical Society* **385**, 719 (02 2008).
27. S. Sazonov, E. Churazov, R. Sunyaev and M. Revnivtsev, Hard X-ray emission of the Earth's atmosphere: Monte Carlo simulations, *Monthly Notices of the Royal Astronomical Society* **377**, 1726 (05 2007).
28. M. Türler, M. Chernyakova, T. J.-L. Courvoisier, P. Lubiński, A. Neronov, N. Produit and R. Walter, Integralhard x-ray spectra of the cosmic x-ray background and galactic ridge emission, *Astronomy and Astrophysics* **512**, p. A49 (Mar 2010).

Prospect for WHIM detection in the cosmic web by *SRG/eROSITA*[1]

H. Tanimura* and N. Aghanim

*Université Paris-Saclay, CNRS, Institut d'Astrophysique Spatiale,
Bâtiment 121, 91405 Orsay, France*
E-mail: hideki.tanimura@ias.u-psud.fr

Hydrodynamical simulations predict that the cosmic web contains the majority of the missing baryons in the form of plasma, called the warm-hot intergalactic medium (WHIM). However, its direct measurement through X-ray emissions has been prevented for decades due to the weak signal and the complex morphology of cosmic filaments.

We report the first statistical detection of X-ray emission from cosmic web filaments with the *ROSAT* data. We identified more than 15,000 large-scale filaments, spanning 30-100 Mpc length, in the SDSS survey and statistically detected X-ray emissions from the WHIM at 4.2 sigma confidence level using the *ROSAT* maps. Given this detection, we can expect a much more significant detection from *SRG/eROSITA* and indeed predicted the detectability of the WHIM. The prediction shows that stacking ~2000 filaments only would lead to a 5σ detection with an average gas temperature of the WHIM as low as ~0.3 keV.

Keywords: Clusters; intracluster medium; large-scale structure of Universe; cosmic background radiation

1. Missing baryon problem

Recent CMB observations indicate that baryons comprise 4.9% of the total energy density of the Universe,[2] and it is in agreement with the detected baryons at early times ($z > 2$), for example, through measurements of quasar absorption lines. However, at late times ($z < 2$), ~30% of baryons have not been confirmed,[3] called the "Missing Baryon Problem." Hydrodynamical simulations predict that most of the missing baryons are expected to be in the form of hot plasma with the temperature range of 10^5–10^7 K and density of about 10–100 times the average cosmic value, referred to as the warm-hot intergalactic medium (WHIM), and to be located in filaments between galaxy clusters.[4] Therefore, extensive searches have been performed for the WHIM with far-UV, X-ray, and the thermal Sunyaev-Zel'dovich (tSZ) effect. However, the measurement is difficult because the signal is relatively weak, and the morphology of the source is complex.

2. WHIM detection with *ROSAT* data

To probe the WHIM in filaments, we used the filament catalog identified in the SDSS spectroscopic galaxies[5] and the *ROSAT* X-ray count-rate maps at six energy bands in 0.1 – 2.0 keV[6] [a]. We stacked the *ROSAT* maps at the positions of ~15,000

---

[a] http://www.jb.man.ac.uk/research/cosmos/rosat/

cosmic filaments (30 to 100 Mpc at $0.2 < z < 0.6$) and detected the X-ray emissions for the first time at a significance of 4.2σ in the energy band of 0.56–1.21 keV (left panel in Fig. 1). While no significant detection was found at the other five energy bands, this result is predicted by hydrodynamic simulations,[7,8] which suggest that the relative contribution of the WHIM to the total CXB peaks at about 0.4–0.9 keV.

We performed an X-ray spectral analysis with the APEC model for the stacked signals at six energy bands and estimated the average gas density and temperature at the cores (< 2 Mpc) of the filaments (right panel in Fig. 1). The average central gas overdensity was found to be $\delta = 30 \pm 15$, assuming a cylindrical filament with a density distribution following a β-model with $\beta = 2/3$. We compared this measurement with the other statistical tSZ measurement[9] and found that these results are consistent. The average gas temperature was also found to be $0.9^{+1.0}_{-0.6}$ keV, and it is a bit larger than the tSZ result of ~ 0.1 keV. This difference may imply that the gas temperature is higher at the core than at the outskirt, considering that the X-ray gas temperature was estimated within ~ 2 Mpc from the filament spines, whereas the tSZ temperature was the average within ~ 5 Mpc.

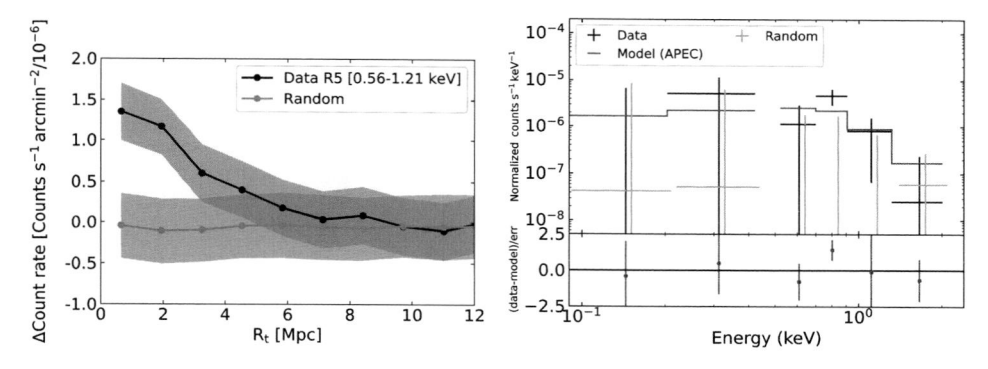

Fig. 1. *Left*: Average radial X-ray profile of 15,165 filaments in the energy band of 0.56–1.21 keV in black with the 1σ uncertainties in gray. Average radial X-ray profile from 1,000 random samplings in cyan. For each random sampling, 15,165 filaments are displaced at random positions on the *ROSAT* map. *Right*: Excesses of X-ray emission at the cores of 15,165 filaments in the six *ROSAT* energy bands in black. Amplitudes of X-ray emissions from 1,000 random samplings in cyan. Fit to the data with the APEC model in red. Ratio of data and model at each energy band is shown at the bottom in magenta.

3. Prospect of WHIM detection with *SRG/eROSITA*

A definitive statement on the gas temperature trend in filaments requires higher quality data, such as from the ongoing *SRG/eROSITA* all-sky survey. Therefore, we simulated the *SRG/eROSITA* observation of the X-ray emission from cosmic filaments based on the gas density and temperature estimated with the *ROSAT* data and evaluated its detectability. The result shows that we can expect a $\sim 5\sigma$ detection by stacking only 100 filaments (left panel in Fig. 2).

While the detection becomes more challenging when the gas temperature is lower, we found that the stacking of $\sim$2,000 filaments would lead to a 5σ detection of X-ray emission, even with an average gas temperature as low as $\sim$0.3 keV (right panel in Fig. 2).

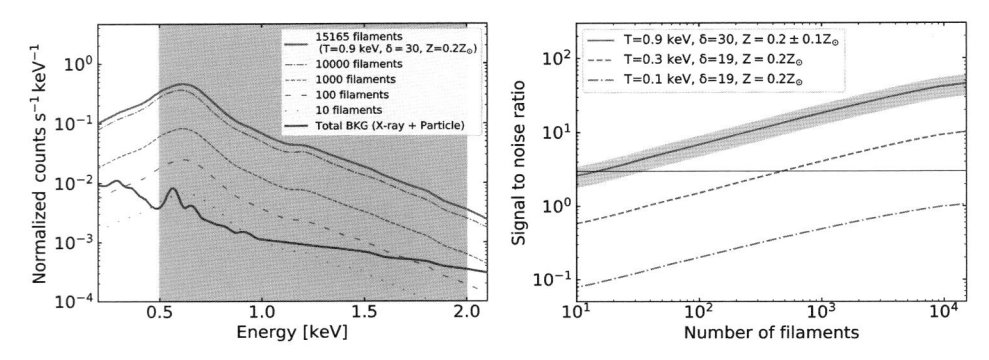

Fig. 2. *Left*: Simulated *SRG/eROSITA*'s energy spectra from the gas at the cores of the stacked 10, 100, 1,000, 10,000, and 15,165 filaments in red. The stacked spectra are calculated with overdensity = 30, temperature = 0.9 keV, and metallicity = $0.2Z_\odot$. *SRG/eROSITA*'s Background energy spectrum in blue. *Right*: Signal-to-noise ratios as a function of the number of stacked filaments are shown in red for "overdensity = 30, temperature = 0.9 keV and metallicity = $0.2Z_\odot$ at 0.5–2.0 keV", "overdensity = 19, temperature = 0.3 keV and metallicity = $0.2Z_\odot$ at 0.3–0.8 keV", and "overdensity = 19, temperature = 0.1 keV and metallicity = $0.2Z_\odot$ at 0.3–0.5 keV". Uncertainties due to the metallicity of $(0.2\pm 0.1)Z_\odot$ are shown in light red area. Horizontal black line indicates a 3σ detection line.

Acknowledgement

This research has been supported by the funding for the ByoPiC project from the European Research Council (ERC) under the European Union's Horizon 2020 research and innovation programme grant agreement ERC-2015-AdG 695561.

References

1. H. Tanimura *et al.*, *A&A* **643**, p. L2 (November 2020).
2. Planck Collaboration, *A&A* **641**, p. A6 (September 2020).
3. J. M. Shull, B. D. Smith and C. W. Danforth, *ApJ* **759**, p. 23 (November 2012).
4. R. Cen and J. P. Ostriker, *ApJ* **650**, 560 (October 2006).
5. N. Malavasi *et al.*, *A&A* **642**, p. A19 (October 2020).
6. S. L. Snowden *et al.*, *ApJ* **485**, 125 (August 1997).
7. L. A. Phillips *et al.*, *ApJ* **554**, L9 (June 2001).
8. E. Ursino and M. Galeazzi, *ApJ* **652**, 1085 (December 2006).
9. H. Tanimura *et al.*, *A&A* **637**, p. A41 (May 2020).

The role of eXTP in the multi-messenger astronomy era

G. Stratta

INAF, Istituto di Astrofisica e Planetologia Spaziali,
Rome, Italy
E-mail: giulia.stratta@inaf.it

Gor Oganesyan

Gran Sasso Science Institute,
Viale F. Crispi 7, I-67100, L'Aquila (AQ), Italy

INFN - Laboratori Nazionali del Gran Sasso,
I-67100, L'Aquila (AQ), Italy

The first detection of gravitational waves on 2015 with the Advanced LIGO and Advanced Virgo interferometers has opened a new observational window in the Universe. The last decade has also welcomed decisive discoveries in neutrino astronomy. Expected advances of gravitational wave and neutrino detectors by the end of the 2020s will mark the start of a golden era of multi-messenger astrophysics. The most promising multi-messenger sources in the high-energy sky, e.g. GRBs, AGNs, magnetars, are among the main targets for the enhanced X-ray Timing and Polarimetry (eXTP). In this proceeding, we describe the possible role of eXTP in the context of multi-messenger astronomy and in particular on the synergies with gravitational wave interferometers at the sensitivity expected by the end of the twenties.

Keywords: X-ray sources; gravitational waves; neutrinos; multi-messenger astrophysics.

1. Introduction

In the quickly evolving framework of multi-messenger astronomy, two breakthrough results have been achieved in the last few years that magnificently show the power of combining different "messengers" from the same source as well as the crucial role of high-energy observatories.

On 17 August 2017 a binary neutron star merger (GW170817) has been detected with the network of Advanced LIGO (aLIGO,[1]) and Advanced Virgo (AdV,[2]) gravitational wave interferometers. The source was found to be spatially and temporally coincident with a short Gamma Ray Burst GRB170817.[3,4] This association marked the first direct evidence that at least a fraction of short GRB progenitors are NS-NS mergers. Short GRB progenitor nature so far was based on indirect evidence collected in the last 15 years that goes from the lack of any core collapse supernova associated with a short GRB to the explosion site within the host galaxy, typically far from star forming regions (see[5] for a review). Both the burst and afterglow properties of GRB 170817 were found to be consistent with a significant inclination angle of the binary system. In particular, the afterglow properties provided the first empirical evidence of a narrowly collimated jet and allowed to define its energy angular distribution.[6,7] Another emission component distinguished from the afterglow was also detected as a fading opt-NIR source (AT2017gfo)[8] and identified with the theoretically predicted thermal emission (kilonova) powered by the intense radioactive decay from instable heavy nuclei freshly-formed during the neutron star merger.[8,9] Past kilonova observations where claimed in few short GRBs and their identification relied on few data points (e.g.[10]). The exceptional high-quality temporal and spectral data of AT2017gfo allowed us to study in great details the kilonova properties for the first time.[11,12]

The other breakthrough discovery was achieved on 22 September 2017 when a high-energy neutrino event was detected with IceCube[13] and found to be spatially consistent with a gamma-ray emitting blazar at z=0.34 (TXS0506+056). The association has a confidence level lower than the case of GW/GRB170817 (i.e. $\sim 3\sigma$) but is an important finding that provide crucial hints on the origin of the identified diffuse flux of astrophysical very-high-energy neutrinos (10 TeV-10 PeV) detected by IceCube[14] and the possible role of blazars within most extreme particle accelerators in the Universe.

In the next few years, gravitational wave and neutrino detectors will undergo significant upgrades reaching unprecedented sensitivities. A new gravitational wave detector located in India (LIGO-India[a]) will join the current network of second generation (2G) interferometers formed by the two aLIGO in the USA, AdV in Italy and KAGRA in Japan.[15,16] Both aLIGO and AdV will reach a sensitivity larger than the nominal one with the upgraded configurations "A+" and "Virgo+"[17] during the fifth observation run (the start of which is currently scheduled for mid 2025). The completed network will be able to detect neutron star binary mergers (the most promising source for an associated electromagnetic counterpart) up to 330 Mpc, with an expected rate of few tens of detections per year (updated to the third observation run results).[17] By the end of the twenties, major upgrades are under consideration for aLIGO in the "Voyager" configuration[18] that will test some of the key technologies need for the third generation (3G) interferometers as the Cosmic Explorer (CE,[18,19]) and Einstein Telescope (ET,[20–22]) expected to be operational by mid-thirties. The "Voyager" configuration will possibly place the GW detection rate mid-way between the 2G and 3G detectors by the end of the twenties. The 3G detectors will have about one order of magnitude better sensitivity than current ones, with an expected rate of compact binary coalescences (CBCs) per year of the order of $O(10^5)$, up to distances that will cover the peak of star formation epoch and far beyond.[22]

Gravitational wave source sky localisation from the interferometer network is based on the triangulation method. By the end of the twenties, the completed GW detector network will have improved sky localisation capabilities, with average

---

[a]https://dcc.ligo.org/LIGO-M1100296/public

uncertainty regions of the order of few tens of square degrees for CBCs.[17] At distances larger than $\sim$ 100 Mpc, this scenario challenges the identification of the electromagnetic counterparts at optical wavelengths due to the large number of transient sources expected in such large areas and the incompleteness of galaxy catalogs above 100 Mpc. On the contrary, the high-energy transient sky is much less populated and gamma-ray or X-ray counterparts detected with all sky monitors might represent the most suitable way to pinpoint the GW source in the sky.

The GW source localisation uncertainties strongly depends on the presence of a network. This is still uncertain for the 3G interferometers during the thirties. A single GW detector such as ET, thanks to its sensitivity at low frequency, is able to localize about 100 binary neutron star merger per years within a few tens of square degrees up to a redshift of 0.3. These sources are detected before the mergers (some of them also few hours before the merger). For a network of detectors including ET and CE, the number of well localized events increases of an order of magnitude. However, going to large distances the sky-localization becomes of hundreds of square degrees for a large majority of events (e.g.,[22, 23]). Early warnings from GW detectors allows ground and space-based telescopes to slew onto the identified sky region before the advent of the expected electromagnetic transient emission. Early warning alerts of the order of few minutes for the most nearby sources (i.e. NS-NS mergers at few tens of Mpc) are planned also for the 2G next observation runs[b].

For neutrino detectors, the Km3NeT[24] in the Mediterrean Sea will provide IceCube comparable sensitivites in the Northern Emisphere on the second half of the twenties and it will work in synergies with the Gigaton Volume Baikal late neutrino detector. In the Southern Emisphere, IceCube-gen2 will gradually increase the current IceCube sensitivity up to one order of magnitude,[25] boosting the current astrophysical neutrino detection rate to values that will significantly increase the chances to find the electromagnetic counterparts. The neutrino sky localization accuracy depends on neutrino flavour, where long tracks topology (for ν_μ) provide angular resolution down to 0.1-0.2 deg and a 2π sr sky coverage, while cascade topology (for ν_e and most ν_τ) angular resolution are typically 3-5 deg for the whole 4π sky, thus still requiring an electromagnetic counterpart and detectors with sky localization capabilities better than few arcmin to pinpoint the host galaxy and/or identify the source.

The launch of the enhanced X-ray Timing and Polarimetry mission eXTP,[26] currently scheduled by 2027[c], coincides with the middle/final stages of the above described major upgrades of neutrino and gravitational wave detectors. The recent breakthrough results described above, point to the gamma-ray bursts and active galactic nuclei among the most promising classes of multi-messenger sources that will be observed in the next years. Further promising candidates are represented by

---

[b]$https://emfollow.docs.ligo.org/userguide/early_warning.html$
[c]https://www.isdc.unige.ch/extp/

magnetars and core collapsing supernovae. All these sources are among the main targets for eXTP and a number of white papers describe all the science we will be able to do with eXTP.[27–30] The onboard wide field monitor (WFM, 2-50 keV, 3.7 sr field of view), with few arcmin-scale sky localization capabilities, and two sets of focusing telescope arrays with spectroscopic and polarimetric capabilities (SFA and PFA), will allow eXTP to play a crucial role in finding and characterizing the electromagnetic counterparts of the gravitational wave and neutrino sources by the end of the twenties.

In the following sections we focus on the capabilities of eXTP to observe two specific classes of multi-messenger sources: the compact binary coalescences (CBC) formed by two neutron stars (NS-NS) or a neutron star and a stellar-mass black hole (NS-BH), and core collapsing massive stars (ccSNe). For NS-NS mergers and ccSNe, a metastable or stable neutron star remnant may form after the main event. Both NS-N/NS-BH and ccSNe, as well as the possible NS remnant, have a number of theoretically expected emission components in the electromagnetic spectrum and in particular at high energies.

2. NS-NS/NS-BH mergers

Several electromagnetic components are expected in the soft/hard X-ray bands after the merger phase of coalescing NS-NS/NS-BH systems. A short GRB, possibly accompanied by a soft extended emission (see below), is expected soon after[d] the coalescence if the observer line of sight lies along the jet axis or within a certain angle range that depends on the combination of the source distance, the jet energetic angular distribution and the detector sensitivity. The collimated nature of gamma-ray emission implies that only a fraction of GW-detected NS-NS/NS-BH can be observed as short GRBs. To make a rough estimate, by assuming that all NS-NS/NS-BH produce a GRB, the number of GW+GRB detection is $f_b = (1-cos\theta_{jet})$ times lower, where f_b can be as low as 0.001 for $\theta_{jet} \sim 2-3$ deg. Interestingly, recent results on the jet structure based on the observation of GRB170817,[31] shows that at large viewing angles gamma-ray emission get fainter but also softer, thus allowing sensitive wide field monitors to cover energies down to a few keV, as eXTP/WFM, best suited for detecting the electromagnetic counterpart of most nearby NS-NS/NS-BH events that are more likely off-axis. Simultaneous detection of GRB+GW can provide a wealth of information on jet launching mechanisms exploiting for instance the temporal delay between the GRB trigger and the GW detection. Also a non-detection of a GRB counterpart can provide useful insights on jet formation efficiencies in NS-NS/NS-BH.

The impact of the jet with the circumburst environment gives rise to an afterglow emission that, depending on the viewing angle from the jet axis, it can show an initial steep decay followed by a plateau and then a typical $t^{-\alpha}$ decay (with $\alpha \sim 1-2$), or an

---

[d]For GW170817, the short burst was observed 1.7 seconds after the merger epoch.[4]

initial slow rising behaviour followed by a late time power law decay in case of large viewing angles. At very late time, e.g. months up to years after the NS-NS/NS-BH merger, the impact of the nearly isotropic ejecta of neutron-rich matter released during the merger, may eventually produce a mildy-relativistic blast wave from which synchrotron radiation could be observed in X-rays (e.g.,[32] see also §2.1.3). For NS-NS mergers, if a NS remnant is formed, nearly isotropic X-ray emission produced from the pulsar nebula might escape if successfully ionizes the surrounding ejecta of matter released during the merger. Such non-thermal X-ray emission is expected on timescales of the order of days for certain values of the pulsar magnetic field and ejecta mass and with luminosities up to $\sim 5 \times 10^{44}$ erg s^{-1}.[33,34]

We will see in the next sections how eXTP will play an important role in detecting these high-energy components, significantly contributing to multi-messenger observational campaigns by the end of the twenties.

2.1. *eXTP and GRB 170817-like sources*

In this section we present preliminary results from data simulations of X-ray emission from a GRB170817-like source observed with eXTP. For these simulations we used calibration files released by March 2021 and the data analysis software package XSPECv12.10.[35]

2.1.1. *Prompt emission*

GRB 170817 is so far the only short GRB that has been associated with a NS-NS merger system detected through GW emission (see §1). Despite a high-energy signal rather typical for short GRBs, with duration of $\sim$ 2s and peak photon flux of 3.7 ± 0.9 ph cm^{-2} s^{-1} in the 10-1000 keV band,[36] given the very small distance of the source ($\sim$ 40 Mpc,[3]), the isotropic equivalent luminosity $L_{iso} = 1.6 \times 10^{47}$ erg s^{-1}[37] is several orders of magnitude lower than the average value for short GRBs ($\sim 10^{52}$ erg s^{-1}, see e.g.[38]). According to Goldstein et al.,[36] the burst spectrum is best fitted by a power-law model with exponential cut-off $f(E) = A(E/E_0)^\alpha e^{-E(2+\alpha)/E_p}$ in the first 0.6 s, with $\alpha = -0.62 \pm 0.40$, peak energy[e] $E_p = 185 \pm 62$ keV, 10-1000 keV flux $(3.1 \pm 0.7) \times 10^{-7}$ erg cm^{-2} s^{-1} and fluence $(1.8 \pm 0.4) \times 10^{-7}$ erg cm^{-2}. During the tail of the burst, the spectrum is best fitted by a black-body with KT=(10.3 ± 1.5) keV, flux $(0.5 \pm 0.1) \times 10^{-7}$ erg cm^{-2} s^{-1} and fluence $(0.61 \pm 0.12) \times 10^{-7}$ erg cm^{-2} in the 10-1000 keV. By using these best-fit models, and introducing photoelectric absorption with equivalent hydrogen column density[f] $N_H = 7.5 \times 10^{20}$ cm^{-2},[36] we perform simulations of eXTP/WFM observations of the main burst in the 2-50 keV energy band and find that a GRB 170817-like burst at the same distance could be

---

[e]The peak energy is the cut-off energy multiplied by $(\alpha + 2)$
[f]based on the host galaxy NGC4993 dust extinction $A_V = 0.338$

confidently detected ($\sim 7\sigma$) during the first 0.6 s, if spectral parameters were at the 1σ soft side of the error margins, confirming past results.[27] We estimate that a GRB170817-like source could be detectable with eXTP/WFM under this spectral assumption up to about 70 Mpc.

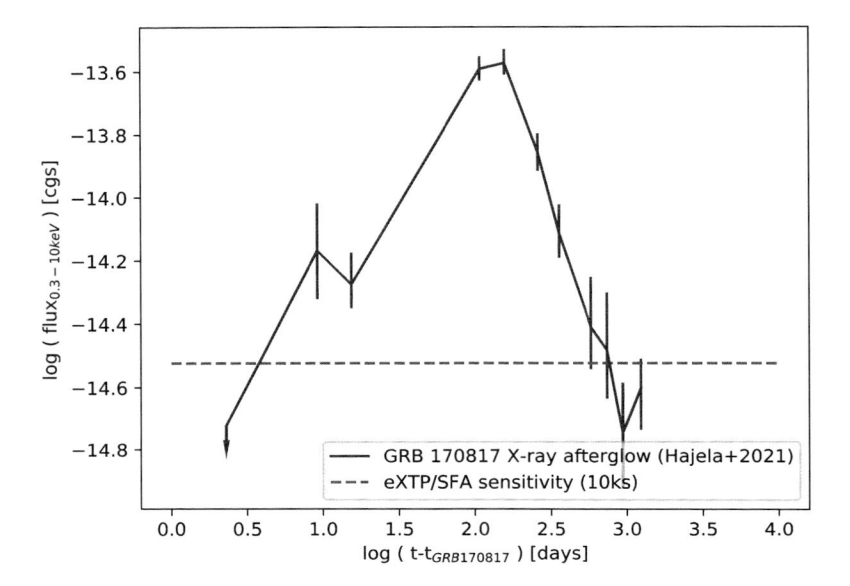

Fig. 1. X-ray (0.3-10 keV) flux of the short GRB 170817 afterglow that was associated with a NS-NS merger progenitor. Data are from Hajela et al. 2021 and references therein. The eXTP/SFA sensitivity will allow us to monitor a similar source from the very first phases up to the late ones, providing accurate sky localization. Horizontal line indicates the eXTP/SFA sensitivity for 10 ks of exposure from Zhang et al. 2016 and[26] computed in the 0.3-10 keV by assuming an absorbed power law model with phton index $\Gamma = 1.7$ and $N_H = 5 \times 10^{20}$ cm^{-2}.

2.1.2. *Afterglow emission*

The X-ray afterglow emission of GRB 170817 was detected with Chandra only 9 days after the merger as a faint source spatially coincident with the optical counterpart AT2017gfo and with flux $\sim 5 \times 10^{-15}$ erg cm^{-2} s^{-1} (0.3-10 keV,[39]). GRB170817 X-ray afterglow showed a slow rising behaviour that reached a peak of the emission after 100 days, with X-ray peak flux of a few 10^{-14} erg cm^{-2} s^{-1} (see Fig. 1). The overall properties of GRB170817 are in good agreement with the predictions for a GRB observed with a large inclination angle ($\sim 20-40$ deg) with respect to the jet axis. Given the eXTP/SFA sensitivities by assuming 10 ks of exposure ($\sim 2 \times 10^{-15}$ in the 2-10 keV energy band and $\sim 5 \times 10^{-16}$ in the 0.5-2 keV energy band, see Zhang et al. 2016), an X-ray afterglow of a GRB 170817-like source could be observed at almost all epochs, if accurate source sky localization is provided. The light curve long monitoring provided by eXTP/SFA is crucial to disentangle among different jet structure modellings that in turn encode the physics of jet formation and launching mechanisms in GRBs.

2.1.3. Very late time X-ray emission

Currently, the X-ray emission of GRB 170817 is still detectable and shows an intriguing possible rebrightening phase 4 years after the merger epoch.[40] Among the possible interpretations, this rebrightening could be the evidence of the theoretically predicted non-thermal emission produced by the impact of the kilonova ejecta into the circumburst medium,[32,41] though other interpretations are under investigations.[42] Measured spectrum during this phase assuming a power-law model, has photon index $\Gamma = 1.6$ and an integrated flux of 2.5×10^{-14} erg cm^{-2} s^{-1} in the 0.3-10 keV energy range.[32] We find that by assuming the spectral parameters provided by,[32] such late time X-ray emission could be detected with eXTP/SFA at more than 5σ level with 20 ks of exposure.

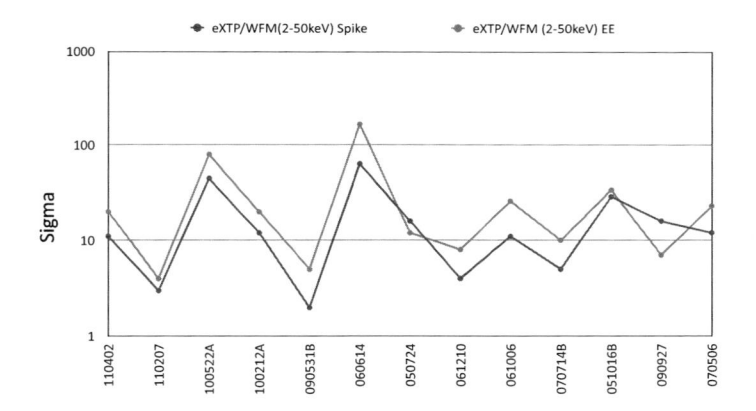

Fig. 2. Detection significance of a sample of short GRB spikes (blue) with Extended Emission (EE, orange). The x-axis shows the short GRB names, where the last 8 has measured redshift and cover a range from z=0.125 for GRB060614 to z=2.31 for GRB070506.

2.2. Short GRB with Extended Emission

An interesting perspective that potentially can increase the simultaneous GRB+GW detection is represented by the subclass of short GRBs that, following the main spike with hard spectral properties, show a prolongued softer and fainter Extended Emission (EE) that lasts after few tens of seconds.[43–46] The fraction of short GRBs with EE is still very uncertain and from high-energy detector catalogues range from $\sim 2 - 20\%$. However, recent studies over a large sample of short GRBs detected with the coded mask telescope onboard the Neil Gehrels Swift Observatory (Swift, hereafter,[47]) and for which the X-ray telescope (XRT) observations could start during the EE, showed that providing a spectral coverage down to sof X-rays (i.e. ~ few keV), the fraction of short GRBs with EE can be as high as 50% or more.[48] Among the possible hypothesis on the origin of the extended emission there is the presence of a magnetar formed soon after the merger of two neutron stars.[49,50] The important consequence in this case is that the extended emission component is expected to have a much lower degree of collimation with respect to the main spike that characterizes the short GRB.[33,50] If so, the EE detection rate can be in principle higher than short GRBs, making wide field monitors sensitive to the X-ray band as eXTP/WFM best suited to detect the electromagnetic counterparts of a potentially large fraction of NS-NS mergers.

We simulate 5 short GRB with EE with measured spectral parameters from Fermi/GBM and Swift/BAT joint analysis plus 8 short GRB with EE observed with Swift/BAT with known redshift. We take best fit parameters from Kaneko et al.[44] For these simulations we used calibration files released by March 2021 and the data analysis software package XSPECv12.10.[35] We find that EE component is always detected with eXTP/WFM and in most cases with better significance than the hard spike (see Figure 2).

2.3. *Polarisation of GRB jets*

2.3.1. *The prompt emission*

Despite the fact that GRBs have been observed more than forty years, the basic properties of the GRB jets are not yet constrained. We still can not discriminate baryonic jets[51,52] from ones dominated by the Poynting flux[53,54] by only analysing the spectral and temporal properties of short lasting prompt emission pulses (~0.1 s) at the keV-MeV energy range (see[55] and[56] for a review). We also do not have a clear understanding of the dissipation processes that lead to the GRB production. Our knowledge is limited by the lack of an interpretation of the GRB spectra which are typically modelled by the two broken power laws smoothly connected at ~ 200 keV for LGRBs and at higher energies for SGRBs.[57] The observed spectra are too narrow to fit the fast cooling synchrotron radiation model and they are too broad compared with the simple thermal emission.[57,58] The absence of a single and straightforward emission mechanism to explain the typical GRB spectra has left us with big number of diverse physical models that correspond to very different GRB jet models. We can roughly classify the GRB production models by their dissipation side. The "standard" model assumes that the prompt emission is produced above the jet photosphere by the synchrotron emission of the non-thermal electrons that are produced by the internal shocks.[59,60] The "expected" parameters of the internal shocks model return fast cooling regime of the synchrotron radiation to dominate in the prompt phase, however it contradicts the observed values of the photon indices at the low energies.[58] Other class of models assume that the dissipation of the jet takes the place below the jet photosphere via the radiation dominated shocks.[61,62] The complex nature of the formation of the final spectrum via many Compton scatterings allows to produce spectra much broader than a simple thermal ones, thus close to the observed GRB spectra. However, it remains quite challenging to explain the observed variability, the power law structure of the high energy tail of the GRB spectra and the long lasting X-ray tails of the GRB pulses in these models.[63] There are numerous effects that can modify the spectral expectations from internal shocks model or any other optically thin synchrotron sources (e.g. non-thermal particles from magnetic re-connection), including the anisotropy of electron's pitch angles or presence of an external source of photons (see[64] for a brief review). While all these models could explain some of the observed GRB spectra, or at least partially (at the low or the high energy part), their prediction on the level of polarisation and the evolution of the polarisation angle is quite different, also depending on the structure of the local magnetic field (see[65] for a review). Therefore, the polarisation measure of the prompt phase is crucial for discriminating among GRB jet models including the acceleration processes (the magnetic field orientation).

So far the attempts to measure the GRB polarisation over short time-scales in the soft γ-rays returned inconclusive results due to contradictions between instruments and methods of data reduction performed by the Gamma-Ray Burst Polarimeter (GAP) (Yonetoku et al. 2011), POLAR,[66] and the Astrosat CZTI[67] instruments. The future γ-ray polarimeters, such as POLAR-2, LEAP and SPHiNX, have the capabilities to improve the polarisation measure accuracy of the prompt emission phase. However, measuring the polarization in the X-rays is equally interesting and has its own advantages. While the prompt emission pulses are very short in the soft γ-rays, we do observe regularly their tails (X-ray steep decay phase) for much longer time (100-1000 s) in 0.3-10 keV thanks to Swift/XRT. The X-ray steep decay is quite bright and starts at $\sim 10^{-7}\,\mathrm{erg\,s^{-1}\,cm^{-2}}$ at the peak of the prompt pulse and drops in two orders of magnitude in 100-1000 s. This phase is modelled as remnant of the prompt emission, i.e. the emission we observe when the GRB pulse is diminished at the jet co-moving frame.[68] Recently, it was demonstrated that X-ray steep decay is the lower energy prompt emission originated by the adiabatically cooling jet after its heat source is switched off.[69] Measuring X-ray polarization in the steep decay phase by the Polarimetry Focusing array (PFA) onboard eXTP would be a direct probe of the prompt emission polarisation (see[70]). The sensitivity of PFA is enough to constrain the linear polarisation degree for exposures of 100-1000 s given the extraordinary brightness of the X-ray steep decay phase. It requires a precise sky localisation of each detected GRB by the wide field γ or X-ray instruments, comparable with the extremely narrow FoV of PFA. The localisation level of arcminutes are expected to be provided by the eXTP/WFM and also by the next generation nano-satellite detectors such as HERMES.[71] Therefore, the prompt communication between eXTP instruments and advanced networks of γ-ray telescopes could provide a unique tool to study early X-ray polarisation. The presence of precursors and the quiescent periods in the temporal structure of LGRBs could be useful to send early trigger to detect bright X-ray counterparts of GRBs by PFA.

While *Swift*/XRT has been able to detect the steep decay phase of LGRBs, it is still technically challenging to promptly slew in the case of SGRBs. Given the spectral differences between long and short GRBs, one would expect physical differences between their jets and the dissipation processes. Therefore, the early detection of the X-ray emission from SGRBs and the measurement of its polarisation is of a great interest. The early warning and localisation of GWs prior to the BNS merger by the next generation GW detectors, such as the Einstein Telescope,[72] could be a unique trigger for the detection of the early X-ray polarisation of the the tail of the prompt emission from SGRBs.

2.3.2. *The afterglow emission*

Although we have very little knowledge on the physics of the prompt emission production, GRB afterglow emission (lasting for days) has a quite convincing interpretation. It is widely accepted that the dissipation of the GRB jet in the circumburst medium via shocks produces afterglow emission.[73–75] There have been several indications of detection of the linear polarisation in the late afterglow emission at the level of few percent[76] and a detection of circular polarisation in the afterglow of GRB 121024A.[77] The linear polarisation of level of few percent has been found at very early times,[78] when the emission is dominated by the reverse shock propagating into the GRB jet ejecta. Thus these measurements result to be essential for probing the shock physics by constraining the orientation of the magnetic field relative to the bulk motion, as well as for understanding the nature of the GRB jet by itself (reverse shock). Furthermore, nearby GRB sources can be detected off-axis, as the multi-messenger event of GW 170817/GRB 170817A. An upper limit of 12 percent in the linear polarisation at 2.8 GHz was obtained 244 days after the binary neutron star merger.[79] This upper limit allowed us to establish that the magnetic field has a finite parallel component, calling for turbulence amplified magnetic field in the external shock.[80]

X-ray domain in the physics of the GRB afterglow has a special importance for the following reasons. While the radio, optical and Very High Energy emissions in the afterglow phase are typically consistent with the standard external shocks model, *Swift* has discovered, that roughly half of the X-ray afterglow emission deviated from the standard forward shock emission, showing a long lasting (up to $\sim 10^4$ s) plateau phase, which is characterised by nearly constant flux. The X-ray plateau emission is can be produced by the additional energy input from the GRB central engine (e.g. newborn magnetar)[68] or it can be caused by the viewing angle effects[81] or by the delayed prompt emission from the jet wings.[82,83] In either case, the measure of the polarisation would be essential for constraining the physics of this mysterious GRB phase, simply because the polarisation would probe the structure of the magnetic field of the emission surface. From the observational perspective, the plateau phase has some advantages; it appears later compared to the steep decay phase giving more time to slew on, lasts longer ($\sim 10^4$ s), it is relatively bright ($\sim 10^{-10}\,\mathrm{erg\,s^{-1}\,cm^{-2}}$ comparable with the PFA sensitivity) and with absence of significant spectral evolution, which could remove polarisation. In the era of the Einstein Telescope, it would be also possible to constrain the BNS postmerger signal for relatively nearby sources. Combining the information from the BNS postmerger signals together with the X-ray polarisation from the plateau phase will be extremely powerful to shed light on our understanding of the origin of the central engine powering SGRBs.

Another intriguing possibility to probe the prompt emission is to measure the polarisation of the late-time X-ray flares. *Swift* has discovered numerous X-ray flares superimposed to the afterglow emission.[84] These flares appear up to 10^5 s after the GRB detection and their variability suggests their internal nature, i.e. they could be hardly produced by the external shocks. Therefore, they are often interpreted as late-time prompt emission. Their late-time appearance and relative brightness increases the chances for PFA to measure their linear polarisation,[85] thus providing complementary observations to the the next generation γ-ray polarimeters. From one side, the X-ray flares polarisation measurements would probe the prompt emission zone, and on the other side, the comparison between the polarisation measurements at early times in γ-rays and at late times in X-rays would finally help us to establish the nature of the late time X-ray activity.

3. Core collapse supernovae and magnetars

Core collapse supernovae (ccSNe) have been claimed as another potential class of high-frequency gravitational wave sources,[86–88] as well as neutrino sources,[89] that current and/or future ground-based GW detectors and neutrino detectors may reveal in the next years. The ccSNe energy output transferred with GWs however is still very uncertain depending on the rather unnown explosion mechanism. Recent modelling contraints on possible GW energy values, obtained from a search of GW transients associated with optically detected ccSNe within ~ 20 Mpc during the first two observational runs of aLIGO and AdV (between 2015 and 2017), suggest that ccSNe GW detection may happen in the next years for sources up to few tens of Mpc in a few, very optimistic scenarios.[90] The GW signal detection from ccSNe, possibly combined with neutrinos detection, represents a unique opportunity to probe the inner dynamics inaccessible to electromagnetic observations. The electromagnetic counterpart of ccSNe plays a key role in allowing to confirm or discard the likely very faint GW signal by providing a precise sky localization and an estimate of the epoch of the explosion.

At high-energies, the best GW-detected ccSNe electromagnetic counterparts would be the typical long GRBs due to their brightness and the expected temporal proximity to the epoch of the GW burst originating from the core collapse. The rate of typical long GRBs, however, is expected to be extremely low due to the small fraction of ccSNe known to be associated with such energetic events (only about few %, e.g.[91]), and to the combination of the GRB collimated nature and the short distances that GW detectors may reach for this type of burst signals. However, a subclass of anomalously faint and soft long GRBs, named Low Luminosity GRBs (LLGRBs), have been suggested to represent a distincted class of long GRBs that populate the local Universe at a much higher rate (up to 10^3 times the typical long GRBs). The redshift distribution of LLGRBs detected so far is well below 1, where the most nearby was detected at z=0.0085 (37 Mpc).[92] These properties make LLGRBs an interesting class of sources that may enhance the chances of simultaneous detection with GWs with high-energy wide field monitors. LLGRBs are also softer than typical long GRBs and this highlight the role of wide field monitors with peak sensitivity between few to few tens of keV as eXTP/WFM. We simulated how eXTP/WFM would detect GRB 060218, a typical LLGRB observed with Swift/BAT. This was a close GRB at 139 Mpc showing an unusual long and soft burst, with duration 2740s.[93] The burst was best fitted by a simple power law spectrum in the 15-150 keV with photon index $\Gamma = 2.5 \pm 0.1$, fluence of 5.8×10^{-6} erg cm^{-2} and peak flux 2×10^{-8} erg cm^{-2} s^{-1}. By simulating with XSPECv12.0 the eXTP/WFM observations using the most recent calibration files we find that with 1ks of exposure this burst could have been clearly detected with significance of $\sim 40\ \sigma$.

Another electromagnetic counterpart at high-energy is represented by the X-ray emission from the ccSNe shock breakout (SBO). The advantage of such component with respect to LLGRBs is that it is thought to be not collimated. However, the SBO phenomenology lack of statistics so far, with only one event observed (XRO 080109/SN2008D,[94]). The 0.3-10 keV spectrum of XRO080109 was consistent with a power law with photon index $\Gamma = 2.3 \pm 0.3$, equivalent hydrogen column density $N_H = 6.8^{+1.8}_{-1.5} \times 10^{21}$ cm^{-2} and peak flux of 7×10^{-10} erg s^{-1} cm^{-2}.[94] Such low fluxes could not had been detected by the majority of current wide field monitors. Indeed, its discovery happened serendipitously by falling within the Swift/XRT field of view while performing a follow-up campaign of another source in the very same galaxy. By assuming the best fit spectral model of XRO080109, very preliminary simulations with eXTP/WFM with 400 s of exposure show that this source would not be detected, confining the SBO detection with eXTP/WFM within our Galaxy.

4. Conclusions

The eXTP expected launch date and lifetime are timely for a full synergy with upgraded second generation GW detectors and with next generation neutrino detectors. Among the most promising multimessenger sources there are the compact binary mergers from which the high-energy electromagnetic counterpart is expected in the form of short GRBs and their afterglows and possibly additional X-ray emission, yet to be confirmed, as from the impact of the kilonova with the circumburst medium. We have shown how eXTP/WFM can observe short GRBs, including the "Extended emission" observed in a fraction of short GRBs. The eXTP/SFA could have monitored almost all the evolution of the associated X-ray afterglow of GRB 170817 up to very late times and the eXTP/WFM detect the soft component of the prompt emission up to 70 Mpc. Both neutrino and GW are expected from cc-SNe, a subclass of which is the progenitor of long GRBs and in particular of the much more numerous low luminosity GRBs that are populating the nearby Universe. eXTP/WFM can play a crucial role in detecting the associated GRB and providing accurate burst timing and sky localization that will help in refining GW/neutrino event detection confidence and parameter estimation. In particular, the eXTP/WFM sky localization will allow us to trigger follow-up campaigns by next generation facilities as ELT, SKA, CTA, etc. to characterize GW sources with unprecedented sensitivities. eXTP/SPA is capable to detect the GRB prompt and afterglow emission polarisation to disentangle among different jet launching mechanisms as well as to shed light on the nature of the late time activity observed in the X-ray afterglow of several events.

References

1. J. Aasi, B. P. Abbott, R. Abbott, T. Abbott, M. R. Abernathy, K. Ackley, C. Adams, T. Adams, P. Addesso, R. X. Adhikari et al., Advanced LIGO, *Class. Quantum Grav.* **32**, p. 074001 (April 2015).
2. F. Acernese, M. Agathos, K. Agatsuma, D. Aisa, N. Allemandou, A. Allocca, J. Amarni, P. Astone, G. Balestri, G. Ballardin et al., Advanced Virgo: A second-generation interferometric gravitational wave detector, *Class. Quantum Grav.* **32**, p. 024001 (January 2015).
3. B. P. Abbott, R. Abbott, T. D. Abbott, F. Acernese, K. Ackley, C. Adams, T. Adams, P. Addesso, R. X., V. B. Adya et al., GW170817: Observation of Gravitational Waves from a Binary Neutron Star Inspiral, *Phys. Rev. Letter* **119**, p. 161101 (October 2017).
4. B. P. Abbott, R. Abbott, T. D. Abbott, F. Acernese, K. Ackley, C. Adams, T. Adams, P. Addesso, R. X. Adhikari et al., Gravitational Waves and Gamma-Rays from a Binary Neutron Star Merger: GW170817 and GRB 170817A, *ApJL* **848**, p. L13 (October 2017).
5. E. Berger, Short-Duration Gamma-Ray Bursts, *Ann. Rev. Astron. Astrophys.* **52**, 43 (August 2014).
6. G. Ghirlanda, O. S. Salafia, Z. Paragi, M. Giroletti, J. Yang, B. Marcote, J. Blanchard, I. Agudo, T. An, M. G. Bernardini, R. Beswick, M. Branchesi, S. Campana, C. Casadio, E. Chassand e-Mottin, M. Colpi, S. Covino, P. D'Avanzo, V. D'Elia, S. Frey, M. Gawronski, G. Ghisellini, L. I. Gurvits, P. G. Jonker, H. J. van Langevelde, A. Melandri, J. Moldon, L. Nava, A. Perego, M. A. Perez-Torres, C. Reynolds, R. Salvaterra, G. Tagliaferri, T. Venturi, S. D. Vergani and M. Zhang, Compact radio emission indicates a structured jet was produced by a binary neutron star merger, *Science* **363**, 968 (Mar 2019).
7. K. P. Mooley, A. T. Deller, O. Gottlieb, E. Nakar, G. Hallinan, S. Bourke, D. A. Frail, A. Horesh, A. Corsi and K. Hotokezaka, Superluminal motion of a relativistic jet in the neutron-star merger GW170817, *Nature* **561**, 355 (September 2018).

8. B. P. Abbott, R. Abbott, T. D. Abbott, F. Acernese, K. Ackley, C. Adams, T. Adams, P. Addesso, R. X. Adhikari et al., Multi-messenger Observations of a Binary Neutron Star Merger, *ApJL* **848**, p. L12 (October 2017).
9. D. A. Coulter, R. J. Foley, C. D. Kilpatrick, M. R. Drout, A. L. Piro, B. J. Shappee, M. R. Siebert, J. D. Simon, N. Ulloa, D. Kasen, B. F. Madore, A. Murguia-Berthier, Y. C. Pan, J. X. Prochaska, E. Ramirez-Ruiz, A. Rest and C. Rojas-Bravo, Swope Supernova Survey 2017a (SSS17a), the optical counterpart to a gravitational wave source, *Science* **358**, 1556 (Dec 2017).
10. N. R. Tanvir, A. J. Levan, A. S. Fruchter, J. Hjorth, R. A. Hounsell, K. Wiersema and R. L. Tunnicliffe, A 'kilonova' associated with the short-duration γ-ray burst GRB 130603B, *Nature* **500**, 547 (August 2013).
11. E. Pian, P. D'Avanzo, S. Benetti, M. Branchesi, E. Brocato, S. Campana, E. Cappellaro, S. Covino, V. D'Elia, J. P. U. Fynbo, F. Getman, G. Ghirlanda, G. Ghisellini, A. Grado, G. Greco, J. Hjorth, C. Kouveliotou, A. Levan, L. Limatola, D. Malesani, P. A. Mazzali, A. Melandri, P. Møller, L. Nicastro, E. Palazzi, S. Piranomonte, A. Rossi, O. S. Salafia, J. Selsing, G. Stratta, M. Tanaka, N. R. Tanvir, L. Tomasella, D. Watson, S. Yang, L. Amati, L. A. Antonelli, S. Ascenzi, M. G. Bernardini, M. Boër, F. Bufano, A. Bulgarelli, M. Capaccioli, P. Casella, A. J. Castro-Tirado, E. Chassande-Mottin, R. Ciolfi, C. M. Copperwheat, M. Dadina, G. De Cesare, A. di Paola, Y. Z. Fan, B. Gendre, G. Giuffrida, A. Giunta, L. K. Hunt, G. L. Israel, Z. P. Jin, M. M. Kasliwal, S. Klose, M. Lisi, F. Longo, E. Maiorano, M. Mapelli, N. Masetti, L. Nava, B. Patricelli, D. Perley, A. Pescalli, T. Piran, A. Possenti, L. Pulone, M. Razzano, R. Salvaterra, P. Schipani, M. Spera, A. Stamerra, L. Stella, G. Tagliaferri, V. Testa, E. Troja, M. Turatto, S. D. Vergani and D. Vergani, Spectroscopic identification of r-process nucleosynthesis in a double neutron-star merger, *Nature* **551**, 67 (Nov 2017).
12. S. J. Smartt, T. W. Chen, A. Jerkstrand, M. Coughlin, E. Kankare, S. A. Sim, M. Fraser, C. Inserra, K. Maguire, K. C. Chambers, M. E. Huber, T. Krühler, G. Leloudas, M. Magee, L. J. Shingles, K. W. Smith, D. R. Young, J. Tonry, R. Kotak, A. Gal-Yam, J. D. Lyman, D. S. Homan, C. Agliozzo, J. P. Anderson, C. R. Angus, C. Ashall, C. Barbarino, F. E. Bauer, M. Berton, M. T. Botticella, M. Bulla, J. Bulger, G. Cannizzaro, Z. Cano, R. Cartier, A. Cikota, P. Clark, A. De Cia, M. Della Valle, L. Denneau, M. Dennefeld, L. Dessart, G. Dimitriadis, N. Elias-Rosa, R. E. Firth, H. Flewelling, A. Flörs, A. Franckowiak, C. Frohmaier, L. Galbany, S. González-Gaitán, J. Greiner, M. Gromadzki, A. N. Guelbenzu, C. P. Gutiérrez, A. Hamanowicz, L. Hanlon, J. Harmanen, K. E. Heintz, A. Heinze, M. S. Hernandez, S. T. Hodgkin, I. M. Hook, L. Izzo, P. A. James, P. G. Jonker, W. E. Kerzendorf, S. Klose, Z. Kostrzewa-Rutkowska, M. Kowalski, M. Kromer, H. Kuncarayakti, A. Lawrence, T. B. Lowe, E. A. Magnier, I. Manulis, A. Martin-Carrillo, S. Mattila, O. McBrien, A. Müller, J. Nordin, D. O'Neill, F. Onori, J. T. Palmerio, A. Pastorello, F. Patat, G. Pignata, P. Podsiadlowski, M. L. Pumo, S. J. Prentice, A. Rau, A. Razza, A. Rest, T. Reynolds, R. Roy, A. J. Ruiter, K. A. Rybicki, L. Salmon, P. Schady, A. S. B. Schultz, T. Schweyer, I. R. Seitenzahl, M. Smith, J. Sollerman, B. Stalder, C. W. Stubbs, M. Sullivan, H. Szegedi, F. Taddia, S. Taubenberger, G. Terreran, B. van Soelen, J. Vos, R. J. Wainscoat, N. A. Walton, C. Waters, H. Weiland, M. Willman, P. Wiseman, D. E. Wright, Ł. Wyrzykowski and O. Yaron, A kilonova as the electromagnetic counterpart to a gravitational-wave source, *Nature* **551**, 75 (Nov 2017).
13. IceCube Collaboration, Multimessenger observations of a flaring blazar coincident with high-energy neutrino IceCube-170922A, *Science* **361**, p. eaat1378 (July 2018).

14. IceCube Collaboration, Evidence for High-Energy Extraterrestrial Neutrinos at the IceCube Detector, *Science* **342**, p. 1242856 (November 2013).
15. K. Somiya, Detector configuration of KAGRA-the Japanese cryogenic gravitational-wave detector, *Classical and Quantum Gravity* **29**, p. 124007 (June 2012).
16. Y. Aso, Y. Michimura, K. Somiya, M. Ando, O. Miyakawa, T. Sekiguchi, D. Tatsumi and H. Yamamoto, Interferometer design of the kagra gravitational wave detector, *Phys. Rev. D* **88**, p. 043007 (Aug 2013).
17. B. P. Abbott, R. Abbott, T. D. Abbott, S. Abraham, F. Acernese, K. Ackley, C. Adams, V. B. Adya, C. Affeldt, L. S. C. Kagra Collaboration and VIRGO Collaboration, Prospects for observing and localizing gravitational-wave transients with Advanced LIGO, Advanced Virgo and KAGRA, *Living Reviews in Relativity* **23**, p. 3 (September 2020).
18. D. Reitze *et al.*, Cosmic Explorer: The U.S. Contribution to Gravitational-Wave Astronomy beyond LIGO, *Bull. Am. Astron. Soc.* **51**, p. 035 (2019).
19. B. P. Abbott, R. Abbott, T. D. Abbott, M. R. Abernathy, K. Ackley, C. Adams, P. Addesso, R. X. Adhikari, V. B. Adya, C. Affeldt, N. Aggarwal, O. D. Aguiar, A. Ain, P. Ajith, B. Allen, P. A. Altin, S. B. Anderson, W. G. Anderson, K. Arai, M. C. Araya, C. C. Arceneaux, J. S. Areeda, K. G. Arun, G. Ashton, M. Ast, S. M. Aston, P. Aufmuth, C. Aulbert, S. Babak, P. T. Baker, S. W. Ballmer, J. C. Barayoga, S. E. Barclay, B. C. Barish, D. Barker, B. Barr, L. Barsotti, J. Bartlett, I. Bartos, R. Bassiri, J. C. Batch, C. Baune, A. S. Bell, B. K. Berger, G. Bergmann, C. P. L. Berry, J. Betzwieser, S. Bhagwat, R. Bhandare, I. A. Bilenko, G. Billingsley, J. Birch, R. Birney, S. Biscans, A. Bisht, C. Biwer, J. K. Blackburn, C. D. Blair, D. G. Blair, R. M. Blair, O. Bock, C. Bogan, A. Bohe, C. Bond, R. Bork, S. Bose, P. R. Brady, V. B. Braginsky, J. E. Brau, M. Brinkmann, P. Brockill, J. E. Broida, A. F. Brooks, D. A. Brown, D. D. Brown, N. M. Brown, S. Brunett, C. C. Buchanan, A. Buikema, A. Buonanno, R. L. Byer, M. Cabero, L. Cadonati, C. Cahillane, J. C. Bustillo, T. Callister, J. B. Camp, K. C. Cannon, J. Cao, C. D. Capano, S. Caride, S. Caudill, M. Cavaglià, C. B. Cepeda, S. J. Chamberlin, M. Chan, S. Chao, P. Charlton, B. D. Cheeseboro, H. Y. Chen, Y. Chen, C. Cheng, H. S. Cho, M. Cho, J. H. Chow, N. Christensen, Q. Chu, S. Chung, G. Ciani, F. Clara, J. A. Clark, C. G. Collette, L. Cominsky, M. Constancio, D. Cook, T. R. Corbitt, N. Cornish, A. Corsi, C. A. Costa, M. W. Coughlin, S. B. Coughlin, S. T. Countryman, P. Couvares, E. E. Cowan, D. M. Coward, M. J. Cowart, D. C. Coyne, R. Coyne, K. Craig, J. D. E. Creighton, J. Cripe, S. G. Crowder, A. Cumming, L. Cunningham, T. D. Canton, S. L. Danilishin, K. Danzmann, N. S. Darman, A. Dasgupta, C. F. D. S. Costa, I. Dave, G. S. Davies, E. J. Daw, S. De, D. DeBra, W. D. Pozzo, T. Denker, T. Dent, V. Dergachev, R. T. DeRosa, R. DeSalvo, R. C. Devine, S. Dhurandhar, M. C. Díaz, I. D. Palma, F. Donovan, K. L. Dooley, S. Doravari, R. Douglas, T. P. Downes, M. Drago, R. W. P. Drever, J. C. Driggers, S. E. Dwyer, T. B. Edo, M. C. Edwards, A. Effler, H.-B. Eggenstein, P. Ehrens, J. Eichholz, S. S. Eikenberry, W. Engels, R. C. Essick, T. Etzel, M. Evans, T. M. Evans, R. Everett, M. Factourovich, H. Fair, S. Fairhurst, X. Fan, Q. Fang, B. Farr, W. M. Farr, M. Favata, M. Fays, H. Fehrmann, M. M. Fejer, E. Fenyvesi, E. C. Ferreira, R. P. Fisher, M. Fletcher, Z. Frei, A. Freise, R. Frey, P. Fritschel, V. V. Frolov, P. Fulda, M. Fyffe, H. A. G. Gabbard, J. R. Gair, S. G. Gaonkar, G. Gaur, N. Gehrels, P. Geng, J. George, L. Gergely, A. Ghosh, A. Ghosh, J. A. Giaime, K. D. Giardina, K. Gill, A. Glaefke, E. Goetz, R. Goetz, L. Gondan, G. González, A. Gopakumar, N. A. Gordon, M. L. Gorodetsky, S. E. Gossan, C. Graef, P. B. Graff, A. Grant, S. Gras, C. Gray, A. C. Green, H. Grote, S. Grunewald, X. Guo, A. Gupta, M. K. Gupta, K. E. Gushwa, E. K. Gustafson, R. Gustafson, J. J. Hacker, B. R. Hall, E. D. Hall, G. Hammond,

M. Haney, M. M. Hanke, J. Hanks, C. Hanna, M. D. Hannam, J. Hanson, T. Hardwick, G. M. Harry, I. W. Harry, M. J. Hart, M. T. Hartman, C.-J. Haster, K. Haughian, M. C. Heintze, M. Hendry, I. S. Heng, J. Hennig, J. Henry, A. W. Heptonstall, M. Heurs, S. Hild, D. Hoak, K. Holt, D. E. Holz, P. Hopkins, J. Hough, E. A. Houston, E. J. Howell, Y. M. Hu, S. Huang, E. A. Huerta, B. Hughey, S. Husa, S. H. Huttner, T. Huynh-Dinh, N. Indik, D. R. Ingram, R. Inta, H. N. Isa, M. Isi, T. Isogai, B. R. Iyer, K. Izumi, H. Jang, K. Jani, S. Jawahar, L. Jian, F. Jiménez-Forteza, W. W. Johnson, D. I. Jones, R. Jones, L. Ju, K. Haris, C. V. Kalaghatgi, V. Kalogera, S. Kandhasamy, G. Kang, J. B. Kanner, S. J. Kapadia, S. Karki, K. S. Karvinen, M. Kasprzack, E. Katsavounidis, W. Katzman, S. Kaufer, T. Kaur, K. Kawabe, M. S. Kehl, D. Keitel, D. B. Kelley, W. Kells, R. Kennedy, J. S. Key, F. Y. Khalili, S. Khan, Z. Khan, E. A. Khazanov, N. Kijbunchoo, C.-W. Kim, C. Kim, J. Kim, K. Kim, N. Kim, W. Kim, Y.-M. Kim, S. J. Kimbrell, E. J. King, P. J. King, J. S. Kissel, B. Klein, L. Kleybolte, S. Klimenko, S. M. Koehlenbeck, V. Kondrashov, A. Kontos, M. Korobko, W. Z. Korth, D. B. Kozak, V. Kringel, C. Krueger, G. Kuehn, P. Kumar, R. Kumar, L. Kuo, B. D. Lackey, M. Landry, J. Lange, B. Lantz, P. D. Lasky, M. Laxen, A. Lazzarini, S. Leavey, E. O. Lebigot, C. H. Lee, H. K. Lee, H. M. Lee, K. Lee, A. Lenon, J. R. Leong, Y. Levin, J. B. Lewis, T. G. F. Li, A. Libson, T. B. Littenberg, N. A. Lockerbie, A. L. Lombardi, L. T. London, J. E. Lord, M. Lormand, J. D. Lough, H. Lück, A. P. Lundgren, R. Lynch, Y. Ma, B. Machenschalk, M. MacInnis, D. M. Macleod, F. Magaña-Sandoval, L. M. Zertuche, R. M. Magee, V. Mandic, V. Mangano, G. L. Mansell, M. Manske, S. Márka, Z. Márka, A. S. Markosyan, E. Maros, I. W. Martin, D. V. Martynov, K. Mason, T. J. Massinger, M. Masso-Reid, F. Matichard, L. Matone, N. Mavalvala, N. Mazumder, R. McCarthy, D. E. McClelland, S. McCormick, S. C. McGuire, G. McIntyre, J. McIver, D. J. McManus, T. McRae, S. T. McWilliams, D. Meacher, G. D. Meadors, A. Melatos, G. Mendell, R. A. Mercer, E. L. Merilh, S. Meshkov, C. Messenger, C. Messick, P. M. Meyers, H. Miao, H. Middleton, E. E. Mikhailov, A. L. Miller, A. Miller, B. B. Miller, J. Miller, M. Millhouse, J. Ming, S. Mirshekari, C. Mishra, S. Mitra, V. P. Mitrofanov, G. Mitselmakher, R. Mittleman, S. R. P. Mohapatra, B. C. Moore, C. J. Moore, D. Moraru, G. Moreno, S. R. Morriss, K. Mossavi, C. M. Mow-Lowry, G. Mueller, A. W. Muir, A. Mukherjee, D. Mukherjee, S. Mukherjee, N. Mukund, A. Mullavey, J. Munch, D. J. Murphy, P. G. Murray, A. Mytidis, R. K. Nayak, K. Nedkova, T. J. N. Nelson, A. Neunzert, G. Newton, T. T. Nguyen, A. B. Nielsen, A. Nitz, D. Nolting, M. E. N. Normandin, L. K. Nuttall, J. Oberling, E. Ochsner, J. O'Dell, E. Oelker, G. H. Ogin, J. J. Oh, S. H. Oh, F. Ohme, M. Oliver, P. Oppermann, R. J. Oram, B. O'Reilly, R. O'Shaughnessy, D. J. Ottaway, H. Overmier, B. J. Owen, A. Pai, S. A. Pai, J. R. Palamos, O. Palashov, A. Pal-Singh, H. Pan, C. Pankow, F. Pannarale, B. C. Pant, M. A. Papa, H. R. Paris, W. Parker, D. Pascucci, Z. Patrick, B. L. Pearlstone, M. Pedraza, L. Pekowsky, A. Pele, S. Penn, A. Perreca, L. M. Perri, M. Phelps, V. Pierro, I. M. Pinto, M. Pitkin, M. Poe, A. Post, J. Powell, J. Prasad, V. Predoi, T. Prestegard, L. R. Price, M. Prijatelj, M. Principe, S. Privitera, L. Prokhorov, O. Puncken, M. Pürrer, H. Qi, J. Qin, S. Qiu, V. Quetschke, E. A. Quintero, R. Quitzow-James, F. J. Raab, D. S. Rabeling, H. Radkins, P. Raffai, S. Raja, C. Rajan, M. Rakhmanov, V. Raymond, J. Read, C. M. Reed, S. Reid, D. H. Reitze, H. Rew, S. D. Reyes, K. Riles, M. Rizzo, N. A. Robertson, R. Robie, J. G. Rollins, V. J. Roma, G. Romanov, J. H. Romie, S. Rowan, A. Rüdiger, K. Ryan, S. Sachdev, T. Sadecki, L. Sadeghian, M. Sakellariadou, M. Saleem, F. Salemi, A. Samajdar, L. Sammut, E. J. Sanchez, V. Sandberg, B. Sandeen, J. R. Sanders, B. S. Sathyaprakash, P. R. Saulson, O. E. S. Sauter, R. L. Savage, A. Sawadsky, P. Schale, R. Schilling, J. Schmidt, P. Schmidt,

R. Schnabel, R. M. S. Schofield, A. Schönbeck, E. Schreiber, D. Schuette, B. F. Schutz, J. Scott, S. M. Scott, D. Sellers, A. S. Sengupta, A. Sergeev, D. A. Shaddock, T. Shaffer, M. S. Shahriar, M. Shaltev, B. Shapiro, P. Shawhan, A. Sheperd, D. H. Shoemaker, D. M. Shoemaker, K. Siellez, X. Siemens, D. Sigg, A. D. Silva, A. Singer, L. P. Singer, A. Singh, R. Singh, A. M. Sintes, B. J. J. Slagmolen, J. R. Smith, N. D. Smith, R. J. E. Smith, E. J. Son, B. Sorazu, T. Souradeep, A. K. Srivastava, A. Staley, M. Steinke, J. Steinlechner, S. Steinlechner, D. Steinmeyer, B. C. Stephens, R. Stone, K. A. Strain, N. A. Strauss, S. Strigin, R. Sturani, A. L. Stuver, T. Z. Summerscales, L. Sun, S. Sunil, P. J. Sutton, M. J. Szczepańczyk, D. Talukder, D. B. Tanner, M. Tápai, S. P. Tarabrin, A. Taracchini, R. Taylor, T. Theeg, M. P. Thirugnanasambandam, E. G. Thomas, M. Thomas, P. Thomas, K. A. Thorne, E. Thrane, V. Tiwari, K. V. Tokmakov, K. Toland, C. Tomlinson, Z. Tornasi, C. V. Torres, C. I. Torrie, D. Töyrä, G. Traylor, D. Trifirò, M. Tse, D. Tuyenbayev, D. Ugolini, C. S. Unnikrishnan, A. L. Urban, S. A. Usman, H. Vahlbruch, G. Vajente, G. Valdes, D. C. Vander-Hyde, A. A. van Veggel, S. Vass, R. Vaulin, A. Vecchio, J. Veitch, P. J. Veitch, K. Venkateswara, S. Vinciguerra, D. J. Vine, S. Vitale, T. Vo, C. Vorvick, D. V. Voss, W. D. Vousden, S. P. Vyatchanin, A. R. Wade, L. E. Wade, M. Wade, M. Walker, L. Wallace, S. Walsh, H. Wang, M. Wang, X. Wang, Y. Wang, R. L. Ward, J. Warner, B. Weaver, M. Weinert, A. J. Weinstein, R. Weiss, L. Wen, P. Weßels, T. Westphal, K. Wette, J. T. Whelan, B. F. Whiting, R. D. Williams, A. R. Williamson, J. L. Willis, B. Willke, M. H. Wimmer, W. Winkler, C. C. Wipf, H. Wittel, G. Woan, J. Woehler, J. Worden, J. L. Wright, D. S. Wu, G. Wu, J. Yablon, W. Yam, H. Yamamoto, C. C. Yancey, H. Yu, M. Zanolin, M. Zevin, L. Zhang, M. Zhang, Y. Zhang, C. Zhao, M. Zhou, Z. Zhou, X. J. Zhu, M. E. Zucker, S. E. Zuraw, J. Zweizig and J. H. and, Exploring the sensitivity of next generation gravitational wave detectors, *Classical and Quantum Gravity* **34**, p. 044001 (Jan 2017).
20. M. Punturo, M. Abernathy, F. Acernese, B. Allen, N. Andersson, K. Arun, F. Barone, B. Barr, M. Barsuglia, M. Beker, N. Beveridge, S. Birindelli, S. Bose, L. Bosi, S. Braccini, C. Bradaschia, T. Bulik, E. Calloni, G. Cella, E. Chassande Mottin, S. Chelkowski, A. Chincarini, J. Clark, E. Coccia, C. Colacino, J. Colas, A. Cumming, L. Cunningham, E. Cuoco, S. Danilishin, K. Danzmann, G. De Luca, R. De Salvo, T. Dent, R. De Rosa, L. Di Fiore, A. Di Virgilio, M. Doets, V. Fafone, P. Falferi, R. Flaminio, R. Franc, F. Frasconi, A. Freise, P. Fulda, J. Gair, G. Gemme, A. Gennai, A. Giazotto, K. Glampedakis, M. Granata, H. Grote, G. Guidi, G. Hammond, M. Hannam, J. Harms, D. Heinert, M. Hendry, I. Heng, E. Hennes, S. Hild, J. Hough, S. Husa, S. Huttner, G. Jones, F. Khalili, K. Kokeyama, K. Kokkotas, B. Krishnan, M. Lorenzini, H. Lück, E. Majorana, I. Mandel, V. Mandic, I. Martin, C. Michel, Y. Minenkov, N. Morgado, S. Mosca, B. Mours, H. Müller Ebhardt, P. Murray, R. Nawrodt, J. Nelson, R. Oshaughnessy, C. D. Ott, C. Palomba, A. Paoli, G. Parguez, A. Pasqualetti, R. Passaquieti, D. Passuello, L. Pinard, R. Poggiani, P. Popolizio, M. Prato, P. Puppo, D. Rabeling, P. Rapagnani, J. Read, T. Regimbau, H. Rehbein, S. Reid, L. Rezzolla, F. Ricci, F. Richard, A. Rocchi, S. Rowan, A. Rüdiger, B. Sassolas, B. Sathyaprakash, R. Schnabel, C. Schwarz, P. Seidel, A. Sintes, K. Somiya, F. Speirits, K. Strain, S. Strigin, P. Sutton, S. Tarabrin, A. Thüring, J. van den Brand, C. van Leewen, M. van Veggel, C. van den Broeck, A. Vecchio, J. Veitch, F. Vetrano, A. Vicere, S. Vyatchanin, B. Willke, G. Woan, P. Wolfango and K. Yamamoto, The Einstein Telescope: a third-generation gravitational wave observatory, *Class. Quantum Grav.* **27**, p. 194002 (October 2010).

21. S. Hild, M. Abernathy, F. Acernese, P. Amaro-Seoane, N. Andersson, K. Arun, F. Barone, B. Barr, M. Barsuglia et al., Sensitivity studies for third-generation gravitational wave observatories, *Classical and Quantum Gravity* **28**, p. 094013 (May 2011).
22. M. Maggiore, C. Van Den Broeck, N. Bartolo, E. Belgacem, D. Bertacca, M. A. Bizouard, M. Branchesi, S. Clesse, S. Foffa, J. García-Bellido, S. Grimm, J. Harms, T. Hinderer, S. Matarrese, C. Palomba, M. Peloso, A. Ricciardone and M. Sakellariadou, Science case for the Einstein telescope, *J. Cosmol. Astropart. Phys.* **2020**, p. 050 (March 2020).
23. M. L. Chan, C. Messenger, I. S. Heng and M. Hendry, Binary neutron star mergers and third generation detectors: Localization and early warning, *Phys. Rev. D* **97**, p. 123014 (June 2018).
24. S. Adrián-Martínez, M. Ageron, F. Aharonian, S. Aiello, A. Albert, F. Ameli, E. Anassontzis, M. Andre, G. Androulakis, M. Anghinolfi and et al., Letter of intent for KM3NeT 2.0, *J. Phys. G Nucl. Phys.* **43**, p. 084001 (August 2016).
25. IceCube-Gen2 Collaboration, IceCube-Gen2: A Vision for the Future of Neutrino Astronomy in Antarctica, *arXiv e-prints*, p. arXiv:1412.5106 (December 2014).
26. S. Zhang, A. Santangelo, M. Feroci, Y. Xu, F. Lu, Y. Chen, H. Feng, S. Zhang, S. Brandt, M. Hernanz, L. Baldini, E. Bozzo, R. Campana, A. De Rosa, Y. Dong, Y. Evangelista, V. Karas, N. Meidinger, A. Meuris, K. Nandra, T. Pan, G. Pareschi, P. Orleanski, Q. Huang, S. Schanne, G. Sironi, D. Spiga, J. Svoboda, G. Tagliaferri, C. Tenzer, A. Vacchi, S. Zane, D. Walton, Z. Wang, B. Winter, X. Wu, J. J. M. in 't Zand, M. Ahangarianabhari, G. Ambrosi, F. Ambrosino, M. Barbera, S. Basso, J. Bayer, R. Bellazzini, P. Bellutti, B. Bertucci, G. Bertuccio, G. Borghi, X. Cao, F. Cadoux, R. Campana, F. Ceraudo, T. Chen, Y. Chen, J. Chevenez, M. Civitani, W. Cui, W. Cui, T. Dauser, E. Del Monte, S. Di Cosimo, S. Diebold, V. Doroshenko, M. Dovciak, Y. Du, L. Ducci, Q. Fan, Y. Favre, F. Fuschino, J. L. Gálvez, M. Gao, M. Ge, O. Gevin, M. Grassi, Q. Gu, Y. Gu, B. Han, B. Hong, W. Hu, L. Ji, S. Jia, W. Jiang, T. Kennedy, I. Kreykenbohm, I. Kuvvetli, C. Labanti, L. Latronico, G. Li, M. Li, X. Li, W. Li, Z. Li, O. Limousin, H. Liu, X. Liu, B. Lu, T. Luo, D. Macera, P. Malcovati, A. Martindale, M. Michalska, B. Meng, M. Minuti, A. Morbidini, F. Muleri, S. Paltani, E. Perinati, A. Picciotto, C. Piemonte, J. Qu, A. Rachevski, I. Rashevskaya, J. Rodriguez, T. Schanz, Z. Shen, L. Sheng, J. Song, L. Song, C. Sgro, L. Sun, Y. Tan, P. Uttley, B. Wang, D. Wang, G. Wang, J. Wang, L. Wang, Y. Wang, A. L. Watts, X. Wen, J. Wilms, S. Xiong, J. Yang, S. Yang, Y. Yang, N. Yu, W. Zhang, G. Zampa, N. Zampa, A. A. Zdziarski, A. Zhang, C. Zhang, F. Zhang, L. Zhang, T. Zhang, Y. Zhang, X. Zhang, Z. Zhang, B. Zhao, S. Zheng, Y. Zhou, N. Zorzi and J. F. Zwart, The enhanced X-ray Timing and Polarimetry mission—eXTP, *Science China Physics, Mechanics, and Astronomy* **62**, p. 29502 (February 2019).
27. J. J. M. in 't Zand, E. Bozzo, J. Qu, X.-D. Li, L. Amati, Y. Chen, I. Donnarumma, V. Doroshenko, S. A. Drake, M. Hernanz, P. A. Jenke, T. J. Maccarone, S. Mahmoodifar, D. de Martino, A. De Rosa, E. M. Rossi, A. Rowlinson, G. Sala, G. Stratta, T. M. Tauris, J. Wilms, X. Wu, P. Zhou, I. Agudo, D. Altamirano, J.-L. Atteia, N. A. Andersson, M. C. Baglio, D. R. Ballantyne, A. Baykal, E. Behar, T. Belloni, S. Bhattacharyya, S. Bianchi, A. Bilous, P. Blay, J. Braga, S. Brandt, E. F. Brown, N. Bucciantini, L. Burderi, E. M. Cackett, R. Campana, S. Campana, P. Casella, Y. Cavecchi, F. Chambers, L. Chen, Y.-P. Chen, J. Chenevez, M. Chernyakova, C. Jin, R. Ciolfi, E. Costantini, A. Cumming, A. D'Aì, Z.-G. Dai, F. D'Ammando, M. De Pasquale, N. Degenaar, M. Del Santo, V. D'Elia, T. Di Salvo, G. Doyle, M. Falanga, X. Fan, R. D. Ferdman, M. Feroci, F. Fraschetti, D. K. Galloway, A. F. Gambino, P. Gandhi, M. Ge, B. Gendre, R. Gill, D. Götz, C. Gouiffès, P. Grandi, J. Granot, M. Güdel, A. Heger,

C. O. Heinke, J. Homan, R. Iaria, K. Iwasawa, L. Izzo, L. Ji, P. G. Jonker, J. José, J. S. Kaastra, E. Kalemci, O. Kargaltsev, N. Kawai, L. Keek, S. Komossa, I. Kreykenbohm, L. Kuiper, D. Kunneriath, G. Li, E.-W. Liang, M. Linares, F. Longo, F. Lu, A. A. Lutovinov, D. Malyshev, J. Malzac, A. Manousakis, I. McHardy, M. Mehdipour, Y. Men, M. Méndez, R. P. Mignani, R. Mikusincova, M. C. Miller, G. Miniutti, C. Motch, J. Nättilä, E. Nardini, T. Neubert, P. T. O'Brien, M. Orlandini, J. P. Osborne, L. Pacciani, S. Paltani, M. Paolillo, I. E. Papadakis, B. Paul, A. Pellizzoni, U. Peretz, M. A. Pérez Torres, E. Perinati, C. Prescod-Weinstein, P. Reig, A. Riggio, J. Rodriguez, P. Rodríguez-Gil, P. Romano, A. Różańska, T. Sakamoto, T. Salmi, R. Salvaterra, A. Sanna, A. Santangelo, T. Savolainen, S. Schanne, H. Schatz, L. Shao, A. Shearer, S. N. Shore, B. W. Stappers, T. E. Strohmayer, V. F. Suleimanov, J. Svoboda, F. K. Thielemann, F. Tombesi, D. F. Torres, E. Torresi, S. Turriziani, A. Vacchi, S. Vercellone, J. Vink, J.-M. Wang, J. Wang, A. L. Watts, S. Weng, N. N. Weinberg, P. J. Wheatley, R. Wijnands, T. E. Woods, S. E. Woosley, S. Xiong, Y. Xu, Z. Yan, G. Younes, W. Yu, F. Yuan, L. Zampieri, S. Zane, A. A. Zdziarski, S.-N. Zhang, S. Zhang, S. Zhang, X. Zhang and M. Zingale, Observatory science with eXTP, *Science China Physics, Mechanics, and Astronomy* **62**, p. 29506 (February 2019).

28. A. Santangelo, S. Zane, H. Feng, R. Xu, V. Doroshenko, E. Bozzo, I. Caiazzo, F. Coti Zelati, P. Esposito, D. González-Caniulef, J. Heyl, D. Huppenkothen, G. Israel, Z. Li, L. Lin, R. Mignani, N. Rea, M. Orlandini, R. Taverna, H. Tong, R. Turolla, C. Baglio, F. Bernardini, N. Bucciantini, M. Feroci, F. Fürst, E. Göğüş, C. Güngör, L. Ji, F. Lu, A. Manousakis, S. Mereghetti, R. Mikusincova, B. Paul, C. Prescod-Weinstein, G. Younes, A. Tiengo, Y. Xu, A. Watts, S. Zhang and S.-N. Zhan, Physics and astrophysics of strong magnetic field systems with eXTP, *Science China Physics, Mechanics, and Astronomy* **62**, p. 29505 (February 2019).

29. A. De Rosa, P. Uttley, L. Gou, Y. Liu, C. Bambi, D. Barret, T. Belloni, E. Berti, S. Bianchi, I. Caiazzo, P. Casella, M. Feroci, V. Ferrari, L. Gualtieri, J. Heyl, A. Ingram, V. Karas, F. Lu, B. Luo, G. Matt, S. Motta, J. Neilsen, P. Pani, A. Santangelo, X. Shu, J. Wang, J.-M. Wang, Y. Xue, Y. Xu, W. Yuan, Y. Yuan, S.-N. Zhang, S. Zhang, I. Agudo, L. Amati, N. Andersson, C. Baglio, P. Bakala, A. Baykal, S. Bhattacharyya, I. Bombaci, N. Bucciantini, F. Capitanio, R. Ciolfi, W. K. Cui, F. D'Ammando, T. Dauser, M. Del Santo, B. De Marco, T. Di Salvo, C. Done, M. Dovčiak, A. C. Fabian, M. Falanga, A. F. Gambino, B. Gendre, V. Grinberg, A. Heger, J. Homan, R. Iaria, J. Jiang, C. Jin, E. Koerding, M. Linares, Z. Liu, T. J. Maccarone, J. Malzac, A. Manousakis, F. Marin, A. Marinucci, M. Mehdipour, M. Méndez, S. Migliari, C. Miller, G. Miniutti, E. Nardini, P. T. O'Brien, J. P. Osborne, P. O. Petrucci, A. Possenti, A. Riggio, J. Rodriguez, A. Sanna, L. Shao, M. Sobolewska, E. Sramkova, A. L. Stevens, H. Stiele, G. Stratta, Z. Stuchlik, J. Svoboda, F. Tamburini, T. M. Tauris, F. Tombesi, G. Torok, M. Urbanec, F. Vincent, Q. Wu, F. Yuan, J. J. M. in 't Zand, A. A. Zdziarski and X. Zhou, Accretion in strong field gravity with eXTP, *Science China Physics, Mechanics, and Astronomy* **62**, p. 29504 (February 2019).

30. A. L. Watts, W. Yu, J. Poutanen, S. Zhang, S. Bhattacharyya, S. Bogdanov, L. Ji, A. Patruno, T. E. Riley, P. Bakala, A. Baykal, F. Bernardini, I. Bombaci, E. Brown, Y. Cavecchi, D. Chakrabarty, J. Chenevez, N. Degenaar, M. Del Santo, T. Di Salvo, V. Doroshenko, M. Falanga, R. D. Ferdman, M. Feroci, A. F. Gambino, M. Ge, S. K. Greif, S. Guillot, C. Gungor, D. H. Hartmann, K. Hebeler, A. Heger, J. Homan, R. Iaria, J. i. Zand, O. Kargaltsev, A. Kurkela, X. Lai, A. Li, X. Li, Z. Li, M. Linares, F. Lu, S. Mahmoodifar, M. Méndez, M. Coleman Miller, S. Morsink, J. Nättilä, A. Possenti, C. Prescod-Weinstein, J. Qu, A. Riggio, T. Salmi, A. Sanna, A. Santangelo,

H. Schatz, A. Schwenk, L. Song, E. Šrámková, B. Stappers, H. Stiele, T. Strohmayer, I. Tews, L. Tolos, G. Török, D. Tsang, M. Urbanec, A. Vacchi, R. Xu, Y. Xu, S. Zane, G. Zhang, S. Zhang, W. Zhang, S. Zheng and X. Zhou, Dense matter with eXTP, *Science China Physics, Mechanics, and Astronomy* **62**, p. 29503 (February 2019).
31. O. S. Salafia, G. Ghirlanda, S. Ascenzi and G. Ghisellini, On-axis view of GRB 170817A, *Astron. Astrophys.* **628**, p. A18 (Aug 2019).
32. A. Hajela, R. Margutti, J. S. Bright, K. D. Alexander, B. D. Metzger, V. Nedora, A. Kathirgamaraju, B. Margalit, D. Radice, E. Berger, A. MacFadyen, D. Giannios, R. Chornock, I. Heywood, L. Sironi, O. Gottlieb, D. Coppejans, T. Laskar, Y. Cendes, R. Barniol Duran, T. Eftekhari, W. Fong, A. McDowell, M. Nicholl, X. Xie, J. Zrake, S. Bernuzzi, F. S. Broekgaarden, C. D. Kilpatrick, G. Terreran, V. A. Villar, P. K. Blanchard, S. Gomez, G. Hosseinzadeh, D. J. Matthews and J. C. Rastinejad, The emergence of a new source of X-rays from the binary neutron star merger GW170817, *arXiv e-prints*, p. arXiv:2104.02070 (April 2021).
33. B. D. Metzger and A. L. Piro, Optical and X-ray emission from stable millisecond magnetars formed from the merger of binary neutron stars, *Mon. Not. R. Astron. Soc.* **439**, 3916 (April 2014).
34. R. Ciolfi, W. Kastaun, J. V. Kalinani and B. Giacomazzo, First 100 ms of a long-lived magnetized neutron star formed in a binary neutron star merger, *Phys. Rev. D* **100**, p. 023005 (Jul 2019).
35. K. Arnaud, B. Dorman and C. Gordon, XSPEC: An X-ray spectral fitting package (October 1999).
36. A. Goldstein, P. Veres, E. Burns, M. S. Briggs, R. Hamburg, D. Kocevski, C. A. Wilson-Hodge, R. D. Preece, S. Poolakkil, O. J. Roberts, C. M. Hui, V. Connaughton, J. Racusin, A. von Kienlin, T. Dal Canton, N. Christensen, T. Littenberg, K. Siellez, L. Blackburn, J. Broida, E. Bissaldi, W. H. Cleveland, M. H. Gibby, M. M. Giles, R. M. Kippen, S. McBreen, J. McEnery, C. A. Meegan, W. S. Paciesas and M. Stanbro, An Ordinary Short Gamma-Ray Burst with Extraordinary Implications: Fermi-GBM Detection of GRB 170817A, *Astrophys. J. Lett.* **848**, p. L14 (October 2017).
37. B. B. Zhang, B. Zhang, H. Sun, W. H. Lei, H. Gao, Y. Li, L. Shao, Y. Zhao, Y. D. Hu, H. J. Lü, X. F. Wu, X. L. Fan, G. Wang, A. J. Castro-Tirado, S. Zhang, B. Y. Yu, Y. Y. Cao and E. W. Liang, A peculiar low-luminosity short gamma-ray burst from a double neutron star merger progenitor, *Nature Communications* **9**, p. 447 (January 2018).
38. G. Ghirlanda, O. S. Salafia, A. Pescalli, G. Ghisellini, R. Salvaterra, E. Chassande-Mottin, M. Colpi, F. Nappo, P. D'Avanzo, A. Melandri, M. G. Bernardini, M. Branchesi, S. Campana, R. Ciolfi, S. Covino, D. Götz, S. D. Vergani, M. Zennaro and G. Tagliaferri, Short gamma-ray bursts at the dawn of the gravitational wave era, *Astron. Astrophys.* **594**, p. A84 (October 2016).
39. E. Troja, L. Piro, H. van Eerten, R. T. Wollaeger, M. Im, O. D. Fox, N. R. Butler, S. B. Cenko, T. Sakamoto, C. L. Fryer, R. Ricci, A. Lien, R. E. Ryan, O. Korobkin, S.-K. Lee, J. M. Burgess, W. H. Lee, A. M. Watson, C. Choi, S. Covino, P. D'Avanzo, C. J. Fontes, J. B. González, H. G. Khandrika, J. Kim, S.-L. Kim, C.-U. Lee, H. M. Lee, A. Kutyrev, G. Lim, R. Sánchez-Ramírez, S. Veilleux, M. H. Wieringa and Y. Yoon, The X-ray counterpart to the gravitational-wave event GW170817, *Nature* **551**, 71 (November 2017).
40. A. Hajela, R. Margutti, J. Bright, K. D. Alexander, W. Fong, E. Berger, R. Chornock, D. L. Coppejans, P. Blanchard, V. A. Villar, T. Eftekhari, A. Kathirgamaraju, D. Giannios, T. Laskar, J. Zrake, A. MacFadyen and K. Paterson, Continued Chandra observations of GW170817 at 3.3 years since merger, *GRB Coordinates Network* **29375**, p. 1 (January 2021).

41. V. Nedora, D. Radice, S. Bernuzzi, A. Perego, B. Daszuta, A. Endrizzi, A. Prakash and F. Schianchi, Dynamical ejecta synchrotron emission as a possible contributor to the changing behaviour of GRB170817A afterglow, *MNRAS* **506**, 5908 (October 2021).
42. E. Troja, B. O'Connor, G. Ryan, L. Piro, R. Ricci, B. Zhang, T. Piran, G. Bruni, S. B. Cenko and H. van Eerten, Accurate flux calibration of GW170817: is the X-ray counterpart on the rise?, *arXiv e-prints*, p. arXiv:2104.13378 (April 2021).
43. Z. F. Bostancı, Y. Kaneko and E. Göğüş, Gamma-ray bursts with extended emission observed with BATSE, *MNRAS* **428**, 1623 (January 2013).
44. Y. Kaneko, Z. F. Bostancı, E. Göğüş and L. Lin, Short gamma-ray bursts with extended emission observed with Swift/BAT and Fermi/GBM, *MNRAS* **452**, 824 (September 2015).
45. J. P. Norris and J. T. Bonnell, Short Gamma-Ray Bursts with Extended Emission, *ApJ* **643**, 266 (May 2006).
46. A. Lien, T. Sakamoto, S. D. Barthelmy, W. H. Baumgartner, J. K. Cannizzo, K. Chen, N. R. Collins, J. R. Cummings, N. Gehrels, H. A. Krimm, C. B. Markwardt, D. M. Palmer, M. Stamatikos, E. Troja and T. N. Ukwatta, The Third Swift Burst Alert Telescope Gamma-Ray Burst Catalog, *ApJ* **829**, p. 7 (September 2016).
47. P. T. O'Brien, R. Willingale, J. Osborne, M. R. Goad, K. L. Page, S. Vaughan, E. Rol, A. Beardmore, O. Godet, C. P. Hurkett, A. Wells, B. Zhang, S. Kobayashi, D. N. Burrows, J. A. Nousek, J. A. Kennea, A. Falcone, D. Grupe, N. Gehrels, S. Barthelmy, J. Cannizzo, J. Cummings, J. E. Hill, H. Krimm, G. Chincarini, G. Tagliaferri, S. Campana, A. Moretti, P. Giommi, M. Perri, V. Mangano and V. LaParola, The Early X-Ray Emission from GRBs, *ApJ* **647**, 1213 (August 2006).
48. S. Kisaka, K. Ioka and T. Sakamoto, Bimodal Long-lasting Components in Short Gamma-Ray Bursts: Promising Electromagnetic Counterparts to Neutron Star Binary Mergers, *ApJ* **846**, p. 142 (September 2017).
49. B. D. Metzger, D. Giannios, T. A. Thompson, N. Bucciantini and E. Quataert, The protomagnetar model for gamma-ray bursts, *MNRAS* **413**, 2031 (May 2011).
50. N. Bucciantini, J. Arons and E. Amato, Modelling spectral evolution of pulsar wind nebulae inside supernova remnants, *MNRAS* **410**, 381 (January 2011).
51. B. Paczynski, Gamma-ray bursters at cosmological distances, *ApJl* **308**, L43 (September 1986).
52. J. Goodman, Are gamma-ray bursts optically thick?, *ApJl* **308**, p. L47 (September 1986).
53. V. V. Usov, Millisecond pulsars with extremely strong magnetic fields as a cosmological source of γ-ray bursts, *Nature* **357**, 472 (June 1992).
54. C. Thompson, A model of gamma-ray bursts., *MNRAS* **270**, 480 (October 1994).
55. T. Piran, The physics of gamma-ray bursts, *Rev. Mod. Phys.* **76**, 1143 (October 2004).
56. P. Kumar and B. Zhang, The physics of gamma-ray bursts and relativistic jets, *Phys. Rep.* **561**, 1 (February 2015).
57. R. D. Preece, M. S. Briggs, R. S. Mallozzi, G. N. Pendleton, W. S. Paciesas and D. L. Band, The Synchrotron Shock Model Confronts a "Line of Death" in the BATSE Gamma-Ray Burst Data, *ApJl* **506**, L23 (October 1998).
58. G. Ghisellini, A. Celotti and D. Lazzati, Constraints on the emission mechanisms of gamma-ray bursts, *MNRAS* **313**, L1 (March 2000).
59. R. Narayan, B. Paczynski and T. Piran, Gamma-ray bursts as the death throes of massive binary stars, *ApJl* **395**, L83 (August 1992).
60. M. J. Rees and P. Meszaros, Unsteady outflow models for cosmological gamma-ray bursts, *ApJl* **430**, L93 (August 1994).

61. D. Eichler and A. Levinson, A Compact Fireball Model of Gamma-Ray Bursts, *ApJ* **529**, 146 (January 2000).
62. A. Pe'er, P. Mészáros and M. J. Rees, The Observable Effects of a Photospheric Component on GRB and XRF Prompt Emission Spectrum, *ApJ* **642**, 995 (May 2006).
63. R. Barniol Duran and P. Kumar, Adiabatic expansion, early X-ray data and the central engine in GRBs, *MNRAS* **395**, 955 (May 2009).
64. S. Ascenzi, G. Oganesyan, M. Branchesi and R. Ciolfi, Electromagnetic counterparts of compact binary mergers, *J. Plasma Phys.* **87**, p. 845870102 (February 2021).
65. R. Gill, M. Kole and J. Granot, Grb polarization: A unique probe of GRB physics (2021).
66. N. Produit, T. W. Bao, T. Batsch, T. Bernasconi, I. Britvich, F. Cadoux, I. Cernuda, J. Y. Chai, Y. W. Dong, N. Gauvin, W. Hajdas, M. Kole, M. N. Kong, R. Kramert, L. Li, J. T. Liu, X. Liu, R. Marcinkowski, S. Orsi, M. Pohl, D. Rapin, D. Rybka, A. Rutczynska, H. L. Shi, P. Socha, J. C. Sun, L. M. Song, J. Szabelski, I. Traseira, H. L. Xiao, R. J. Wang, X. Wen, B. B. Wu, L. Zhang, L. Y. Zhang, S. N. Zhang, Y. J. Zhang and A. Zwolinska, Design and construction of the POLAR detector, *Nuclear Instruments and Methods in Physics Research A* **877**, 259 (January 2018).
67. S. Vadawale, Prospects of hard X-ray polarimetry with pixillated CZT detectors, in *Astronomical Society of India Conference Series, year = 2013, series = Astronomical Society of India Conference Series*,
68. B. Zhang, Y. Z. Fan, J. Dyks, S. Kobayashi, P. Meszaros, D. N. Burrows, J. A. Nousek and N. Gehrels, Physical processes shaping gamma-ray burst x-ray afterglow light curves: Theoretical implications from the SwiftX-ray telescope observations, *The Astrophysical Journal* **642**, 354 (May 2006).
69. S. Ronchini, G. Oganesyan, M. Branchesi, S. Ascenzi, M. G. Bernardini, F. Brighenti, S. Dall'Osso, P. D'Avanzo, G. Ghirlanda, G. Ghisellini, M. E. Ravasio and O. S. Salafia, Spectral index-flux relation for investigating the origins of steep decay in γ-ray bursts, *Nature Communications* **12**, p. 4040 (January 2021).
70. R. Gill and J. Granot, Temporal evolution of prompt GRB polarization, *Monthly Notices of the Royal Astronomical Society* **504**, 1939 (04 2021).
71. F. Fuschino, R. Campana, C. Labanti, Y. Evangelista, M. Feroci, L. Burderi, F. Fiore, F. Ambrosino, G. Baldazzi, P. Bellutti, R. Bertacin, G. Bertuccio, G. Borghi, D. Cirrincione, D. Cauz, F. Ficorella, M. Fiorini, M. Gandola, M. Grassi, A. Guzman, G. L. Rosa, M. Lavagna, P. Lunghi, P. Malcovati, G. Morgante, B. Negri, G. Pauletta, R. Piazzolla, A. Picciotto, S. Pirrotta, S. Pliego-Caballero, S. Puccetti, A. Rachevski, I. Rashevskaya, L. Rignanese, M. Salatti, A. Santangelo, S. Silvestrini, G. Sottile, C. Tenzer, A. Vacchi, G. Zampa, N. Zampa and N. Zorzi, HERMES: An ultra-wide band X and gamma-ray transient monitor on board a nano-satellite constellation, *Nuclear Instruments and Methods in Physics Research A* **936**, 199 (August 2019).
72. M. Maggiore, C. Van Den Broeck, N. Bartolo, E. Belgacem, D. Bertacca, M. A. Bizouard, M. Branchesi, S. Clesse, S. Foffa, J. García-Bellido, S. Grimm, J. Harms, T. Hinderer, S. Matarrese, C. Palomba, M. Peloso, A. Ricciardone and M. Sakellariadou, Science case for the Einstein telescope, *jcap* **2020**, p. 050 (March 2020).
73. B. Paczynski and J. E. Rhoads, Radio Transients from Gamma-Ray Bursters, *ApJl* **418**, p. L5 (November 1993).
74. P. Mészáros and M. J. Rees, Optical and Long-Wavelength Afterglow from Gamma-Ray Bursts, *Astrophys. J.* **476**, 232 (February 1997).
75. R. Sari, T. Piran and R. Narayan, Spectra and Light Curves of Gamma-Ray Burst Afterglows, *ApJl* **497**, L17 (April 1998).

76. S. Covino and D. Gotz, Polarization of prompt and afterglow emission of Gamma-Ray Bursts, *Astronomical and Astrophysical Transactions* **29**, 205 (January 2016).
77. K. Wiersema, S. Covino, K. Toma, A. J. van der Horst, K. Varela, M. Min, J. Greiner, R. L. C. Starling, N. R. Tanvir, R. A. M. J. Wijers, S. Campana, P. A. Curran, Y. Fan, J. P. U. Fynbo, J. Gorosabel, A. Gomboc, D. Götz, J. Hjorth, Z. P. Jin, S. Kobayashi, C. Kouveliotou, C. Mundell, P. T. O'Brien, E. Pian, A. Rowlinson, D. M. Russell, R. Salvaterra, S. di Serego Alighieri, G. Tagliaferri, S. D. Vergani, J. Elliott, C. Fariña, O. E. Hartoog, R. Karjalainen, S. Klose, F. Knust, A. J. Levan, P. Schady, V. Sudilovsky and R. Willingale, Circular polarization in the optical afterglow of GRB 121024A, *Nature* **509**, 201 (May 2014).
78. C. G. Mundell, D. Kopač, D. M. Arnold, I. A. Steele, A. Gomboc, S. Kobayashi, R. M. Harrison, R. J. Smith, C. Guidorzi, F. J. Virgili, A. Melandri and J. Japelj, Highly polarized light from stable ordered magnetic fields in GRB 120308A, *Nature* **504**, 119 (December 2013).
79. A. Corsi, G. W. Hallinan, D. Lazzati, K. P. Mooley, E. J. Murphy, D. A. Frail, D. Carbone, D. L. Kaplan, T. Murphy, S. R. Kulkarni and K. Hotokezaka, An Upper Limit on the Linear Polarization Fraction of the GW170817 Radio Continuum, *ApJl* **861**, p. L10 (July 2018).
80. R. Gill and J. Granot, Constraining the magnetic field structure in collisionless relativistic shocks with a radio afterglow polarization upper limit in GW 170817, *MNRAS* **491**, 5815 (February 2020).
81. P. Beniamini, R. Duque, F. Daigne and R. Mochkovitch, X-ray plateaus in gamma-ray bursts' light curves from jets viewed slightly off-axis, *MNRAS* **492**, 2847 (February 2020).
82. G. Oganesyan, S. Ascenzi, M. Branchesi, O. S. Salafia, S. Dall'Osso and G. Ghirlanda, Structured Jets and X-Ray Plateaus in Gamma-Ray Burst Phenomena, *ApJ* **893**, p. 88 (April 2020).
83. A. Panaitescu, X-Ray Afterglows from the Gamma-Ray Burst "Large-angle" Emission, *ApJ* **895**, p. 39 (May 2020).
84. D. N. Burrows, P. Romano, A. Falcone, S. Kobayashi, B. Zhang, A. Moretti, P. T. O'Brien, M. R. Goad, S. Campana, K. L. Page, L. Angelini, S. Barthelmy, A. P. Beardmore, M. Capalbi, G. Chincarini, J. Cummings, G. Cusumano, D. Fox, P. Giommi, J. E. Hill, J. A. Kennea, H. Krimm, V. Mangano, F. Marshall, P. Mészáros, D. C. Morris, J. A. Nousek, J. P. Osborne, C. Pagani, M. Perri, G. Tagliaferri, A. A. Wells, S. Woosley and N. Gehrels, Bright X-ray Flares in Gamma-Ray Burst Afterglows, *Science* **309**, 1833 (September 2005).
85. Y. Z. Fan, B. Zhang and D. Proga, Linearly Polarized X-Ray Flares following Short Gamma-Ray Bursts, *ApJl* **635**, L129 (December 2005).
86. J. Logue, C. D. Ott, I. S. Heng, P. Kalmus and J. H. C. Scargill, Inferring core-collapse supernova physics with gravitational waves, *Phys. Rev. D* **86**, p. 044023 (August 2012).
87. N. Andersson, J. Baker, K. Belczynski, S. Bernuzzi, E. Berti, L. Cadonati, P. Cerdá-Durán, J. Clark, M. Favata, L. S. Finn, C. Fryer, B. Giacomazzo, J. A. González, M. Hendry, I. S. Heng, S. Hild, N. Johnson-McDaniel, P. Kalmus, S. Klimenko, S. Kobayashi, K. Kokkotas, P. Laguna, L. Lehner, J. Levin, S. Liebling, A. MacFadyen, I. Mandel, S. Marka, Z. Marka, D. Neilsen, P. O'Brien, R. Perna, J. Read, C. Reisswig, C. Rodriguez, M. Ruffert, E. Schnetter, A. Searle, P. Shawhan, D. Shoemaker, A. Soderberg, U. Sperhake, P. Sutton, N. Tanvir, M. Was and S. Whitcomb, The transient gravitational-wave sky, *Classical and Quantum Gravity* **30**, p. 193002 (October 2013).

88. J. Powell and B. Müller, Gravitational wave emission from 3D explosion models of core-collapse supernovae with low and normal explosion energies, *MNRAS* **487**, 1178 (July 2019).
89. D. Guetta, R. Rahin, I. Bartos and M. Della Valle, Constraining the fraction of core-collapse supernovae harbouring choked jets with high-energy neutrinos, *MNRAS* **492**, 843 (February 2020).
90. B. P. Abbott, R. Abbott, T. D. Abbott, S. Abraham, F. Acernese, K. Ackley, C. Adams, V. B. Adya, C. Affeldt, M. Agathos and et al., Optically targeted search for gravitational waves emitted by core-collapse supernovae during the first and second observing runs of advanced LIGO and advanced Virgo, *Phys. Rev. D* **101**, p. 084002 (April 2020).
91. M. Della Valle, Supernovae and gamma-ray bursts connection, *Astronomical and Astrophysical Transactions* **29**, 99 (January 2016).
92. V. D'Elia, S. Campana, A. D'Aì, M. De Pasquale, S. W. K. Emery, D. D. Frederiks, A. Lien, A. Melandri, K. L. Page, R. L. C. Starling, D. N. Burrows, A. A. Breeveld, S. R. Oates, P. T. O'Brien, J. P. Osborne, M. H. Siegel, G. Tagliaferri, P. J. Brown, S. B. Cenko, D. S. Svinkin, A. Tohuvavohu and A. E. Tsvetkova, GRB 171205A/SN 2017iuk: A local low-luminosity gamma-ray burst, *Astronomy and Astrophysics* **619**, p. A66 (November 2018).
93. S. Campana, V. Mangano, A. J. Blustin, P. Brown, D. N. Burrows, G. Chincarini, J. R. Cummings, G. Cusumano, M. Della Valle, D. Malesani, P. Mészáros, J. A. Nousek, M. Page, T. Sakamoto, E. Waxman, B. Zhang, Z. G. Dai, N. Gehrels, S. Immler, F. E. Marshall, K. O. Mason, A. Moretti, P. T. O'Brien, J. P. Osborne, K. L. Page, P. Romano, P. W. A. Roming, G. Tagliaferri, L. R. Cominsky, P. Giommi, O. Godet, J. A. Kennea, H. Krimm, L. Angelini, S. D. Barthelmy, P. T. Boyd, D. M. Palmer, A. A. Wells and N. E. White, The association of GRB 060218 with a supernova and the evolution of the shock wave, *Nature* **442**, 1008 (August 2006).
94. A. M. Soderberg, E. Berger, K. L. Page, P. Schady, J. Parrent, D. Pooley, X. Y. Wang, E. O. Ofek, A. Cucchiara, A. Rau, E. Waxman, J. D. Simon, D. C. J. Bock, P. A. Milne, M. J. Page, J. C. Barentine, S. D. Barthelmy, A. P. Beardmore, M. F. Bietenholz, P. Brown, A. Burrows, D. N. Burrows, G. Byrngelson, S. B. Cenko, P. Chandra, J. R. Cummings, D. B. Fox, A. Gal-Yam, N. Gehrels, S. Immler, M. Kasliwal, A. K. H. Kong, H. A. Krimm, S. R. Kulkarni, T. J. Maccarone, P. Mészáros, E. Nakar, P. T. O'Brien, R. A. Overzier, M. de Pasquale, J. Racusin, N. Rea and D. G. York, An extremely luminous X-ray outburst at the birth of a supernova, *Nature* **453**, 469 (May 2008).

CALET on the ISS: The first 5 years

Pier Simone Marrocchesi* for the CALET Collaboration[†]

Dept. of Physical Sciences, Earth and Environment, Via Roma 56, I-53100 Siena, Italy
and INFN Sezione di Pisa, Largo Bruno Pontecorvo 3, I-56127 Pisa, Italy
*E-mail: piersimone.marrocchesi@pi.infn.it

Abstract—The CALorimetric Electron Telescope CALET is collecting science data on the International Space Station since October 2015 with excellent and continuous performance. Energy is measured with a deep homogeneous calorimeter (1.2 nuclear interaction lengths, 27 radiation lengths) preceded by an imaging pre-shower (3 radiation lengths, 1mm granularity) providing tracking and 10^{-5} electron/proton discrimination. Two independent sub-systems identify the charge Z of the incident particle from proton to iron and above (Z<40). CALET measures the cosmic-ray electron+positron flux up to 20 TeV, gamma rays up to 10 TeV, and nuclei up to 1 PeV. In this paper, we report the on-orbit performance of the instrument and summarize the main results obtained during the first 5 years of operation, including the electron+positron energy spectrum and the individual spectra of protons, heavier nuclei and iron. Solar modulation and gamma-ray observations are also concisely reported, as well as transient phenomena and the search for gravitational wave counterparts.

Keywords: Cosmic rays; high energy astrophysics; space-borne experiments.

1. INTRODUCTION

CALET is a cosmic-ray experiment designed for long-term observations of charged and neutral cosmic radiation on the ISS. The instrument is managed by an international collaboration led by the Japanese Space Agency (JAXA) with the participation of the Italian Space Agency (ASI) and NASA. It was launched on August 19, 2015 with the Japanese carrier H-IIB, delivered to the ISS by the HTV-5 Transfer Vehicle, and installed on the Japanese Experiment Module Exposure Facility (JEM-EF). The science program of CALET addresses several outstanding questions of high-energy astroparticle physics including the origin of cosmic rays (CR), the possible presence of nearby astrophysical CR sources, the acceleration and propagation of primary and secondary elements in the galaxy, and the nature of dark matter. The design of CALET is optimised for high precision measurements of the electron+positron spectrum with an accurate scan of the energy interval already covered by previous experiments and its extension to the region above 1 TeV. Given the high energy resolution of CALET for electrons, a detailed study of the spectral shape might reveal the presence of nearby sources of acceleration as well as possible indirect signatures of dark matter.[1,2]

With its individual element resolution in the charge identification of cosmic rays, CALET is also carrying out direct measurements of the spectra and relative

---

[†]See the last page for the full authors list.

abundances of light and heavy cosmic nuclei[3,4] from proton to iron, in the energy interval from ~ 50 GeV (10 GeV/n) for the lighter (heavier) nuclei to several hundred TeV. The abundances of the rare CR trans-iron elements up to $Z \sim 40$ are studied with a dedicated program of long term observations.[5]

2. THE CALET INSTRUMENT

The CALET main telescope is an all-calorimetric instrument comprised of three sub-detectors. The CHarge Detector (CHD) is positioned at the top of the apparatus and consists of a two layered hodoscope of plastic scintillators paddles (14 paddles per layer). It performs the charge identification of individual nuclear species, providing a measurement of the charge Z of the incident particle over a wide dynamic range (from Z = 1 up to Z = 40).[6] The IMaging Calorimeter (IMC) is a fine grained sampling calorimeter, segmented longitudinally into 16 layers of scintillating fibers (with 1 mm^2 square cross-section), read out individually and arranged in pairs along orthogonal directions. Each pair is interleaved with thin tungsten absorbers (for a total thickness of 3 X_0). It reconstructs the early shower profile and the impinging particle trajectory with good angular resolution, while providing also a redundant charge measurement.[1] The third detector is the Total AbSorption Calorimeter (TASC), an homogeneous calorimeter with 12 layers of lead-tungstate (PWO) logs arranged in pairs along orthogonal directions. With its 27 X_0 thickness and shower imaging capability, it measures electrons and gamma-rays with an excellent energy resolution, providing high discrimination against hadronic cascades. The total thickness of the main telescope is equivalent to 30 X_0 and 1.3 proton interaction lengths (λ_I), the geometrical factor is 0.12 m^2 sr. A more detailed description of the instrument can be found in Ref. 7 and in the Supplemental Material (SM) of Ref. 9.

3. FLIGHT OPERATIONS AND CALIBRATIONS

The commissioning of CALET aboard the ISS was successfully completed at the beginning of October 2015. Since then, the instrument has been taking science data continuously with no significant interruptions.[2] The on-orbit operations are controlled via the JAXA Ground Support Equipment (JAXA-GSE) in Tsukuba by the Waseda CALET Operations Center (WCOC) at Waseda University, Tokyo.

As of April 30, 2021 a total observation time of more than 2027 days was integrated with a live time fraction $\sim$85% of the total time, and $\sim$2.7 billion events collected above 1 GeV. The exposure with the high-energy (HE) trigger mode, designed to maximize the collection power for electrons above 10 GeV, and other high-energy shower events was $\sim 178\ m^2$ sr day.

Energy calibrations of each channel of CHD, IMC, and TASC is performed with penetrating proton and He particles selected in-flight by a dedicated trigger mode. Raw signals are corrected for light output non-uniformity, gain differences among the channels, position and temperature dependence, as well as temporal gain variations.[7,8] Correlations among the four gain ranges for each TASC channel are calibrated with flight data, and responses from consecutive ranges are linked together to provide a seamless transition. In this way, a dynamic range spanning more than six orders of magnitude is achieved, allowing observations from one minimum ionizing particle to 1 PeV showers.

4. COSMIC-RAY DIRECT MEASUREMENTS WITH CALET ON THE ISS

4.1. *The Electron Spectrum*

The CALET collaboration reported their first measurement of the inclusive electron+positron spectrum in the energy range from 10 GeV to 3 TeV (Ref. 9) within a fiducial subset of the acceptance. Soon after, the DArk Matter Particle Explorer (DAMPE) collaboration published their all-electron spectrum in the energy interval from 25 GeV to 4.6 TeV (Ref. 10).

The latter publication was followed by a number of papers speculating about the origin of a possible peak-like structure near 1.4 TeV in DAMPE data. An updated version of the CALET all-electron spectrum was published, covering the energy

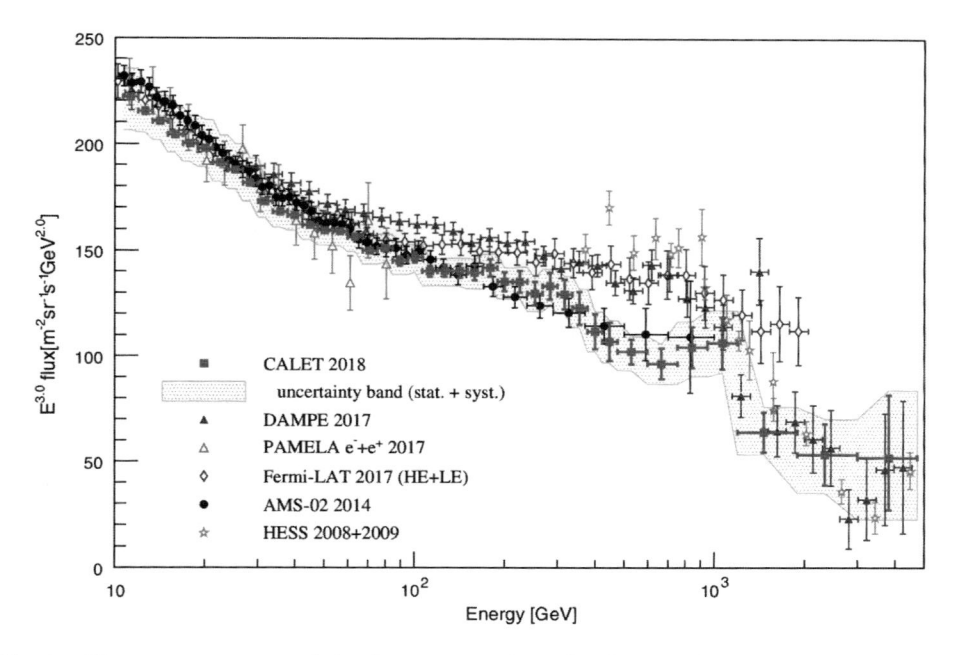

Fig. 1. Direct measurements of the electron + positron flux by space-borne experiments including,[10,11][12-14] and from ground-based experiments.[15,16] The CALET 2018 data[11] are shown as red filled circles in the energy interval 11 GeV to 4.8 TeV. The width of each bin is shown as a horizontal bar, statistical errors as vertical bars. The gray band indicates the quadratic sum of statistical and systematic errors (not including the uncertainty on the energy scale).

range from 11 GeV to 4.8 TeV (Ref. 11) with 780 days of flight data and the full geometrical acceptance. It reported a new analysis with doubled statistics at $E>$ 475 GeV and included one additional energy bin between 3 and 4.8 TeV (Figure 1). The width of each bin is shown as a horizontal bar, the statistical errors as vertical bars, while the gray band is representative of the quadratic sum of statistic and systematic errors. A comprehensive study of the systematic uncertainties was performed as described in Refs. 9, 11 and Supplemental Material therein. A constant electron identification efficiency of 70% was achieved above 30 GeV, with a proton contamination level of 2–5% below 1 TeV and ∼10–20% above.

Taking the currently available experimental data at face-value, we notice that the all-electron spectrum data seem to fork into two groups of measurements: AMS-02 + CALET and Fermi/LAT + DAMPE, with good consistency within each group, but with only marginal overlap between the two, possibly indicating the presence of unknown systematic errors. The CALET spectrum is consistent with AMS-02 below ∼1TeV where both experiments have a good electron identification capability albeit using different detection techniques. CALET observation of a flux suppression above ∼1TeV is consistent with DAMPE within errors. No peak-like structure was found at 1.4 TeV in CALET data, irrespective of the energy binning. After re-binning with the same set of energy bins as DAMPE, an inconsistency between the two measurements emerged[11] with a 4 σ significance, the latter including the systematic errors quoted by both experiments.

New results on the analysis of electrons based on the first five years of CALET observations will be presented at the upcoming ICRC2021 conference.

4.2. *The Proton Spectrum*

Cosmic-ray energies from the GeV scale to the multi-TeV region have been explored – in separate subranges – by magnetic spectrometers (e.g., BESS-TeV, PAMELA, and AMS-02), calorimeters (e.g., ATIC, CREAM, NUCLEON, and DAMPE) and Cherenkov / Transition Radiation instruments (e.g., TRACER). In the intermediate energy region from 200 GeV to 800 GeV a deviation from a single power-law (SPL) was observed in both proton and helium spectra by CREAM,[17–19] PAMELA[20,21] and confirmed with high statistics measurements by AMS-02,[22] CALET,[23] and DAMPE.[24]

The first proton paper published by CALET[23] reported a proton flux measurement where, for the first time, a single space-borne instrument was able to cover the whole interval of proton energies from 50 GeV to 10 TeV thanks to its large dynamic range. The proton flux was extracted from the data collected from October 13, 2015 to August 31, 2018 (1054 days) on the ISS using only 40% of the total acceptance. A detailed study of the systematic uncertainties was reported in the same paper and in the Supplementary Material therein.[23] This is of particular relevance because CR flux measurements are well known to be affected by relatively large systematic errors, often specific of each instrument. CALET proton data (Fig. 2)

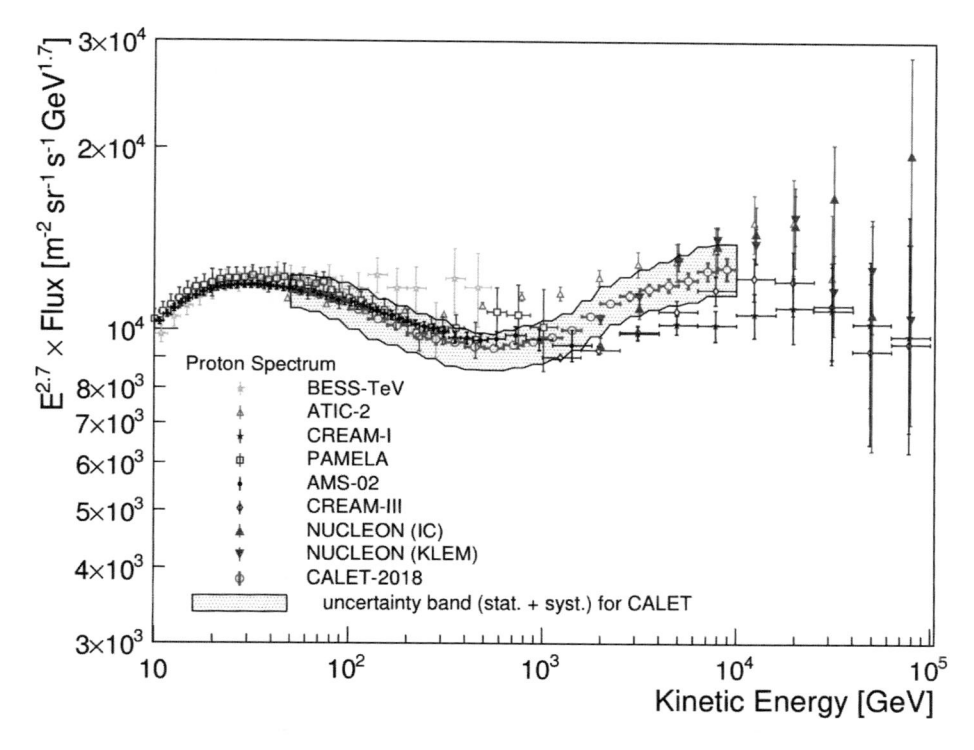

Fig. 2. Cosmic-ray proton spectrum measured by CALET from 50 GeV to 10 TeV published in Ref. 23. The gray band indicates the quadratic sum of statistical and systematic errors.

are consistent with AMS-02 but extend to higher energies by nearly one order of magnitude, showing a very smooth transition of the spectral index from -2.81 ± 0.03 (in the region 50–500 GeV) to -2.56 ± 0.04 (in 1–10 TeV), thereby confirming the existence of a spectral hardening and providing evidence of a deviation from a single power law by more than 3σ.

An update of CALET proton analysis, based on 5 years of data on the ISS, will be presented at the upcoming ICRC2021 conference together with preliminary results on the helium flux.

4.3. The Spectra of Heavier Nuclei

The observation of a spectral hardening in proton and helium, as well as in carbon and oxygen spectra,[18,20,22,25,26] have opened a new and unexpected scenario in CR phenomenology. In particular, the high statistics observations by AMS-02, up to a maximum detectable rigidity (MDR) of a few TV, clearly show that primary elements have a very similar rigidity dependence above ∼60 GV and that secondary elements (like Li, Be and B) also show a flux hardening, though with subtle differences that might be attributed to propagation effects (secondaries propagate first as primaries and then as secondaries). Therefore, it is very important to extend the presently available measurements to the multi-TeV region and investigate the energy dependence of the spectral index for individual nuclear species with high accuracy. CALET is carrying out extensive measurements of the energy spectra, relative abundances and secondary-to-primary ratios of cosmic-ray nuclei.

Preliminary CALET results on the B/C ratio and on the spectra of heavier nuclei from neon to iron (Fig. 3) were previously reported (see for instance Refs. 4, 27, 28). In the following we will focus on the CALET published spectra of C, O and Fe.

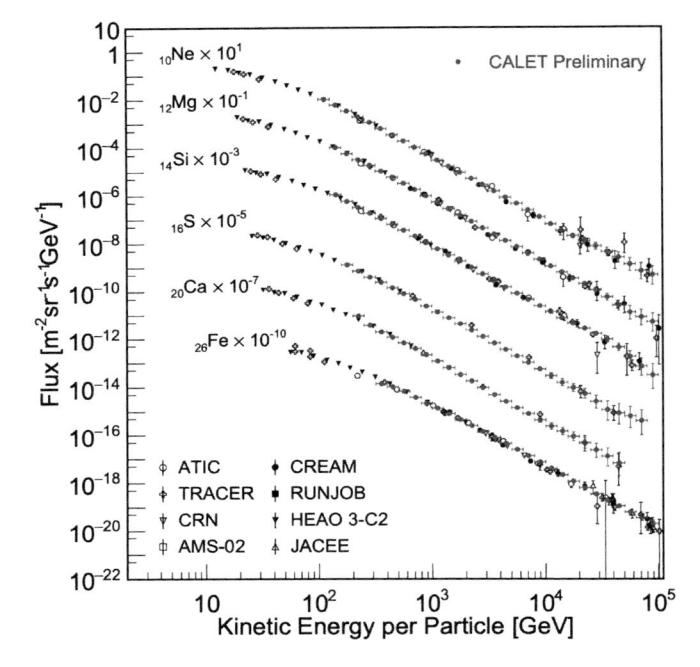

Fig. 3. Preliminary results of energy spectra of heavy primary components of Ne, Mg, Si, S, Ca and Fe as a function of energy par particle compared with previous observations. The Error bars of CALET data[28] represent the statistical uncertainty only.

4.4. Carbon and Oxygen Spectra

The energy spectra of carbon and oxygen and their flux ratio were measured by CALET in the energy range from 10 GeV/n to 2.2 TeV/n and published in Ref. 29. CALET observations (Fig. 4) allow to exclude a single power law spectrum for C and O at the level of more than 3σ. A spectral index increase (spectrum flattening) $\Delta\gamma = 0.166 \pm 0.042$ (carbon) and $\Delta\gamma = 0.158 \pm 0.053$ (oxygen) were measured above 200 GeV/n, respectively. The fluxes of C and O were found to share the same energy dependence with a constant C/O flux ratio 0.911 ± 0.006 above 25 GeV/n.

While the above results are consistent with the ones reported by AMS-02 for the same elements, the absolute normalization of CALET data is significantly lower than AMS-02, but in agreement with previous experiments (including PAMELA for carbon). For more details please refer to Ref. 29 and the Supplementary Material therein.

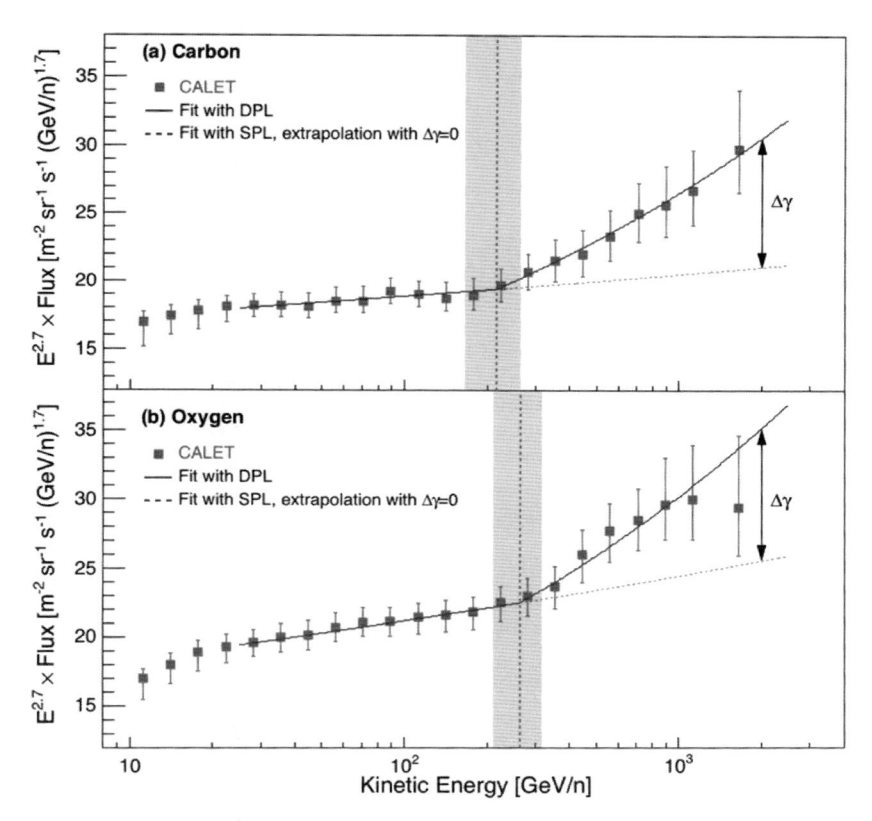

Fig. 4. Fit of the CALET (a) C and (b) O energy spectra[29] with a Double Power Law (DPL) function (blue line) in the energy range [25, 2000] GeV/n. The flux is multiplied by $E^{2.7}$ where E is the kinetic energy per nucleon. Error bars are the sum in quadrature of statistical and systematic uncertainties. The dashed blue lines represent the extrapolation of an Single Power Law function fitted to the data in the energy range [25, 200] GeV/n. $\Delta\gamma$ is the spectral index change above the transition energy E_0 (vertical green dashed line). The green band shows the uncertainty error on E_0 from the DPL fit.

4.5. *The Iron Spectrum*

In a recent paper,[30] the CALET collaboration reported their first measurement of the energy spectrum of cosmic-ray iron from 10 GeV/n to 2.0 TeV/n.

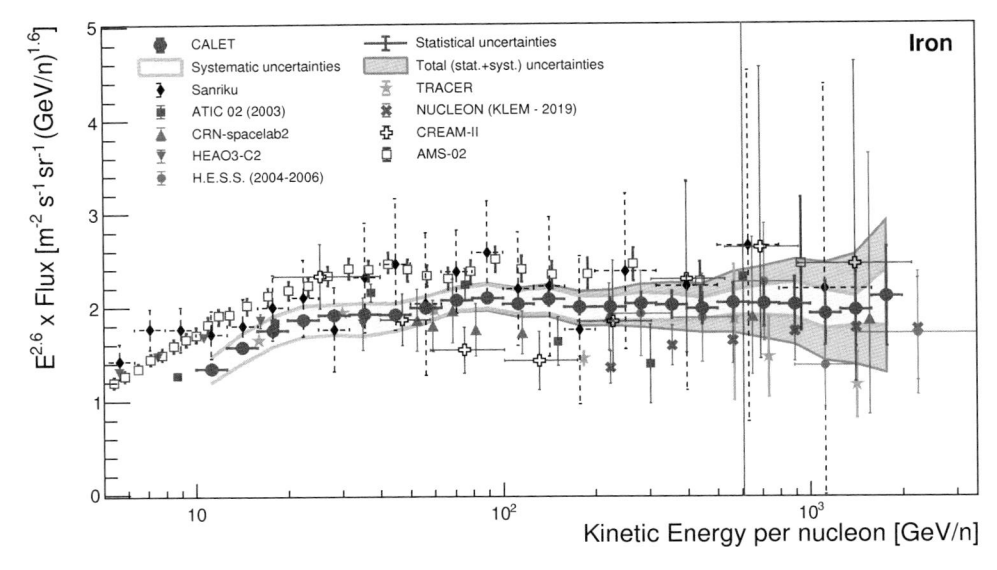

Fig. 5. CALET iron flux[30] as a function of kinetic energy per nucleon in GeV (with multiplicative factor $E^{2.6}$). The error bars of the CALET data (red filled circles) represent the statistical uncertainty only. The yellow band indicates the quadrature sum of systematic errors, while the green band indicates the quadrature sum of statistical and systematic errors. Also plotted are the data points from other direct measurements.[31–39]

The analysis is based on 4.4 years of observations and the measurement achieves a significantly better precision than most of the existing measurements of the same element. The CALET iron differential spectrum in kinetic energy per nucleon is shown in Fig. 5, where uncertainties including statistical and systematic errors are bounded within a green band. The spectrum is compared with the results from space-based (HEAO3-C2,[31] CRN,[32] AMS 02,[33] NUCLEON[34]) and balloon-borne experiments (ATIC-02,[35] TRACER,[36] CREAM-II,[37] Sanriku[38]), as well as ground-based observations (H.E.S.S.[39]). The CALET spectrum is consistent with ATIC 02 and TRACER at low energy and with CRN and HESS at high energy. CALET and NUCLEON iron spectra have similar shapes, while they differ in the absolute normalization of the flux. The latter turns out to be higher for CALET than for CRN by ∼10% on average, while it is lower by 14% with respect to Sanriku. CALET and AMS-02 iron spectra have a very similar shape (Fig. S12 of the Supplemental Material of Ref. 30), but differ in the absolute normalization of the flux by ∼ 20%.

Taking into account the average size of the large systematic errors reported in the literature, CALET data turn out to be consistent with previous measurements within the uncertainty error band, both in spectral shape and normalization. Below 50 GeV/n the spectral shape is found to be similar to the one observed for primaries lighter than iron. Above the same energy, CALET observations are consistent with the hypothesis of an SPL spectrum up to 2 TeV/n, i.e., the flattening observed above a few hundred GeV/nucleon in the p-C-O spectra does not appear to be present in the iron spectrum in the sub-TeV region. Beyond this limit, the uncertainties given by the available statistics and large systematics do not allow yet to draw a significant conclusion on a possible deviation from a single power law. An SPL fit in this region yields a spectral index value $\gamma = -2.60 \pm 0.03$.

4.6. *The Observation of Gamma-Rays*

CALET can identify gamma-rays and measure their energies from $\sim$1 GeV to the TeV region. Both CHD and the first IMC layers are used in the offline analysis as anti-coincidence against incoming charged particles, taking advantage of the high granularity of the IMC.

Gamma-ray candidates are also required to deposit more energy in the bottom IMC layers than in the upper ones where pair conversion takes place. In addition to the HE trigger, CALET implements a LE-γ trigger extending the sensitivity to gamma rays with primary energies down to $\sim$1 GeV. This dedicated trigger is activated only at low geomagnetic latitudes (to avoid an increase of the dead-time) and it is also enabled whenever a gamma-ray burst is triggered by the Calet Gamma-Ray Burst Monitor (CGBM).[40] The first two years of data allowed a complete characterization of the performance of CALET as a gamma-ray instrument, the optimization of the event selection criteria, the determination of the effective area, Point Spread Function (PSF) and absolute pointing accuracy. Measured signals from gamma-ray bright point sources and diffuse galactic emission were found to be in agreement with simulated results and expectations from Fermi-LAT data.[41] The spectra from sources like Crab, Geminga, and Vela pulsars were measured by CALET and tested for consistency with parameterised LAT spectra. These results confirmed the sensitivity of the calorimeter in observing bright, persistent sources.[42] The gamma-ray sky observed by CALET using the LE-γ trigger is shown in Fig. 6.

CALET can also detect gamma-ray transients by means of the CGBM operating in the energy range of 7 keV–20 MeV. As of April 2021, 246 GRBs have been detected, 12% of which were classified as short, with an average rate of $\sim$44.6 /year.

A search for electromagnetic counterparts of gravitational waves (GW) triggered by LIGO/Virgo was performed with a combined analysis of the CGBM and the calorimeter. Candidate signals compatible with gamma-ray emission were searched for in time intervals of tens of seconds centered on the reported trigger times of GW151226, GW170104, GW170608, GW170814, and GW170817 events. No signal was detected for all GW events; upper limits on gamma-ray emission were set for GW151226 (CAL + CGBM) and GW170104 (CAL), while GW170608, GW170814, GW170817 turned out to be outside the CALET field-of-view.[43,44]

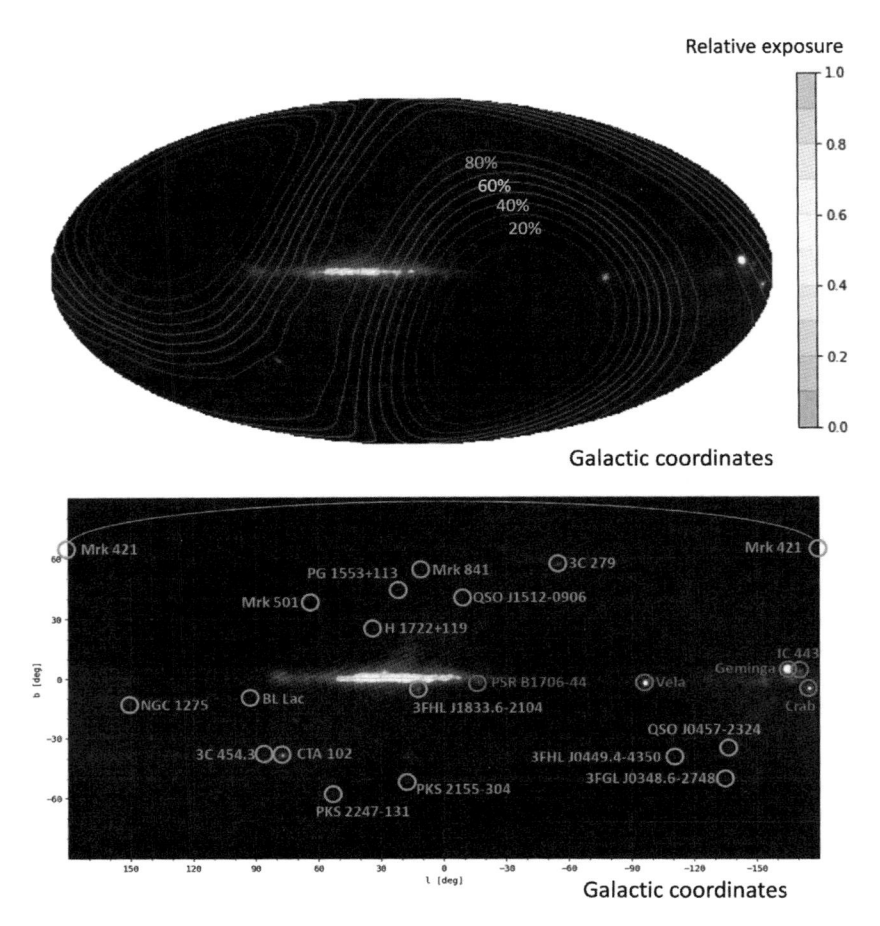

Fig. 6. Top: CALET gamma-ray sky map (observation period: 2015.11.01-2020.07.31) with the LE-γ trigger (E >1 GeV), shown in a Mollweide projection of galactic coordinates. White contours show the relative level of exposure compared to the maximum on the sky; bottom: point sources observed during the same period (with >1 GeV), including the Crab, Geminga, and Vela pulsars.

5. SUMMARY AND PERSPECTIVES

CALET was successfully launched on Aug. 19, 2015. The instrument performance has been very stable during all the scientific observation period from Oct. 13, 2015. CALET measurements of the electron spectrum were published in two papers,[9,11] the latter with improved statistics and extended energy range from 11 GeV to 4.8 TeV. The extension to five years of CALET on-orbit operations provided an increase of the available statistics in the electron observations by a factor $\sim$3 thereby contributing to a better understanding of the detector and of the systematic errors. A search for possible spectral footprints of nearby electron sources in the region above $\sim$1 TeV is in progress.

The wide dynamic range and excellent charge identification capability allow CALET to measure nuclei in cosmic rays from proton to iron and above, with an energy reach approaching the PeV scale. The proton spectrum was published up to 10 TeV (Ref. 23); C and O spectra to 2.2 TeV/n (Ref. 29), and Fe to 2.0 TeV/n (Ref. 30). The spectral index dependence on energy confirmed a spectral hardening for p, C, O with a smooth onset at a few hundred GeV. Measurements of the energy spectra and composition of all primary and secondary nuclei (and of their ratios) are ongoing. The relative abundance of the ultra heavy nuclei up to $Z = 40$ has also been preliminarily analyzed.[5]

The performance of the gamma-ray measurements has confirmed CALET's capability to observe the diffuse component and bright point-sources in the gamma-ray sky from ∼1 GeV to 100 GeV and above (Fig. 6). The continuous GeV gamma-ray sky observation with CALET complements the coverage by other missions and may help to identify unexplored high-energy emissions from future transient events. The latter phenomena are studied with the CGBM.

Follow-up observations were carried out in the X-ray and gamma-ray band of GW events during LIGO/Virgo observation campaigns.[43,44]

Solar modulation is constantly monitored and studied. Since the start of observations in 2015/10, a steady increase in the 1-10 GeV all-electron flux has been observed to present. In the past two years, the flux has reached the maximum flux observed with PAMELA during the previous solar minimum period.[45] Solar energetic particles (SEP) are also studied at high geomagnetic latitudes.

High statistics detection of MeV electrons originating from the radiation belt allows the study of relativistic electron precipitation.[46] This is one of the topics of Space Weather studies[47] which were added as additional observational targets for CALET after the start of on-orbit operations.

Important updates of CALET electron and proton analyses, as well as preliminary results on He, B, B/C analyses, will be presented at the upcoming ICRC2021 conference (highlights in Ref. 48).

The so far excellent performance of the instrument and the outstanding quality of the data suggest that a long-term strategy of CALET observations will contribute to a deeper understanding of cosmic-ray phenomena. CALET operations on the ISS have been recently approved for an extension to the end of 2024 (at least).

ACKNOWLEDGMENTS

We gratefully acknowledge JAXA's contributions to the development of CALET and to the operations aboard the JEM-EF on the International Space Station. We also wish to express our sincere gratitude to Agenzia Spaziale Italiana (ASI) and NASA for their support of the CALET project. This work was supported in part by JSPS Grant-in-Aid for Scientific Research (S) Number 26220708 and 19H05608, JSPS Grant-in-Aid for Scientific Research (B) Number 17H02901, JSPS Grant-in-Aid for Research Activity Start-up No.20K22352 and by the MEXT-Supported

Program for the Strategic Research Foundation at Private Universities (2011–2015) (No.S1101021) at Waseda University. The CALET effort in Italy is supported by ASI under agreement 2013-018-R.0 and its amendments. The CALET effort in the United States is supported by NASA through Grants No. NNX16AB99G, No. NNX16AC02G, and No. NNH14ZDA001N-APRA-0075.

References

1. S. Torii (for the CALET Collab.), PoS (ICRC2019) 142 (2019).
2. Y. Asaoka (for the CALET Collab.), PoS (ICRC2019) 001 (2019).
3. S. Torii and P. S. Marrocchesi (for the CALET Collab.), Adv. Sp. Res. **64**(12), 2531 (2019).
4. Y. Akaike (for the CALET Collab.), PoS (ICRC2019) 034 (2019).
5. B. F. Rauch (for the CALET Collab.), PoS (ICRC2019) 130 (2019).
6. P. S. Marrocchesi, O. Adriani, Y. Akaike, M. G. Bagliesi, A. Basti, G. Bigongiari, S. Bonechi, M. Bongi, M. Y. Kim, T. Lomtadze, P. Maestro, T. Niita, S. Ozawa, Y. Shimizu, and S. Torii, Nucl. Instrum. Methods A **659**, 477 (2011).
7. Y. Asaoka, Y. Akaike, Y. Komiya, R. Miyata, S. Torii, O. Adriani, K. Asano, M. G. Bagliesi, G. Bigongiari, W. R. Binns, S. Bonechi, M. Bongi, P. Brogi, J. H. Buckley, N. Cannady, G. Castellini, et al. (CALET Collab.), Astropart. Phys. **91**, 1 (2017).
8. Y. Asaoka, S. Ozawa, S. Torii, O. Adriani, Y. Akaike, K. Asano, M. G. Bagliesi, G. Bigongiari, W. R. Binns, S. Bonechi, M. Bongi, P. Brogi, J. H. Buckley, N. Cannady, G. Castellini, C. Checchia, et al. (CALET Collab.), Astropart. Phys. **100**, 29 (2018).
9. O. Adriani, Y. Akaike, K. Asano, Y. Asaoka, M. G. Bagliesi, G. Bigongiari, W. R. Binns, S. Bonechi, M. Bongi, P. Brogi, J. H. Buckley, N. Cannady, G. Castellini, C. Checchia, M. L. Cherry, G. Collazuol, et al. (CALET Collab.), Phys. Rev. Lett. **119**, 181101 (2017).
10. G. Ambrosi, Q. An, R. Asfandiyarov, P. Azzarello, P. Bernardini, B. Bertucci, M. S. Cai, J. Chang, D. Y. Chen, H. F. Chen, J. L. Chen, W. Chen, M. Y. Cui, T. S. Cui, A. D'Amone, A. De Benedittis, et al. (DAMPE Collab.), Nature **552**, 63 (2017).
11. O. Adriani, Y. Akaike, K. Asano, Y. Asaoka, M. G. Bagliesi, E. Berti, G. Bigongiari, W. R. Binns, S. Bonechi, M. Bongi, P. Brogi, J. H. Buckley, N. Cannady, G. Castellini, C. Checchia, M. L. Cherry, et al. (CALET Collab.), Phys. Rev. Lett. **120**, 261102 (2018).
12. O. Adriani, G. C. Barbarino, G. A. Bazilevskaya, R. Bellotti, M. Boezio, E. A. Bogomolov, M. Bongi, V. Bonvicini, S. Bottai, A. Bruno, F. Cafagna, D. Campana, P. Carlson, M. Casolino, G. Castellini, C. De Santis, et al. (PAMELA Collab.), Riv. Nuovo Cimento **40**, 473 (2017).
13. S. Abdollahi et al. (The Fermi-LAT Collab.), Phys. Rev. D **95**, 082007 (2017).
14. M. Aguilar, D. Aisa, A. Alvino, G. Ambrosi, K. Andeen, L. Arruda, N. Attig, P. Azzarello, A. Bachlechner, F. Barao, A. Barrau, L. Barrin, A. Bartoloni, L. Basara, M. Battarbee, R. Battiston, et al. (AMS Collab.), Phys. Rev. Lett. **113**, 221102 (2014).
15. F. Aharonian, A. G. Akhperjanian, U. Barres de Almeida, A. R. Bazer-Bachi, Y. Becherini, B. Behera, W. Benbow, K. Bernlöhr, C. Boisson, A. Bochow, V. Borrel, I. Braun, E. Brion, J. Brucker, P. Brun, R. Bühler, et al. (H.E.S.S. Collab.), Phys. Rev. Lett. **101**, 261104, (2008).
16. F. Aharonian, A. G. Akhperjanian, G. Anton, U. Barres de Almeida, A. R. Bazer-Bachi, Y. Becherini, B. Behera, K. Bernlöhr, A. Bochow, C. Boisson, J. Bolmont, V. Borrel, J. Brucker, F. Brun, P. Brun, R. Bühler, et al. (H.E.S.S. Collab.), Astron. Astrophys. **508**, 561 (2009).

17. Y. S. Yoon, T. Anderson, A. Barrau, N. B. Conklin, S. Coutu, L. Derome, J. H. Han, J. A. Jeon, K. C. Kim, M. H. Kim, H. Y. Lee, J. Lee, M. H. Lee, S. E. Lee, J. T. Link, A. Menchaca-Rocha, et al., Astrophys. J. **839**, 5 (2017).
18. H. S. Ahn, P. Allison, M. G. Bagliesi, J. J. Beatty, G. Bigongiari, J. T. Childers, N. B. Conklin, S. Coutu, M. A. DuVernois, O. Ganel, J. H. Han, J. A. Jeon, K. C. Kim, M. H. Lee, L. Lutz, P. Maestro, et al., Astrophys. J. Lett. **714**, L89 (2010).
19. Y. S. Yoon, H. S. Ahn, P. S. Allison, M. G. Bagliesi, J. J. Beatty, G. Bigongiari, P. J. Boyle, J. T. Childers, N. B. Conklin, S. Coutu, M. A. DuVernois, O. Ganel, J. H. Han, J. A. Jeon, K. C. Kim, M. H. Lee, et al., Astrophys. J. **728**, 122 (2011).
20. O. Adriani, G. C. Barbarino, G. A. Bazilevskaya, R. Bellotti, M. Boezio, E. A. Bogomolov, L. Bonechi, M. Bongi, V. Bonvicini, S. Borisov, S. Bottai, A. Bruno, F. Cafagna, D. Campana, R. Carbone, P. Carlson, et al. (PAMELA Collab.), Science **332**, 69 (2011).
21. O. Adriani, G. C. Barbarino, G. A. Bazilevskaya, R. Bellotti, M. Boezio, E. A. Bogomolov, M. Bongi, V. Bonvicini, S. Borisov, S. Bottai, A. Bruno, F. Cafagna, D. Campana, R. Carbone, P. Carlson, M. Casolino, et al. (PAMELA Collab.), Astrophys. J. **765**, 91 (2013).
22. M. Aguilar, D. Aisa, B. Alpat, A. Alvino, G. Ambrosi, K. Andeen, L. Arruda, N. Attig, P. Azzarello, A. Bachlechner, F. Barao, A. Barrau, L. Barrin, A. Bartoloni, L. Basara, M. Battarbee, et al. (AMS Collab.), Phys. Rev. Lett. **114**, 171103 (2015).
23. O. Adriani, Y. Akaike, K. Asano, Y. Asaoka, M. G. Bagliesi, E. Berti, G. Bigongiari, W. R. Binns, S. Bonechi, M. Bongi, P. Brogi, A. Bruno, J. H. Buckley, N. Cannady, G. Castellini, C. Checchia, et al. (CALET Collab.), Phys. Rev. Lett. **122**, 181102 (2019).
24. Q. An, R. Asfandiyarov, P. Azzarello, P. Bernardini, X. J. Bi, M. S. Cai, J. Chang, D. Y. Chen, H. F. Chen, J. L. Chen, W. Chen, M. Y. Cui, T. S. Cui, H. T. Dai, A. D'Amone, A. De Benedittis, et al. (DAMPE Collab.), Sci. Adv. **5** eaax3793 (2019).
25. M. Aguilar, D. Aisa, B. Alpat, A. Alvino, G. Ambrosi, K. Andeen, L. Arruda, N. Attig, P. Azzarello, A. Bachlechner, F. Barao, A. Barrau, L. Barrin, A. Bartoloni, L. Basara, M. Battarbee, et al. (AMS Collab.), Phys. Rev. Lett. **115**, 211101 (2015).
26. M. Aguilar, L. Ali Cavasonza, B. Alpat, G. Ambrosi, L. Arruda, N. Attig, S. Aupetit, P. Azzarello, A. Bachlechner, F. Barao, A. Barrau, L. Barrin, A. Bartoloni, L. Basara, S. Başeğmez-du Pree, M. Battarbee, et al. (AMS Collab.), Phys. Rev. Lett. **119**, 251101 (2017).
27. P. Maestro, P. S Marrocchesi, G. Bigongiari, and P. Brogi, Adv. Space Res. 64, 2538 (2019).
28. Y. Akaike (for the CALET Collab.), J. Phys.: Conf. Ser. **1181**, 012042 (2019).
29. O. Adriani, Y. Akaike, K. Asano, Y. Asaoka, M. G. Bagliesi, E. Berti, G. Bigongiari, W. R. Binns, M. Bongi, P. Brogi, A. Bruno, J. H. Buckley, N. Cannady, G. Castellini, C. Checchia, M. L. Cherry, et al. (CALET Collab.), Phys. Rev. Lett. **125**, 251102 (2020).
30. O. Adriani, Y. Akaike, K. Asano, Y. Asaoka, E. Berti, G. Bigongiari, W. R. Binns, M. Bongi, P. Brogi, A. Bruno, J. H. Buckley, N. Cannady, G. Castellini, C. Checchia, M. L. Cherry, G. Collazuol, et al. (CALET Collab.), Phys. Rev. Lett. **126**, 241101 (2021).
31. J. J. Engelmann, P. Ferrando, A. Soutoul, P. Goret, E. Juliusson, L. Koch-Miramond, N. Lund, P. Masse, B. Peters, N. Petrou, and I. L. Rasmussen, Astron. Astrophys. **233**, 96 (1990).
32. D. Müller, S. P. Swordy, P. Meyer, J. L'Heureux, and J. M. Grunsfeld, Astrophys. J. 374, **356** (1991).
33. M. Aguilar, L. Ali Cavasonza, M. S. Allen, B. Alpat, G. Ambrosi, L. Arruda, N. Attig, F. Barao, L. Barrin, A. Bartoloni, S. Başeğmez-du Pree, R. Battiston, M. Behlmann,

B. Beischer, J. Berdugo, B. Bertucci, et al. (AMS Collab.), Phys. Rev. Lett. **126**, 041104 (2021).

34. V. Grebenyuk, D. Karmanov, I. Kovalev, I. Kudryashov, A. Kurganov, A. Panov, D. Podorozhny, A. Tkachenko, L. Tkachev, A. Turundaevskiy, O. Vasiliev, A. Voronin (NUCLEON Collaboration), Adv. Space Res. **64**, 2546 (2019).

35. A. D. Panov, J. H. Adams, H. S. Ahn, G. L. Bashinzhagyan, J. W. Watts, J. P. Wefel, J. Wu, O. Ganel, T. G. Guzik, V. I. Zatsepin, I. Isbert, K. C. Kim, M. Christl, E. N. Kouznetsov, M. I. Panasyuk, E. S. Seo, et al. (ATIC Collaboration), Bull. Russ. Acad. Sci. **73**, 564 (2009).

36. M. Ave, P. J. Boyle, F. Gahbauer, C. Höppner, J. R. Hörandel, M. Ichimura, D. Müller, and A. Romero-Wolf (TRACER Collab.), Astrophys. J. **678**, 262 (2008).

37. H. S. Ahn, P. Allison, M. G. Bagliesi, L. Barbier, J. J. Beatty, G. Bigongiari, T. J. Brandt, J. T. Childers, N. B. Conklin, S. Coutu, M. A. DuVernois, O. Ganel, J. H. Han, J. A. Jeon, K. C. Kim, M. H. Lee, et al. (CREAM Collab.), Astrophys. J. **707**, 593 (2009).

38. M. Ichimura, M. Kogawa, S. Kuramata, H. Mito, T. Murabayashi, H. Nanjo, T. Nakamura, K. Ohba, T. Ohuchi, T. Ozawa, Y. Yamada, H. Matsutani, Z. Watanabe, E. Kamioka, K. Kirii, M. Kitazawa, et al., Phys. Rev. D **48**, 1949 (1993).

39. F. Aharonian, A. G. Akhperjanian, A. R. Bazer-Bachi, M. Beilicke, W. Benbow, D. Berge, K. Bernlöhr, C. Boisson, O. Bolz, V. Borrel, I. Braun, E. Brion, A. M. Brown, R. Bühler, I. Büsching, S. Carrigan, et al. (H.E.S.S. Collab.), Phys. Rev. D **75**, 042004 (2007).

40. K. Yamaoka, A. Yoshida, T. Sakamoto, I. Takahashi, T. Hara, T. Yamamoto, Y. Kawakubo, R. Inoue, S. Terazawa, R. Fujioka, K. Senuma, S. Nakahira, H. Tomida, S. Ueno, S. Torii, M. L. Cherry, S. Ricciarini (CALET Collab.), in *Proceedings of the 7th Huntsville Gamma-Ray Burst Symposium, GRB 2013, eConf C1304143, 41 (2013)*.

41. N. Cannady, Y. Asaoka, F. Satoh, M. Tanaka, S. Torii, M. L. Cherry, M. Mori, O. Adriani, Y. Akaike, K. Asano, M. G. Bagliesi, E. Berti, G. Bigongiari, W. R. Binns, S. Bonechi, M. Bongi, et al. (CALET Collab.), Astrophys. J. Suppl. S. **238**, 5 (2018).

42. M. Mori et al. (for the CALET Collab.), PoS (ICRC2019) 586 (2019).

43. O. Adriani, Y. Akaike, K. Asano, Y. Asaoka, M. G. Bagliesi, E. Berti, G. Bigongiari, W. R. Binns, S. Bonechi, M. Bongi, P. Brogi, J. H. Buckley, N. Cannady, G. Castellini, C. Checchia, M. L. Cherry, et al. (CALET Collab.), Astrophys. J. Lett. **863**, 160 (2018).

44. O. Adriani, Y. Akaike, K. Asano, Y. Asaoka, M. G. Bagliesi, G. Bigongiari, W. R. Binns, S. Bonechi, M. Bongi, P. Brogi, J. H. Buckley, N. Cannady, G. Castellini, C. Checchia, M. L. Cherry, G. Collazuol, et al. (CALET Collab.), Astrophys. J. Lett. **829**, L20 (2016).

45. S. Miyake et al. (for the CALET Collab.), PoS (ICRC2019) 1126 (2019).

46. R. Kataoka, Y. Asaoka, S. Torii, T. Terasawa, S. Ozawa, T. Tamura, Y. Shimizu, Y. Akaike, M. Mori (CALET Collab.), Geophys. Res. Lett. **43**, 4119 (2016).

47. A. Bruno et al. (for the CALET Collab.), PoS (ICRC2019) 1063 (2019).

48. P. S. Marrocchesi et al. (for the CALET Collab.), PoS (ICRC2021) 010 (2021).

Full Authors List: CALET Collaboration

O. Adriani[1,2], Y. Akaike[3,4], K. Asano[5], Y. Asaoka[5], E. Berti[1,2], G. Bigongiari[6,7], W. R. Binns[8], M. Bongi[1,2], P. Brogi[6,7], A. Bruno[9,10], J. H. Buckley[8], N. Cannady[11,12,13], G. Castellini[14], C. Checchia[6], M. L. Cherry[15], G. Collazuol[16,17], K. Ebisawa[18], A. W. Ficklin[15], H. Fuke[18], S. Gonzi[1,2], T. G. Guzik[15], T. Hams[11], K. Hibino[19], M. Ichimura[20], K. Ioka[21], W. Ishizaki[5], M. H. Israel[8], K. Kasahara[22], J. Kataoka[23], R. Kataoka[24], Y. Katayose[25], C. Kato[26], N. Kawanaka[27,28], Y. Kawakubo[15], K. Kobayashi[3,4], K. Kohri[29], H. S. Krawczynski[8], J. F. Krizmanic[11,12,13], P. Maestro[6,7], P. S. Marrocchesi[6,7], A. M. Messineo[30,7], J.W. Mitchell[12], S. Miyake[32], A. A. Moiseev[33,12,13], M. Mori[34], N. Mori[2], H. M. Motz[35], K. Munakata[26], S. Nakahira[18], J. Nishimura[18], G. A. de Nolfo[9], S. Okuno[19], J. F. Ormes[36], N. Ospina[16,17], S. Ozawa[37], L. Pacini[1,14,2], P. Papini[2], B. F. Rauch[8], S. B. Ricciarini[14,2], K. Sakai[11,12,13], T. Sakamoto[38], M. Sasaki[33,12,13], Y. Shimizu[19], A. Shiomi[39], P. Spillantini[1], F. Stolzi[6,7], S. Sugita[38], A. Sulaj[6,7], M. Takita[5], T. Tamura[19], T. Terasawa[40], S. Torii[3], Y. Tsunesada[41], Y. Uchihori[42], E. Vannuccini[2], J. P. Wefel[15], K. Yamaoka[43], S. Yanagita[44], A. Yoshida[38], K. Yoshida[22], and W. V. Zober[8]

[1]Department of Physics, University of Florence, Via Sansone, 1, 50019 Sesto, Fiorentino, Italy, [2]INFN Sezione di Florence, Via Sansone, 1, 50019 Sesto, Fiorentino, Italy, [3]Waseda Research Institute for Science and Engineering, Waseda University, 17 Kikuicho, Shinjuku, Tokyo 162-0044, Japan, [4]JEM Utilization Center, Human Spaceflight Technology Directorate, Japan Aerospace Exploration Agency, 2-1-1 Sengen, Tsukuba, Ibaraki 305-8505, Japan, [5]Institute for Cosmic Ray Research, The University of Tokyo, 5-1-5 Kashiwa-no-Ha, Kashiwa, Chiba 277-8582, Japan, [6]Department of Physical Sciences, Earth and Environment, University of Siena, via Roma 56, 53100 Siena, Italy, [7]INFN Sezione di Pisa, Polo Fibonacci, Largo B. Pontecorvo, 3, 56127 Pisa, Italy, [8]Department of Physics and McDonnell Center for the Space Sciences, Washington University, One Brookings Drive, St. Louis, Missouri 63130-4899, USA, [9]Heliospheric Physics Laboratory, NASA/GSFC, Greenbelt, Maryland 20771, USA, [10]Department of Physics, Catholic University of America, Washington, DC 20064, USA, [11]Center for Space Sciences and Technology, University of Maryland, Baltimore County, 1000 Hilltop Circle, Baltimore, Maryland 21250, USA, [12]Astroparticle Physics Laboratory, NASA/GSFC, Greenbelt, Maryland 20771, USA, [13]Center for Research and Exploration in Space Sciences and Technology, NASA/GSFC, Greenbelt, Maryland 20771, USA, [14]Institute of Applied Physics (IFAC), National Research Council (CNR), Via Madonna del Piano, 10, 50019 Sesto, Fiorentino, Italy, [15]Department of Physics and Astronomy, Louisiana State University, 202 Nicholson Hall, Baton Rouge, Louisiana 70803, USA, [16]Department of Physics and Astronomy, University of Padova, Via Marzolo, 8, 35131 Padova, Italy, [17]INFN Sezione di Padova, Via Marzolo, 8, 35131 Padova, Italy, [18]Institute of Space and Astronautical Science, Japan Aerospace Exploration Agency, 3-1-1 Yoshinodai, Chuo, Sagamihara, Kanagawa 252-5210, Japan, [19]Kanagawa University, 3-27-1 Rokkakubashi, Kanagawa, Yokohama, Kanagawa 221-8686, Japan, [20]Faculty of Science and Technology, Graduate School of Science and Technology,, Hirosaki University, 3, Bunkyo, Hirosaki, Aomori 036-8561, Japan, [21]Yukawa Institute for Theoretical Physics, Kyoto University, Kitashirakawa Oiwakecho, Sakyo, Kyoto 606-8502, Japan, [22]Department of Electronic Information Systems, Shibaura Institute of Technology, 307 Fukasaku, Minuma, Saitama 337-8570, Japan, [23]School of Advanced Science and Engineering, Waseda University, 3-4-1 Okubo, Shinjuku, Tokyo 169-8555, Japan, [24]National Institute of Polar Research, 10-3, Midori-cho, Tachikawa, Tokyo 190-8518, Japan, [25]Faculty of Engineering, Division of Intelligent Systems Engineering, Yokohama National University, 79-5 Tokiwadai, Hodogaya, Yokohama 240-8501, Japan, [26]Faculty of Science, Shinshu University, 3-1-1 Asahi, Matsumoto, Nagano 390-8621, Japan, [27]Hakubi Center, Kyoto University, Yoshida Honmachi, Sakyo-ku, Kyoto 606-8501, Japan, [28]Department of Astronomy, Graduate School of Science, Kyoto University, Kitashirakawa Oiwake-cho, Sakyo-ku, Kyoto 606-8502, Japan, [29]Institute of Particle and Nuclear Studies, High Energy Accelerator Research Organization, 1-1 Oho, Tsukuba, Ibaraki 305-0801, Japan, [30]University of Pisa, Polo Fibonacci, Largo B. Pontecorvo, 3, 56127 Pisa, Italy, [31]Astroparticle Physics Laboratory, NASA/GSFC, Greenbelt, Maryland 20771, USA, [32]Department of Electrical and Electronic Systems Engineering, National Institute of Technology, Ibaraki College, 866 Nakane, Hitachinaka, Ibaraki 312-8508, Japan [33]Department of Astronomy, University of Maryland, College Park, Maryland 20742, USA, [34]Department of Physical Sciences, College of Science and Engineering, Ritsumeikan University, Shiga 525-8577, Japan, [35]Faculty of Science and Engineering, Global Center for Science and Engineering, Waseda University, 3-4-1 Okubo, Shinjuku, Tokyo 169-8555, Japan, [36]Department of Physics and Astronomy, University of Denver, Physics Building, Room 211, 2112 East Wesley Avenue, Denver, Colorado 80208-6900, USA, [37]Quantum ICT Advanced Development Center, National Institute of Information and Communications Technology, 4-2-1 Nukui-Kitamachi, Koganei, Tokyo 184-8795, Japan, [38]College of Science and Engineering, Department of Physics and Mathematics, Aoyama Gakuin University, 5-10-1 Fuchinobe, Chuo, Sagamihara, Kanagawa 252-5258, Japan, [39]College of Industrial Technology, Nihon University, 1-2-1 Izumi, Narashino, Chiba 275-8575, Japan [40]RIKEN, 2-1 Hirosawa, Wako, Saitama 351-0198, Japan, [41]Division of Mathematics and Physics, Graduate School of Science, Osaka City University, 3-3-138 Sugimoto, Sumiyoshi, Osaka 558-8585, Japan, [42]National Institutes for Quantum and Radiation Science and Technology, 4-9-1 Anagawa, Inage, Chiba 263-8555, Japan, [43]Nagoya University, Furo, Chikusa, Nagoya 464-8601, Japan, [44]College of Science, Ibaraki University, 2-1-1 Bunkyo, Mito, Ibaraki 310-8512, Japan

The fluxes of charged cosmic rays as measured by the DAMPE satellite

Paolo Bernardini (on behalf of the DAMPE Collaboration)

*Dipartimento di Matematica e Fisica, Università del Salento
and Istituto Nazionale di Fisica Nucleare
Lecce, 73100, Italy
E-mail: paolo.bernardini@le.infn.it*

DAMPE (DArk Matter Particle Explorer) is a satellite-born experiment promoted by the Chinese Academy of Sciences, with the collaboration of Italian and Swiss agencies. Since December 2015, DAMPE flies at the altitude of 500 km and collects data smoothly. The detector is made of four sub-detectors: top layers of plastic scintillators, a silicon-tungsten tracker, a BGO calorimeter (32 radiation lengths), and a bottom boron-doped scintillator to detect delayed neutrons. The main goal of the experiment is the search for indirect signals of Dark Matter in the electron and photon spectra with energies up to 10 TeV. Furthermore DAMPE studies cosmic charged and gamma radiation. Moreover, the calorimeter depth and the large acceptance allow to measure cosmic ray fluxes in the range from 20 GeV up to hundreds of TeV with unprecedented precision. An overview of the latest results about the charged cosmic rays will be presented.

Keywords: Cosmic rays; Satellite; DAMPE.

1. Introduction

The DArk Matter Particle Explorer (DAMPE) is a satellite-born experiment and it is funded by the strategic space projects of the Chinese Academy of Sciences with the active contribution of Italian and Swiss universities and institutions.[1,2] It is devoted to search for indirect dark matter signatures, to measure the fluxes of charged cosmic rays and to study the high energy gamma signal of astrophysical origin. In this paper the dark matter search and the gamma astronomy will be neglected to focus the reader's attention on the recent results about charged cosmic rays (electrons, protons and heavier nuclei).

2. The detector

The detector has been designed not only to reach the research goals. The final setup is an optimal compromise between scientific needs and reduction of power consumption and weight. In Fig. 1 the four sub-detectors of the DAMPE experiment are shown:

- PSD, in place of Plastic Scintillator strip Detector, used to measure the charge (Z) of incoming particles thanks to the Bethe-Bloch formula. The anti-coincidence with the PSD signal is also exploited to select gamma events.

- STK, in place of Silicon-Tungsten tracKer-converter, to reconstruct the trajectory of particles and to confirm the charge measurement. The tungsten is devoted to convert photons in electron-positron pairs.
- BGO, in place of bismuth germanate calorimeter (14 layers) of about 32 radiation lengths, that is ~ 1.6 nuclear interaction lengths, enough to get high resolution in energy measurement. The BGO bars allow to reconstruct the shower image in two views, then it is possible to distinguish between hadronic and electromagnetic ones.
- NUD, in place of NeUtron Detector, to further increase the hadronic shower rejection power.

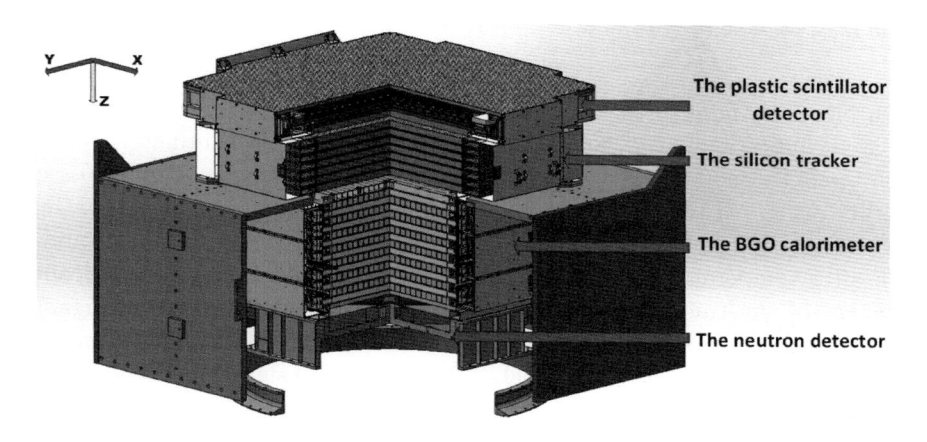

Fig. 1. The DAMPE detector with its 4 sub-detectors.

DAMPE performances were verified by a series of beam tests at CERN.[1,3,4] The wide energy range of electron beam and the high purity of proton beam allowed to check energy resolution, linearity (Fig. 2, left) and e/p separation (see Fig. 7 in the following). Also beams of argon and lead fragments were used to check the PSD capability to measure Z for heavy ions (Fig. 2, right for the argon beam). Furthermore sea-level muon test have been performed during different stages of the DAMPE assembly. Then the energy response to Minimum Ionizing Particles (MIPs), the efficiency and the detector alignment have been checked with a large sample of atmospheric muon tracks.

3. In-flight DAMPE performances

The satellite has been successfully launched on December 17, 2015. After few days all detectors were powered on and the data acquisition began very soon. We would like to stress that the detector works properly and flies at the altitude of 500 km on a Sun-synchronous orbit since almost 6 years, in spite of its foreseen 3-years life.

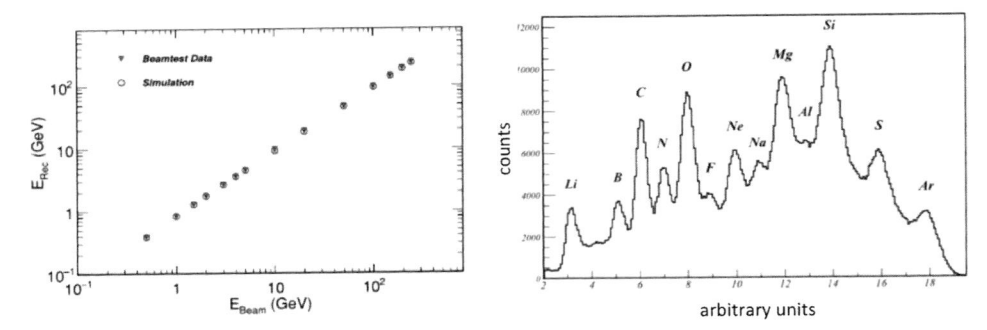

Fig. 2. Beam test - Left panel: Reconstructed energy versus electron beam energy (simulated and beam-test data are shown). Right panel: PSD charge spectrum of fragments of an argon beam (helium peak has been removed).

On orbit the detector is calibrated by using the standard scientific data and dedicated calibration data. The data acquisition system runs continuously in observation mode for most of the time and switches to calibration mode for 40 seconds twice per orbit. All the calibration results (pedestal values, dynode ratios, energy gains, trigger thresholds and so on) are consistent with the ground ones and very stable after temperature correction. The STK alignment allows a significant improvement of the tracking resolution.[5] In Fig. 3 (left panel) the PSD signal due to MIP protons is plotted as a function of time in a period of about 4 months. A similar plot is shown in the right panel of Fig. 3 for BGO signal due to no-showering helium nuclei. The high stability of the detectors is confirmed by these and many other checks.

4. Cosmic Rays (CR)

After more than 100 years since the CR discovery many questions are yet without answer. The spectra before the knee do not fit perfectly with a simple power-law and the canonical model of CR acceleration in Super Nova shock does not explain the observed structures. Precise measurements for different chemical components are essential for testing the CR models (sources, production, acceleration, diffusion in the galaxy, presence of different populations, and so on).

DAMPE can contribute to CR studies measuring the spectrum structures for different nuclei in the range from tens of GeV up to hundreds of TeV. The possibility to reach such high energies with on-orbit detectors put a bridge between space and ground experiments and pave the way to a combined analysis.

The measurement of CR spectra is based on the estimate of charge and energy of incoming particles. By means of the STK tracking (supported also by the information on the fired BGO bars) the path-length in PSD is reconstructed. Then the PSD signal allows to measure the charge (square root of the energy release in PSD is proportional to path-length and Z). In Fig. 4 the elemental CR spectrum is

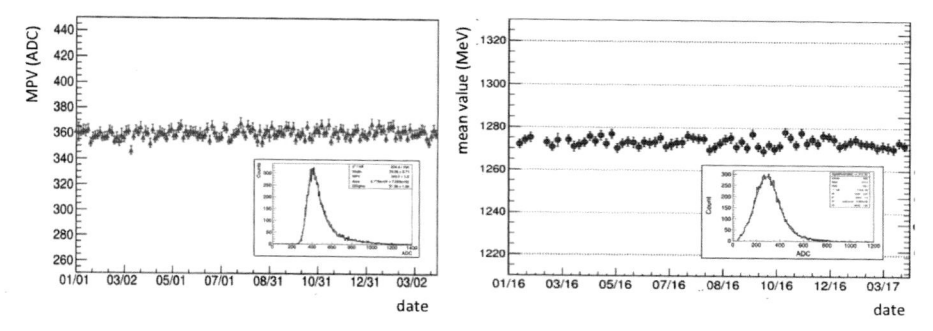

Fig. 3. Left panel: the deposited energy in PSD for minimum ionizing protons is fitted with the convolution of a Landau function with a Gaussian one (insert). The Most Probable Value (MPV) is shown as a function of time. Right panel: similar plot for minimum ionizing helium nuclei in BGO (the mean value of the deposited energy is displayed versus time instead of MPV).

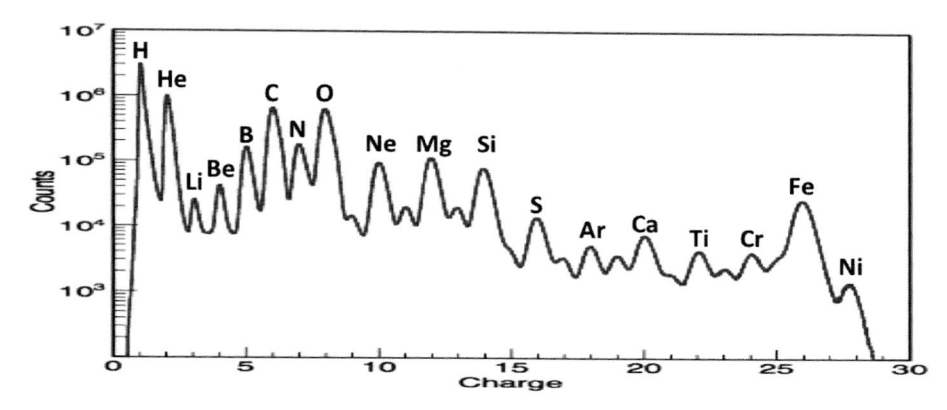

Fig. 4. Charge spectrum reconstructed on the basis of the deposited energy in the PSD. Almost all Z-peaks are visible up to nickel.

shown from hydrogen up to iron and beyond. By means of the template-fit procedure the different peaks are separated and the mutual contamination is estimated (an example is shown in Fig. 5 where the data-Montecarlo agreement is excellent).

Lastly the energy is estimated by the signal in the BGO calorimeter. Its unprecedented thickness allows to push the direct measurement of CR spectra to highest energies. The imaging allows also to distinguish the features of hadronic showers from electromagnetic ones.

The DAMPE spectra for protons[6] and helium nuclei[7] are presented in Fig. 6. The analyses for heavier nuclei are in progress. Both the spectra in Fig. 6 show a similar shape inconsistent with a single power-law. The fit of these spectra improves significantly using smoothly-broken power-laws in order to reproduce a hardening followed by a softening. The observation of the hardening confirms previous measurements, instead the softening is observed for the first time by DAMPE with such

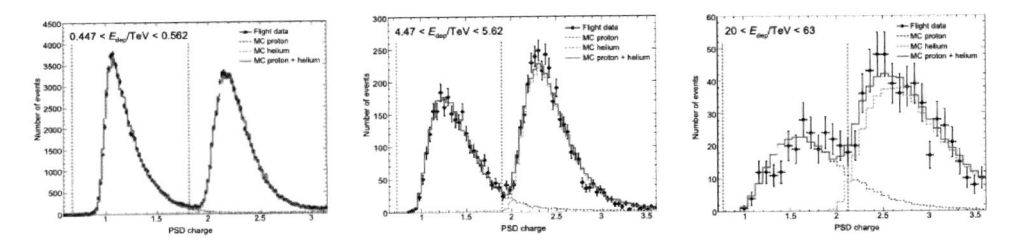

Fig. 5. Combined PSD signal for protons and helium nuclei, for different ranges of BGO energy (447-562 GeV, 4.47-5.62 TeV, 20-63 TeV). The colour codes to distinguish on-orbit and simulated data are shown in the plot. The cut used to select proton candidates is represented by the vertical dotted lines.

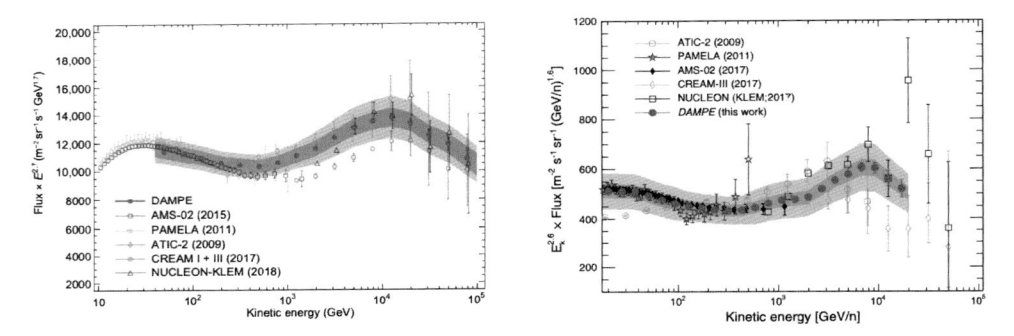

Fig. 6. Spectra for cosmic protons (left panel) and helium nuclei (right panel). For protons (helium) the flux is multiplied for $E^{2.7}$ ($E^{2.6}$). Two changes of spectral index are visible in both the spectra (hardening followed by softening).

significance. The break-energy for the softening suggests a dependence on particle charge, although a dependence on mass can not be ruled out yet.

5. Cosmic electrons and positrons (CRE)

Some measurements[8-14] reported an unexpected structure of CRE flux. Furthermore evidence for a spectral break in the TeV range of the CRE flux has been provided by indirect measurements[15,16] affected by significant uncertainties.

In two years of data taking DAMPE measured CRE spectrum in the range from 25 GeV to 4.6 TeV[17] with very low background. Indeed the imaging properties of the BGO calorimeter are exploited to recognise the showers initiated by CRE. The PID algorithm is based on the spread of the BGO hits (*spread*) and on the fraction (F_{last}) of energy on the lower layer with respect to the sum of energies released on all the BGO layers. The quantities *spread* and F_{last} are combined in the parameter

$$\zeta = F_{\text{last}} \frac{(spread/\text{mm})^4}{8 \times 10^6}. \quad (1)$$

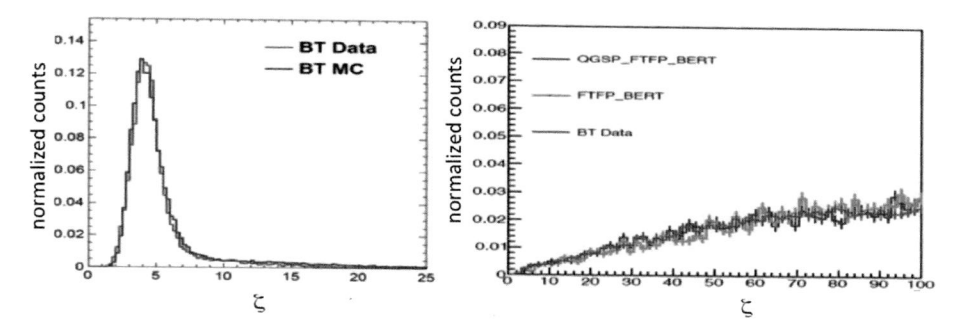

Fig. 7. Beam test (BT) - The ζ-distributions for electrons (left panel) and for protons (right panel). In the proton plot the real data are compared with simulations based on different models of the hadronic interactions.

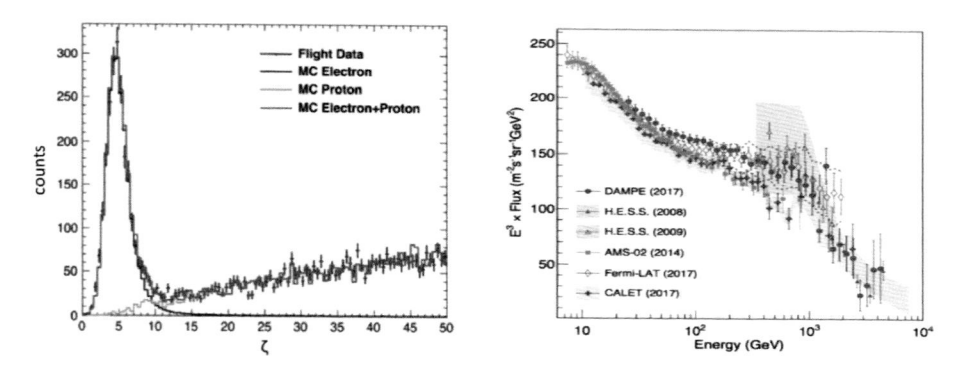

Fig. 8. Left: Distribution of the ζ parameter (the cut $\zeta < 8.5$ is applied to select the CRE sample). Right: electron and positron spectrum measured by different experiments (DAMPE: red dots, HESS systematic errors: grey band).

The efficiency of the ζ-parameter in order to distinguish electrons and protons has been verified in the beam test (Fig. 7). Then the CRE sample is selected by requiring $\zeta < 8.5$ (see Fig. 8, left panel). The CRE flux measured by DAMPE as a function of energy is shown in right panel of Fig. 8 with measurements of others experiments. Also in this case a smoothly broken power-law is preferred to fit the largest part of the spectrum.

6. Conclusions

The DAMPE detector works extremely properly since its launch more than 5 years ago and it is expected to operate stably in the next few years. Many analyses based on DAMPE data are going on successfully. The measurements of CRE, proton and helium spectra are particularly remarkable. Indeed the direct detection of spectral breaks confirms previous direct and indirect measurements, clarifies the shape of the spectra at highest energies. These results put severe constraints about models of acceleration and diffusion of galactic cosmic rays. Many new results are expected from the analysis of the complete sample of DAMPE data.

References

1. Chang J., Chinese J. Space Science **34**, 550 (2014).
2. Chang J. *et al.*, Astropart. Physics **95**, 6 (2017).
3. Azzarello P. *et al.*, Nuclear Instruments and Methods A **831**, 378 (2016).
4. Zhang Z. *et al.*, Nuclear Instruments and Methods A **836**, 98 (2016).
5. Tykhonov A. *et al.*, Nuclear Instruments and Methods A **893**, 43 (2018).
6. Ambrosi G. *et al.* (DAMPE Collaboration), *Science Advances 5* (2019) eaax3793.
7. Alemanno F. *et al.* (DAMPE Collaboration), *Physics Review Letters 126* (2021) 201102.
8. Chang J. *et al.* (ATIC Collaboration), Nature **456**, 362 (2008).
9. Abdo A.A. *et al.* (Fermi-LAT Collaboration), Phys. Rev. Lett. **102**, 181101 (2009).
10. Abdollahi S. *et al.* (Fermi-LAT Collaboration), Phys. Rev. D **95**, 082007 (2017).
11. Aguilar M. *et al.* (AMS-02 Collaboration), Phys. Rev. Lett. **113**, 221102 (2014).
12. Adriani O. *et al.* (PAMELA collaboration), Phys. Rev. Lett. **106**, 201101 (2011).
13. Adriani O. *et al.* (CALET Collaboration), Phys. Rev. Lett. **119**, 181101 (2017).
14. Adriani O. *et al.* (CALET Collaboration), Phys. Rev. Lett. **120**, 261102 (2018).
15. Aharonian F. *et al.* (H.E.S.S. Collaboration), Phys. Rev. Lett. **101**, 261104 (2008).
16. Aharonian F. *et al.* (H.E.S.S. Collaboration), Astron. Astrophys. **508**, 561 (2009).
17. Ambrosi G. *et al.* (DAMPE Collaboration), Nature **552**, 63 (2017).

Recent results from the Pierre Auger Observatory

E. Roulet for the Pierre Auger Collaboration

Centro Atómico Bariloche
Av. Bustillo 9500, Bariloche, 8400, Argentina
E-mail: roulet@cab.cnea.gov.ar
Full author list: https://www.auger.org/archive/authors_2021_07.html

The Pierre Auger Observatory has by now achieved an exposure of order 10^5 km^2 sr yr, exploring about 85% of the sky. In this talk, I will review some of the recent results, including the detailed measurements of the features in the cosmic ray spectrum, the study of the anisotropies in the cosmic ray arrival directions both at large and intermediate angular scales, the inferred mass composition, and multimessenger searches.

Keywords: Cosmic rays

The Pierre Auger Observatory has been operational since January 2004 and has by now reached an accumulated exposure of order 10^5 km^2 yr sr (see Fig. 1). This enormous increase in the number of detected cosmic rays (CRs) with ultrahigh energies, by more than an order of magnitude with respect to previous observations, has allowed measuring the CR spectrum with unprecedented detail,[1] firmly establishing the suppression at the highest energies, above 47 EeV, as well as the various features of the spectrum, including the discovery of a softening at 14 EeV, the observation of the ankle at 5 EeV, the second-knee at 0.16 EeV, and the low-energy ankle at 28 PeV (see Fig. 2).

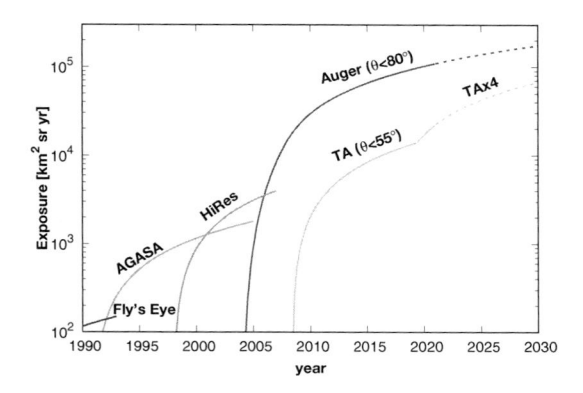

Fig. 1. Exposure vs. time of ultrahigh-energy air shower arrays. The previous experiments (Fly's Eye, HiRes and AGASA) as well as the Auger and Telescope Array exposures used in anisotropy searches at the highest energies are shown, together with the extrapolations to the next years involving the enlarged TAx4 upgrade.

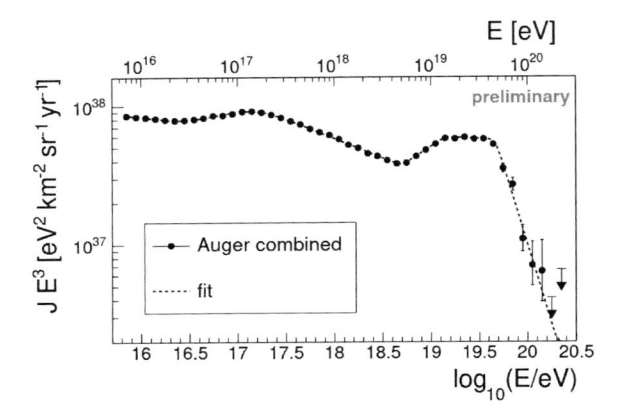

Fig. 2. Combined spectrum from measurements obtained with different techniques together with a broken power-law fit (see ref.1 for details).

By observing events with zenith angles up to 80°, i.e., covering 85% of the sky, it also became possible to determine with high significance an anisotropy in the CR arrival direction distribution at energies above 8 EeV, which has a characteristic dipolar pattern with an amplitude of about 7%.[2] The direction of this anisotropy, with the reconstructed dipole pointing about 115° away from the direction towards the Galactic center, provides a clear indication supporting the extragalactic origin of the CRs at these energies (see left panel of Fig. 3). Considering several energy bins above 8 EeV, the dipole amplitude is found to actually increase with energy, and the direction of the fitted dipole in all bins lies not far from the direction of the outer spiral arm of the Galaxy.[3] At energies below 8 EeV, no significant anisotropies were observed, so that relevant upper bounds on the equatorial dipole amplitudes were set down to energies of 0.03 EeV, and interestingly the right ascension phase of the flux modulations below about 1 EeV is not far from the right ascension of the Galactic center.[4] Hints of anisotropies at intermediate angular scales, of order 20°, have been obtained at energies above about 40 EeV, with the main excess lying around the direction towards the nearby radiogalaxy Centaurus A (right panel of Fig. 3). This radiogalaxy then provides a possible candidate source of ultrahigh-energy CRs, although other potential CR sources are also located in the same region of the sky, such as the starburst galaxies NGC4945 and M83. A likelihood ratio test comparing the CR arrival directions above different threshold energies with a catalog of nearby starburst galaxies, flux-weighted and smeared, reveals a maximum significance above a threshold of 38 EeV for an angular scale of a top-hat window of 25°.[5]

The hybrid nature of the Auger Observatory, with both surface detectors (SD) and fluorescence detectors (FD), allows it to perform sensitive measurements of the mass composition of the primary CRs. The SD consists of instrumented water tanks that measure the Cherenkov light emitted by relativistic secondary charged particles

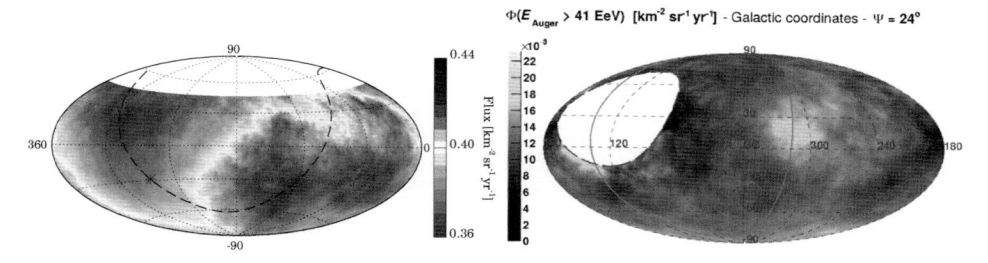

Fig. 3. CR flux map above 8 EeV averaged on windows of 45° radius (left panel, in Equatorial coordinates) and above 41 EeV averaged of 24° radius windows (right panel, Galactic coordinates).

crossing them and is hence sensitive to both the muonic and the electromagnetic components of the showers reaching ground level. The FD telescopes measure instead the longitudinal development in the atmosphere of the CR induced showers by observing, with a $\sim 15\%$ duty cycle, the light emitted by the N_2 air molecules that get excited by the passage of the electromagnetic component of the shower. The FD allows for an almost calorimetric measurement of the primary energy, which is also used to calibrate the SD energy assignment. Moreover, the atmospheric depth at which the showers reach their maximum development, $X_{\max}$, provides crucial information about the mass composition of the CRs, because lighter primaries give rise to more penetrating showers than heavier ones since these last can be considered as a superposition of many lower energy showers induced by the individual nucleons. The measurements of the distribution of $X_{\max}$ values allowed us to establish[6] that at energies of a few EeV the average CR masses are light, being dominated by H and He primaries, and they become increasingly heavier as the energy is further increased, lying in the ballpark of the expectations from primary N nuclei at energies of 30 EeV and possibly even heavier at higher energies (the actual masses inferred depend, however, on the hadronic interaction model adopted in the analysis). The narrow spread in the fluctuations on the values of $X_{\max}$ measured above the ankle energy also implies that there is little admixture between elements with disparate masses at these energies. These measurements are depicted in Fig. 4.

A combined fit to the spectrum and anisotropy measurements within an astrophysical scenario with equal luminosity sources having power-law spectra with rigidity dependent cutoffs has been performed in ref. 7.

Besides the measurement of $X_{\max}$ with FD, also the SD has been used to obtain composition information,[8] exploiting the rise-times of the measured signals in the triggered detectors. Given that the shower muons travel straight from their production points high in the atmosphere, while the electromagnetic component of photons, electrons, and positrons have a more diffusive propagation in the atmosphere, the muonic signal is expected to be more concentrated in the early part of the shower front while the electromagnetic one will have a larger spread. Hence, shorter rise times are expected in the signals from showers with a more abundant

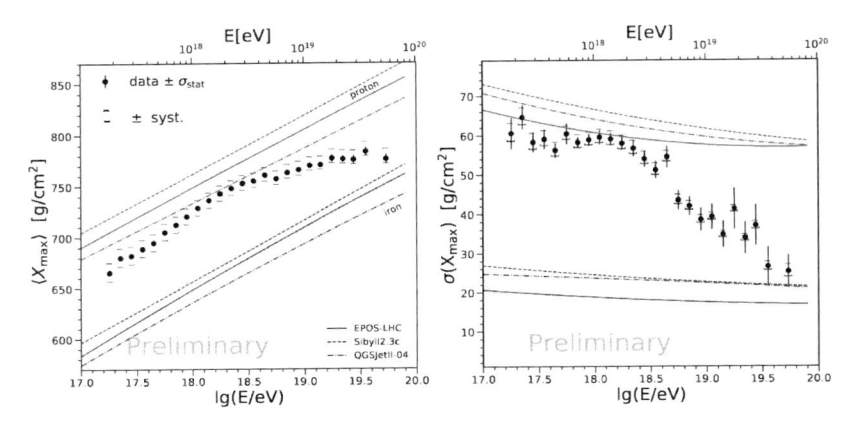

Fig. 4. Mean $X_{\max}$ and its dispersion as a function of energy, as measured with the Auger fluorescence detectors.

muonic component, as is the case for the showers induced by heavier nuclei. These measurements can then be correlated with the FD measurements of the depth of shower maxima. Given the larger statistics obtained with SD, which has a 100% duty cycle, it has become possible to obtain more detailed information about the composition at the highest energies, actually splitting the highest energy FD bin in four SD bins. In this way the trend towards a heavier composition for increasing masses is confirmed with SD up to the highest energies.

Another search performed has been to look for a component of photon-induced showers, which would be very poor in muons, and this allowed to set stringent bounds on the primary photon fluxes above EeV energies.[9] The upper bounds strongly disfavor exotic scenarios for the production of UHECRs, such as those involving superheavy particle decays (see left panel in Fig. 5).

Also ultrahigh-energy neutrinos have been searched through the study of inclined showers.[10] Very inclined showers produced by ordinary nuclear-induced cascades, which initiate high in the atmosphere, would have their electromagnetic component totally attenuated by the time they reach ground level. On the other hand, neutrino-induced showers can be initiated at any depth in the atmosphere, and those originating close to the detector will have a significant electromagnetic component, looking then 'younger' than the hadronic ones, what could be exploited to single them out from the background. Actually, the most sensitive neutrino search is that looking for showers produced by Earth-skimming tau neutrinos interacting in the crust of the Earth and producing tau leptons that manage to exit from the soil before decaying to produce the atmospheric shower that may be observed. The most sensitive energy range for these searches is around the EeV, which just happens to be the range where the fluxes of cosmogenic neutrinos are expected to peak. In particular, cosmogenic neutrinos could arise from the photo-pion production taking place when CR protons with energies exceeding the GZK threshold of about 40 EeV

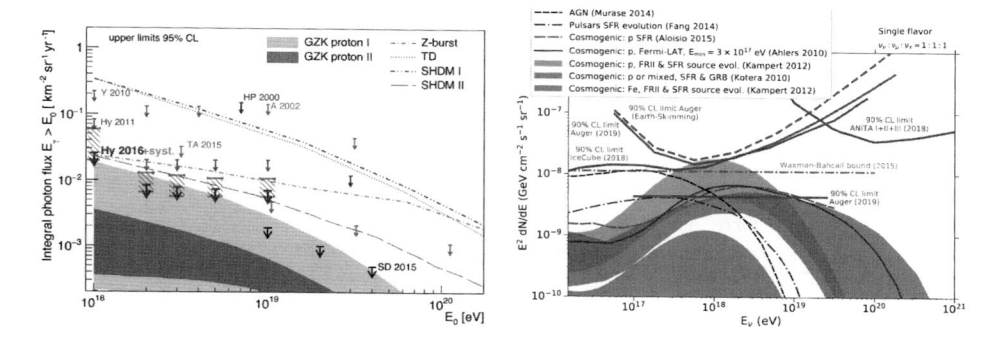

Fig. 5. Bounds on photon fluxes (left) and neutrino fluxes (right), compared to some model expectations.

interact with CMB photons, and the neutrinos produced in the charged pion decays have typical energies of about $E_p/20$. No neutrino candidates have yet been observed in these searches, allowing us to set bounds that start to constrain some of the most optimistic scenarios for the production of cosmogenic neutrinos, which are those with protons dominating the CR fluxes at the highest energies. However, more realistic scenarios with a predominantly heavier composition at the highest energies predict fluxes below the present bounds (see right panel of Fig. 5).

Searches of neutrinos in association with the first neutron star binary merger detected by the LIGO-Virgo Collaboration also led to negative results,[11] in spite of the lucky coincidence that the event just happened to be a few degrees below the horizon, a situation in which the sensitivity to Earth-skimming tau neutrinos is largely enhanced. It is interesting to note that the model predictions for the case in which the jet of this closeby merger had been aligned with the line of sight were not very far from the Auger sensitivity, but the lack of an observed signal is not unexpected, given the slight misalignment of the jet in this particular merger. Also searches in the direction towards the blazar TXS 0506+056, from which a ~ 300 TeV neutrino was observed by IceCube, revealed no neutrino candidate, allowing to constrain the neutrino flux from this object at the highest energies.[12]

The Pierre Auger Observatory is at present undergoing an upgrade, consisting in adding 4 m^2 scintillators on top of each SD and using faster electronics, which in combination with the water-Cherenkov detectors should allow for a cleaner separation between the electromagnetic and muonic components of the showers. This separation should make it possible to obtain composition information on an event by event basis with the SD detector, allowing, for instance, to improve the sensitivity of the anisotropy studies by restricting them to just the lighter CR component (which is less deflected by the Galactic and extragalactic magnetic fields). Also radio antennas are being added to each SD detector to observe the radio emission from the electromagnetic component of the showers, which should help in particular to study the composition of the inclined showers. This new phase of the Observatory should allow for improved studies of all the topics just discussed, as well as to better handle the still remaining open issues.

References

1. Aab et al. (Pierre Auger Collaboration), Phys. Rev. Lett. 125 (2020) 121106; V. Novotný for the Pierre Auger Collaboration, PoS(ICRC2021)324
2. A. Aab et al. (Pierre Auger Collaboration), Science 357 (2017) 1266
3. A. Aab et al. (Pierre Auger Collaboration), Astrophys. J. 868 (2018) 4
4. A. Aab et al. (Pierre Auger Collaboration), Astrophys. J. 891 (2020) 142
5. A. Aab et al. (Pierre Auger Collaboration), Astrophys. J. Lett. 853 (2018) L29; J. Biteau for the Pierre Auger Collaboration, PoS(ICRC2021)307
6. A. Aab et al. (Pierre Auger Collaboration), Phys. Rev. D 90 (2014) 122005; A. Yushkov for the Pierre Auger Collaboration, PoS(ICRC2019)483
7. A. Aab et al. (Pierre Auger Collaboration), JCAP 04 (2017) 038
8. A. Aab et al. (Pierre Auger Collaboration), Phys. Rev. D 96 (2017) 122003; C. Todero Peixoto for the Pierre Auger Collaboration, PoS(ICRC2019)440
9. A. Aab et al. (Pierre Auger Collaboration), JCAP 04 (2017) 009
10. A. Aab et al. (Pierre Auger Collaboration), JCAP 10 (2019) 022
11. ANTARES Collaboration, IceCube Collaboration, The Pierre Auger Collaboration, and LIGO Scientific Collaboration and Virgo Collaboration, Astrophys. J. Lett. 850 (2017) L35
12. A. Aab et al. (Pierre Auger Collaboration), Astrophys. J. 902 (2020)105

The HERD space mission

F.C.T. Barbato on behalf of the HERD Collaboration

Gran Sasso Science Institute, L'Aquila, Italy
INFN Laboratori Nazionali del Gran Sasso, Assergi, L'Aquila, Italy
E-mail: felicia.barbato@gssi.it

The High Energy cosmic-Radiation Detection (HERD) space mission is now being designed, as a result of an international collaboration among several chinese and european institutions, to make cosmic ray (CR) direct measurements at the highest possible energies with current technologies.

HERD primary scientific goals include precise measurements of the energy spectra of CR individual species up to few PeV, reaching the knee of the all-particle spectrum, and study electrons and photon of spectra from GeV up to tens of TeV, also contributing to multimessenger observations together with other satellites and ground-based experiments.

In order to reach these goals HERD is configured to accept incident particles from its top and the four lateral sides. The baseline design includes covering the top and fours sides with: the Silicon Charge Detector (SCD), for incident particle trajectory and charge measurement, the Plastic Scintil- lator Detector (PSD), for photon tagging and precise charge measurement, and a scintillating Fiber Tracker (FIT). The core of the facility is made by a LYSO crystal calorimeter (CALO) that with its 3 interaction lengths and 55 radiation lengths will allow the measurement of incident gamma-rays, electrons and cosmic ray nuclei with unprecedented resolution and 3D reconstruction. In addition, on one side a Transition Radiation detector (TRD) will be installed for on-orbit calibration of the CALO.

Keywords: Cosmic rays; Chinese Space Station; space missions; SiPM; LYSO.

1. Introduction

Cosmic rays are messengers with which we use to explore the Universe and its laws. Despite being discovered more than one century ago, our knowledge about them is still limited. In the recent years, some progresses have been made in our knowledge and understanding of them thanks to several experiments. Nevertheless, many fundamental questions on this topic are still open: where are they produced? how are they accelerated to such energies? how do they propagate in the Universe?

A big issue concerns the so-called *knee* region of the primary cosmic ray spectrum. Here (at $\sim$ PeV energies), the spectrum steepens. This behaviour was firstly observed in 1958, nevertheless the cause remains still unknown. Because of the rapidly falling intensity of the cosmic ray flux with energy, in order to explore this region we need experiments with a large acceptance and operating over years. In past this role was played by ground based experiments. Nevertheless, this kind of experiments are not able to perform mass composition studies. For this reason, we need new spaceborne observatories performing studies aiming at finding an answer to this question.

The High Energy cosmic Radiation Detection (HERD) facility is an international space mission that will start operation around 2027 to make cosmic ray direct measurements at the highest possible energies with advanced technologies. It will be installed on the Chinese Space Station (CSS) where it will observe the high energy sky for more than 10 years. The HERD project involves researchers from Chinese institutions, Italy, Switzerland and Spain. The unprecedented acceptance and the 3D segmented calorimeter allow HERD to represent the future of the direct cosmic ray detection and a missing observational link among space-based and ground-based experiments.

2. Scientific objectives

HERD primary scientific goals include:

- extending the measurement of cosmic ray flux up to a few PeV testing the theory of the knee structure as due to galactic source acceleration limit;
- extending the measurement of $e^+ + e^-$ flux up to several tens of TeV testing the hypothesis of the expected cutoff at high energy distinguishing between DM or astrophysical origin of positron excess and looking for possible other structures of the spectra and eventual anisotropies;
- large acceptance, high sensitivity to γ-rays up to several hundreds of GeV for a long term gamma ray sky also searching for γ-lines associated to DM annihilation, while accomplishing a γ-ray sky survey up to very high energy.

Cosmic ray origins Since their discovery in 1910, our knowledge about cosmic ray physics experienced several progresses. Today, we are in another golden era for cosmic rays, due mainly to their connection with physics at the highest energy, indirect search for particle dark matter and site and mechanism of cosmic accelerators. Information about the latter topic can be obtained from the energy spectrum of cosmic rays. It is expected to follow a power-law for energies below the "knee" (at 3-4 PeV) because of the canonical shock acceleration of particles, see FIG. 1.

Nevertheless, several experiments observed changes in the power-law spectral indices for protons, helium, and heavy nuclei. Current data suggest a hardening of the spectra above about 0.2 TeV/nucleon. The hardening at energies above 200-400 GeV is well established since the first observation by PAMELA,[2] while the softening at energies above 10 TeV is observed by different experiments with the first strong evidence in DAMPE data.[3] The deviations from single power law of the spectra motivate extensive investigations for deeper understanding of the acceleration and propagation mechanisms or of new possible cosmic ray sources. Several theoretical solutions have been proposed, exploiting different hypotheses on source properties/populations, acceleration/propagation mechanisms and particle physics issues at high energies, in order to give a satisfactory explanation of this behaviour.[4]

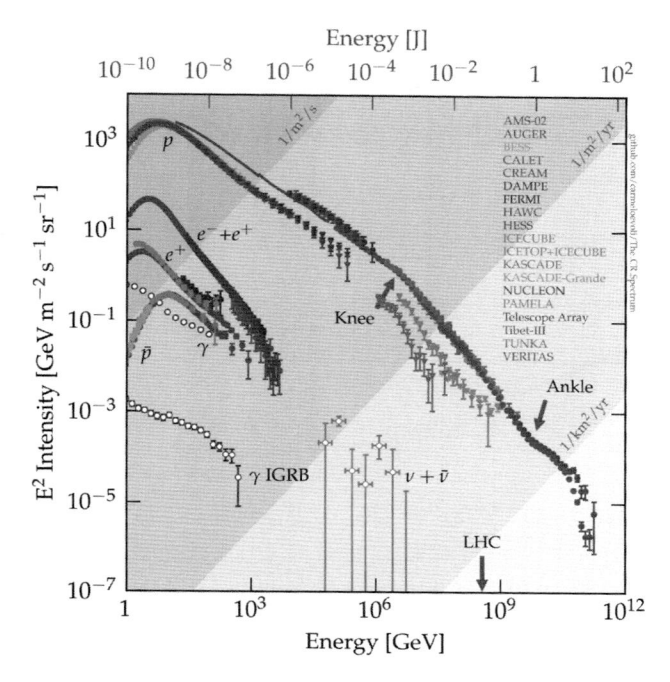

Fig. 1. Up-to-date summary of measurements of CR energy spectra.[1] For energies below ∼ 100 TeV, the spectra of different species are shown, and for higher energies the all-particle spectra are plotted. References of data: CREAM; ATIC; AMS-02; PAMELA; Fermi-LAT; HESS; IceCube; Akeno; Tibet; AGASA; HiRes; Auger.

So one of the HERD objectives will be the extension of the measurement of p and He flux up to a few PeV. The HERD data can clearly reveal the knee structure of both protons and Helium nuclei and can critically address the possible Z-dependence, A-dependence, or constant knee of different compositions, which are very important to understand the physical nature of the knee of CRs, see FIG. 2. Measurements of secondary over primary ratio, such as B/C, are important to probe the propagation of CRs. HERD will extend the precise measurements of B/C up to a few TeV/nucleon, thus accurately determine the propagation behaviour of CRs.

Finally, taking into account that the Iron nuclei are the end-products of stellar nucleosynthesis, they are thus very good tracer of the acceleration sites of CRs. HERD is expected to strongly improve such measurements.

Measurement of cosmic electron+positron spectrum and Dark Matter signal search In 2009, PAMELA experiment reported a positron excess[5] in the CR flux at energies 10-100 GeV, later it was very precisely measured by AMS-02 in an extended energy range up to 700 GeV.[6] Such a signal is generally expected from dark matter annihilation. However, the hard positron spectrum and large amplitude are difficult to achieve in most conventional WIMP models. A variety of theoretical

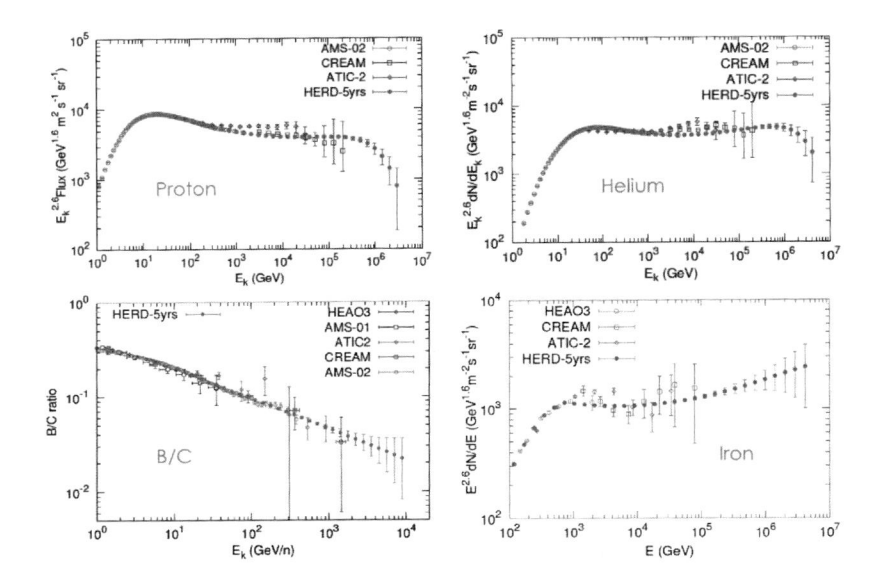

Fig. 2. Expected p, He, B/C and Fe energy spectra measured with 5yr exposure of HERD, compared with that observed by other experiments.

studies focusing on the DM interpretation of this excess have been performed in the literature, however the origin of these high energy positrons remains debatable.

Evidently, it is of a great importance to extend this measurement with greater precision at higher energy scales in order to distinguish the origin of the high energy electrons/positrons, either from DM annihilation or from astrophysical sources.

In this sense, progress has been made by the satellite experiment DAMPE (launched in 2015) which in 2017 reported its first result of CR electrons/positrons, showing a cutoff at ~ 0.9 TeV.[7] It has long been believed that the shape of the spectral cutoff is different for the astrophysical source (softer) and DM annihilation (harder).

Compared with DAMPE, the HERD experiment will have a larger acceptance and can extend the measurement of the electron-positron spectrum to higher energies with optimal precision, see FIG. 3, thus providing valuable insight on high energy astrophysics and DM studies.

A high energy gamma ray observatory HERD will be the most sensitive sky surveyer with very wide field of view for gamma rays between tens of GeV and several TeV, thus extending the Fermi-LAT observations at higher energies (E>300 GeV) and additionally complementing CTA, the most sensitive high energy γ-ray telescope with a narrow field of view.

The observation of the γ-ray sky is among the main scientific objectives of the HERD collaboration being relevant in understanding the nature of DM while also studying cosmic ray acceleration and propagation mechanisms in the Galaxy.[8]

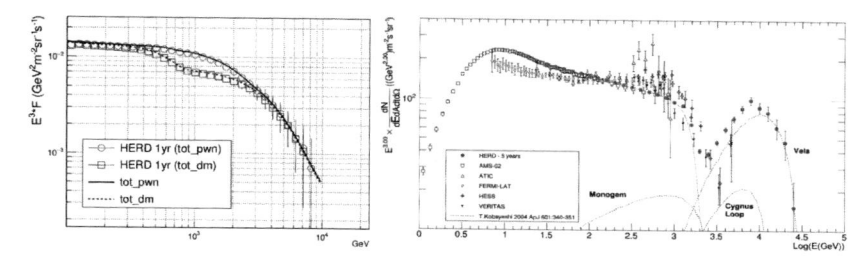

Fig. 3. Expected $e^+ + e^-$ flux in 1 year with PWN or DM sources on the left. Expected e++e- flux in 5 years on the right.

Information about cosmic ray spectra and intensities in distant locations, indeed, could be extracted by measuring the diffuse γ-ray emission, that traces energetic particle interactions, primarily protons and electrons, in the Interstellar Medium (ISM).[9] Moreover, the understanding of Galactic diffuse emission is also crucial to dark matter studies, since γ-rays can be produced in cosmic ray interactions mainly via decay of neutral pions and possibly from the annihilation of dark matter weakly interacting massive particles (WIMPs). The Galactic Center (GC) is expected to be the brightest source of DM annihilations in the γ-ray sky by several orders of magnitude. Although due to several astrophysical processes in the crowded GC region make it extremely difficult to disentangle the DM signal from conventional emissions, the DM-induced γ-ray emission is expected to be so large there that its search is of crucial relevance.[10] In the analyses of Fermi data of the Galactic center, the diffuse γ-ray backgrounds and discrete sources, as we model them today, seem to account for the majority of the detected γ-ray emission. Nevertheless, residual emission not accounted for by the above mentioned models of standard sources could still be present,[11][12] and be interpreted as product of DM annihilation.[13] The spectrum and spatial distribution of the GeV excess is consistent with what can be expected from Weakly Interacting Massive Particle (WIMP) with mass of a few tens of GeV of annihilating to standard model particles in the inner Galactic halo. With significantly improved sensitivity, HERD could measure with high resolution these spectra. Furthermore, the higher effective area especially at TeV energies may help in extending the energy range in which we detect the Galactic diffuse emission. This would provide a unique bridge for ground-based experiments sensitive in the TeV energy range.

3. The HERD payload

The HERD payload will be installed onboard of the CSS around 2027 and will be operating for 5 to 10 years, see TAB 1. Its heart, the calorimeter (CALO), will be surrounded on 5 sides by the other subdetectors i.e. the Fiber Tracker (FIT), the Plastic Scintillator Detector (PSD) and the Silicon Charge Detector (SCD), while a Transition Radiation Detector (TRD) will be placed only on one lateral side, see FIG. 4. This configuration will guarantee a wide field of view and more than one order of magnitude increase in acceptance with respect to current experiments, see TAB 2.

Table 1. Mission requirements of the HERD payload

Mission requirements	Value
Life Time	>10 years
Orbit	Circular LEO
Altitude	340-450 km
Inclination	42°
FOV	± 70 °
Mass	4t

Table 2. Main requirements of the HERD payload

Item	Value
Energy range (e/γ)	10 GeV - 100 TeV; >0.1 GeV(γ)
Energy range (nucleus)	30 GeV - 3 PeV
Angular resolution (e/γ)	0.1 deg.@10 GeV
Charge measurement (nucleus)	0.05 - 0.15 c.u.
Energy resolution (e)	1% @ 200 GeV
Energy resolution (p)	20% @ 100 GeV - PeV
e/p separation	$\sim 10^{-6}$
Geometric factor (e)	>3 m^{2}Sr @ 200 GeV
Geometric factor (p)	>2 m^{2}Sr @ 100 GeV

The Silicon Charge Detector The silicon charge detector is the outermost shell of HERD. It will measure the incident particle trajectory and charge of cosmic rays up to Z=26. Its position is chosen to ensure a reliable charge measurement and to avoid fragmentation phenomena of high energy particles. The current design follows the example of the DAMPE Silicon Tracker (STK). Each detection unit, i.e. each side, contains 8 layers of 300 μm microstrip silicon detectors mounted with alternating orthogonal direction strip directions onto low-density aluminum honeycombs, see FIG. 5. It is highly segmented to minimize the backscattered secondary particles coming from the CALO. The global active area is about 60 m^2.

We simulated several samples of proton, helium, carbon, oxygen, silicon, and iron nuclei with energies from 10 GeV/n to 1 TeV/n and with isotropic incidence to study the performances of the SCD. We found that the combined charge resolution of 8 layers is below 0.3 c.u. for all samples. Test beams are ongoing at the CERN SPS and PS ion beam lines to directly measure charge resolution of SCD prototypes.

The Plastic Scintillator Detector The PSD is the second detector encountered by an incoming particle. It works as an anticoincidence detector (i.e. it is able to discriminate incident γ-rays from charged particles) and provides an additional charge measurement of incoming cosmic-ray nuclei in a range up to Z $\leq$26.[14]

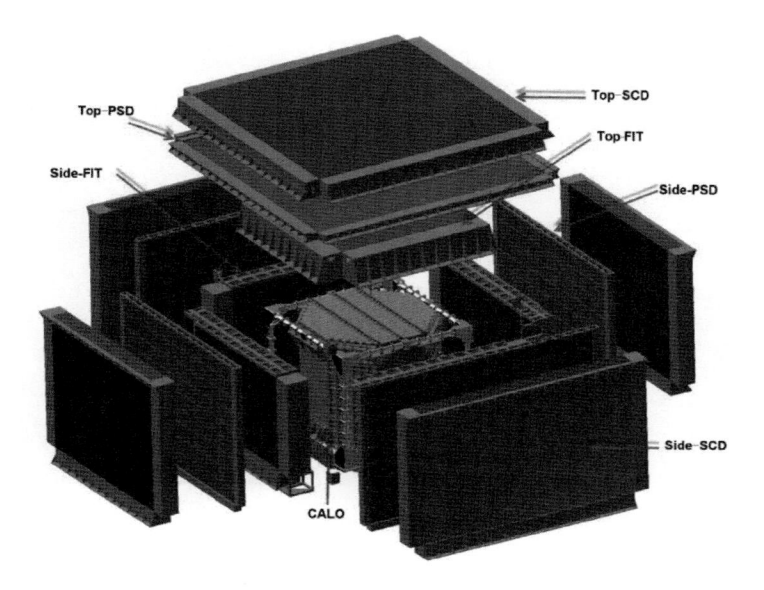

Fig. 4. Exploded model of HERD. In orange the silicon charge detector (SCD), in dark yellow the plastic scintillator detector (PSD), in green the fiber tracker (FIT) and in light yellow the calorimeter (CALO).

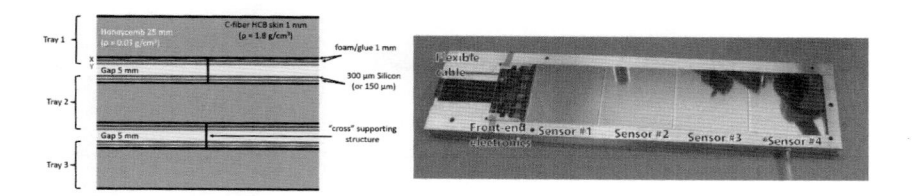

Fig. 5. Scheme of the SCD on the left. A prototype of SCD on the right.

Currently there are two designs for the PSD: one made by plastic scintillator bars the other made by plastic scintillator tiles. In both cases the single detection unit (i.e. bar, tile) is readout by silicon photomultipliers (SiPMs). The use of SiPMs will ensure, in addition to exceptional detection performances, low-weight, negligible power consumption, compactness and non-sensitivity to magnetic fields.

The bar option forsees two orthogonal layers of trapezoidal bars, see FIG. 6
The tile option forsees two staggered layers of square tiles, see FIG. 7.
Both configurations show advantages and disadvantages, mainly related to the optimal number of readout channels versus back–splash (or back–scattering) effects.
Currently both prototypes are undergoing beam tests at CERN with the aim to define the best scintillator type and size as well as SiPM quantity and model.

Fig. 6. Scheme of the PSD made with bars on the upper left. The PSD bar prototype undergoing the beam test at CERN on central left. A detail of the SiPMs used for the readout on the bottom left. A detail of the complete detection unit (the bar) undergoing the beam test at CERN on the right.

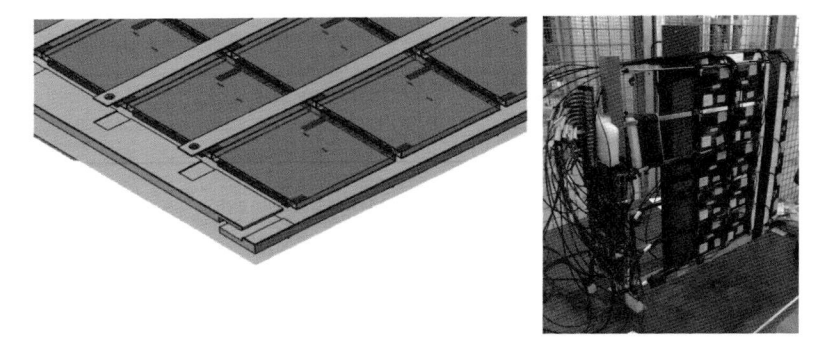

Fig. 7. Detail of the scheme of the PSD made with tiles on the left. The PSD tiles prototype undergoing the beam test at CERN on the right.

Fiber Tracker The FIT is the third detector hit by an impinging particle. It has several aims:

- reconstructing the trajectories and the charge absolute value (Z) of charged cosmic rays;
- favouring the conversion of low energy gamma rays and reconstructing the tracks of the generated electrons and positrons;
- acting as a redundance of the SCD and offering the possibility of cross-calibration among subdetectors.

In the current design,[15] each side of the FIT is made by 7 tracking planes, for 7 independent measurements of the position of a traversing charged particle, see FIG. 8. Each tracking plane consists of two layers measuring the two orthogonal spatial coordinates.

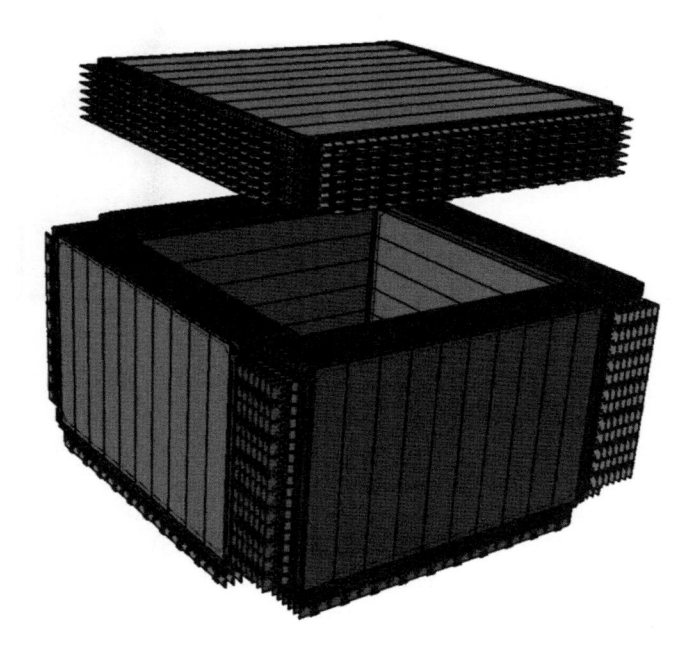

Fig. 8. Scheme of the FIT detector.

The tracking planes of the top sector are made of 10 FIT modules on both the x layers and y layers, while the tracking planes of the side sectors are made of 6 FIT modules on the x layers and 10 FIT modules on the y layers. A module includes one scintillating fiber mat and three SiPM-arrays to readout the scintillation light induced by the particles hitting the mat.

A FIT module prototype made of a 77 cm long fiber mat and one SiPM array was exposed to a 400 GeV/c primary proton beam and a fragmentation ion beam created by a 150 GeV/c lead beam hitting a beryllium target at CERN. A spatial resolution of 45 m and a mean hit efficiency of 99.6% were measured for protons. The response to nuclei from helium up to beryllium was studied and a charge resolution better than 15% was found.

The calorimeter The heart of the HERD instrument is the CALO: it is a homogeneous, isotropic, 3D segmented calorimeter accepting particles coming from each surface.[16] The performance of a detector based on these ideas was accurately studied by the CaloCube R&D project. By exploiting those results, the baseline design of the CALO consists of about 7500 LYSO cubes with edge length of 3 cm, corresponding to about 2.6 radiation lengths (X_0) and 1.4 Moliere radius. The CALO external envelope is similar to an octagonal prism and the crystals are arranged on vertical layers with different dimension, see FIG. 9.

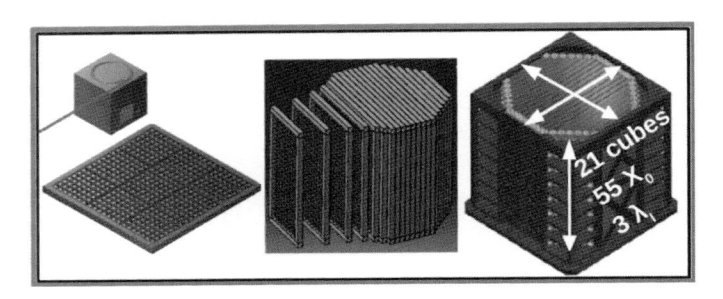

Fig. 9. Scheme of the CALO detector.

The total depth of the CALO for vertical particles is about 55 X_0 (radiation length) and $3\lambda_I$ (interaction length).

The scintillation light of each crystal is read-out by two independent systems: the first one consists of WaveLength Shifting fibers (WLS) coupled to image Intensified scientific CMOS (IsCMOS) cameras, the second one is made of photo-diodes (PD) connected to custom front-end electronics chips named HIDRA. This design, here named "double read-out system", achieves the capability of cross-calibrating the scintillation light measurement. Recent articles by calorimetric CR experiments speculated about the energy scale calibration as a possible source of unknown uncertainty, particularly for the electron flux measurement. Both the "double read-out" system and the TRD detector will strongly increase the understanding of HERD calorimeter energy scale with respect to previous CR detectors. Furthermore, both WLS and PD systems provide independent fast trigger information which will be employed to improve the HERD trigger capabilities.

The Transition Radiation Detector The TRD, installed on a lateral face of the detector, is needed to calibrate the response of the calorimeter to high energy hadronic showers. Ground calibration of space calorimeters, indeed, can only go to 400 GeV at maximum by using CERN SPS beam. For TeV protons, only few particles have showers all contained in the calorimeter and only visible deposited energy is recorded by detectors. Energy of primary proton is then derived by data extrapolation of low energy protons, which is not reliable.

A Transition Radiation Detector (TRD) could be used to calibrate the incident particle with energy in a range in which transition radiation is generated but not saturated. The energy of TR is proportional to the Lorentz factor γ of the incident

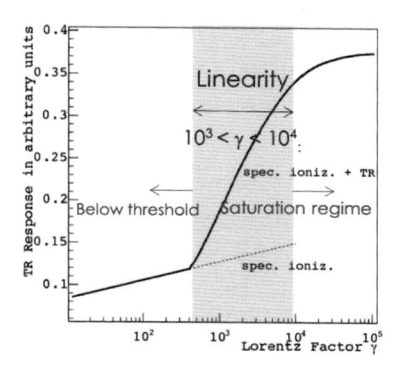

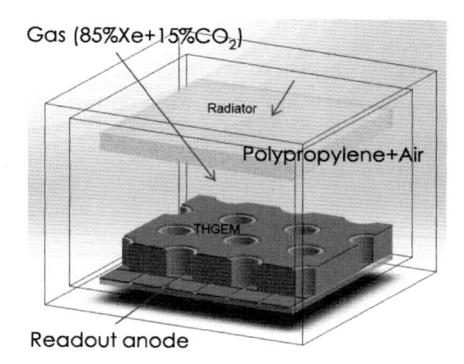

Fig. 10. Working principle of the TRD detector on the left. Scheme of the TRD detector on the right.

charged particle. The radiant photons will be generated at $\gamma \sim 10^3$ and saturated at $\gamma \sim 10^4$, the corresponding energy region of proton is about 1-10 TeV, see FIG. 10.

By detecting the X rays generated by TR, the absolute energy of the incident charged particle in the TeV region can be obtained by measuring the Lorentz factor.

The large effective area of TRD is achieved by a modular and highly redundant design. The TRD is arranged in 3 layers each consisting of 9 detection modules. Each detection module consists of a TR radiator, an X-ray gaseous detector with an effective area of 20×20 cm^2 and read-out electronics, supported by grid-like frames.

4. Summary

The HERD detector will be installed onboard CSS on 2027, with a lifetime of 5–10 years. The main scientific objectives regarding this initiative reside in the fields of CR physics, gamma-rays and (indirect) DM searches.

HERD will be capable of providing high-precision measurements including single-element spectral indexes along with spectral hardenings/softenings of nuclei and it will investigate the "knee" in hadronic CRs, for the first time via direct observations.

Moreover it will provide precise measurements of secondary-to-primary ratios (i.e., B/C) in an extended energy range,giving information on CR propagation in the Galaxy.

A great effort will also be invested in probing fine structures in the leptonic component ($e^+ + e^-$), especially at the highest-achievable energies with great precision.

HERD will also be involved in high energy gamma-ray observations throughout a broad energy range due to its wide FOV, as well as assisting in observations of ground-based experiments with a narrow FOV.

Acknowledgements

The author would like to thank all members of the HERD Collaboration for supporting this work with valuable comments and fruitful discussions.

References

1. C. Evoli, *The Cosmic-Ray Energy Spectrum* (Zenodo, 2020).
2. O. Adriani, G. C. Barbarino, G. A. Bazilevskaya, R. Bellotti, M. Boezio, E. A. Bogomolov, L. Bonechi, M. Bongi, V. Bonvicini, S. Borisov, S. Bottai, A. Bruno, F. Cafagna, D. Campana, R. Carbone, P. Carlson, M. Casolino, G. Castellini, L. Consiglio, M. P. D. Pascale, C. D. Santis, N. D. Simone, V. D. Felice, A. M. Galper, W. Gillard, L. Grishantseva, G. Jerse, A. V. Karelin, S. V. Koldashov, S. Y. Krutkov, A. N. Kvashnin, A. Leonov, V. Malakhov, V. Malvezzi, L. Marcelli, A. G. Mayorov, W. Menn, V. V. Mikhailov, E. Mocchiutti, A. Monaco, N. Mori, N. Nikonov, G. Osteria, F. Palma, P. Papini, M. Pearce, P. Picozza, C. Pizzolotto, M. Ricci, S. B. Ricciarini, L. Rossetto, R. Sarkar, M. Simon, R. Sparvoli, P. Spillantini, Y. I. Stozhkov, A. Vacchi, E. Vannuccini, G. Vasilyev, S. A. Voronov, Y. T. Yurkin, J. Wu, G. Zampa, N. Zampa and V. G. Zverev, Pamela measurements of cosmic-ray proton and helium spectra, *Science* **332**, 69 (2011).
3. F. Alemanno, Q. An, P. Azzarello, F. C. T. Barbato, P. Bernardini, X. J. Bi, M. S. Cai, E. Catanzani, J. Chang, D. Y. Chen, J. L. Chen, Z. F. Chen, M. Y. Cui, T. S. Cui, Y. X. Cui, H. T. Dai, A. D'Amone, A. De Benedittis, I. De Mitri, F. de Palma, M. Deliyergiyev, M. Di Santo, T. K. Dong, Z. X. Dong, G. Donvito, D. Droz, J. L. Duan, K. K. Duan, D. D'Urso, R. R. Fan, Y. Z. Fan, K. Fang, F. Fang, C. Q. Feng, L. Feng, P. Fusco, M. Gao, F. Gargano, K. Gong, Y. Z. Gong, D. Y. Guo, J. H. Guo, X. L. Guo, S. X. Han, Y. M. Hu, G. S. Huang, X. Y. Huang, Y. Y. Huang, M. Ionica, W. Jiang, J. Kong, A. Kotenko, D. Kyratzis, S. J. Lei, S. Li, W. L. Li, X. Li, X. Q. Li, Y. M. Liang, C. M. Liu, H. Liu, J. Liu, S. B. Liu, W. Q. Liu, Y. Liu, F. Loparco, C. N. Luo, M. Ma, P. X. Ma, T. Ma, X. Y. Ma, G. Marsella, M. N. Mazziotta, D. Mo, X. Y. Niu, X. Pan, A. Parenti, W. X. Peng, X. Y. Peng, C. Perrina, R. Qiao, J. N. Rao, A. Ruina, M. M. Salinas, G. Z. Shang, W. H. Shen, Z. Q. Shen, Z. T. Shen, L. Silveri, J. X. Song, M. Stolpovskiy, H. Su, M. Su, Z. Y. Sun, A. Surdo, X. J. Teng, A. Tykhonov, H. Wang, J. Z. Wang, L. G. Wang, S. Wang, X. L. Wang, Y. Wang, Y. F. Wang, Y. Z. Wang, Z. M. Wang, D. M. Wei, J. J. Wei, Y. F. Wei, S. C. Wen, D. Wu, J. Wu, L. B. Wu, S. S. Wu, X. Wu, Z. Q. Xia, H. T. Xu, Z. H. Xu, Z. L. Xu, Z. Z. Xu, G. F. Xue, H. B. Yang, P. Yang, Y. Q. Yang, H. J. Yao, Y. H. Yu, G. W. Yuan, Q. Yuan, C. Yue, J. J. Zang, F. Zhang, S. X. Zhang, W. Z. Zhang, Y. Zhang, Y. J. Zhang, Y. L. Zhang, Y. P. Zhang, Y. Q. Zhang, Z. Zhang, Z. Y. Zhang, C. Zhao, H. Y. Zhao, X. F. Zhao, C. Y. Zhou and Y. Zhu, Measurement of the cosmic ray helium energy spectrum from 70 gev to 80 tev with the dampe space mission, *Phys. Rev. Lett.* **126**, p. 201102 (May 2021).
4. J. Blumer, R. Engel and J. R. Horandel, Cosmic Rays from the Knee to the Highest Energies, *Prog. Part. Nucl. Phys.* **63**, 293 (2009).
5. I. Cholis, D. P. Finkbeiner, L. Goodenough and N. Weiner, The PAMELA positron excess from annihilations into a light boson, **2009**, 007 (Dec 2009).
6. L. Feng, R.-Z. Yang, H.-N. He, T.-K. Dong, Y.-Z. Fan and J. Chang, AMS-02 positron excess: new bounds on dark matter models and hint for primary electron spectrum hardening, *Phys. Lett. B* **728**, 250 (2014).

7. G. Ambrosi et al., Direct detection of a break in the teraelectronvolt cosmic-ray spectrum of electrons and positrons, *Nature* **552**, 63 (2017).
8. R. C. Haight, M. B. Chadwick, T. Kawano and P. Talou, Front matter for volume 769, *AIP Conference Proceedings* **769**, p. frontmatter (2005).
9. S. D. Hunter, D. L. Bertsch, J. R. Catelli, T. M. Dame, S. W. Digel, B. L. Dingus, J. A. Esposito, C. E. Fichtel, R. C. Hartman, G. Kanbach, D. A. Kniffen, Y. C. Lin, H. A. Mayer-Hasselwander, P. F. Michelson, C. von Montigny, R. Mukherjee, P. L. Nolan, E. Schneid, P. Sreekumar, P. Thaddeus and D. J. Thompson, Egret observations of the diffuse gamma-ray emission from the galactic plane, *apj* **481**, 205 (May 1997).
10. G. A. Gómez-Vargas, M. A. Sánchez-Conde, J.-H. Huh, M. Peiró, F. Prada, A. Morselli, A. Klypin, D. G. Cerdeño, Y. Mambrini and C. Muñoz, Constraints on WIMP annihilation for contracted dark matter in the inner Galaxy with the Fermi-LAT, *Journal of Cosmology and Astroparticle Physics* **2013**, p. 029 (2013).
11. V. Vitale, A. Morselli et al., Indirect search for dark matter from the center of the milky way with the Fermi-Large Area Telescope, *arXiv:0912.3828* (2009).
12. B. Zhou, Y.-F. Liang, X. Huang, X. Li, Y.-Z. Fan, L. Feng and J. Chang, GeV excess in the Milky Way: The role of diffuse galactic gamma-ray emission templates, *Physical Review D* **91**, p. 123010 (2015).
13. A. Achterberg, S. Amoroso, S. Caron, L. Hendriks, R. R. De Austri and C. Weniger, A description of the Galactic Center excess in the Minimal Supersymmetric Standard Model, *Journal of Cosmology and Astroparticle Physics* **2015**, p. 006 (2015).
14. D. Kyratzis, F. Alemanno, C. Altomare, F. Barbato, P. Bernardini, P. Cattaneo, I. D. Mitri, F. de Palma, L. D. Venere, M. D. Santo, P. Fusco, F. Gargano, F. Loparco, S. Loporchio, G. Marsella, M. Mazziotta, F. Pantaleo, A. Parenti, R. Pillera, A. Rappoldi, G. Raselli, M. Rossella, D. Serini, L. Silveri, A. Surdo and L. Wu, The plastic scintillator detector of the herd space mission, *Proceeding of Science* **ICRC 2021**.
15. C. P. et al., Fit: the scintillating fiber tracker of the herd space mission, *Proceeding of Science* **ICRC 2021**.
16. L. P. et al., Design and expected performances of the large acceptance calorimeter for the herd space mission, *Proceeding of Science* **ICRC 2021**.